Discrete Mathematics & Computing

A Set of Lectures

The book website DMC-book.com contains supporting material for instructors and readers.

(Solutions to pop-quizzes and exercises, slides, ...)

Book feedback: magdondmcbook@gmail.com.

Discrete Mathematics
&
Computing

A Set of Lectures

Malik Magdon-Ismail
Rensselaer Polytechnic Institute

Malik Magdon-Ismail
Department of Computer Science
Rensselaer Polytechnic Institute
Troy, NY 12180, USA
magdon@cs.rpi.edu

ISBN 10: 0-578-56787-7
ISBN 13: 978-0-578-56787-7

 v. 2020.01

This book was typeset by the authors and was printed and bound in the United States of America.

To my teachers, and to my students.

Mathematics

She is patient.
She sits,
She waits in silence.

A truth once found,
A truth shall be,
In antiquity and hereafter.

Preface

> So please, oh please, we beg, we pray,
> Go throw your TV set away,
> And in its place you can install
> A lovely bookshelf on the wall. – **Roald Dahl**
>
> No wi-fi. Please just talk to each other and get drunk.
> – **bar on Kollwitzstrasse, Berlin.**
>
> I have been a happy man ever since January 1, 1990, when I no longer had an email address. – **Donald E. Knuth**

This book is a story which starts with discrete mathematics and ends at the theory of computing. The end points as well as the journey are beautiful. Due to physical constraint, our passage through the complex landscape is linear, character by character, word by word. The true story is neither linear nor short, so it goes without saying that our tale is not entire. We strive to make the story relavent to the life of a computer scientist, who, after all, is the biggest consumer of discrete mathematics in the modern era.

Be sure to distinguish the programmer from the computer scientist. Programming is but one of the skills required of a competent computer scientist. The other is to *solve problems* using *algorithms*. This trifecta of problem solving using algorithms programmed on one of a myriad different computing platforms is everywhere. And everywhere in this trifecta, you will find a role for theory and formal reasoning. It behoves us to solve these computing problems carefully because, today, the common citizen trusts their life to computing systems. It's best that those systems work as they are supposed to, provably so. We are not alone in this observation.

> "Too few people recognize that the high technology so celebrated today is a mathematical technology."
>
> "A programmer must *demonstrate* that their program has the required properties. If this comes as an afterthought, it is all but certain that they won't be able to meet this obligation. Only if this obligation influences the design is there hope to meet it. Pure *a posteriori* verification denies you that wholesome influence and is therefore putting the cart before the horse. But that is exactly what happens in the software houses where "programming" and "quality assurance" are done by different groups. Needless to say, those houses deliver without warranty."
>
> "The required techniques of effective reasoning are pretty formal, but as long as programming is done by people who don't master them, the software crisis will remain with us and will be considered an incurable disease. And you know what incurable diseases do: they invite the quacks and charlatans in, who in this case take the form of Software Engineering Gurus." – Edsger Dijkstra

You may use the book for self-study, but the spirit of the presentation is a set of lectures for a theory *course*. We are old fashioned and adhere to the teacher-apprentice philosophy. Maximum value will be reaped with an instructor at the helm, for one shouldn't underestimate the guide's ability to dampen the meanderings of the fledgling-trekker. A course imposes an inflexible bandwidth constraint and effort was needed to respect that constraint. We had to carefully choose what to include, and more importantly what to *exclude*.[1] It is on good authority that effort spent identifying only that which is absolutely necessary is effort well spent:

> "I didn't have time to write a short letter, so I wrote a long one instead." – Mark Twain
>
> "This report, by its very length, defends itself against the risk of being read." – Winston Churchill

To compensate for omitted topics, there are 250^+ worked quizzes and exercises and $1,500^+$ problems suitable for homeworks or exams. Many of the problems are a springboard into more advanced techniques.

To the instructor. Each lecture is short and meant to be covered in whole. Once or twice, we reneg on that intention ☹, to present topics of particular relevance to computer science (for example the RSA-cryptosystem). The material is suitable for a fast-paced single-semester course. One could also teach each part (part I on discrete mathematics and part II on the theory of computing) as separate semester courses, in which case all the details could be covered, including some challenging problems.

[1] Suggestions that further *shorten* the text will receive my gratitude squared. All other feedback is greatly appreciated too.

The flexibility offered by standard texts adapts well to a variety of teaching philosophies. But, that flexibility is at a price. Experience shows that students react well to a linear path without diversions. While a lecturer is skilled at selecting what to cover, a student may not be skilled at deciding what to focus on as they read. Our presentation does not offer a wealth of options for meandering. I have picked a path. Students eager to explore can quench that thirst in the problems section. In the end, it is not the student's path but the passion they develop that matters.

> To build a ship, don't drum up people to collect wood and don't assign them tasks and work. Rather, teach them to long for the endless immensity of the sea. – Antoine de Saint-Exupery

To the student. Don't be a spectator. You have to do theory, not read about it. A typical begining student should make an effort to work all the pop-quizzes and attempt all the exercises. The pop-quizzes check if you are still awake. The exercises are to stretch the muscles. Treat the pop-quizzes and exercises as worked examples. To reap maximum benefit you must try to solve them first, before looking to the solutions. The end-of-chapter problems give an opportunity to strain the muscles, and in some cases strain them a lot. An advanced student may quickly read the text, do the exercises and focus on the problems. You can learn a lot by mastering all the problems.

Blanket Acknowledgement. Everything in this book has been done before. Perhaps some of the presentation is original, but even there, I cannot say to what extent I was influenced by the many beloved texts I grew up on. So, what then is the purpose of such a book, which produces nothing new? Purely pedagogical! To give an analogy, everything is on the internet. So, what then is the purpose of Google™? Google™ does not create novel content, rather it plays a search and discovery role. When you want something, Google™ finds it and presents it in just the right order – Google's™ opinion of the right order. There's a wealth of mathematics out there, and you can get it all using Google™. But you don't need it all for a sophomore-level theory course. I've collected what *I* think is needed, and presented it in my own way and my own order. Hopefully, my thoughts match up with some higher order truth, who knows. To focus on pedagogy, I gave up on detailed references in the text. Instead, I pay a blanket tribute here, to:

Biggs	Epp	Graham; Knuth; Patashnik
Grimmett; Stirzaker	Hopcroft; Motwani; Ullman	Kleinberg; Tardos
Lehman; Leighton; Meyer	Lewis; Papadimitriou	Lovász; Pelikán; Vesztergombi
Polya	Rosen	Sipser
Scheinerman	Skiena	Stanley
van Lint; Wilson	West	Zeitz

The above authors developed ideas in unique ways that may have affected the way I present certain topics, either explicitly or intangibly. When the resemblence is extreme, I have tried to give credit within the local context. In cases where I have underestimated the resemblence, I apologize in advance, and hope the acknowledgement above reduces a little of the wrongdoing. A similar consideration goes for exercises and problems, which in some cases have been lifted form olympiads, problem-books, etc. With age comes the ability to forget the original source of many a problem, especially those encountered many years ago.

I give a special thanks to those students, colleagues and teaching assistants who were the sandbox for early drafts of this book, especially Mark K. Goldberg who took on the first draft.

Rumpelstiltskin is still spinning gold for Zainab, Zain, Deen, Rafi and Sofya who patiently endured the demands of writing a book. When the little ones grow into their mathematics shoes, I hope they will read this book. It's time to turn on the lights and enter.

Malik Magdon-Ismail
Troy, New York
magdondmcbook@gmail.com
January 8, 2020.

Contents

A table of the notation used in this book starts on page 435, before the index. We suggest referring to it as needed.

Part I

Discrete Mathematics

> Good mathematics is not about how many answers you know. It's about how you behave when you don't know. – **unknown**
>
> The only way to learn math is to do math. – **Paul Halmos**
>
> Don't let anyone work harder than you. – **Serena Williams**
>
> To make a great dream come true, the first requirement is a great capacity to dream; the second is persistence. – **Cesar Chavez**

Chapter 0

Background and Pep Talk

1: The basics, the resources and putting yourself in the right mood.

Even "self-contained" books start somewhere and build. We cater to 2nd-year undergraduates in a mathematical, engineering or scientific discipline who have had one year of computer science (programming/data-structures) and one year of calculus. In short, we assume high-school mathematics (numbers, geometry, algebra, ...), some programming and some calculus. Here are some refresher questions. Answer them, perhaps with a little help from the solutions ☺.

TO STUDY THIS BOOK YOU MUST NOT USE ELECTRONIC DEVICES UNLESS **EXPLICITLY** ASKED TO DO SO.

Numbers and Sets.

1. What is the prime factorization of 252?
2. What is the minimum element in the set $\{8, 9, 3, 10, 19\}$?
3. What is the union of the sets $\{8, 9, 3, 10, 19\}$ and $\{3, 10, 1, 7\}$? What is the intersection?
4. Does this set of positive numbers have a minimum element:
$$\{25, 97, 107, 100, 18, 33, 99, 27, 2014, 2200, 23, \ldots\}$$
The set could be infinite. You only know that every number is positive.
5. Give examples of an integer, a rational number and a real number.
6. Let k be a whole number (e.g. $k = 7$). Which of the following are divisible by 3:
$$3k,\ 3k + 1,\ 3k + 2,\ 3k + 3,\ 3k + 4,\ 3k + 5.$$

Logarithms and Exponentials.

1. $\ln(2) \approx 0.693$; $\ln(3) \approx 1.098$. What is $\ln(12)$?
2. $2^{10} = 1024 \approx 1,000$. What is 2^{20}?
3. How are $\ln(1 \times 2 \times 3 \times \cdots \times 10)$ and $(\ln 1 + \ln 2 + \ln 3 + \cdots + \ln 10)$ related?
4. How are $2^a/2^b$ and 2^{a-b} related? What is 2^0?
5. Show $\log_2 100 = \log_2 10 \times \log_{10} 100$. More generally, show that $\log_\alpha x = \log_\alpha \beta \times \log_\beta x$.

Sums and Products.

1. What are: (a) $1 + 2 + 3 + \cdots + 1000$ (b) $1 + 2 + 3 + \cdots + n$ (c) $1 + \frac{1}{7} + \frac{1}{7^2} + \frac{1}{7^3} + \frac{1}{7^4} + \cdots$?
2. What is $5!$? What is $n!$? What is $0!$?

3. $\sum$ is an invitation to add. $\sum_{i\geq 1}^{i\leq 10} f(i)$ asks you to add $f(i)$ for the whole numbers i which satisfy the lower bound in the lower limit and the upper bound in the upper limit,
$$\sum_{i\geq 1}^{i\leq 10} f(i) = f(1) + f(2) + \cdots + f(10).$$
Similarly, $\prod$ is an invitation to multiply,
$$\prod_{i\geq 1}^{i\leq 10} f(i) = f(1) \times f(2) \times \cdots \times f(10).$$
We often simplify the notation even more and write $\sum_{i=1}^{10} f(i)$ and $\prod_{i=1}^{10} f(i)$.

What is $\sum_{i=1}^{1000} i$? What is $\sum_{k=1}^{1000} k$? What is $\sum_{k=1}^{1000} i$? What is $\sum_{|i-1|\leq 5} i$?

4. What is $1 + 2 + 3 + \cdots + k$? What is $\sum_{i=1}^{k} i$? What is $\sum_{k=1}^{n} k$?

5. Write the next two quantities using factorials: $\sum_{i=1}^{k} \ln(i)$; $\prod_{i=1}^{k} i$.

6. "Empty" sums, e.g. $\sum_{i\geq 3}^{i\leq 1} i$, are 0. "Empty" products, e.g. 2^0 and $0!$, are 1. Here's why.

   You want the sum of the numbers in the set $\{3, 10, 1, 7\}$. You are lazy, but your two friends are not. You split the set into two disjoint subsets $\{3, 10\}$ and $\{1, 7\}$, give one subset to each friend, and request the subset-sums. You receive the subset-sums 13 and 8, and add these two numbers to get the full sum of 21. This simple procedure should work no matter how you split up your original set. Suppose you gave one friend all the numbers, and the other none of them. For the procedure to work, your friend with none of the numbers (who computes an empty sum) must return 0.
   To get the product instead of the sum, your friends would give you the subset-products 30 and 7, which you multiply to get 210. If one friend gets all the numbers, and the other none of them, the procedure still works if the friend with no numbers (who computes an empty product) returns 1.

Algebra.

1. What is $(1 + 2)^2$?
2. What is $(a + b)^2$? What about $(a + b)^3$?
3. What are the solutions to $x^2 - 5x - 6 = 0$?
4. What are the solutions to $e^{2x} - 5e^x - 6 = 0$?
5. What are x and y when $x + y = 2$ and $2x + 3y = 7$?
6. Use partial fractions to simplify the expressions $\dfrac{3x + 11}{x^2 - x - 6}$ and $\dfrac{3x + 11}{x^2 + 6x + 9}$.

Calculus.

1. Which of these series converges:
$$1 + 2 + 2^2 + 2^3 + 2^4 + \cdots$$
$$1 + \tfrac{1}{2} + (\tfrac{1}{2})^2 + (\tfrac{1}{2})^3 + (\tfrac{1}{2})^4 + \cdots$$
$$1 - 1 + 1 - 1 + 1 - 1 + 1 - 1 + \cdots$$
$$1 + \tfrac{1}{2} + \tfrac{1}{3} + \tfrac{1}{4} + \cdots$$
$$1 - \tfrac{1}{2} + \tfrac{1}{3} - \tfrac{1}{4} + \tfrac{1}{5} - \tfrac{1}{6} + \cdots$$
2. What are the derivatives of: x^3; e^{2x}; 2^x; $\dfrac{1}{x}$; $\dfrac{1}{x^2}$; $\ln x$; $\log_2 x$; $\ln 2x$?

3. What are the indefinite integrals of: x^3; e^{2x}; 2^x; x^{-1}; x^{-2}?
4. What is the limit as $x \to 0$ of the functions:
$$\frac{e^x-1}{\sin(2x)};\qquad \frac{e^x-1}{1+x};\qquad \frac{e^x-1}{\sin(x^2)};\qquad \frac{e^x-1}{x+x^2};\qquad \frac{e^x-1}{e^{2x}-1}.$$
5. What is the limit as $x \to \infty$ of the functions: $\dfrac{e^x-1}{e^{2x}-1}$; $\dfrac{e^x-1}{x^3+2e^x}$; $\dfrac{e^x}{x^x}$.
6. What is the Taylor expansion of $f(x) = 1/(2 + \sin(x))$ around $x = \pi/2$?
7. What is $\int_0^T dx\ (1 + x^2)^{-1}$?
8. Define the function $f(t) = \int_0^t dx\ \sin(1 + x^2 e^x)$. What is $\frac{d}{dt} f(t)$?

Setting Up Expectations

This book is by no means a complete coverage of discrete mathematics and computing. We chose some topics to cover, and within those topics we left out many advanced concepts to satisfy the bandwidth constraints of a course. To compensate, we have given a generous helping of quizzes, exercises and problems:

- pop quizzes ask you if you are still awake;
- exercises stretch your muscles within the current context;
- easier problems test your knowledge and provide practice with the concepts;
- harder problems guide you through some of the more advanced concepts.

There are several books which delve more deeply or more completely into discrete mathematics. As for the deeper books, we will say more in the epilogue. Here are some more complete books at this level:

- *Discrete Mathematics and its Applications,* by Rosen.
- *Discrete Mathematics with Applications,* by Epp.
- *Mathematics for Computer Science,* by Lehman, Leighton, and Meyer. (MIT **open** course.)

Analogous books for the theory of computation are

- *Introduction to the Theory of Computation,* by Sipser.
- *Elements of the Theory of Computation,* by Lewis and Papadimitriou.
- *Introduction to Automata Theory, Languages, and Computation,* by Hopcroft, Motwani, and Ullman.

The internet is an endless resource for enrichment. Combined with the above books which have many solved exercises, there is no shortage of practice problems. Mathematics is like any sport. You have to train.

Final Exam. You relaxed all winter and ran the spring Boston Marathon. You got destroyed. The next year, you put in some intense 5-hour workouts three days before the race. You got destroyed. The third year you wisened up and got a coach 3 months ahead of the race. You took notes which helped fine-tune your 5-hour workouts three days before the race. You still got destroyed. Finally on the 4th attempt you tried something new. You got the coach as before and incorporated the coach's teachings into a 3 hour work-out every day. You were getting fitter. Three days before the race, you ramped up your training. Wow! You finished in the top-10% of runners in the race. ☺ *Your* Boston Marathon is the final exam in the course.

Pep Talk

Society won't object if you say "Math isn't for me," and yet it's as ridiculous as saying "Running isn't for me," or "English isn't for me." If you move to USA, to get around you learn English. Anyone can do it. If you wish to precisely model "stuff", you learn math. Anyone can do it, enough said. Yes, math is hard. But so is learning English. Math is for anyone who will put in the effort. You *must* put the effort.

You also can learn to "think", to be creative and solve problems. Solving a problem starts with strategic considerations, the foremost being to prepare the psychology. Two classics on that front are

How to Solve It: A New Aspect of Mathematical Method by George Polya;
The Art and Craft of Problem Solving, by Paul Zeitz.

To get into the right state of mind, listen well to the story of Polya's little mouse.

> "A mouse tries to escape from an old fashioned cage. After many futile attempts bouncing back-and-forth, thumping his body against the cage bars, he finally finds one place where the bars are slightly wider apart. The mouse, bruised and battered escapes through this small opening, and to his elation, finds freedom." – Polya

Try, try and try again. Vary the trials that you may find the rare favorable path to a discovery. The story of the mouse is for everyone. When you hit an interesting problem just outside the reach of your familiar realm, don't throw your hands in the air out of submission because a solution doesn't magically appear.

The solution to an interesting problem is not obvious.

That is the law. When you don't see the solution immediately, don't be discouraged. Realize that such situations are faced by every explorer entering the unknown. All that Columbus needed was a curiosity, perseverance and a little good luck. Columbus marched forward despite adversity. A mathematics problem can throw much adversity your way. Don't fret; don't give up. Be patient; persevere. Be that mouse, trying this and that. Eventually a small opening will appear and you may then walk through. Most importantly, realize that these are the rules for everyone, from the amateur to the professional mathematician.

It may be true that there is an innateness to mathematical creativity, just as not everyone is a Mozart. Alas, some may appear better at mathematics than others. They may be better trained, or just better. In all cases, it doesn't matter. Leave them to their business, and you focus on yours. To warm up to the importance of perseverance, try not to turn another page until you solve this visual connection puzzle, which we have lifted directly from *The Art and Craft of Problem Solving*.

Pop Quiz 0.1

Connect tiles of the same letter with wires that don't cross, enter tiles, or exit the box (you may bend wires). If you think it can't be done, why not?

Don't be too quick to dismiss either conclusion, or to peek at the answer. Patience. Try this and that. Fiddle around. Make sure you understand the challenge.

To solve such problems, "You need brains and good luck. But, you must also sit tight and wait till you get a bright idea." – Polya

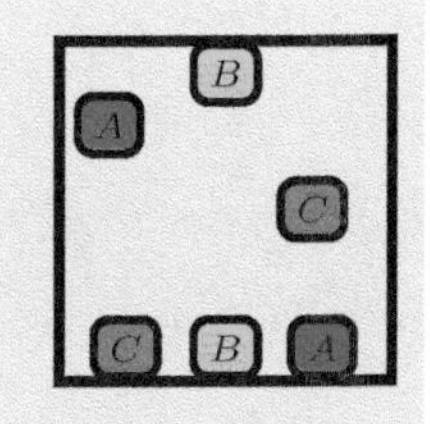

Ask this puzzle of your best mathematician friends. It will drive home the fact that everyone has to think about a problem. Everyone has to try one or two things that fail, then one or two things that partially succeed. Through perseverance, these failures and partial successes are what ultimately shine light on the way out.

Our primary goal is to impart the knowledge and tools of discrete mathematics to you. But, you are the one who must use these tools to solve problems. And, to solve problems, you must prepare yourself mentally for a tough road. Don't be afraid to experiment. Don't be afraid to crash your CPU or corrupt your operating system – you can always perform a fresh install of linux. Put yourself in the right frame of mind.

Be the mouse!

Let us begin.

Go down deep enough into anything and you will find mathematics.
– **Dean Schlicler**

If you don't believe mathematics is simple, it is only because you don't realize how complicated life is. – **John von Neumann**

To ask the right question is harder than to answer it. – **Georg Cantor**

Learning is a treasure that follows its owner. – **Chinese Proverb**

Chapter 1

A Taste of Discrete Mathematics

1: Wheting the appetite: epidemics; speed-dating; and, friendship networks.

Discrete mathematics deals with "objects that we count." When you cook your favorite Thai dish, you perform "discrete" steps in a sequence. We can count those steps. When delegates sit at a banquet, each "discrete" delegate sits at a single "discrete" seat. Processes that take place in well defined steps, involving objects that come in indivisible units are the focus of discrete mathematics. The most famous discrete object is the digital computer which executes instructions in sequential steps and uses a discrete scratch-paper called RAM to store intermediate results during its calculations. If that is not enough reason to study the subject, then for beauty's sake do it. Let us begin with some examples of discrete mathematics in the real world.

1.1 Modeling Epidemics

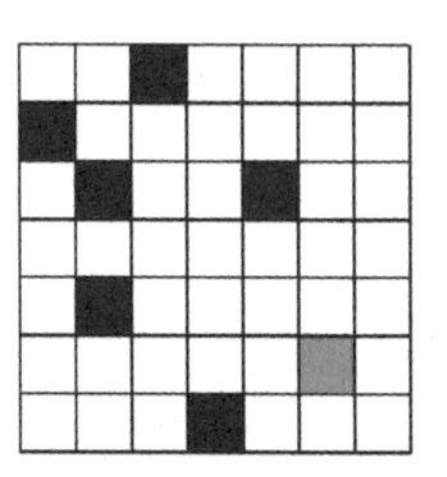

Outbreaks of a deadly virus EBOLA recur every now and then. The name of the virus is not important. People live on a grid, think of a chess board with only white squares. Each grid square is a person. Adjacent squares that share a side are neighbors. Initially, some people are infected, in gray. Infection is permanent and if at least two of your neighbors are infected today, then tomorrow you will be infected. Who will ultimately get infected? For example, will the square shaded red eventually get infected on the 7×7 grid shown? Let us tinker. Tinkering is an essential part of discrete mathematics. So, starting from the initial gray infections, let's see how the infection spreads over a few days. On each day, the previous infections are in black and the new infections are in gray.

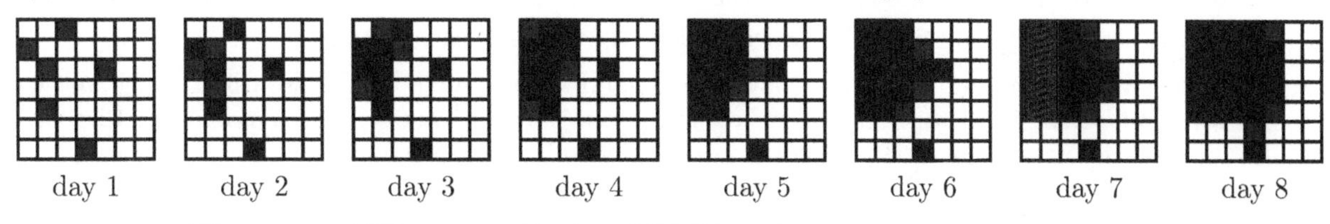

Pop Quiz 1.1
Continue to tinker with the epidemic spread above. Does the red square eventually get infected?

The epidemic spread we described is indeed a discrete process. People are either infected or not. Time is discretized into days. We identified the actors as people living on a grid and the process dynamics – at least two of your neighbors must be infected to infect you. These are modeling assumptions. Modeling assumptions are critical, and you may argue with them. People may not live on a grid. Perhaps a single neighbor being infected is enough to infect you. A good model is more likely to give correct conclusions. The beginning of a discrete mathematical analysis is always a model of the phenomenon you are analyzing. In our case, the model was a 2-contact threshold for epidemic spread on a grid. We will not address modeling, which, for starters, is very application dependent. We are interested in what happens next. So, what does happen next? You ask questions. Here are a few interesting questions.

1. Given the initial infection, who will ultimately get infected?
2. What is the fewest initial infections needed to ultimately infect the whole community?
3. If you had a few vaccines, who should you immunize to minimize the ultimate infection?
4. Given the current observed state of the epidemic, can one determine the "points of entry", defined as the smallest set of initially infected people that could have produced the observed infections?

You now answer these questions and that is where discrete mathematics comes in. The answers and the difficulty of getting them will depend on the model and the application.

Exercise 1.2
Can you infect the entire 7×7 grid, starting with an initial infection of just 6 people?

Before we switch gears, observe that our model for EBOLA spread can apply to other contexts: virus spread in a computer network; company-defaults in an economic crisis; adoption of a technology in a social network.

1.2 Speed Dating

You analyze disease spread in your spare time, but your real job is to run a speed-dating club. Every night you get 16 people, 8 boys and 8 girls. Anyone can date any other person. Here is how the night plays out. You have four tables, and there are 4 rounds of speed dating. In each round, 4 people sit at each table to "speed date" in a group setting. Round 1 of speed dating is shown below. The letters are the first initial of the clients. In round 1, A meets B, C and D; B meets A, C and D; and so on.

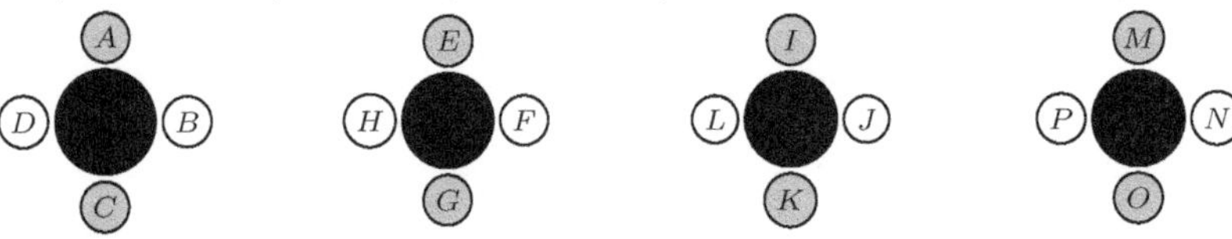

You succeed if you hook up many couples, so you want everyone to meet as many people as possible during the night. That's the model. Here are some interesting questions.

1. What does "...meet as many people as possible ..." mean? Do you care about the average number of encounters your clients had or the client who had the fewest encounters?
2. Can one efficiently configure the rounds so that everyone meets at least 10 people?
3. What would happen if you randomly assigned clients to tables in each round?

Tinker a little. Can you come up with good ways to configure the 4 rounds of speed-dating. See if you can figure out why I am so confident that no matter how much you tinker, no one will meet more than 12 people. I can also say that if you configured the rounds randomly, everyone would expect to meet about 9 people, so random is not that bad. You cannot beat 12 for anyone, and random gets you to about 9 for everyone.

1.3 Friendship Networks and Ads

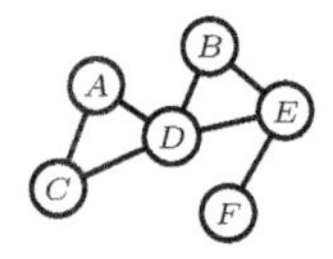

Six people Alice (A), Bob (B), Charles (C), David (D), Edward (E) and Fiona (F) form a friendship or social network. Circles are the people and the links are the friendships between pairs of people. Two people, i.e. circles, are friends if they are connected by a line. You might recognize the friendship cliques between $\{A, C, D\}$ and $\{D, B, E\}$ while F looks like a loner.[1]

We can visually analyze our small friendship network, but what about an online social network with a billion people? We certainly can't draw it on this page. So how would you go about identifying all the large friendship cliques? This turns out to be a very interesting challenge, but why do we care?

An advertiser who wants to market a new smartphone may try to convince David (D) to adopt the device in the hopes that everyone in David's friendship cliques might also buy the device. That would be a huge payoff. To make such advertising dreams into realities, we need to model social networks in a way that can be represented on a computer, and find all the large friendship-cliques or social "communities" so the advertiser can identify whom to target. Finding the large cliques is a tough discrete mathematics problem.

1.4 Modeling Computers

You've now seen some flavors of discrete mathematics. Computer scientists use discrete mathematics to model, analyze and solve real world problems. The summit of our adventure is going to be a grand model, a model of the digital computer – a *model of computing*. We want a realistic model that captures your desktop as well as smartphone, GPU or fitbit. But, it should be simple enough to analyze, for we have deep questions to ask.

1. What can we compute?
2. What *can't* we compute?
3. Are there things we can compute in principle, but it takes too long?

In answering these questions, we will journey through the world of discrete mathematics.

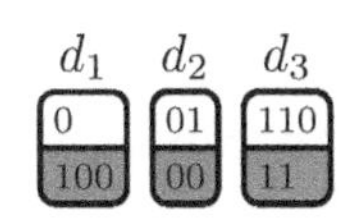

What is computing? Let's get a feel for it using a domino puzzle. The top and bottom entry in each of the three dominos d_1, d_2, d_3 on the right is a binary string. A sequence of dominoes produces a combined domino in which the top string is the concatenation of all the top strings in order, and similarly for the bottom string. For example,

$d_3d_1d_3$ = 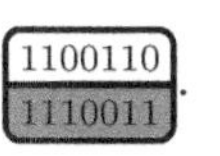, which gives the combined domino 1100110 / 1110011.

To solve the domino puzzle, find a sequence of dominos for which the combined top and bottom strings match. Repetition of dominos is allowed and you need not use all dominos. In this case, you can verify that $d_3d_2d_3d_1$ solves the puzzle. That's nice, but what does a simple kids' puzzle have to do with computing? Could you write a program to solve the domino puzzle? Your program would read in a text file where each row of the file describes a domino, two comma separated binary strings. Your program should output a sequence of dominos which solves the puzzle, or say it can't be done. Now, does that look like a computing problem to you, something that could be on a programming assignment?

> **Challenge.** I'm feeling sly and evil. A prize of **$1,000** inflation adjusted goes to the first correct program that solves the domino puzzle for any input file of dominos. There are two catches.
> (i) Your program must *stop* and output the correct answer no matter what the input domino file.
> (ii) You must give a *proof* that your program is correct.

We can't rely on intuition to say what is and is not computing. We need a precise model. Stay tuned. 

1.5 Proof

It is Human to seek proof, to ask why. If your neighbor says evacuate because of hurricanes, wouldn't you seek verification? If you claim to have a perpetual motion machine, I won't take you at your word. We each have different thresholds to be convinced of something. In life, a few true instances are often enough – that is inductive proof. The sun has risen every morning. That's enough for us earthy beings to conclude that the sun will always rise. Logically, a few cases of the sun having risen does not prove "The sun rises every morning." It only means the statement is not obviously false. In mathematics, we have the same urge for verification, but our expectations are high. We require deductive proof.

In the speed-dating ritual on page 8, nobody meets more than 12 people. Here is a proof. In any round a person meets at most 3 new people. So, after 4 rounds they meet at most $4 \times 3 = 12$ new people. Aren't you utterly convinced? The beauty of deductive proof is that it leaves no room for doubt.

Becoming Good at Discrete Math. You're no stranger to reasoning in real life. You can look at a rental contract and determine when you can break the lease without penalty. Mathematics, reasoning about abstract objects, is similar yet seems difficult. Don't fret. You had a lifetime of training for everyday reasoning. With similar training, you can build stamina for mathematics. But you must be diligent. Mathematics is no spectator sport. Don't "read" or "study". *Do*! Work the examples, exercises and problems. Write in the book. Annotate definitions and theorems with pictures or simple examples. Make sure you understand what is being said. No one speed reads mathematics. Even to those fluent in the language, it is a foreign tongue.

> In mathematics, if you're missing something, you're missing everything. *Work* the text, quizzes and exercises, with pencil and paper in hand. You must agree with the smallest detail.

It is worth showcasing the recurring workflow an expert uses to solve a problem. Memorize it.

1: Model the problem you are trying to solve using a discrete mathematical object.
2: Tinker with easy cases to understand the model. **Tinkering is essential.**
3: Based on the tinkering, formulate a conjecture about your problem/model.
4: Prove the conjecture and make it a theorem. You now *know* something new.

The novice builds the model and stares at it without knowing what to prove, because of a failure to tinker.

Exercise 1.3 [A Sisyphean Puzzle to Teethe On]

Zeus punished King Sisyphus of Corinth to an eternity of rolling a boulder up a hill only to see it roll down when near the top. Sisyphean tasks are laborious yet futile.

Three boxes start with 100, 200 and 300 boulders, the configuration $(100, 200, 300)$. A move places a stone from one box into another. For example, moving a stone from the box with 200 to the box with 100 gives configuration $(101, 199, 300)$. Each move gains or loses gold coins and debt is allowed. The gain is larger for a move from a box with many stones to a box with few stones. Specifically,

gain = # stones left in originating box (after move) − # stones in destination box (before move).

Here is a sequence of moves with the corresponding payments.

start configuration	end configuration	gain
$(100, 200, 300)$	$(101, 199, 300)$	$199 - 100 = +99$
$(101, 199, 300)$	$(101, 198, 301)$	$198 - 300 = -102$
$(101, 198, 301)$	$(102, 198, 300)$	$300 - 101 = +199$

The profit for these three moves is +196 coins $(= 99 - 102 + 199)$. Sisyphus can move stones, but must return to the start configuration. How much can Sisyphus profit? Can you prove it?

Mathematics and "Partial Credit". They don't mesh well. In school, partial credit is a learning-aide. It's comforting to know you're close to a solution, and partial credit delivers the message. Mathematics is not so forgiving. A proof is right or wrong. There's no almost proven. Computer programs are mathematical objects running on mathematical devices. A program works or it doesn't. If a builder makes one wrong join the whole structure can fall. You don't get $\frac{1}{2}$-credit for sending someone to the moon but forgetting to bring them back. A program that mostly works is a catastrophe waiting to happen. Check out Therac-25 on Wikipedia:

> "Because of concurrent programming errors, it sometimes gave its patients radiation doses that were hundreds of times greater than normal, resulting in death or serious injury."

Who cares if Therac-25 had one bug or 17 bugs? Should we be lenient because Therac-25 worked 99.9% of the time, only failing in rare boundary cases? There is a fundamental difference between algorithms that always work and heuristics which often work, but without guarantee. Life does not give credit for partial solutions.

Critical computer systems from traffic control to robotic surgery to self-driving cars must fully work all the time, otherwise people will suffer. Take the precaution to *prove* your program works. Others rely on it.

1.6 Problems

Problem 1.1. The parity of an integer is 0 if it is even and 1 if it is odd. Which operations preserve parity:
(a) Multiplying by an even. (b) Multiplying by an odd. (c) Raising to a positive integer power.

Problem 1.2. What's wrong with this comparison: Google's nett worth in 2017, about $700 billion, exceeds the GDP of many countries, e.g. Argentina's 2016-GDP was about $550 billion. (Look up nett worth and GDP.)

Problem 1.3. Consider 2-contact EBOLA on a grid. You have one immunization vaccine. We show two different immunization scenarios, where you immunize the green square. Show the final infection in each case and determine which person you prefer to immunize? How many vaccines are needed to ensure that nobody else gets infected?

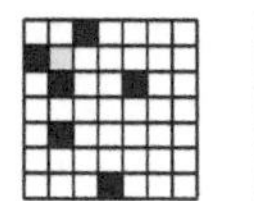

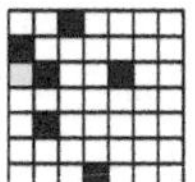

Problem 1.4. For the speed-dating problem with 16 people, $A, B, \ldots, P$ and four tables, arrange the rounds so that:
(a) In two rounds, everyone meets 6 people.
(b) In three rounds, everyone meets 9 people.
(c) In four rounds, everyone meets 12 people.
(d) In five rounds, everyone meets 15 people?

Problem 1.5 (Social Golfer Problem). 32 golfers form 8 groups of 4 each week. Each group plays a round of golf. No two golfers can be in the same group more than once. For how many weeks can this golfing activity go on?
(a) "Prove" that this golfing activity cannot go on for more than 10 weeks.
(b) Try to create a scheduling of players for as many weeks as you can. (10 is possible.)
(c) How is this problem related to the speed-dating problem?
In general you must schedule g groups of golfers each of size s for w weeks so that no two golfers meet more than once in the same group. Given (g, s, w), can it can be done and what is the schedule? This is a hard problem.

Problem 1.6. Students $A, \ldots, H$ form a friendship network (right). To advertise a new smartphone, you plan to give some students free samples. Here are two models for the spread of phone-adoption.
Model 1 (WEAK MAJORITY): People buy a phone if at least as many friends have the phone as don't.
Model 2 (STRONG MAJORITY): People buy a phone if more friends have the phone than don't

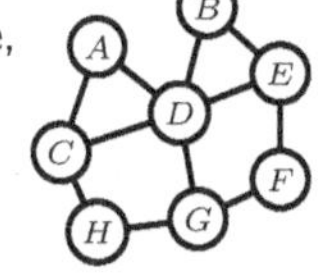

(a) Use your intuition and determine the most "central" of the people in this friend-network.
(b) If you give a phone only to this central node, who ultimately has a phone in: (i) Model 1 (ii) Model 2?
(c) How many phones must you distribute, and to whom, so that everyone switches to your phone in Model 2?
(d) Repeat part (c), but now you cannot give a phone to the central node.
(A slight change to a model can have a drastic impact on the conclusions. A good model is important.)

Problem 1.7. Five radio stations (red stars) broadcast to different regions, as shown. The FCC assigns radio-frequencies to stations. Two radio stations with overlapping broadcast regions must use different radio-frequencies so that the common listners do not hear garbled nonsense. What is the minimum number of radio-frequencies the government needs?

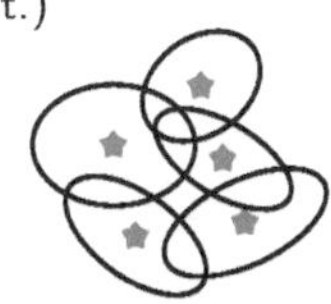

Discrete math problems are like childhood puzzles. Parity, symmetry and invariance often yield simple solutions.

Problem 1.8. Two players take turns placing identical circular quarters on a circular table. Coins cannot overlap and must remain on the table. The last person to play wins. Do you want to go first or second? *[Hint: symmetry.]*

Problem 1.9. A chocolate-bar has 50 squares (5×10). How many breaks are necessary to break the bar into its 50 individual squares? You may only break a piece along a straight line from one side to the other. No stacking allowed. *[Hint: Define the invariant $\Delta = \#$pieces $- \#$breaks. What happens to Δ with each break?]*

Problem 1.10. A single-elimination tournament has 57 players. Players may receive byes in some rounds. How many matches are played before a winner is declared? Does it depend on how the tournament is configured? *[Hint: Define the invariant $\Delta = \#$players remaining $+ \#$matches played. What happens to Δ after a match?]*

Problem 1.11. Five pirates must share 100 gold coins. The most senior pirate proposes a division of coins and all pirates vote. If at least half the pirates agree, the coins are divided as proposed. If not, the proposer is killed and the process continues with the next most senior pirate. A pirates priority is to stay alive, and then to get as much gold as possible. What should the senior pirate propose? *[Hint: Sometimes it is better to start with a smaller problem.]*

Problem 1.12. Can you color squares of a 9×9 grid blue or red so that every square has one opposite color neighbor (neighbors are left, right, up or down).

Problem 1.13. 57 security guards are positioned so that no two pairs of guards are the same distance apart. Every guard watches the guard closest to him. Is there an arrangement of the guards so that every guard is being watched?

Problem 1.14. 10 trucks each have 100 gallons of fuel and use 1 gallon of fuel per mile. How far can you deliver a chest that fits in one truck? (You can transfer the chest and/or fuel from truck to truck.)

Problem 1.15. A camel owner wants to sell his 300 bananas at a market 100 miles away. The camel can carry at most 100 bananas, but eats a banana for every mile travelled. How many bananas can be sold at the market?

Problem 1.16. Show that fewer than n initial infections cannot infect the whole $n \times n$ grid in 2-contact EBOLA. *[Hint: For a square, define 4-outgoing links (N,S,E,W) to its 4 neighbors. Pretend boundary-squares have neighbors. For an infected square, remove all outgoing links to infected neighbors. Let Δ, the "wavefront" of the infected area, be all remaining outgoing links for infected squares. Can Δ increase? What is Δ when all squares are infected?]*

Problem 1.17 (Chomp). In the grid of chocolate, if you eat the top-left square, you lose. Each player takes turns to eat a square plus all the chocolate below it and to the right. We show a possible first move and the chocolate that removed in blue. Do you want to go first or second? *[Hint: Either eating the bottom right piece wins or not. If not, what should you do?]*

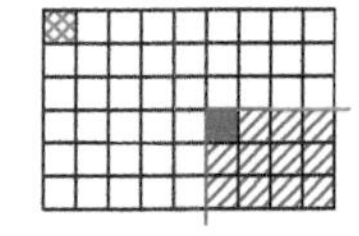

Problem 1.18. A man has a boat which can carry him and one other thing. How can the man get a fox, a chicken and a bag of corn across the river, if, when unattended, the fox eats the chicken and the chicken eats the corn.

Problem 1.19. Tasks involving covering an area using different shaped tiles are a treasure trove of interesting puzzles.

(a) Remove the top left and bottom right squares on an 8×8 chess board. Can you tile the remaining 62 squares with 31 dominos? *[Hint: Show that #black squares − #white squares is an <u>invariant</u> when you place a domino?]*

(b) On an 8×8 chess board, show that if you remove any two squares of different colors, you can tile the remainder of the board with dominos. *[Hint: See illustration on the right. We show a path starting from the top-left. You can tile the board by placing dominos along this path. You may assume that the first square removed is white (why?). Show that you can still tile the remaining board along the path.]*.

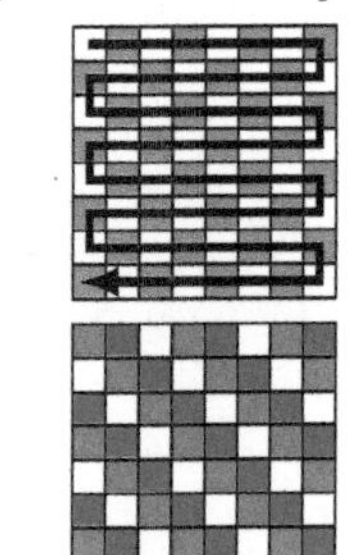

(c) On a 8×8 chess board, show that if you remove any corner square, you cannot tile the remainder of the board with straight triominos (▭▭▭). It is possible to tile the board with triominos after removing one square. Can you identify which squares can be removed (there are 4)? *[Hint: See illustration on the right. We have colored the squares on the chess board so that a triomino must cover one square of each color.]*.

(d) Can you cover a 10×10 chessboard with 25 straight tetrominos (▭▭▭▭). If yes, how?

Problem 1.20. There are 13 purple, 15 red and 17 green chameleons. When chameleons of different colors meet they both transform to the third color. Will all 45 chameleons ever be the same color? *[Hint: Consider $\Delta = \#purple - \#red$.]*

Problem 1.21. A building has 1000 floors. You wish to determine the highest floor from which you can drop an egg without the egg breaking. If you had 1000 identical eggs, you could drop one from each floor and see which eggs survive. How many egg drop trials do you need if you have: (a) One egg. (b) Two identical eggs.

Problem 1.22. Four boys take 1min, 2min, 7min and 10min to cross a bridge. The bridge only holds two boys at a time. It is dark and there is only one flashlight, which is needed to cross the bridge. Two boys cross at the speed of the slower boy who holds the flashlight. All four boys must get across the bridge. If the fastest boy acts as chauffeur for the other three, all four can cross in 21 min. Can all four get across the bridge faster?

Problem 1.23. Two consecutive positive numbers n and $n+1$ are given to you and a friend. One player gets n and the other gets $n+1$, at random. You look at your number and shout out your opponents number if you know it, otherwise you pass the turn to your opponent. Will this game ever stop?

Problem 1.24. You have a gold chain with 63 links. You would like to cut some links to obtain a set of links of different sizes. You goal is to be able to represent any number of links from 1 to 63 as a collection of some of your pieces in order to trade. What is the minimum number of links you need to cut to be able to do so?

Problem 1.25. Three ants a, b, c are on the vertices A, B, C of a triangle. Each ant randomly picks one of the other vertices and walks to it. What are the chances that no ants colide on an edge or at a destination vertex)? What if there are four ants a, b, c, d on the vertices A, B, C, D of a tetrahedron?

Problem 1.26. Two players alternately pick numbers without replacement from the set $\{1, 2, 3, \ldots, 9\}$. The first player to obtain three numbers that sum to 15 wins. What is your strategy?

Problem 1.27. A maharaja has 100 amphoras of wine. A traitor poisons one amphora, gets detected and killed. The poisoned amphora is not known and the poison kills in exactly one month. The maharaja uses tasters to tell if wine is safe, depending on whether the taster lives or dies after a month.

(a) The maharaja wants to safely drink wine in a month, what is the minimum number of tasters he needs.

(b) The maharaja wants to use all safe amphoras to throw an orgy in a month. What is the minimum number of tasters he needs. A simple solution is 100 tasters, one on each amphora. One can do much better though.

Problem 1.28. Two players take turns picking a coin from either end of a line of 20 coins. In the example below, if player 1 always takes from the left and player 2 from the right, then player 1's coins total 80, and player 2's total is 146.

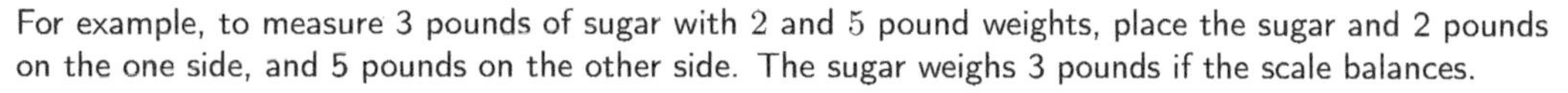

The player with the highest total wins, player 2 in the example. Do you want to play first or second?

Problem 1.29. To weigh sugar, you have a comparison scale that can compare weights (illustrated). Give the fewest weights that are needed to measure out $1, 2, \ldots, 121$ pounds of sugar.

For example, to measure 3 pounds of sugar with 2 and 5 pound weights, place the sugar and 2 pounds on the one side, and 5 pounds on the other side. The sugar weighs 3 pounds if the scale balances.

Problem 1.30. More than half of 99 processors are good and the rest are bad. You may ask a processor to evaluate another processor. A good processor always gives the correct answer and a bad one gives the wrong answer. How many times must you ask some (any) processor to evaluate another before you can identify a good processor?

Problem 1.31. A plane has fuel capacity to fly half way around the world. A plane can refuel from another plane in mid-air. All planes are at the airport. How many planes and tanks of gas do you need so that you can support a single plane to fly around the world? All planes must return to the airport.

Problem 1.32. 25 horses have different speeds. You can race up to 5 horses at a time and observe the order in which the horses finish. You have no stop-watch. Show that 7 races suffice to determine the fastest 3 horses.

Problem 1.33. 100 prisoners are up for a pardon. Prisoners will be lined in random order with a randomly chosen red or blue hat on each head. A prisoner sees only those ahead of them in the line. The last in line shouts the color of his hat. If he gets it right, he is pardoned. Then the second-last prisoner gets a chance and so on until the first in line.

The night before pardoning, the prisoners may strategize. During the pardoning process, the prisoners cannot communicate except to shout out a hat color. If the prisoners optimally strategize the night before, what are the chances that the first to shout is pardoned, the second to shout, the third to shout and so on up to the final prisoner?

Problem 1.34. At a puzzle-party with 32 guests, the host will shuffle a 52-card deck and paste a card on each guest's forhead. A guest will see every other guest's card but not their own card. After the cards are pasted on forheads, each guest, one by one, must shout out a card (e.g. 4♠). At the end the number of guests who correctly shouted out their card is multiplied by $1,000 to get a prize amount which is split evenly among all guests.

Intense discussion breaks out among the guests as they arrive. A philosopher suggests breaking into 16 pairs. In each pair, the first to shout says their partner's card so the partner can guess correctly. This strategy guarantees $16,000. A FOCS-student claims, "I can guarantee we will share $31,000." Can you come up with a strategy to guarantee $31,000?

Problem 1.35. Three friends A, B, C each have tokens a, b, c. At every step a random pair of friends is picked to swap whatever tokens they currently have. If the first pair picked is (A, B) and then (A, C) then the tokens are distributed c, a, b after the two swaps. What are the chances each friend has their own token after 2015 swaps?

Problem 1.36. On a table are some red and blue cards. Two players take turns picking two cards. If the two cards picked are the same color, both cards are replaced by one red card. If the two cards picked are different colors, both cards are replaced by one blue card. When one card remains, you win if it is blue and your opponent wins if it is red.

(a) Must the game always end, or can it go on forever?

(b) Who wins if there are 8 blue and 11 red cards to start? Does it matter who goes first? *[Hint: Parity invariant.]*

Problem 1.37. Dad normally picks Sue from school which ends at 3pm. School ended early at 2pm, so Sue started walking home and dad picked her up on the way, returning home 20min earlier than usual. For how long did Sue walk?

Problem 1.38. Pick any six kids. Show that either 3 of them know each other or 3 of them do not know each other.

Problem 1.39. Fifteen houses are in a row. A thief robs a house. On each subsequent night, the thief robs a neighbor of the house robbed the previous night. The thief may backtrack and rob the same house. A policeman can watch any one house per night. Is there a strategy for the policeman to guarantee catching the thief?

Problem 1.40. 5 of 10 coins are showing heads. You can move coins to form two sets, and you can flip over any coins you wish. How will you guarantee that both sets have the same number of heads showing, blindfolded?

Problem 1.41. Baniaz and her twin kids pass a gumball machine with 2 red, 3 blue and 4 green gumballs. Gumballs cost 1¢ each and come out randomly. Baniaz buys gumballs until she can give each of her kids one gumball of the same color. In the worst case, how much must Baniaz be willing to spend? What if she had quadruplets instead?

Problem 1.42. Two 1 meter fuses (strings) each burn non-uniformly in 60 sec. How can you measure 45 sec?

Here come hard problems that take you to the boundaries of mathematics and computing.

Problem 1.43 (Collatz/$3n+1$ Problem). Given an integer $n > 1$, repeat as follows until you reach 1:

$$n \longrightarrow \begin{cases} n/2 & \text{if } n \text{ is even;} \\ 3n+1 & \text{if } n \text{ is odd;} \end{cases}$$

Example: $6 \to 3 \to 10 \to 5 \to 16 \to 8 \to 4 \to 2 \to 1$. Do you reach 1 for every n? This "simple" problem is unsolved!

Problem 1.44 (Subset Sum). Find two different subsets of this set of one hundred 27-digit numbers, with the requirement that the numbers in each subset must have the same sum.

#	Number
1:	5719825393567961346558155629
2:	5487945882843158696672157984
3:	4767766531754254874224257763
4:	1855924359757732125866239784
5:	4289776424589197647513647977
6:	7967131961768854889594217186
7:	2572967277666133789225764888
8:	1294587141921952639693619381
9:	4764413635323911361699183586
10:	1474343641823476922667154474
11:	2578649763684913163429325833
12:	5161596985226568681977938754
13:	2242632698981685551523361879
14:	7474189614567412367516833398
15:	6211855673345949471748161445
16:	4942716233498772219251848674
17:	5516264359672753836539861178
18:	5854762719618549417768925747
19:	5313691171963952518124735471
20:	6737691754241231469753717635
21:	4292388614454146728246198812
22:	4468463715866746258976552344
23:	2638621731822362373162811879
24:	1258922263729296589785418839
25:	4482279727264797827654899397
26:	8749855322285371162986411895
27:	1116599457961971796683936952
28:	3879213273596322735993329751
29:	9212359131574159657168196759
30:	3351223183818712673691977472
31:	8855835322812512868896449976
32:	4332859486871255922555418653
33:	2428751582371964453381751663
34:	6738481866868951787884276161
35:	8794353172213177612939776215
36:	2989694245827479769152313629
37:	6117454427987751131467589412
38:	2761854485919763568442339436
39:	6884214746997985976433695787
40:	8671829218381757417536862814
41:	9431156837244768326468938597
42:	4788448664674885883585184169
43:	3624757247737414772711372622
44:	9361819764286243182121963365
45:	9893315516156422581529354454
46:	5913625989853975289562158982
47:	8313891548569672814692858479
48:	2265865138518379114874613969
49:	3477184288963424358211752214
50:	6321349612522496241515883378
51:	1796439694824213266958886393
52:	6366252531759955676944496585
53:	8545458545636898974365938274
54:	3362291186211522318566852576
55:	8464473866375474967347772855
56:	2892857564355262219965984217
57:	4296693937661266715382241936
58:	8634764617265724716389775433
59:	8415234243182787534123894858
60:	2267353254454872616182242154
61:	4689911847578741473186337883
62:	4428766787964834371794565542
63:	7146295186764167268433238125
64:	2273823813572968577469388278
65:	6686132721336864457635223349
66:	3161518296576488158997146221
67:	1917611425739928285147758625
68:	3516431537343387135357237754
69:	7549684656732941456945632221
70:	2397876675349971994958579984
71:	4675844257857378792991889317
72:	2832515241382937498614676246
73:	8755442772953263299368382378
74:	9833662825734624455736638328
75:	5298671253425423454611152788
76:	9857512879181186421823417538
77:	1471226144331341144787865593
78:	3545439374321661651385735599
79:	6735367616915626462272211264
80:	2141665754145475249654938214
81:	8481747257332513758286947416
82:	9961217236253576952797397966
83:	9941237996445827218665222824
84:	6242177493463484861915865966
85:	4344843511782912875843632652
86:	7568842562748136518615117797
87:	2776621559882146125114473423
88:	6174299197447843873145457215
89:	5387584131525787615617563371
90:	5317693353372572284588242963
91:	6612142515552593663955966562
92:	1314928587713292493616625427
93:	2446827667287451685939173534
94:	9786693878731984534924558138
95:	2926718838742634774778713813
96:	3791426274497596641969142899
97:	2831727715176299968774951996
98:	3281287353463725292271916883
99:	9954744594922386766735519674
100:	3414339143545324298853248718

Problem 1.45 (Verifier for "Hello World"). Write a program in your pet language to solve the this problem.

Input: Any C^{++} program F.cpp (an ASCII text file).

Output: *Yes* if: when you compile and run F.cpp, it prints "Hello World", and eventually stops.
No if: when you compile and run F.cpp, the program loops forever or stops without printing "Hello World".

Would you have guessed that a solver for the domino puzzle (Section 1.4) can be used to build a Hello-World-verifier?

Education is not the learning of facts but the training of the mind to think. – **Albert Einstein**

For tech support, press the exact value of pi. – **automated sadistic phone system**

DAD:Can you say the alphabet backwards?
SON: Sure, Z,Y,X,.... Can you say π backwards?
DAD:Urghh ...??!!**&$#??...

Chapter 2

Discrete Objects

1: Sets; sequences; graphs.
2: Building an intuition for proofs.

To say anything about discrete mathematics, at the very least we must introduce the cast of discrete objects.

2.1 Sets

Sets are everywhere. A set is a collection of items. Instead of an axiomatic set theory[1], we rely on your intuition about sets, and focus on set-operations. Here are two sets.

$$M = \{m, a, l, i, k\}; \qquad V = \{a, e, i, o, u\}.$$

We use short descriptive names for sets and list the elements inside curly brackets. Order does not matter and repeated elements can be removed: $\{a, a, r, d, v, a, r, k\}$ and $\{k, r, a, v, d\}$ are the same set of letters. The "belongs to" symbol $\in$ indicates set-membership: $m \in M$ means the letter m is in the set M. The universal set $\mathcal{U}$ contains all items. The elements in $\mathcal{U}$ depend on the context. The empty set $\varnothing$ (also written $\{\}$) contains no items. For our two sets M and V, the natural universal set is the lower-case alphabet,

$$\mathcal{U} = \{a, b, c, d, e, f, g, h, i, j, k, l, m, n, o, p, q, r, s, t, u, v, w, x, y, z\}.$$

It is tedious to list all elements of a large set. We prefer to use compact descriptions of sets. We may write:

$$\mathcal{U} = \{a, b, c, \ldots, x, y, z\}, \qquad \text{or} \qquad \mathcal{U} = \{\text{lower case letters}\}.$$

Compact descriptions are essential for complex large sets which are hard to list out. Two such important sets are the natural numbers $\mathbb{N}$, the numbers we use to count, also called the counting numbers; and, the integers $\mathbb{Z}$.

$$\begin{aligned} \text{natural numbers } \mathbb{N} &= \{1, 2, 3, 4, 5, \ldots\} \\ \text{integers } \mathbb{Z} &= \{0, \pm 1, \pm 2, \pm 3, \pm 4, \pm 5, \ldots\}. \end{aligned}$$

We start counting from 1.[2] As you guessed, "..." ("dot, dot, dot" ☺) means going on forever. Another important set is the real numbers $\mathbb{R}$, which is not so easy to describe, let alone list out. We can build complex sets by specifying the properties of a generic element in the set. Let us work through an example.

$$E = \{2, 4, 6, 8, 10, \ldots\}.$$

How do we continue this list for E? You might guess E is the set of even numbers. But, what if I wrote

$$E' = \{2, 4, 6, 8, 10, 13, \ldots\}.$$

[1] The standard foundation of set theory is based on the Zermelo-Fraenkel axioms with Choice, **ZFC**.

[2] Many texts define $\mathbb{N}$ to include 0. We will use $\mathbb{N}_0 = \{0, 1, 2, 3, \ldots\}$ if we need to refer to the counting numbers together with zero. In enumerative combinatorics, the set of positive integers, which we are calling $\mathbb{N}$, is often called $\mathbb{P}$. We reserve $\mathbb{P}$ to denote probability, to distinguish it from the many other uses we will have for P (predicate, polynomial, etc). P is a polular letter.

How do you interpret the nebulous "..." in E'? We used "..." to define $\mathbb{N}$ because $\mathbb{N}$ is familiar to us, so there is not much at risk. But, from now on, we must try to avoid "...". So, how do we define the positive even numbers E? We use a variable in the definition:

$$\begin{aligned} E &= \{\text{Natural numbers } n \text{ that are twice some other natural number } k.\}. \\ E &= \{n \mid n = 2k, \text{ where } k \in \mathbb{N}\}. \end{aligned} \tag{2.1}$$

To the left of the "|" is the variable n which represents a generic member of the set E. To the right of the "|" are properties that n must satisfy to be in E. Every n that satisfies these properties is in E and any n that does not satisfy these properties is not in E. So, E contains all the natural numbers which are multiples of 2.

Pop Quiz 2.1
Use a variable to define the set of positive odd numbers $O = \{1, 3, 5, 7, \ldots\}$.

Another important set is the rational numbers $\mathbb{Q}$, the ratios of integers. Here is one way to define $\mathbb{Q}$,

$$\text{rational numbers } \mathbb{Q} = \{r \mid r = a/b\ , \text{ where } a \in \mathbb{Z},\ b \in \mathbb{N}\}.$$

To define rational numbers, we used the variable r as a generic representative of a rational number in $\mathbb{Q}$. The property r must satisfy is that it must be the ratio of an integer and a natural number.

The Subset Relation. The subset relation indicates that one set contains another.

	Said out loud	What it means
$A \subseteq B$	A is a subset of B	Everything in A is in B.
$A \subset B$	A is a proper subset of B	Everything in A is in B and something in B is not in A.
$A = B$	A equals B	Everything in A is in B and everything in B is in A, $A \subseteq B$ *and* $B \subseteq A$.

The empty set $\varnothing$ is a subset of any set: $\varnothing \subseteq A$ for any set A. This is vacuously the case because the empty set has nothing in it. Therefore every item in the empty set, there happen to be none, is in the set A.

Exercise 2.2
True or False, and why: "All pigs that fly are green with purple spots." (Relate to $\varnothing \subseteq A$ for any A.)
[Hint: Define two sets: PF $= \{$*pigs that fly*$\}$; GP $= \{$*things that are green with purple spots*$\}$.*]*

Set Operations. The intersection, union and complement can be used to to get new sets from old sets. The union of two sets combines the elements in both, and the intersection takes the common elements. The complement takes all elements outside a set and only makes sense within the context of some universal set.

	Said out loud	Set produced	Formal definition
$A \cap B$	A intersection B	Elements common to A and B.	$\{x \mid x \in A \text{ and } x \in B\}$
$A \cup B$	A union B	Combine elements in A with B.	$\{x \mid x \in A \text{ or } x \in B\}$
$\overline{A}$	A complement	Elements not in A.	$\{x \mid x \notin A\}$ ($x \notin A$ means x is not in A).

$A \cap B$ $\qquad$ $A \cup B$ $\qquad$ $\overline{A}$

Pop Quiz 2.3
$M = \{m, a, l, i, k\}$ and $V = \{a, e, i, o, u\}$. What are $M \cap V$, $M \cup V$ and $\overline{M}$? (State your universal set.)

Power Set. A set can be both a subset and a member of another set. Consider the two sets:

$$A = \{a, b\}; \qquad B = \{\{a, b\}, a, b, c\}.$$

A is a subset of B because every item in A is in B. But, A is also a member of B because B actually contains the *set* $\{a, b\}$ as an element. The power set of A, written $\mathcal{P}(A)$, is a set consisting of all the subsets of A,

$$\mathcal{P}(A) = \{\varnothing, \{a\}, \{b\}, \{a, b\}\}.$$

The power set contains sets that are subsets of the underlying set. Since $\varnothing$ is a subset of any set, $\varnothing \in \mathcal{P}(A)$. The number of elements in a finite set is its size, denoted by $|\cdot|$. So, $|A| = 2$, $|B| = 4$ and $|\mathcal{P}(A)| = 4$.

Venn Diagram. A Venn diagram pictorially shows the relationship between sets. A set is a region whose area corresponds to the size of the set. On the right are sets of students at a school in Troy, NY. The MATH students are fewer than the CS students (from the sizes of the regions). All the MATH students live in Troy (the MATH region is inside the Troy region). Most CS students live in Troy. The red region is CS ∩ MATH, the CS-MATH dual majors. Most MATH-majors are also CS-majors, but many CS-majors are not MATH-majors. Use Venn diagrams to convince yourself of the following relationships for combining set operations.

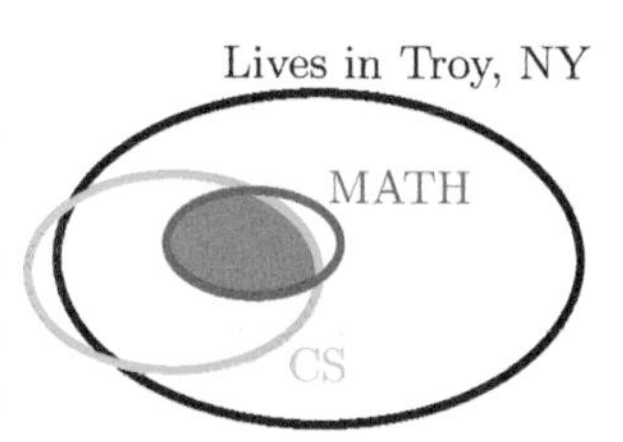

1. *Associative:* $(A \cap B) \cap C = A \cap (B \cap C)$;
   $(A \cup B) \cup C = A \cup (B \cup C)$.
2. *Commutative:* $A \cap B = B \cap A$;
   $A \cup B = B \cup A$.
3. *Complements:* $\overline{(\overline{A})} = A$;
   $\overline{A \cap B} = \overline{A} \cup \overline{B}$;
   $\overline{A \cup B} = \overline{A} \cap \overline{B}$.
4. *Distributive:* $A \cup (B \cap C) = (A \cup B) \cap (A \cup C)$;
   $A \cap (B \cup C) = (A \cap B) \cup (A \cap C)$.

Figure 2.1: Combining set operations.

2.2 Sequences

Like a set, a sequence is a list of objects. Unlike a set, the order is important and repetition matters. Here are 3 different sequences: *malik*; *kilam*; *maalik*. Sometimes we refer to a sequence as a string. Computers deal only in ones and zeros – binary sequences. This is in part due to practical limitations of their hardware implementation: it is only possible to reliably differentiate between high voltage (a "1") and low voltage (a "0"). The 8-bit ASCII code allows us to convert alpha-numeric to binary. Here is an example.

m	a	l	i	k
01101101	01100001	01101100	01101001	01101011

The alpha-numeric sequence *malik* corresponds (via the ASCII code) to the binary sequence

$$0110110101100001011011000110100101101011.$$

Any sequence can be converted to binary in this way. For more details on ASCII, we suggest the Internet.

2.3 Graphs

Sets and sequences represent collections of objects. They don't capture relationships between objects. Relationships are important. Graphs are the discrete-mathematical object for modeling and visualizing relationships. Recall our social network of six friends Alice, Bob, Charles, David, Edward and Fiona. We denote the set of people by V,

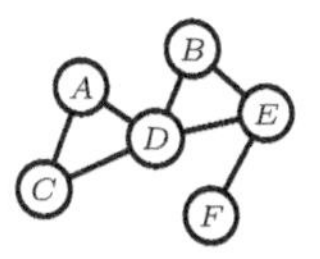

$$V = \{A, B, C, D, E, F\}.$$

A friendship can exist between a pair of people. In the friendship network above, each circle is a person, and two people are friends if they are linked. If there is no link between two people, for example A and B above, it means A and B are not friends. Does that mean they are enemies? That is open to interpretation and depends on the context. If we are modeling foreign relations between countries, then two countries are either friends or they are enemies. This is the interpretation we will take – if you are not friends, you are enemies.

To get a mathematical as opposed to visual representation of this social network, we identify each friend-link by a pair of people. For example the friend-link between A and D could be represented as (A, D). All the friend-links can be collected into a set, let us call it E. For our social network this set E would be

$$E = \{(A,C), (A,D), (C,D), (B,D), (B,E), (D,E), (E,F)\}.$$

Given the set of people V and the set of friendships E, you should feel comfortable that you could draw a picture of the friendship network as we did above.

Exercise 2.4

Compare the friendship network shown on the right with the one above in the text.

(a) Are the two friendship networks visually similar?

(b) Can this network be the same set of friends? Explain.

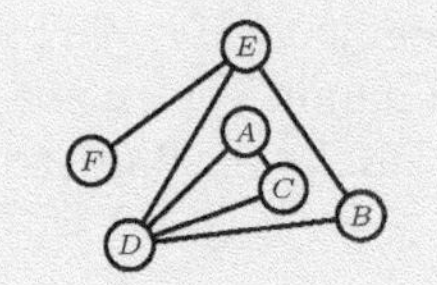

The take away from Exercise 2.4 is that different people may draw the same social network differently. The picture in Exercise 2.4 is very different from the one at the begining of this section, but they are both pictures of the same social network. What matters is who the people are, the set V, and who is friends with whom, the set E of friendships. The sets V and E together are a graph. The picture with circles and links is a visual representation of the graph. In high-school, a graph was a picture of a function $f(x)$ against x. That is not so in this book. When we say graph, visualize circles for objects with links between them identifying relationships. We refer to the picture of a function $f(x)$ against x as a plot or line-plot of the function.

Graphs model a variety of settings, not just social networks: road networks where objects are points of interest and links are roads; airport networks where objects are cities and two cities are linked if there is a non-stop flight from one to the other; etc. Graphs also model different kinds of relationships. Two examples, which occur often in computer science are affiliation graphs and conflict graphs. Affiliation graphs model the membership relationship between objects and groups to which those objects are affiliated. Conflict graphs model contention or competition between objects, for example different animals competing with each other in a food web. We illustrate affiliation and conflict graphs in the next two figures.

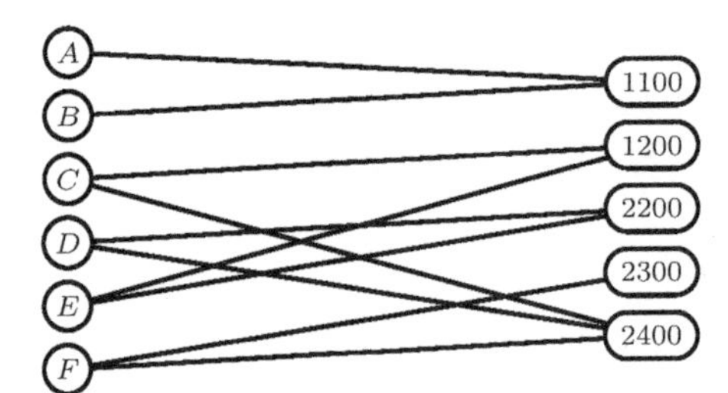

Affiliation graphs. Our friends are taking courses. The friends are on the left and the course numbers on the right. A link between a person and a course means the person is taking the course.

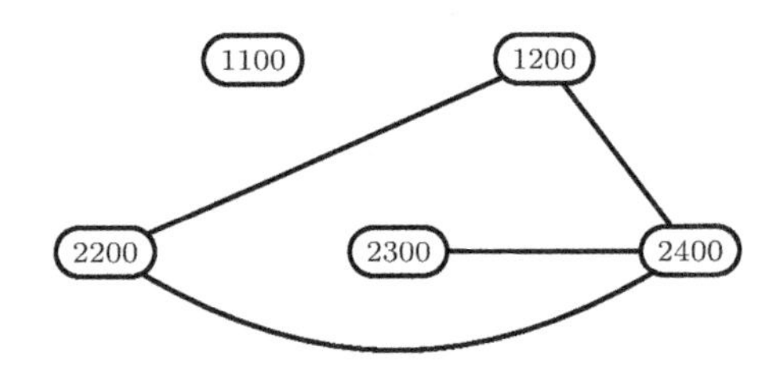

Conflict graphs. A student enrolled in two courses creates a conflict for those courses. The exams of the two courses must be at different times. A link between two courses means they conflict.

Affiliation graphs and conflict graphs are often related. The conflict graph on the right is derived from the affiliation graph on the left by linking two courses if some student is in both courses.

Pop Quiz 2.5

Which discrete object would you use to model the grid in the 2-contact EBOLA model. Explain.

2.4 Easing into Proofs

Let us ease you into proofs informally, before developing the formal infrastructure.

When is a Number a Square?

Suppose n is an integer, written $n \in \mathbb{Z}$. We would like to understand when n^2 is even. Let us tinker with the squares of the first few numbers.

n	0	± 1	± 2	± 3	± 4	± 5	± 6	± 7	± 8	± 9	± 10	± 11	...
n^2	**0**	1	**4**	9	**16**	25	**36**	49	**64**	81	**100**	121	...

We observe a few things. The squares are growing much faster than the numbers themselves. But what we care about is "When is the square even?" The even squares have been highlighted for you. At this point, it is not hard to make a guess – a conjecture.

Conjecture 2.1. Every even square came from an even number and every even number has an even square.

If we prove our conjecture, it becomes a theorem – a mathematical truth – and you can take it to the bank. Let us prove the conjecture. When n is even it means n is a multiple of 2, or $n = 2k$ for an integer k. Then,

$$n^2 = 4k^2 = 2 \cdot (2k^2).$$

Thus, n^2 is also a multiple of 2 because $2k^2$ is an integer, hence n^2 is even. Are we done? Not quite. What we have shown is that the squares of even numbers are even. That does not mean that every even square came from an even number. Since integers are either even or odd, consider an odd integer $n = 2k + 1$ for an integer k. Taking the square, we get

$$n^2 = 4k^2 + 4k + 1 = 2(2k^2 + 2k) + 1.$$

This time, n^2 is odd since it is 1 larger than a multiple of 2. So an odd integer cannot give rise to an even square, therefore an even square must have come from an even integer. Are we done? Have we shown that every even square came from an even number and every even number has an even square? Is our proof general? Yes, because we made no assumptions about n in our argument. So, our argument applies to any even n and any even n^2 which means we proved the conjecture. The conjecture is now a theorem.

Theorem 2.2. Every even square is the square of an even number and every even number has an even square.

You should be convinced of the theorem, and that is the purpose of a proof. We will slowly build a language for mathematical proofs and an infrastructure of proof patterns to standardize the notion of a proof and make things more concise. However, the purpose of a proof will always remain the same.

A proof must **convince** someone that a claim is true.

Every 6-person party has a 3-person friend clique or a 3-person war.

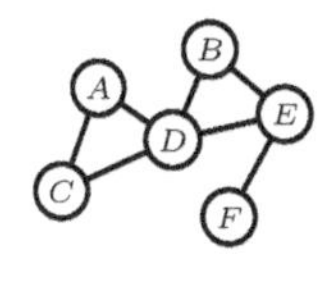

We model friendship networks using graphs. Our six friends $V = \{A, B, C, D, E, F\}$ are having a party. We reproduced their friendship network on page 17 here. Observe that $\{A, C, D\}$ are all mutual friends, and so form a 3-person friend clique. Also observe that $\{A, B, F\}$ are all mutual enemies as there are no friendships between them, so they could have a 3-person war if left unchaperoned. Our little social network has both a 3-person friend clique and a 3-person war. Is this always the case? Let's tinker with some easy examples.

If everyone was mutual friends, there can't be a 3-person war. Similarly, if everyone were enemies, there can't be a 3-person friend clique. So, in general, we cannot expect both a 3-person friend clique and a 3-person war. Is there any network with neither a 3-person friend clique nor a 3-person war? You can think of a 3-person friend clique as some kind of structure. Similarly, a 3-person war is also a kind of structure. We are asking whether there is a 6-person friendship network that has no structure.

Let's try to build a 6-person friendship network with no structure. To do so, we consider the network from the perspective of one of the friends, it might as well be Alice. If Alice has more friends than enemies, then she has at least 3 friends because there are 5 other people. The only other possibility is that she has more enemies than friends, in which case she has at least 3 enemies, again because there are 5 other people. We illustrate the two possible situations for Alice in the figure below. In (a) we show three of her friends (she has at least 3 friends) and in (b) we show three of her enemies (she has at least 3 enemies).

(a) More friends than enemies. (b) More enemies than friends.

In (a), if any pair of A's friends are also friends as indicated by the dashed line then 3 people form a friend clique. If all A's friends are mutual enemies, we have a 3-person war. So in case (a), there is either a 3-person friend clique or a 3 person war. The argument in (b) is similar. If any pair of A's enemies are also enemies, then together with A we have a 3-person war. If all A's enemies in (b) are mutual friends there is a 3-person friend clique. Since (a) and (b) are the only possibilities, in all cases it is not possible to construct such a friend network with neither a 3-person friend clique nor a 3-person war.

Theorem 2.3. Every 6-person friend network has either a 3-person friend clique or a 3-person war or both.

Every 6-person friendship network must have some structure. Isn't that interesting!

2.4.1 An Axiom: The Well-Ordering Principle

Can we prove everything? No. Some things, which we must take for granted, are the starting point for proving other things. In mathematics, we have three main types of claims:

1. **Axioms:** A self-evident statement that is asserted as true without proof.
2. **Conjectures:** A claim that is believed true but is not true until proven so.
3. **Theorems:** A proven truth. You can take it to the bank.

Axioms are taken to be true on faith. Therefore, axioms should be believable. We take high-school math for granted, for example the rules of algebra, geometry, etc., and some basic calculus. We also assume a very powerful fact that might seem obvious to you. Consider any set of positive integers. Such a set is a subset of the natural numbers, for example

$$\{2, 5, 4, 11, 7, 296, 81\}; \qquad \text{or,} \qquad \{6, 19, 24, 18, \ldots\}.$$

The first set is finite. In the second set, the "..." indicates that the set goes on forever, but we don't know how, except that every number is positive. The first set has a minimum element equal to 2. Does the second set have a minimum element? You might feel that somehow the answer is yes, but unfortunately it cannot be proved. We have to assume this fact of the natural numbers, i.e. the natural numbers are well-ordered.

Axiom 2.4 (Well-ordering principle). Any non-empty subset of $\mathbb{N}$ has a minimum element.

This seems obvious. The next exercise might convince you that the axiom is non-trivial.

> **Exercise 2.6**
> (a) Construct a subset of the integers $\mathbb{Z}$ that has no minimum element.
> (b) Construct a <u>positive</u> subset of the rationals $\mathbb{Q}$ that has no minimum element.

The well-ordering principle looks benign but it's very powerful. The game in mathematics is to string together previously established facts, i.e. axioms or theorems, to prove new interesting facts. The starting point is axioms. Let us use the well-ordering principle to prove something that looks completely unrelated.

$\sqrt{2}$ is not a rational number.[3]

$\sqrt{2}$ is not a discrete object. Our interest lies not in $\sqrt{2}$ *per-se* but in using the well-ordering principle to prove something apparently unrelated. If you believe the well-ordering principle, then you must accept that $\sqrt{2}$ is irrational. The method of proof is a little strange, and we will say much more about it later. If a number is rational, there are many ways to represent it as a ratio. For example, $\frac{2}{3} = \frac{4}{6}$. So let us try to write $\sqrt{2}$ as a ratio. If it can be done, there are many ways to do it. We collect all these ways into a hypothetical set:[4]

$$\boxed{\sqrt{2}} = \left\{ \frac{a_1}{b_1}, \frac{a_2}{b_2}, \frac{a_3}{b_3}, \frac{a_4}{b_4}, \cdots \right\},$$

where $\{a_1, a_2, \ldots\}$ are all integers and $\{b_1, b_2, \ldots\}$ are all natural numbers. The set $\boxed{\sqrt{2}}$, given that it is non-empty, implicitly defines two other sets: the numerators $\{a_1, a_2, \ldots\}$ and the denominators $\{b_1, b_2, \ldots\}$. The denominators form a set containing only natural numbers, so by the well-ordering principle, there is a minimum element. Call this minimum element b_* and the corresponding numerator a_*. So,

$$\sqrt{2} = \frac{a_*}{b_*}.$$

For b_* to be the minimum possible, it must be that a_* and b_* have no factors in common, for otherwise you could divide out that factor and get a smaller b_*.[5] Squaring both sides gives $2 = a_*^2/b_*^2$, or

$$a_*^2 = 2b_*^2.$$

Observe that a_*^2 is even since it is a multiple of 2. Recall that we proved the only way for a_*^2 to be even is for a_* to be even, that is $a_* = 2k$ (Theorem 2.2). Alas, $(2k)^2 = 2b_*^2$, or

$$b_*^2 = 2k^2.$$

Ha! b_*^2 is also even, which means b_* is even. Both a_* and b_* are even, so 2 is a common factor. Something smells fishy. What is going on? If the set $\boxed{\sqrt{2}}$ is non-empty, by the well-ordering principle there must be a minimum denominator b_*, and a_* and b_* have no common factor. But, we showed that a_* and b_* have the common factor 2. We have an impossible situation if $\boxed{\sqrt{2}}$ is non-empty. Therefore, $\boxed{\sqrt{2}}$ must be empty, in which case $\sqrt{2}$ is not a ratio and hence not rational.[6] Are you convinced?

Theorem 2.5. $\sqrt{2} \notin \mathbb{Q}$. That is, the square-root of two is not a rational number.

The method of proof is subtle, and goes by the name *reductio ad absurdum*, reduction to the absurd. In modern mathematics it is called a proof by contradiction. As Hardy comments, contradiction is far finer a gambit than a mere pawn or queen sacrifice in chess. With contradiction you give away the game and hope to steal it back later. The endpoint in the proof was something that smelled fishy. Another way to arrive at something smelling fishy is to make a mistake in the proof, and therein lies the danger in this type of gambit.

To prove $\sqrt{2}$ is not rational, we strung together several known facts. Here is a summary of those facts.

- The well-ordering principle (an axiom). Axioms are fundamental, plausible facts, and we do not prove them. Axioms are simply believed to be true. Axioms are the starting points in mathematics.
- Highschool knowledge that you either have or must accept as true without proof (e.g. algebra, basic properties of numbers, addition, multiplication, etc.). For example, we will not prove that $(x+1)^2 = x^2 + 2x + 1$. Use judgement in deciding whether some basic knowledge can be assumed. When in doubt, err on the cautious side and state your assumptions.
- Theorem 2.2 on the evenness of a square. We proved this using basic highschool math.

The final proof used these facts to convince you that $\sqrt{2}$ is not rational.

[3]Hipassus of the Pythagorean school discovered this around 500BC. The discovery was a crime, going against the Pythagorean school which held that all numbers are ratios of integers. Hipassus was sentenced to death by drowning for this crime, or his other crime which was to show how to inscribe a dodecahedron in a sphere. Mathematics is a dangerous profession.

[4]Listing the ratios implies the elements of the set can be listed out. Don't worry, we don't need this, even though it's true.

[5]In high-school, we knew this as reducing a fraction to its simplest form, or lowest terms.

[6]We take for granted a property of logic called the law of the excluded middle which says a statement is either true or false, there's no in-between. So $\boxed{\sqrt{2}}$ is either non-empty or it's empty. If it can't be non-empty, it must therefore be empty.

We did not set up any formal infrastructure for proofs. Our goal was to introduce basic proofs in the context of some elementary problems. In doing so, we have demonstrated three basic proof methods in action. Here are the proof methods we have seen.

- Direct and contrapositive proof. We used this to prove that even squares come from even numbers.
- Exhaustive proof using case by case analysis. We used this to prove our little facts about friendship cliques and wars in a 6-person social network.
- Proof by contradiction. We used this to show that $\sqrt{2}$ is irrational.

Without detailing the formal mechanics for how these proofs work, we hoped to give you an intuition for what it takes to convince somebody that a claim is true. Just as in a court of law you are innocent until proven guilty, in mathematics a claim is treated as false until proven true. Anytime you see the word proof, get prepared to be convinced, but also be skeptical.

We want to convince you of many things. So, you will see many proofs in this book. We also want you to convince others of many things, so you must become an expert in proofs. There are three main phases to making and proving a claim: identify the claim, prove it, and finally check that your proof is correct.

Three Steps for Making and Proving a Claim

Step 1: Precisely state the right thing to prove. Often, creativity and imagination are needed to identify the right claim. A trade off is usually achieved: the claim should be non-trivial otherwise it won't be useful, but the claim should also be within the realm of "the provable" given the tools you have. Most importantly, the claim should be true and how do you know that before proving it? The knack to come up with the right things to prove is a gift. Some people, like Paul Erdős, had an inordinate amount of this gift.

Step 2: Prove the claim. In any proof, some "genius" but often simple idea may be needed to make the proof go through. Again, creativity and imagination play a role. Sometimes standard proof techniques can be used. You can become proficient in these standard techniques through training and practice.

Step 3: Check the proof for correctness. No creativity is needed to look a proof in the eye and determine if it is correct, to determine if you are convinced. Never let anyone claim bogus things and convince you with invalid proofs. Make it a second nature to seek and validate proofs. Be skeptical. This advice will never let you down.

At a minimum, you should be able to precisely state what you want to prove. That is our next order of business. We will then set up an infrastructure of proof templates for proving different types of precisely stated claims. Needless to say, we cannot cover all possible proof strategies.[7] As you work through this book, and in general with all things mathematical, keep an eye out for nifty tricks and tactics for proving things. File them away, for someday they may come in handy.

A trick that is used twice becomes a method. — G. Polya

[7] It would be nice if we could list all proof strategies and write a program to prove any given theorem by exhaustively trying every strategy – an automated theorem prover. Then, we wouldn't have to worry about proving things. Ironically, it is a deep theorem of mathematics that there does not exist a general automated theorem prover. It appears that creativity will always have a place in mathematics.

2.5 Problems

Problem 2.1. What is the difference between a Theorem, a Conjecture and an Axiom?

Problem 2.2. List the elements in the following sets (E is the set of even numbers).

(a) $A = \{n \mid -4 \le n \le 15;\ n \in E\}$.
(b) $B = \{x \mid x^2 = 9;\ x \in \mathbb{Z}\}$.
(c) $C = \{x \mid x^2 = 6;\ x \in \mathbb{Z}\}$.
(d) $D = \{x \mid x = x^2 - 1;\ x \in \mathbb{R}\}$.

Problem 2.3. Give formal definitions of these sets using a variable.

(a) $A = \{0, 1, 4, 9, 16, 25, 36, \ldots\}$.
(b) $B = \{0, 4, 16, 36, 64, 100, \ldots\}$.
(c) $C = \{1, 2, 4, 7, 11, 16, 22, \ldots\}$.
(d) $D = \{\ldots, \frac{1}{8}, \frac{1}{4}, \frac{1}{2}, 1, 2, 4, 8, \ldots\}$.

Problem 2.4. On the x–y plane, sketch the points in the sets:

(a) $A = \{(x, y) \mid x \in [0, 1], y \in [0, 1]\}$.
(b) $B = \{(x, y) \mid x, y \in \mathbb{R}, x^2 + y^2 = 1\}$.
(c) $C = \{(x, y) \mid x, y \in \mathbb{R}, x^2 + y^2 \le 1\}$.
(d) $D = \{(x, y) \mid x \ge 1, y \in \mathbb{R}\}$.
(e) $E = \{(x, x^2) \mid x \in \mathbb{R}\}$.
(f) $F = \{(x, x + y) \mid x \in \mathbb{R}, y \in \mathbb{Z}\}$.

Problem 2.5. Express the shaded region using unions, intersections and complements.

(a) 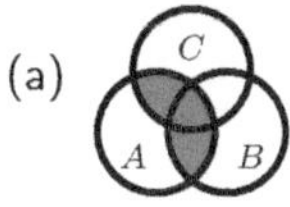

(b) 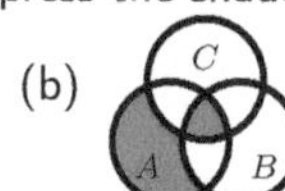

(c) 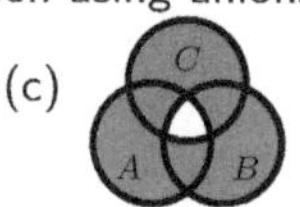

(d) 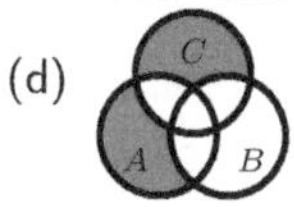

(e) 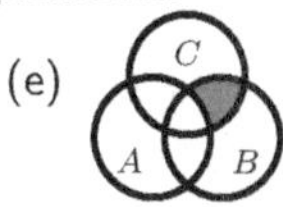

(f) 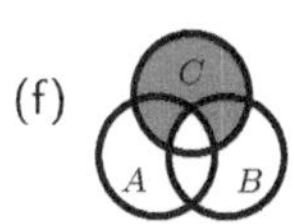

Problem 2.6. Give two sets A, B for which $A \not\subseteq B$ and $B \not\subseteq A$.

Problem 2.7. Complement depends on the universal set $\mathcal{U}$. Let $X = \{a, e\}$. What is $\overline{X}$ when:
(a) $\mathcal{U} = \{$lower case vowels$\}$. (b) $\mathcal{U} = \{$lower case letters$\}$

Problem 2.8. True or False: (a) $\mathbb{N} \subseteq \mathbb{Z}$ (b) $\mathbb{N} \subset \mathbb{Z}$ (c) $\mathbb{Z} \subseteq \mathbb{Q}$ (d) $\mathbb{Z} \subset \mathbb{Q}$

Problem 2.9. For each case, find $\bigcup_{i=1}^{\infty} A_i = A_1 \cup A_2 \cup A_3 \cup \cdots$ and $\bigcap_{i=1}^{\infty} A_i = A_1 \cap A_2 \cap A_3 \cap \cdots$.
(a) $A_i = \{n | n \in \mathbb{N}, n \ge i\}$. (b) $A_i = \{0, i\}$. (c) $A_i = \{x | x \in \mathbb{R}, 0 < x < i\}$.

Problem 2.10. Let $A_i = \{(x, y) \mid x \in [0, 1], y \in [1/(i + 1), 1/i]\}$. On the x–y plane, sketch:
(a) A_1 and A_2. (b) $A_1 \cup A_2$. (c) $A_1 \cup A_5$. (d) $A_1 \cup A_2 \cup \cdots \cup A_n = \bigcup_{i=1}^{n} A_i$. (e) $A_1 \cup A_2 \cup \cdots = \bigcup_{i=1}^{\infty} A_i$.

Problem 2.11. Let $B = \{\{a, b\}, a, b, c\}$. List the power set $\mathcal{P}(B)$ (it has 16 elements)?

Problem 2.12. List all subsets of $\{a, b, c, d\}$ that contain c but not d.

Problem 2.13. (a) What are $|M \cap V|$ and $|\mathcal{P}(M \cap V)|$ for $M = \{m, a, l, i, k\}, V = \{a, e, i, o, u\}$? (b) What is $|\,\mathbb{N}\,|$?

Problem 2.14. $|A| = 7$ and $|B| = 4$. What are the possible values for $|A \cap B|$ and $|A \cup B|$?

Problem 2.15. What is the set $\mathbb{Z} \cap \overline{\mathbb{N}} \cap S$, where $S = \{z^2 \mid z \in \mathbb{Z}\}$ is the set perfect squares.

Problem 2.16 (Cartesian Product). Let $A = \{1, 2, 3\}$ and $B = \{a, b, c, d\}$. The Cartesian product $A \times B$ is the set of pairs formed from elements of A and elements of B,

$$A \times B = \{(a, b) \mid a \in A, b \in B\}.$$

(a) List the elements in $A \times B$. What is $|A \times B|$? ($|X|$ is the number of elements in X.)
(b) List the elements in $B \times A$. What is $|B \times A|$?
(c) List the elements in $A \times A = A^2$. What is $|A \times A|$?
(d) List the elements in $B \times B = B^2$. What is $|B \times B|$?

Generalize the definition of $A \times B$ to a Cartesian product of three sets $A \times B \times C$.

Problem 2.17. Sketch the Cartesian products $\mathbb{R} \times \mathbb{R} = \mathbb{R}^2$, $\mathbb{R} \times \mathbb{N}$, $\mathbb{N} \times \mathbb{R}$, $\mathbb{N} \times \mathbb{N} = \mathbb{N}^2$. (See Problem 2.16.)

Problem 2.18. List as a set all the 4-bit binary sequences. How many did you get? Now, list all the 4-bit binary sequences in which 00 does not occur. How many did you get?

Problem 2.19. How many binary sequences are of length 1,2,3,4,5? Guess the pattern.

Problem 2.20. A sequence $s_0, s_1, s_2, s_3, \ldots$ is described below. Give a "simple" formula for the nth term s_n in the sequence, for $n = 0, 1, 2, 3, \ldots$. Your answer should be of the form $s_n = f(n)$ for some function $f(n)$.

(a) $0, 1, 2, 3, 4, 5, 6 \ldots$
(b) $1, -1, 1, -1, 1, -1, \ldots$
(c) $0, 1, -2, 3, -4, 5, -6, \ldots$
(d) $2, 0, 2, 0, 2, 0, \ldots$
(e) $1, 2, 4, 8, 16, \ldots$
(f) $1, 3, 5, 7, 9, \ldots$
(g) $1, 0, 0, 1, 1, 1, 0, 0, 0, 0, 0, 0, 0, 0, 1, 1, \ldots$
(h) $0, 3, 8, 15, 24, 35, 48, 63, \ldots$
(i) $1, 2, \frac{1}{3}, 4, \frac{1}{5}, 6, \frac{1}{7}, 8, \frac{1}{9}, 10, \frac{1}{11}, 12, \ldots$
(j) $1, \frac{1}{2}, 4, \frac{1}{8}, 16, \frac{1}{32}, 64, \frac{1}{128}, \ldots$

Problem 2.21. For each case in Problem 2.20, use a variable as in (2.1) to formally define the set of numbers.

Problem 2.22. Draw a picture of each graph representing friendships among our 6 friends $V = \{A, B, C, D, E, F\}$.
(a) $E = \{(A, B), (B, C), (C, D), (D, E), (E, F), (F, A)\}$.
(b) $E = \{(A, B), (A, C), (A, D), (A, E), (A, F)\}$.
(c) $E = \{(A, D), (B, D), (C, D), (A, E), (B, E), (C, E), (A, F), (B, F), (C, F)\}$.
(d) $E = \{(A, B), (B, C), (A, C), (D, E), (E, F), (D, F)\}$.
You should recognize familiar social structures in your pictures.

Problem 2.23. How do you get the conflict graph from the affiliation on page 18?

Problem 2.24. Model the relationship between radio-stations in Problem 1.7 using a graph.
(a) Would you use friendship networks, affiliation graphs or conflict graphs?
(b) Draw a picture of your graph for the 5 radio stations.
(c) Show that 3 radio frequencies $(1, 2, 3)$ suffice for no listener to hear garbled nonsense.

Problem 2.25 (Internet Exercise). Research these settings and explain how they can be represented by graphs:
(a) Infectious disease spread.
(b) Collaborations between academic authors.
(c) Niche overlap in ecology.
(d) Protein interactions in human metabolism.

Problem 2.26. True or false and why? Every square which is a multiple of 4 came from a multiple of 4 and every multiple of 4 has a square which is a multiple of 4.

Problem 2.27. Do you believe this method for amplifying money? Explain why or why not.

$$1¢ = \$0.01 = (\$0.1)^2 = (10¢)^2 = 100¢ = \$1.$$

Problem 2.28 (Quotient Remainder Theorem). Given are $n \in \mathbb{Z}$ and a divisor $d \in \mathbb{N}$.

Theorem. There are a unique quotient $q \in \mathbb{Z}$ and remainder $r \in \mathbb{Z}$, with $0 \le r < d$, such that $n = qd+r$.

Suppose $n = 27$ and $d = 5$; compute q and r. Can you think of a way to prove the theorem?

Problem 2.29. Mimic the method we used to prove $\sqrt{2}$ is irrational and prove $\sqrt{3}$ is irrational. Now use the same method to try and prove $\sqrt{9}$ is irrational. What goes wrong?

Problem 2.30 (Simple Continued Fractions).
For $n \ge 1$, a non-terminating continued fraction x is shown on the right.

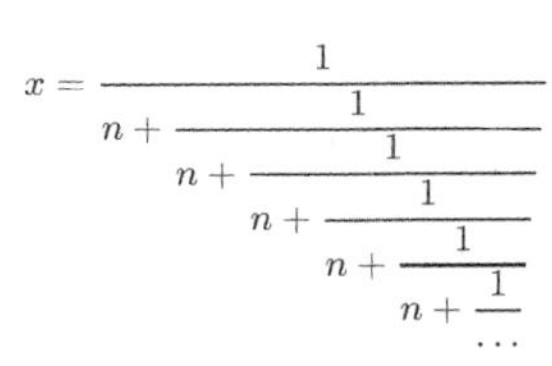

$$x = \cfrac{1}{n + \cfrac{1}{n + \cfrac{1}{n + \cfrac{1}{n + \cfrac{1}{n + \cdots}}}}}$$

Can you think of a way to show that x is irrational, for any $n \in \mathbb{N}$?
(Tinker with $n = 1$ first.)

Problem 2.31 (Ramsey). Prove a crude generalization of the 6-person party theorem. Specifically, in any n-person party, there is either a friend-clique or war with more than $\frac{1}{2}\log_2 n$ people. Here is a "constructive" proof. Make three sets C (for clique), W (for war) and V. Sets C and W are initially empty and V has all the people. We run a process in steps and continue until no one is left in V. At each step, pick any person x from V and:

- Place x in C if x is friends with more than half of V. Discard from V all the enemies of x.
- Place x in W if x is enemies with at least half of V. Discard from V all the friends of x.

(a) Show that at every step in the process, everyone in C are mutual friends and everyone in W are mutual enemies.
(b) Show that at each step in the process, the size of V shrinks from $|V|$ to no less than $\frac{1}{2}(|V| - 1)$.
(c) Show that the process continues for at least $\log_2 n$ steps, where in each step a person is added to either C or W.
(d) Show that either C or W has more than $\frac{1}{2}\log_2 n$ people at the end. Are we done?

Girl: I say there is one true soul mate for every person.
Boy: That's one busy soul mate. – **old, haggard joke**

When things get too complicated, it sometimes makes sense to stop and wonder: Have I asked the right question? – **Enrico Bombieri**

There's no sense in being precise when you don't even know what you're talking about – **John von Neumann**

Chapter 3

Making Precise Statements

Proofs are a mathematician's "rigorous" way of convincing you of something. A rigorous proof is worthless if the point being made is not clear. Here are some statements.

1. 2+2=4.
2. 2+2=5.
3. You may have cake OR candy.
4. IF pigs can fly THEN you get an A.
5. EVERY person has A soul mate.

Each statement above is either true T or false F (law of the excluded middle). The first is true and the second is false. We underlined potentially confusing words in the other statements. In the 3rd statement, can you have both cake and candy? In the 4th, clearly pigs can't fly. Does that mean you can't get an A? In the 5th statement, does every person have their own special soul mate (for me it's "Z" and for you it's "Joe"). Or, is there is a universal soul mate and all people share that same soul mate, whoever that may be?

5(a) There is a single soul mate that EVERY person shares.
5(b) EVERY person has their own special soul mate.

Big deal you say. Yes, when it comes to proof! To verify 5(b) we asked our friends $\{A, B, C, D, E, F\}$ from Chapter 1 to name a soul mate. Their replies are on the right. They all have some soul mate, so 5(b) is true. 5(a) is much harder to prove. The responses neither prove nor disprove 5(a).

A says Sue's their soul mate;
B says Joe's their soul mate;
C says Sue's their soul mate;
D's soul mate is a red Porshe;
E says Sue's their soul mate;
F says Sam's their soul mate.

Pop Quiz 3.1
(a) How would you verify 5(a) by asking questions to our 6 friends?
(b) Give two interpretations of "Every American has a dream."

Before seeking proof you must have the correct logical meaning of the claim. The building blocks of a claim are propositions. A proposition is true (T) or false (F). It may be hard (or impossible) to assign a truth value to a proposition, but the claim should be unambiguous. We use the letters $p, q, r, s, \ldots$ for propositions.

Exercise 3.2
If you can, evaluate the truth value of these propositions (true T or false F):
(a) p: Porky the pig can fly. (b) q: You got an A. (c) r: Kilam is an American. (d) s: 4^2 is even.

3.1 Compound Propositions

We build more complex claims called compound propositions by connecting basic propositions using 4 basic connectors. We must give a precise meaning to these connectors to avoid ambiguity in claims involving them.

Connector	Symbol	An example in words
NOT	$\neg p$	IT IS NOT THE CASE THAT (Porky the pig can fly)
AND	$p \wedge q$	(Porky the pig can fly) AND (You got an A)
OR	$p \vee q$	(Porky the pig can fly) OR (You got an A)
IF...THEN...	$p \to q$	IF (Porky the pig can fly) THEN (You got an A)

A compound proposition is either true or false, just like a basic proposition.

Exercise 3.3
Here are three propositions p : It is raining. q : Kilam has his umbrella. r : It is cloudy.
Write out the compound propositions below and use common sense to assign true T or false F for each:
$p \wedge r \quad p \to q \quad p \to r \quad q \to r \quad q \to p \quad r \to p.$

A mathematical claim is most often an "IF...THEN..." compound proposition. Proving a mathematical claim amounts to proving that the compound proposition is true. Therefore, we need to understand the meaning of compound propositions: When is a compound proposition true? Let us take each connector in turn.

Negation, NOT: IT IS NOT THE CASE THAT(Porky the pig can fly). A negation is true when the original proposition "Porky the pig can fly" is false. It's that simple.

The negation $\neg p$ is true when p is false, and $\neg p$ is false when p is true.

Conjunction, AND: (Porky the pig can fly) AND (You got an A). AND is as expected from English.

Both p and q must be true for $p \wedge q$ to be true. Otherwise $p \wedge q$ is false.

Since pigs cannot fly, the proposition "Porky the pig can fly" is F. We don't know whether you got an A or not in the course, but it does not matter. The conjunction is F.

Disjunction, OR: (You can have cake) OR (You can have ice-cream). OR is slightly different from common English, where you can have exactly one of cake and ice-cream (exclusive-OR). In mathematics, OR is true even if you have both cake and ice-cream. An OR is false only when both propositions are false.

Both p and q must be false for $p \vee q$ to be false. Otherwise $p \vee q$ is true.

(Porky the pig can fly) OR (You got an A) is true if you got an A and false otherwise, as pigs can't fly.

Implication, IF ..., THEN: IF (Porky the pig can fly) THEN (You got an A). Intuition says you can't get an A because pigs can't fly. Wrong! Implication is subtle but important. Most theorems are implications, e.g. "IF n^2 is even, THEN n is even." Implication is also the basis for deductions. You find out that n^2 is even. You can now infer $n \neq 5$. Here is a more familiar example not involviing flying pigs.

p : it rained last night
q : the grass is wet
$p \to q$: IF (it rained last night) THEN (the grass is wet).

What does it mean for this common-sense implication to be true? What can you conclude? Not much. Did it rain last night? Is the grass wet? We don't know. So what use is an implication?

The morning news reports rain last night. Can we say anything about the grass? Here's what we know.

IF (it rained last night) THEN (the grass is wet)	T		$p \to q$	T
It rained last night (from the morning news)	T		p	T
Is the grass wet?	**YES!**	$\therefore$	q	T

($\therefore$ means "therefore.") On the right is the general pattern of this inference using a true implication (p and q are arbitrary). Instead of watching the news, you went out and found wet grass. Did it rain last night?

IF (it rained last night) THEN (the grass is wet)	T		$p \to q$	T
The grass is wet (from walking outside)	T		q	T
Did it rain last night?	☹	$\therefore$	p	T or F

Wet grass does not mean rain – maybe sprinklers came on. The implication remains valid even if it didn't rain. Let's keep going. Suppose the morning news reports no rain last night:

IF (it rained last night) THEN (the grass is wet)	T		$p \to q$	T
It rained last night (from the morning news)	F		p	F
Is the grass wet?	☹	$\therefore$	q	T or F

No surprise here. No rain last night does not mean dry grass (perhaps sprinklers came on). Lastly, suppose you went out and the grass is dry. We surely can conclude that it couldn't have rained last night.

IF (it rained last night) THEN (the grass is wet)	T		$p \to q$	T
The grass is wet (from walking outside)	F		q	F
Did it rain?	**NO!**	$\therefore$	p	F

Here is a summary of these inferences.

For a **true** implication $p \to q$:
When p is true, you can conclude that q is true.
When q is true, you **cannot** conclude p is true.
When p is false, you **cannot** conclude q is false.
When q is false, you can conclude p is false.

Exercise 3.4

Use practical experience to determine T/F for each implication and then answer the related questions.

(a) T or F: IF it is cloudy THEN it is raining. It is cloudy. Is it raining?

(b) T or F: IF it is cloudy THEN you have your umbrella.
  (i) You have your umbrella. Is it cloudy? (ii) You do not have your umbrella. Is it cloudy?

(c) T or F: IF you study hard THEN you will get an A.
  (i) You studied hard. Did you get an A? (iii) You did not study hard. Did you get an A?
  (ii) You got an A. Did you study hard? (iv) You did not get an A. Did you study hard?

(d) T or F: IF (you are hungry OR you are thirsty) THEN you will visit the cafeteria.
  (i) You are thirsty. Did you visit the cafeteria?
  (ii) You did visit the cafeteria. Are you hungry? Are you thirsty?
  (iii) You did not visit the cafeteria. Are you hungry? Are you thirsty?

A scientist collects data to verify an implication. One night it rained. The next morning the grass was bone dry. What do you think about our implication now? It cannot be valid, because the implication says that if it rained the grass must be wet. We have a falsifying scenario where it rained and the grass is dry – a counterexample. This is the only scenario in which the implication is false. Let us define implication,

$p \to q$ is false in only one case: when p is true and q is false. In all other cases $p \to q$ is true.

We have identified when an implication is true and when it's false. Now, back to our implication

IF (Porky the pig can fly) THEN (You got an A).

Pigs can't fly, so this is like the case where it did not rain last night. When it did not rain, the grass could be wet or not. Similarly, pigs can't fly, but you can get an A ☺ (or not) and the implication is still true. It is extremely important to understand implication. All the following are the implication $p \to q$ in English.

If it rained last night then the grass is wet.	IF p THEN q
It rained last night implies the grass is wet.	p IMPLIES q
It rained last night only if the grass is wet.	p ONLY IF q
The grass is wet if it rained last night.	q IF p
The grass is wet whenever it rains.	q WHENEVER p

3.2 Truth-Tables

We summarize what we know about our 4 connectors in a truth-table, shown below.

p	q	$\neg p$	$p \wedge q$	$p \vee q$	$p \to q$
F	F	T	F	F	T
F	T	T	F	T	T
T	F	F	F	T	F
T	T	F	T	T	T

On the left are the basic propositions p and q, and all their possible truth values. On the right are the compound propositions you are interested in. The truth-table tells you the truth-value of the compound propositions for all possible truth-values of the basic propositions – that is the mathematical "meaning" of the compound proposition. When intuition fails you, always use a truth-table to figure things out. An example will help clarify things, as well as introduce us to even more complex compound propositions.

Example 3.1. Let us solve Exercise 3.4(d). Certainly if you are hungry or thirsty, then you will visit the cafeteria. So, $(p \vee q) \to r$ is true for propositions p, q and r defined by

p : you are hungry $\qquad$ q : you are thirsty $\qquad$ r : you will visit the cafeteria,

Let us construct the truth-table for $(p \vee q) \to r$. First list the eight possible truth value combinations for the basic propositions p, q and r. A systematic way to list the possible truth values is to alternate T and F for r; then, alternate two T's and two F's for q; lastly, alternate four T's and four F's for p between. In the table below, as an intermediate step we show the truth-table for $p \vee q$ and use that to get the truth-table for $(p \vee q) \to r$. We highlighted the five rows with $(p \vee q) \to r$ true. We can restrict our analysis of the three cases in Exercise 3.4(d) to these highlighted rows since the compound proposition is known to be true.

(i) *You are thirsty:* q is true, (rows 4 and 8). In both cases r is true, i.e. you visit the cafeteria.

(ii) *You did visit the cafeteria:* r is true (rows 2, 4, 6 and 8). In some cases you are hungry, and in some you are thirsty. Are you hungry? We don't know. Are you thirsty? We don't know. You could be neither (row 2) and just wander into the cafeteria.

(iii) *You did not visit the cafeteria:* r is false (only row 1). Now p and q are both false. You are neither hungry nor thirsty.

	p	q	r	$(p \vee q)$	$(p \vee q) \to r$
1.	F	F	F	F	**T**
2.	F	F	T	F	**T**
3.	F	T	F	T	**F**
4.	F	T	T	T	**T**
5.	T	F	F	T	**F**
6.	T	F	T	T	**T**
7.	T	T	F	T	**F**
8.	T	T	T	T	**T**

Truth-tables makes these kinds of logical deductions mechanical. □

Equivalent Compound Propositions. English has many ways to say the same thing. Consider these statements using p = "it rained last night" and q = "the grass is wet".

(*i*) If it rained last night then the grass is wet.	$p \to q$
(*ii*) If the grass is not wet, then it did not rain last night.	$\neg q \to \neg p$
(*iii*) Either it did not rain last night or the grass is wet.	$\neg p \vee q$

These different statements are logically equivalent – they mean the same thing. To see this mathematically,

1. *Associative:* $(p \wedge q) \wedge r \overset{\text{eqv}}{\equiv} p \wedge (q \wedge r)$;
   $(p \vee q) \vee r \overset{\text{eqv}}{\equiv} p \vee (q \vee r)$.
2. *Commutative:* $p \wedge q \overset{\text{eqv}}{\equiv} q \wedge p$;
   $p \vee q \overset{\text{eqv}}{\equiv} q \vee p$.
3. *Negations:* $\neg(\neg p) \overset{\text{eqv}}{\equiv} p$;
   $\neg(p \wedge q) \overset{\text{eqv}}{\equiv} \neg p \vee \neg q$;
   $\neg(p \vee q) \overset{\text{eqv}}{\equiv} \neg p \wedge \neg q$.
4. *Distributive:* $p \vee (q \wedge r) \overset{\text{eqv}}{\equiv} (p \vee q) \wedge (p \vee r)$;
   $p \wedge (q \vee r) \overset{\text{eqv}}{\equiv} (p \wedge q) \vee (p \wedge r)$.
5. *Implication:* $p \to q \overset{\text{eqv}}{\equiv} \neg q \to \neg p$;
   $p \to q \overset{\text{eqv}}{\equiv} \neg p \vee q$.

Figure 3.1: Rules for manipulating logical connectors.

we use their truth-tables. You should verify the truth-table below (we added $q \to p$, the converse of $p \to q$).

		(i)	*(ii)*	*(iii)*	Converse of $p \to q$
p	q	$p \to q$	$\neg q \to \neg p$	$\neg p \vee q$	$q \to p$
F	F	T	T	T	T
F	T	T	T	T	F
T	F	F	F	F	T
T	T	T	T	T	T

Compound propositions with the same truth-table are logically equivalent (mean the same thing). We use $\overset{\text{eqv}}{\equiv}$ for logical equivalence, The first three implications are logically equivalent and mean the same thing.

$$p \to q \overset{\text{eqv}}{\equiv} \neg q \to \neg p \overset{\text{eqv}}{\equiv} \neg p \vee q$$

The last proposition, the converse $q \to p$, does not have the same truth-table as $p \to q$.

Order is very important: $p \to q$ and $q \to p$ **do not** mean the same thing.

"IF you're dead, THEN your eyes are shut" and "IF you're eyes are shut, THEN you're dead" are very different!

Rather than compute a massive truth table, it is often easier to show equivalence using the rules for manipulating logical connectors in Figure 3.1. These rules are similar to the set-operation rules in Figure 2.1 on page 17. Negation is like set-complement; AND is like set-intersection; and, OR is like set-union. For example, the negation of a conjunction, $\neg(p \wedge q) \overset{\text{eqv}}{\equiv} \neg p \vee \neg q$. The negation IT'S NOT(cold and rainy) means that either it is not cold or it is not rainy, exactly as the rule says. You may verify all the rules with truth-tables.

Example 3.2. We use the rules in Figure 3.1 to derive equivalent propositions to $(q \wedge \neg r) \to \neg p$.

$$
\begin{aligned}
\boldsymbol{(q \wedge \neg r) \to \neg p} &\overset{\text{eqv}}{\equiv} \neg(q \wedge \neg r) \vee \neg p && \text{(implication)}\\
&\overset{\text{eqv}}{\equiv} (\neg q \vee r) \vee \neg p && \text{(negation)}\\
&\overset{\text{eqv}}{\equiv} \neg q \vee (r \vee \neg p) && \text{(associative)}\\
&\overset{\text{eqv}}{\equiv} \neg q \vee (\neg p \vee r) && \text{(commutative)}\\
&\overset{\text{eqv}}{\equiv} (\neg q \vee \neg p) \vee r && \text{(associative)}\\
&\overset{\text{eqv}}{\equiv} \boldsymbol{(\neg p \vee \neg q) \vee r} && \text{(commutative)}\\
&\overset{\text{eqv}}{\equiv} \neg(p \wedge q) \vee r && \text{(negation)}\\
&\overset{\text{eqv}}{\equiv} \boldsymbol{(p \wedge q) \to r} && \text{(implication)}
\end{aligned}
$$

All propositions in a derivation chain are equivalent. The ones in bold appear in Exercise 3.6. Many of our steps are trivial (e.g. commutativity). With experience you'll start omitting such trivial steps. □

Pop Quiz 3.5 [Compound Propositions and Programming]

Compound propositions are used to control the flow of a program Look at these snippets of C^{++} code.

```
if(x > 0 || (y > 1 && x < y))
    Execute instructions A, B, C.
```

```
if(x > 0 || y > 1)
    Execute instructions A, B, C.
```

Use truth-tables to show that both do the same thing. Which do you prefer and why?

Exercise 3.6

Use truth-tables or logical derivations to arrange these propositions into groups that are logically equivalent.

$\neg p \to q$ $\quad \neg q \to p$ $\quad p \vee q$ $\quad \neg(p \wedge q)$ $\quad \neg p \vee \neg q$

$(p \wedge q) \to r$ $\quad (\neg p \vee \neg q) \vee r$ $\quad (q \wedge \neg r) \to \neg p$ $\quad p \vee (q \vee r)$ $\quad \neg r \to (p \vee q)$

3.2.1 Proving an Implication

We will say more about proofs later. Here, we discuss the logic of proving a simple implication.

IF (n^2 is even) THEN (n is even).

It may be confusing that n is unknown, unlike in Exercise 3.4 where everything was concrete. What is n? Is n^2 even? Is n even? We don't know and don't care. We only care about the truth of the implication. How can we know the truth of an implication without knowing anything about the basic propositions involved? This is what is subtle about proving an implication. Let us start by introducing the basic propositions, as usual.

p : n^2 is even
q : n is even

$p \to q$

p	q	$p \to q$
F	F	T
F	T	T
T	F	F
T	T	T

The shaded row in the truth-table is the only case in which $p \to q$ is false. To prove an implication, we must prove that the shaded row cannot happen. How can we do that without knowing n? Here is how. That row asserts that q is false and p is true. If q is false, n is odd, $n = 2k + 1$. Then p is also false as n^2 is odd:

$$n^2 = 4k^2 + 4k + 1 = 2(2k^2 + 2k) + 1. \qquad \leftarrow \text{odd}$$

p and q can be true or false, but p being true *and* q being false can't occur together. We don't know n, yet we know the shaded row in the truth-table is impossible. In all other rows of the truth-table, $p \to q$ is true, hence we have proved that $p \to q$ is true. That is, "if n^2 is even then n is even" is a true implication.

3.3 Quantifiers: Statements About Many Things

EVERY Person has A soul mate.

We need to deal with this complex sentence. Let's start simple. Here are other similar claims.

Kilam has **some** gray hair.
Everyone has **some** gray hair.
Any map can be colored with 4 colors with adjacent countries having different colors.
Every even integer $n > 2$ is the sum of 2 primes *(Goldbach, 1742)*.
Someone broke this faucet.
There exists a creature with blue eyes and blonde hair.
All cars have four wheels.

All the statements are well formed claims. They are either true or false. The complexity of these claims stems form their use of words/phrases called quantifiers:

EVERY; A; SOME; ANY; ALL; THERE EXISTS.

Quantifiers are attached to nouns, e.g. "EVERYone;" "SOME hair;" and, "THERE EXISTS a creature." The noun identifies some set and the quantifier indicates that we are making a statement about some of the members of the set. The quantifier tell us about how many objects in the set we are making a statement. Compare:

My Ford Escort has four wheels;
ALL cars have four wheels.

The first statement talks about a particular car. The second makes a general statement about cars. The quantifier ALL tells us which cars. Let's formally define the set of cars,

$$C = \{c \mid c \text{ is a car}\}.$$

It seems pedantic, so bear with us. A long winded way to say "ALL cars have four wheels" is

$$\text{for all cars } c \in C, \text{ car } c \text{ has four wheels.} \tag{3.1}$$

3.3.1 Predicates

We like precise, not long-winded. We use the symbol $\forall$ to stand for "for all". Let's shorten "car c has four wheels" to $P(c)$. Our statement from (3.1) in condensed form becomes

$$\forall c \in C : P(c).$$

Read aloud: "for all c in C, the statement $P(c)$ is true." In $P(c)$ is a new concept, the predicate. A predicate $P(c)$ looks like a function $f(x)$. Like a function, a predicate takes an input or inputs. In this case $P(c)$ takes input c. Unlike a typical function which outputs a value $f(x)$, a predicate outputs a statement $P(c)$. Just like a function, the input to a predicate can be any element within its domain, which is some set. In our example, the domain is the set of cars. An example of an input is $c =$ My Ford Escort and

$$P(\text{My Ford Escort}) = \text{"car 'My Ford Escort' has four wheels."}$$

It sounds odd and it's simpler to just say "My Ford Escort has four wheels". The statement is not that odd if you view 'My Ford Escort' as the label of a particular car. When we assert $P(c)$, we mean that the statement output by predicate P for input c is true.

You've used predicates before. $\forall x \in \mathbb{R},\ x^2 \geq 0$ is an informal version of $\forall x \in \mathbb{R} : Q(x)$, where the predicate $Q(x)$ returns the statement "the value x^2 is ≥ 0". The technical term is predicate. Don't be paralyzed, it is just notation. But, the concept is very important. A predicate defines a set of statements, one for each input. Each statement output by the predicate can be true or false. Let us compare a predicate to a function.

	Predicate	Function
	$P(c)$ = "car c has four wheels"	$f(x) = x^2$
Input	object $c \in C$	parameter $x \in \mathbb{R}$
Output	**statement** $P(c)$	**value** $f(x)$
Example	$P(\text{Jen's VW})$ = "car 'Jen's VW' has four wheels"	$f(5) = 25$
	$\forall c \in C : P(c)$	$\forall x \in \mathbb{R},\ f(x) \geq 0$
Meaning	For all $c \in C$, the statement $P(c)$ is true.	For all $x \in \mathbb{R}$, $f(x)$ is ≥ 0.

Pop Quiz 3.7

Consider the predicate $P(n)$ = "n is a perfect square".

(a) Give a domain for predicate P?
(b) Is the predicate P true or false?
(c) What is $P(4)$?
(d) Which are true: $P(4)$, $P(5)$, $P(9)$.

We use predicates to make multiple claims by specifying the inputs on which the predicate is true. A common case in mathematics is to assert the predicate is true for all inputs. This is what $\forall c \in C : P(c)$ claims, that all cars have four wheels. $\forall$ is the universal quantifier. Another common quantifier in mathematics is the existential quantifier, which claims that a predicate is true for at least one possible input, for example

There EXISTS a creature with blue eyes and blonde hair.

Define the set of creatures, $A = \{a \mid a \text{ is a creature}\}$, and the predicate

$$Q(a) = \text{“}a \text{ has blue eyes and blonde hair.”}$$

We use the symbol $\exists$ to stand for "there exists." Our statement becomes

$$\exists a \in A: \ Q(a).$$

Read aloud, "There exists a creature a in the set of creatures A for which $Q(a)$ is true (i.e., a has blue eyes and blonde hair)." Words like "for all," "every," "any" and "all" are translated into mathematics using the universal quantifier $\forall$. Words like "some," "at least one" and "there exists" are translated into mathematics using the existential quantifier. The universal and existential quantifier are the main ones used in mathematics.

Exercise 3.8
Formulate predicates (and domains) and translate the following into "mathematics".
(a) Kilam has some gray hair.
(b) Any map can be 4-colored with adjacent countries having different colors.
(c) Every even integer $n > 2$ is the sum of 2 primes.
(d) There is no creature with blue eyes and blonde hair.

Universal and existential quantifiers are very different, especially when it comes to proof. To convince you that "Every car has four wheels," I must show you every car and count its wheels. It's much easier to convince you that "There is a creature with blue eyes and blonde hair." I simply find one creature with blue eyes and blonde hair. The same goes for proving a mathematical statement with the universal versus the existential quantifier. Think about what it takes to convince you of these three claims.

Claim 1. Every even integer $n \geq 2$ is the sum of two primes. [hard]
Claim 2. There is a triple of integers (a, b, c) for which $a^2 + b^2 = c^2$. [easy]
Claim 3. There is no triple of integers (a, b, c) for which $a^3 + b^3 = c^3$. [hard]

Combining quantifiers with connectors

A predicate produces a statement. That statement can be a compound statement formed using connectors. Consider the claim "There exists a creature with blue eyes and blonde hair." Define two predicates,

$$G(a) = \text{“}a \text{ has blue eyes;”} \qquad H(a) = \text{“}a \text{ has blonde hair.”}$$

Our claim is "there exists a for which $G(a) \wedge H(a)$ is true",

$$\exists a \in A : (G(a) \wedge H(a)).$$

We are quantifying a compound statement involving predicates. Notice the use of parentheses to indicate the scope of the quantifier. When the context is clear, we often leave out the domain in our quantified statements. For example, if it's clear we are talking about creatures, then we simply write $\exists a : (G(a) \wedge H(a))$. We can also define the compound predicate $R(a) = G(a) \wedge H(a)$ and write $\exists a : R(a)$.

Exercise 3.9
Which expressions below are valid statements? For the valid ones, write an "English translation". (G and H are the same predicates defined above in the text.)

$$(\exists a : G(a)) \wedge (\exists a : H(a)); \qquad (\exists b : G(b)) \wedge (\exists c : H(c)); \qquad (\exists a : G(a)) \wedge H(c).$$

3.3.2 Negation

Consider the sentence "There is no creature with blue eyes and blonde hair." That is, "IT IS NOT THE CASE THAT(There is creature with blue eyes and blonde hair),"

$$\neg(\exists a : (G(a) \wedge H(a))).$$

An equivalent claim is: for all creatures a, a does not have blue eyes and blonde hair:

$$\forall a : \neg(G(a) \wedge H(a))).$$

Now consider the negation of "All cars have four wheels," which is

"IT IS NOT THE CASE THAT(all cars have four wheels)."

This means there is a car which does not have four wheels. Using the predicate $P(c)$ = "car c has four wheels,"

$$\neg(\forall c : P(c)) \overset{\text{eqv}}{\equiv} \exists c : \neg P(c).$$

In general, you can take the negation inside the quantifier, negating the predicate, provided you change the quantifier (existential to universal or universal to existential).

For any predicate $P(x)$,
$$\neg(\forall x : P(x)) \overset{\text{eqv}}{\equiv} \exists x : \neg P(x);$$
$$\neg(\exists x : P(x)) \overset{\text{eqv}}{\equiv} \forall x : \neg P(x).$$

3.3.3 Mixing Quantifiers

We finally get to the claim which began this section,

"EVERY person has A soul mate."

As we already mentioned, in English, this sentence is ambiguous. Does every person have the same soul mate or does every person have their own soul mate? To make things precise, let's define the set of people, $A = \{a \mid a \text{ is a person}\}$. We assume a soul mate is a person. Now, define a predicate for two inputs $a, b \in A$:

$$P(a, b) = \text{"Person } a \text{ has as a soul mate person } b.\text{"}$$

Note, you can be my soul mate while I need not be yours. If we mean every person shares the same soul mate, then there exists this special soul mate who is soul mate to everyone. Here it is in mathematical notation:

$$\exists b : (\forall a : P(a, b)). \tag{3.2}$$

Read aloud: there is a soul mate b such that for every person a, $P(a, b)$ is true. We first identify this unique hard-working soul mate, then claim all people have said person as soul mate. If, instead, every person has their own soul mate, then for every person, there exists this personalized soul mate. In our notation,

$$\forall a : (\exists b : P(a, b)). \tag{3.3}$$

The mathematical meanings of (3.2) and (3.3) are now precise, and they are very different. The two statements only differ in the order of the quantifiers.

When quantifiers are mixed, the order in which they appear in the statement is important for the meaning, and the order generally cannot be switched.

Exercise 3.10

(a) For $P(a, b)$ write out the quantified proposition. Does changing the quantifier order preserve meaning?
   (i) $\forall a : (\forall b : P(a, b))$. Reversing order, is $\forall b : (\forall a : P(a, b))$ logically equivalent?
   (ii) $\exists a : (\exists b : P(a, b))$. Reversing order, is $\exists b : (\exists b : P(a, b))$ logically equivalent?

(b) Are the following valid predicates, $Q(a) = \exists b : P(a, b)$ and $R(b) = \forall a : P(a, b)$?
   Use Q and R to rewrite the statements in (3.2) and (3.3).

Exercise 3.11
In our haggard joke, the girl really meant "There is one [and only one] true soul mate for every person." Use the predicate $P(a, b)$, quantifiers and connectors to formulate this claim precisely.

3.3.4 Proofs with Quantifiers

Here are two claims, more on the mathematical side.

Claim 1. $\forall n > 2$: IF n is even, THEN n is a sum of two primes. *(Goldbach, 1742)*
Claim 2. $\exists(a, b, c) \in \mathbb{N}^3 : a^2 + b^2 = c^2$.

In claim 1, the domain of the quantifier is the natural numbers greater than 2. In claim 2, the domain is triples of natural numbers (a, b, c) and this domain is written as $\mathbb{N}^3$. Claim 1 (known as Goldbach's conjecture) has no known proof. One must show that the predicate is true for every value of $n > 2$:

"IF 3 is even, THEN 3 is the sum of two primes" [true because 3 is not even.]
"IF 4 is even, THEN 4 is the sum of two primes" [true because $4 = 2 + 2$.]
"IF 5 is even, THEN 5 is the sum of two primes" [true because 5 is not even.]
"IF 6 is even, THEN 6 is the sum of two primes" [true because $6 = 3 + 3$.]
"IF 7 is even, THEN 7 is the sum of two primes" [true because 7 is not even.]
"IF 8 is even, THEN 8 is the sum of two primes" [true because $8 = 5 + 3$.]
⋮ ⋮

We have to show that an infinite number of IF... THEN... statements are true, one for every $n > 2$. You can imagine that this is going to be tough.

Here is a proof of claim 2. Set $a = 3, b = 4, c = 5$ and observe that $3^2 + 4^2 = 5^2$. That's it! To prove an existential claim, you just need to find one instance where the predicate is true. Proving an existential claim is usually much easier than proving a universal claim.

Exercise 3.12
Which of the following claims are easier to disprove, and why?
(a) $\forall n \in \mathbb{N} : 2^{(2^n)} + 1$ is prime. ($2^{(2^n)} + 1$ is called a Fermat number.)
(b) $\exists(a, b, c) \in \mathbb{N}^3 : a^3 + b^3 = c^3$. (This is a special case of Fermat's last theorem.)
(To disprove a claim you show that the negation of the claim is true.)

3.4 Deduction Versus Induction

Here is a classic deductive argument. Someone tells you that p is true, where p is the strange claim:

p: IF (The earth is not flat) THEN (Pigs can fly)

With age comes the wisdom that the earth is round. Now, you can deductively conclude that pigs can fly. Deduction gives a hardcore proof that you can take to the bank. As long as p is true, the deduction is sound. The deduction is based on the knowledge that p is true and later the knowledge that the earth is round. How did we get this knowledge? In life it is a process called induction. With "enough" evidence for a claim you assert its truth. From the fanciful we move to the mundane.

ALL ravens are black.

Indeed, all 27 ravens I know are black. Every black raven I observe strengthens my belief in this claim and at some point I put it into my knowledge bank as a fact. That's induction and its very tricky (see Problem 3.58). Later, we will see a technique called mathematical induction which does indeed allow you to make a few observations and conclude something is true always, but one more ingredient will be added.

3.5 Problems

Problem 3.1. Determine T/F. If you think a statement is not a valid proposition, explain why.

(a) "2+7=10."
(b) "There are no wild killer bees in Alaska."
(c) "Miami is not in Florida."
(d) "Where is the train station?"
(e) "$2x > 5$."
(f) "$2^n < 100$."
(g) "There is a lot of pollution in Mumbai."
(h) "The answer to this question is F."

Problem 3.2. True or False: "The function f equals 5?" Explain.

Problem 3.3. True or False: "IF God exists, THEN the square of any real number is non-negative.". Explain

Problem 3.4. Define the propositions p = "Kilam is a CS major" and q = "Kilam is a hockey player". Use the connectors $\wedge, \vee, \neg$ to formulate these claims.

(a) Kilam is a hockey player and CS major.
(b) Kilam either plays hockey or is a CS major.
(c) Kilam plays hockey, but he is not a CS major.
(d) Kilam is neither plays hockey nor is a CS major.
(e) Kilam is a CS major or a hockey player, not both.
(f) Kilam is not a hockey player, but is a CS major.

Problem 3.5. What is the negation of these statements?

(a) Jan is rich and happy.
(b) If Kilam was born yesterday, then pigs fly.
(c) Niaz was born yesterday and pigs can't fly.
(d) Kilam's phone has at least 8GB of RAM.
(e) If Kilam is in pajamas, then all lights are off.
(f) Every student is a friend of another student.
(g) Some student is a friend of another student.
(h) All Kilam's friends are big and strong.

Problem 3.6. Kilam's has 2GB of RAM Liamsi has 4GB of RAM. Which propositions are true?

(a) IF Kilam has more RAM than Liamsi THEN pigs fly.
(b) IF Liamsi has more RAM than Kilam THEN pigs fly.
(c) Kilam has more RAM than Liamsi AND pigs fly.
(d) Kilam has more RAM than Liamsi OR pigs fly.
(e) Liamsi has more RAM than Kilam AND pigs fly.
(f) Liamsi has more RAM than Kilam OR pigs fly.

Problem 3.7. There are 3 spoons, 4 forks and 4 knives. How many utensils are:
(a) Forks or knives. (b) Forks and knives. (c) Neither Forks nor knives.

Problem 3.8. Rewrite each sentence in "IF..., THEN..." form.

(a) You pass the FOCS-final exam only if you studied this book for at least one week.
(b) Attending class is necessary for passing the course.
(c) For a quadrilateral to be square, it is sufficient that it have four equal angles.
(d) For a quadrilateral to be square, it is necessary that it have four equal sides.
(e) A natural number can't be an odd prime unless it is greater than 2.
(f) The giant flies come out whenever it is hot.
(g) All roads lead to Rome.

Problem 3.9. If the blind-spot indicator on the wing-mirror of a car lights up, there is car in your blind spot and it's not safe to switch lanes. The blind-spot indicator is not lit. Does it mean you can switch lanes or should you look first?

Problem 3.10. Ifar's parents always told him: "If you don't eat your peas, you can't have ice-cream." Naturally, Ifar always ate his peas and eagerly expected his ice-cream to come. Are Ifar's parents obliged to give him ice-cream? What statement did Ifar think he heard, and is that logically equivalent to what his parents actually said.

Problem 3.11. What's the difference between these marketing slogans? Which is the more impressive claim?

"If you didn't buy your car from FOCS-Auto, then you paid too much."
"If you bought you car from FOCS-Auto, then you didn't pay too much."

Problem 3.12. Trolls are knights who are honest or knaves who are liars. Troll 1 says: "If we are brothers, then we are knaves." Troll 2 says: "We are brothers or knaves." (a) Can both trolls be knights? (b) Can both trolls be knaves?

Problem 3.13. If it rains on a day, it rains the next day. Today it didn't rain. On which days must there be no rain?
(a) Tommorrow. (b) All future days. (c) Yesterday. (d) All previous days.

Problem 3.14. For $p=$ "You're sick", $q=$ "You miss the final", $r=$ "You pass FOCS". Translate into English:
(a) $q\to\neg r$. (b) $(p\to\neg r)\vee(q\to\neg r)$. (c) $(p\wedge q)\vee(\neg q\wedge r)$.

Problem 3.15. Here is a logic puzzle from a pshchology experiment studying how humans perform deductive analysis. You have before you the cards (only the top is visible). Each card has a number on one side and a letter on the other.

 5  T 3 4

Rule: If a card has a P on it, then the other side must be a 5.

To verify that the rule is not been broken, which are the fewest cards that you need to turn over, and why?

Problem 3.16. Here is a logic puzzle from a bar setting.

Law: If you are drinking beer, then you must be 21 or older.

The bouncer sees 4 people A,B,C,D shown on the right. Which of the following must the bouncer check to ensure the bar abides by the law.
(a) A's age. (b) B's age. (c) C's drink. (d) D's drink.

A is drinking a beer;
B is drinking a coke;
C is drinking something and looks under 21;
D is drinking something and looks over 50.

Problem 3.17. Here's what we know about Kilam.

1: Kilam eats Italian or French each night.
2: He eats French or wears dress shoes.
3: Whenever he eats Italian and wears a coat, he does not wear a bow tie.
4: He never eats French unless he also wears a coat or dress shoes.
5: If he wears dress shoes, he wears a coat.

(a) Will Kilam ever be without a coat? (b) Today, Kilam was wearing a bow tie. What else did he wear? What did he eat?

Problem 3.18 (Converse, Contrapositive). The converse of an implication $p\to q$ is $q\to p$; the contrapositive is $\neg q\to\neg p$. For each implication, give the converse and contrapositive.

(a) If $\frac{a}{b}$ and $\frac{b}{c}$ are in $\mathbb{Z}$, then $\frac{a}{c}\in\mathbb{Z}$.
(b) $x^2=1\to x=1$.
(c) If $x^2=x+1$, then $x=\frac{1}{2}(1\pm\sqrt{5})$.
(d) If $p>2$ is prime, then p is odd.
(e) $ab=0\to a=0$ or $b=0$.
(f) If $n\in\mathbb{N}$ ends in 3, then 3 divides n.
(g) For $n\in\mathbb{Z}$, $3n=9\to n^2=9$.
(h) For $n\in\mathbb{Z}$, $n^2>9\to n>3$.
(i) For $n\in\mathbb{N}$, $n^2>9\to n>3$.
(j) If $n\in\mathbb{N}$ is odd then n^2+n-2 is even.
(k) Every connected graph G has 32 vertices.
(l) Honk if you love FOCS.

In each case, if you can, determine true or false for the converse and contrapositive (both can be true or false).

Problem 3.19. Mathematically formulate the usual meaning of each sentence using p,q,r.

(a) p: "you will succeed at this job"; q: "you know Java"; r: "you know Python".
Sentence: IF you know Java or Python, you will succeed at this job."
(b) p: "you buy a lunch entree"; q: "you can have soup"; r: "you can have salad".
Sentence: IF you buy a lunch entree, you can have soup or salad."
(c) p: "you may enter the US"; q: "you have a job"; r: "you have a green-card".
Sentence: IF you have a job or green-card, you may enter the US."

Problem 3.20 (DNF). Use $\neg,\wedge,\vee$ to give compound propositions with these truth-tables. *[Hints: Consider only rows which are* T *and use* OR *of* AND*'s.]*

(a)

q	r	
T	T	F
T	F	T
F	T	F
F	F	F

(b)

q	r	
T	T	F
T	F	T
F	T	F
F	F	T

(c)

p	q	r	
T	T	T	F
T	T	F	F
T	F	T	F
T	F	F	F
F	T	T	F
F	T	F	T
F	F	T	F
F	F	F	F

(d)

p	q	r	
T	T	T	F
T	T	F	T
T	F	T	F
T	F	F	F
F	T	T	T
F	T	F	T
F	F	T	F
F	F	F	F

(AND-OR-NOT formulas use only $\neg,\wedge,\vee$. Any truth-table can be realized by an AND-OR-NOT formula. Even more, one can construct an OR of AND's, the disjunctive normal form (DNF).)

Problem 3.21. Give pseudocode for a program that takes the input $n \in \mathbb{N}$ and outputs all the possible truth values (rows in the truth table) for the statements $p_1, p_2, \ldots, p_n$. The correct output for $n = 1$ and $n = 2$ are shown. We suggest you either use recursion or a while loop.

p_1
F
T

p_1	p_2
F	F
F	T
T	F
T	T

Problem 3.22. How many rows are in the truth table of $\neg(p \vee q) \wedge \neg r$? Give the truth table.

Problem 3.23.
(a) Give the truth-table for these compound propositions.

$$p \wedge \neg p; \quad p \vee \neg p; \quad p \rightarrow (p \vee q); \quad ((p \rightarrow q) \wedge (\neg q)) \rightarrow \neg p.$$

(b) How many rows are in the truth-table of the proposition $(p \vee q) \rightarrow (r \rightarrow s)$.
(c) Show that $(p \rightarrow q) \vee p$ is ALWAYS true. This is called a tautology.

Problem 3.24. Let $q \rightarrow p$ be F and $q \rightarrow r$ be T. Answer T/F: (a) $p \vee q$ (b) $p \rightarrow q$ (c) $p \wedge q \wedge r$.

Problem 3.25. Given the information, answer the question true, false or I don't know.
(a) IF you ace the quiz and final, THEN you get an A. You aced the final. Did you get an A?
(b) IF you ace the quiz or final, THEN you get an A. You aced the final. Did you get an A?
(c) IF you ace the quiz and final, THEN you get an A. You got an A. Did you ace the final?
(d) IF you ace the quiz or final, THEN you get an A. You got an A. Did you ace the final?
(e) IF you ace the quiz and final, THEN you get an A. You got a B. Did you ace the final?
(f) IF you ace the quiz or final, THEN you get an A. You got a B. Did you ace the final?

Problem 3.26. Given the information, answer the question true, false or I don't know.
(a) IF it rains, THEN Kilam brings an umbrella. It did not rain. Did Kilam bring an umbrella?
(b) EVERYONE who eats apples is healthy. Kilam is healthy. Does Kilam eat apples?
(c) EVERYONE who eats apples is healthy. Kilam is not healthy. Does Kilam eat apples?
(d) EVERYONE who eats apples is healthy. Kilam eats apples. Is Kilam healthy?
(e) You can have cake OR ice-cream. You had cake. Can you have ice-cream?
(f) Lights are turned on in the night. Lights are off. Is it day?
(g) Lights are turned on in the night. It is day. Are the lights on?
(h) IF you are a singer, THEN you don't eat cheese. You don't eat cheese. Are you a singer?

Problem 3.27. It rains on Tuesdays. When it rains, Kilam does not run. When it's dry, Kilam either runs or goes to work early. When Kilam runs, he must eat breakfast. All people have coffee with breakfast. Answer T/F/I don't know.
(a) Today is Wednesday, so Kilam had coffee.
(b) Today, Kilam went to work early, so it did not rain.
(c) Today, Kilam did not go for a run, so either it is Tuesday or Kilam went early to work.
(d) On Friday, Kilam did not go to work early, so he must have had coffee.
(e) On Friday, Kilam did not go to work early, so either it rained or Kilam had coffee.

Problem 3.28. On your back bumper is a sticker saying "Honk if you love FOCS." What can you conclude about the driver in the car behind you if: (a) You hear honking? (b) You don't hear any honking?

Problem 3.29. For each pair of implications, determine which one is likely to be true in practice.
(a) If I was in the rain, then my hair is wet.
If my hair is wet, then I was in the rain.
(b) If you have a CS-degree, then you took FOCS.
If you took FOCS, then you have a CS-degree.

Problem 3.30. Sherrif Suzie and Big Mike debate the implication

If $n \in \mathbb{N}$ is odd, then $n^2 + 4$ is prime.

Suzie tries to convince Mike it's false by giving a counterexample (right).
(a) Why is Sherrif Suzie only trying odd n to find a counterexample?
(b) Does the conversation convince you that the implication is true? If not, why not?
(c) Find a counterexample to show that the implication is false.

SS: Perhaps 1 is a counterexample.
BM: Nope: $1^2 + 4 = 5$, which is prime.
SS: What about 3?
BM: Nope: $3^2 + 4 = 13$, which is prime.
SS: Let's try 5?
BM: No again: $5^2 + 4 = 29$, a prime.
SS: You win. The implication seems true.
BM: Phew! I'm tired. Let's have a drink.

Problem 3.31. Use truth tables to determine logical equivalence of compound statements.
(a) Are $(p \to q) \to r$ and $p \to (q \to r)$ (b) $(p \wedge \neg q) \vee q$ and $p \vee q$.

Problem 3.32. Use truth-tables to verify the rules for derivations in Figure 3.1 on page 29. Now use the rules in Figure 3.1 to show logical equivalence $\neg((p \wedge q) \vee r) \overset{\text{eqv}}{\equiv} (\neg p \wedge \neg r) \vee (\neg q \wedge \neg r)$.

Problem 3.33. Show that $(p \to q) \vee (q \to p)$ is always true for arbitrary statements p, q.

Problem 3.34 (Satisfiability). We list four clauses using the propositions p, q, r, s.

$$(\overline{p} \vee q) \qquad (\overline{q} \vee r) \qquad (\overline{r} \vee s) \qquad (\overline{s} \vee q)$$

Give a truth assignment (T/F) to each of p, q, r, s so that every clause is true, i.e. satisfied.

Problem 3.35. Assign T/F to p, q, r, s to make the compound proposition true (if possible).
(a) $(p \to q) \wedge (q \leftrightarrow \neg p)$. (b) $(p \vee \neg r) \wedge (r \wedge s) \wedge (\neg s \wedge \neg p) \wedge (p \wedge (q \to r))$. (c) $(p \leftrightarrow q) \to \neg(p \to q)$.

Problem 3.36. Using statements p, q, r, s, we list eight clauses. Each clause is an OR of 3 terms, where a term is a statement or its negation. A proposition appears at most once in a clause.

$$(p \vee q \vee r) \quad (\overline{q} \vee r \vee s) \quad (\overline{p} \vee q \vee s) \quad (\overline{p} \vee q \vee r) \quad (p \vee r \vee \overline{s}) \quad (\overline{p} \vee \overline{q} \vee s) \quad (\overline{p} \vee \overline{r} \vee s) \quad (\overline{p} \vee q \vee \overline{s})$$

(a) Give a truth assignment (T or F) to each of p, q, r, s so that every clause is true (satisfied).
(b) Construct eight clauses for which no truth assignment to p, q, r, s can satisfy all eight clauses.
(c) Show that it is always possible to satisfy at least 7 of the 8 clauses, no matter how many variables there are, as long as there are exactly three terms in each clause.

Problem 3.37. For the domain of all students, use the predicates $S(x)$ = "x is a student", $I(x)$ = "x is a smart" and $F(x, y)$ = "x is a friend of y" to formulate the following statements.
(a) Kilam is a student.
(b) All students are smart.
(c) No student is a friend of Kilam.
(d) Every student is a friend of some other student.
(e) There is a student who is a friend of every other student.
(f) All smart students have a friend.

Problem 3.38. What is the negation of each statement. You are being asked to "translate" a negation like IT IS NOT THE CASE THAT(Kilam is a student) into "normal" English.
(a) Kilam is a student.
(b) All students are smart.
(c) No student is a friend of Kilam.
(d) Every student is a friend of some other student.
(e) There is a student who is a friend of every other student.
(f) All smart students have a friend.

Problem 3.39. Use predicates and connectors to precisely state each interpretation of "Every American has a dream."
(a) There is a single dream, the "American dream," and every American has that same special dream.
(b) Every American has their own personal dream (possibly a different one for each person).
(c) Every American has one (and only one) personal dream (possibly a different one for each person).

Problem 3.40. Give the negation of each claim in sensible English. Start with IT IS NOT THE CASE THAT($\cdot$) and then take the negation inside the quantifiers.
(a) There is a constant C for which $n^3 \leq Cn^2$ for all $n \in \mathbb{N}$.
(b) For some $x > 0$, there is a constant C for which, for all $n \in \mathbb{N}$, $n^{2+x} \leq Cn^2$.

Problem 3.41. Give the negation of each claim. Simplify your statement so that the negation, $\neg$, is not to the left of any quantifier. Determine which of the original statement or the negation is T. (Can both be T? Can neither be T?)
(a) $\forall x \in \mathbb{Z} : (\exists y \in \mathbb{Z} : x{+}2y = 3)$. (b) $\exists x > 0 : (\forall y > 0 : xy < x)$. (c) $\exists (x, y) \in \mathbb{Z}^2 : (x{+}y = 13) \wedge (xy = 36)$.

Problem 3.42. On the Isle-of-FOCS are Saints who always tell the truth and Sinners who always lie.
(a) Two people, A and B, made these statements. Which (if any) of them must be Saints?
A: "Exactly one of us is lying." B: "At least one of us is telling the truth."
(b) Three people, A, B, C, made these statements. Which (if any) of them must be Saints?
A: "Exactly one of us speaks the truth." B: "We are all lying." C: "The other two are lying."

Problem 3.43. For $x \in \{1, 2, 3, 4, 5\}$ and $y \in \{1, 2, 3\}$, determine T/F with short justifications.
(a) $\exists x : x{+}3 = 10$ (b) $\forall x : y{+}3 \leq 7$ (c) $\exists x : (\forall y : x^2 < y{+}1)$ (d) $\forall x : (\exists y : x^2{+}y^2 < 12)$

Problem 3.44. For $x, y \in \mathbb{Z}$, determine T/F with short justifications.
(a) $\forall x : (\exists y : x = 5/y)$ (b) $\forall x : (\exists y : y^4 - x < 16)$ (c) $\forall x : (\forall y : \log_2 x \neq y^3)$

Problem 3.45. Let $P(x,h)$ = "Person x has hair h" and $M(h)$ = "Hair h is grey". Formulate:

(a) Kilam has some grey hair.
(b) Someone has all grey hair.
(c) Nobody is bald.
(d) Kilam does not have all grey hair.

Problem 3.46. Formulate the appropriate predicates, identify the domain of the predicate and give the "mathematical" version of the following statements.

(a) Every person has at most one job.
(b) Kilam has some grey hair.
(c) Everyone has some grey hair.
(d) Everyone is a friend of someone.
(e) All professors consider their students as a friend.
(f) No matter what integer you choose, there is always an integer that is larger.
(g) Every natural number has a prime factorization.
(h) Two courses which have the same student cannot have exam times that overlap.
(i) No student has won a TV game-show.
(j) There is a soul-mate for everyone.
(k) 15 is a multiple of 3. (In your predicate you must define what a multiple is.)
(l) 15 is not a multiple of 4.
(m) 16 is a perfect square. (In your predicate you must define what a perfect square is.)
(n) Every student in FOCS has taken a course in calculus and a course in programming.
(o) Every CS-major who graduates has taken FOCS.
(p) Between any two rational numbers there is another rational number.
(q) Between any rational number and larger irrational number is another irrational number.
(r) Between any rational number and larger irrational number is another rational number.

Problem 3.47. Use quantifiers to precisely formulate the associative laws for multiplication and addition and the distributive law for multiplication over addition.

Problem 3.48. For the predicates $F(x)$="x is a freshman" and $M(x)$="x is a math major', translate into English:
(a) $\exists x : M(x)$ (b) $\neg\exists x : F(x)$ (c) $\forall x : (M(x) \to \neg F(x))$ (d) $\neg\exists x : (M(x) \wedge \neg F(x))$

Problem 3.49. What is the difference between $\forall x : (\neg\exists y : P(x) \to Q(y))$ and $\neg\exists y : (\forall x : P(x) \to Q(y))$?

Problem 3.50. P and Q are predicates. Are these pairs of statements equivalent. Explain.
(a) $\forall x : (\neg\exists y : P(x) \to Q(y))$ and $\neg\exists x : (\exists y : P(x) \to Q(y))$.
(b) $\forall x : (\neg\exists y : P(x) \to Q(y))$ and $\neg\exists y : (\forall x : P(x) \to Q(y))$.

Problem 3.51. Let $P(x)$ and $Q(y)$ be predicates. Verify that these quantified compound propositions are equivalent. (To show that quantified predicates are equivalent, show that when one is true, the other is true and *vice versa*.)

$$\forall x : (\neg\exists y : P(x) \to Q(y)) \quad \text{and} \quad \neg\exists x : (\exists y : P(x) \to Q(y)).$$

Problem 3.52. Let $P(x)$ and $Q(x)$ be arbitrary predicates. Prove or disprove:
(a) $\forall x : (P(x) \wedge Q(x)) \overset{\text{eqv}}{\equiv} (\forall x : P(x)) \wedge (\forall x : Q(x))$ (b) $\forall x : (P(x) \vee Q(x)) \overset{\text{eqv}}{\equiv} (\forall x : P(x)) \vee (\forall x : Q(x))$

Problem 3.53. Suppose P and Q are predicates taking an input whose domain is D which happens to be an empty domain. If you can, determine the truth values of:
(a) $\forall x : P(x)$ (b) $\exists y : P(y)$ (c) $(\forall x : P(x)) \vee (\exists y : P(y))$ (d) $(\forall x : P(x)) \vee P(y)$

Problem 3.54. Determine if each quantified compound statement is always true. If no, give a counterexample (specify the predicate and domain). If yes, explain why. (a) $(\exists x : P(x)) \to (\forall x : P(x))$ (b) $(\forall x : P(x)) \to (\exists x : P(x))$.

Problem 3.55. x and y are integers. Answer true or false, explaining your reasoning.
(a) $\forall x : (\exists y : 2x - y = 0)$
(b) $\forall y : (\exists x : 2x - y = 0)$
(c) $\exists x : (\forall y : 2x - y = 0)$
(d) $\exists y : (\forall x : 2x - y = 0)$
(e) $\exists x : (\forall y : x2^y = 0)$
(f) $\exists y : (\forall x : x2^y = 0)$

Problem 3.56. In which (if any) of the domains $\mathbb{N}, \mathbb{Z}, \mathbb{Q}, \mathbb{R}$ are these claims T. (x and y can have different domains.)
(a) $\exists x : x^2 = 4$ (b) $\exists x : x^2 = 2$ (c) $\forall x : (\exists y : x^2 = y)$ (d) $\forall y : (\exists x : x^2 = y)$

Problem 3.57. True or false. A counterexample to "ALL ravens are black" must be: (a) Non-raven. (b) Non-black.

Problem 3.58 (Hempel's Paradox). Do you believe in induction? Consider the claim "ALL ravens are black."

(a) You observe a black raven. Does that strengthen your belief that "ALL ravens are black?" Is it a proof?

(b) You observe a white sock. Does that strengthen your belief that "ALL non-black things are not ravens?"

(c) Show that "ALL ravens are black." is logically equivalent to "ALL non-black things are not ravens." So, does inductive logic suggest that observing a white sock strengthens your belief that "ALL ravens are black?" Hmm...

Problem 3.59 (Closure). A set $\mathcal{S}$ is closed under an operation if performing that operation on elements of $\mathcal{S}$ returns an element in $\mathcal{S}$. Here are five examples of closure.

$\mathcal{S}$ is closed under addition $\rightarrow$ $\forall(x, y) \in \mathcal{S}^2 : x + y \in \mathcal{S}$.
$\mathcal{S}$ is closed under subtraction $\rightarrow$ $\forall(x, y) \in \mathcal{S}^2 : x - y \in \mathcal{S}$.
$\mathcal{S}$ is closed under multiplication $\rightarrow$ $\forall(x, y) \in \mathcal{S}^2 : xy \in \mathcal{S}$.
$\mathcal{S}$ is closed under division $\rightarrow$ $\forall(x, y \neq 0) \in \mathcal{S}^2 : x/y \in \mathcal{S}$.
$\mathcal{S}$ is closed under exponentiation $\rightarrow$ $\forall(x, y) \in \mathcal{S}^2 : x^y \in \mathcal{S}$.

Which of the five operations are the following sets closed under? (a) $\mathbb{N}$. (b) $\mathbb{Z}$. (c) $\mathbb{Q}$. (d) $\mathbb{R}$.

Problem 3.60. Compute the number of positive divisors of the following integers:

$$6, 8, 12, 15, 18, 30 \qquad\qquad 4, 9, 16, 25, 36$$

State a precise conjecture that relates a property of the number of divisors of n to a property of n (proof not needed). (You may define convenient notation, for example let $\phi(n)$ be the number of positive divisors of n).

Problem 3.61. Use dominos to tile an 8×8 chessboard with two opposite-color squares removed. Tinker. Formulate a precise conjecture about whether the board with missing squares can be tiled. You don't have to prove your conjecture.

Problem 3.62. In the Ebola model, a square is infected if at least two (non-diagonal) neighbors are infected.

(a) An initial infection is shown. Show the final state of the grid, i.e., who is ultimately infected.

(b) Are there 5 initial infections that can infect the whole 6×6 square. What about with 6 initial infections? Also try the 4×4 and 5×5 grids.

(c) For the $n \times n$ grid, $n \in \mathbb{N}$, formulate a conjecture for the fewest initial infections required to infect the whole square. You do not have to prove your claim, but be **precise** in your statement.

(d) **[Hard]** Can you think of a way to justify your conjecture?

Problem 3.63. For n numbers $x_1, \ldots, x_n$, the average $\mu = \frac{1}{n}\sum_{i=1}^{n} x_i$ and the average of squares $s^2 = \frac{1}{n}\sum_{i=1}^{n} x_i^2$. Tinker with some numbers and $n = 2, 3$, computing μ^2 and s^2. Make a conjecture that relates μ^2 and s^2.

Problem 3.64 (Josephus Problem). From n children, a winner is to be picked by standing the children in a circle and then proceeding around the circle removing every other child until one remains (the winner). (Variants of this method are popular: 1 potato, 2 potato, 3 potato, 4; 5 potato, 6 potato, 7 potato, more and Eeny, meeny, miny, moe.) Number the children $1, \ldots, n$, in order as they stand in the circle (the process starts at child 1, and child 2 is the first to be removed). Let $J(n)$ be the winner when there are n children.

(a) For $n = 8$, in what order are the children removed? Who is the winner (what is $J(8)$).

(b) Compute $J(2), J(4), J(8), J(16), J(32)$. Can you guess $J(64)$?

(c) Compute $J(3), J(6), J(12), J(24), J(48)$. Can you guess $J(96)$?

(d) Formulate a conjecture for $J(2^k)$ for $k \geq 0$. You don't have to prove it.

(e) Formulate a conjecture for $J(q2^k)$ in terms of $J(q)$, for $k \geq 0$. You don't have to prove it.

(f) **[Hard]** Tinker like crazy and formulate a conjecture for $J(n)$. You don't have to prove it.

(In one version of the legend, Jewish historian Flavius Josephus and 40 other Jews are trapped in a cave by Romans. Instead of surrender, they stood in a circle, picking every seventh person to die at the hand of the next person picked (the last man standing commits suicide). Josephus determined where he and a friend should stand to be the last two men standing, at which point they promptly surrendered. Can you figure out where they stood?)

Problem 3.65 (Internet task). The function $f : A \mapsto B$ maps A to B. Lookup definitions of 1-to-1 (injection), onto (surjection), invertible (bijection) and give examples of each type of function when A and B are given by:

(a) $A = \{1, 2\}$, $B = \{a, b\}$ (b) $A = \{1, 2\}$, $B = \{a, b, c\}$ (c) $A = \{1, 2, 3\}$, $B = \{a, b\}$.

(If you think it cant be done for specific cases, explain why.)

Obvious is the most dangerous word in mathematics. – **E. T. Bell**

A heavy warning used to be given that pictures are not rigorous; this has never had its bluff called and has permanently frightened its victims into playing for safety. – **John E. Littlewood**

Few things are harder to put up with than a good example. – **Mark Twain**

Chapter 4

Proofs

1: Implication: IF ..., THEN ...
2: Proof patterns: direct proof; contraposition; contradiction; proofs about sets.

A common task is to reason from known facts and deduce something new.

It rained last night (fact); the grass is wet ("deduced").

Mathematicians are a curious lot who live in an abstract world and reason about facts that are not known to be true. What does that mean? Compare what we just deduced above with the following statement.

IF it rained last night, THEN the grass is wet.

This claim connects two facts. The connection is useful even though, at this moment, we have no facts. One day, you may learn that it rained last night and can infer that the grass is wet. Here is a more useful example.

IF one can quickly find the largest friend-clique in a friendship network, THEN one can quickly assign non-conflicting frequencies to radio stations using a minimum number of frequencies.

Is this claim true? Yes. Is it useful? Not yet! If you discover a way to quickly find the largest friend-clique, only then can you assign radio frequencies efficiently. We wish to prove implications, $p \to q$ for arbitrary propositions p and q, even if the implication is not of immediate use – reasoning in the absence of facts.

Pop Quiz 4.1
Identify p and q in the following implications $p \to q$.
(a) If n is greater than 2 and even, then n is the sum of two primes.
(b) If x and y are rational, then $x + y$ is rational.
(c) If $ax^2 + bx + c = 0$ and $a \neq 0$ then $x = (-b + \sqrt{b^2 - 4ac})/2a$ or $x = (-b - \sqrt{b^2 - 4ac})/2a$.

4.1 Direct Proof

We already saw a proof technique for implication. The only case where $p \to q$ is false is when p is true and q is false. To show $p \to q$ is true, show that this counterexample cannot happen. Consider the example

IF x and y are rational, THEN $x + y$ is rational.

This is the statement $p \to q$ with $p =$ "x and y are rational" and $q =$ "$x + y$ is rational". We want to show that p is true and q is false cannot happen. Suppose p is true. What does that mean? It means x and y are ratios, $x = a/b$ and $y = c/d$, where $a, c \in \mathbb{Z}$ and $b, d \in \mathbb{N}$. We now get an expression for $x + y$,

$$x + y = \frac{a}{b} + \frac{c}{d} = \frac{ad + bc}{bd}.$$

Observe that $x + y$ is a ratio of an integer $ad + bc$ and a natural number bd. That is $x + y$ is rational and q is true. The case with p being true and q being false can't occur, so the implication must be true. Our proof above is called direct proof. To show p being true and q being false cannot occur together, assume p is true and show q must be true. This proves the implication. Here is the formal proof. Pay attention to the steps.

Theorem 4.1. If $x, y \in \mathbb{Q}$, then $x + y \in \mathbb{Q}$.

Proof. We prove the theorem using a direct proof.
1: Assume that $x, y \in \mathbb{Q}$, that is x and y are rational.
2: Then, $x = a/b$ and $y = c/d$ for $a, c \in \mathbb{Z}$ and $b, d \in \mathbb{N}$. (That's what "x and y are rational" means.)
3: Then $x + y = (ad + bc)/bd$. (High-school algebra.)
4: Since $ad + bc \in \mathbb{Z}$ and $bd \in \mathbb{N}$, $(ad + bc)/bd$ is rational.
5: Thus, we conclude (from steps 3 and 4) that $x + y \in \mathbb{Q}$. ■

A proof is a mathematical essay, and, as with a literary essay, a proof must be well written. The goal of a proof is to convince a reader of a theorem. A badly written proof that leaves a reader with some doubts has failed. Adhering to a structure in a proof is a good idea. Always start with the word "Proof" (surprise ☺) and tell the reader when the proof is over using the end of proof symbol "■". To begin your proof, state the method you are using, in this case direct proof. The remaining steps are summarized in the template below.

> **Proof Template I: Direct proof of an implication $p \to q$.**
> *Proof.* We prove the implication using a direct proof.
> 1: Start by assuming that the statement claimed in p is true.
> 2: Restate your assumption in mathematical terms.
> 3: Use mathematical and logical derivations to relate your assumption to q.
> 4: Argue that you have shown that q must be true.
> 5: End by concluding that q is true. ■

Example 4.2. Let x be any real number, i.e. $x \in \mathbb{R}$.

IF $4^x - 1$ is divisible by 3, THEN $4^{x+1} - 1$ is divisible by 3.

This is the claim $p \to q$ with $p =$ "$4^x - 1$ is divisible by 3" and $q =$ "$4^{x+1} - 1$ is divisible by 3".

Proof. We prove the claim using a direct proof.
1: Assume that p is true, that is $4^x - 1$ is divisible by 3.
2: This means that $4^x - 1 = 3k$ for an integer k, or that $4^x = 3k + 1$.
3: Observe that $4^{x+1} = 4 \cdot 4^x$, and since $4^x = 3k + 1$, it follows that

$$4^{x+1} = 4 \cdot (3k + 1) = 12k + 4.$$

Therefore $4^{x+1} - 1 = 12k + 3 = 3(4k + 1)$, which is a multiple of 3 as $4k + 1$ is an integer.
4: Since $4^{x+1} - 1$ is a multiple of 3, we have shown that $4^{x+1} - 1$ is divisible by 3.
5: Therefore, the statement claimed in q is true. ■

A common mistake made after a direct proof is to think that p is true. No! We made a local assumption that p is true inside the proof as our way of proving the implication. After our proof, we no longer can assume $4^x - 1$ is divisible by 3. Can we claim $4^{x+1} - 1$ is divisible by 3? No! Is x an integer? We don't know! None of these things are specified in the claim. Only the *implication*

$$(4^x - 1 \text{ is divisible by } 3) \to (4^{x+1} - 1 \text{ is divisible by } 3)$$

is true. If you have an $x = \frac{1}{2}\log_2(22) = 2.229\cdots$ for which $4^x - 1 = 21$ is divisible by 3, now you conclude $4^{3.229\cdots} - 1 = 87$ is divisible by 3. The implication allows you to deduce this new fact. □

As you become a professional mathematician, you might relax the formal structure of a proof, making it more streamlined. There are different techniques and styles, but the goal is always the same, to convince the reader of some claim. It is therefore important to convey the idea at the heart of the proof, above almost anything else. Always bear in mind that the proof will be read by a human. Help your reader to follow your proof.

Guidelines for Writing Readable and Good Proofs

(I) **State your strategy.** Start with the type of proof, e.g. direct proof. Break long proofs into parts and tie up the parts at the end. Even if it is obvious, don't leave tying up to the reader. The reader must have *no* doubts.
(II) **Have a logical flow.** Recall how hard it is to follow movies that jump between story lines or back and forth in time. A reader follows a proof linearly, from beginning to end.
(III) **Keep it simple.** A proof is an essay with equations to justify steps, not a sequence of equations with a few words sprinkled here and there. At the heart of a proof is an idea. Make the idea clear. Avoid overload of symbols and new notation unless it's absolutely necessary.
(IV) **Justify your steps.** The reader must have no doubts. Avoid phrases like "It's obvious that ..." If it is so obvious, give a short explanation. Be honest in your proof. Don't try to hide anything.
(V) **End your proof.** Explain why what you set out to show is true.
(VI) **Read your proof.** Finally, check correctness. Edit. Simplify.

"For all." In Example 4.2, nothing was said about x. The argument was general, in that it applied to any x. In the derivation, x was just a place holder for a number. We could substitute any number for x. Thus, the implication is true for all $x \in \mathbb{R}$. We could define a compound predicate

$$P(x) : \text{“IF } 4^x - 1 \text{ is divisible by 3, THEN } 4^{x+1} - 1 \text{ is divisible by 3”}$$

and we proved $\forall x \in \mathbb{R} : P(x)$. This is one way to prove a universally quantified claim.

Proof Template II: Proving $\forall x \in \mathcal{D} : P(x)$ using a general x.
Proof. We prove $P(x)$ for a general (arbitrary) element $x \in \mathcal{D}$.
1: Start by assuming that x is an arbitrary element of $\mathcal{D}$.
2: Mathematically determine properties x must have because it is in D.
3: Use valid derivations to show that $P(x)$ is true for this generic x.
4: Since $P(x)$ is true for arbitrary $x \in \mathcal{D}$, conclude $\forall x \in \mathcal{D} : P(x)$. ■

A note on style and difficulty. You don't have to number the steps in a proof, but all the steps should be there. We numbered the steps so you can compare a proof with a proof template. A proof can be easy or hard, but all the key steps must be there in either case. What makes a proof hard? In Proof Template II, steps 1 and 4 are easy. Step 2 is somewhat non-trivial, in that you may have to think a little about what properties you can infer of elements in the domain $\mathcal{D}$. Step 3 is likely to be the hard one, to use mathematical and logical derivations to show what you want and creativity is often required.

Example 4.3. For all pairs of odd integers m, n, the sum $m+n$ is an even integer. Before proving this claim, let's make it precise by first defining the sets of odd and even integers.

$$E = \{n | n = 2k; k \in \mathbb{Z}\}; \qquad O = \{n | n = 2k + 1; k \in \mathbb{Z}\};$$

Our claim is $\forall (m, n) \in O^2 : m + n \in E$. Note, O^2 just means pairs of elements from O. O^3 is tripples, etc.
Proof. We prove that $m + n \in E$ for general odd integers m and n.
1: To begin let $m \in O$ and $n \in O$ be arbitrary odd integers.
2: Since m and n are odd, there are integers k and ℓ for which $m = 2k + 1$ and $n = 2\ell + 1$.
3: We need to show that $m + n$ is even. Indeed, we have that

$$m + n = 2k + 1 + 2\ell + 1 = 2k + 2\ell + 2 = 2 \cdot (k + \ell + 1).$$

Since $k + \ell + 1$ is an integer, $m + n$ is twice an integer and hence $m + n$ is even.
4: Since $m + n$ is even for arbitrary odd m and n, $\forall (m, n) \in O^2 : m + n \in E$. ■

"All" versus "IF... THEN..." The two statements below are saying the same thing.

p : ALL cars have 4 wheels.
q : IF x is a car, THEN x has 4 wheels.

For this equivalence to hold, it is critical that the condition "x is a car," in the IF-statement, matches exactly the condition for membership in the set "cars", the domain to which ALL refers. Define this domain as $\mathcal{D} = \{x \mid x \text{ is a car}\}$. Our two statements are:

$$p: \ \forall x \in \mathcal{D} : \text{"}x \text{ has 4 wheels"}$$
$$q: \ \text{"}x \text{ is a car"} \rightarrow \text{"}x \text{ has 4 wheels"}$$

Proposition p is universally quantified; q is an implication. If q is false, some car does not have 4 wheels and p is false. If q is true, every car has 4 wheels and p is true. Either p and q are both true, or both false. If you prove p then you have also proven q and *vice versa*. The universal statement and the implication are equivalent. Both are used frequently and interchangeably. Here is the formal statement of this equivalence.

> For predicates $P(n)$ and $Q(n)$, define a domain $\mathcal{D} = \{n \mid P(n) \text{ is true}\}$. Then,
>
> $\forall n \in \mathcal{D} : Q(n)$ and $P(n) \rightarrow Q(n)$
>
> are equivalent statements. If you prove one, you have proved both.

Exercise 4.2
Use direct proof to prove the following claims.
(a) If a is divisible by b and b is divisible by c, then a is divisible by c.
(b) For all real numbers x, y, $|x + y| \leq |x| + |y|$ ($|\cdot|$ is the absolute value).
(c) The product of any 4 consecutive integers is divisible by 8.

4.1.1 Disproving Implication

To disprove the implication $P(n) \rightarrow Q(n)$, you only need one special n_* for which both $P(n_*)$ is true and $Q(n_*)$ is false. For such a counterexample n_*, $P(n_*) \rightarrow Q(n_*)$ is false. Let us disprove the implication

$$\text{IF } x \geq 0, \text{ THEN } x^2 > 0.$$

Our counterexample is $x_* = 0$, for which $x_* \geq 0$, but ${x_*}^2 \leq 0$. A single counterexample suffices.

Example 4.4. We illustrate the difference between proving and disproving an implication.

(i) **Disprove:** IF $x^2 > y^2$, THEN $x > y$. The implication is false.

Proof. To disprove $x^2 > y^2 \rightarrow x > y$, consider the counterexample $x = -2$ and $y = 1$. Then, $x^2 = 4$ and $y^2 = 1$, and so $x^2 > y^2$ is true. But $x \leq y$, and so $x > y$ is false. A single counterexample suffices. ■

(ii) **Prove:** IF $x^2 > y^2$ and $x > 0$, THEN $x > y$. The implication is true.

Proof. We use a direct proof. Assume that $x^2 > y^2$ and $x > 0$. There are two cases.

Case 1 ($y < 0$). Trivially, $x - y > 0$ because $x > 0$.

Case 2 ($y \geq 0$). From $x^2 > y^2$ we get $x^2 - y^2 > 0$, or $(x - y)(x + y) > 0$. Since $x > 0$ and $y \geq 0$, $x + y > 0$. Hence $x - y > 0$, or else the product can't be positive.

In both cases $x - y > 0$ as was to be shown. ■

The disproof in (i) is short and easy: you find a single counterexample. The proof in (ii) is long and complicated. Disproving an implication is "easy"; proving is hard. The proof in (ii) used cases, a common tactic. When you use cases, it is important to consider all possible cases. Here, there are only two possible cases, $y < 0$ and $y \geq 0$. Please re-read these two proofs to appreciate the difference in their nature. □

Pop Quiz 4.3
For a predicate $Q(n)$, how do you disprove the statement $\forall n \in \mathcal{D} : Q(n)$.

4.2 Proof by Contraposition

To prove $p \to q$, you show that the counterexample p is true and q is false can't occur. In a direct proof, you assume p and prove q. Instead, one could start by assuming q to be false and show that p cannot be true, which also means p being true and q being false cannot happen. Let us use this method to show

IF x^2 is even, THEN x is even.

To show (x^2 is even) $\to$ (x is even) using the new approach, first assume x is not even (q is false). Now show that x^2 is not even (p must be false). If x is not even, then x is odd and $x = 2k + 1$ for some integer k. Then,

$$x^2 = (2k+1)^2 = 4k^2 + 4k + 1 = 2(2k^2 + 2k) + 1 = 2\ell + 1,$$

where $\ell = 2k^2 + 2k$ is an integer. That is, when x is not even, x^2 is also not even. We have proved the implication. This method of proof is called proof by contraposition.

Proof Template III: Proof of $p \to q$ by Contraposition.
Proof. We prove the theorem using contraposition.
1: Start by assuming that the statement claimed in q is false.
2: Restate your assumption in mathematical terms.
3: Use mathematical and logical derivations to relate your assumption to p.
4: Argue that you have shown that p must be false.
5: End by concluding that p is false. ■

Such an odd name, contraposition. The name comes from the contrapositive of the statement $p \to q$, which is the statement $\neg q \to \neg p$. The next exercise will illuminate matters.

Exercise 4.4
(a) Use a truth-table to show that $p \to q \overset{\text{eqv}}{\equiv} \neg q \to \neg p$. That is, an implication and its contrapositive are logically equivalent. Either both are true or both are false and proving one proves the other.
(b) Give the contrapositive statement.
(i) IF it rained last night THEN the grass is wet. (ii) IF the mall is crowded, THEN you stay at home.
(c) Give the contrapositive statement and a proof by contraposition of the implication.
(i) IF $x, y > 0$ and $xy > 100$ THEN $x > 10$ or $y > 10$. (ii) IF r is irrational, THEN $\sqrt{r}$ is irrational.

Since $p \to q$ and the contrapositive $\neg q \to \neg p$ are logically equivalent, proving one also proves the other. Let us examine how we would prove the contrapositive $\neg q \to \neg p$, using a direct proof. We start by assuming that $\neg q$ is true, or that q is false. We then show that $\neg p$ must be true, i.e., p must be false. But, this is exactly what a proof by contraposition does. Proof by contraposition is a direct proof of the contrapositive.

4.3 Equivalence: If and Only If

Equivalence is stronger than implication. James likes all apples. James likes only apples. We conclude that "James likes x" and "x is an apple" are equivalent statements, for either both are true or both are false:

James likes x is true means x must be an apple (he likes *only* apples).
x is an apple is true means James must like x (he likes *all* apples).
James likes x is false means x cannot be an apple (he likes *all* apples).
x is an apple is false means James cannot like x (he likes *only* apples).

We use the IF AND ONLY IF connector for equivalent statements that are either both true or both false,

James likes x IF AND ONLY IF x is an apple.

The symbol for IF AND ONLY IF is $\leftrightarrow$. Equivalence, p IF AND ONLY IF q, is written $p \leftrightarrow q$.

The truth-table for IF AND ONLY IF is on the right. For p IF AND ONLY IF q to be true, p and q must both be true or both be false: when both are true, $p \to q$ is true; when both are false, $\neg p \to \neg q$ is true, i.e. the contrapositive $q \to p$ is true.[1]

p	q	$p \leftrightarrow q$
F	F	T
F	T	F
T	F	F
T	T	T

$$p \leftrightarrow q \overset{\text{eqv}}{\equiv} (p \to q) \wedge (q \to p).$$

Pop Quiz 4.5

Use truth-tables to verify $p \leftrightarrow q \overset{\text{eqv}}{\equiv} (p \to q) \wedge (q \to p)$.

To prove an IF AND ONLY IF claim, you prove each implication. Here is an example.

Integer x is divisible by 3 IF AND ONLY IF x^2 is divisible by 3.

Proof. The proof has two main steps, one for each implication:

(i) Prove: IF x is divisible by 3, THEN x^2 is divisible by 3.

We use a direct proof. Assume x is divisible by 3, so $x = 3k$ for some $k \in \mathbb{Z}$. Then, $x^2 = 9k^2 = 3 \cdot (3k^2)$, which is clearly a multiple of 3. So, x^2 is divisible by 3, as was to be shown.

(ii) Prove: IF x^2 is divisible by 3, THEN x is divisible by 3.

We use contraposition. Assume x is not divisible by 3. There are two cases for x,

Case 1: $x = 3k + 1 \to x^2 = 3k(3k + 2) + 1$ (1 more than a multiple of 3).

Case 2: $x = 3k + 2 \to x^2 = 3(3k^2 + 4k + 1) + 1$ (1 more than a multiple of 3).

In both cases, x^2 is not divisible by 3, as was to be shown. ■

Always remember that an IF AND ONLY IF proof contains the proofs of two implications. Each implication may be proved in different ways. In our proof above, we used direct proof and contraposition.

Proof Template IV: Proving IF AND ONLY IF, $p \leftrightarrow q$.

Proof.

1: Prove $p \to q$ using a proof method for implications (forward step).

2: Prove $q \to p$ using a proof method for implications (backward step). ■

Definitions and Equivalence. A definition gives an alternative but equivalent description of a concept. The IF AND ONLY IF connector is often used in definitions. Here are some examples.

US citizen You are a US citizen IF AND ONLY IF you were born on US soil.

Set equality Sets A and B are equal IF AND ONLY IF $A \subseteq B$ and $B \subseteq A$.

Parallel Two line segments on a plane are parallel IF AND ONLY IF after extending both segments to infinity in both directions there is no intersection.

You cannot dispute a definition. You may prefer a different one, for example the US government defines US citizen differently, but a definition is the author's choice. Definitions give a more convenient way to describe something. "These lines are parallel" is simpler than "these lines when extended to infinity..." Introduce definitions only to help with clarity. Too many definitions can be counter productive.

Exercise 4.6

(a) Here is an erroneous definition of parallel in 2-dimensions: Two line segments are parallel IF AND ONLY IF they do not intersect. Draw line segments that are parallel according to this definition, but not parallel according to the correct definition in the text.

(b) Give a definition for parallel in 3 dimensions:

(c) Give a definition of isosceles (you don't need to define "triangle").

[1]The symbol $\leftrightarrow$ can be interpreted as a merging of $p \to q$ and $p \leftarrow q$ (i.e. $p \rightleftarrows q$) to $p \leftrightarrow q$.

4.4 Proof by Contradiction (Reductio ad Absurdum)

A contradiction is something that is false; something that sounds **FISHY**. For example:

$$1 = 2; \qquad n^2 < n \text{ (for integer } n); \qquad |x| < x; \qquad p \wedge \neg p.$$

Clearly $1 \neq 2$, $n^2 \geq n$ and $|x| \geq x$ (high-school math). The last, $p \wedge \neg p$, is the classical contradiction; no matter whether p is true or false, $p \wedge \neg p$ is false. If you show $a < b$, and subsequently $a \geq b$, then something must be **FISHY** in your derivations because $a < b$ and $a \geq b$ cannot both hold. You derived a contradiction. In mathematics, you cannot derive contradictions (falsehoods). This fact leads us to a very useful method of proof. Let us see this method of proof in action by revisiting the proof that $\sqrt{2}$ is not rational.

1: **Assume $\sqrt{2}$ is rational.**
2: This means $\sqrt{2} = a_*/b_*$ for a smallest possible denominator b_*. [well-ordering]
3: **a_* and b_* have no common factors** (b_* is the smallest possible denominator).
4: So, $2 = a_*^2/b_*^2 \to a_*^2 = 2b_*^2$, or a_*^2 is even. Hence, a_* is even, $a_* = 2k$. [we proved this]
5: Therefore, $4k^2 = 2b_*^2$ and so $b_*^2 = 2k^2$, or b_*^2 is even. Hence, b_* is even.
6: **a_* and b_* have the common factor 2** (FISHY)

Steps 3 and 6 contradict each other. That's **FISHY**. Now for the crux of the matter.

> **Principle of Contradiction.** If you derive (using valid steps) a **FISHY** conclusion, at least one assumption in the derivation must be **FISHY**.

Step 6 in the proof is a **FISHY** conclusion obtained via steps 2–5 which are all valid. By the principle of contradiction, at least one assumption is **FISHY** (false), and it can only be the assumption in step 1 that $\sqrt{2}$ is rational. This means that $\sqrt{2}$ must not be rational. And, we have proved it via a contradiction.

> **Proof Template V: Proof by Contradiction that p is true.**
> *Proof.*
> 1: To derive a contradiction, assume that p is false.
> 2: Restate your assumption in mathematical terms.
> 3: Derive a **FISHY** statement – a contradiction that must be false.
> 4: Therefore, the assumption in step 1 is false, and p is true. ∎

Contradiction is powerful because the assumption in step 1 gives something to work with. Assuming $\sqrt{2}$ is rational, gives a starting point for deriving that $\sqrt{2}$ is not rational.

Example 4.5. Let a, b be integers. Prove that $a^2 - 4b \neq 2$.

Proof. To derive a contradiction, assume that $a^2 - 4b = 2$. Then, $a^2 = 2 + 4b = 2(1 + 2b)$ is even, so a is even. This means $a = 2k$ for an integer k. Therefore, $(2k)^2 - 4b = 2$. Divide both sides by 2 to get

$$2(k^2 - b) = 1,$$

which is **FISHY**: the LHS is even but the RHS is odd. Therefore, $a^2 - 4b \neq 2$. ∎

> **Exercise 4.7**
> Prove the following by contradiction.
> (a) Let $m, n \in Z$. Prove that $21m + 9n \neq 1$.
> (b) Let x, y be positive real numbers. Prove that $x + y \geq 2\sqrt{xy}$
> (c) Let $m, n \in \mathbb{Z}$ with $m^2 + n^2$ divisible by 4. Then, m and n are not both odd.

Example 4.6. You can use contradiction to prove any claim, even claims inside another proof. Let a, b, c be real numbers. If $a > c$ and $b > c$, then $\max(a, b) - c > 0$.

Proof. We use direct proof. Assume $a > c$ and $b > c$; we show $\max(a, b) - c > 0$.

1: To derive a contradiction, **assume** $\max(a, b) - c \leq 0$, which means $c \geq \max(a, b)$.

2: Since $c \geq \max(a,b)$, $c \geq a$ (because $\max(a,b) \geq a$).
3: Therefore $c < a$ and $c \geq a$ (a very **FISHY** contradiction).
4: Our assumption in step 1 must be false. That means $\max(a,b) - c > 0$ ■

We used contradiction inside a direct proof, a powerful method worth summarizing.

Proof Template VI: Direct Proof of $p \to q$ using Contradiction.
Proof. Using a direct proof, assume p is true and show q is true.
1: To derive a contradiction, assume q is false.
2: Use valid derivations to obtain something **FISHY** – a contradiction.
3: At least one assumption must be false: either p is false or q is true.
4: In either case, conclude that $p \to q$ is true. ■

When the contradiction in step 2 is that p is false (contradicting p assumed true), you assumed $\neg q$ and showed $\neg p$, similar to a proof by contraposition. Unlike proof by contraposition, you get to assume two things: that p is true and q is false. That's a lot to start with. The proof succeeds if you derive any contradiction.

DANGER! Be especially careful in contradiction proofs. A tiny mistake can easily lead to a contradiction and a false sense that you proved your claim.

Picking Proof Templates. Here is a useful cheat sheet for picking a proof method.

Situation you are faced with	Suggested proof method
1. Clear how result follows from assumption	**Direct proof**
2. Clear that if result is false, the assumption is false	**Contraposition**
3. Disprove an implication	**Show a counterexample**
4. Prove something exists	**Show an example**
5. Prove something does not exist	**Contradiction**
6. Prove something is unique	**Contradiction**
7. Prove something is true for all objects	**Show for general object**
8. Disprove something is true for all objects	**Show a counterexample**

Exercise 4.8
Determine which proof technique to use for each claim (you don't need to give a proof).
(a) There is no real x for which $x^2 < 0$
(b) If n^2 is odd, then n is odd.
(c) If n is odd, then n^2 is odd.
(d) Not every natural number is a square.
(e) The product of two rational numbers is rational.
(f) The product of two odd numbers can never be even.
(g) There does not exist a rational number equal to $\sqrt{6}$.
(h) At least one number in a set of numbers is as large (or larger) than the average.

4.5 Proofs about Sets

The common proof tasks involving sets are to show:

- one set is a subset of another, $A \subseteq B$;
- one set is a not a subset of another, $A \not\subseteq B$;
- two sets are equal, $A = B$, which means $A \subseteq B$ and $B \subseteq A$.

To show $A \subseteq B$, you must show that every element of A is in B. That is,

$$x \in A \to x \in B.$$

Suppose $A = \{\text{multiples of } 6\}$ and $B = \{\text{multiples of } 3\}$. Then, $A \subseteq B$ but $B \nsubseteq A$. To prove $A \subseteq B$, suppose $x \in A$. Then $x = 6k = 3 \cdot (2k)$ which is a multiple of 3. So, $x \in B$ and we showed $x \in A \to x \in B$. To show $B \nsubseteq A$ we must show a counterexample for $x \in B \to x \in A$, specifically an element of B not in A. The counterexample $x = 3$ will do. One counterexample suffices to show $B \nsubseteq A$.

Set equality involves two implications, because $A = B$ means $A \subseteq B$ and $B \subseteq A$. That is, one must show:

$$x \in A \leftrightarrow x \in B.$$

Example 4.7. We will show that $A \cup (B \cap C) = (A \cup B) \cap (A \cup C)$. You can use similar techniques to show all the laws for combining set operations in Figure 2.1 on page 17. A formal proof must prove an IF AND ONLY IF. An informal "proof by picture" using Venn diagrams often suffices, as illustrated below.

Informal proof by picture:

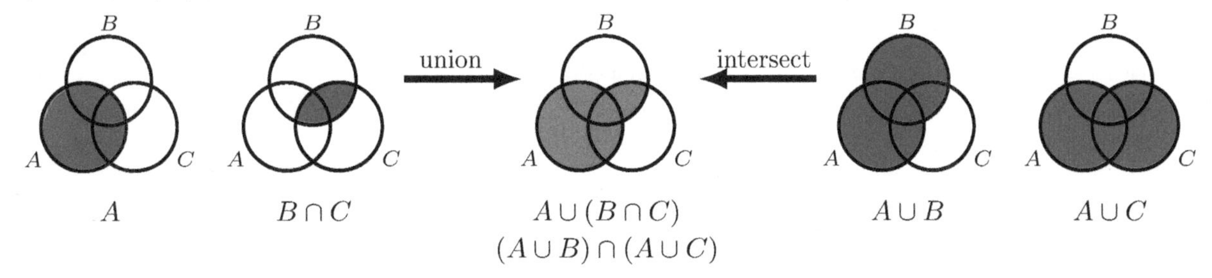

Proof. Let $X = A \cup (B \cap C)$ and $Y = (A \cup B) \cap (A \cup C)$. To prove $X = Y$, we prove two implications:

(i) Show $X \subseteq Y$, or $x \in A \cup (B \cap C) \to x \in (A \cup B) \cap (A \cup C)$.
We use a direct proof. Assume $x \in A \cup (B \cap C)$. There are two cases.
Case 1: $x \in A$. This means $x \in A \cup B$ and $x \in A \cup C$, so $x \in (A \cup B) \cap (A \cup C)$.
Case 2: $x \notin A$. Since $x \in A \cup (B \cap C)$, we conclude $x \in B \cap C$. That is, $x \in B$ and $x \in C$. Because $x \in B$, we have $x \in (A \cup B)$. Because $x \in C$, we have $x \in (A \cup C)$. Therefore, $x \in (A \cup B) \cap (A \cup C)$.

(ii) Show $Y \subseteq X$, or $x \in (A \cup B) \cap (A \cup C) \to x \in A \cup (B \cap C)$.
We use contraposition and contradiction. Suppose that $x \notin A \cup (B \cap C)$. We need to show that $x \notin (A \cup B) \cap (A \cup C)$. To derive a contradiction, assume $x \in (A \cup B) \cap (A \cup C)$.
Since $x \notin A \cup (B \cap C)$, $x \notin A$. Since $x \in (A \cup B) \cap (A \cup C)$ it means $x \in (A \cup B)$ and $x \in (A \cup C)$. But, because $x \notin A$ and $x \in (A \cup B)$, it must be that $x \in B$; similarly, because $x \in (A \cup C)$, it must be that $x \in C$. Therefore $x \in B \cap C$, which means $x \in A \cup (B \cap C)$. This contradicts $x \notin A \cup (B \cap C)$. Hence, $x \notin (A \cup B) \cap (A \cup C)$.

We proved $X \subseteq Y$ and $Y \subseteq X$, which proves $X = Y$. ■

Pop Quiz 4.9
$A = \{\text{multiples of } 2\}$; $B = \{\text{multiples of } 9\}$; $C = \{\text{multiples of } 6\}$. Prove $A \cap B \subseteq C$.

Exercise 4.10
Give formal as well as pictorial (Venn diagram) proofs for:
(a) $A \cap (B \cup C) = (A \cap B) \cup (A \cap C)$. (b) $\overline{A \cup \overline{B}} = \overline{A} \cap B$.

Exercise 4.11 [Inverse of a union.]
Let $f : A \mapsto B$ be an invertible function with domain A and range B. The inverse image of a set $C \subseteq B$ is the set of elements in A which map to C, $f^{-1}(C) = \{a \in A \mid f(a) \in C\}$. Prove that the inverse of a union of sets in B is the union of the corresponding inverses in A. That is, for $C, D \subseteq B$,

$$f^{-1}(C \cup D) = f^{-1}(C) \cup f^{-1}(D).$$

4.6 Problems

Problem 4.1. The six (or seven) "C's" of a good proof. Explain why each is important.

(a) Correct.
(b) Clear.
(c) Complete.
(d) Concise.
(e) Continuous (moving forward).
(f) Coordinated (well organized).

The seventh "C", which many mathematicians value dearly is Clever (elegant or beautiful).

Problem 4.2. What's wrong with this proof of "If n is even, then n^2 is even"? What is proved?

1: Suppose n^2 is even.
2: Let n have a prime factorization $n = p_1^{q_1} p_2^{q_2} \cdots p_k^{q_k}$.
3: Then, $n^2 = p_1^{2q_1} p_2^{2q_2} \cdots p_k^{2q_k}$ (each prime appears an even number of times).
4: Since n^2 is even, 2 is a prime factor of ($p_1 = 2$), so $n^2 = 2^{2q_1} p_2^{2q_2} \cdots p_k^{2q_k}$, with $q_1 > 0$.
5: So, $n = 2^{q_1} p_2^{q_2} \cdots p_k^{q_k}$, with $q_1 > 0$.
6: That means 2 is a factor of n and, so n is even as claimed. ■

Problem 4.3. Usinig $0 = 0$ and standard algebra, we prove $7 = 7$. Which proofs are valid? Why or why not?

(a)
1. $7 = 7$
2. $7 - 7 = 7 - 7$
3. $0 = 0$ ☺

$\rightarrow$ $7 = 7$ ✓

(b)
1. Assume $7 \neq 7$
2. $7 - 7 \neq 7 - 7$
3. $0 \neq 0$ **!FISHY**

$\rightarrow$ $7 = 7$ ✓

(c)
1. $0 = 0$
2. $0 + 7 = 0 + 7$
3. $7 = 7$ ☺

$\rightarrow$ $7 = 7$ ✓

Problem 4.4. What is wrong with this bad proof that $4 = 7$? You know that 0=0.

1: $\mathbf{4 = 7}$ (what we are trying to prove)
2: $7 = 4$ ($a = b$ implies $b = a$)
3: $4 + 7 = 7 + 4$ ($a = b$ and $c = d$ implies $a + c = b + d$)
4: $4 + 7 - 11 = 7 + 4 - 11$ (subtract 11 from both sides)
5: $\mathbf{0 = 0}$ ✓ (we derived a known fact, hence our first step can't be wrong)

Problem 4.5. Here are two proofs that $2 = 1$. In each case, what went wrong?

(a) Let $a = 1$ and $b = 1$. Then,
1: We know $a = b$.
2: So, $2a^2 = a^2 + a^2 = a^2 + ab$.
3: So, $2a^2 - 2ab = a^2 - ab$.
4: Or, $2 \cdot (a^2 - ab) = 1 \cdot (a^2 - ab)$.
5: Dividing by $a^2 - ab$ gives $2 = 1$ ■

(b) We use the fact that $-2 = -2$.
1: Hence, $4 - 6 = 1 - 3$,
2: So, $4 - 6 + 9/4 = 1 - 3 + 9/4$.
3: That is, $(2 - 3/2)^2 = (1 - 3/2)^2$.
4: So, $2 - 3/2 = 1 - 3/2$.
5: Which means $2 = 1$. ■

Problem 4.6. Determine the true implications. If true, prove it. If false, give a counterexample. $\mathcal{H}$ is a set of horses. *[Hint: Consider separately the cases where $\mathcal{H}$ has fewer than 11 horses and $\mathcal{H}$ has at least 11 horses separately.]*

(a) IF all 10-horse subsets of $\mathcal{H}$ have only gray horses, THEN all 11-horse subsets of $\mathcal{H}$ have only gray horses.
(b) IF some 10-horse subset of $\mathcal{H}$ has a black horse, THEN some 11-horse subset of $\mathcal{H}$ has a black horse.

Problem 4.7. Give direct proofs:

(a) $x, y \in \mathbb{Q} \rightarrow xy \in \mathbb{Q}$.
(b) $n \in \mathbb{Z} \rightarrow n^2 + n$ is even.
(c) For $x, y \in \mathbb{Z}$, $x^2 + y^2$ is even $\rightarrow x + y$ is even.
(d) For $a, b, c \in \mathbb{Z}$, (a divides b AND b divides c) $\rightarrow a$ divides c.

Problem 4.8. Give the contrapositive of each statement.

(a) If p is prime, then p is odd.
(b) For $n \in \mathbb{Z}$, $n/(n+1) \notin \mathbb{Z}$.
(c) If $n \in \mathbb{N}$ has remainder 2 or 3 when divided by 4, then n is not square.
(d) If $n \in \mathbb{N}$ is composite, then n has a prime divisor that is at most $\sqrt{n}$.

Problem 4.9. You may assume n is an integer. Give direct and contraposition proofs of:

(a) ($n^3 + 5$ is odd) $\rightarrow$ (n is even).
(b) (3 does not divide n) $\rightarrow$ (3 divides $n^2 + 2$).

Problem 4.10. You may assume n is an integer. Prove by contraposition (explicitly state the contrapositive).

(a) x is irrational $\rightarrow \sqrt{x}$ is irrational.
(b) $n^2 + 4n + 2$ is even $\rightarrow n$ is even.
(c) $2^n - 1$ is prime $\rightarrow n$ is prime.
(d) n^3 is odd $\rightarrow n$ is odd.
(e) n^2 is not divisible by 4 $\rightarrow n$ is odd.
(f) If $p > 2$ is prime, then p is odd.
(g) If $2^n - n$ is prime, then n is odd.
(h) For $x, y > 0$, $y^3 + x^2 y \leq x^3 + xy^2 \rightarrow y \leq x$.
(i) d doesn't divide $mn \rightarrow d$ doesn't divide m or n.
(j) $x^5 + 7x^3 + 5x \geq x^4 + x^2 + 8 \rightarrow x \geq 0$.
(k) 3 divides $n - 2 \rightarrow n$ is not a perfect square.
(l) If $p > 2$ is prime, then $p^2 + 1$ is composite.
(m) For $x, y \in \mathbb{Z}$, $x^2 + y^2$ is even $\rightarrow x + y$ is even.
(n) If xy is even, then x is even or y is even.

Problem 4.11. For $x, y \in \mathbb{N}$, which statements below are contradictions (cannot possibly be true). Explain.
(a) $x^2 < y$ (b) $x^2 = \frac{1}{2}y$ (c) $x^2 - y^2 \leq 1$ (d) $x^2 + y^2 \leq 1$ (e) $2x + 1 = y^2 + 5y$ (f) $x^2 - \frac{1}{2}y^2 = 1$ (g) $x^2 - y^2 = 1$.

Problem 4.12. Prove by contradiction:

(a) $\sqrt[3]{2}$ is irrational.
(b) $\sqrt{6}$ is irrational.
(c) $\log_2 9$ is irrational.
(d) $\forall (x, y) \in \mathbb{Z}^2 : 9x - 15y \neq 2$.
(e) $3 + 5\sqrt{2}$ is irrational.
(f) $\sin x + \cos x \geq 1$, where $x \in [0, \pi/2]$.
(g) There is no $q \in \mathbb{Q}$ for which $q - 1 = 1/q$.
(h) $(x, y) \in \mathbb{Z}^2 \to x^2 - 4y - 3 \neq 0$.
(i) For all real, positive x, y: $x + y \geq 2\sqrt{xy}$.
(j) $\forall (a, b, c) \in \mathbb{Z}^3 : (a^2 + b^2 = c^2) \to (a \text{ or } b \text{ is even})$.
(k) For $k \in \mathbb{N}$, $\sqrt{k} + \sqrt{k+1} < \sqrt{4k+2}$.
(l) There are no $x, y \in \mathbb{Q}$ for which $x^2 + y^2 = 3$.
(m) If 4 kids share 29 toys, someone gets at least 8 toys.
(n) Every prime number $p \geq 5$ is of the form $6k \pm 1$, where $k \in \mathbb{N}$.

Problem 4.13. Prove by contradiction:

(a) For real numbers a and b, $\lfloor a + b \rfloor \geq \lfloor a \rfloor + \lfloor b \rfloor$, where the floor $\lfloor \cdot \rfloor$ rounds down.
(b) In a right triangle with integer sides, the two shorter sides cannot both be odd.
(c) Given \$1, \$10, \$100 and \$1,000 bills, you can't get a value of 2^{n+1} using 2^n bills, for $n \in \mathbb{N}$.
(d) Let x, y, a be positive with $x \leq y$. Then, $(x + a)/(y + a) \geq x/y$.
(e) Let $a_1, a_2, \ldots, a_{10}$ be integers with $1/a_1 + 1/a_2 + \cdots + 1/a_{10} = 1$. Then, at least one of the a_i is even.
(f) If all points in the plane are red or blue, then between points of one color, all positive real distances are realized.
(g) Suppose, for $n > 3$, $a_1 + a_2 + \cdots + a_n \geq n$ and $a_1^2 + a_2^2 + \cdots + a_n^2 \geq n^2$. Then, $\max(a_1, a_2, \ldots, a_n) \geq 2$.
(h) The fraction $(21n + 4)/(14n + 3)$ is irreducible.
(i) If you cover an 8×8 chessboard with 32 dominos, some pair of adjacent dominos must form a 2×2 square.

Problem 4.14. Prove: If $a, b, c \in \mathbb{Z}$ are odd, then for all $x \in \mathbb{Q}$, $ax^2 + bx + c \neq 0$. (Contradiction in a direct proof.)

Problem 4.15. Prove these if and only if claims. You must prove two implications. (Break the proof into cases.)

(a) Prove: 4 divides $n \in \mathbb{Z}$ IF AND ONLY IF $n = 1 + (-1)^k(2k - 1)$ for $k \in \mathbb{N}$. (Try $n < 0, n = 0, n > 0$; k even/odd.)
(b) Let $w, x, y, z \in \mathbb{N}$ satisfy $z^2 = w^2 + x^2 + y^2$. Prove that z is even IF AND ONLY IF w, x, y are all even. (Try w, x, y being even/odd.)

Problem 4.16. Determine the type of proof and prove. Tinker, tinker, tinker.

(a) The product of any two odd integers is odd.
(b) $\sqrt{5} + \sqrt{22} < \sqrt{48}$. (No calculators allowed!)
(c) If $3n + 2$ is odd then n is odd. Here, $n \in \mathbb{Z}$.
(d) For real numbers a, b with $a \neq b$, $a^2 + b^2 > 2ab$.
(e) For $n \in \mathbb{Z}$, $n^2 + 3n + 4$ is even. (Try cases).
(f) If xy is odd, then both x and y are odd. Here, $x, y \in \mathbb{Z}$.
(g) There is no fixed constant C for which $n^3 \leq Cn^2$ for all $n \in \mathbb{N}$.
(h) For any positive rational x, there is another positive rational $y < x$.
(i) If $n^2 - 4n + 5$ is even then n is odd. Here, $n \in \mathbb{Z}$.
(j) If $x - y$ is divisible by d, then $x^2 - y^2$ is divisible by d. Here, $x, y, d \in \mathbb{Z}$.
(k) If n is odd, then $n^2 - 1$ is divisible by 8.
(l) If $2^n - 1$ is prime, then n is prime. Here, $n \in \mathbb{N}$.
(m) If $n \in \mathbb{Z}$, then $n^2 - 3$ is not divisible by 4. Here, $n \in \mathbb{N}$.
(n) Every nonzero rational number is a product of two irrational numbers.
(o) There exist integers m and n for which $2m + 3n = 13$.
(p) If m is divisible by d and $m + n$ is divisible by d then n is divisible by d. Here, $m, n, d \in \mathbb{N}$.
(q) When dividing n by d, the quotient q and remainder $0 \leq r < d$ are unique. Here, $n, d, q, r \in \mathbb{Z}$.
(r) For $n \geq 2$, prove that none of $n! + 2, n! + 3, \ldots, n! + n$ are prime. Here, $n \in \mathbb{N}$.
(s) If $\sqrt{3}$ is irrational, then $\sqrt{3^k}$ is irrational for any positive odd number k.
(t) Every odd number is the difference of two squares.
(u) A perfect square number has remainder 0 or 1 when divided by 4.
(v) The numbers $a = 3^{2017} + 25$ and $b = 3^{2017} + 26$ cannot both be perfect squares.
(w) If a and b are positive real numbers with $ab < 10{,}000$, then $\min(a, b) < 100$.
(x) For all positive real x, $x^2 + x^{-2} \geq 2$.
(y) A right triangle with integer sides can't be isoceles. *[Hint: Pythagoras and $\sqrt{2}$ is irrational.]*
(z) For $n \in \mathbb{N}$, $\sqrt{n(n+1)} \leq n + 1/2$.

Problem 4.17. Prove or disprove. Tinker, tinker, tinker.

(a) For all $n \in \mathbb{Z}$, $n/(n+1) \notin \mathbb{Z}$.
(b) For all $n \in \mathbb{N}$, $n/(n+1) \notin \mathbb{N}$.
(c) Every even square number is a multiple of 4.
(d) If $\sqrt{r}$ is irrational, then r is irrational.
(e) If r is irrational, then $\sqrt{r}$ is irrational.
(f) There exist integers a, b for which $\sqrt{a+b} = \sqrt{a} + \sqrt{b}$.
(g) For all integers a, b, if $a < b$ then $a^2 < b^2$.
(h) If n is an integer and n^2 is divisible by 3, then n is divisible by 3.
(i) If n is an integer and n^2 is divisible by 4, then n is divisible by 4.
(j) If n is an integer and n^2 is divisible by 6, then n is divisible by 6.
(k) For every $n \in \mathbb{N}$, $3^n + 2$ is prime.
(l) For every $n \in \mathbb{N}$, $n^2 + n$ is even.
(m) The product of four consecutive positive integers can never be a perfect square.
(n) If $x \in \mathbb{R}$ then $x \le x^2$.
(o) If x, y are irrational, then y^x is irrational. *[Hint:* $(\log_2 9, \sqrt{2})$ *or* $(\sqrt{2}, \sqrt{2}^{\sqrt{2}})$*.]*
(p) If x, y are rational, then y^x is rational.
(q) For any two sets A and B, $A \not\subseteq B \to B \subseteq A$.
(r) There exist $x, y \in \mathbb{Z}$ for which $2x^2 + 5y^2 = 14$.
(s) $x \in \mathbb{Q}$ and $y \notin \mathbb{Q} \to xy \notin \mathbb{Q}$.
(t) $x \in \mathbb{Q}$, $x \neq 0$ and $y \notin \mathbb{Q} \to xy \notin \mathbb{Q}$. *[Hint: Which method gives you most to work with?]*
(u) For $x \in \mathbb{R}$ and $x \ge 0$, $\lfloor x \rfloor + \lfloor x + 1/3 \rfloor + \lfloor x + 2/3 \rfloor = \lfloor 3x \rfloor$.
(v) For $x \in \mathbb{N}$, $\lfloor x/2 \rfloor + \lceil x/2 \rceil = x$.
(w) For some $x > 0$, there is a constant C for which $n^{2+x} \le Cn^2$ for all $n \in \mathbb{N}$.
(x) If $n \ge 2$ is not prime, then $2n + 13$ is not prime. Here, $n \in \mathbb{N}$.
(y) If d divides the product mn, then d divides m or d divides n. Here, $m, n, d \in \mathbb{N}$.
(z) x is odd if and only if $x^2 - 1$ is divisible by 8. Here, $x \in \mathbb{Z}$.

Problem 4.18. Prove or disprove.

(a) Between any rational number and larger irrational number is another irrational number. *[Hint: Average]*
(b) Between any rational number and larger irrational number is another rational number.

Problem 4.19. Prove this complicated implication:

$$(\neg\exists(x,y) \in \mathbb{Q}^2 : x^2 + y^2 = 3) \to (\text{for all odd } k, \neg\exists(v,w) \in \mathbb{Q}^2 : v^2 + w^2 = 3^k).$$

Problem 4.20 (Binary cyclic shift). A binary number $\mathbf{b} = b_m b_{m-1} \cdots b_2 b_1 b_0$, where $b_i \in \{0, 1\}$ and $b_m = 1$ equals the integer $n(\mathbf{b}) = b_0 2^0 + b_1 2^1 + \cdots + b_m 2^m$. The cyclic shift of the binary number is $\mathbf{b}_c = b_{m-1} \cdots b_2 b_1 b_0 b_m$, which corresponds to taking the leftmost bit and moving it to the front (now, b_{m-1} could possibly be 0). Let $n(\mathbf{b}_c)$ be the integer corresponding to the cyclic shift of the binary number.

(a) For $\mathbf{b} = 101001$, what is the cyclic shift $\mathbf{b}_c$, and what are the integers $n(\mathbf{b})$, $n(\mathbf{b}_c)$.
(b) Given $\mathbf{b} = b_m b_{m-1} \cdots b_2 b_1 b_0$, what is an algebraic expression for $n(\mathbf{b}_c)$.
(c) Prove that $n(\mathbf{b}_c) \le n(\mathbf{b})$ for all $\mathbf{b}$. You may assume $2^0 + 2^1 + 2^2 + \cdots + 2^k = 2^{k+1} - 1$.
(d) When does equality occur, i.e. $n(\mathbf{b}_c) = n(\mathbf{b})$?

Problem 4.21. A number n is triangular if $n = 1 + 2 + \cdots + k = \frac{1}{2}k(k+1)$ for some $k \in \mathbb{N}$ (you may use this formula without proof). A number n is square if $n = k^2$ for some $k \in \mathbb{N}$.

(a) List the first 10 triangular and square numbers. Compare with $\frac{1}{2}k(k+1)$ for $k = 1, 2, \ldots, 10$.
(b) Prove: if n is triangular, then so too are $9n + 1$, $25n + 3$, $49n + 6$ and $81n + 10$.
(c) Prove: n is triangular if and only if $8n + 1$ is square.

Problem 4.22. You may assume any number n has a unique factorization into primes.

(a) Prove: An integer n is divisible by prime p IF AND ONLY IF n^2 is divisible by p.
(b) Show (using contradiction) that $\sqrt{p}$ is irrational for any prime p.

Problem 4.23. A triangle is drawn on the plane. The vertices of the triangle have integer coordinates. Prove that the triangle cannot be equilateral. *[Hints: You must prove something does not exist – what proof method would you pick? Pythagoras' Theorem will be useful, as will irrational numbers. Persevere.]*

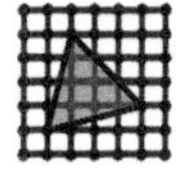

Problem 4.24. A comparison scale can only compare weights.

(a) You have 3 balls, one is heavier. Can you can determine which ball is heavier in one weighing? Prove it. Repeat for 9 balls and two weighings.

(b) You have 4 balls, one is heavier. Can you can determine which ball is heavier in one weighing? Prove it. Repeat for 10 balls and two weighings.

Problem 4.25. The points in the plane are colored red, blue or green. Prove by contradiction.

(a) If there are no green points, then there is an equilateral triangle of side 1 or $\sqrt{3}$ with monochromatic vertices.

(b) There are two points of the same color a distance 1 apart.

(c) Fix any 16×9 rectangular grid. One can form a rectangle using monochromatic points on the grid.

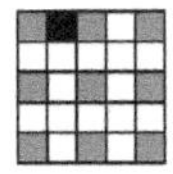

Problem 4.26. A 5×5 board is missing a square (black). Cover the remaining squares with L-shaped tiles, ▟. You may rotate tiles, but tiles cannot overlap or hang off the board. Don't be upset if you fail. Prove there is no L-tiling of this deficient board. As a hint, we have shaded in some squares gray.

Problem 4.27. Explain how to prove and disprove the following statements.

(a) $\neg P(n) \to Q(n)$
(b) $\neg(P(n) \to Q(n))$
(c) $\forall n : (P(n) \to Q(n))$
(d) $\forall x : ((\forall n : P(n)) \to Q(x))$
(e) $\exists n : (P(n) \to Q(n))$
(f) $\exists x : ((\exists n : P(n)) \to Q(x))$

Problem 4.28. For $(a, b) \in \mathbb{R}^2$, which mathematical claim below do you think is true?

(a) If $(\forall (a, b) : ax + b = 0)$, then $x = 0$. (b) $\forall (a, b) :$ (if $ax + b = 0$, then $x = 0$).

Problem 4.29. Let $\mathcal{D} = \{n \mid P(n) \text{ is T}\}$. Prove $(\forall n \in \mathcal{D} : Q(n)) \leftrightarrow (P(n) \to Q(n))$.

(a) $(\forall n \in \mathcal{D} : Q(n)) \to (P(n) \to Q(n))$. (b) $(P(n) \to Q(n)) \to (\forall n \in \mathcal{D} : Q(n))$.

Problem 4.30. Suppose $p \to q$ is true. Show $(p \wedge r) \to q$ is true, the stronger assumption p and r also implies q.

Problem 4.31. Recall $p \leftrightarrow q \overset{\text{eqv}}{\equiv} (p \to q) \wedge (q \to p)$. Show that $p \leftrightarrow q \overset{\text{eqv}}{\equiv} (p \wedge q) \vee (\neg p \wedge \neg q)$:

(a) Use truth-tables. (b) Use the rules in Figure 3.1 on page 29. *[Hints: $p \wedge \neg p \overset{\text{eqv}}{\equiv} \text{F}$ and $x \vee \text{F} \overset{\text{eqv}}{\equiv} x$.]*

Problem 4.32. In 1637, Pierre de Fermat made a claim (Fermat's Last Theorem) that was only proved 357 years later by Andrew Wiles. You may assume Fermat's Last Theorem:

If a, b, c, n are natural numbers with $n > 2$, then $a^n + b^n \neq c^n$.

Use contradiction to show that $2^{1/p}$, p-th root of 2 is irrational for integer $p > 2$.

Problem 4.33. Prove $p \to p$ is true for any statement p.

Problem 4.34. "q is necessary and sufficient for p" is another way to say $p \leftrightarrow q$.

(a) For p to be true, it is necessary that q be true. Which of the statements below must be true:

$$p \to q; \qquad q \to p; \qquad p \leftrightarrow q.$$

(b) For p to be true, it is sufficient that q be true. Now, which statements must be true.

Problem 4.35. Given that every natural number is either prime or divisible by a prime, prove by contradiction that there are infinitely many primes. *[Hint: For $x_1, x_2, \ldots, x_n \geq 2$, $x_1 x_2 \cdots x_n + 1$ is not divisible by any of $x_1, x_2, \ldots, x_n$.]*

Problem 4.36. Prove $\overline{A \cap B \cap C} = \overline{A} \cup \overline{B} \cup \overline{C}$. (a) Using Venn diagrams. (b) Show: $x \in \overline{A \cap B \cap C} \leftrightarrow x \in \overline{A} \cup \overline{B} \cup \overline{C}$. (c) Derive $\overline{A} \cup \overline{B} \cup \overline{C}$ from $\overline{A \cap B \cap C}$ using the rules in Figure 2.1 on page 17.

Problem 4.37. Give "proof" by pictures using Venn diagrams for each set relationship:

(a) $\overline{A \cap B} = \overline{A} \cup \overline{B}$.
(b) $\overline{A \cup B} = \overline{A} \cap \overline{B}$.
(c) $A \cap (B \cup C) = (A \cap B) \cup (A \cap C)$.
(d) $(A \cap B) \cup (A \cap \overline{B}) = A$.
(e) $(A \cup B) \cap \overline{A} = B \cap \overline{A}$.
(f) $A \cap \overline{A} = \varnothing$.
(g) $A \cap B \subseteq A$.
(h) $(\overline{A \cup B}) \cap A = \varnothing$.
(i) $(\overline{A \cap B}) \cap A = A \cap \overline{B}$.
(j) $|A| + |B| = |A \cup B| + |A \cap B|$.

Problem 4.38. Give formal proofs for each equality in Problem 4.37.

Problem 4.39. The set difference $A - B$ contains the elements in A that are not in B.

(a) Give $A - B$ and $B - A$ for (i) $A = \{1, 2, 3, 4\}$, $B = \{2, 4, 6, 8, 10\}$. (ii) $A = \{3k \mid k \in \mathbb{N}\}$, $B = \{p | p \in \mathbb{N} \text{ is prime}\}$.

(b) Give an expression for $A - B$ in terms of A and B using only intersection, union and complements.

(c) Use Venn diagrams to prove or disprove: $A \cup (B - C) = (A \cup B) - C$.

Problem 4.40. Prove that $A = B$, where A and B are the sets defined below.

(a) $A = \{x \mid x = 2k + 1, k \in \mathbb{Z}\}$ $\quad B = \{x \mid x = 2m - 17, m \in \mathbb{Z}\}$

(b) $A = \{(i, j) \mid 1 \leq i \leq n \text{ and } 1 \leq j \leq i\}$ $\quad B = \{(i, j) \mid j \leq i \leq n \text{ and } 1 \leq j \leq n\}$

Problem 4.41. $A = \{(x, y) \in \mathbb{R}^2 \mid y = x^2\}$; $B = \{(x, y) \in \mathbb{R}^2 \mid y = 2 - x\}$. What is $A \cap B$?

Problem 4.42. In each case, prove (or disprove) a relationship between the sets.

(a) $A = \{2k, k \in \mathbb{N}\}$, $B = \{3k, k \in \mathbb{N}\}$, and $C = \{6k, k \in \mathbb{N}\}$. Prove $A \cap B = C$.

(b) $A = \{7k, k \in \mathbb{N}\}$ and $B = \{3k, k \in \mathbb{N}\}$. Prove $A \cap B \neq \varnothing$.

(c) $A = \{4k - 3, k \in \mathbb{N}\}$ and $B = \{4k + 1, k \in \mathbb{N}\}$. Prove or disprove $A = B$.

(d) $A = \{4k + 1, k \in \mathbb{Z}\}$ and $B = \{4k + 5, k \in \mathbb{Z}\}$. Prove or disprove $A = B$.

(e) $A = \{12m + 21n, m, n \in \mathbb{Z}\}$. Prove or disprove $A = \mathbb{Z}$.

(f) $A = \{12m + 25n, m, n \in \mathbb{Z}\}$. Prove or disprove $A = \mathbb{Z}$.

Problem 4.43. Prove the following facts about the power set of A and B.

(a) $\mathcal{P}(A) \cup \mathcal{P}(B) \subseteq \mathcal{P}(A \cup B)$. $\quad$ (b) $\mathcal{P}(A) \subseteq \mathcal{P}(B) \leftrightarrow A \subseteq B$.

Problem 4.44. Prove that there exists a unique set A for which $A \cup B = B$ for all sets B.

Problem 4.45 (Closure). A set system is a collection of sets, $\mathcal{C} = \{\mathcal{A}_1, \mathcal{A}_2, \ldots\}$, where $\mathcal{A}_i$ are sets of elements from a universal set $\mathcal{U}$. The set system $\mathcal{C}$ is closed under a set-operation if performing the operation on sets in $\mathcal{C}$ produces only sets in $\mathcal{C}$. Here are examples of closure:

- **Closed under finite union.** If $\mathcal{A}_1, \mathcal{A}_2 \in \mathcal{C}$, then $\mathcal{A}_1 \cup \mathcal{A}_2 \in \mathcal{C}$.
- **Closed under finite intersection.** If $\mathcal{A}_1, \mathcal{A}_2 \in \mathcal{C}$, then $\mathcal{A}_1 \cap \mathcal{A}_2 \in \mathcal{C}$.
- **Closed under complement.** If $\mathcal{A}_1 \in \mathcal{C}$, then $\overline{\mathcal{A}_2} \in \mathcal{C}$.

(a) Let $\mathcal{C} = \{\mathcal{A}\}$ have one set $\mathcal{A}$. Show that $\mathcal{C}$ is closed under union and intersection. What about complement?

(b) Let $\mathcal{C} = \{\varnothing, \mathcal{A}, \overline{\mathcal{A}}, \mathcal{U}\}$. Show that $\mathcal{C}$ is closed under union, intersection and complement.

(c) Prove that if $\mathcal{C}$ is closed under union and complement, then $\mathcal{C}$ is closed under intersection.

(d) Give a set system $\mathcal{C}$ containing at least 4 sets that is closed under union and intersection, but not closed under complement. (Make sure to specify the universal set.)

Problem 4.46. Study these definitions of convergence and prove or disprove the claims. (In all cases, $n \in \mathbb{N}$.)

Definition. $f(n) \to \infty$ if for every $C > 0$, there is n_C such that for all $n \geq n_C$, $f(n) \geq C$.

Definition. $f(n) \to a$ if for every $\varepsilon > 0$, there is n_ε such that for all $n \geq n_\varepsilon$, $|f(n) - a| \leq \varepsilon$.

(a) $f(n) = (2n^2 + 3)/(n + 1)$. (i) $f(n) \to \infty$. (ii) $f(n) \to 1$. (iii) $f(n) \to 2$.

(b) $f(n) = (n + 3)/(n + 1)$. (i) $f(n) \to \infty$. (ii) $f(n) \to 1$. (iii) $f(n) \to 2$.

(c) $f(n) = n \sin^2(\frac{1}{2}n\pi)$. (i) $f(n) \to \infty$. (ii) $f(n) \to 1$. (iii) $f(n) \to 2$.

Problem 4.47 (Without Loss Of Generality (wlog)). Consider the following claim.

If x and y have opposite parity (one is odd and one is even), then $x + y$ is odd.

Explain why, in a direct proof, we may assume that x is odd and y is even? Prove the claim.
(Such a proof starts "Without loss of generality, assume x is odd and y is even. Then, ...")

Problem 4.48. Use the concept of "without loss of generality" to prove these claims.

(a) If d does not divide mn, then d does not divide m or n. (Use contraposition.)

(b) For integers x, y, if xy is not divisible by 5 then x and y are both not divisible by 5.

(c) For any nonzero real number x, $x^2 + 1/x^2 \geq 2$.

(d) For non-negative x, y, $\max(x, y) \leq x + y$.

(e) **Triangle Inequality.** For all $x, y \in \mathbb{R}$, $|x + y| \leq |x| + |y|$.

(f) **Schur's Inequality.** For $a, b, c \geq 0$ and $r > 0$, $a^r(a - b)(a - c) + b^r(b - a)(b - c) + c^r(c - a)(c - b) \geq 0$.

(g) Points in $\mathbb{R}^2$ are colored red or blue. Prove there are two points of the same color a distance d apart, for $d > 0$.

(h) No right triangle has sides which are Fibonacci numbers $(1, 1, 2, 3, 5, 8, 13, \ldots$, each number being the sum of the previous two). *[Hint: Triangle inequality; contradiction.]*

> Induction makes you feel guilty for getting something out of nothing, and it is artificial, but it is one of the greatest ideas of civilization. – **Herbert Wilf**
>
> Line up dominoes close enough for each domino to knock over the next. If the first domino falls, they all fall. The fault in this analogy is that a domino takes time to fall, so a far-away domino won't fall for a long time. A chain of mathematical implications is outside time. – **Peter J. Eccles (adapted)**

Chapter 5

Induction: Proving "FOR ALL ..."

1: Why do we need induction?
2: The principle of induction and the induction proof pattern.
3: Induction and well-ordering.

In the previous chapter, we discussed one method for proving a universally quantified statement,

"FOR ALL n, ..."

You prove the statement for a general, arbitrary n. Often, we have to resort to a more powerful tool known as mathematical induction. Induction is our most powerful tool for proving such "FOR ALL" claims. If you put just one thing on your wish-list, wish to become an expert on induction. Induction is not only a powerful proof technique, but it is also at the heart of important algorithm design strategies such as recursion and dynamic programming. Induction opens up a whole new world of computer science, so try to pick it up early.

Pop Quiz 5.1
The first person in line is a girl and behind any girl is a girl. Is everyone in line a girl?

Let us wade in with an example. The postal stamp machine in the student union should dispense stamps for any postage. In 2015, postcard-postage was 34¢, so you'll never need less than 34¢ in postage. Postage for various types of mail increases from year to year, but it's inconvenient to restock our machine with different stamps every year. We stocked the machine with a huge supply of 5¢ and 7¢ stamps. Can the machine dispense any postage demanded by a customer, assuming it is at least 34¢? Let us tinker with small postages.

postage	19¢	20¢	21¢	22¢	23¢
stamp combination	7,7,5	5,5,5,5	7,7,7	5,5,5,7	?

Things are not looking good. You can't dispense 23¢ (prove it). But, we don't need 23¢. The machine only needs to dispense postages of 34¢ or more. Let us continue. Perseverance is a virtue when tinkering.

19¢	20¢	21¢	22¢	23¢	24¢	25¢	26¢	27¢	28¢
7,7,5	5,5,5,5	7,7,7	5,5,5,7	✗	7,7,5,5	5,5,5,5,5	7,7,7,5	5,5,5,5,7	7,7,7,7

It looks like postages above 23¢ can be dispensed. Are we certain the situation with 23¢ won't recur at a higher postage, say 1023¢? That's where induction comes in. Here is a hint of how it works. If you can dispense some postage n, for example $n = 24$¢, then you can easily dispense $n + 5 = 29$¢ by adding a 5¢ stamp. Continue to tinker. Can you see why the hint means you can dispense the higher postages. The crux of induction is captured by our stamp dispenser. Induction uses the solution for some value of n ($n = 24$¢), to find an "easy" solution for a larger value of n ($n = 29$¢). In this chapter, we formalize this intuitive reasoning.

Induction begins with a predicate $P(n)$ where n is a natural number, and a claim that $P(n)$ is true for all n above some value. Let us begin with some examples of predicates and claims.

	Predicate	Claim
(i)	$P(n) =$ "Can make postage n with 5¢ and 7¢ stamps."	For all $n \geq 24$, $P(n)$ is true.
(ii)	$P(n) =$ "$n^2 - n + 41$ a prime number."	For all $n \geq 1$, $P(n)$ is true.
(iii)	$P(n) =$ "$4^n - 1$ is divisible by 3."	For all $n \geq 1$, $P(n)$ is true.
(iv)	$P(n) =$ "$1 + 2 + \cdots + n = n(n+1)/2$."	For all $n \geq 1$, $P(n)$ is true.
(v)	$P(n) =$ "$1 + 1/\sqrt{2} + 1/\sqrt{3} + \cdots + 1/\sqrt{n} \leq 2\sqrt{n}$."	For all $n \geq 1$, $P(n)$ is true.

Why do we need induction? Tinker with claims (ii) and (iii). For $n = 1, \ldots, 8$ the check marks show that $n^2 - n + 41$ is prime, and 3 divides $4^n - 1$ because $(4^n - 1)/3$ is an integer. Both claims look good so far.

n	1	2	3	4	5	6	7	8	...
$n^2 - n + 41$	41✓	43✓	47✓	53✓	61✓	71✓	83✓	97✓	...
$(4^n - 1)/3$	1✓	5✓	21✓	85✓	341✓	1365✓	5461✓	21845✓	...

But, this is not a proof of the claims for all $n \geq 1$. Continue to tinker. You will soon see that $n^2 - n + 41$ is not always prime, for example when $n = 41$. You will also find that $4^n - 1$ is divisible by 3, even for very large n. How large an n do you have to verify before you are convinced that $4^n - 1$ is divisible by 3 for all n?

No matter how big an n you verify, you fear that the next one will fail, and so you verify one more, and one more, ..., it never ends. Ilan Vardi gave this extreme example of a false claim that looks true:

$$n^{17} + 9 \text{ and } (n+1)^{17} + 9 \text{ have no factors in common for all } n \geq 1.$$

Try verifying this claim and see how high you get. You might even start to believe it, until you reach the first counterexample at $n = 8424432925592889329288197322308900672459420460792433$. Even a computer can't count that high. It's too dangerous to rely on verification, we need proof. How do we prove a claim for all $n \geq 1$? We certainly can't verify it for all n. One way is to prove the claim for a general n. This is not very systematic and often requires creativity. The next exercise proves that 3 divides $4^n - 1$ for a general n.

Exercise 5.2

Consider the geometric sum $S(n) = 1 + 4 + 4^2 + \cdots + 4^{n-1}$.

(a) Show that $S(n)$ is an integer.

(b) Compute a formula for $S(n)$ using the geometric sum formula, $1 + r^2 + \cdots + r^n = (r^{n+1} - 1)/(r - 1)$.

(c) Show that $4^n - 1$ is divisible by 3 for a general $n \geq 1$.

In Exercise 5.2, it took clairvoyance to attack the problem indirectly using a geometric sum. On the other hand, a proof by induction is systematic. It may be hard or it may not work, but the method is systematic.

Let us focus on the predicate $P(n) =$ "$4^n - 1$ is divisible by 3". We already verified $P(1)$, that $4^1 - 1$ is divisible by 3. We repeat an implication that was proved in Example 4.2 on page 42,

$$\text{IF } 4^n - 1 \text{ is divisible by 3, THEN } 4^{n+1} - 1 \text{ is divisible by 3.}$$

For the moment, the proof of this implication is not important, though we did prove it. In terms of our predicate $P(n)$, this means $P(n)$ implies $P(n+1)$ for any n,

$$P(n) \rightarrow P(n+1).$$

We referred to proving implications as reasoning without facts. Our hope was that in time, a new fact would make it worthwhile. We now reap the payday. A fact has come to light, namely $P(1)$ is true, $4^1 - 1$ is divisible by 3. And $P(1) \rightarrow P(2)$, so $P(2)$ is true, because if not, then $P(1) \rightarrow P(2)$ would be false. But $P(2) \rightarrow P(3)$, so $P(3)$ is true, and so on. The inference-chain never ends, and so for an arbitrary, general n, we ultimately infer $P(n)$ is true. That means $P(n)$ is true for all $n \geq 1$. In our case, $4^n - 1$ is divisible by 3 for all $n \geq 1$.

The table on the left summarizes the inferences. It's like tipping a domino-chain as shown on the right.

	Proved	**Inferred**
$P(1)$	$P(1) \to P(2)$	$\boldsymbol{P(2)}$
	$P(2) \to P(3)$	$\boldsymbol{P(3)}$
	$P(3) \to P(4)$	$\boldsymbol{P(4)}$
	$P(4) \to P(5)$	$\boldsymbol{P(5)}$
	$P(5) \to P(6)$	$\boldsymbol{P(6)}$
	$\vdots$	$\vdots$
	$P(n-1) \to P(n)$	$\boldsymbol{P(n)}$
	$\vdots$	$\vdots$

Analogy. The $P(n)$ form a chain of dominos,

$$\boxed{P(1)} \to P(2) \to P(3) \to P(4) \to P(5) \to \cdots$$

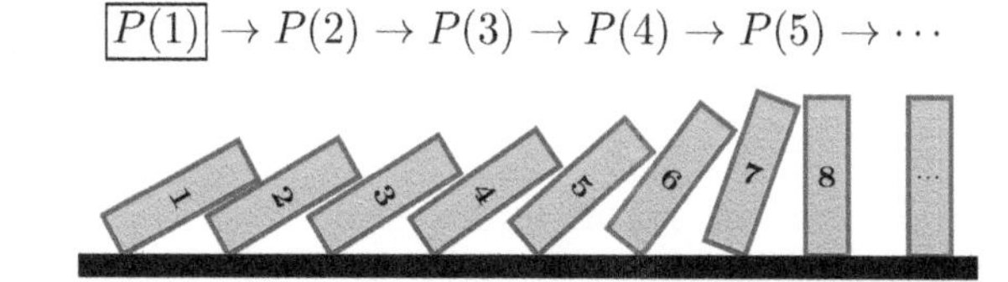

Domino Chain Principle: Line up dominos and tip the first domino. If the dominos are close together, they all fall.

It is crucial that:

(i) The first domino is tipped, $P(1)$ is true.
(ii) Adjacent dominos are close enough, $P(n) \to P(n+1)$.

The principle of induction summarizes our discussion for a general predicate $P(n)$.

Principle of Induction. Let $P(n)$ be a predicate for natural number $n \geq 1$.
(i) If you have proved $P(1)$. [base case]
(ii) And you have proved $P(n) \to P(n+1)$ for $n \geq 1$. [induction]
Then, you can conclude $P(n)$ is true for all $n \geq 1$.

The principle of induction follows from well-ordering. For now, the intuition suffices, but if you prefer a proof see Exercise 5.10. To repeat, $P(n) \to P(n+1)$ sets up an infinite chain of implications. If you prove the LHS of a true implication, you can infer the RHS. Proving $P(1)$ establishes the leftmost claim, hence, the entire chain is true. Prove (i) and (ii) in the principle of induction and $P(n)$ is true for all $n \geq 1$.

Exercise 5.3
For which n can you be sure $P(n)$ is true.
(a) $P(2)$ is true and $P(n) \to P(n+1)$ is true for $n \geq 1$.
(b) $P(1)$ is true and $P(n) \to (P(2n) \wedge P(n-1))$ is true for $n \geq 1$.
(c) $P(1)$ is true and $P(n) \to (P(n^2) \wedge P(n-1))$ is true for $n \geq 1$.
(d) $P(1) \wedge P(2)$ is true and $P(n) \to P(n+2)$ is true for $n \geq 1$.
(e) $P(1) \wedge P(2)$ is true and $P(n) \to (P(n^2) \wedge P(n-1))$ is true for $n \geq 2$.

5.1 Ordinary Induction

Ordinary induction uses the principle of induction "as is" to prove $P(n)$ for $n \geq 1$. The ingredients are:

- Carefully formulate the predicate $P(n)$. In particular you must identify n.
- Verify $P(1)$, the base case.
- Prove the implication $P(n) \to P(n+1)$ for every $n \geq 1$, the induction step.

You have to prove the implication for every $n \geq 1$. So, how did we gain? Why not just prove $P(n)$ for every $n \geq 1$? Because proving the implication is much easier. To prove $P(n) \to P(n+1)$, you get to assume $P(n)$ in the proof. We now give the formal proof by induction that $4^n - 1$ is divisible by 3.

Theorem 5.1. $4^n - 1$ is divisible by 3 for all $n \geq 1$.

Proof. (By induction.) Define the claim $P(n) : 4^n - 1$ is divisible by 3. (Technically a predicate)
1: **[Base case]** $P(1)$ claims that $4^1 - 1 = 3$ is divisible by 3, which is clearly true.

2: **[Induction step]** We prove $P(n) \to P(n+1)$ for all $n \geq 1$, using a direct proof.
Assume $P(n)$: $4^n - 1$ is divisible by 3. ← called the induction hypothesis
Prove $P(n+1)$: $4^{n+1} - 1$ is divisible by 3.
By the induction hypothesis, $4^n - 1 = 3k$ for an integer k, or $4^n = 3k + 1$. This means

$$4^{n+1} = 4 \cdot 4^n = 4(3k+1) = 12k + 4.$$

Subtracting 1 from both sides, $4^{n+1} - 1 = 12k + 3 = 3(4k + 1)$, which is a multiple of 3. Hence, $4^{n+1} - 1$ is divisible by 3, which proves $P(n+1)$.

3: By the principle induction, $P(n)$ is proved $\forall n \geq 1$. ■

Induction is one of humanity's great inventions. Learn it well.

Proof Template VII: Induction to prove $\forall n \geq 1 : P(n)$.
Proof. We use induction to prove $\forall n \geq 1 : P(n)$.
1: Prove $P(1)$. (Usually a simple verification.) **[base case]**
2: Prove $P(n) \to P(n+1)$ for $n \geq 1$ **[induction step]**

Prove the implication using direct proof or contraposition.

Direct	Contraposition
Assume $P(n)$.	Assume $P(n+1)$ is false.
↓ valid steps for any $n \geq 1$; must use $P(n)$	↓ valid steps for any $n \geq 1$; must use $\neg P(n+1)$
Show $P(n+1)$ **is true.**	**Show** $P(n)$ **is false.**

3: Conclude, by induction, $P(n)$ is true for all $n \geq 1$. ■

As we work through examples, you'll see that induction is plug and play, almost always following the standard template. Though the induction step (step 2) may vary with the predicate $P(n)$, several things are essential:

- Make sure to prove the implication $P(n) \to P(n+1)$ for a general $n \geq 1$.
- To use direct proof, start with the assumption that $P(n)$ is true, and reformulate it mathematically.
- Somewhere in your direct proof you must use $P(n)$ to prove the claim in $P(n+1)$.
- The direct proof always ends with a statement that $P(n+1)$ is true.

5.1.1 Sum of Powers of Integers

After some effort, you can confirm that $1 + 2 + \cdots + 99 + 100 = 5050$.[1] Let us prove, for any $n \geq 1$,

$$1 + 2 + 3 + \cdots + (n-1) + n = \tfrac{1}{2}n(n+1).$$

Commit this important sum to memory. Why? Many programs do something once, then twice, then 3 times, and so on up to n times. The total work is given by this sum. First, we give the "proof by genius". A teacher, to occupy the legendary Gauss, asked him to add $1 + 2 + \cdots + 100$. In seconds, the 8-year-old Gauss yelled 5050. He computed the answer using the formula above, no doubt, but how did he get the formula? Gauss wrote the sum $S(n) = 1 + 2 + \cdots + n$ forwards and backwards and added.

$$\begin{array}{rcl} S(n) &=& 1 \;+\; 2 \;+\cdots+\; n \\ S(n) &=& n \;+\; n-1 \;+\cdots+\; 1 \\ \hline 2S(n) &=& (n+1) + (n+1) + \cdots + (n+1) \\ &=& n \times (n+1) \end{array}$$

The RHS has n pairs and each pair adds to $n+1$. The conclusion is $S(n) = \frac{1}{2}n(n+1)$.

[1]The sum of powers of the integers has a rich 2,500 year history: Pythagoras (~500BC) knew how to sum the integers; Jakob Bernoulli (~1700) fathered the current state of the art, relating the sums of integer powers to the Bernoulli numbers.

The idea to reverse the sum and combine is just pure genius for an 8-year-old. The picture with black and white balls illustrates Gauss' idea with $n = 6$. The white balls are the sum, and the black balls are the reversed sum. Together they form an $n \times (n+1)$ rectangle with twice the number of balls in the desired sum. Now for the proof by induction. It is methodical and straightforward, not requiring such creative genius.

Theorem 5.2. The sum of the first n numbers is $1 + 2 + \cdots + n = \frac{1}{2}n(n+1)$.

Proof. (By induction.) Define the claim $P(n) : 1 + 2 + \cdots + n = \frac{1}{2}n(n+1)$.

1: **[Base case]** $P(1)$ claims that $1 = \frac{1}{2} \times 1 \times (1+1)$, which is clearly true.

2: **[Induction step]** We show $P(n) \to P(n+1)$ for all $n \geq 1$, using a direct proof.
Assume (induction hypothesis) $P(n)$*:* $1 + 2 + \cdots + n = \frac{1}{2}n(n+1)$.
Prove $P(n+1)$*:* $1 + 2 + \cdots + n + (n+1) = \frac{1}{2}(\boldsymbol{n+1})(\boldsymbol{n+1}+1)$.
We compute the sum $1 + 2 + \cdots + n + (n+1)$ as follows:

$$\begin{aligned} 1+2+\cdots+n+(n+1) &= [\mathbf{1+2+\cdots+n}] + (n+1) && \text{[key step]} \\ &= \tfrac{1}{2}\boldsymbol{n(n+1)} + (n+1) && \text{[by the induction hypothesis]} \\ &= \tfrac{1}{2}(\boldsymbol{n+1})(\boldsymbol{n+1}+1) && \text{[algebra, please verify]} \end{aligned}$$

This is exactly what was to be shown. So, $P(n+1)$ is true.

3: By induction, we proved $P(n)$ for all $n \geq 1$. ■

The key step breaks the sum in $P(n+1)$ into two parts, where one part resembles the induction hypothesis $P(n)$. The creative stroke in an induction is usually to relate $P(n+1)$ to $P(n)$.

A BIG error in the induction step is to start from $P(n+1)$ and show $P(n)$, proving $P(n+1) \to P(n)$, not $P(n) \to P(n+1)$.

Never assert $P(n+1)$ as true (first step of bad proof). This is what you must *prove*.

BAD!

We are to prove:
$1 + \cdots + n + (n+1) = \frac{1}{2}(n+1)(n+2)$
Subtracting $n+1$ from both sides,

$$\begin{aligned} 1+\cdots+n &= \tfrac{1}{2}(n+1)(n+2) - (n+1) \\ 1+\cdots+n &= (n+1)(\tfrac{n}{2}+1-1) \\ 1+\cdots+n &= \tfrac{1}{2}n(n+1) \quad ✗ \end{aligned}$$

In the bad proof, $P(n)$ isn't used to justify any step. The proof ends with $P(n)$ not $P(n+1)$, and $P(n)$ was assumed, so deriving it proves nothing. This flawed proof is a relic of a misplaced youth, but it is an epidemic. The student on this route appears to think:

"Let's see what happens by assuming $P(n+1)$, what we are to prove. Look, nothing bad happens! We got to a known truth, namely $P(n)$. So the starting point, $P(n+1)$, must be true." ✗

This cozy "logic" is wrong, see Problem 4.4. Here are two similar correct proofs. Be sure to grasp the differences between the good proofs and the bad one. In particular, $P(n+1)$ is never asserted. Only $P(n)$ is used.

GOOD

$$\begin{aligned} 1+\cdots+n &= \tfrac{1}{2}n(n+1) \quad [P(n) \text{ is } \textit{true}] \\ 1+\cdots+(n+1) &= \tfrac{1}{2}n(n+1) + (n+1) \\ &= \tfrac{1}{2}(n+1)(n+2) \quad ✓ \end{aligned}$$

This proof starts with the true assertion $P(n)$.

GOOD

$$\begin{aligned} 1+\cdots+(n+1) &= (1+\cdots+n) + (n+1) \\ &= \tfrac{1}{2}n(n+1) + (n+1) \quad [P(n) \text{ is } \textit{true}] \\ &= \tfrac{1}{2}(n+1)(n+2) \quad ✓ \end{aligned}$$

This proof correctly manipulates the sum in $P(n+1)$.

Exercise 5.4

Prove, by induction, the following claims for $n \geq 1$.

(a) **[Arithmetic sum]** $a + (a+d) + (a+2d) + (a+3d) + \cdots + (a+(n-1)d) = na + \frac{1}{2}n(n-1)d$.

(b) **[Geometric sum]** $a + ar^a r^2 + ar^3 + \cdots + ar^{n-1} = a(r^n - 1)/(r-1)$, where $r \neq 1$.

(c) $n \leq 2^n$. (d) $5^n - 1$ is divisible by 4. (e) $1 \cdot 1! + 2 \cdot 2! + 3 \cdot 3! + n \cdot n! = (n+1)! - 1$.

Finding the Formula

Gauss' derivation was indeed ingenious, but we can't all be a Gauss. Induction was systematic, not requiring the insight of Gauss, but there is a glaring deficiency. Did you spot it? Induction gives a proof of the formula, not a derivation. Therein lies the challenge. Induction does not work until you have something to prove. To prove the answer, you must already have the answer. It seems circular, but it's not. To get going with an induction, you can make a guess and induction can prove your guess. How do you get a plausible guess? **Tinker!** Tinker with small values of n and make a guess by observation on these few n. Beware! Verification on a few n is never a proof. But, once you have a guess, you can use induction to hammer out the proof for all n. Let's work through obtaining a formula for the sum of the first n squares,

$$S(n) = 1^2 + 2^2 + 3^2 + \cdots + n^2.$$

We start by tinkering, and, in doing so, we illustrate the method of differences. Here is a table with $S(n)$.

	n	1	2	3	4	5	6	7	8	9	10
	$S(n)$	1	5	14	30	55	91	140	204	285	385
1st difference	$S'(n)$		4	9	16	25	36	49	64	81	100
2nd difference	$S''(n)$			5	7	9	11	13	15	17	19
3rd difference	$S'''(n)$				2	2	2	2	2	2	2

There is no pattern to $S(n)$. Look at the 1st difference $S'(n) = S(n) - S(n-1)$, the difference between consecutive values. The 1st difference is like a 1st derivative from calculus. The 1st differences are squares, no surprise there. Consider the 2nd difference (changes in the 1st difference, $S''(n) = S'(n) - S'(n-1)$), and the 3rd difference (changes in the 2nd difference, $S'''(n) = S''(n) - S''(n-1)$). A pattern emerges in the 2nd difference, the odd numbers. A stronger pattern appears in the 3rd difference, the constant 2. Think back to calculus. If the 3rd derivative is constant, the function is a 3rd order polynomial. We make the same guess here. Since the third difference is a constant, we guess that $S(n)$ is a 3rd order polynomial in n,

$$S(n) = a_0 + a_1 n + a_2 n^2 + a_3 n^3.$$

If this formula is to work for all n, it had better work for $n = 1, 2, 3, 4$. This means

$$\begin{array}{lr} a_0 + a_1 + a_2 + a_3 = 1 & \leftarrow n = 1 \\ a_0 + 2a_1 + 4a_2 + 8a_3 = 5 & \leftarrow n = 2 \\ a_0 + 3a_1 + 9a_2 + 27a_3 = 14 & \leftarrow n = 3 \\ a_0 + 4a_1 + 16a_2 + 64a_3 = 30 & \leftarrow n = 4 \end{array}$$

Pop Quiz 5.5
Verify $a_0 = 0$, $a_1 = \frac{1}{6}$, $a_2 = \frac{1}{2}$ and $a_3 = \frac{1}{3}$ solves the 4 equations in 4 unknowns above.

So, our guess is $S(n) = \frac{1}{6}n + \frac{1}{2}n^2 + \frac{1}{3}n^3$. Let us verify that this guess works for small n,

n	1	2	3	4	5	6	7	8	9	10
$\frac{1}{6}n + \frac{1}{2}n^2 + \frac{1}{3}n^3$	1	5	14	30	55	91	140	204	285	385

It's looking good. We now use induction to prove our guess $S(n) = \frac{1}{6}n + \frac{1}{2}n^2 + \frac{1}{3}n^3 = \frac{1}{6}n(n+1)(2n+1)$.

Theorem 5.3 (Sum of Squares). The sum of the first n squares is $1^2 + 2^2 + \cdots + n^2 = \frac{1}{6}n(n+1)(2n+1)$.

Proof. (By induction.) Define the claim $P(n) : 1^2 + 2^2 + \cdots + n^2 = \frac{1}{6}n(n+1)(2n+1)$.

1: **[Base case]** $P(1)$, claims that $1 = \frac{1}{6} \times 1 \times 2 \times 3$, which is clearly true.

2: **[Induction step]** We prove $P(n) \to P(n+1)$ for all $n \geq 1$, using a direct proof.
Assume (induction hypothesis) $P(n)$: $1^2 + 2^2 + \cdots + n^2 = \frac{1}{6}n(n+1)(2n+1)$.
Prove $P(n+1)$: $1^2 + 2^2 + \cdots + n^2 + (n+1)^2 = \frac{1}{6}(n+1)(n+2)(2n+3)$.

Compute the sum $1^2 + 2^2 + \cdots + n^2 + (n+1)^2$ as follows:

$$\begin{aligned} 1^2 + 2^2 + \cdots + n^2 + (n+1)^2 &= [\mathbf{1^2 + 2^2 + \cdots + n^2}] + (n+1)^2 && \text{[key step]} \\ &= \tfrac{1}{6}\boldsymbol{n(n+1)(2n+1)} + (n+1)^2 && \text{[by the induction hypothesis]} \\ &= \tfrac{1}{6}(n+1)(n+2)(2n+3) && \text{[algebra, please verify]} \end{aligned}$$

This is exactly the expression claimed in $P(n+1)$, which proves $P(n+1)$.

3: By induction, we have proved $P(n)$ for all $n \geq 1$. ∎

It is possible to derive a formula for the sum of the first n squares without induction (see Problem 5.77 for the magic). Induction is systematic and straightforward in comparison.

Exercise 5.6
Obtain a formula for each sum. First tinker, then make a guess and prove it by induction for $n \geq 1$.
(a) The odd numbers, $S(n) = 1 + 3 + \cdots + (2n-1)$. (b) The cubes, $S(n) = 1^3 + 2^3 + \cdots + n^3$.

5.1.2 Induction Gone Wrong

Induction creates an infinite chain of implications. Proving the first claim (base case) sets the chain into motion, implying all subsequent claims. You must have the base case and the entire infinite chain of implications:

$$\boxed{P(1)} \to P(2) \to P(3) \to P(4) \to P(5) \to P(6) \to P(7) \to \cdots$$

Induction fails if you don't have the base case, or if any link is missing. Here are two failed inductions.

No Base Case: $P(1) \to P(2) \to P(3) \to P(4) \to \cdots$

Let us misuse induction to "prove" the false claim $P(n) : n + 1 \leq n$ for all $n \geq 1$.

We show $P(n) \to P(n+1)$. Assume $P(n)$, so $n + 1 \leq n$. Then, $(n+1) + 1 \leq n + 1$, proving $P(n+1)$. Hence, we proved $P(n) \to P(n+1)$ for all $n \geq 1$. There is nothing wrong with the proof of the implication.

[Every link is proved, but without the base case, you have nothing.]

Broken Chain of Implications: $\boxed{P(1)}$ $P(2) \to P(3) \to P(4) \to \cdots$

Let us misuse induction to "prove" the false claim $P(n)$: "all balls in any set of n balls are the same color."

For the base case, $P(1)$ is clearly true as when there is 1 ball there is just one color.

We show $P(n) \to P(n+1)$. Assume $P(n)$, that in any set of n balls, all balls are the same color. Now consider any set of $n+1$ balls $\{b_1, b_2, \ldots, b_n, b_{n+1}\}$. The n balls $\{b_1, b_2, \ldots, b_n\}$ have the same color because $P(n)$ is true. The n balls $\{b_2, \ldots, b_n, b_{n+1}\}$ have the same color because $P(n)$ is true. Since b_2 is common to both sets, $\{b_1, b_2, \ldots, b_n, b_{n+1}\}$ must have the same color, which proves $P(n+1)$.

The claim "b_2 is common to both sets" only holds when $n \geq 2$. So, the argument fails to prove $P(1) \to P(2)$.

[A single broken link kills the entire proof.]

The first proof emphasizes that the implication $P(n) \to P(n+1)$ may be easy to prove, but the entire chain of implications is useless without the base case. The second proof shows how easy it is to overlook boundary cases when proving $P(n) \to P(n+1)$. Every implication in the chain must be solid for induction to work.

Pop Quiz 5.7
For which n can you infer $P(n)$. The implications have been proved and claims known to be true are boxed.

(a) $P(1) \to P(2) \to \boxed{P(3)} \to P(4) \to P(5) \to P(6) \to P(7) \to P(8) \to \cdots$

(b) $P(1) \to P(2) \to \boxed{P(3)} \to P(4) \quad P(5) \to P(6) \to P(7) \to P(8) \to \cdots$

(c) $\boxed{P(1)} \to P(2) \to P(3) \to P(4) \quad \boxed{P(5)} \to P(6) \to P(7) \to P(8) \to \cdots$

Example 5.4. Induction can be used to prove much more than just formulas for sums. Here is an example.

> A circle has $2n$ distinct points, n are red and n are blue. Prove that one can start at a blue point and move clockwise always having passed as many blue points as red.

Stop and **tinker**. Make sure you understand the claim. For an example with 3 red and blue points, find a blue point to start at. Now try 4 red and blue points, as in the example on the right. Try to convince yourself of the claim. Be curious. Ask additional questions.

- Can there be more than one valid blue point to start the trip?
- Can a blue point whose counter-clockwise neighbor is a blue point be a valid start?
- Can one start at any blue point which has a red point for counter-clockwise neighbor?

Now for the proof by induction. The base case $n = 1$ is illustrated. Start at the blue point. The clockwise trip has always passed as many blue as red points, since there is only one red point. For the induction step. Assume the claim for any arrangement of n red and blue points on the circle.

We must prove the claim for any $n+1$ red and blue points. Consider an arbitrary arrangement of $n+1$ red and blue points on the circle. We show one such arrangement with $n+1=5$.

Important: You must start from the general case of the claim for $n+1$.

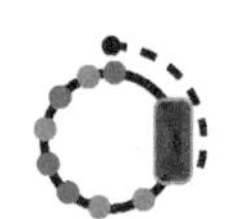

[Key Step.] We must link the claim for $n+1$ with the induction hypothesis. We can apply the induction hypothesis after removing a pair of red and blue points, leaving n pairs of red and blue points. But which pair of points should we remove? Start at any blue point and move clockwise to a red point. The red point and its preceeding blue point are shaded. Remove the two shaded points. (We can pick any consecutive blue-red pair. Why pick such a specific pair?)

We now have n pairs of red and blue points. By the induction hypothesis, there is a clockwise trip that has always passed as many blue points as red. We show a valid clockwise trip in the figure.

> How did we find this trip? We don't need to! That's the crux of induction. We have blind faith in the induction hypothesis and simply assert the trip exists without spending any effort to find it.

How does this clockwise trip help with proving the claim for the original $n+1$ red and blue points? The same trip starting from the same blue point works for the original $n+1$ red and blue points! You can verify this for the example. Let us prove it for a general case.

Observe that the trip given by the induction hypothesis cannot start between the two removed points (there is no blue point in that region). Define the score as the number of blue minus red points passed. As the trip moves clockwise, the score is non-negative until the trip hits the removed blue point (by construction from the induction hypothesis). At the removed blue point, the score goes up by 1 and then returns to its original non-negative score at the removed red point. So, the score for the rest of the trip is exactly what it was before adding back the removed points, and hence remains non-negative by the induction hypothesis. We have proved that there is a valid trip starting at a blue point for the general case of $n+1$ red and blue points, proving the induction step. By induction, the claim holds for $n \geq 1$. ■

The key step in almost all induction proofs is the same: link the claim for $n+1$ to the claim for n. This is also usually where most creativity is needed. There are no rules to follow. If a superhero told you that link, then the proof is often routine from there. That superhero is you. *You* have to tinker around until a lightbulb turns on. The pictures accompanying the proof down the righthand side are exactly our tinkering.

Look back at the proof. Try to come up with alternative, perhaps easier proofs. Does the proof give an algorithm for finding the starting blue point? How efficient an algorithm? These follow on thoughts are the path to an airtight understanding of the problem. It's the path a scholar would take. □

Exercise 5.8 [L-tile land]

A patio is a $2^n \times 2^n$ square grid. The top-left square is blacked out for a pot-plant. The rest of the patio must be tiled with L-shaped tiles, ▟. Prove that this can always be done. We show the 2×2 and 4×4 grids.

5.2 Induction and Well-ordering

The well-ordering principle is simple and looks innocuous, but it's as powerful as induction.

Well-ordering Principle: Any non-empty set of natural numbers has a minimum element.

Any induction-proof can be done using well-ordering. To compare induction and well-ordering, let us prove

$$n < 2^n \qquad \text{for all } n \geq 1.$$

Proof. **[Induction]** Define the claim $P(n) : n < 2^n$. We prove $P(n)$ for $n \geq 1$ by induction.
Base case. $P(1)$ is clearly true because $1 < 2^1$.
Induction step. Assume $P(n)$: $n < 2^n$. Since $n \geq 1$, $n + 1 \leq n + n = 2n$. By the induction hypothesis, $2n < 2 \times 2^n = 2^{n+1}$, so $n + 1 < 2^{n+1}$, which proves $P(n + 1)$. By induction, $P(n)$ is proved for $n \geq 1$. ■

A well-ordering proof uses contradiction. You assume there is a counterexample n for which $P(n)$ is false, and consider the smallest counterexample. You then find an even smaller counterexample, a contradiction.

Proof. **[Well-ordering]** We use contradiction. Assume there is a counterexample $n \geq 1$ with $n \geq 2^n$. Collect all the counterexamples into a "bad" set $\mathcal{B}$. By well-ordering, $\mathcal{B}$ has a minimum element n_* with $n_* \geq 2^{n_*}$. Clearly $1 < 2^1$, so n_* can't be 1, which means $n_* \geq 2$ and $\frac{1}{2}n_* \geq 1$. We prove $n_* - 1$ is a counterexample:

$$n_* - 1 \geq n_* - \tfrac{1}{2}n_* = \tfrac{1}{2}n_* \geq \tfrac{1}{2} \times 2^{n_*} = 2^{n_*-1}.$$

So, $n_* - 1 \in \mathcal{B}$, a FISHY contradiction because n_* is the minimum element in $\mathcal{B}$. Thus, $n < 2^n$ for $n \geq 1$. ■

The two proof techniques are equivalent. Some would argue that the smallest counterexample approach illuminates the structure in the problem. Nevertheless, induction is much more popular.

Exercise 5.9

(i) A non-empty set $\mathcal{B}$ has only integers greater than z_0. Use well-ordering to prove that $\mathcal{B}$ has a minimum.
(ii) Give a well-ordering proof for problems (a)–(e) in Exercise 5.4

It's no coincidence that induction proofs can be done with well-ordering. Induction is well-ordering in disguise. Induction can be proved from well-ordering. Indeed, suppose we have proved the induction chain of implications as well as $P(1)$. Let n_* be the smallest n for which $P(n)$ is false. Here is the situation, with the statements known to be true in boxes and the first false statement $P(n_*)$ in red.

$$\boxed{P(1)} \to \boxed{P(2)} \to \boxed{P(3)} \to \boxed{P(4)} \to \cdots \to \boxed{P(n_* - 1)} \to P(n_*) \to P(n_* + 1) \cdots$$

Do you see the problem? If $P(n_* - 1)$ is true and $P(n_*)$ is false, then the implication $P(n_* - 1) \to P(n_*)$ is false, which can't be since the entire implication chain has been proved. So, there is no such n_*.

Exercise 5.10

Use the well-ordering principle to prove the the principle of induction for any predicate P.

IF ($P(1)$ is true AND $P(n) \to P(n + 1)$ is true for $n \geq 1$), THEN $P(m)$ is true for $m \geq 1$.

Induction is a powerful off-the-shelf tool that is practical, convenient and easy to apply in a variety of settings. Induction follows from well-ordering, yet it is not the "Induction Theorem." Just as induction follows from well-ordering, so too does well-ordering follow from induction (Problem 5.78). The two are equivalent principles. You may assume one or other. Why didn't we start with induction? Why introduce well-ordering in the first place? Because well-ordering is a simple plausible principle which is easy to accept on face value, as we did in Chapter 1. Little did we expect back then that well-ordering is equivalent to this mammoth proof technique induction. Had we started with the principle of induction, a subtle principle, you might have been skeptical.

5.3 Problems

Problem 5.1. Is $2^p - 1$ prime for the primes $p = 2, 3, 5, 7$? Is $2^p - 1$ prime whenever p is prime?

Problem 5.2. Is $n^2 + n + 41$ prime for $n = 1, 2, \ldots, 10$. Is $n^2 + n + 41$ prime for all $n \in \mathbb{N}$?

Problem 5.3. For which n is $P(n)$ true? Explain by showing the "chain" of implications.
(a) $P(2)$ is true and $P(n) \to P(n+1)$ for $n \geq 0$.
(b) $P(1)$ is true and $P(n) \to (P(2n) \wedge P(2n+1))$ for $n \geq 1$.
(c) $P(2)$ is true and $P(n) \to (P(n^2) \wedge P(n-2))$ for $n \geq 2$.
(d) $P(1), P(2), P(3)$ are true and $P(n) \to P(n+4)$ for $n \geq 1$.
(e) $P(0), P(1)$ are true and $P(n) \to P(n+2)$ for $n \geq 0$.
(f) $P(0), P(1), P(2)$ are true and $P(n) \to P(3n)$ for $n \geq 1$.

Problem 5.4. Which of the following, if any, is a valid way to prove $P(n) \to P(n+1)$.

(i) Let's see what happens if $P(n+1)$ is true.
⋮ (valid derivations)
Look! $P(n)$ is true. ✓

(ii) Let's see what happens if $P(n+1)$ is F.
⋮ (valid derivations)
Look! $P(n)$ is F. ✓

(Compare with the **BAD** proof on page 59. It is very important to understand this problem.)

Problem 5.5. Let us prove the conjecture: "If every person in a n-person social network has at least one friend, then everyone is linked to everyone else by a chain of friendships. Such a network is connected."

> We use induction. When $n = 2$ the claim is easy to verify. For $n \geq 2$, assume any n-person network with people $p_1, \ldots, p_n$ is connected. Now add a person p_{n+1} to get an $(n+1)$-person network. All original people are linked to each other. The new person p_{n+1} has at least one friend, so is linked to (say) p_j. Since p_j is linked to $p_1, \ldots, p_n$, this means p_{n+1} is linked to everyone else. Thus everyone is linked to everyone else, and the claim holds for $n+1$. ■

Show that the conjecture is not true, and explain what is wrong with the induction proof above.

Problem 5.6. Prove by induction: $2 \times 2^1 + 3 \times 2^2 + 4 \times 2^3 + \cdots + (n+1) \times 2^n = n \times 2^{n+1}$, for $n \geq 1$.

Problem 5.7. Determine for which n the claim is true and use induction to prove it.
(a) $2^0 + 2^1 + 2^2 + \cdots + 2^n = 2^{n+1} - 1$.
(b) $1 + 3 + 5 + \cdots + (2n-1) = n^2$.
(c) $\frac{1}{1\cdot 2} + \frac{1}{2\cdot 3} + \frac{1}{3\cdot 4} + \cdots + \frac{1}{n\cdot(n+1)} = \frac{n}{n+1}$.
(d) $0 \cdot 1 + 1 \cdot 2 + \cdots + n \cdot (n+1) = \frac{1}{3}n(n+1)(n+2)$.
(e) $\frac{1}{2} + \frac{2}{4} + \frac{3}{8} + \cdots + \frac{n}{2^n} = 2^{-n}(2^{n+1} - n - 2)$.
(f) $(1 - \frac{1}{2})(1 - \frac{1}{3})(1 - \frac{1}{4}) \cdots (1 - \frac{1}{n}) = \frac{1}{n}$.

Problem 5.8. Prove by induction, for $n \geq 2$, $(1 - \frac{1}{1+2})(1 - \frac{1}{1+2+3}) \cdots (1 - \frac{1}{1+2+\cdots+n}) = \frac{n+2}{3n}$.

Problem 5.9. Prove by induction, for $n \geq 1$,
(a) $1 + \frac{1}{\sqrt{2}} + \frac{1}{\sqrt{3}} + \cdots + \frac{1}{\sqrt{n}} \geq \sqrt{n}$. (b) $1 + \sqrt{2} + \sqrt{3} + \cdots + \sqrt{n} \leq n\sqrt{n}$. (c) $\frac{1\times 3\times 5\times(2n-3)\times(2n-1)}{2\times 4\times 6\times(2n-2)\times 2n} \leq \frac{1}{\sqrt{n+1}}$.

Problem 5.10. Determine for which n the claim is true and use induction to prove it.
(a) 5 divides $11^n - 6$.
(b) 7 divides $n^7 - n$.
(c) 24 divides $5^{2n} - 1$.
(d) 8 divides $3^{2n} - 1$.
(e) 5 divides $2^{3n} - 3^n$.
(f) 7 divides $5^{2n+1} + 2^{2n+1}$.
(g) 6 divides $17n^3 + 103n$.
(h) 5 divides $4 \cdot 3^n + (-2)^n$.
(i) 3 divides $5^n + 2 \cdot 11^n$.
(j) 3 divides $n^3 + 5n + 6$.
(k) 3 divides $n^3 + 2n$.
(l) 6 divides $n^3 - n$.
(m) 4 divides $n^4 - n^2$.
(n) 5 divides $6^n + 4$.
(o) 3 divides $2^{2n-1} + 1$.
(p) 9 divides $4^{3n} + 8$.
(q) 80 divides $3^{4n} - 1$.
(r) 10 divides $13^n - 3^n$.
(s) 12 divides $5 \cdot 9^n + 3$.
(t) 8 divides $7^n - (-1)^n$.

Problem 5.11. Use induction to prove these facts about divisibility.
(a) $n^2 - 1$ is divisible by 8 for all odd natural numbers n.
(b) $n^4 - 1$ is divisible by 16 for all odd natural numbers n.
(c) $2^{3^n} + 1$ is divisible by 3^{n+1} for $n \geq 0$.
(d) $4^{2n+1} + 5^{2n+1} + 6^{2n+1}$ is divisible by 15 for $n \geq 0$.

Problem 5.12. For $n \geq 1$, prove by induction:
(a) $4n \leq 2^{n+1}$.
(b) $n^2 \leq 2^{n+1}$.
(c) $n! \geq 2^{n-1}$.
(d) $3^n > n^2$.
(e) $n! \leq n^n$.
(f) $1 + 2 + \cdots + n \leq n^2$.
(g) $1^2 + 2^2 + \cdots + n^2 > n^3/3$.
(h) $10^0 + 10^1 + \cdots + 10^n < 10^{n+1}$.
(i) $n! \geq n^n e^{-n}$. *[Hint: $(1 + \frac{1}{n})^n \leq e$.]*
(j) Bernoulli's inequality: $(1+x)^n \geq 1 + nx$ for $x \geq -1$.

Problem 5.13. Determine for which n the claim is true and prove it by induction.

(a) k is odd implies k^n is odd.
(b) $\sqrt[n]{n} \le 2 - \frac{1}{n}$.
(c) $2^{1/2^n}$ is not rational.
(d) 5 divides $(x-2)$ implies 5 divides $x^n - 2^n$.
(e) For $x > 0$, (i) $(1+x)^n \le 1+nx+n^2x^2$ (ii) $(1-x)^n \le 1-nx+\frac{1}{2}n^2x^2$.
(f) **[Challenging!]** $\text{Re}[(\cos x + i\sin x)^n] = \cos nx$.

Problem 5.14. Prove that the last digit of 3^{4n} is 1, for $n \ge 0$.

Problem 5.15. Prove: 9 divides $10^n - 1$ for $n \ge 0$. Hence, show: 9 divides x if and only if 9 divides x's digit-sum.

Problem 5.16. Prove that $(3^{2^n} - 1)/2^{n+2}$ is an odd integer for $n \ge 1$.

Problem 5.17. Prove that $1+\frac{1}{2}+\frac{1}{3}+\cdots+\frac{1}{2^k} \ge 1+\frac{1}{2}k$, for $k \ge 0$. Hence prove that $1+\frac{1}{2}+\frac{1}{3}+\cdots+\frac{1}{n} \ge \frac{1}{2}(1+\log_2 n)$.

Problem 5.18. The nth Harmonic number is $H_n = 1 + \frac{1}{2} + \frac{1}{3} + \cdots + \frac{1}{n}$, for $n \ge 1$. Prove:

(a) $H_1 + H_2 + \cdots + H_n = (n+1)H_n - n$.
(b) $1 + \frac{1}{2}\ln n \le H_n \le 1 + \ln n$. *[Hint: For $0 \le x \le \frac{1}{2}$, $-2x \le \ln(1-x) \le -x$.]*

Problem 5.19. Let $x_1, \ldots, x_n$ be positive and sum to $\frac{1}{2}$, $x_1 + x_2 + \cdots + x_n = \frac{1}{2}$. Prove:

$$\frac{1-x_1}{1+x_1} \times \frac{1-x_2}{1+x_2} \times \frac{1-x_3}{1+x_3} \times \cdots \times \frac{1-x_n}{1+x_n} \ge \frac{1}{3}.$$

Problem 5.20. Prove, by induction, that every $n \ge 1$ is a sum of distinct powers of 2.

Problem 5.21. Let A be a finite set of size $n \ge 1$, prove by induction that $|\mathcal{P}(A)| = 2^n$.

Problem 5.22. Prove each case by induction. Then, guess the general pattern and prove your guess by induction.

(a) $\sum_{i=1}^n i = 1 + 2 + \cdots + n = \frac{1}{2}n(n+1)$
(b) $\sum_{i=1}^n i(i+1) = 1\cdot 2 + 2\cdot 3 + \cdots + n\cdot(n+1) = \frac{1}{3}n(n+1)(n+2)$
(c) $\sum_{i=1}^n i(i+1)(i+2) = 1\cdot 2\cdot 3 + 2\cdot 3\cdot 4 + \cdots + n\cdot(n+1)\cdot(n+2) = \frac{1}{4}n(n+1)(n+2)(n+3)$

Problem 5.23. After determining for which n the claim holds, prove it by induction:

(a) $(1-\frac{1}{\sqrt{2}})(1-\frac{1}{\sqrt{3}})(1-\frac{1}{\sqrt{4}})\cdots(1-\frac{1}{\sqrt{n}}) \le \frac{2}{n^2}$.
(b) $(1-\frac{1}{2})(1-\frac{1}{4})(1-\frac{1}{8})\cdots(1-\frac{1}{2^n}) \ge \frac{1}{4} + \frac{1}{2^{n+1}}$.
(c) $1 - \frac{1}{n+1} < 1 + \frac{1}{4} + \frac{1}{9} + \cdots + \frac{1}{n^2} \le 2 - \frac{1}{n}$.
(d) $\frac{1}{n+1} + \frac{1}{n+2} + \cdots + \frac{1}{2n} > \frac{11}{18}$.

Problem 5.24. Prove by induction on n: $\overline{A_1 \cup A_2 \cup A_3 \cup \cdots \cup A_n} = \overline{A_1} \cap \overline{A_2} \cap \overline{A_3} \cap \cdots \cap \overline{A_n}$.

Problem 5.25. Use the method of differences to guess a formula for $S(n)$. Prove your guess.

(a) $S(n) = 1 + 4 + 7 + \cdots + (3n-2)$
(b) $S(n) = \sum_{i=1}^n i(i+1)^2$
(c) $S(n) = \sum_{i=1}^{2n} (-1)^i i^2$.

Problem 5.26. In each problem, compute a formula for the quantity of interest. Use the following strategy: (i) Tinker with small values of n, for example $n = 1, 2, 3, 4, 5$. (ii) Guess a solution. (iii) Prove your guess by induction.

(a) The product $\Pi(n) = (1-\frac{1}{2})(1-\frac{1}{3})\cdots(1-\frac{1}{n+1})$, for $n \ge 1$.
(b) The product $\Pi(n) = (1-\frac{1}{4})(1-\frac{1}{9})\cdots(1-\frac{1}{n^2})$, for $n \ge 2$.
(c) The sum $S(n) = \sum_{i=1}^{2n} (-1)^i i$, for $n \ge 1$.
(d) The sum $S(n) = 1\cdot 3 + 3\cdot 5 + 5\cdot 7 + \cdots + (2n-1)(2n+1)$, for $n \ge 1$.
(e) The sum $S(n) = \frac{1}{1\cdot 2} + \frac{1}{2\cdot 3} + \frac{1}{3\cdot 4} + \cdots + \frac{1}{n(n+1)}$, for $n \ge 1$.
(f) The sum $S(n) = \frac{1}{2!} + \frac{2}{3!} + \frac{3}{4!} + \cdots + \frac{n}{(n+1)!}$, for $n \ge 1$.
(g) The sum $S(n) = \frac{1}{2} + \frac{2}{3} + \frac{3}{4} + \cdots \frac{n}{n+1}$.
(h) The product $\Pi(n) = \cos\theta \times \cos(2\theta) \times \cos(4\theta) \times \cdots \times \cos(2^n\theta)$, for $n \ge 0$. *[Hint: Multiply by $\sin\theta$; $\sin 2A = ?$.]*
(i) The product $\Pi(n) = (1+\frac{1}{3})(1+\frac{1}{3^2})(1+\frac{1}{3^4})\cdots(1+\frac{1}{3^{2^n}})$, for $n \ge 0$. *[Hint: $(1-\frac{1}{3}) \times \Pi(n)$.]*
(j) The nth derivative of x^2e^x, that is $\frac{d^n}{dx^n}(x^2e^x)$, for $n \ge 1$.
(k) The integral $\Gamma(n) = \int_0^\infty dx\, x^{n-1}e^{-x}$, for $n \ge 1$.
(l) The sum $S(n) = \sum_{\substack{\mathcal{A}\subseteq[n] \\ \mathcal{A}\neq\varnothing}} \prod_{x\in\mathcal{A}} \frac{1}{x}$, for $n \ge 1$. (The index $\mathcal{A}$ is over the non-empty subsets of $[n] = \{1, \ldots, n\}$.)

Problem 5.27. Place n circles on the plane, dividing the plane into regions. Prove that you can color the regions red and blue so that no two regions which share a boundary at a circle have the same color.

Problem 5.28. Prove each claim by induction for $n \geq 3$.

(a) There is a set with n numbers $x_1, \ldots, x_n$ such that each x_i divides the sum $s = x_1 + \cdots + x_m$.
(b) There is a convex polygon with at least 3 acute internal angles.
(c) There are n distinct positive numbers whose reciprocals sum to 1.

Problem 5.29. Prove by induction that the derivative of x^n is nx^{n-1}, for $n \geq 1$. *[Hint: $(fg)' = f'g + fg'$.]*

Problem 5.30. Prove that the nth derivative of x^n is $n!$, for $n \geq 1$.

Problem 5.31 (Nested Roots). Let $x_1 = \sqrt{1}$, $x_2 = \sqrt{1+\sqrt{1}}$, $x_3 = \sqrt{1+\sqrt{1+\sqrt{1}}}$, and so on. We can get x_{n+1} from x_n using $x_{n+1} = \sqrt{1+x_n}$. Prove that: (a) $x_n \leq 2$. (b) x_n is monotonically increasing. By monotone convergence (calculus), x_n converges. Make a conjecture for $\lim_{n\to\infty} x_n$.

Problem 5.32 (A Formula of Ramanujan). The math prodigy Ramanujan derived the remarkable formula:

$$2 = \sqrt{1 + 1\sqrt{1 + 2\sqrt{1 + 3\sqrt{1 + 4\sqrt{1 + \cdots}}}}}. \tag{5.1}$$

(a) Numerically verify (5.1) by computing the RHS to a high accuracy using many terms.
(b) Assume Ramanujan's formula is valid. Generalize the formula by proving, for all $n \geq 1$:

$$n + 1 = \sqrt{1 + n\sqrt{1 + (n+1)\sqrt{1 + (n+2)\sqrt{1 + (n+3)\sqrt{1 + \cdots}}}}}.$$

Problem 5.33. Prove, for $n \geq 3$, that every convex n-gon has $n(n-3)/2$ diagonals (that are not sides).

Problem 5.34. Prove that the sum of interior angles of a convex polygon with n sides is $(n-2)\pi$. You may assume the result is true for triangles ($n = 3$), and that one can cut a convex n-gon into a convex $(n-1)$-gon and a triangle as shown. (A convex polygon has all interior angles smaller than π.)

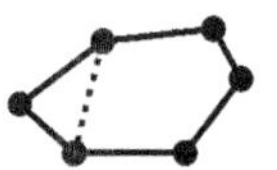

Problem 5.35. Suppose $a, b \geq 0$ (non-negative reals). Prove by induction:

(a) $(a+b)^n \geq a^n + b^n$, for $n \geq 1$.
(b) $(a+b)^n \geq a^n + b^n + 2ab(a+b)^{n-2}$, for $n \geq 2$.
(c) $(a+b)^n \geq a^n + b^n + nab(a^{n-2} + b^{n-2})$, for $n \geq 2$.

Problem 5.36. Suppose $|x_i|, |y_i| \leq M$. Prove: $\left|\prod_{i=1}^n x_i - \prod_{i=1}^n y_i\right| \leq M^{n-1} \sum_{i=1}^n |x_i - y_i|$.

Problem 5.37. Prove that n lines through the origin create $2n$ regions in the plane.

Problem 5.38. $M(n)$ is the maximum number of regions into which n lines can divide a plane.

(a) Tinker. Three lines are shown on the right, creating regions $R_1, \ldots, R_6$. What is the maximum number of regions possible with three lines?
(b) Continue to tinker. Compute $M(n)$ for small values of n.
(c) Make a conjecture for $M(n)$.
(d) Prove your conjecture using induction.

R_1 R_2 R_3 R_4 R_5 R_6

Problem 5.39. Prove you can make any postage greater than 12¢ using only 4¢ and 5¢ stamps. (The USPS can set any postage above 12¢ and you don't have to by any new stamps.)

Problem 5.40. A cap of a disk is a region subtended by a cord. We show three caps, which do not cover the disk. Suppose n caps do cover the entire disk. Prove by induction on n that one can cover the disk using at most 3 of the caps. *[Hint: Consider the complements of the caps and show that if every 3 cap-complements have nonempty intersection then all n complements have nonempty intersection which contradicts the caps covering the disk. (A special case of Helly's Theorem.)]*

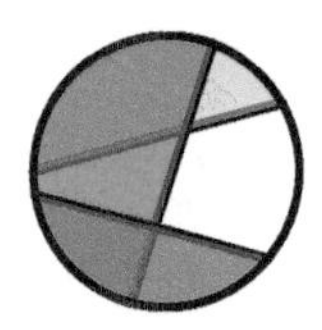

Problem 5.41 (Binomial Theorem). For integers $0 \leq k \leq n$, the binomial coefficient $\binom{n}{k}$ is given by the formula $\binom{n}{k} = n!/k!(n-k)!$ (recall the empty product $0! = 1$).

(a) Show that $\binom{n+1}{k} = \binom{n}{k} + \binom{n}{k-1}$, for $1 \leq k \leq n$. Hence prove that $\binom{n}{k}$ is an integer for $n \geq 0$ and $0 \leq k \leq n$.
(b) Prove, for $n \geq 1$, $(1+x)^n = \sum_{i=0}^n \binom{n}{i} x^i = \binom{n}{0}x^0 + \binom{n}{1}x^1 + \cdots + \binom{n}{n}x^n$.
(c) Use (b) to give the expansions of $(1+x)^2$, $(1+x)^3$, $(1+x)^4$.
(d) Show that $(x+y)^n = \sum_{i=0}^n \binom{n}{i} x^i y^{n-i}$.

Problem 5.42 (Central Binomial Coefficient). Prove by induction that $\frac{1}{n+1}4^n < \binom{2n}{n} < 4^{n-1}$ for $n \geq 5$.

Problem 5.43 (Binomial Coefficients are Integers). Let k be a positive integer.

(a) Prove by induction on k that the product of k consecutive positive numbers is divisible by $k!$. *[Hint: Let $P(k)$ be the claim that $n(n+1)\cdots(n+k-1)$ is divisible by $k!$ for all $n \geq 1$. To prove $P(k+1)$, use induction on n. Also, $(n+1)(n+2)\cdots(n+k-1)(n+k) = n(n+1)(n+1)\cdots(n+k-1) + k(n+1)(n+2)\cdots(n+k-1)$ is a product of k consecutive numbers plus k times a product of $k-1$ consecutive numbers.]*

(b) Prove that the binomial coefficient $\binom{n}{k} = \frac{n!}{k!(n-k)!}$ is an integer, where $0 \leq k \leq n$.

Problem 5.44 (Fermat's Little Theorem). Prove, by induction: if p is prime, then p divides $n^p - n$ for $n \geq 1$. *[Hint: Show p divides $\binom{p}{i}$ for $0 < i < p$. Use the Binomial Theorem.]*

Problem 5.45. For $n \geq 1$, prove by induction that $\dfrac{(2n-1)!!}{(2n)!!} \leq \dfrac{1}{\sqrt{2n+1}}$, where the double factorials are:

$$(2n)!! = 2 \times 4 \times 6 \times \cdots \times 2n; \qquad (2n-1)!! = 1 \times 3 \times 5 \times \cdots \times (2n-1).$$

Problem 5.46. Prove by induction that for $n \geq 1$,

$$\frac{1}{\pi}\int_0^{\pi} dx\ \sin^{2n} x = \frac{(2n-1)!!}{(2n)!!}.$$

[Hint: Show, using integration by parts, that $\int_0^{\pi} dx\ \sin^k x = \frac{k-1}{k}\int_0^{\pi} dx\ \sin^{k-2} x$.]

Problem 5.47. Choose any $n+1$ numbers from $\{1, 2, \ldots, 2n\}$. For the numbers choser, prove by induction that:

(a) Two are consecutive. (b) One of the numbers is a multiple of another.

Problem 5.48. For $x_1, \ldots, x_n$, the average is $\mu = \frac{1}{n}\sum_{i=1}^{n} x_i$ and the average of the squares is $s^2 = \frac{1}{n}\sum_{i=1}^{n} x_i^2$. A well known fact is $\mu^2 \leq s^2$. Prove it by induction on n.

Problem 5.49. Prove that the regions created by n lines on a plane can be colored with two colors so that no two regions which share a side have the same color.

Problem 5.50. Let A be the 2×2 matrix $\left[\begin{smallmatrix}1 & 1\\ 0 & 1\end{smallmatrix}\right]$. Compute the n-term matrix product A^n.

(a) Tinker. Compute the matrix products A^2, A^3, A^4. ($\mathrm{A}^n = \mathrm{A} \times \mathrm{A} \times \cdots \times \mathrm{A}$ with n terms.)

(b) Formulate a guess about A^n and prove it by induction.

Problem 5.51. For two sequences $a_1, \ldots, a_n$ and $b_1, \ldots, b_n$, let $A = a_1 + \cdots + a_n$ and $B = b_1 + \cdots + b_m$ be the sums. Let S be the sum of all pairwise products $a_i b_j$. Prove by induction that $S = AB$. That is,

$$S = a_1b_1 + \cdots + a_1b_m + a_2b_1 + \cdots + a_2b_m + \cdots + a_nb_1 + \cdots + a_nb_m = (a_1 + \cdots + a_n)(b_1 + \cdots + b_m).$$

Problem 5.52. A comparison scale can only compare weights (see illustration on the right). Show that if you have the weights (in pounds) $1, 3, 3^2, 3^3, \ldots, 3^k$, you can measure any integer number of pounds of sugar from $1, 2, \ldots, \frac{1}{2}(3^{k+1} - 1)$.

For example, with the weights $1, 3, 3^2$, you can weigh 5 pounds of sugar by placing the sugar on the same side of the scale as the 1 and 3 pound weights, and placing the 9 poind weight on the other side of the scale (the sugar weighs 5 pounds if the scale balances).

Problem 5.53. Recall our 6 social friends A, B, C, D, E, F from Chapter 1. We show two possible friendship networks, G_1 and G_2 (G for graph). Let n be the number of nodes.

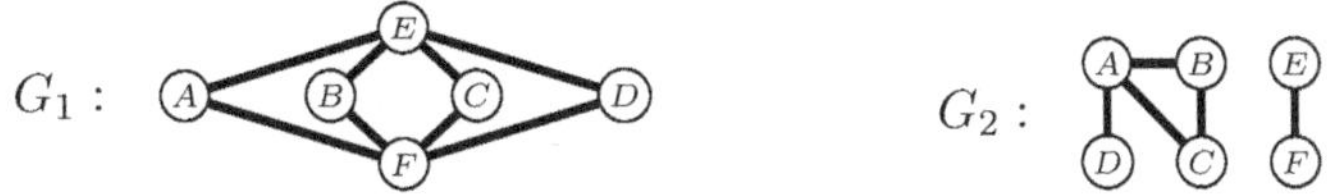

Two people are connected if they can reach each other using friendship links. In G_1, A and D can connect via E. The friendship network is connected if every pair of people can connect.

(a) Determine whether G_1 and G_2 are connected.

(b) Two people who are not friends are enemies. Give the enemy networks $\overline{G}_1$ and $\overline{G}_2$ ($\overline{G}$ for complement, because the enemy edges are the complement of the friend edges).

(c) Determine whether $\overline{G}_1$ and $\overline{G}_2$ are connected.

(d) Is it possible for both the friendship and enemy networks to be connected?

(e) Prove, by induction on n: For any friendship network G, either G or $\overline{G}$ is connected.

Problem 5.54. In a social network with n friends, everyone shakes everyone else's hand once. Prove by induction that the total number of handshakes is $\frac{1}{2}n(n-1)$.

Problem 5.55. A round-robin tournament has n players $p_1, p_2, \ldots, p_n$. There is a match between every pair of players. Prove by induction that the number of matches played is $\frac{1}{2}n(n-1)$.

Problem 5.56. At a party are n people. Some people shake hands with others, No one shakes another's hand more than once. Use well-ordering to prove that there are two people who make the same number of handshakes. *[Hint: Assume the claim is false for a smallest possible party size of n_* which makes a smallest possible number of total handshakes k_*. Show that someone in this party make no handshakes, and derive a contradiction.]*

Problem 5.57. In a round robin tournament, everyone plays everyone else. A 4-person tournament is shown in the graph below. The arrow $A \rightarrow B$ means A beat B.

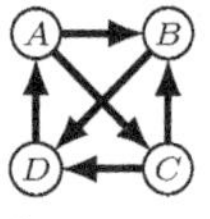

tournament

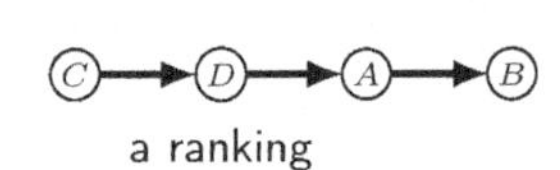

a ranking

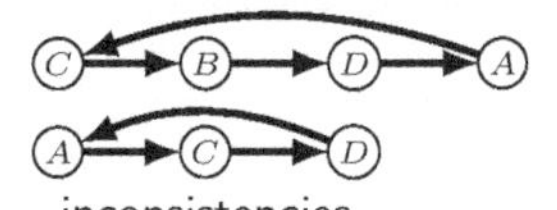

inconsistencies

A ranking is an ordering of the players for which the first player beats the second, the second beats the third and so on. An example ranking for the tournament is shown.

An inconsistency is a sequence of players where the first beats the second, the second beats the third, ..., and the last beats the first. We show 4-person and 3-person inconsistencies.

(a) Prove by induction on the number of people: Every tournament has a ranking.

(b) Prove: Every tournament has a ranking with the first player having the most wins. *[Hint: Consider the longest ranking that starts with the player having the most wins.]*

(c) Give a tournament with 5 people that has no inconsistency.

(d) Prove by induction: In every tournament with no incônsistency, one player beats all other players and one player loses to all other players.

(e) Prove by induction: Every tournament with an inconsistency has a 3-person inconsistency. (You must carefully define the induction claim $P(n)$.)

Problem 5.58. Let S_n be the points with integer coordinates (x, y) where $x, y \geq 0$ and $x + y \leq n$. Show that S_n cannot be covered by the union of n lines. At least $n + 1$ lines are required.

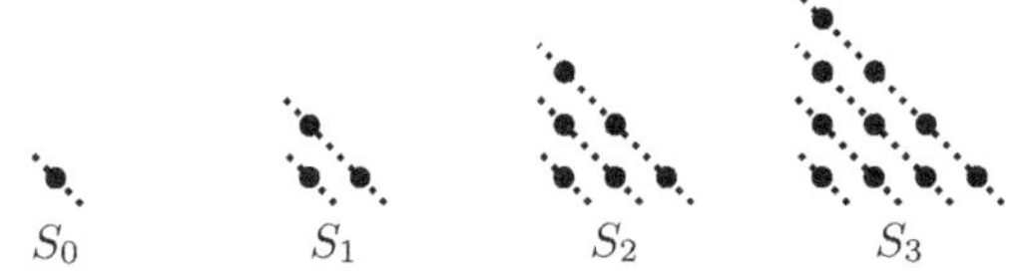

Problem 5.59. Three friends A, B, C each have tokens a, b, c. At every step a random pair of friends is picked to swap whatever tokens they currently have. If the first pair picked is (A, B) and then (A, C) then the token are distributed c, a, b. Prove that it is not possible for each friend to have their own token after 2015 such swaps. *[Hint: Consider any odd number of swaps.]*

Problem 5.60. A robot has a repetoire of moves on an infinite grid as shown in the figures.

(a) The robot moves one diagonal step at a time. Prove that no sequence of moves takes the robot to the shaded square. *[Hint: Let (x, y) be the robot's position. Consider $x + y$.]*

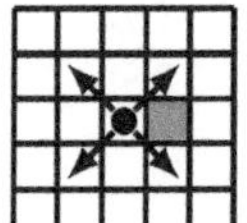

(b) One of the moves changed. Now prove that any square (m, n) can be reached by a finite sequence of moves.

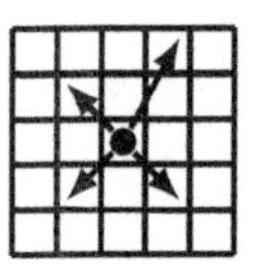

Problem 5.61. A knight's possible moves are shown by the arrows on the right. The knight starts at position $(0, 0)$ on an infinite board. Prove that the knight can move to any square (m, n) using at most $3(|m| + |n|)$ moves. *[Hint: First show the knight can move one square up, down, left or right.]*

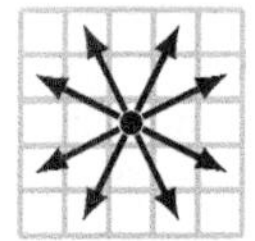

Problem 5.62. There are n squares shaded on an infinite grid.

(a) Compute the perimeter of the shaded area as highlighted by the thick line.

(b) Prove by induction that the perimeter of the shaded area is even for all $n \geq 1$.

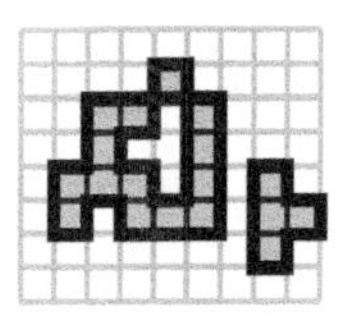

Problem 5.63. Prove a famous result in geometry: the n-polygon with maximum area incribed in a circle is regular (has equal sides). Let $\theta_1, \ldots, \theta_n$ be the angles subtended by the sides of the polygon at the center, $0 < \theta_i \leq \pi$.

(a) For $0 \leq \lambda \leq 1$ and $0 \leq x, y \leq \pi$, show that $\lambda \sin x + (1-\lambda)\sin y \leq \sin(\lambda x + (1-\lambda)y)$.

(b) Prove $\sin\theta_1 + \cdots + \sin\theta_n \leq n \sin(\frac{\theta_1 + \cdots \theta_n}{n})$. Hence, prove the result. *[Hint: Area(isocelles triangle) =* $\frac{1}{2}r^2\sin\theta$*.]*

Problem 5.64 (Josephus Problem). In the Josephus problem (Problem 3.64) n objects in a circle are numbered 1 to n. Starting at 1, every other object is removed (object 2 is the first to be removed). Prove that for $n = 2^k$, object 1 is the last object to be removed, for $k \geq 0$.

Problem 5.65 (Pick's Theorem). Five polygons are shown on a grid: red; purple; blue; green; and, blue-union-green. The vertices of each polygon are grid points.

(a) Compute the areas of these five polygons.

(b) For a polygon, let B be the number of grid points on the boundary and I the number of grid points inside. For each polygon, compute $I + \frac{1}{2}B - 1$. Do you see a pattern?

Pick's Theorem. Area(polygon with vertices at grid points) $= I + \frac{1}{2}B - 1$.

(c) Prove Pick's Theorem for axis aligned rectangles (purple).

(d) Prove Pick's Theorem for triangles (red). *[Hint: Start with right-triangles. Enclose the triangle in a rectangle.]*

(e) A polygon P with vertices on grid points satisfies Pick's Theorem (blue). P is joined at a face to a triangle whose third vertex is a grid point (green). Show that the area of the new polygon satisfies Pick's Theorem.

(f) A polygon P with vertices at grid points is obtained by repeatedly joining n triangles at common faces. Prove by induction that P satisfies Pick's Theorem. (Fact: Any polygon can be built by joining triangles.)

Problem 5.66. A roll of two 6-faced dice has 36 possible outcomes, one for each pair of outcomes (dice 1, dice 2):

$$(1,1)\cdots(1,6),(2,1)\cdots(2,6),(3,1)\cdots(3,6),(4,1)\cdots(4,6),(5,1)\cdots(5,6),(6,1)\cdots(6,6).$$

When the dice are indistinguishable, several pairs of outcomes are identical and should be considered the same outcome. For example $(1,6)$ and $(6,1)$ are the same outcome because we cannot distinguish which dice rolled 6.

(a) How may of the 36 outcomes are distinguishable?

(b) For n indistinguishable dice, prove by induction that the number of distinguishable outcomes is

$$\binom{n+5}{5} = \frac{1}{5!}(n+1)(n+2)(n+3)(n+4)(n+5).$$

[Hints: Let $Q_k(n) = \#$ *distinguishable outcomes for n dice with* k *sides. Induction on* k*. Problem 5.22]*

Problem 5.67 (Quotient-remainder Theorem). Use well-ordering to prove: Given $n \in \mathbb{Z}$ and a divisor $d \geq 0$, there are a unique quotient $q \in \mathbb{Z}$ and unique remainder $r \in \mathbb{Z}$, with $0 \leq r < d$, such that $n = qd + r$.

Problem 5.68 (The number e). One of the most important mathematical constants is $e \approx 2.71828\cdots$.

(a) Prove that $1 + \frac{k}{n} \leq (1+\frac{1}{n})^k < 1 + \frac{k}{n} + \frac{k^2}{n^2}$ for $k \leq n$. Hence prove that $2 < \left(1+\frac{1}{n}\right)^n < 3$, for $n \geq 1$.

(b) Prove that for $m > n \geq 2$,

$$\left(1+\frac{1}{n}\right)^n < \left(1+\frac{1}{m}\right)^m \quad \text{and} \quad \left(1+\frac{1}{n}\right)^{n+1} > \left(1+\frac{1}{m}\right)^{m+1}.$$

That is, the sequence $(1+\frac{1}{n})^n$ is increasing and bounded above by 3. Therefore it converges. The limit is defined as e. The sequence $(1+\frac{1}{n})^{n+1}$ is decreasing and converges to the same value. Therefore for any $n \geq 2$,

$$\left(1+\frac{1}{n}\right)^n < e < \left(1+\frac{1}{n}\right)^{n+1}.$$

(c) Prove that, for $n > 6$, $\left(\frac{n}{3}\right)^n < n! < \left(\frac{n}{2}\right)^n$.

(d) Prove that, for $n \geq 1$, $\left(\frac{n}{e}\right)^n < n! < n\left(\frac{n}{e}\right)^n$.

Problem 5.69. Define a polynomial in x, $P_n(x)$ as

$$P_n(x) = 1 + \frac{x}{1!} + \frac{x(x+1)}{2!} + \frac{x(x+1)(x+2)}{3!} + \cdots + \frac{x(x+1)(x+2)\cdots(x+n-1)}{n!}.$$

(a) Show that $P_n(-n) = (-1)^0\binom{n}{0} + (-1)^1\binom{n}{1} + (-1)^2\binom{n}{2} + \cdots (-1)^n\binom{n}{n}$, and hence $P_n(-n) = 0$.

(b) Use part (a) and the Binomial Theorem to prove that $-n$ is a root of $P_n(x)$.

(c) What is the degree of $P_n(x)$? Prove by induction that the roots of $P_n(x)$ are $-1, -2, -3, \ldots, -n$.

(d) Deduce a formula of the form $P_n(x) = c(x+r_1)(x+r_2)\cdots(x+r_n)$ and prove it by induction.

Problem 5.70. The positive numbers $x_1, \ldots, x_n$ and $y_1, \ldots, y_m$ have equal sum at most mn. Prove that one can cancel terms from the equation $x_1 + \cdots + x_n = y_1 + \cdots + y_m$ and still maintain equality. *[Hint: Induction on* $n+m$*.]*

Problem 5.71. The sequence $x_1, x_2, \ldots$ is defined by: $x_1 = 1$; $x_{2n} = x_n + 1$; $x_{2n+1} = 1/x_{2n}$. Prove:

(a) Every number in the sequence is rational. *[Hint: Use well-ordering.]*

(b) Every positive rational r equals some x_n for a unique n. ($x_1, x_2, \ldots$ is a "list" of the positive rationals.) *[Hints: Let $r = a/b$ (a and b have no common divisor). Use well-ordering w.r.t. $a+b$.]*

Problem 5.72. A circle has $2n$ distinct points, n are red and n are blue. By examining the proof by induction in Example 5.4 on page 62, construct a method to find a blue point x such that a clockwise trip starting from x will always have passed as many blue points as red.

Problem 5.73. For $n+2$ statements $p, r_1, \ldots, r_n, q$ ($n \geq 1$), prove that you can conclude $p \leftrightarrow q$ from a chain of IF AND ONLY IF's or a chain of implications. Specifically, prove the following are true:

(a) $((p \leftrightarrow r_1) \wedge (r_1 \leftrightarrow r_2) \wedge \cdots \wedge (r_{n-1} \leftrightarrow r_n) \wedge (r_n \leftrightarrow q)) \rightarrow (p \leftrightarrow q)$.

(b) $((p \rightarrow r_1) \wedge (r_1 \rightarrow r_2) \wedge \cdots \wedge (r_{n-1} \rightarrow r_n) \wedge (r_n \rightarrow q) \wedge (q \rightarrow p)) \rightarrow (p \leftrightarrow q)$.

Problem 5.74. Use the well-ordering principle to prove these principles of induction.

(a) $P(1)$ and $P(n) \rightarrow (P(2n) \wedge P(2n+1))$ implies $P(n)$ for all $n \geq 1$.

(b) $P(1)$ and $P(n) \rightarrow (P(2n) \wedge P(n-1))$ implies $P(n)$ for all $n \geq 1$.

Problem 5.75 (Telescoping Sum/Product). For a function f, and $n \geq 1$, prove by induction:

(a) $\sum_{i=1}^{n}(f(i+1) - f(i)) = f(n+1) - f(1)$, and more generally $\sum_{i=1}^{n}(f(i+k) - f(i)) = \sum_{i=1}^{k}(f(n+i) - f(i))$.

(b) $\prod_{i=1}^{n} f(i+1)/f(i) = f(n+1)/f(1)$, and more generally $\prod_{i=1}^{n} f(i+k)/f(i) = \prod_{i=1}^{k} f(n+i)/f(i)$.

Problem 5.76. Find a formula in each case. Prove it. *[Hints: Induction; partial fractions; telescoping sum/product.]*

(a) $S(n) = \frac{1}{1\cdot 2} + \frac{1}{2\cdot 3} + \frac{1}{3\cdot 4} + \cdots + \frac{1}{n(n+1)}$.

(b) $S(n) = \frac{1}{1\cdot 2\cdot 3} + \frac{1}{2\cdot 3\cdot 4} + \frac{1}{3\cdot 4\cdot 5} + \cdots + \frac{1}{n(n+1)(n+2)}$.

(c) $S(n) = \frac{1}{2!} + \frac{2}{3!} + \frac{3}{4!} + \cdots + \frac{n}{(n+1)!}$.

(d) $S(n) = \frac{1}{2\cdot 5} + \frac{1}{5\cdot 8} + \frac{1}{8\cdot 11} + \cdots + \frac{1}{(3n-1)(3n+2)}$.

(e) $\Pi(n) = (1+\frac{k}{1}) \times (1+\frac{k}{2}) \times (1+\frac{k}{3}) \times \cdots \times (1+\frac{k}{n})$.

(f) $\Pi(n) = (1-\frac{1}{1+2}) \times (1-\frac{1}{1+2+3}) \times \cdots \times (1-\frac{1}{1+2+\cdots+n})$.

Problem 5.77. Define the sum of the first n numbers raised to the pth power as $S_p(n)$,

$$S_p(n) = \sum_{i=1}^{n} i^p = 1^p + 2^p + \cdots + n^p.$$

(a) What is $S_0(n)$?

(b) Show that $\sum_{i=1}^{n}((i+1)^{p+1} - i^{p+1}) = (n+1)^{p+1} - 1$. *[Hint: Problem 5.75.]*

(c) Use the Binomial Theorem to show that $\sum_{i=1}^{n}((i+1)^{p+1} - i^{p+1}) = \sum_{j=0}^{p}\binom{p+1}{j} S_j(n)$.

(d) Use (b) and (c) to show that $S_p(n) = \frac{1}{p+1}\Big((n+1)^{p+1} - 1 - \sum_{j=0}^{p-1}\binom{p+1}{j} S_j(n)\Big)$.
(A formula for the sum of the pth powers using sums for lower order powers.)

(e) Start with (a) and use (d) to get explicit formulas for $S_1(n)$, $S_2(n)$, $S_3(n)$, $S_4(n)$.

(f) Prove your formula for $S_4(n)$ by induction.

Using this approach, you can continue the derivation and obtain an explicit formula

$$S_p(n) = \frac{1}{p+1}\sum_{j=0}^{p}\binom{p+1}{j} B_j n^{p+1-j},$$

where B_j are the Bernoulli numbers, the first few being $B_0 = 1$; $B_1 = -\frac{1}{2}$; $B_2 = \frac{1}{6}$; $B_3 = 0$; $B_4 = -\frac{1}{30}$; ...

Problem 5.78. Assume the principle of induction and prove the well-ordering principle.

Suppose $\mathcal{B}$ is a non-empty set of natural numbers. Then, $\mathcal{B}$ has a minimum element.

[Hints: Define $P(n)$: $\mathcal{B}$ does not contain any of $1, 2, \ldots, n$. Prove IF *$\mathcal{B}$ has no minimum,* THEN *$P(n)$ is true for all $n \geq 1$. Hence, $\mathcal{B} = \varnothing$. That is, prove the contraposition. Note that $P(n)$ makes a claim for all of $1, 2, \ldots, n$. Induction with such predicates is called strong induction. Can you prove the claim using the simpler predicate "$P(n)$: $\mathcal{B}$ does not contain n." What goes wrong? Choosing the right predicate a skill learned through practice.]*

> We've taught you that the earth is round,
> That red and white make pink,
> And something else that matters more,
> We've taught you how to think. – **Dr. Seuss**
>
> Spoon feeding, in the long run teaches us nothing but the shape of the spoon. – **E. M. Forster**

Chapter 6

Strong Induction

1: Different types of induction: ordinary induction; leaping induction; strong induction.

Induction by osmosis! We work through a diverse set of problems, starting with a tough one. For $n \geq 1$,

$$1+\frac{1}{\sqrt{2}}+\frac{1}{\sqrt{3}}+\cdots+\frac{1}{\sqrt{n}} \leq 2\sqrt{n}. \tag{6.1}$$

A useful organizational tool for complex proofs is the lemma. A lemma is not of direct interest. Its role is to aid the main task of proving some theorem. We need a peripheral fact to prove (6.1), and state it as a lemma.

Lemma 6.1. $2\sqrt{n}+1/\sqrt{n+1} \leq 2\sqrt{n+1}$, for $n \geq 1$.

> **Pop Quiz 6.1**
> Prove Lemma 6.1 using a proof by contradiction.

Proof. (of (6.1)) We use induction. Define the claim $P(n): 1+1/\sqrt{2}+1/\sqrt{3}+\cdots+1/\sqrt{n} \leq 2\sqrt{n}$.

1: **[Base case]** $P(1)$ claims that $1 \leq 2 \times \sqrt{1}$, which is clearly true.

2: **[Induction step]** We prove $P(n) \rightarrow P(n+1)$ for all $n \geq 1$, using a direct proof.
Assume (induction hypothesis) $P(n)$: $1+1/\sqrt{2}+1/\sqrt{3}+\cdots+1/\sqrt{n} \leq 2\sqrt{n}$.
Prove $P(n+1)$: $1+1/\sqrt{2}+1/\sqrt{3}+\cdots+1/\sqrt{n}+1/\sqrt{n+1} \leq 2\sqrt{n+1}$.

$$1+\frac{1}{\sqrt{2}}+\cdots+\frac{1}{\sqrt{n}}+\frac{1}{\sqrt{n+1}} = \left(1+\frac{1}{\sqrt{2}}+\cdots+\frac{1}{\sqrt{n}}\right)+\frac{1}{\sqrt{n+1}} \overset{(a)}{\leq} 2\sqrt{n}+\frac{1}{\sqrt{n+1}} \overset{(b)}{\leq} 2\sqrt{n+1}$$

(a) follows from the induction hypothesis and (b) from Lemma 6.1. So, $P(n+1)$ is proved.

3: By induction, $P(n)$ is true for all $n \geq 1$. ■

What clairvoyance to know ahead of time the exact lemma we would need ☺. In practice, the proof comes first. When we get stuck at inequality (b), we know what to prove in the lemma. The organizational value of the lemma is to keep the induction clear and simple. Our proof above is very structured. In practice, it is okay to be less formal as long as you adequately address the base case and induction step.

6.1 Strengthening the Induction Hypothesis

The title derives from the peculiar phenomenon that, with induction, it can be easier to prove a stronger claim. Let us prove, for $n \geq 4$, that $n^2 \leq 2^n$. Define the claim $P(n): n^2 \leq 2^n$. The chain we need is:

$$\boxed{P(4)} \rightarrow P(5) \rightarrow P(6) \rightarrow P(7) \rightarrow P(8) \rightarrow P(9) \rightarrow \cdots$$

As usual, we start with the base case $P(4) : 4^2 \leq 2^4$, that is $16 \leq 16$, a no brainer. Now comes the induction step. For the induction hypothesis, assume $P(n)$: $n^2 \leq 2^n$. We must prove $P(n+1)$: $(n+1)^2 \leq 2^{n+1}$.

$$(n+1)^2 \;=\; n^2 + 2n + 1 \;\leq\; 2^n + 2n + 1.$$

The inequality uses the induction hypothesis that $n^2 \leq 2^n$. If $2n+1 \leq 2^n$, the RHS is at most $2^n + 2^n = 2^{n+1}$ and we are done. We can assume $2n+1 \leq 2^n$ in the induction hypothesis only if we were proving the stronger claim $n^2 \leq 2^n$ AND $2n+1 \leq 2^n$. So, define a new claim

$$Q(n) : (n^2 \leq 2^n) \text{ AND } (2n+1 \leq 2^n).$$

We do the unthinkable and prove $Q(n)$ instead of $P(n)$. It's unsettling because $P(n)$ was hard, and $Q(n)$ is even stronger because $Q(n)$ implies $P(n)$. Let's give it a go. The chain we need for $Q(n)$ is:

$$\boxed{Q(4)} \to Q(5) \to Q(6) \to Q(7) \to Q(8) \to Q(9) \to \cdots$$

Proof. We use induction for the stronger claim $Q(n)$: (i) $n^2 \leq 2^n$; AND, (ii) $2n+1 \leq 2^n$.

1: **[Base case]** $Q(4)$ claims (i) $4^2 \leq 2^4$; AND, (ii) $2 \times 4 + 1 \leq 2^4$. Both are clearly true.

2: **[Induction step]** We prove $Q(n) \to Q(n+1)$ for all $n \geq 4$, using a direct proof.
Assume (induction hypothesis) $Q(n)$: (i) $n^2 \leq 2^n$; AND, (ii) $2n+1 \leq 2^n$.
Prove $Q(n+1)$: (i) $(n+1)^2 \leq 2^{n+1}$; AND, (ii) $2(n+1)+1 \leq 2^{n+1}$.

(i) $$(n+1)^2 = n^2 + 2n + 1 \leq 2^n + 2^n = 2^{n+1} \checkmark$$
(because from the induction hypothesis $n^2 \leq 2^n$ **and** $2n+1 \leq 2^n$)

(ii) $$2(n+1)+1 = 2 + 2n + 1 \leq 2^n + 2^n = 2^{n+1} \checkmark$$
(because $2 \leq 2^n$ and from the induction hypothesis $2n+1 \leq 2^n$)

This proves $Q(n+1)$. Note, proving $Q(n+1)$ involves proving two things.

3: By induction, $Q(n)$ is true for all $n \geq 4$. ∎

Pause. Is $Q(n)$ really a stronger claim than $P(n)$. Yes! How come it was easier to prove? This is a peculiarity with induction. A harder claim can be easier to prove because there is a trade-off in the induction step that proves $Q(n) \to Q(n+1)$. You have to prove more in $Q(n+1)$, but you get to assume more in $Q(n)$, which gives you more to work with. You also should take note that, because we want to prove our claim for $n \geq 4$, the base case is $Q(4)$ and we only need to prove $Q(n) \to Q(n+1)$ for $n \geq 4$.

Exercise 6.2

(a) Prove $P(n) : n^3 < 2^n$, for $n \geq 10$. (Strengthen P to Q and, if needed, strengthen Q to R.)
(b) Prove $n^2 \leq 2^n$ for $n \geq 4$ without having to strengthen the claim. Similarly prove $n^3 < 2^n$, for $n \geq 10$.
(c) Prove $1+\frac{1}{2^2}+\frac{1}{3^2}+\cdots+\frac{1}{n^2} \leq 2$, for $n \geq 1$. What goes wrong? Now prove $1+\frac{1}{2^2}+\frac{1}{3^2}+\cdots+\frac{1}{n^2} \leq 2-\frac{1}{n}$.

***L*-Tile Land.** A patio is a $2^n \times 2^n$ square grid. One of the four center-squares of the patio is blacked out for a pot-plant. The rest of the patio must be tiled with L-shaped tiles, ▟. Figure 6.1 illustrates tilings of grids for $n = 1, 2, 3$. Can we always tile the patio, no matter how large it is?

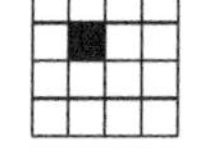

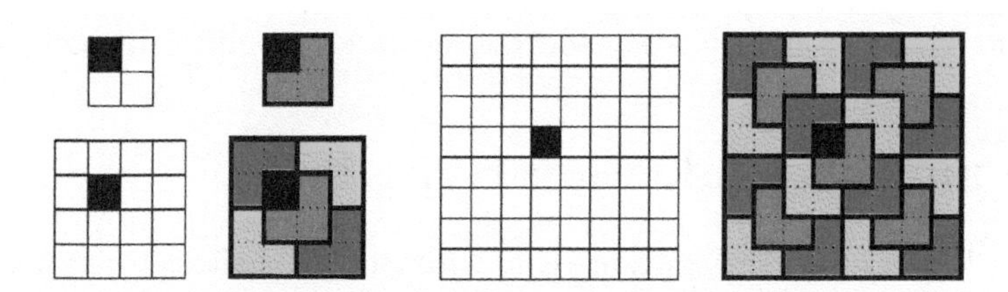

Figure 6.1: L-tiling of grids which are missing a center-square.

Let's prove there is always an L-tiling by induction. First we define the claim $P(n)$, which means you must identify n. A natural candidate is the n appearing in the size of the grid. We wish to prove for $n \geq 1$,

$$P(n): \text{The } 2^n \times 2^n \text{ grid minus a center-square can be } L\text{-tiled.}$$

The base case, $P(1)$, is the 2×2 grid with a "center" square blacked out, which is easy.

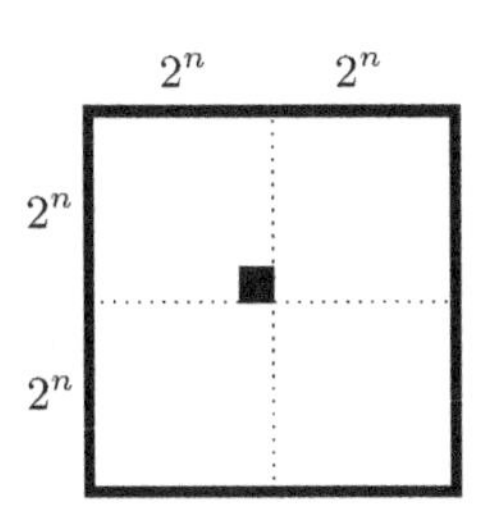

For the induction step, we assume (induction hypothesis) $P(n)$, i.e. the $2^n \times 2^n$ grid minus a center-square can be L-tiled. We must prove $P(n+1)$: the $2^{n+1} \times 2^{n+1}$ grid minus a center-square can be L-tiled. The $2^{n+1} \times 2^{n+1}$ grid has four $2^n \times 2^n$ sub-grids. For induction to work, we must L-tile this configuration using the assumption that the $2^n \times 2^n$ grid minus a center-square can be L-tiled. First challenge: the four $2^n \times 2^n$ sub-grids are not similar. One has a square missing in the corner and the others have no missing square. A grid with no missing square cannot be L-tiled by itself.

Pop Quiz 6.3
Why can't the 3 grids with no missing square be L-tiled on their own? *[Hint: Is 4^n divisible by 3?]*

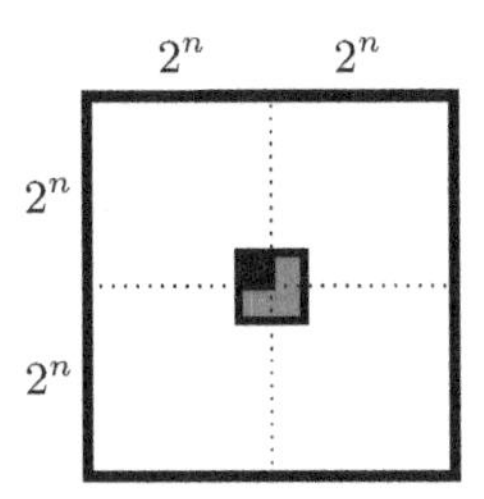

Placing an L-tile in the center as shown in red on the right makes all the $2^n \times 2^n$ sub-grids similar – they all have a corner-square missing. Second challenge: how do we tile these four sub-grids with a missing corner-square? Our induction hypothesis does not help us because it says we can L-tile the $2^n \times 2^n$ square if a center-square is missing. We have corner-squares missing. That's a signal to strengthen our claim so that it includes missing corner-squares, not just center squares.

$Q(n)$: (i) The $2^n \times 2^n$ grid missing a center-square can be L-tiled; AND
(ii) The $2^n \times 2^n$ grid missing a corner-square can be L-tiled.

Proof. We will prove the stronger claim $Q(n)$ for $n \geq 1$ by induction.

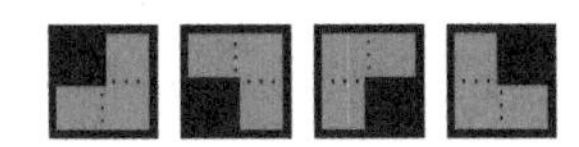

1: **[Base case]** The four cases on the right verify $Q(1)$ which claims that the 2×2 grid with a center or corner-square missing can be L-tiled.

2: **[Induction step]** We prove $Q(n) \to Q(n+1)$ for $n \geq 1$, using a direct proof.
Assume (induction hypothesis) $Q(n)$: (i) The $2^n \times 2^n$ grid missing a center-square can be L-tiled; AND
(ii) The $2^n \times 2^n$ grid missing a corner-square can be L-tiled.
Prove $Q(n+1)$: (i) The $2^{n+1} \times 2^{n+1}$ grid missing a center-square can be L-tiled; AND
(ii) The $2^{n+1} \times 2^{n+1}$ grid missing a corner-square can be L-tiled.

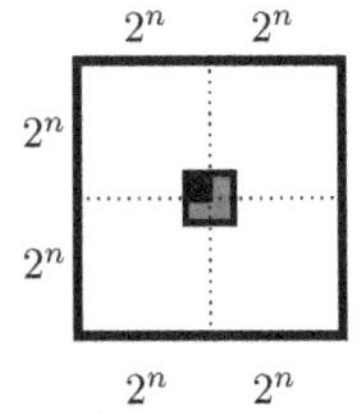

(i) For a $2^{n+1} \times 2^{n+1}$ grid missing a center-square, place an L-tile to cover the remaining 3 center-squares. This creates four $2^n \times 2^n$ sub-grids, each missing a corner-square. By part (ii) of the induction hypothesis, each sub-grid can be L-tiled independently. This gives an L-tiling of the $2^{n+1} \times 2^{n+1}$ grid missing a center-square. An identical argument applies, no matter which center-square is missing.

(ii) For a $2^{n+1} \times 2^{n+1}$ grid missing a corner-square, place an L-tile to cover three of the center-squares as shown in the figure. Each $2^n \times 2^n$ sub-grid is now missing a corner-square. By part (ii) of the induction hypothesis, each sub-grid can be L-tiled independently. The same argument applies no matter which corner-square is missing. So, the $2^{n+1} \times 2^{n+1}$ grid missing a corner-square can be L-tiled.

The conclusion is that $Q(n+1)$ is true, as was to be shown.

3: By induction, $Q(n)$ is true for all $n \geq 1$. ■

Comment: Use pictures whenever possible to clarify the logic of a proof.

Exercise 6.4
Show that you can L-tile a $2^n \times 2^n$ with a missing black square at position (n, n). The patios for $n = 1, 2, 3, 4$ are illustrated.

[Hint: Tinker with the $2^3 \times 2^3$ patio missing a square anywhere. What is the strongest claim you can make? Remember, with induction, it can be much easier to prove a much stronger claim.]

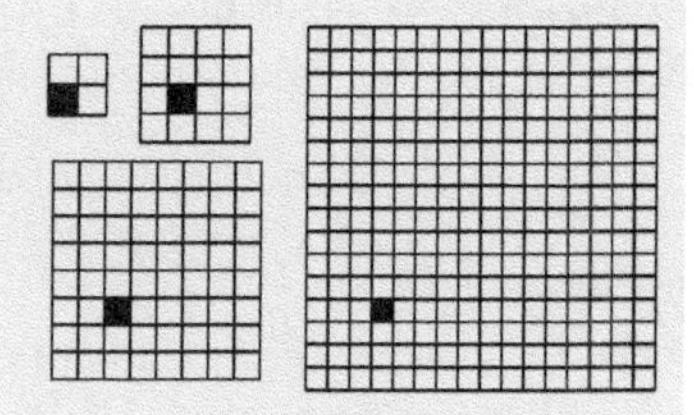

6.2 Leaping Induction

In Exercise 6.2 you proved $P(n) : n^3 < 2^n$, for $n \geq 10$ by strengthening the claim. Here is an easier approach. Assume for the induction step $P(n)$. Instead of $P(n+1)$, let us prove $P(n+2)$, i.e. $(n+2)^3 < 2^{n+2}$.

$$\begin{aligned} (n+2)^3 &= n^3 + \mathbf{6}\boldsymbol{n}^2 + \mathbf{12}\boldsymbol{n} + \mathbf{8} \\ &< n^3 + \boldsymbol{n} \cdot n^2 + \boldsymbol{n}^\mathbf{2} \cdot n + \boldsymbol{n}^\mathbf{3} && \text{(because, for } n \geq 10,\ 6 < n,\ 12 < n^2 \text{ and } 8 < n^3) \\ &= 4n^3 \\ &< 4 \cdot 2^n = 2^{n+2} && \text{(because the induction hypothesis } P(n) \text{ gives } n^3 < 2^n). \end{aligned}$$

We have proved that $P(n) \rightarrow P(n+2)$. How is that useful? It helps to visualize the chain of implications.

P(10) P(11) P(12) P(13) P(14) P(15) P(16) P(17) P(18) P(19) P(20) P(21) ...

You can appreciate the name leaping induction. Starting from the base case $P(10)$, the implications leap-frog over the odd n and only touch the even n. What about the implications from $P(n)$ for odd n, for example $P(11) \rightarrow P(13)$? All those implication arrows are also present.

P(10) P(11) P(12) P(13) P(14) P(15) P(16) P(17) P(18) P(19) P(20) P(21) ...

The grayed-out implications don't help, as none of them start from a true claim to imply an unknown claim. The easy fix is to prove $P(11)$, which follows because $11^3 = 1331 < 2048 = 2^{11}$. The situation now becomes:

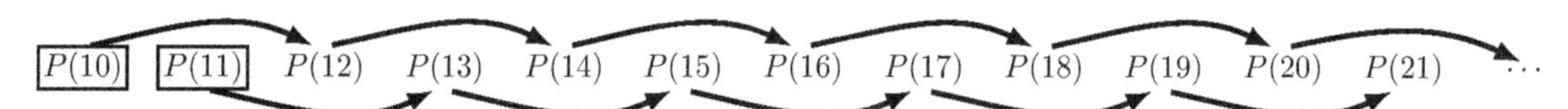

Now, start from $P(10)$ and repeatedly use the leaping implication $P(n) \rightarrow P(n+2)$ to prove $P(n)$ for even n. Start from $P(11)$ and repeatedly use the leaping implication to prove $P(n)$ for odd n. So, $P(n)$ is true for all $n \geq 10$. In ordinary induction, there is one base case. Here, there are two base cases. We call it 2-leaping induction. Leaping induction helps when it is difficult to prove $P(n) \rightarrow P(n+1)$, but easier to prove the leaping implication $P(n) \rightarrow P(n+k)$ for some $k > 1$. The trade-off is more base cases.

Proof Template VIII: k-Leaping Induction.
Proof. We prove $\forall n \geq 1 : P(n)$ by induction.
1: Show that $P(1), P(2), \ldots, P(k)$ are true. **[k base cases]**
2: Show $P(n) \rightarrow P(n+k)$ for $n \geq 1$ **[induction step]**
3: Conclude: By induction, $P(n)$ is true for $n \geq 1$. ■

Pop Quiz 6.5 [3-leaping induction]
You wish to prove $P(n)$ for $n \geq 1$ and have proved the leaping implication $P(n) \rightarrow P(n+3)$ for $n \geq 1$.
(a) Show in a picture the implication links. (b) How many base cases do you need? What are they?

Example 6.2. Back to postage, where we began induction in Chapter 5. To change things up, consider making postage using 3¢ and 4¢ stamps. Let's tinker to come up with a claim.

3¢	4¢	5¢	6¢	7¢	8¢	9¢	10¢	11¢	12¢
3	4	–	3,3	3,4	4,4	3,3,3	3,3,4	3,4,4	4,4,4

$$P(n): \text{Postage of } n¢ \text{ can be made using only } 3¢ \text{ and } 4¢ \text{ stamps.}$$

Leaping induction pops out. If you have postage n, then you get postage $n+3$ by adding a 3¢ stamp, so $P(n) \to P(n+3)$. The three base cases $P(6)$, $P(7)$, $P(8)$ prove $P(n)$ for $n \geq 6$. Please fill in the details using Proof Template VIII. Note: The base cases start at $n = 6$ because we want $P(n)$ for $n \geq 6$.

Tickle your curiosity. Consider other pairs of denominations. For example, (3¢, 5¢) works for any postage greater than 7¢. But, (3¢, 6¢) won't work. Can you prove it (hint: 3 and 6 are both divisible by 3)? □

Exercise 6.6

(a) Consider an induction using the leaping implication $P(n) \to P(2n)$ for $n \geq 1$.
 (i) Show a picture of the implications. (ii) What "base-cases" do you need? *[Hint: Odd n.]*

(b) Now consider the leaping implication $P(n) \to P(2n) \wedge P(2n+1)$ for $n \geq 1$.
 (i) Show a picture of the implications. (ii) What base-cases do you need? Justify your answer.

6.3 Strong Induction

Induction proves $P(1), P(2), P(3), \ldots, P(n), \ldots$ step by step, moving up one value in n each time,

✓ $P(1)$ ✓ $P(1) \to$ ✓ $P(2)$ ✓ $P(1) \to$ ✓ $P(2) \to$ ✓ $P(3)$ ✓ $P(1) \to$ ✓ $P(2) \to$ ✓ $P(3) \to P(4)$

When it is time to infer $P(4)$, $P(1), P(2)$ and $P(3)$ are all known to be true. Induction only needs $P(3)$ to infer $P(4)$. However, if needed, we could use any or all the smaller n to infer $P(4)$.

Let us use this idea to prove the Fundamental Theorem of Arithmetic, which establishes the prime numbers $\{2, 3, 5, 7, 11, \ldots\}$, as the atomic units for all numbers. If you are seeking fame, there are many important open questions involving the prime numbers. A prime number is greater than 1 and has no divisor other than itself and 1. Let us consider a non-prime, for example 2015 (the year we started writing this book).

$$2015 = 5 \times 13 \times 31.$$

Curious. 2015 is not prime, but it is a product of factors which are all prime.

Theorem 6.3 (Fundamental Theorem of Arithmetic)**.** Suppose $n \geq 2$. Then,

(i) Either n is prime or can be written as a product of factors all of which are prime.

(ii) The representation of n as a product of primes is unique up to reordering of the factors.

We only prove part (i) of the Fundamental Theorem of Arithmetic here. The claim we prove is:

$$P(n): n \text{ can be written as a product of factors all of which are prime.} \tag{6.2}$$

Since 2 is prime, it is the product of (one) prime factor, so $P(2)$ is true (base case). To use induction, we need to move up one step, for example from 2015 to 2016. Let's see what happens with 2016,

$$2016 = 2 \times 2 \times 2 \times 2 \times 2 \times 3 \times 3 \times 7.$$

Wow! There is no similarity between the factors of 2015 and those of 2016. The prime factorization of 2015 won't help with factoring 2016 into primes. We are not toast yet. Perhaps some other smaller values can be of more help, and indeed this is the case because $2016 = 32 \times 63$. The prime factorizations of 32 and 63 do help with the prime factorization of 2016 – just multiply those two prime factorizations together, which means

$$P(32) \wedge P(63) \to P(2016).$$

Knowing that $P(k)$ holds for smaller k does help. For general n, we don't know which smaller values will be useful, but that won't be an issue if we can assume $2, 3, \ldots, n$ are all products of primes. Now, either $n+1$ is prime (a product of one prime), or $n+1$ is composite, in which case $n+1 = k\ell$, where $2 \le k, \ell \le n$. Since k and ℓ are at most n, they have prime factorizations. That is, $k = s_1 \cdots s_\alpha$ and $\ell = t_1 \cdots t_\beta$. Hence,

$$n+1 = k\ell = (s_1 \cdots s_\alpha) \cdot (t_1 \cdots t_\beta).$$

The last expression proves $n+1$ is a product of primes. Effectively, assuming that $2, 3, \ldots, n$ are all products of primes to prove $n+1$ is a product of primes corresponds to proving a much stronger claim by induction. We explicitly state this strong-induction claim in the formal proof below.

Proof. To prove n is a product of primes for all $n \ge 1$, we use induction to prove the stronger claim:

$$Q(n) : 2, 3, \ldots, n \text{ are all products of primes.}$$

1: **[Base case]** $Q(2)$ claims that 2 is a product of primes, which is clearly true.

2: **[Induction step]** We show $Q(n) \to Q(n+1)$ for all $n \ge 2$, using a direct proof.
Assume (induction hypothesis) $Q(n)$: $2, 3, \ldots, n$ are all products of primes.
Prove $Q(n+1)$: $2, 3, \ldots, n, n+1$ are all products of primes.

By the induction hypothesis, $2, 3, \ldots, n$ are products of primes. We only need to prove $n+1$ is a product of primes. Either $n+1$ is a prime or $n+1 = k\ell$, where $2 \le k, \ell \le n$. By the induction hypothesis, k and ℓ are products of primes which can be multiplied to write $n+1$ as a product of primes, proving $Q(n+1)$.

3: By induction, $Q(n)$ is true for all $n \ge 2$. Certainly, if $Q(n)$ is true, then so is $P(n)$ in (6.2). ■

In the proof, the stronger claim $Q(n)$ has a special form. The original claim $P(n)$ in (6.2) is that n is a product of primes. The stronger claim $Q(n)$ asserts $P(n)$ for n and all smaller values,

$$Q(n) = P(2) \wedge P(3) \wedge P(4) \wedge \cdots \wedge P(n).$$

This is a much stronger claim than $P(n)$. The induction step is also interesting. Though we are proving the stronger claim $Q(n+1)$, we only needed to prove $P(n+1)$, because $P(2), \ldots, P(n)$ came for free from the induction hypothesis. Proving this type of stronger claim is called a proof by strong induction.

Strong Induction. To prove $P(n)$ for all $n \ge 1$, use induction to prove the stronger claim:

$$Q(n) : \text{each of } P(1), P(2), \ldots, P(n) \text{ are true.}$$

Proof Template IX: Strong Induction.

Proof. We prove $P(n)$ for all $n \ge 1$, by strong induction.

1: Prove $P(1)$. **[base case]**

2: Prove $P(1) \wedge P(2) \wedge \cdots \wedge P(n) \to P(n+1)$ for all $n \ge 1$ **[induction step]**
Assume: $P(1)$, $P(2), \ldots,$ $P(n)$ are all true.
Prove: $P(n+1)$.

3: Conclude, by induction, $P(n)$ is true for all $n \ge 1$. ■

Let's compare the mechanics of strong induction and induction.

	Ordinary Induction	**Strong Induction**
Base Case	Prove $P(1)$	Prove $Q(1) = P(1)$
Induction Step	Assume: $P(n)$ Prove: $P(n+1)$	Assume: $Q(n) = P(1) \wedge P(2) \wedge \cdots \wedge P(n)$ Prove: $P(n+1)$

In both methods, the base cases are the same and you prove $P(n+1)$ in the induction step. The difference is that in strong induction, you get to assume more but prove the same thing, so strong induction must be easier. It is a good idea to default to strong induction. Ironic. It is always easier to prove this stronger claim.[1]

[1] A counterpart to induction is recursion. You solve a "hard" problem of size $n+1$ by first solving easier smaller problems. Strong induction corresponds to solving all the smaller problems. That's overkill if you only need the problem of size n.

The Fundamental Theorem of Arithmetic is a representation theorem. Some object, in this case n, is represented using other objects, in this case primes. The theorem ensures that the representation exists and is unique, but does not tell us how to find the representation. Computer scientists spend a lot of effort on prime factorization. We know how to do it, but not efficiently. Why do computer scientists care about such representations? Well, mathematics has a funny way of creeping into life. The representation of LARGE integers as a product of two primes plays a fundamental role in cryptography. Thanks to cryptography, we have secure online banking, email, social media accounts, etc. Imagine a life without cryptography.

Strong induction is particularly useful for representation theorems because one typically builds the representation of a bigger object using the representation of many smaller objects of unknown sizes, and the induction hypothesis in strong induction ensures existence of the representation for all smaller sizes. Here come more examples of representation theorems.

Theorem 6.4 (Binary Numbers). Every $n \geq 1$ is a sum of distinct powers of 2. The representation is unique.

Let us tinker a little to see what is going on. Consider $n = 22$,

$$22 = 2^1 + 2^2 + 2^4.$$

We could write this in binary as 10110, which means (reading from right to left)

$$0 \times 2^0 + 1 \times 2^1 + 1 \times 2^2 + 0 \times 2^3 + 1 \times 2^4.$$

For induction to work, we should be able to get the representation for $n+1$ from n. So let's look at $22+1 = 23$. Since 22 is even, 2^0 is not in its representation, so we can just add 2^0 to get $23 = 2^0 + 2^1 + 2^2 + 2^4$, or more compactly the binary representation of 23 is 10111. Let's keep going, with $23 + 1 = 24$. Now, unfortunately, things get complicated. You cannot just add 2^0 to 23, as 2^0 is already in the binary representation of 23. This makes ordinary induction tricky.[2] With strong induction, to handle 24 simply divide by 2, to get 12. The strong induction hypothesis gives that all values smaller than 24 are a sum of distinct powers of 1. So, 12 is a sum of distinct powers,

$$12 = 2^2 + 2^3.$$

We immediately get the representation for 24 by multiplying by 2,

$$24 = 2 \times 12 = 2 \times 2^2 + 2 \times 2^3 = 2^3 + 2^4.$$

Our argument does not prove the binary representation is unique. One way to prove uniqueness is by contradiction. For another way to prove uniqueness, see Problem 6.27.

Exercise 6.7

(a) Write 21 as a sum of distinct powers of 2.

(b) Give the full proof that every $n \geq 1$ is a sum of distinct powers of 2. In your induction step you should consider $n + 1$ even and $n + 1$ odd separately.

(c) **(Factorial representation)** Use Exercise 5.4(e) to show that every $n \geq 1$ has a representation

$$n = \sum_{i=1}^{\infty} a_i i!, \qquad \text{where } a_i \in \{0, 1, \ldots, i\}.$$

Example 6.5 (Equal pile Nim). Strong induction is also a powerful tool for proving optimal strategies, especially for strategic two player games. Nim (old English/German) means to steal or pilfer. A popular two person game has this name. Here is a simple version. There are two rows of pennies. Each row has the same number of pennies. A player, at his turn, can remove any number of pennies (at least 1) from one row. The last player to remove pennies is the winner. Here is an example of a game being played.

player 1 → player 2 → player 1 → player 2 → player 1 →

[2] If you did Problem 5.20 your proof would have been something along the line: By the well-ordering principle, there is a smallest power i for which 2^i is not in the representation of 23 ($i = 3$ for 23, because 2^3 is absent). You needed to prove that you can add this power and remove all the smaller powers. So for 24, you would get 11000. This is how to add one in binary.

Player 1, being the last to play, wins. Player 2 can do better. Player 2 has a simple optimal strategy to guarantee a win by ensuring that the two rows are always equal. Here is a proof by strong induction that Player 2 can always win. Let n be the number of pennies in each row when the game starts.

$$P(n): \text{Player 2 can win the game that starts with } n \text{ pennies in each row.}$$

The base case is $P(1)$, 1 penny in each row. Player 2 wins because Player 1 must take a penny from one of the rows and Player 2 takes the other penny, ending the game.

Now for the induction step. Assume $P(1) \wedge \cdots \wedge P(n)$ and consider $P(n+1)$, the game with $n+1$ pennies. Suppose Player 1 takes $k \geq 1$ pennies from a row. If $k = n+1$, then Player 2 takes the entire other row and wins. If $k < n+1$, then Player 2 takes k pennies from the other pile. This results in $r = n+1-k$ pennies in each pile, and it is Player 1's turn to play. The situation is exactly the start of a game with r pennies. Since $1 \leq r \leq n$ (because $1 \leq k < n+1$), $P(r)$ is true, that is Player 2 can win from here. This proves $P(n+1)$, and, by induction, $P(n)$ for all $n \geq 1$. We needed strong induction because, in the induction step, we do not know k, the number of pennies player 1 takes. □

Checklist When Approaching an Induction Problem.

- ✓ Are you trying to prove a "For all ..." claim?
- ✓ Identify the claim $P(n)$, especially the parameter n. Here is an example.
  Prove: geometric mean ≤ arithmetic mean. What is $P(n)$? What is n?
  A candidate for n is the number of terms in the mean.
  $P(n)$: geometric mean ≤ arithmetic mean for every set of n positive numbers.
- ✓ Tinker. Does the claim hold for small n ($n = 1, 2, 3, \ldots$)? These become base cases.
- ✓ Tinker. Can you see why (say) $P(5)$ follows from $P(1), P(2), P(3), P(4)$?
  This is the crux of induction, to build from a smaller n to a larger n.
- ✓ Determine the type of induction: try strong induction first.
- ✓ Write out the skeleton of the proof to see exactly what you need to prove.
- ✓ Determine and prove the base cases.
- ✓ Prove $P(n+1)$ in the induction step. You must use the induction hypothesis $P(n)$.

An induction may fail because you try to prove too much: $P(n+1)$ is too heavy a burden. Then again, your proof may fail because you try to prove too little: $P(n)$ is too weak a support. In general you must balance the strength of your claim so that the support is just enough for the burden. — G. Polya.

6.4 Many Flavors of Induction

There are many types of induction: ordinary induction, strong induction, leaping induction, etc. You can even invent your own induction. You set up a chain of implications and prove some base cases. The base cases start the dominoes falling, and the chain of implications eventually topples all the other dominos, proving the claim for all $n \geq 1$. Ordinary induction, the basic flavor, is like climbing a ladder. If you can get to the first rung, and you know how to climb up one rung, then you can climb as high as you want. All the flavors of induction are equivalent, but a proof may be much easier in one flavor than another.

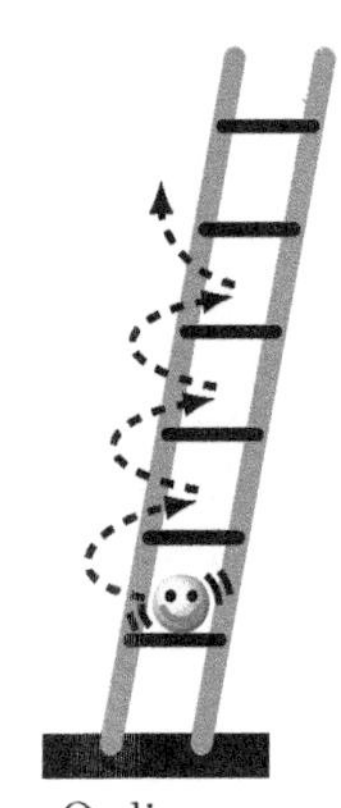

Ordinary Induction

Induction is your buddy in computer science, not merely as a proof technique, but also as a basis for designing algorithms. Just as induction proves a claim for large n using the claim for smaller n, there are algorithm design techniques that solve a large hard problem by starting using solutions of smaller simpler problems, for example recursion, dynamic programming and greedy algorithms. You need some form of induction to prove that these "inductive" algorithms work correctly for every input. You will learn the details in an algorithms course. Exercise 6.8 is an example of using induction to prove that a greedy algorithm works.

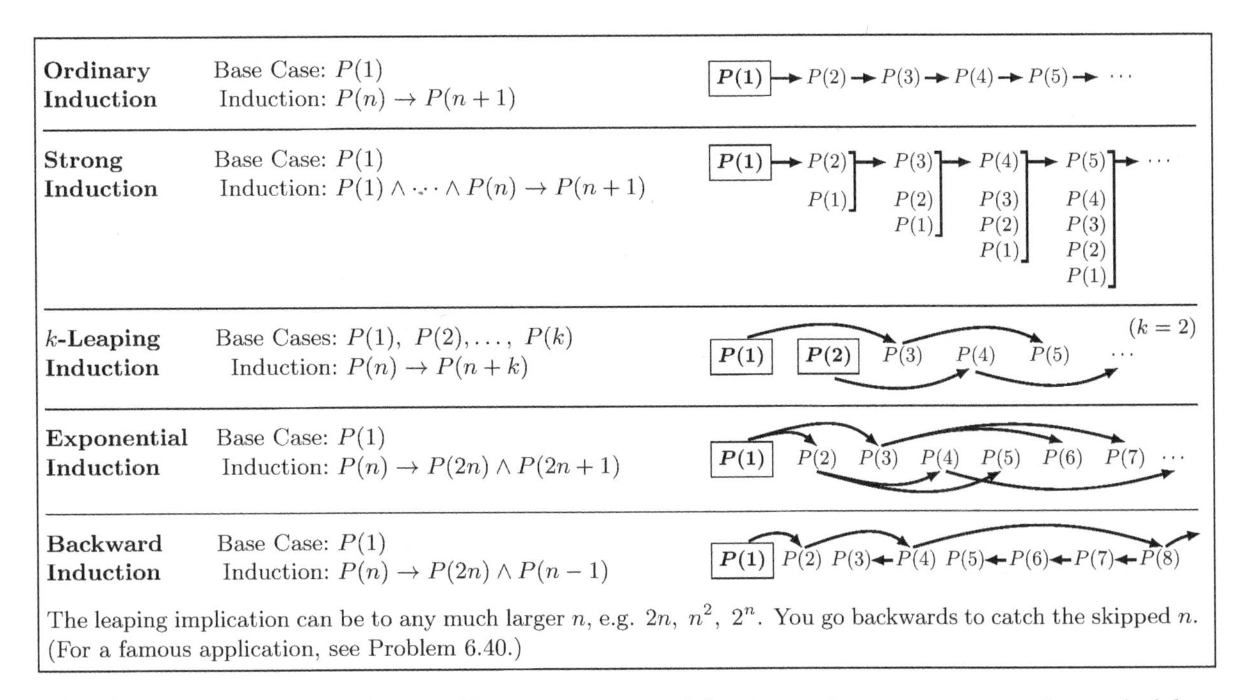

Ordinary Induction	Base Case: $P(1)$ Induction: $P(n) \to P(n+1)$	
Strong Induction	Base Case: $P(1)$ Induction: $P(1) \wedge \cdots \wedge P(n) \to P(n+1)$	
k-Leaping Induction	Base Cases: $P(1),\ P(2), \ldots,\ P(k)$ Induction: $P(n) \to P(n+k)$	$(k=2)$
Exponential Induction	Base Case: $P(1)$ Induction: $P(n) \to P(2n) \wedge P(2n+1)$	
Backward Induction	Base Case: $P(1)$ Induction: $P(n) \to P(2n) \wedge P(n-1)$	

The leaping implication can be to any much larger n, e.g. $2n$, n^2, 2^n. You go backwards to catch the skipped n. (For a famous application, see Problem 6.40.)

Table 6.1: Common types of induction. To set up your own induction, make sure every n can be reached from a proven base case using implication arrows. To prove your induction works, use well-ordering.

Induction should be on your fingertips. Table 6.1 is a summary of common types of induction. Understand and commit the first three to memory. Your goto-method should be strong induction. Strong induction is a little more cumbersome than ordinary induction but always easier. Keep your eyes open for applications of leaping induction. When you can't see how to prove the claim for $n+1$ from n, check to see if you can prove the claim for $n+2$ or $n+3$, etc. If you can prove the claim for one of these much higher values of n, then some version of leaping induction may work.

Exercise 6.8

The US coin system has 4 denominations of coins: 1¢, 5¢, 10¢ and 25¢. The task is to generate n¢ using the fewest coins. The "greedy" algorithm is universal: start with the largest denomination and work down to the smallest. Specifically, use as many 25¢ coins as possible; then, 10¢; then, 5¢; and, finally, 1¢. The greedy algorithm for 68¢ gives:

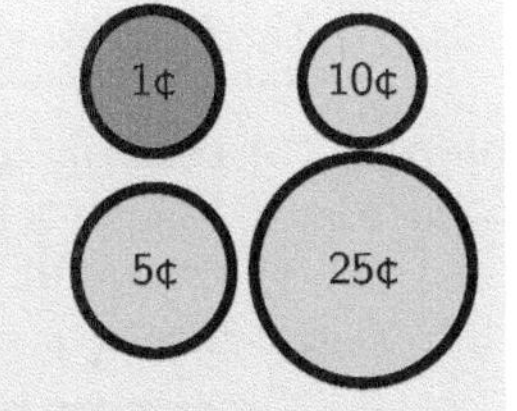

$$68¢ = 25¢ + 25¢ + 10¢ + 5¢ + 1¢ + 1¢ + 1¢$$

(a) Show that the greedy algorithm produces the fewest coins for all $n \geq 1$.

(b) Give a coin system for which the greedy algorithm does not produce the fewest coins. Give the coin denominations and an n for which the greedy algorithm fails.

Pop Quiz 6.9

Suppose $P(1) \wedge P(2) \wedge \cdots \wedge P(n) \to P(n+4)$ and $P(1)$ is true. Is $P(n)$ true for all $n \geq 1$? What base cases do you need? *[Hint: You could call this leaping strong induction.]*

6.5 Problems

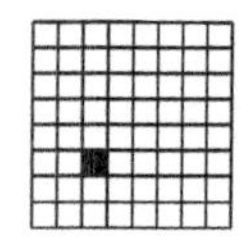

Problem 6.1. We proved the strong claim that a $2^n \times 2^n$ grid missing any square can be L-tiled. The induction proof constructively tiles the $2^n \times 2^n$ from four smaller problems on $2^{n-1} \times 2^{n-1}$ grids. You can therefore build an algorithm using the ideas in the proof. Use the algorithm suggested by the proof to obtain an L-tiling of the 8×8 grid shown, which is missing a square at position $(3, 3)$.

Problem 6.2. Prove: (a) $1+1/\sqrt{2}+1/\sqrt{3}+\cdots+1/\sqrt{n} > 2\sqrt{n+1}-2$. (b) $1+\sqrt{2}+\sqrt{3}+\cdots+\sqrt{n} \le 2(n+1)\sqrt{n}/3$.

Problem 6.3. Strengthen the claim and prove by induction, for $n \ge 1$:

(a) The sum of the first n odd numbers is a square. *[Hint: Strengthen to a specific square.]*

(b) (Uses complex numbers) Re$[(\cos x + i \sin x)^n] = \cos nx$. *[Hint: Im$[(\cos x + i \sin x)^n] =?$.]*

Problem 6.4. Consider the product $\Pi(n) = (1/2) \times (3/4) \times (5/8) \times \cdots \times (2n-1)/2n = (2n-1)!!/(2n)!!$.

(a) Use induction to show: (i) $\Pi(n) \le 1/\sqrt{2n}$. What goes wrong? (ii) $\Pi(n) \le 1/\sqrt{2n+1}$.

(b) Is (a)(ii) a stronger claim than (a)(i)? Is (a)(i) true? Why is (a)(ii) easier to prove than (a)(i)?

(c) Use induction to prove an even stronger claim that $\Pi(n) \le 1/\sqrt{3n+1}$.

Problem 6.5. (i) Identify the weaker claim and prove it by induction. If you can't, why? (ii) Prove the stronger claim.

(a) Let $\Pi(n) = (1+1^{-3})(1+2^{-3})(1+3^{-3})\cdots(1+n^{-3})$. Claim $\Pi(n) < 3$ or $\Pi(n) < 3 - 1/n$, for $n \ge 1$.

(b) Let $\Pi(n) = (1+2^{-1})(1+2^{-2})(1+2^{-3})\cdots(1+2^{-n})$. Claim $\Pi(n) < 5/2$ or $\Pi(n) < 5(1-2^{-n})/2$, for $n \ge 2$.

(c) Claim $\sqrt[n]{n} \le 2$ or $\sqrt[n]{n} \le 2 - 1/n$, for $n \ge 1$.

Problem 6.6. Let $H_n = 1/1 + 1/2 + \cdots + 1/n$, the nth Harmonic number, and $S_n = H_1/1 + H_2/2 + \cdots + H_n/n$.

(a) Prove $S_n \le H_n^2/2 + 1$ by induction. What goes wrong?

(b) Prove the stronger claim $S_n \le H_n^2/2 + (1/1^2 + 1/2^2 + \cdots + 1/n^2)/2$. Why is this stronger?

Problem 6.7. Prove $\sqrt{2\sqrt{3\cdots\sqrt{n}}} \le 3$ by induction. Did it work? Find and prove a stronger claim.

Problem 6.8. Prove $n^7 < 2^n$ for $n \ge 37$. (a) Use induction. (b) Use leaping induction.

Problem 6.9. What is wrong with this bad proof by strong induction that $3^k = 1$ for $k \ge 0$.

> **Base Case:** $3^0 = 1$. ✓
> **Induction:** Assume $3^k = 1$ for $k = 0, \ldots n$ and show $3^{n+1} = 1$.
> $3^{n+1} = 3^n \times 3^n/3^{n-1} = 1 \times 1/1 = 1$ (by the induction hypothesis, $3^n = 3^{n-1} = 1$)
> Therefore, by induction, $3^n = 1$ for $n \ge 0$. ✓

Problem 6.10. Let $P(m, n)$ be a predicate (claim) with two inputs $m, n \ge 1$.

(a) Determine if $P(m, n)$ is true for all $m, n \ge 1$ by showing pictorially the "grid" of implications when:
(i) $P(1, 1)$ is true; AND (ii) $P(m, n) \to (P(m, n+1) \wedge P(m+1, n))$ is true for $m, n \ge 1$.

(b) Use the well-ordering principle to prove the following principle of double induction.

> **Principle of Double Induction.** Let $P(m, n)$ be a predicate for $m, n \ge 1$.
> (i) If $P(1, 1)$ is true; AND
> (ii) $P(m, n) \to (P(m, n+1) \wedge P(m+1, n))$ is true for $m, n \ge 1$.
> Then, $P(m, n)$ is true for all $m, n \ge 1$.

(c) Use double induction to prove that $4^m - 4^n$ is divisible by 3, for $m, n \ge 1$.

Problem 6.11. Let $P(m, n)$ be a predicate (claim) with two inputs $m, n \ge 1$. Suppose

(i) $P(1, 1)$ is true;

(ii) $P(1, n) \to P(1, n+1)$ for $n \ge 1$ and $P(m, 1) \to P(m+1, 1)$ for $m \ge 1$;

(iii) $P(m, n) \to P(m+1, n+1)$ for $m, n \ge 1$.

Show the grid of implications that is created. Is $P(m, n)$ true for all $m, n \ge 1$?

Problem 6.12. Consider the "double sum" of $i \times j$ over all pairs (i, j) with $1 \le i \le m$ and $1 \le j \le n$,

$$S(m, n) = (1 \times 1 + 1 \times 2 + \cdots + 1 \times n) + (2 \times 1 + 2 \times 2 + \cdots + 2 \times n) + \cdots + (m \times 1 + m \times 2 + \cdots + m \times n).$$

(a) Compute $S(3, 2)$. (b) Prove $S(m, n) = mn(m+1)(n+1)/4$, for $m, n \ge 1$.

Problem 6.13. Prove the following claims.

(a) Any postage greater than 11¢ can be made using 4¢ and 5¢ stamps.
(b) Infinitely many postages cannot be made using 4¢ and 6¢ stamps.

Problem 6.14. For what n can n students be broken into teams of 4 or 7? Prove it.

Problem 6.15. Prove that there are $2^{\lceil n/2 \rceil}$ distinct n-bit binary palindromes (strings that equal their reversal).

Problem 6.16. A grill has space for two pancakes and cooks one side of a pancake in 1 minute. How long does it take to cook n pancakes (both sides of each pancake must be cooked)? Prove your answer.

Problem 6.17. Prove that a square can be cut exactly into n squares of possibly distinct positive sizes for $n \geq 6$.

Problem 6.18. Prove that $\lfloor 1/2 \rfloor + \lfloor 2/2 \rfloor + \lfloor 3/2 \rfloor + \cdots + \lfloor n/2 \rfloor = \begin{cases} n^2/4 & n \text{ even;} \\ (n^2-1)/4 & n \text{ odd.} \end{cases}$ ($\lfloor \cdot \rfloor$ rounds down.)

Problem 6.19. For $n \geq 1$, show that $n = \pm 1^2 \pm 2^2 \pm 3^2 \cdots \pm k^2$ (for some k and appropriate choice of each $\pm$). *[Hint: What is $(k+4)^2 - (k+3)^2 - (k+2)^2 + (k+1)^2$?]*

Problem 6.20. Prove by strong induction that $n \leq 3^{n/3}$ for $n \geq 0$.

Problem 6.21. Prove that, for $n \geq 1$, there is $k \geq 0$ and ℓ odd such that $n = 2^k \ell$.

Problem 6.22. Prove by strong induction that the kth prime number $p_k \leq 2^{2^{k-1}}$.

Problem 6.23. For $x \in \mathbb{R}$, suppose $x + 1/x \in \mathbb{Z}$. Prove $x^n + 1/x^n \in \mathbb{Z}$ for $n \geq 1$.

Problem 6.24. If $\cos x + \sin x$ is rational, prove that $\cos^n x + \sin^n x$ is rational for any $n \geq 1$.

Problem 6.25. For $n \geq 1$, prove by induction that $F_n = (\phi_+^n - \phi_-^n)/\sqrt{5}$ is a natural number, where $\phi_\pm = (1 \pm \sqrt{5})/2$. *[Hint: Use induction. First show that $F_n = F_{n-1} + F_{n-2}$.]*

Problem 6.26. Use strong induction to prove, for all $n \geq 1$, that $n/q \neq \sqrt{2}$ for any $q \in \mathbb{N}$. What does it mean?

Problem 6.27. Prove the uniqueness of binary representation (Theorem 6.4). Suppose

$$n = 2^{i_1} + 2^{i_2} + \cdots + 2^{i_r} = 2^{j_1} + 2^{j_2} + \cdots + 2^{j_\ell}, \qquad \text{where } i_1 < i_2 < \cdots < i_r \text{ and } j_1 < j_2 < \cdots < j_\ell.$$

(a) Prove that $i_1 = j_1$. *[Hint: If $i_1 < j_1$, divide both sides by 2^{i_1}. The LHS will be odd.]*
(b) Prove by induction on k that $2^{i_k} = 2^{j_k}$.

Problem 6.28. Use strong induction together with a greedy algorithm to prove that any $n \geq 0$ is a sum of distinct powers of 2 in a unique way. *[Hint: Let i_1 be the highest power of 2 that is at most n, so $n = 2^{i_1} + k$, where $k < 2^{i_1}$.]*

Problem 6.29. At one end of a line containing only boys and girls is a boy and at the other end is a girl. Prove that the number of boy–girl pairs who are standing next to each other is odd.

Problem 6.30. Problem 5.57 used induction to prove every tournament has a ranking. Show it by strong induction. *[Hint: Remove any player v and consider two sub-tournaments: those players who lost to v; and those who beat v.]*

Problem 6.31. Between every pair of major US cities is a one-way flight (the direction is not known). Washington DC has the most out-going flights to major US cities. The president starts in Washington DC and visits each major city once in some sequence, flying from one city to the next. Prove that the president's city-tour is always possible.

Problem 6.32. We are back in L-tile land.

(a) This time the potted plant needs more room than just one square. For $n \geq 1$, a $2^n \times 2^n$ grid-patio is missing a (large) 2×2 square in a corner as shown in the figure. Prove that the remainder of the patio can be L-tiled, for $n \geq 1$.
(b) We are no longer sure what the size of the potted plant is. The size may be $2^k \times 2^k$, and so a $2^k \times 2^k$ square will be missing from the corner of the $2^n \times 2^n$ grid-patio. Prove that the remainder of the patio can always be L-tiled, for $k \geq 1$ and $n \geq k$. *[Hint: Tinker: try $k = 2; n = 3$ and $k = 2; n = 4$ to figure out what is going on.]*

Problem 6.33. Consider the $5^n \times 5^n$ patio with the top-left square removed.

(a) Prove that the number of remaining squares is divisible by 3.
(b) For $n \geq 1$, prove by induction that the rest of the patio can be L-tiled.

Problem 6.34. For which n can these grids be L-tiled: (a) $3^n \times 3^n$ (b) $5^n \times 5^n$ (c) $6^n \times 6^n$?

Problem 6.35. Prove that a $(3n+1) \times (3n+1)$ grid missing one square can be L-tiled, for $n \geq 1$. Use 2-leaping induction and the figure to the right as a guide to the proof.

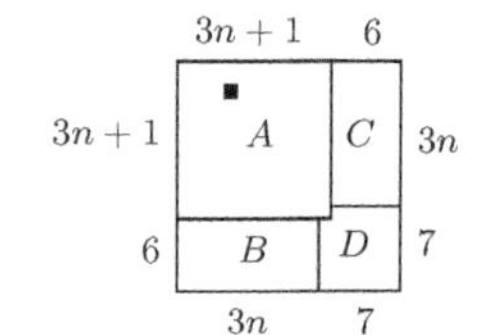

(a) What are the base cases? Prove them.
(b) Prove that a $2k \times 3r$ grid can be tiled for $k, n \in \mathbb{N}$.
(c) Prove that A, B, C, D can be tiled and prove the claim.

Problem 6.36. We wish to L-tile a grid that is missing its top-right quadrant (we show $k = 3$). Prove that this is always possible for $k \geq 1$. Prove $P(k)$ for $k \geq 1$, where $P(k)$ is defined as

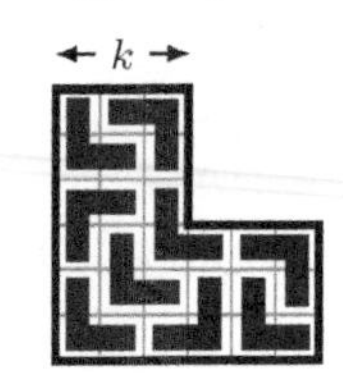

$$P(k) : \text{The } \tfrac{3}{4}\text{-grid missing the top right } k \times k \text{ quadrant can be } L\text{-tiled.}$$

(a) Prove $P(k)$ for $k = 1, \ldots, 4$.
(b) Prove $P(k_1) \wedge P(k_2) \rightarrow P(k_1 k_2)$.
(c) Prove $P(k)$ for $k \geq 1$. *[Hint: For $k \geq 5$, either $k = 3r, 3r+2$ or $3r+4$ for $r \in \mathbb{N}$.]*

Problem 6.37 (Local Minimum). For $n = 2^k$, n^2 distinct values are concealed in each square of an $n \times n$ We wish to find a local minimum, which is a square whose value is lower than its four neighbors (up, down, left, right). It is costly to reveal any specific grid square's value, so we would like to peek at as few values as possible before declaring a local minimum. Prove that you can find a local minimum by revealing at most $8n$ values.

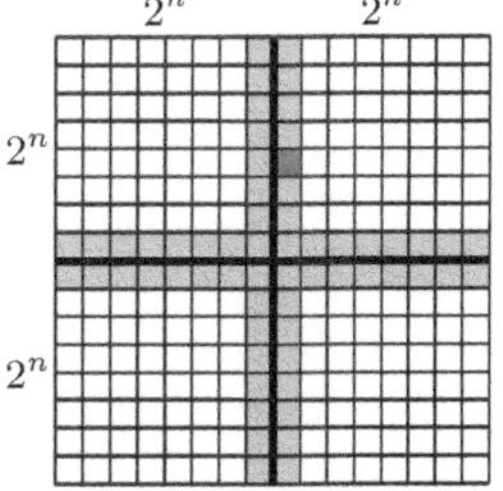

(a) Break the $2^{k+1} \times 2^{k+1}$ grid, into 4 smaller subgrids as we did in L-tile land. Reveal the values in the vertical and horizontal central bands shaded in gray in the figure. Among these revealed values, consider the minimum (highlighted in red).
 (i) How many values are revealed?
 (ii) Prove that the subgrid with the minimum value (red square) has a local minimum.
(b) Let $R(k)$ be the number of squares revealed to find a local minimum in the $2^k \times 2^k$ grid. Show that $R(k) \leq R(k-1) + 2^{k+2} - 4$. Why is it inequality, not equality?
(c) Unfold the recursion and prove that $R(n) \leq 8n - 4(\ln n + 2)$.

Problem 6.38. You have a stack of n boxes. You may split a stack into two. If you split a stack of k boxes into two stacks of k_1, k_2 ($k_1 + k_2 = k$), you earn \$$k_1 k_2$ (the product). Your must reduce the stack of n boxes to n stacks of one box and earn as much money as possible.
(a) Tinker with different ways of unstacking 4 and 5 boxes.
(b) Make a conjecture for the number of turns you need. Prove it by strong induction.
(c) Make a conjecture for the maximum \$ you can earn. Prove it by strong induction.

Problem 6.39. The general version of Nim has k piles with $n_1, \ldots, n_k$ coins in each pile. In 1902, Charles Bouton discovered an optimal strategy for Nim. Represent n_i in binary. For three piles of 6, 7 and 23 coins, $n_1 = 6 = 00110$, $n_2 = 7 = 00111$ and $n_3 = 23 = 10111$ (equalize the lengths of the binary numbers by front-padding with zeros). The "Nim-sums" $s_1, s_2, \ldots$ are obtained by summing each column of digits, so $s_1 = 2$, $s_2 = 3$, $s_3 = 3$, $s_4 = 0$ and $s_5 = 1$, as shown on the right.

n_1: 0 0 1 1 0
n_2: 0 0 1 1 1
n_3: 1 0 1 1 1
s: 1 0 3 3 2

(a) If every Nim-sum is even, show that any move will make at least one Nim sum odd.
(b) Prove: if any Nim-sum is odd, there is a move to make every Nim-sum even.
(c) Prove: if one of the Nim-sums is odd, the first player can force a win.
(d) What is your move for the (6,7,23)-pile Nim game in our example?

Problem 6.40. The arithmetic mean AM, the geometric mean GM and the harmonic mean HM are

$$\text{AM} = \frac{x_1 + x_2 + \cdots + x_n}{n}, \qquad \text{GM} = (x_1 x_2 \cdots x_n)^{1/n} \qquad \text{and} \qquad \text{HM} = \frac{n}{1/x_1 + 1/x_2 + \cdots + 1/x_n},$$

where $x_1, \ldots, x_n$ are positive real numbers. Prove that, for $n \geq 2$, HM $\leq$ GM $\leq$ AM.
(a) Prove GM $\leq$ AM. What is your induction claim $P(n)$? Here is Cauchy's famous proof using backward induction.
 (i) What is the base case? Prove it. *[Hint: $(\sqrt{x_1} - \sqrt{x_2})^2 \geq 0$.]*
 (ii) Prove that $P(2) \wedge P(n) \rightarrow P(2n)$.
 (iii) Prove $P(n) \rightarrow P(n-1)$. *[Hint: $(x_1 + \cdots + x_{n-1})/(n-1) = (x_1 + \cdots + x_{n-1} + \frac{x_1 + \cdots + x_{n-1}}{n-1})/n$.]*
 (iv) Collect everything together into a full proof by induction.
(b) To show HM $\leq$ GM, use GM $\leq$ AM for the numbers $\{1/x_1, 1/x_2, \ldots, 1/x_n\}$.

Problem 6.41 (Jensen's Inequality). A function $f(x)$ is concave if every chord of f is entirely below f. That is, for all $\alpha_1, \alpha_2 \geq 0$ and $\alpha_1 + \alpha_2 = 1$,

$$f(\alpha_1 x_1 + \alpha_2 x_2) \geq \alpha_1 f(x_1) + \alpha_2 f(x_2).$$

(a) Prove by induction that if $\alpha_i \geq 0$ and $\alpha_1 + \cdots + \alpha_n = 1$, then

$$f(\alpha_1 x_1 + \alpha_2 x_2 + \cdots + \alpha_n x_n) \geq \alpha_1 f(x_1) + \alpha_2 f(x_2) + \cdots + \alpha_n f(x_n).$$

(Evaluating f on a weighted average is at least as large as the weighted average of f.)

(b) Show that if $f''(x) < 0$, then $f(x)$ is concave. Use this to show that $\log(x)$ is concave.

(c) Prove the AM-GM inequality (see Problem 6.40). *[Hint: Take the* log.*]*

Problem 6.42. In a line are n disks (black on one side and white on the other). In each step you remove a black disk and flip its neighbors (if they are still there). The goal is to remove all disks. Here is a sample game.

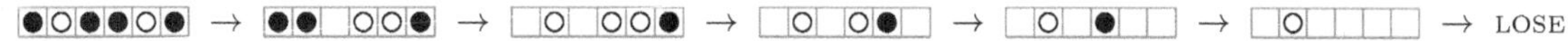

(a) Tinker. Determine when you can win, and when you can't. *[Hint: Consider the parity of black disks.]*

(b) Give an optimal strategy. Prove that your strategy wins all winnable games, and if it fails, the game is not winnable.

Problem 6.43. A sliding puzzle is a grid of 9 squares with 8 tiles. The goal is to get the 8 tiles into order (the target configuration). A move slides a tile into an empty square. Below we show first a row move, then a column move.

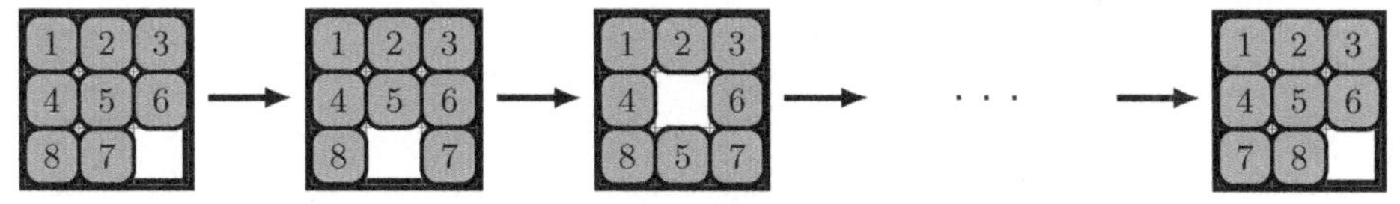

Prove that no sequence of moves produces the target configuration. *[Hint: The tiles form a sequence going left to right, top to bottom. An inversion is a pair that is out of order. Prove by induction that the number of inversions stays odd.]*

Problem 6.44. Here is a generalization of Problem 1.43(k). An $m \times n$ rectangular grid has at least two squares on each side ($m, n \geq 2$) and one side is even (so the total number of squares is even). Two squares of opposite colors are removed. Prove by strong induction that the remainder of the board can be tiled by dominos.

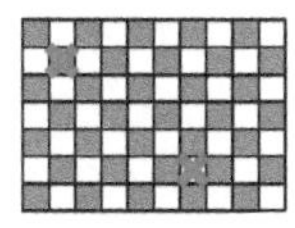

Problem 6.45. We prove, using well-ordering, that every natural number has a description of 13 words or less.

Assume some numbers cannot be described in 13 words or less. By well-ordering, there is a smallest such n_*. Here is a description of n_* using 13 words or less, a contradiction:

"The smallest natural number that cannot be described in thirteen words or less"

Do you think this proof is correct? If no, why not? If yes, is anything unsatisfying about the proof?

Problem 6.46. Here is another proof of the first part of the fundamental theorem of arithmetic.

(a) Prove by strong induction that every number greater than 1 is divisible by a prime.

(b) Use (a) to prove by strong induction that every $n > 1$ is a product of primes, $n = p_1 p_2 \cdots p_k$.

Problem 6.47. What's wrong with this proof of part (ii) of the Fundamental Theorem of Arithmetic, Theorem 6.3?

$Q(n)$: each of $2, 3, \ldots, n$ have a unique factorization into a product of primes..

[Base case] $Q(2)$ is true because 2 is a product of one prime, and that is unique.

[Induction step] Assume $Q(n) : 2, 3, \ldots, n$ have a unique factorization into a product of primes. If $n+1$ is prime, then there is no problem. If $n+1$ is composite, then $n+1 = k\ell$. Each of k and ℓ have a unique factorization into a product of primes. The product of these unique factorizations gives the unique factorization of $n+1$. Therefore, $Q(n+1)$ is true. By induction, $Q(n)$ is true $\forall n \geq 2$.

Problem 6.48.[Hard] Prove part (ii) of the Fundamental Theorem of Arithmetic (uniqueness of prime factorization). If n is prime, there is nothing to prove. Let $n = p_1 p_2 \cdots p_r$. Suppose $n = q_1 q_2 \cdots q_\ell$. is an alternate prime factorization. To prove that the q_is are the same as the p_is, you will need Euclid's Lemma:

Lemma 6.6 (Euclid's Lemma). IF a prime p divides the product $a_1 a_2$, THEN either p divides a_1 p or p divides a_2.

(a) Argue that n is divisible by p_1.

(b) Generalize Euclid's lemma: IF $a_1 a_2 \cdots a_\ell$ is divisible by a prime p, THEN one of the a_i's is divisible by p. *[Hint: Use induction on ℓ; Euclid's Lemma is the base case.]*

(c) Show that one of the q_i's is divisible by p_1 and hence that $p_1 = q_i$ for one of the q_i's.

(d) Prove that the primes in $q_1 \cdots q_\ell$ all appear in $p_1 \cdots p_r$ and *vice versa*. (Strong induction on n.)

(e) Prove Euclid's Lemma. Suppose p divides a_1a_2, but not a_1. Show that p divides a_2.

(i) Prove Bézout's identity: there exist integers x and y for which $px + a_1y = 1$.
[Hint: Let d be the smallest positive integer for which $px + a_1y = d$. Show that d divides both p and a_1.]

(ii) Use Bézout's identity to prove that a_2 is divisible by p. *[Hint: Multiply by a_2.]*

Problem 6.49. For $x \in \mathbb{R}$, one can write $x = k + \alpha$ where $k \in \mathbb{Z}$ is the integer part and $0 \le \alpha < 1$ is the fractional part. The rounding operation $\{x\}$ is defined as follows. If $\alpha \ge 1/2$, $\{x\} = k + 1$, and if $\alpha < 1/2$, $\{x\} = k$. Note that $1/2$ is rounded up. For $n \ge 1$, a problem from an old Russian mathematics olympiad asks to compute

$$f(n) = \sum_{i=1}^{\infty} \left\{\frac{n}{2^i}\right\} = \left\{\frac{n}{2}\right\} + \left\{\frac{n}{4}\right\} + \left\{\frac{n}{8}\right\} + \left\{\frac{n}{16}\right\} + \cdots$$

(a) Compute the sum without rounding, $n \cdot 2^{-1} + n \cdot 2^{-2} + n \cdot 2^{-3} + \cdots$. *[Hint: What is $1/2 + 1/4 + 1/8 + \cdots$?]*

(b) Compute $f(n)$ for $n = 1, 2, 3, 4, 5$, and make a conjecture for $f(n)$.

(c) Prove your conjecture. *[Hint: Exponential induction. Show $\{n/2^k + 1/2^{k+1}\} = \{n/2^k\}$.]*

Problem 6.50. Here are some interesting/challenging problems for you to prove by induction. Tinker, tinker.

(a) There is a one-way flight between every pair of cities. Prove that there is at least one special city that can be reached from every other city either directly or via one stop.

(b) For $n \ge 0$, there are integers x, y for which $x(21n + 4) + y(14n + 3) = 1$.

(c) Let $x_1, x_2, \ldots, x_n$ be any sequence of positive real numbers. Prove that
$$(x_1^2 + 1)(x_2^2 + 1) \cdots (x_n^2 + 1) \ge (x_1x_2 + 1)(x_2x_3 + 1)(x_3x_4 + 1) \cdots (x_{n-1}x_n + 1)(x_nx_1 + 1).$$

(d) Enough gas for a car to travel around a circle is spread among n gas stations on the circle. Prove that the car can start at one of the gas stations and make it around the circle.

(e) Prove $\binom{j}{j} + \binom{j+1}{j} + \binom{j+2}{j} + \cdots + \binom{n}{j} = \binom{n+1}{j+1}$, for $n \ge j$. The binomial coefficient is $\binom{n}{i} = \frac{n!}{i!(n-i)!}$.

(f) Compute a formula for $S_n = \binom{n}{0} - \binom{n-1}{1} + \binom{n-2}{2} - \binom{n-3}{3} \cdots + (-1)^i\binom{n-i}{i} + \cdots$, where the binomial coefficient is $\binom{n}{i} = \frac{n!}{i!(n-i)!}$ if $n \ge i$ and zero for $n < i$. *[Hint: $\binom{n}{i} = \binom{n-1}{i} + \binom{n-1}{i-1}$.]*

(g) Given n positive numbers $x_1 < x_2 < \cdots < x_n$ with sum $s = x_1 + \cdots + x_n$ and $n - 1$ positive numbers $M = \{a_1 < a_2 < \cdots < a_{n-1}\}$ with $s \notin M$, show that one can arrange the x_i into a sequence so that no prefix-sum is in M. *[Hint: Induction on n. In the induction step, consider $(s - x_{n+1}) \in M \backslash a_n$ and $(s - x_{n+1}) \notin M \backslash a_n$.]*

(h) The picture shows a cricket making jumps of sizes 2,3,4,1 and 5 to reach a destination at square 15, while avoiding spiders who lie in wait at squares 1,4,7,13.

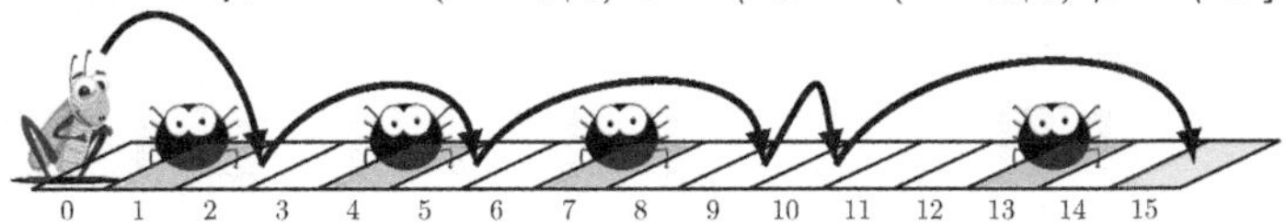

A cricket makes n jumps of distinct positive integer sizes $a_1, \ldots, a_n$ to reach the destination $s = a_1 + \cdots + a_n$. Along the way are $n - 1$ spiders at positions $x_1, \ldots, x_{n-1}$. Prove that the cricket can always reorder the jump sizes and reach the destiniation while avoiding all spiders, providing no spider is at the destination.

(i) The numbers $\{1, \ldots, n\}$ are painted on the $2n$ faces of n cards (each number is used twice). Show that it is always possible to place the cards on a table so that the numbers $1, \ldots, n$ are facing up.

(j) You have n slabs, each with a positive integer weight in $\{1, 2, \ldots, n\}$. The slabs have a total weight less than $2n$. Prove that some combination of the slabs has a total weight of exactly n.

(k) Fix $n \in \mathbb{N}$. Prove Hermite's identity: $\lfloor x \rfloor + \lfloor x + \frac{1}{n} \rfloor + \lfloor x + \frac{2}{n} \rfloor + \cdots + \lfloor x + \frac{n-1}{n} \rfloor = \lfloor nx \rfloor$, for all $x \ge 0$.

(i) Suppose x satisfies Hermite's identity, prove that $x + k/n$ satisfies Hermite's identity for $k \in \mathbb{N}$.

(ii) Show that $x \in [0, \frac{1}{n})$ satisfies Hermite's identity. Hence prove Hermite's identity for all $x > 0$.

(l) We arranged n^2 numbers in a square $n \times n$ table as shown on the right. The number in the ith row and jth column of the table is given by
$$a_{ij} = \frac{1}{i + j - 1}.$$
Pick any n numbers no two of which are in the same row or column. Show that the sum of the numbers picked is at least 1.

$$\begin{array}{ccccc} \frac{1}{1} & \frac{1}{2} & \frac{1}{3} & \cdots & \frac{1}{n} \\ \frac{1}{2} & \frac{1}{3} & \frac{1}{4} & \cdots & \frac{1}{n+1} \\ \vdots & \vdots & \vdots & & \vdots \\ \frac{1}{n} & \frac{1}{n+1} & \frac{1}{n+2} & \cdots & \frac{1}{2n-1} \end{array}$$

(m) For $a, n \in \mathbb{N}$ with $a \le n!$, prove that a is a sum of at most n distinct divisors of $n!$. For example, for $a = 23, n = 4$, the divisors of $n! = 24$ are $\{1, 2, 3, 4, 6, 8, 12, 24\}$ and $a = 12 + 8 + 3$. *[Hint: Quotient-remainder theorem.]*

> The grand thing is to be able to reason backwards. – **Arthur Conan Doyle**
>
> Get your facts first, and then you can distort them as much as you please. – **Mark Twain**
>
> To err is human, but to really foul things up you need a computer. – **Paul Ehrlich**
>
> We can't solve our problems with the same thinking that created them. – **Albert Einstein**

Chapter 7

Recursion

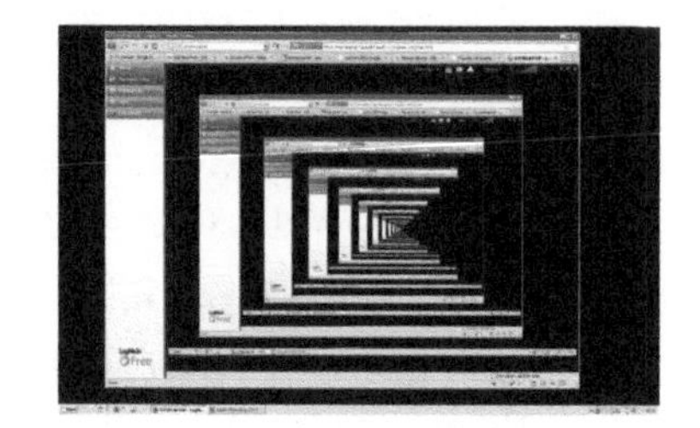

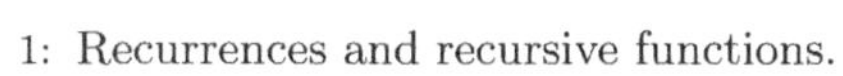

1: Recurrences and recursive functions.
2: Recursive definitions of sets, strings and structures.

The graphic above came from a "demo" of a tool for online lectures that allows the lecturer (me) to monitor the screen of a remote student who watches my screen. Here is a cartoon of what happened in slow motion.

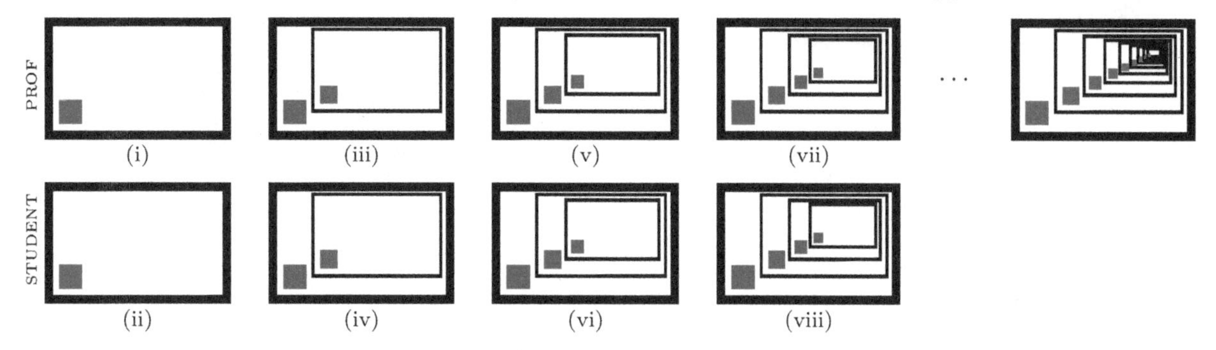

(i) My screen with a blue square. (ii) The student sees my screen. (iii) Launch the tool: a window pops up showing me the students view. (iv) Student's screen updates to my new screen (the student is watching my screen). (v) Tool updates to show me the student's new view. (vi) Student's view updates. (vii) Tool updates. (viii) Student's view updates. .... The process never ends, causing a system crash. Spectacular!.

The tool shows the student's view. But, the student views my screen, which contains what the tool showed. That is, the tool shows what the tool showed, a form of "self reference," and the trademark of recursion. You use recursion when you look-up the meaning of a word:

look-up(word w): Get definition of w. If a word x in the definition is unknown, *look-up*(word x).

To look-up a word, you may need to look-up another word: self-reference. A function or procedure which refers to itself in its definition is called recursive. The look-up(word) procedure works only if every word is ultimately defined using some known basic words. Recursion is powerful, but dangerous. A small error can result in a never ending process. Even the professionals can fall into traps, as with the demo above.

> **Pop Quiz 7.1**
> Define a function: $f(n) = f(n-1) + 2n - 1$. What is $f(3)$?

Program the function $f(n)$ from Pop Quiz 7.1 in your favorite language (Java, C^{++}, Python, R, MATLAB, ...). Call $f(3)$ and await a spectacle. Your program will crash, complaining that "you exceeded the stack space". This is typical in a recursion gone bad. A good programming platform may have a maximum recursion-depth or warn you that its running out of stack space, asking for confirmation on whether to continue.

7.1 Recursive Functions

The function in Pop Quiz 7.1 is missing base cases, cases where $f(n)$ is explicitly specified. The new ingredient in Exercise 7.2 is an explicit value for $n \leq 0$.

Exercise 7.2
Our self-referential function with base cases is $f(n) = \begin{cases} 0 & n \leq 0; \\ f(n-1) + 2n - 1 & n > 0. \end{cases}$

(a) Compute $f(-1), f(0), f(1), f(2), f(3)$. (b) Make a conjecture for the value of $f(n)$.

In Exercise 7.2, $f(n)$ is only partially self-referential. The self-referential part of $f(n)$ is the recursive case. Two requirements for a recursive function to be well defined are:

1. **[Base Cases]** You must explicitly specify the value of $f(n)$ for at least one n.
2. **[Recursive Progress]** If you compute $f(n)$ using $f(k)$, then k must be strictly closer to a base case than n. Ultimately, the recursive case must use base cases, or else the recursive function is ill-defined.

Typically the base case is $n = 0$ and the recursive part of $f(n)$ uses $f(k)$ for $k < n$.

Exercise 7.3
Which of these recursive functions are well defined for integer $n \geq 0$.

(a) $f(n) = \begin{cases} 1 & n = 0; \\ 2f(n-1) & n > 0. \end{cases}$

(b) $f(n) = \begin{cases} 1 & n = 0; \\ nf(n-1) & n > 0. \end{cases}$

(c) $f(n) = \begin{cases} 1 & n = 0; \\ f(n+1) - 1 & n > 0. \end{cases}$

(d) $f(n) = \begin{cases} 1 & n = 0; \\ f(n-2) + 2 & n > 0. \end{cases}$

There is a tight link between induction and recursion. Let us highlight the similarities.

Induction	Recursion
$P(0)$ is true; $P(n) \rightarrow P(n+1)$	$f(0) = 0$; $f(n+1) = f(n) + 2n + 1$
You can conclude $P(n+1)$ if $P(n)$ is true	You can compute $f(n+1)$ if $f(n)$ is known
Therefore, $P(n)$ is true for all $n \geq 0$.	Therefore we can compute $f(n)$ for all $n \geq 0$.

Induction uses small n to prove a claim for larger n. Recursion uses small n to compute a function for larger n. Our experience with different types of induction will help us determine if a recursive function is well defined. For example, is the recursive function $f(n)$ in Exercise 7.3(d) well defined for integers $n \geq 0$, where

$$f(n) = \begin{cases} 1 & n = 0; \\ f(n-2) + 2 & n > 0. \end{cases}$$

Tinker: $f(1) = f(-1) + 2$. The recursion for $f(-1)$ needs $f(-3)$, then $f(-5)$ and so on, never ending.

n	0	1	2	3	4	5	6	7	8
$f(n)$	1	✗	3	✗	5	✗	7	✗	9

An ✗ means you can't compute $f(n)$. Our recursion says $f(n) \rightarrow f(n+2)$, where the arrow means "knowing $f(n)$ implies one can compute $f(n+2)$". Starting at $f(0)$, we get a chain as follows,

$f(0) = 1;$
$f(n) \rightarrow f(n+2)$

$f(0)$ $f(1)$ $f(2)$ $f(3)$ $f(4)$ $f(5)$ $f(6)$ $f(7)$ $f(8)$ $\cdots$

The computation chain should remind you of leaping induction (see page 74), and its no surprise that the recursion does not work for all n. The fix is no surprise. We need one more base case, namely $f(1)$. The formal proof that the recursive function is well-defined after adding this base case is left as an exercise.

Exercise 7.4
After adding the base case $f(1) = 2$, we obtain the recursive function as shown.

$$f(n) = \begin{cases} 1 & n = 0; \\ 2 & n = 1; \\ f(n-2) + 2 & n > 1. \end{cases}$$

Prove that $f(n)$ is well defined for integer $n \geq 0$.
To do so, define your induction claim $P(n)$ as:

$P(n)$: "$f(n)$ can be computed."

Prove by leaping induction that $P(n)$ is true for all $n \geq 0$.

We listed many types of induction in the previous chapter, on page 79. Recursion is similar. There are many different types of recursion, and they are valid whenever the corresponding induction is valid. Drawing the implication arrows with the base cases will help you determine whether you can compute $f(n)$ for every n.

A recursive function must be well defined and compute what you want. Let's go back to the recursion $f(n) = f(n-1) + 2n - 1$ for $n > 0$ and $f(n) = 0$ otherwise. Tinkering shows,

n	0	1	2	3	4	5	6	7	8	$\cdots$
$f(n)$	0	1	4	9	16	25	36	49	64	$\cdots$

A good guess is $f(n) = n^2$. To derive this formula, we "unfold the recursion," which usually means manually implement the recursion and see if quantities cancel and/or simplify into a simple form.

To Unfold a Recursion

1: Obtain $f(n)$ from $f(n-1)$ using the recursion.
2: Stack below this the expression for $f(n-1)$, which needs $f(n-2)$.
3: To get $f(n-2)$, we need $f(n-3)$ (third equation stacked below second one). Continue in this way until you hit the base case.
4: Equate the sum of LHS terms to the sum of RHS terms.
5: Here, every term except $f(n)$ on the LHS cancels with a term on the RHS. The remaining terms on the RHS are the odd numbers.

Hence, $f(n)$ is the sum of the first n odd numbers, which equals n^2.

$$\begin{array}{rcll} f(n) &=& \cancel{f(n-1)} &+\ 2n-1 \\ \cancel{f(n-1)} &=& \cancel{f(n-2)} &+\ 2n-3 \\ \cancel{f(n-2)} &=& \cancel{f(n-3)} &+\ 2n-5 \\ &\vdots& & \\ \cancel{f(3)} &=& \cancel{f(2)} &+\ 5 \\ \cancel{f(2)} &=& \cancel{f(1)} &+\ 3 \\ \cancel{f(1)} &=& \cancel{f(0)}^{\,0} &+\ 1 \\ \hline + \quad f(n) &=& 1+3+\cdots+2n-1 & \end{array}$$

Unfolding the recursion gives an informal derivation of the formula $f(n) = n^2$, a principled guess. To be sure, we must prove that $f(n) = n^2$. The proof uses induction, which is typical of recursion proofs.

Proof. Our claim is $P(n) : f(n) = n^2$. We prove $P(n)$ for $n \geq 0$ by induction.

1: **[Base case]** $P(0)$ claims $f(0) = 0^2$ which is clearly true.
2: **[Induction step]** We prove $P(n) \to P(n+1)$ for $n \geq 0$ using direct proof.
Assume $P(n)$: $f(n) = n^2$.
Prove $P(n+1)$: $f(n+1) = (n+1)^2$.

$$\begin{array}{rcll} f(n+1) &=& f(n) + 2(n+1) - 1 & \text{(by the recursion)} \\ &=& n^2 + 2n + 1 & \text{(induction hypothesis: } f(n) = n^2) \\ &=& (n+1)^2 & (\therefore\ P(n+1) \text{ is true}) \end{array}$$

3: By induction, $P(n)$ is true for all $n \geq 0$. ■

Slightly different recursive functions can yield drastically different results, and this is why recursion is dangerous. Make sure you always prove, using induction, that your recursive function computes the right thing.

Exercise 7.5
These three recursive function appear only slightly different. In each case, tinker to guess the function $f(n)$, and prove your guess by induction.

(a) $f(0) = 0$; $f(n) = 2 + f(n-1)$ for integer $n > 0$.
(b) $f(0) = 0$; $f(n) = 2 \times f(n-1)$ for integer $n > 0$.
(c) $f(0) = 1$; $f(n) = 2 \times f(n-1)$ for integer $n > 0$.

Example 7.1. Let's analyze a complicated recursive function to build some muscle.

$$f(n) = \begin{cases} 1 & n = 1; \\ f(n/2) + 1 & n > 1, \text{ even}; \\ f(n+1) & n > 1, \text{ odd}; \end{cases}$$

(This recursion looks esoteric, but it's not. An algorithm may halve a problem, if it is even, or pad it by one and then halve it. For example binary search)

You should be suspicious. One recursive case needs $f(n+1)$ which is further from the base case $n = 1$. However, the next step halves $n+1$, drastically reducing n and getting it closer to the base case. Let's tinker.

n	1	2	3	4	5	6	7	8	9	10	11	12	13	14	15	16	$\cdots$
$f(n)$	1	2	3	3	4	4	4	4	5	5	5	5	5	5	5	5	$\cdots$

The arrows show how $f(n)$ is obtained, for example, $f(6) \leftarrow f(3) \leftarrow f(4) \leftarrow f(2) \leftarrow f(1)$. There is a path to every n from the base case $n = 1$, as required in a good recursion. The pattern in red, suggests that

$$f(n) = 1 + \lceil \log_2 n \rceil,$$

where $\lceil x \rceil$, the ceiling of x, is x rounded up. We use strong induction to prove that $f(n) = 1 + \lceil \log_2 n \rceil$.

Proof. (By strong induction.) Define the claim $P(n) : f(n) = 1 + \lceil \log_2 n \rceil$.

1: **[Base case]** $P(1)$ is true because and $\log_2 1 = 0$, so $1 + \lceil \log_2 1 \rceil = 1$.

2: **[Induction step]** We prove $P(1) \wedge \cdots \wedge P(n) \rightarrow P(n+1)$ for $n \geq 1$ using direct proof.
Assume $P(1) \wedge P(2) \wedge \cdots \wedge P(n)$: $f(k) = 1 + \lceil \log_2 k \rceil$ for $1 \leq k \leq n$.
Show $P(n+1)$: $f(n+1) = 1 + \lceil \log_2(n+1) \rceil$.
The recursion replaces $f(n+1)$ with $1 + f((n+1)/2)$ if $n+1$ is even or $f(n+2)$ otherwise. The strong induction hypothesis gives f for these smaller inputs (ordinary induction wouldn't work).

(i) <u>$n+1$ is even</u>, in which case

$$\begin{aligned} f(n+1) &= 1 + f(\tfrac{n+1}{2}) \\ &= 1 + 1 + \lceil \log_2(\tfrac{n+1}{2}) \rceil && \text{(by the strong induction hypothesis)} \\ &= 1 + 1 + \lceil \log_2(n+1) - 1 \rceil && \text{(because } \log_2(x/2) = \log_2 x - 1) \\ &= 1 + 1 + \lceil \log_2(n+1) \rceil - 1. && \text{(because } \lceil x - 1 \rceil = \lceil x \rceil - 1) \end{aligned}$$

The last expression is $1 + \lceil \log_2(n+1) \rceil$, as was required to be shown.

(ii) <u>$n+1$ is odd</u>, in which case $n+1 \geq 3$ (or, $n \geq 2$), and

$$f(n+1) = f(n+2) = 1 + f(\tfrac{n+2}{2}).$$

Since $n \geq 2$, $\frac{n+2}{2} \leq \frac{n+n}{2} = n$, so $P(\frac{n+2}{2})$ is true by the strong induction hypothesis.

$$\begin{aligned} f(\tfrac{n+2}{2}) &= 1 + \lceil \log_2(\tfrac{n+2}{2}) \rceil \\ &= 1 + \lceil \log_2(n+2) - 1 \rceil \\ &= \lceil \log_2(n+2) \rceil. \end{aligned}$$

Therefore, $f(n+1) = 1 + \lceil \log_2(n+2) \rceil$. If $\lceil \log_2(n+2) \rceil = \lceil \log_2(n+1) \rceil$, we're done. We state this fact as a lemma, which you may prove in Problem 7.31.

Lemma 7.2. If $n+1 \geq 3$ is odd, then $\lceil \log_2(n+1) \rceil = \lceil \log_2(n+2) \rceil$.

In both cases, $f(n+1) = 1 + \lceil \log_2(n+1) \rceil$, and so $P(n+1)$ is true.

3: By induction, $P(n)$ is true for all $n \geq 1$. ■

That was challenging, but it made us stronger. Observe that its perfectly okay to break the induction step into cases and use lemmas to reduce clutter. □

Exercise 7.6

In each case, tinker and unfold the recursion to guess $f(n)$. Prove your guess by induction.

(a) $f(1) = 0$; $f(n) = f(n-1) + \log_2 n$ for $n > 1$.
(b) $f(1) = 1$; $f(n) = 2f(n-1)$ for $n > 1$.
(c) $f(0) = 1$; $f(n) = nf(n-1)$ for $n > 0$.
(d) $f(1) = 2$; $f(n) = f(n-1)^2$ for $n > 1$.

7.1.1 Recurrences

A recurrence is a recursive function on $\mathbb{N}$. We denote $f(n)$ using a more compact notation like A_n. The recursion in Exercise 7.6(a) using this more compact notation is:

$$A_1 = 0; \quad A_n = A_{n-1} + \log_2 n \quad \text{for } n > 1.$$

Example 7.3 (Fibonacci Sequence)**.** In 1202, Leonardo Bonacci in *Liber Abaci* (Book of Calculation) introduced Fibonacci Numbers as an unrealistic model for rabbit birth rates. The Fibonacci recurrence is:

$$F_1 = 1; \; F_2 = 1; \qquad F_n = F_{n-1} + F_{n-2} \quad \text{for } n > 2.$$

Using the recurrence, we obtain the Fibonacci sequence, where each term is the sum of the previous two terms,

F_1	F_2	F_3	F_4	F_5	F_6	F_7	F_8	F_9	F_{10}	F_{11}	F_{12}	$\cdots$
1	1	2	3	5	8	13	21	34	55	89	144	$\cdots$

This recurrence appeared much earlier in Indian mathematics in conjunction with Sanskrit poetry. A long syllable L has duration 2 time units and a short syllable S has duration 1 time unit. The task was to determine the number of different patterns of long and short syllables that could constitute a duration of n time units. For example, consider a duration $n = 4$ time units. Here are the 5 possibilities:

$$LL \qquad LSS \qquad SLS \qquad SSL \qquad SSSS$$

Let T_n be the number of patterns of duration n. Tinker. List the patterns for $n \leq 6$ and verify the data below.

duration n time units	1	2	3	4	5	6	$\cdots$
# of possible patterns T_n	1	2	3	5	8	13	$\cdots$

It appears that $T_n = F_{n+1}$. To see why, consider the patterns for n time units. A pattern either starts with an S and has $n-1$ time units remaining, or it starts with an L and has $n-2$ time units remaining. Since there are T_{n-1} patterns of duration $n-1$ and T_{n-2} patterns of duration $n-2$, we have:

duration n time units	number of possibilities
S + any pattern of duration $n-1$	T_{n-1}
L + any pattern of duration $n-2$	T_{n-2}

The number of patterns of duration n is the sum of those starting with S and those starting with L. That is,

$$T_n = T_{n-1} + T_{n-2}.$$

We recovered the Fibonacci recurrence, except that the base cases are $T_1 = 1$ and $T_2 = 2$.

Exercise 7.7

Prove by induction that $T_n = F_{n+1}$. *[Hint: Use the claim $P(n) : T_n = F_{n+1}$ AND $T_{n+1} = F_{n+2}$.]*

As with meter in Sanskrit poetry, the Fibonacci recurrence emerges unexpectedly in areas ranging from computer science (Euclid's GCD algorithm, Fibonacci heaps) to biology (branching in trees, arrangement of leaves on stems, family trees of bees, ...) to economics, etc. As a result, the Fibonacci numbers are well studied. We ask the simplest question, how quickly do they grow? Proving things about a recurrence involves induction, and to illustrate, let us show that the Fibonacci numbers grow exponentially by proving

$$F_n \geq (3/2)^n, \qquad \text{for } n \geq 11.$$

$F_{11} = 89 \geq (3/2)^{11} \approx 86.5$ and $F_{12} = 144 \geq (3/2)^{12} \approx 129.7$, so these two base cases are true. We use strong induction. For the induction step, assume the claim holds for $11 \wedge 12 \wedge 13 \wedge \cdots \wedge n$, where $n \geq 12$ (strong induction). We show $F_{n+1} \geq (3/2)^{n+1}$. The recurrence relates F_{n+1} to F_n and F_{n-1}:

$$F_{n+1} = F_n + F_{n-1} \overset{(a)}{\geq} \left(\frac{3}{2}\right)^n + \left(\frac{3}{2}\right)^{n-1} = \left(\frac{3}{2}\right)^{n-1}\left(\frac{3}{2}+1\right) = \left(\frac{3}{2}\right)^{n-1} \cdot \frac{5}{2}$$

In (a) we used the induction hypothesis (recall $n-1 \geq 11$). Since $5/2 > (3/2)^2$, $F_{n+1} \geq (3/2)^{n+1}$, as required. By induction, $F_n \geq (3/2)^n$ for all $n \geq 11$ and so F_n grows at least exponentially with base $3/2$.

Exercise 7.8
Show by induction that $F_n \leq 2^n$ for $n \geq 1$.

To conclude, $(3/2)^n \leq F_n \leq 2^n$ for $n \geq 11$. These are crude bounds. In fact $F_n \approx \varphi^n/\sqrt{5}$ where the so-called golden ratio $\varphi = (1+\sqrt{5})/2 \approx 1.618$. That is, F_n grows exponentially with base ≈ 1.618. □

7.1.2 Recursive Programs

We show a pseudocode for a recursive function `Big(n)`, for integer $n \geq 0$. Two important questions face the programmer who creates such a function. Does the program compute correctly? Does the program run quickly? To prove correctness, use induction. To analyze runtime, one usually solves a recurrence.

```
out=Big(n)
  if(n==0) out=1;
  else out=2*Big(n-1);
```

Exercise 7.9
First tinker. Then, prove by induction that the output of `Big(n)` is 2^n.

How do you analyze the runtime of `Big(n)`? As usual, start by tinkering. Let's walk through `Big(0)`. First test if $n = 0$; it is, and so you output 1. That is 2 operations, or two time steps. We assume every operation takes one unit of time, a simple model of computation. Let's consider `Big(1)`. Again, test if $n = 0$; it is not. Now compute `2*Big(0)`, which is 1 multiplication plus two operations to compute `Big(0)` (we just analyzed this). Your final operation is to output the result, 5 operations in all, taking 5 time steps. Brimming with confidence, we now attack `Big(n)`. One operation to test if $n = 0$; but here we hit a snag. How long does it take to compute `2*Big(n-1)`? Certainly there is 1 multiplication, but we don't know how long it takes for `Big(n-1)`. If only we knew the time to compute `Big(n-1)`, then the time to compute `Big(n)` is just 3 time units more for the test that $n \neq 0$, the multiplication by 2 and the assignment to output. Let T_n be the number of time steps needed to compute `Big(n)`. We have a recurrence for T_n:

$$T_0 = 2; \quad T_n = T_{n-1} + 3.$$

Exercise 7.10
First tinker. Then, prove by induction that $T_n = 3n + 2$.

Checklist for Analyzing a Recursion or Recurrence.

- ✓ Tinker. Draw the implication arrows. Is the function/recurrence well defined?
- ✓ Tinker. Compute $f(n)$ for small values of n.
- ✓ Make a guess for $f(n)$. "Unfolding" the recursion can be helpful here.
- ✓ Prove your conjecture for $f(n)$ by induction.
  - The type of induction to use will often be related to the type of recursion.
  - In the induction step, use the recursion to relate the claim for $n+1$ to lower values.

7.2 Recursive Sets

We now have the infrastructure of recursion, and can finally give a formal definition of the natural numbers

$$\mathbb{N} = \{1, 2, 3, 4, 5, 6, \ldots\}.$$

Pay careful attention to all three parts of the definition.

Recursive definition of the natural numbers $\mathbb{N}$.

① $1 \in \mathbb{N}$. **[basis]**
② $x \in \mathbb{N} \to x + 1 \in \mathbb{N}$. **[constructor]**
③ Nothing else is in $\mathbb{N}$. **[minimality]**

All three parts to the definition are important, but we often leave out minimality which is always there by default.[1] The basis, as with any recursive definition, establishes that some elements are in the set. The constructor rule gives new elements from known elements in the set. The basis gives us that $1 \in \mathbb{N}$. Applying the constructor rule to $x = 1$ gives us that $2 \in \mathbb{N}$. Applying the constructor rule to $x = 2$ gives us that $3 \in \mathbb{N}$. Thus, $\mathbb{N}$ contains $\{1, 2, 3, 4, 5, \ldots\}$. The reason $\mathbb{N}$ equals $\{1, 2, 3, 4, 5, \ldots\}$ is because nothing else is in $\mathbb{N}$. The minimality clause effectively asserts that $\mathbb{N}$ is the smallest set satisfying ① and ②.

Pop Quiz 7.11

To appreciate why we need part ③ in the recursive definition of $\mathbb{N}$, which of the following sets would satisfy just parts ① and ② in the recursive definition?

(a) $\mathbb{R}$. (b) $\mathbb{Q}$. (c) $\{1, \frac{3}{2}, 2, 3, 4, \ldots\}$. (d) $\{1, \frac{3}{2}, 2, \frac{5}{2}, 3, \frac{7}{2}, \ldots\}$. (e) $\{2, 3, 4, \ldots\}$.

A recursively defined set can contain strings. The set of finite binary strings Σ^* has a recursive definition. The base case is the empty string ε which, like the empty set, is the string containing nothing.

Recursive definition of Σ^*, the finite binary strings.

① $\varepsilon \in \Sigma^*$. **[basis]**
② $x \in \Sigma^* \to x\bullet 0 \in \Sigma^*$ AND $x\bullet 1 \in \Sigma^*$. **[constructor]**

Remember, by minimality, nothing else is in Σ^* (the default). The notation $x\bullet 0$ means concatenation of the string x and 0. So, if $x = 10$ then $x\bullet 0 = 100$ and $x\bullet 1 = 101$. Note, for general x, $x\bullet 0 \neq 0\bullet x$. Let us apply the constructor rule to "derive" the strings in Σ^*.

$$\varepsilon \to 0, 1 \to 00, 01, 10, 11 \to 000, 001, 010, 011, 100, 101, 110, 111 \to \cdots.$$

As you can see, we are listing all the binary strings in a systematic, lexicographic order, at each step appending 0 and 1 to the previous strings.

$$\Sigma^* = \{\varepsilon, 0, 1, 00, 01, 10, 11, 000, 001, 010, 011, 100, 101, 110, 111, \ldots\}$$

Exercise 7.12

Give recursive definitions for the set $\mathcal{S}$ in each of the following cases.

(a) $\mathcal{S} = \{3^0, 3^1, 3^2, 3^3, 3^4, \ldots\}$, the powers of 3.
(b) $\mathcal{S} =$ {all strings which are palindromes}, e.g. 010, 110011, 000 are palindromes but 011 is not.
(c) $\mathcal{S} =$ {all strings of matched parentheses}, matched in the usual arithmetic sense. For example [[][]] and [][] are matched but][and []][are not matched.

[1] In other books, you might see minimality referred to as the "extremal clause"

7.3 Recursive Structures – Trees

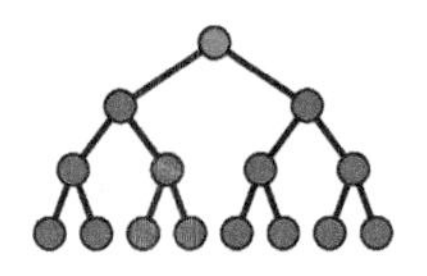

A tree is a special graph (an example is on the right). From the picture, you see that a tree might be a good representation of the hierarchical relationships at a company, with the CEO on top, or of your family ancestry with you on top. The circles are vertices and the links are relationships. The top-vertex colored red is called the root. The mathematician Arthur Cayley invented trees to model the organic hydrocarbons C_nH_{2n+2}:

methane, CH_4	ethane, C_2H_6	propane, C_3H_8	butane, C_4H_{10}	iso-butane, C_4H_{10}

```
    H              H H             H H H            H H H H            H     H     H
  H-C-H          H-C-C-H         H-C-C-C-H        H-C-C-C-C-H        H-C-----C-----C-H
    H              H H             H H H            H H H H            H   H-C-H   H
                                                                             H
```

Cayley discovered that the carbon backbone of butane, C_4H_{10}, could be one of two different trees, which explained why experiments showed two types of butane with different properties (propane, ethane and methane have only one form). Trees are important in computer science and have many uses: search trees (e.g. efficient access to data); game trees (e.g. strategic games); decision trees (e.g. machine learning); compression trees (file compression, e.g. Huffman codes); multi-processor trees (e.g. distributed computing); parse trees (e.g. compilers); expression trees (e.g. computer arithmetic). The list goes on.

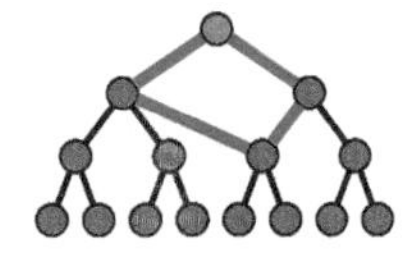

The graph on the right is not a tree. If you remove any blue edge, it becomes a tree. The properties a tree must have are not obvious. We focus on rooted binary trees (RBTs) which have a compact recursive definition that gives a prescription for constructing all RBTs. In our drawings, the root will usually be highlighted in red.

Recursive definition of Rooted Binary Trees (RBT).

① The empty tree ε is an RBT.

② If T_1, T_2 are disjoint RBTs with roots r_1 and r_2, then linking r_1 and r_2 to a new root r gives a new RBT with root r.

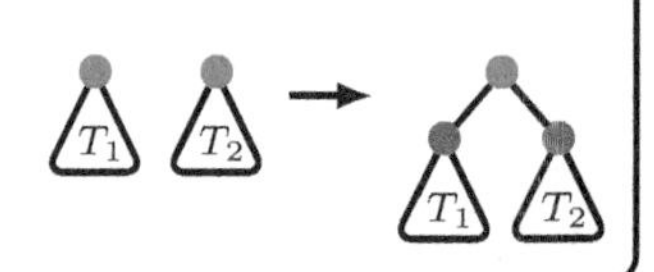

Nothing else is an RBT. We call T_1 and T_2 the child subtrees of the new root. If T_1 and T_2 are empty, you get just a root (no links). We distinguish between the left and right "child", so order matters and our trees are "ordered" RBTs. When T_1 and T_2 are different, the constructor can produce two different trees:

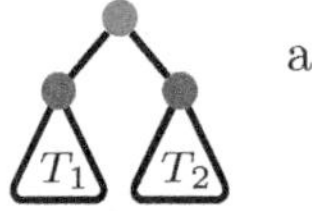

and

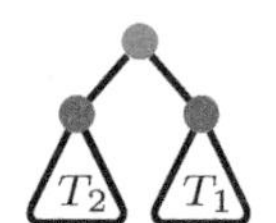

Let's use the recursive definition to generate RBTs. Starting with the base case and systematically using the constructor rule gives trees in order of increasing height. One tree has height 0, just a root. Three trees have height 1 obtained from the ordered pairs of lower height trees. Twenty-one trees have height 2, and so on.

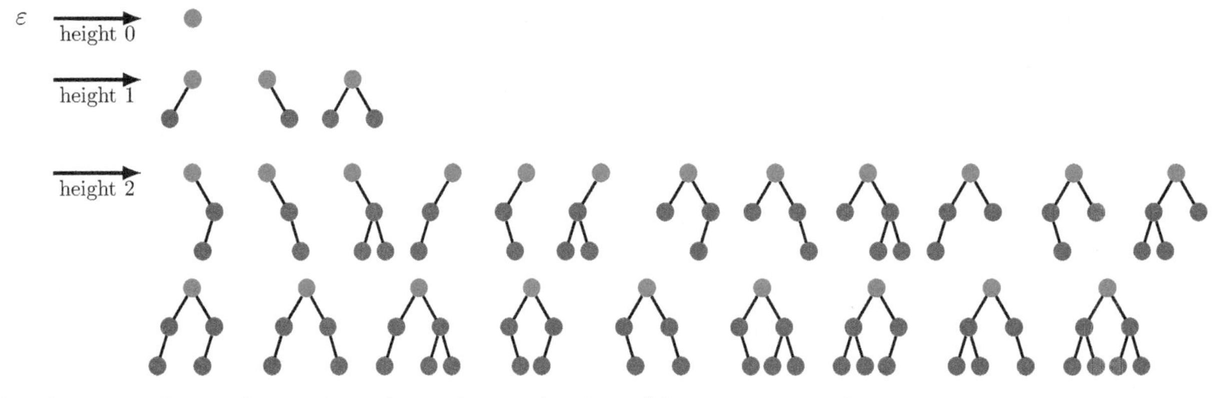

See if you can derive the number of trees having height 3 (the answer is 651).

To show that a graph G is an RBT, you must give a derivation of G which starts from a base case and continues to apply the constructor rule until you obtain G. Here is a derivation of one of the height-2 trees

$\varepsilon \xrightarrow[T_2=\varepsilon]{T_1=\varepsilon} \bullet \xrightarrow[T_2=\varepsilon]{T_1=\bullet} \cdots \xrightarrow[T_2=\bullet]{T_1=\bullet} \cdots \xrightarrow[T_2=\ \cdots]{T_1=\ \cdots} \cdots$

In each step, we apply the constructor and generate a new tree. At each step, we showed the trees T_1 and T_2 which are input to the constructor. The trees which are inputs to the constructor must already have appeared in the derivation, because the constructor rule can only be used if T_1 and T_2 are valid trees.

Pop Quiz 7.13
Give a derivation of the tree at the top of page 92, which proves it is an RBT.

Here are several questions we can't answer yet, but you can think about them.

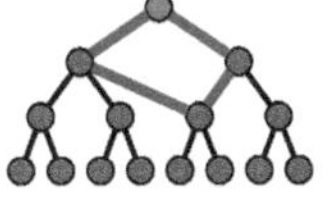

1. How do we show that the second graph on page 92, reproduced here, is not an RBT? It seems one has to show than no derivation could end in that tree. But how do we check every possible derivation? This seems a daunting task, if not impossible.
2. Is there only one way to derive an RBT, by deriving the children subtrees of the root and then applying the constructor to join these children to a new root?
3. Trees have many interesting properties, which we state here without proof. Any one of these equivalent properties could serve as an alternate definition of a general tree (more general than an RBT).
   - A tree is a connected graph with n nodes and $n-1$ edges.
   - A tree is a connected graph with no cycles.
   - A tree is a graph in which any two nodes are connected by exactly one path.

   Can we be sure every RBT has these properties? How would we prove it?
   Is any graph with these properties an RBT? If yes, how do we prove it? If no, how do we prove it?

Exercise 7.14 [Rooted Full Binary Trees (RFBT) – new base case]
① A single root-node ● is an RFBT.
② If T_1, T_2 are disjoint RFBTs with roots r_1 and r_2, then linking r_1 and r_2 to a a new root r gives a new RFBT with root r.
(a) Is every RFBT an RBT? Give an RBT that is not an RFBT.
(b) Give RFBTs with 5 and 6 vertices, together with derivations.

Epilogue on Solving Recurrences. Recursion is an important algorithm design tool and recursive sets are the "root" ☺ of useful structures in computer science. To apply recursion, the key step in developing the algorithm is to reduce a hard problem to simpler cases, e.g. from input-size $n+1$ to sizes n or smaller. This key step can involve creativity, and you will get lots of practice in a follow on algorithms course. Analysis of such algorithms, for example determining runtime, reduces to solving a recurrence. Proving that some formula solves a recurrence is by induction, once you have the formula. But how do you get that formula? Finding a formula that solves a recurrence can involve guesswork and you get better at it with practice. You learn to recognize the patterns. The chapter problems are an opportunity for lots of practice.

- For standard types of recurrences, one can reduce the guesswork to a "science". Linear recurrences arise often in practice and we highly recommend Problems 7.22–7.26. The Akra-Bazzi formula is also a useful general tool, see Problem 7.27.
- There are systematic tools for analyzing recurrences that do not involve guesswork, e.g. generating functions, Problems 8.41–8.44.

7.4 Problems

Problem 7.1. $f(n) = f(n-1)+1$ for $n \geq 1$ and $f(n) = 0$ otherwise. Some would say this is a "circular" definition because we use f to define f. Explain why it is not circular.

Problem 7.2. Define $f(n)$ for $n \in \mathbb{N}$ by $f(1) = 1$, $f(n) = f(n/2)$ for $n > 1$ even, and $f(n) = f(5n-9)$ for $n > 1$ odd. Is f a well defined function? Explain your answer.

Problem 7.3. Give a recursive definition of the function $f(n) = n! \times 2^n$, where $n \geq 1$.

Problem 7.4. Guess a formula for A_n and prove it by induction.
(a) $A_0 = 0$ and $A_n = A_{n-1} + 1$ for $n \geq 1$.
(b) $A_1 = 1, A_2 = 2$ and $A_n = A_{n-1} + 2A_{n-2}$ for $n \geq 2$.
(c) $A_0 = 1$; $A_1 = 2$; $A_n = 2A_{n-1} - A_{n-2} + 2$ for $n \geq 2$. *[Hint: Method of differences.]*
(d) $A_0 = 1$; $A_n = \alpha A_{n-1} + 1$ for $n \geq 2$

Problem 7.5. For each recurrence, (i) Write a program and compute T_{20}. (ii) Tinker. "Unfold" the recurrence and obtain a formula for T_n. Verify T_{20}. (iii) Prove your formula by induction.
(a) $T_0 = 2$ and $T_n = T_{n-1} + 3n$ for $n \geq 1$.
(b) $T_0 = 3$ and $T_n = 2T_{n-1}$ for $n \geq 1$.
(c) $T_0 = 3$ and $T_n = 2T_{n-1} + n$ for $n \geq 1$.
(d) $T_0 = 0$ and $T_n = 4 - T_{n-1}$ for $n \geq 1$.

Problem 7.6. Define $f(n)$ for $n \in \mathbb{N}$ by $f(1) = 0$ and $f(n) = f(\lfloor n/2 \rfloor) + f(\lceil n/2 \rceil) + 1$ for $n > 1$. ($\lceil \cdot \rceil$ and $\lfloor \cdot \rfloor$ round up and down.) (a) Is f a well defined function? Explain. (b) Tinker, guess a formula for $f(n)$ and prove it.

Problem 7.7. Define $f(n)$ for $n \in \mathbb{N}$ by $f(1) = 1$, $f(n) = f(n/2) + 1$ for $n > 1$ even, and $f(n) = f(3n+1)$ for $n > 1$ odd. (a) Compute $f(3), f(5), f(6)$. (b) Is f defined for all $n \in \mathbb{N}$? (See the Collatz conjecture, Problem 1.43.)

Problem 7.8. Give a recurrence for A_n ($n \in \mathbb{N}$), and prove A_n solves the recurrence. Don't forget base cases.
(a) $A_n = 3 \cdot 2^n$.
(b) $A_n = 3^n - 2$.
(c) $A_n = 2 \cdot 3^n - 1$.
(d) $A_n = 2^{2n}$.
(e) $A_n = (n!)^2$.
(f) $A_n = n^3$.
(g) $A_n = n + (-1)^n$.
(h) $A_n = 2^{n^2}$.

Problem 7.9. $G_0 = 0, G_1 = 1$ and $G_n = 7G_{n-1} - 12G_{n-2}$ for $n > 1$. Compute G_5. Show $G_n = 4^n - 3^n$ for $n \geq 0$.

Problem 7.10. $A_1 = 1, A_2 = 2, A_3 = 3$ and $A_n = A_{n-1} + A_{n-2} + A_{n-3}$, for $n > 3$. Prove that $\frac{1}{2}(\frac{9}{5})^n < A_n < 2^n$.

Problem 7.11. In each case tinker. Then, guess a formula that solves the recurrence, and prove it.
(a) $P_0 = 0, P_1 = a$ and $P_n = 2P_{n-1} - P_{n-2}$, for $n > 1$.
(b) $G_1 = 1$; $G_n = (1 - 1/n) \cdot G_{n-1}$, for $n > 1$.

Problem 7.12. In each case $A_1 = 1$. Tinker. Then, guess and prove a formula that solves the recurrence.
(a) $A_n = 10A_{n-1} + 1$ for $n > 1$.
(b) $A_n = \dfrac{n}{n-1}A_{n-1} + n$ for $n > 1$.
(c) $A_n = \dfrac{10n}{n-1}A_{n-1} + n$ for $n > 1$.

Problem 7.13. Analyze these very fast growing recursions. *[Hint: Take logarithms.]*
(a) $M_1 = 2$ and $M_n = aM_{n-1}^2$ for $n > 1$. Guess and prove a formula for M_n. Tinker, tinker.
(b) $L_1 = 2, L_2 = 2$ and $L_n = L_{n-1}L_{n-2}$ for $n > 2$. Prove bounds of the form $2^{a^n} \leq L_n \leq 2^{b^n}$. Tinker, tinker.

Problem 7.14. You have wealth $W_0 = \$100$ in the bank. At the end of every year, the bank gives you 5% interest and you add an extra \$100 in savings. Let W_n be your wealth at year n.
(a) Give a recursion for your wealth in the form $W_n = (?)W_{n-1} + (?)$. Compute W_{10}, W_{20}, W_{30}.
(b) Unfold your recursion to guess a formula for W_n and prove it by induction.

Problem 7.15 (Mortgage Calculator). In a mortgage, you borrow a principal P. At the end of every month you pay X, your monthly mortgage payment. Unfortunately, your debt increases by the monthly interest rate r (for example, if $r = 0.5\%$ then your debt increases by a factor 1.005). Let P_n be your debt after the nth monthly payment.
(a) Show that $P_0 = P$ and $P_n = (1+r)P_{n-1} - X$ for $n \geq 1$. Unfold the recursion, make a guess for P_n and prove it.
(b) Show that the monthly payment $X = rP/(1-(1+r)^{-N})$ will payoff your mortgage after N payments.
(c) A 15-year mortgage has 180 monthly payments. For a loan with principal $P = \$300,000$ and monthly interest $r = 0.5\%$ (6% annual interest rate), compute the monthly payment X.

Problem 7.16. Let $x_1 = 1$ and $x_{n+1} = \sqrt{1 + 2x_n}$ for $n \geq 1$. Prove, for $n \geq 1$, that $x_n < 4$.

Problem 7.17. Define $f(x) = 0$ for $x \leq 0$ and $f(x) = f(x-1) + 2x - 1$ for $x > 0$. Prove $f(x) = \lceil x \rceil(2x - \lceil x \rceil)$, for $x \geq 0$. (The ceiling, $\lceil x \rceil$, is x rounded up.) *[Hint: Let $0 < \alpha \leq 1$. Prove $f(n+\alpha) = n^2 + 2n\alpha + 2\alpha - 1$ for $n \geq 0$.]*

Problem 7.18. Define $f_0(x) = 0$, $f_1(x) = x$ and, for $n \geq 2$, $f_n(x) = xf_{n-1}(x) + (1-x)f_{n-2}(x)$. Note that $f_n(x)$ is a polynomial in x. Prove that $f_n(x) = x((x-1)^n - 1)/(x-2)$.

Problem 7.19. Recall the Fibonacci numbers: $F_1, F_2 = 1$; and, $F_n = F_{n-1} + F_{n-2}$ for $n > 2$.
(a) Compute $F_1, \ldots, F_{10}$ and verify that $F_n < (7/4)^{n-1}$, for $n \geq 1$. Now prove the bound for all $n \geq 1$.
(b) Let $\phi_\pm = (1 \pm \sqrt{5})/2$. Prove that $F_n = (\phi_+^n - \phi_-^n)/\sqrt{5}$ for $n \geq 1$.
(c) $F_{n-1}F_{n+1} - F_n^2 = (-1)^n$, for $n \geq 2$.
(d) Prove that every third Fibonacci number, F_{3n}, is even.
(e) (Sum) Prove: $F_1 + F_2 + F_3 + \cdots + F_n = F_{n+2} - 1$, for $n \geq 1$.
(f) (Sum of odd terms) Prove: $F_1 + F_3 + F_5 + \cdots + F_{2n-1} = F_{2n}$, for $n \geq 1$.
(g) (Sum of even terms) Prove: $F_2 + F_4 + F_6 + \cdots + F_{2n} = F_{2n+1} - 1$, for $n \geq 1$.
(h) (Alternating sum) Prove: $F_1 - F_2 + \cdots + (-1)^n F_{n+1} = (-1)^n F_n + 1$, for $n \geq 1$.
(i) (Linear weighted sum) Prove: $F_1 + 2F_2 + 3F_3 + \cdots + nF_n = nF_{n+2} - F_{n+3} + 2$, for $n \geq 1$.
(j) (Consecutive products) Prove: $F_1F_2 + F_2F_3 + \cdots + F_{2n-1}F_{2n} = F_{2n}^2$, for $n \geq 1$.
(k) Prove that F_n and F_{n+1} have no common factor other than 1, for $n \geq 1$.
(l) Prove that F_{2n} is divisible by F_n, for $n \geq 1$, and more generally that F_{kn} is divisible by F_n, for $n, k \geq 1$.
(m) Prove that $\gcd(F_m, F_n) = F_{\gcd(m,n)}$.
(n) Prove $F_n^2 + F_{n+1}^2 = F_{2n+1}$. *[Hint: You will need to prove a stronger claim, see part (q).]*
(o) Prove $F_{m+n+1} = F_mF_n + F_{m+1}F_{n+1}$ for $m, n \geq 1$

Problem 7.20. Let $U_n = F_{2n}/F_n$ (F_n are Fibonacci numbers). Tinker. Compute $U_1, \ldots, U_5$. Do you see a pattern?
(a) Prove that $U_n = F_{n-1} + F_{n+1}$. Hence, prove that F_n divides F_{2n}. *[Hint: Problem 7.19(o).]*
(b) Prove that U_n satisfies the Fibonacci recursion and compute a formula for U_n

Problem 7.21. Show that every $n \geq 1$ is a sum of distinct Fibonacci numbers, e.g. $11 = F_4 + F_6$; $20 = F_3 + F_5 + F_7$. (There can be many ways to do it, e.g. $6 = F_1 + F_5 = F_2 + F_3 + F_4$.) *[Hints: Greedy algorithm; strong induction.]*

Problem 7.22. A linear kth order recurrence is: $T_n = a_0 + a_1T_{n-1} + a_2T_{n-2} + \cdots + a_kT_{n-k}$, for $n > k$ (T_n uses k previous terms). Given base cases $T_1, \ldots, T_k$, prove that T_n is uniquely defined for $n \geq 1$. (Induction or well-ordering.)

Problem 7.23. Suppose $T_n = a + br^n$ is an exponential sequence.
(a) Show that $T_{n+2} = (r+1)T_{n+1} - rT_n$.
(b) Find a formula for T_n where $T_0 = 1, T_1 = 2$ and $T_{n+2} = 4T_{n+1} - 3T_n$. *[Hint: Use T_0, T_1 to find a, b.]*
(c) Are there any other possible formulas for T_n in (b)? *[Hint: Problem 7.22.]*

Problem 7.24. Suppose, $r \neq s$ and $T_n = ar^n + bs^n$ is a sum of exponential sequences.
(a) Show that $T_{n+2} = (r+s)T_{n+1} - rsT_n$.
(b) Find a formula for T_n where $T_0 = 1, T_1 = 2$ and $T_{n+2} = 3T_{n+1} - 2T_n$. *[Hint: Use T_0, T_1 to find a, b.]*
(c) Find a formula for T_n where $T_0 = 1, T_1 = 2$ and $T_{n+2} = T_{n+1} + 6T_n$.
(d) Are there any other possible formulas for T_n in (b) and (c)? *[Hint: Problem 7.22.]*

Problem 7.25. Suppose, $T_n = (a + bn)r^n$ is a product of a polynomial with an exponential.
(a) Show that $T_{n+2} = 2rT_{n+1} - r^2T_n$. (This is the case $r = s$ in Problem 7.24(a).)
(b) Find a formula for T_n where $T_0 = 1, T_1 = 4$ and $T_{n+2} = 4T_{n+1} - 4T_n$. *[Hint: Use T_0, T_1 to find a, b.]*
(c) Are there any other possible formulas for T_n in (b)? *[Hint: Problem 7.22.]*

Problems 7.24–7.25 give a complete prescription for solving a 2nd-order linear recurrence. (Note that Problem 7.23 is a special case of Problem 7.24 with $s = 1$.) This "dictionary" approach can be extended to kth-order linear recurrences.

Problem 7.26. The dictionary method in Problems 7.22–7.25 may appear out of the blue. Here is a more systematic approach to the 2nd-order linear recurrence. Suppose $T_n = a_1T_{n-1} + a_2T_{n-2}$, with T_0, T_1 given and $a_1, a_2 \neq 0$. We guess a solution of the form $T_n = (\alpha + \beta n)\phi^n$ for constants α, β, ϕ. Your task is to determine α, β, ϕ from a_1, a_2, T_0, T_1.
(a) If $T_0 = T_1 = 0$, what is the solution? From now, assume T_0 and T_1 are not both zero. Can α and β both be zero?
(b) To satisfy the recurrence for $n \geq 2$, show that $\beta(\phi^2 - a_1\phi - a_2) = 0$ and $\alpha(\phi^2 - a_1\phi - a_2) + \beta(a_1\phi + 2a_2) = 0$.
(c) By considering $\beta = 0$ and $\beta \neq 0$, show that $\phi^2 - a_1\phi - a_2 = 0$, hence $\phi = (a_1 \pm \sqrt{a_1^2 + 4a_2})/2$.
(d) There are two cases to consider: (i) $a_1^2 + 4a_2 \neq 0$ (ii) and, $a_1^2 + 4a_2 = 0$. Analyze these two cases.

(i) $a_1^2 + 4a_2 \neq 0$. Show by contradiction that $a_1\phi + 2a_2 \neq 0$. Hence show that $\beta = 0$ and there are two possible solutions that satisfy the recurrence: $T_n = \alpha_+\phi_+^n$ and $T_n = \alpha_-\phi_-^n$, where $\phi_\pm = (a_1 \pm \sqrt{a_1^2 + 4a_2})/2$. More generally, show that the sum of the two possibilities, $T_n = \alpha_+\phi_+^n + \alpha_-\phi_-^n$ satisfies the recurrence.

(ii) $a_1^2 + 4a_2 = 0$. Show that $a_1\phi + 2a_2 = 0$, hence the solution of the recurrence is $T_m = (\alpha + \beta n)(a_1/2)^n$.

(e) Solve these recurrences. *[Hint: Use T_0 and T_1 to determine $\alpha_\pm$ in (d)(i) or α, β in (d)(ii).]*

(i) $T_0 = 1, T_1 = 6, a_1 = 6, a_2 = -9$. (ii) $T_0 = 1, T_1 = 3, a_1 = 8, a_2 = -12$. (iii) $T_0 = T_1 = 1, a_1 = a_2 = 1$.

Problem 7.27 (Akra-Bazzi formula). Suppose $T(n)$ satisfies $T(n) = \sum_{i=1}^k a_i T(b_i n + h_i) + g(n)$ where $a_i > 0$, $0 < b_i < 1$, $|h_i| \le C$ and $|g(n)| \le$ polynomial(n). Let p satisfy $\sum_{i=1}^k a_i b_i^p = 1$. The Akra-Bazzi formula uses integration to obtain $f(n)$, an approximation to $T(n)$ as $n \to \infty$:

$$T(n) \sim f(n) = n^p + n^p \int_1^n dx\, \frac{g(x)}{x^{p+1}}. \qquad (T(n) \sim f(n) \text{ means } T(n)/f(n) \overset{n\to\infty}{\longrightarrow} \text{constant.})$$

In each case, determine $a_i, b_i, C, g(n)$, compute the approximation $f(n)$, and plot $T(n)$ and $f(n)$ versus n.

(a) $T(0) = 0$, $T(1) = 1$ and $T(n) = T(\lfloor n/2 \rfloor) + T(\lceil n/2 \rceil) + n^k$, where: (i) $k = 0$. (ii) $k = 1$. (iii) $k = 2$.

(b) Example 7.1 on page 88.

Problem 7.28. One can use recurrences to define a sequence of strings. Define A_n as follows:

$$A_0 = a; \qquad A_n = a \bullet A_{n-1} \bullet ba \quad \text{for } n \ge 1.$$

(Concatenation, $x \bullet y$, for strings x, y appends y to x producing the string xy, e.g. $ab \bullet ba = abba$.)

(a) What are $A_1, \ldots, A_{10}$. (b) Prove $A_n = a^{\bullet n} b (ab)^{\bullet n}$, where $x^{\bullet k}$ is k copies of the string x concatenated together.

Problem 7.29. Give recurrences to generate these string-sequences.

(a) $A_1 = a$, $A_2 = aa$, $A_3 = aaa$, $\ldots$, $A_k = a^{\bullet k}$. ($a^{\bullet k}$ is k copies of a concatenated together.)

(b) $A_1 = abb$, $A_2 = aabb$, $A_3 = aaabb$, $\ldots$, $A_k = a^{\bullet k} bb$.

(c) $A_1 = ab$, $A_2 = aabb$, $A_3 = aaabbb$, $\ldots$, $A_k = a^{\bullet k} b^{\bullet k}$.

(d) $A_1 = abb$, $A_2 = aabbbb$, $A_3 = aaabbbbbb$, $\ldots$, $A_k = a^{\bullet k} b^{\bullet 2k}$.

Problem 7.30. Define the sequence of strings $A_1, A_2, A_3, \ldots$ by $A_1 = a$, and

$$A_n = \begin{cases} A_{n/2} \bullet a & n \text{ even;} \\ A_{(n-1)/2} \bullet b & n \text{ even.} \end{cases} \quad (\text{for } n > 1)$$

(Concatenation, $x \bullet y$, for strings x, y appends y to x producing the string xy, e.g. $ab \bullet ba = abba$.)

(a) What are $A_1, \ldots, A_{10}$? Prove that A_n is a string that always begins with a.

(b) **[Harder]** Prove that every string begining with a appears in the sequence $A_1, A_2, A_3, \ldots$.

Problem 7.31. Prove $\lceil \log_2(n+1) \rceil = \lceil \log_2(n+2) \rceil$ for even $n \ge 2$. *[Hints: Let $k = \lceil \log_2(n+2) \rceil$, so $n + 2 = 2^k - x$ where $x \in \{0, 2, 4, \ldots, 2^{k-1} - 2\}$. Also note, $\lceil \log_2(2^k - x) \rceil = k$ for $0 \le x < 2^{k-1}$.]*

Problem 7.32. Analyze Example 7.1 using a different method of induction.

(a) Assume $P(1) \wedge P(2)$ are T and $P(n) \to P(2n-1) \wedge P(2n)$ for $n \ge 2$. Prove $P(n)$ for $n \ge 1$. *[Hint: Well-ordering.]*

(b) Use the method of induction in (a) to prove that $f(n) = 1 + \lceil \log_2 n \rceil$ in Example 7.1.

Problem 7.33. Tinker. Guess $f(n)$ and prove your guess, where $f(1) = 1$ and $f(n) = 2f(\lfloor n/2 \rfloor)$ for $n > 1$. *[Hint: Exponential induction.]*

Problem 7.34. A stick is 100 units long. You wish to cut it into 100 unit-length pieces. You can stack multiple pieces and cut them all with one cut. What is the minimum number of cuts you need.

(a) Let n be the length of the longest piece you have. Argue that the number of cuts depends only on n.

(b) Let $C(n)$ the number of cuts needed. What is $C(1)$? Show $C(n) = C(\lceil n/2 \rceil) + 1$ for $n > 1$.

(c) Solve the recursion to get a formula for $C(n)$. How many cuts do you need for the 100-unit stick?

Problem 7.35. Let $x_1 = 1$ and $x_{n+1} = x_n/n + n/x_n$ for $n \ge 1$. Prove $\lfloor x_n^2 \rfloor = n$ for $n \ge 4$. *[Hints: You must show $\sqrt{n} \le x_n < \sqrt{n+1}$. Show $x/n + n/x$ is decreasing for $x \le n$. Prove by induction that $\sqrt{n} \le x_n \le n/\sqrt{n-1}$. Use this to prove $x_n \ge (n-1)/\sqrt{n-2}$, and finally that $x_{n+1} < \sqrt{n+2}$.]*

Problem 7.36. Let $x_0 = 0$ and for $n \ge 1$, $x_n = \sqrt{x_{n-1} + 6}$. Tinker. Compute x_1, x_2, x_3. Now, prove that x_n is monotonically increasing. Also prove that $x_n < 3$.

Problem 7.37. $A_1 = 1/2$ and $A_n^{-1} = 2n + A_{n-1}^{-1}$ for $n > 1$. Tinker. Guess and prove a formula for $S_n = A_1 + \cdots + A_n$.

Problem 7.38. Let $I_n = \int_0^{\pi/2} dx\ \sin^n x$. Compute a formula for I_n.

(a) Compute I_0, I_1, I_{10}, I_{11}. *[Hint: Use integration by parts to show $I_n = (n-1)I_{n-2}/n$ for $n \geq 2$.]*

(b) Show that $I_{2k} = (\pi/2) \cdot (2k)!/(2^{2k}(k!)^2)$ and $I_{2k+1} = (2^{2k}(k!)^2)/(2k+1)!$ for $k = 0, 1, 2, \ldots$.

Problem 7.39 (Continued Fractions). A continued fraction for 2 is shown. The recurrence $S_0 = 1; S_n = 1 + 2/S_{n-1}$ for $n \geq 1$ approaches continued fraction,

$$1+\cfrac{2}{1+\cfrac{2}{1+\cfrac{2}{1+\cfrac{2}{1+\cfrac{2}{1+\cfrac{2}{\cdots}}}}}}$$

$$S_0 = 1, \quad S_1 = 1 + \frac{2}{1}, \quad S_2 = 1 + \frac{2}{1+\frac{2}{1}}, \quad S_3 = 1 + \frac{2}{1+\frac{2}{1+\frac{2}{1}}}, \ldots$$

Prove $S_n = \dfrac{2^{n+2} + (-1)^{n+1}}{2^{n+1} + (-1)^n}$ and $\lim_{n\to\infty} S_n = 2$.

Problem 7.40. Linear algebra is a powerful tool for analyzing recurrences. From Problem 7.39, let $S_n = a_n/b_n$.

(a) What are a_0, b_0? Show that $a_n = a_{n-1} + 2b_{n-1}$ and $b_n = a_{n-1}$ for $n \geq 1$.

(b) Define the vector $x_n = \left[\begin{smallmatrix} a_n \\ b_n \end{smallmatrix}\right]$. What is x_0? Show that $x_n = \mathrm{A}x_{n-1}$ where $\mathrm{A} = \left[\begin{smallmatrix} 1 & 2 \\ 1 & 0 \end{smallmatrix}\right]$.

(c) Show that $x_n = \mathrm{A}^n x_0$. The rest of the problem develops a method to compute A^n.

(d) Show that $\mathrm{AQ} = \mathrm{QD}$, where $\mathrm{Q} = \left[\begin{smallmatrix} 2 & -1 \\ 1 & 1 \end{smallmatrix}\right]$ and $\mathrm{D} = \left[\begin{smallmatrix} 2 & 0 \\ 0 & -1 \end{smallmatrix}\right]$. (Q has the eigenvectors of A and D the eigenvalues).

(e) Since Q is invertible, show that $\mathrm{A} = \mathrm{QDQ}^{-1}$. Prove by induction that $\mathrm{A}^n = \mathrm{QD}^n\mathrm{Q}^{-1}$. What is D^n?

(f) Derive the formula $S_n = (2^{n+2} + (-1)^{n+1})/(2^{n+1} + (-1)^n)$.

Problem 7.41. Refer to the pseudocode on the right.

(a) What is the function being implemented?

(b) Prove that the output is correct for every valid input.

(c) Give a recurrence for the runtime T_n, where $n = j - i$.

(d) Guess and prove a formula for T_n.

```
out=S([arr],i,j)
 if(j<i) out=0;
 else
  out=arr[j]+S([arr],i,j-1);
```

Problem 7.42. Give pseudocode for a recursive function that computes 3^{2^n} on input n.

(a) Prove that your function correctly computes 3^{2^n} for every $n \geq 0$.

(b) Obtain a recurrence for the runtime T_n. Guess and prove a formula for T_n.

Problem 7.43. A recursive function takes input of size $n = 2^k$, reduces the problem to two of size $n/2$ and does additional work of at most n to compute the output. The runtime $T(n)$ depends only on n. Show that: (a) $T(n) \leq 2T(n/2) + n$. (b) $T(n) \in \Theta(n \log n)$. *[Hint: Induction. Show $n\log_2 n \leq T(n) \leq 2n\log_2 n$.]*

Problem 7.44. We give two implementations of `Big(n)` from page 90 (`iseven(n)` tests if n is even).

(a)
```
out=Big(n)
 if(n==0) out=1;
 elseif(iseven(n))
    out=Big(n/2)*Big(n/2);
 else out=2*Big(n-1)
```

(b)
```
out=Big(n)
 if(n==0) out=1;
 elseif(iseven(n))
    tmp=Big(n/2); out=tmp*tmp;
 else out=2*Big(n-1)
```

(i) For each, prove that the output is 2^n.

(ii) For each, obtain a recurrence for the running time T_n. (Assume `iseven(n)` is two operations.)

(iii) For each, compute runtimes T_n for $n = 1, \ldots, 10$. Compare runtimes with Exercise 7.10 on page 90.

Problem 7.45. Give recursive definitions for the set $\mathcal{S}$ in each of the following cases.

(a) $\mathcal{S} = \{0, 3, 6, 9, 12, \ldots\}$, the multiples of 3.

(b) $\mathcal{S} = \{1, 2, 3, 4, 6, 7, 8, 9, 11, \ldots\}$, the numbers which are not multiples of 5.

(c) $\mathcal{S} = \{$all strings with the same number of 0's as 1's$\}$ (e.g. 0011,0101,100101).

(d) The set of odd multiples of 3.

(e) The set of binary strings with an even number of 0's.

(f) The set of binary strings of even length.

Problem 7.46. What is the set $\mathcal{A}$ defined recursively as shown? (By default, nothing else is in $\mathcal{A}$ – minimality.)

① $1 \in \mathcal{A}$.
② $x, y \in \mathcal{A} \to x + y \in \mathcal{A}$;
$x, y \in \mathcal{A} \to x - y \in \mathcal{A}$.

Problem 7.47. What is the set $\mathcal{A}$ defined recursively as shown? (By default, nothing else is in $\mathcal{A}$ – minimality.)

① $3 \in \mathcal{A}$.
② $x, y \in \mathcal{A} \to x + y \in \mathcal{A}$;
$x, y \in \mathcal{A} \to x - y \in \mathcal{A}$.

Problem 7.48. A set $\mathcal{S}$ is defined recursively as shown. (By default, nothing else is in $\mathcal{S}$ – minimality.)
Give a derivation of $\neg((p \wedge q) \vee (\neg p \wedge r))$.

① $p, q, r \in \mathcal{S}$.
② $P, Q \in \mathcal{S} \rightarrow (P \wedge Q) \in \mathcal{S}$;
$P, Q \in \mathcal{S} \rightarrow (P \vee Q) \in \mathcal{S}$;
$P \in \mathcal{S} \rightarrow \neg P \in \mathcal{S}$.

Problem 7.49. There are 5 rooted binary trees (RBT) with 3 nodes. How many have 4 nodes?

Problem 7.50 (Rooted Ternary Trees (RTT)). Rooted ternery trees have a recursive definition.
① The empty tree ε is an RTT.
② If T_1, T_2, T_3 are disjoint RTTs with roots r_1, r_2, r_3, then linking r_1, r_2, r_3 to a new root r gives a new RTT.

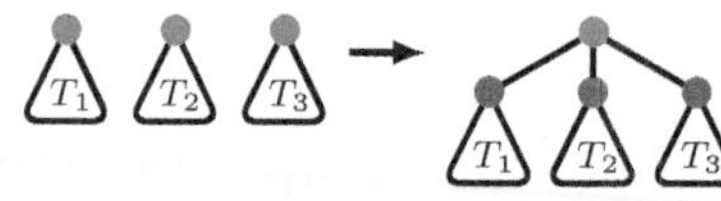

(a) Give all RTT's with at most 5 nodes. (b) Which of your RTT's in (a) are also RTT's?

Problem 7.51 (Rooted Full Ternary Trees (RFTT)). Rooted full ternery trees have a recursive definition.
① A single root-node ● is an RFTT.
② If T_1, T_2, T_3 are disjoint RFTTs with roots r_1, r_2, r_3, then linking r_1, r_2, r_3 to a new root r gives a new RFTT.

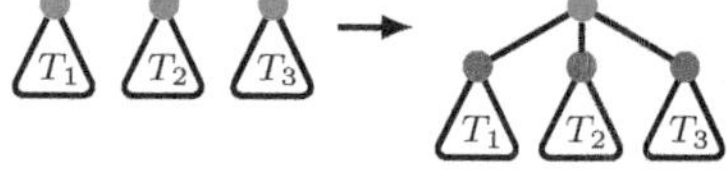

(a) Give all RFTT's with at most 5 nodes. (b) Which of your RFTT's in (a) are also RBT's?

Problem 7.52 (Rooted Trees (RT)). The rooted trees (RT) have the recursive definition.
① The empty tree ε is an RT.
② If $T_1, \ldots T_k$ are disjoint RTs with roots $r_1, \ldots, r_k$, then linking $r_1, \ldots, r_k$ to a new root r gives a new RT.

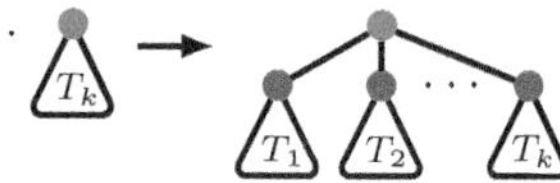

(a) Give all RT's with at most 5 nodes. (b) Which trees in (a) are RBT's. Which are RTTs?

Problem 7.53. The simple continued fractions $\mathcal{F}$ are recursively definined:
① $1 \in \mathcal{F}$.
② $x \in \mathcal{F} \rightarrow n + 1/x \in \mathcal{F}$ for $n \in \{0, 1, 2, \ldots\}$.
(a) For $a_i \in \mathbb{N}$, the tuple $(a_1, a_2, \ldots, a_n)$ represents the continued fraction shown. What is $(4, 3, 2, 1)$ as a fraction a/b in lowest terms?
(b) Start at the base case and repeatedly apply the constructor to derive $(4, 3, 2, 1)$.

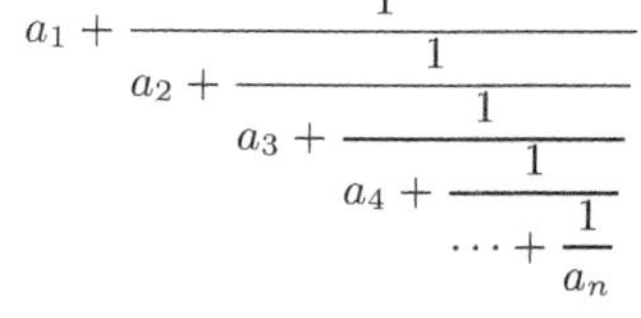

$$a_1 + \cfrac{1}{a_2 + \cfrac{1}{a_3 + \cfrac{1}{a_4 + \cfrac{1}{\cdots + \cfrac{1}{a_n}}}}}$$

Problem 7.54. Recursion is powerful for computing determinants.
(a) Let D_n be the determinant of an $n \times n$ matrix with diagonal a, superdiagonal b and subdiagonal c. D_4 is shown. Show that $D_n = aD_{n-1} - bcD_{n-2}$. For $a = 1, b = -1, c = -1$, what is D_{10}?

$$\begin{vmatrix} a & b & 0 & 0 \\ c & a & b & 0 \\ 0 & c & a & b \\ 0 & 0 & c & a \end{vmatrix}$$

(b) An $n \times n$ matrix A has entries $A_{ij} = a^{|i-j|}$, and D_n is its determinant. D_4 is shown. Derive a recursion for D_n in terms of D_{n-1}. Make a guess for D_n and prove it by induction.

$$\begin{vmatrix} 1 & a & a^2 & a^3 \\ a & 1 & a & a^2 \\ a^2 & a & 1 & a \\ a^3 & a^2 & a & 1 \end{vmatrix}$$

Problem 7.55 (Pascal's recursion). Recursion can involve many variables. Let $n, k \in \mathbb{Z}$.
(a) $f(0,0) = 1$ and $f(0,k) = 0$ for $k \neq 0$. For $n > 0$, $f(n,k) = f(n-1,k) + f(n-1,k-1)$.
(i) Show: $f(n,k)$ is a well defined for $n \geq 1$. (ii) Prove: $f(n,k) = \binom{n}{k} = n!/k!(n-k)!$, for $n \geq 1, 0 \leq k \leq n$.
(b) $g(0,0) = 1$ and $g(0,k) = 0$ for $k \neq 0$. For $n > 0$, $g(n,k) = 2g(n-1,k) + 3g(n-1,k-1)$.(Generalizes (a).)
Tinker. Guess and prove a formula for $g(n,k)$ for $n \geq 1, 0 \leq k \leq n$. *[Hint: kth term of the binomial $(2+3)^n$.]*

Problem 7.56 (Catalan recursion). Let M_n be the number of ways to match n pairs of parentheses to get a well formed arithmetic expression. There are the 5 ways for $n = 3$: [ ] [ ] [ ], [ ] [[ ]], [[ ]] [ ], [[ ] [ ]], [[[ ]]].
(a) What are M_0, M_1, M_2, M_3, M_4? Give the matched sequences for $n = 4$.
(b) Show $M_n = M_0M_{n-1} + M_1M_{n-2} + M_2M_{n-3} + \cdots + M_{n-2}M_1 + M_{n-1}M_0$. Compute M_{10}.

Problem 7.57. A building has n floors. You have k eggs and wish to find the highest safe floor from which you can drop an egg without the egg breaking (Problem 1.21). Let $M(n,k)$ be the number of egg-drops needed. Let $Q(k,d)$ be the largest number of floors n for which you can find the highest safe floor with k eggs using at most d egg-drops.
(a) What are $M(0,k)$, $M(n,1)$. What is $M(n,n)$? *[Hint: Binary search.]*
(b) If the first drop is at floor x, how many drops are needed if: (i) The egg breaks? (ii) The egg survives?
(c) (i) Give a recursion for $M(n,k)$. Program your recursion to get $M(n,3)$ for $n = 7, 8, 9, \ldots$ (high as you can).
(ii) Give a more efficient algorithm that is based on the same recursion and compute $M(1000,3)$.
(d) Give a recursion for $Q(k,d)$ and prove $Q(k,d) = \sum_{i=0}^{k} \binom{d}{i} - 1$. How large an n can 4 eggs and 6 drops handle?

Problem 7.58. Let T_n be the number of prefix-heavy n-bit binary sequences. A sequence is prefix-heavy if every non-empty prefix has more 1's than 0's. Let $F_{n,k}$ be the number of n-bit prefix-heavy sequences ending in $k \geq 1$ zeros.

(a) What are $T_1, \ldots, T_7$? Give all the sequences corresponding to T_7.

(b) What are $F_{7,1}, \ldots, F_{7,7}$. Give all the sequences corresponding to $F_{7,2}$.

(c) Show that $F_{n,1} = T_{n-2} + F_{n,2}$. What are $F_{n,k}$ for $k = \lfloor (n-1)/2 \rfloor$ and $k > \lfloor (n-1)/2 \rfloor$.

(d) Prove that $F_{n,k} = F_{n,k+1} + F_{n-2,k-1}$ for $1 < k < \lfloor (n-1)/2 \rfloor$.

(e) Prove that $T_n = T_{n-1} + T_{n-2} + F_{n-2,1} + F_{n-2,2} + \cdots + F_{n-2,n-2}$. Hence, compute the number of prefix-heavy 10-bit sequences. *[Hint: Consider the possible ways to terminate the sequence: $1, 10, 100, 1000, \ldots$.]*

Problem 7.59 (Foraging Bushman). A bushman foraging in the Kalahari can carry up to 1 gallon of water. He drinks 1 gallon of water per mile walked. On any hike, he must save enough water to walk back to the village (with 1 gallon, he can hike out 1/2-mile and back). He can also place water along his route to increase his range.

(a) The village has 2 gallons of water. Show how the bushman can hike out 3/4-mile and make it back.

(b) Let $M(n)$ be the bushman's maximum range when the village has n gallons of water. Show:
(i) $M(n) \leq n/2$. (ii) $M(2n) \geq M(n) + 1/4$. (iii) Use part (ii) to show $M(n) \geq 1/2 + \lfloor \log_2 n \rfloor/4$.

Can you improve the gap between the bounds in (i) and (iii)? Which bound do you think is tighter?

Problem 7.60 (Towers of Hanoi). Here is a puzzle with n disks and 3 bases. All disks are on base A (smallest on top). You can move a disk from the top of one base to the top of another if all disks on the destination base are larger. The goal is to move all disks from A to C using the fewest moves.

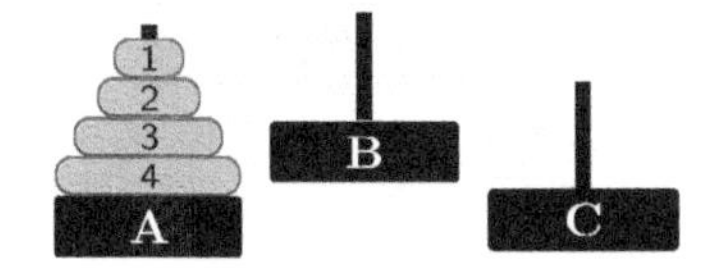

(a) Give a sequence of 16 legal moves to move the 4 disks from A to C.

(b) Let T_n be the fewest moves needed for the task with n disks.
(i) Show that to move disk-n from A to C, the smallest $n-1$ disks must first be moved from A to B.
(ii) Prove that $T_n = 2T_{n-1} + 1$. What is T_1?
(iii) Tinker. Guess a formula for T_n and prove it by induction.

Problem 7.61 (Zeno's Paradox). A hare at 0 chases a tortoise at 1. The tortoise moves at 1 unit per minute and the hare chases at twice that speed. In 1 minute, the hare catches the tortise at position 2.

Zeno argues that the hare never catches the tortise by induction. At iteration 1, the hare is at 0, behind the tortoise at 1. At iteration 2, the hare catches up to tortoise's position at iteration 1, but the tortoise has moved. And so the gambit continues forever. Assume the hare is behind the tortoise at iteration n. At iteration $n+1$ the hare moves to the tortoise's position at iteration n, but the tortoise has moved, so the hare is behind the tortoise at iteration $n+1$.

(a) Zeno concludes, by induction, that the hare is behind the tortise for all iterations. Is the argument correct?

(b) Let t_n be the time the hare takes to execute iteration n. What is t_1? Show that $t_{n+1} = t_n/2$.

(c) Guess and prove formula t_n and show that Zeno's paradox is resolved if $1/2 + 1/2^2 + 1/2^3 + 1/2^4 + \cdots = 1$.

Problem 7.62 (Trash Compactor). A trash bin has unit volume. The trash compactor has compression factor $r > 1$. If you fill the bin with 1 unit of uncompacted trash, the compactor squashes the trash to $(1/r)$-units of compacted trash. For example, if $r = 3$, the 1 unit (uncompacted) becomes $(1/3)$-unit compacted. Now $(2/3)$-unit is free. You can refill and compact again. However, you can't further compress the initial $(1/3)$-unit of compacted trash; you can only compress the new $(2/3)$-unit down to $(2/9)$-unit, which gives a total of $(5/9)$-unit of compacted trash. Each time you use the compactor you create space for new trash, you compact the new trash and keep going like this forever.

Let the step $n = 0, 1, \ldots$ be the number of times the compactor has been used. At step n, let c_n be the amount of compacted trash in the bin and s_n the free space to be filled with new trash and compacted at the next step.

(a) What are c_0 and s_0? For $r = 3$, compute c_n and s_n for $n = 1, 2, 3$.

(b) Show that c_n and s_n satisfy the following recurrences with base cases c_0 and s_0 given in part (a):

$$rc_n = 1 + (r-1)\,c_{n-1} \qquad (n \geq 1); \qquad\qquad rs_n = (r-1)\,s_{n-1} \qquad (n \geq 1).$$

(c) Guess a formula for s_n and prove it by induction.

(d) Explain why the total amount of trash put into the bin is $s_0 + s_1 + s_2 + s_3 + s_4 + \cdots$.

(e) If one continues to compact forever, why must the total trash put into the bin approach r, the compression ratio.

(f) Use (c), (d) and (e) to prove the following infinite geometric sum for any $r > 1$,

$$1 + \left(\frac{r-1}{r}\right) + \left(\frac{r-1}{r}\right)^2 + \left(\frac{r-1}{r}\right)^3 + \left(\frac{r-1}{r}\right)^4 + \cdots = r.$$

Substitute $t = (r-1)/r$ and prove the formula for an infinite geometric sum, $1 + t + t^2 + t^3 + \cdots = 1/(1-t)$.

Problem 7.63 (Josephus Problem). In the Josephus problem (Problems 3.64, 5.64), objects $1, \ldots, n$ are in a circle. Starting at 1, every other object is removed (object 2 is removed first). Let $J(n)$ be the last object removed.

(a) Prove that $J(n)$ satisfies the recursion $J(1) = 1$ and $J(n) = \begin{cases} 2J(n/2) - 1 & n \text{ even;} \\ 2J((n-1)/2) + 1 & n \text{ odd.} \end{cases}$

(b) Use well-ordering (minimum counterexample) to show that $J(n)$ is defined for $n \geq 1$.

(c) Use (a) to compute $J(n)$ for $n \in \{1, \ldots, 32\}$.

(d) Guess a pattern for $J(n)$ based on the data in (c) and predict $J(77), J(78)$.

(e) Guess a formula for $J(n)$ and prove your guess by induction.

Problem 7.64. A cyclic shift transforms a binary number $\mathbf{b} = b_m b_{m-1} \cdots b_0$ with $b_m = 1$ by shifting the leftmost bit to the right, giving $\mathbf{b}_c = b_{m-1} \cdots b_0 b_m$. Problem 4.20 studied some properties of this operation.

(a) Use the data from Problem 7.63(c) to give a table with the binary representations of n and $J(n)$ for $n \in \{1, \ldots, 32\}$. Also include the cyclic shift of the binary representation of n.

(b) Guess at the relationship between the binary representations of n and $J(n)$, and prove it.

Problem 7.65. Generalize the Josephus problem to objects $1, \ldots, n$ with every kth object being removed, $k \geq 1$. Let $J(n, k)$ be the last object to be removed. The Josephus numbers from the previous two problems are $J(n, 2)$.

(a) What is $J(n, 1)$? What is $J(1, k)$?

(b) What is $J(5, 4)$? Use $J(5, 4)$ to deduce $J(6, 4)$. Use $J(6, 4)$ to deduce $J(7, 4)$.

(c) Find a recursion for $J(n, k)$ that uses $J(n-1, k)$. Program your recursion and fill out the following table.

k	n										
	1	2	3	4	5	6	7	8	9	10	100
1											
2											
3											
4											

(d) Where should Josephus stand to be the last one remaining in a band of 41 when every seventh person is removed.

(e) Is the recursion in part (d) or the one from Problem 7.63(a) faster for computing $J(n, 2)$? Informally explain why?

(f) Find a recursion for $J(n, k)$ that would be much more efficient than the one in part (d).

Problem 7.66 (Josephus Permutation). Update the recursion from Problem 7.65 so that instead of computing just the position of the last object to be removed, it computes the entire order in which the objects are removed.

(a) What is the order in which objects are removed when $n = 5$ and $k = 3$?

(b) Use (a) to determine the order in which objects are removed when $n = 6$ and $k = 3$?

(c) Give a recursive function to compute the order of removal for n objects, skipping every k.

(d) Implement your recursion in a program. Determine the order of twenty-six girls with last initials $A, B, \ldots, Z$ in a circle so that when every seventh girl is removed they come off alphabetically.

Problem 7.67 (Fibonacci Tiles). Recursive structures can produce interesting geometric objects. Start with a square of side 1. At each step, attach a square to the longest side of the current rectangle (the side-length of the square is the length of that longest side). We show the rectangle growing with squares numbered by the step at which they were added. Let S_n be the side-length of the square added at step n.

(a) What are $S_1, S_2, S_3, S_4, S_{10}$? *[Hint: Recurrence.]*

(b) Show that $S_n = F_n$ (Fibonacci numbers).

To get the Fibonacci spiral, join a quater-circle in each square (blue curve). This approximates a golden spiral satisfying the polar equation $r = a\varphi^{2\theta/\pi}$ (red curve), where $\varphi \approx 1.618$.

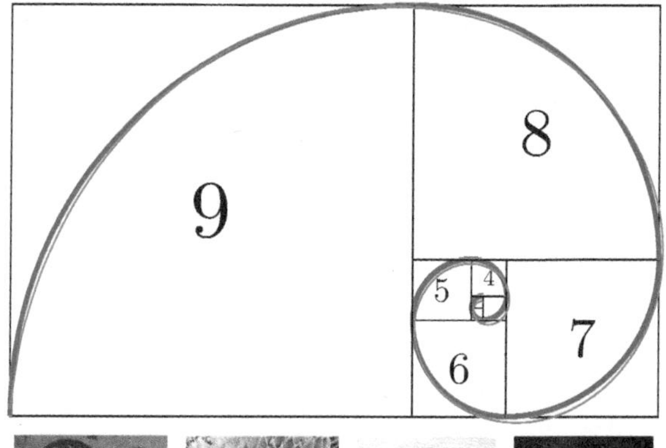

The golden spiral is a logarithmic spiral, $r = ae^{b\theta}$. Such spirals approximate the growth of many structures in Nature, e.g.: Nautilus shell and Aloe (Wikipedia); Storm clouds (NASA); Galaxy (ESA/Hubble). A logarithmic spiral allows growth without changing shape.

> All correct proofs are alike; each incorrect proof is incorrect in its own way.
> – **Tolstoy (*Anna Karenina*, adapted)**
>
> He [Taniyama] was gifted with the special capability of making many mistakes, mostly in the right direction. I envied him and tried to imitate, but found it quite difficult to make good mistakes. – **Goro Shimura**
>
> Mistakes are the portals of discovery. – **James Joyce**

Chapter 8

Proofs with Recursive Objects

1: Structural induction: proving a property for a recursive set.
2: Examples with sets, sequences and trees.

We typically ask two types of questions of a recursive set. Let us be concrete with a very simple set whose recursive definition is on the right,

① $0 \in \mathcal{A}$.
② $x \in \mathcal{A} \to x+4 \in \mathcal{A}$.

$$\mathcal{A} = \{0, 4, 8, 12, 16, \ldots\}.$$

We may ask, (i) What is in $\mathcal{A}$? Is some feature common to every element of $\mathcal{A}$? For example, every element of $\mathcal{A}$ is even. (ii) Is every even number in $\mathcal{A}$? No, for example 2 is not in $\mathcal{A}$. The difference between these two questions is subtle, but important. Please pause to appreciate this difference.

(i)	$x \in \mathcal{A} \to x$ is even	(true)	} Very different statements!
(ii)	x is even $\to x \in \mathcal{A}$	(false)	

Structural induction is a tool for the first question, "Do all members of a recursive set have a given property?"

8.1 Structural Induction

The first two orks had blue eyes. When two blue-eyed orks mate, their child also has blue eyes. Do all orks have blue eyes? Yes. When could a green-eyed ork have arisen? The first two orks had blue eyes, and any new ork has blue eyes because its parents must have blue eyes. This is the essence of structural induction. To crystallize the concept, let's work with the slightly more complex recursive set of matched parentheses $\mathcal{M}$.

Recursive definition of matched parentheses $\mathcal{M}$.
① $\varepsilon \in \mathcal{M}$. **[basis]**
② $x, y \in \mathcal{M} \to [x]\bullet y \in \mathcal{M}$. **[constructor]**

Remember, nothing else is in $\mathcal{M}$. Let us tinker and generate some of the strings in $\mathcal{M}$ using the constructor.

[]	(set $x = \varepsilon$, $y = \varepsilon$ to get $[\varepsilon]\varepsilon = []$)
[[]]	(set $x = []$, $y = \varepsilon$)
[][]	(set $x = \varepsilon$, $y = []$)

Pop Quiz 8.1
Give a derivation to show that [[][]][] $\in \mathcal{M}$.

The strings in $\mathcal{M}$ are balanced, i.e. they have an equal number of open and close parentheses. Let us prove it. To do so, imagine creating the strings $s_1, s_2, s_3, \ldots$ of $\mathcal{M}$ in some order, starting with $s_1 = \varepsilon$,

$$\mathcal{M} = \{\varepsilon, [], [[]], [][], [[]][], \ldots, s_n, \ldots\} \tag{8.1}$$

The list has all strings of $\mathcal{M}$ in their order of creation. The nth string s_n came from two previous strings (s_k, s_ℓ) using the constructor $s_n = [s_k]\bullet s_\ell$. If s_k and s_ℓ are balanced, then so is s_n with one more open-parenthesis and close-parenthesis. Just like orks and blue eyes, when two balanced strings "mate", the resulting "child" is balanced. Since the primordial ancestor $s_1 = \varepsilon$ is balanced, all strings in $\mathcal{M}$ are balanced. Using earlier strings to show that s_n is balanced is just strong induction. Define the property $P(n)$ for string $s_n \in \mathcal{M}$:

$$P(n) : \text{string } s_n \text{ is balanced, i.e. the number of '[' equals the number of ']'.}$$

Proof. ($\mathcal{M}$ contains only balanced strings.) We use strong induction to prove $P(n)$ for $n \geq 1$.

1: **[Base case]** The base case is $n = 1$ and $s_1 = \varepsilon$ which is clearly balanced, so $P(1)$ is true.

2: **[Induction step]** We show $P(1)\wedge\cdots\wedge P(n) \to P(n+1)$ using direct proof. Assume $P(1), P(2), \ldots, P(n)$: $s_1, \ldots, s_n$ are all balanced. We must show $P(n+1)$: s_{n+1} is balanced. We have that $s_{n+1} = [s_k]\bullet s_\ell$, where s_k, s_ℓ appeared earlier than s_{n+1}, so $k, \ell < n+1$. By the strong induction hypothesis, s_k and s_ℓ are balanced. Therefore s_{n+1} is balanced because you add one open-parenthesis and close-parenthesis).

3: By induction, $P(n)$ is true for all $n \geq 1$. ■

Strong induction over a natural ordering of the elements in a recursive set is structural induction. We brushed some subtelties under the rug. Specifically, can one always list out all the elements of $\mathcal{M}$ in a natural order of creation? This is a delicate question, and indeed something needs to be proved. The intuition above should suffice, but if not, see Problem 8.49. We summarize our discussion into a proof template for structural induction. To prove some property for every element in a recursive set, prove the property for the base cases (the primordial ancestors) and show that the constructors (rules for procreation) preserve the property.

Proof Template X: Structural induction on a recursive set.
Let $\mathcal{S}$ be a recursive set. This means there are:

① Bases cases $s_1, \ldots, s_k$ that are in $\mathcal{S}$.
② Constructor rules that use elements in $\mathcal{S}$ to create a new element of $\mathcal{S}$.

For predicate P, to show $P(s)$ for every element $s \in \mathcal{S}$, you must:

1: **[Base cases]** Prove that $P(s_1), P(s_2), \ldots, P(s_k)$ are all true.

2: **[Induction step]** Prove, for *every* constructor rule: IF P is true for the parent elements, THEN P is true for the new child created.

3: By structural induction, conclude that $P(s)$ is true for all $s \in \mathcal{S}$.

You must prove P for every base case, and that every constructor preserves P. ■

To show that an object is in a recursive set, give a derivation. For example $[\,][[\,]] \in \mathcal{M}$. Here is a derivation,

$$\varepsilon \xrightarrow{x=\varepsilon,y=\varepsilon} [\,] \xrightarrow{x=[\,],y=\varepsilon} [[\,]] \xrightarrow{x=\varepsilon,y=[[\,]]} [\,][[\,]].$$

To show that an object is not in a recursive set, you must show that no derivation produces the object. That's a tough call because you must consider every possible derivation. Here is a better strategy.

- Prove that some property is common to all elements of the recursive set.
- Show that the object in question violates that property, and hence cannot belong to the set.

For example $[[\,] \notin \mathcal{M}$ because $[[\,]$ is unbalanced, and every string in $\mathcal{M}$ is balanced. Is every balanced string in $\mathcal{M}$? No, for example $][$ is not in $\mathcal{M}$. To prove it, we need another property of $\mathcal{M}$ that $][$ violates. A string of parentheses is matched in the usual arithmetic sense if it is balanced and every opening parenthesis '[' is closed by a subsequent closing parenthesis ']'. Every string in $\mathcal{M}$ is matched.

Exercise 8.2
Prove by structural induction that every string $s \in \mathcal{M}$ is matched. A string is matched if it is balanced and every prefix of has at least as many '[' as ']'. Hence, prove that $][\notin \mathcal{M}$.

Is every matched string in $\mathcal{M}$. Yes! This is the second question we ask of a recursive set, whether every object of a particular type, in this case matched strings, belongs to the set. How do we prove it? Structural induction is not the tool for this kind of question. We want to prove something doesn't exist outside the recursive set. So contradiction plus well-ordering (induction in disguise) are often the way to go. The details depend on the problem, but we can illustrate the general outline with the set $\mathcal{A} = \{0, 4, 8, \ldots\}$ defined recursively at the begining of the chapter. Let's prove that every non-negative multiple of 4 is in $\mathcal{A}$.

1: Assume there is a smallest non-negative multiple of 4 that is not in $\mathcal{A}$. So, $z = 4k \notin \mathcal{A}$ for $k > 0$.
2: Use the constructor for $\mathcal{A}$ to build your object z from smaller objects having the property you desire. In this case the constructor is pretty simple, $x \to x + 4$. Using the constructor on $x = 4(k-1)$ gives z.
3: Get the contradiction. Since x, a multiple of 4, is smaller than z, we know $x \in \mathcal{A}$ otherwise z is not the smallest multiple of 4 not in $\mathcal{A}$. Applying the constructor to x gives z, which means $z \in \mathcal{A}$. **FISHY!**

Now its your turn. If you want to learn how to work such proofs, do the next exercise carefully.

Exercise 8.3

Show that every matched string is in $\mathcal{M}$, using the following steps.

(a) Let s be any nonempty matched string. Show that there exist matched strings x, y (possibly empty) on which the constructor produces s. That is, $s = [x]y$ for matched strings x and y.
(b) Assume some matched string is not in $\mathcal{M}$ and derive a contradiction.
  (i) Let s be the shortest matched string not in $\mathcal{M}$. Why does such a shortest s exist?
  (ii) Use part (a) to show that $s = [x]y$, where x, y are matched.
  (iii) Show that the lengths of x and y are smaller than the length of s.
  (iv) Show that x and y are in $\mathcal{M}$, and hence that $s \in \mathcal{M}$, a contradiction.

8.2 Structural Induction on $\mathbb{N}$

We recursively defined the set of natural numbers $\mathbb{N} = \{1, 2, 3, \ldots\}$ as follows:

① $1 \in \mathbb{N}$. [base case]
② $x \in \mathbb{N} \to x + 1 \in \mathbb{N}$. [constructor]

Structural induction works with any recursive set. Consider some property of the natural numbers, for example

$$P(n) : 5^n - 1 \text{ is divisible by } 4.$$

We can use structural induction to prove that this property holds for every $n \in \mathbb{N}$.

1: **[Base case]** $P(1)$ claims $5^1 - 1$ is divisible by 4, clearly true.
2: **[Induction step]** In the constructor, x is the parent and $x + 1$ is the child. We must show that if the parent has P, then the child has P, that is if $P(x)$ is true, then $P(x+1)$ is true or $P(x) \to P(x+1)$. We use direct proof. Assume $P(x)$: $5^x - 1$ is divisible by 4, so $5^x - 1 = 4k$, or $5^x = 4k + 1$. Then,

$$5^{x+1} - 1 = 5 \cdot 5^x - 1 = 5 \cdot (4k+1) - 1 = 4(5k+1).$$

So, 4 divides $5^{x+1} - 1$ (the constructor preserves P). By structural induction, P is true for all $n \in \mathbb{N}$. ■

The proof mechanics above should be familiar. Structural induction using the recursive definition of $\mathbb{N}$ is just ordinary induction. A set can have different recursive definitions. Structural induction using different recursive definitions gives different proof techniques.

Exercise 8.4

Define a set of numbers $\mathbb{N}_{\text{STRONG}}$ as follows:

① $1 \in \mathbb{N}_{\text{STRONG}}$.
② If $1, 2, 3, \ldots, n$ are all in $\mathbb{N}_{\text{STRONG}}$, then $n + 1 \in \mathbb{N}_{\text{STRONG}}$.

(a) What is the relationship between $\mathbb{N}$ and $\mathbb{N}_{\text{STRONG}}$?
(b) You have seen structural induction with $\mathbb{N}_{\text{STRONG}}$ before. What form of induction is it?

8.3 Palindromes

"Was it a rat I saw?" reads the same backwards, if you ignore spaces. A string is a palindrome if it equals its reversal. Focus on binary strings, sequences of bits. Let us introduce some notation. The string $s = 01100$ of length 5 has bits $s_1 = 0, s_2 = 1, s_3 = 1, s_4 = 0$ and $s_5 = 0$. A string s of length n has bits $s_1 s_2 \cdots s_n$. The reversal of s, denoted s^{R}, is the string whose bits are in the reverse order. For $s = 01100$, $s^{\mathrm{R}} = 00110$. If s has length n, then $s^{\mathrm{R}}_i = s_{n+1-i}$. Concatenation "$\bullet$" joins two strings, for example $011 \bullet 101 = 011101$.

Exercise 8.5

Let $x = 0101$, $y = 110$ and $z = 10110$.

(a) What are the concatenations $x \bullet y$ and $y \bullet x$? What is $x \bullet y \bullet z$?

(b) What is $(x \bullet y)^{\mathrm{R}}$, the reversal of $x \bullet y$? What is $(x \bullet y \bullet z)^{\mathrm{R}}$

(c) Prove that, for general strings, the reversal of $x \bullet y$ is $y^{\mathrm{R}} \bullet x^{\mathrm{R}}$.

(d) For strings $x_1, \ldots, x_n$, prove by induction that $(x_1 \bullet x_2 \bullet \cdots \bullet x_n)^{\mathrm{R}} = x_n^{\mathrm{R}} \bullet x_{n-1}^{\mathrm{R}} \bullet \cdots \bullet x_1^{\mathrm{R}}$.

Here is a recursive definition of the palindromes $\mathcal{P}$, the set of all binary strings which equal their reversal,

$$\mathcal{P} = \{\varepsilon, 0, 1, 00, 11, 000, 101, 010, 111, \ldots\}.$$

① There are three base cases: $\varepsilon \in \mathcal{P}$, $0 \in \mathcal{P}$, $1 \in \mathcal{P}$.

② There are two constructors: (i) $x \in \mathcal{P} \to 0 \bullet x \bullet 0 \in \mathcal{P}$; (ii) $x \in \mathcal{P} \to 1 \bullet x \bullet 1 \in \mathcal{P}$.

Pop Quiz 8.6

Give a derivation of the string 001100. How many palindromes have length 6?

Let us use structural induction to prove that every element of $\mathcal{P}$ is a palindrome. Clearly the base cases are palindromes. We must prove that the constructor preserves palindromicity. By Exercise 8.5,

$$(0 \bullet x \bullet 0)^{\mathrm{R}} = 0^{\mathrm{R}} \bullet x^{\mathrm{R}} \bullet 0^{\mathrm{R}} = 0 \bullet x^{\mathrm{R}} \bullet 0.$$

If x is a palindrome, then $x^{\mathrm{R}} = x$ and so $(0 \bullet x \bullet 0)^{\mathrm{R}} = 0 \bullet x \bullet 0$. This means that the first constructor rule preserves palindromicity if it starts from a palindrome. Similarly, the second constructor rule preserves palindromicity. By structural induction, every element of $\mathcal{P}$ is a palindrome. The formal proof is an exercise.

Exercise 8.7

(a) Give the proof by structural induction that every string in $\mathcal{P}$ is a palindrome.

(b) Prove that every palindrome is in $\mathcal{P}$. *[Hint: Mimic the proof in Exercise 8.3.]*

8.4 Well-Formed Arithmetic Expressions

Every kindergartner knows that $((1+1+1) \times (1+1+1+1+1)) = 15$. On the left is an arithmetic expression, a string composed of the characters $\{1, (,), \times, +\}$, and on the right is the value of this expression. The value is a number computed from the string using the standard rules of arithmetic. Define the function `value(s)` which returns the value of the arithmetic expression s. We won't formally define `value(s)`. Instead, we rely on your familiarity with evaluating arithmetic expressions from kindergarten.[1] Here is a recursive definition of a set of strings $\mathcal{A}_{\mathrm{ODD}}$ containing some well-formed arithmetic expressions.

① Base case: $1 \in \mathcal{A}_{\mathrm{ODD}}$.

② There are two constructors: (i) $x \in \mathcal{A}_{\mathrm{ODD}} \to (x + 1 + 1) \in \mathcal{A}_{\mathrm{ODD}}$; (ii) $x, y \in \mathcal{A}_{\mathrm{ODD}} \to (x \times y) \in \mathcal{A}_{\mathrm{ODD}}$.

[1]The kindergartner's ability to evaluate arithmetic strings is not trivial to automate. In 1978, Robert Floyd won the Turing Award in part for "simple" parsing algorithms, which includes parsers for arithmetic.

First things first, lets tinker around and generate some of the strings in $\mathcal{A}_{\text{ODD}}$,

$$
\begin{array}{llll}
1 \to (1+1+1) \to & ((1+1+1)+1+1) & ((1+1+1)\times(1+1+1)) \to \ldots \\
\ (1\times 1) & ((1\times 1)+1+1) & ((1+1+1)\times(1\times 1)) \\
 & (1\times(1+1+1)) & ((1\times 1)\times(1+1+1)) \\
 & (1\times(1\times 1)) & ((1\times 1)\times(1\times 1)) \\
 & ((1+1+1)\times 1) & \\
 & ((1\times 1)\times 1) &
\end{array}
$$

There are well-formed expressions which are not in $\mathcal{A}_{\text{ODD}}$, for example

$$((1+1+1+1)\times(1+1+1)).$$

Let's prove that this string is not in $\mathcal{A}_{\text{ODD}}$. Evaluate the arithmetic expressions for the strings in $\mathcal{A}_{\text{ODD}}$ that we generated and verify that they all evaluate to an odd number. For example,

$$((1+1+1)+1+1) = (3+1+1) = 5.$$

If $\texttt{value}(s)$ is odd, we say s is odd. We prove that every expression in $\mathcal{A}_{\text{ODD}}$ is odd. Clearly the base case 1 is odd. We must show that the constructors preserve oddness. In the first constructor rule, the new expression created is $(x+1+1)$, which is odd when x is odd because

$$\texttt{value}((x+1+1)) = \texttt{value}(x)+2 = (\text{odd})+2 = (\text{odd}).$$

The first constructor rule *preserves* oddness because the new string created is odd if the input to the constructor is odd. Now for the second constructor rule. Starting from x, y, the new string is $(x \times y)$, whose value is:

$$\texttt{value}((x\times y)) = \texttt{value}(x)\times\texttt{value}(y) = (\text{odd})\times(\text{odd}) = (\text{odd}).$$

The new string is odd when x and y are odd, because the product of two odd values is odd. So, the second constructor rule also preserves oddness, producing a new odd string from odd strings. By structural induction, every string in $\mathcal{A}_{\text{ODD}}$ is odd. Now, consider the string we claimed is not in $\mathcal{A}_{\text{ODD}}$. Compute its value:

$$
\begin{aligned}
\texttt{value}(((1+1+1+1)\times(1+1+1))) &= \texttt{value}((1+1+1+1))\times\texttt{value}((1+1+1)) \\
&= 4\times 3 = 12.
\end{aligned}
$$

Since the value is even, this proves that the string cannot be in $\mathcal{A}_{\text{ODD}}$ which contains only odd expressions.

Exercise 8.8

(a) Give the formal proof by structural induction that every string in $\mathcal{A}_{\text{ODD}}$ is odd.

(b) Give a well-formed arithmetic expression that is odd but not in $\mathcal{A}_{\text{ODD}}$.

8.5 Properties of Rooted Binary Trees

Recall the recursive definition of rooted binary trees, RBT:

① The empty tree ε is an RBT.

② If T_1, T_2 are disjoint RBTs with roots r_1 and r_2, then linking r_1 and r_2 to a new root r gives a new RBT with root r.

Every rooted binary tree with $n \geq 1$ vertices has $n-1$ links. You can verify this property explicitly for the trees on pages 92–93. To prove the claim, we must show that if the trees T_1 and T_2 start out with this property, then the new tree created by the constructor rule preserves the property. We have to count the number of vertices and links in the new tree and show that there is one more vertex than links. Here is the formal proof by structural induction.

Proof. First, we define our property $P(T)$ for a rooted binary tree T as:

$$P(T): \text{IF tree } T \text{ is a rooted binary tree with } n \geq 1 \text{ vertices, THEN } T \text{ has } n-1 \text{ links.}$$

1: **[Base case]** $P(\varepsilon)$ is vacuously true because ε is not a tree with $n \geq 1$ vertices.

2: **[Induction step]** Now, suppose that T_1 and T_2 are disjoint trees for which both $P(T_1)$ and $P(T_2)$ are true. Let n_1 be the number of vertices in T_1 and let ℓ_1 be the number of links. Similarly, n_2 and ℓ_2 are the number of vertices and links respectively in T_2. Let n and ℓ be the number of vertices and links in the new tree created by the constructor rule. There are four cases to consider.

- Case 1: $T_1 = T_2 = \varepsilon$. The new tree is a vertex with $n = 1$ and $\ell = 0$, and $\ell = n - 1$.
- Case 2: $T_1 = \varepsilon; T_2 \neq \varepsilon$. The left child-subtree in the new tree is empty, so the new tree has one more vertex than T_2 and one more link from r to r_2. So, $n = n_2 + 1$ and
$$\ell = \ell_2 + 1 \overset{(a)}{=} n_2 - 1 + 1 = n_2 = n - 1,$$
where (a) follows from the induction hypothesis because T_2 is nonempty.
- Case 3: $T_1 \neq \varepsilon; T_2 = \varepsilon$. This is similar to case 2. The right child-subtree is empty, so $n = n_1 + 1$ and
$$\ell = \ell_1 + 1 \overset{(a)}{=} n_1 - 1 + 1 = n_1 = n - 1.$$
- Case 4: $T_1 \neq \varepsilon; T_2 \neq \varepsilon$. In the new tree there is one more vertex, the new root, so $n = n_1 + n_2 + 1$. There are two new links, from the new root to the old roots r_1 and r_2, so
$$\ell = \ell_1 + \ell_2 + 2 \overset{(a)}{=} n_1 - 1 + n_2 - 1 + 2 = n_1 + n_2 = n - 1.$$

In all four cases, $\ell = n - 1$ and so the new tree has our property P. We proved that the constructor preserves property P if it starts from trees that have property P.

3: By structural induction, $P(T)$ is true for all trees $T \in$ RBT. ■

Checklist for Structural Induction.

Analogy: if the first ancestors had blue eyes, and blue eyes are inherited from one generation to the next, then all of society will have blue eyes.

✓ You have a recursively defined set $\mathcal{S}$.
✓ You want to prove a property P for all members of $\mathcal{S}$.
✓ Does the property P hold for the base cases?
✓ Is the property P preserved by all the constructor rules?
✗ Structural induction is not how you prove that all objects with property P are in $\mathcal{S}$.

Pop Quiz 8.9

On page 92 we said the graph on the right is not a tree. Prove it isn't an RBT.

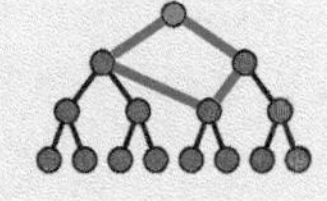

Exercise 8.10

Recursion is powerful for defining functions on recursively defined sets. For a recursive binary tree T, we define height(T) and size(T) recursively as follows.

① height(ε) $= -1$ and size(ε) $= 0$.

② Let T_1, T_2 be disjoint RBTs, and let T be obtained from T_1, T_2 using the RBT constructor rule. Then,

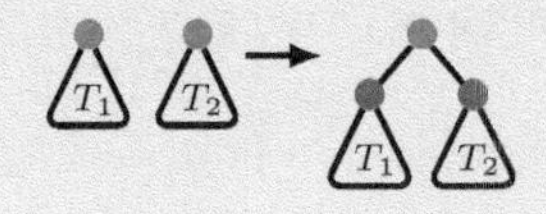

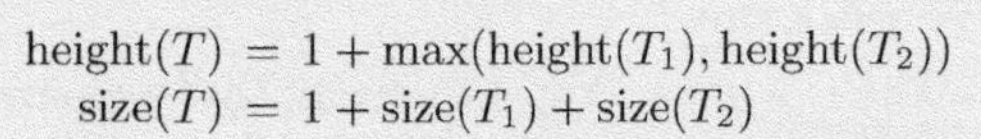

$$\text{height}(T) = 1 + \max(\text{height}(T_1), \text{height}(T_2))$$
$$\text{size}(T) = 1 + \text{size}(T_1) + \text{size}(T_2)$$

Note how the recursive function mimics the recursive definition of the set.

(a) Compute the size and height of the tree at the beginning of Section 7.3 on page 92.
(b) size(T) is better known as what?
(c) Prove by structural induction that for every RBT T, size(T) $\leq 2^{\text{height}(T)+1} - 1$.

8.6 Problems

Problem 8.1. We show a recursive function on the right, whose input is a non-negative integer. Tinker with this function. Make a conjecture for what the function does and prove your conjecture by induction.

```
UP(x):
1: If x = 0, return 1.
2: If x is odd, return 2 × UP(⌊x/2⌋).
3: If x is even, return x + 1
```

Problem 8.2. We show a recursive function on the right, whose inputs are an array $A = [A_0, A_1, \ldots, A_n]$, a real number x and an integer $0 \le j \le n$. The function implements Horner's method to compute the polynomial

$$A_0 + A_1 x + A_2 x^2 + \cdots + A_n x^n.$$

Prove that $\text{H}(0, A, x)$ correctly evaluates the desired polynomial.

```
H(j, A, x):
1: If j = n, return A_n.
2: return A_j + x * H(j + 1, A, x)
```

Problem 8.3. We show a triangle of numbers similar to Pascal's triangle. Row zero has just a 1 (all other numbers in row zero are 0). The numbers in each subsequent row are obtained by summing the three numbers above, as illustrated. Let $T_{n,i}$ be the ith entry of row n, $-n \le j \le n$. Then,

$$T_{i,j} = T_{i-1,j-1} + T_{i-1,j} + T_{i-1,j+1}.$$

(a) Tinker. Make a conjecture for the sum of a row and prove it.
(b) Give a formula for the number of non-zeros in row i. Prove it.

0	0	0	0	0	**1**	0	0	0	0	0
0	0	0	0	**1**	**1**	**1**	0	0	0	0
0	0	0	**1**	**2**	**3**	**2**	**1**	0	0	0
0	0	**1**	**3**	**6**	**7**	**6**	**3**	**1**	0	0
0	**1**	**4**	**10**	**16**	**19**	**16**	**10**	**4**	**1**	0

$\cdots$

Problem 8.4. In Equation (8.1) we listed strings in $\mathcal{M}$ as they are created by applying the constructor. Give an algorithm to systematically create this list. Illustrate your algorithm by listing the first 10 strings in $\mathcal{M}$. You may like to program your algorithm and present the output of your program.

Problem 8.5. For the set $\mathcal{A} = \{0, 4, 8, \ldots\}$ defined on page 101, prove by induction that $4n \in \mathcal{A}$ for integer $n \ge 0$.

Problem 8.6. Give a recursive definition for the set $\mathcal{A} = \{1, 2, 2^2, \ldots\}$, the non-negative powers of 2. Prove
(a) Every element of your set is a non-negative power of 2. (b) Every non-negative power of 2 is in your set.

Problem 8.7. Prove that every non-empty string in the set $\mathcal{M}$ of matched parentheses begins with an opening parenthesis [(structural induction). Prove that $][\notin \mathcal{M}$. Is every string that begins with an opening parenthesis in $\mathcal{M}$?

Problem 8.8. For any string x, show that $x \bullet x^{\text{R}}$ is a palindrome.

Problem 8.9. The set $\mathcal{P}_\text{o}$ of binary strings has a recursive definition.

① $\varepsilon \in \mathcal{P}_\text{o}$.
② $x \in \mathcal{P}_\text{o} \to x \bullet 0 \bullet x \in \mathcal{P}_\text{o}$
$x \in \mathcal{P}_\text{o} \to x \bullet 1 \bullet x \in \mathcal{P}_\text{o}$

(a) Show that every string in $\mathcal{P}_\text{o}$ is a palindrome.
(b) Show that every non-empty string in $\mathcal{P}_\text{o}$ has odd length.
(c) Is every palindrome in $\mathcal{P}_\text{o}$?
(d) Is every palindrome with odd length in $\mathcal{P}_\text{o}$? Prove your answer.

Problem 8.10. Recursively define all binary palindromes of even length and nothing else. Prove your answer.

Problem 8.11. Let T_n be the number of palindromes of length n (palindromes are recursively defined on page 104). Show that T_n satisfies the recurrence $T_0 = 1$, $T_1 = 2$ and $T_n = 2T_{n-2}$ for $n \ge 2$.
Prove that the number of palindromes of length n is $2^{\lceil n/2 \rceil}$ ($\lceil x \rceil$ is x rounded up).

Problem 8.12. A set $\mathcal{P}$ of parenthesis strings has a recursive definition (right).

① $\varepsilon \in \mathcal{P}$
② $x \in \mathcal{P} \to [x] \in \mathcal{P}$
$x, y \in \mathcal{P} \to xy \in \mathcal{P}$

(a) Determine if each string is in $\mathcal{P}$ and give a derivation if it is in $\mathcal{P}$.
 (i) [[[]]]][(ii) [][[]][[]] (iii) [[][][
(b) Give two derivations of [][][[]] whose steps are not a simple reordering of each other.
(c) Prove by structural induction that every string in $\mathcal{P}$ has even length.
(d) Prove by structural induction that every string in $\mathcal{P}$ is balanced.
(e) For a string $x \in \mathcal{P}$, define the inbalance as follows. Start on the left of x and move right. Add $+1$ for every [you encounter, and add -1 for every] you encounter.
 (i) After you traverse x, what is the imbalance?
 (ii) Give an upper bound on the imbalance at any point in x.
 (iii) Prove by structural induction that at any point in x, imbalance ≥ 0.
(f) In the text we defined the set $\mathcal{M}$ of balanced and matched parentheses. Prove that $\mathcal{P} = \mathcal{M}$
 (i) Prove by structural induction that every $x \in \mathcal{P}$ has a derivation using the rules for $\mathcal{M}$.
 (ii) Prove by structural induction that every $x \in \mathcal{M}$ has a derivation using the rules for $\mathcal{P}$.

Problem 8.13. Recursively define the binary strings that contain more 0's than 1's. Prove:
(a) Every string in your set has more 0's than 1's. (b) Every string which has more 0's than 1's is in your set.

Problem 8.14. A set $\mathcal{A}$ is defined recursively as shown.
(a) Prove that every element of $\mathcal{A}$ is a multiple of 3.
(b) Prove that every multiple of 3 is in $\mathcal{A}$.

① $3 \in \mathcal{A}$.
② $x, y \in \mathcal{A} \to x + y \in \mathcal{A}$; $x, y \in \mathcal{A} \to x - y \in \mathcal{A}$.

Problem 8.15. A set $\mathcal{S}$ of points on the 2-D plane has a recursive definition.
(a) On a 2-D xy-plot, show the points in $\mathcal{S}$ (you can't show all of $\mathcal{S}$).
(b) Prove that every point $(x, y) \in \mathcal{S}$ satisfies $y = 2x - 2$.

① $(1, 0) \in \mathcal{S}$
② $(x, y) \in \mathcal{S} \to (x+1, y+2) \in \mathcal{S}$

Problem 8.16. Assume a bee produces only one offspring. A male bee (blue) has only a female (red) parent. A female bee has a male and female parent. We show an ancestry tree of a male bee on the right. Let m_n be the number of ancestor bees at level n. Level 1 contains just the one male bee. For example $m_4 = 3$.
(a) What are $m_1, m_2, \ldots, m_7$?
(b) Get a recurrence for m_n and show $m_n = F_n$ (F_n are the Fibonacci numbers.)
(c) Suppose a hive has m_1 male bees and f_1 female bees in the current generation (level 1). Show that, for the entire hive, there are $m_1 F_n + f_1 F_{n+1}$ ancestor-bees at level n.

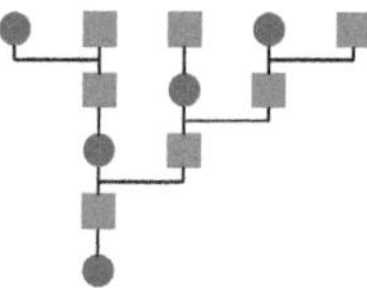

Problem 8.17. We reproduce the recursive definition of simple continued fractions from Problem 7.53.
(a) Prove that every element in $\mathcal{F}$ is a positive rational number.
(b) (Harder) Prove that every positive rational number is in $\mathcal{F}$. Let $x = a/b$ where $a, b \in \mathbb{N}$. Show that $x \in \mathcal{F}$ by strong induction on b.
(i) Base case, $b = 1$. Prove that for all $a \in \mathbb{N}$, $a \in \mathcal{F}$.
(ii) Induction step. Assume $a/b \in \mathcal{F}$ for $b \in \{1, \ldots, n\}$ and $a \in \mathbb{N}$. Prove that $a/(n+1) \in \mathcal{F}$ for $a \in \mathbb{N}$. *[Hint: Quotient remainder theorem.]*

① $1 \in \mathcal{F}$.
② $f \in \mathcal{F} \to n{+}1/f \in \mathcal{F}$ for $n \in \{0, 1, 2, \ldots\}$.

Problems 8.18–8.27 rely on the recursive definitions of RBT and RFBT; RTT and RFTT (ternary trees); and, RT (rooted trees), which are in Chapter 7 and Problems 7.50–7.52.

Problem 8.18. Recursively define rooted binary trees (RBT) and rooted full binary trees (RFBT).
(a) Give examples, with derivations, of RBTs and RFBTs with 5,6 and 7 vertices.
(b) Prove by structural induction that every RFBT has an odd number of vertices.

Problem 8.19. In a tree (RBT or RFBT): a vertex is a leaf if both children are empty; a vertex is half-full if one child is empty and the other is not. A vertex is full if both children are non-empty. Let L be the number of leaves, H the number of half-full vertices and F the number of full vertices. Let $n = L + H + F$ (total number of vertices).
(a) Prove by structural induction that in any RFBT, all vertices are either full or leaves: $H = 0$.
(b) Prove by structural induction that in any RBT, $n = 2L + H - 1$ and $F = L - 1$.
(c) Prove by structural induction that in any RFBT, $n = 2F + 1$.
(d) Use (c) to prove that every RFBT has an odd number of vertices.

Problem 8.20. The height and size of trees are defined recursively in Exercise 8.10. Prove:
(a) $\text{size}(T) \geq \text{height}(T) + 1$ for any rooted binary tree (RBT) T.
(b) $\text{size}(T) \geq 2 \times \text{height}(T) + 1$ for any rooted full binary tree (RFBT) T.

Problem 8.21. Consider these graphs:
(a) Which are RBTs? Explain your answers.
(b) Which are RFBTs? Explain your answers.

I: II: 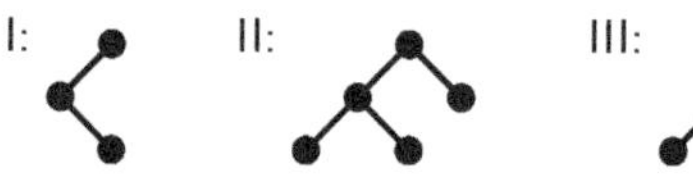 III: 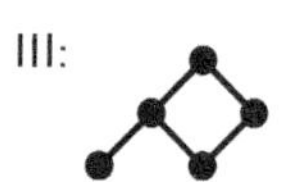 IV: 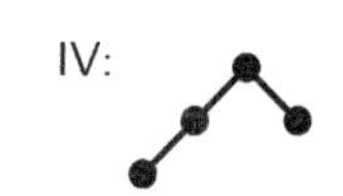

Problem 8.22. Prove that every RBT is connected (there is a chain of links from every vertex to every other vertex).

Problem 8.23. Answer T or F with with explanations.
(a) Every rooted binary tree (RBT) is a rooted ternary tree (RTT).
(b) Every every rooted full binary tree (RFBT) is a rooted ternary tree (RTT).
(c) Every rooted full binary tree (RFBT) is a rooted full ternary tree (RFTT).
(d) Every rooted binary tree (RBT) is a rooted tree (RT). (What about RTT?)
(e) Every every rooted full binary tree (RFBT) is a rooted tree (RT). (What about RFTT?)

Problem 8.24. Prove the following by structural induction.

(a) The degree of the root in any RBT is at most 2.
(b) The degree of the root in any RFBT is 2.
(c) The degree of the root in any RTT is at most 3.
(d) The degree of the root in any RFTT is 3.

Problem 8.25. Prove by structural induction a rooted full ternary tree (RFTT) has $3k-2$ vertices, for $k \in \mathbb{N}$.

Problem 8.26. Prove the following about the rooted tree on the right.

(a) (i) It is a rooted tree (RT). (ii) It is a rooted ternary tree (RTT).
(b) (i) It is not a rooted full ternary tree (RFTT). (ii) It is not a rooted binary tree (RBT).

Problem 8.27. Define size and height (see Exercise 8.10) for rooted ternery trees (RTT) and rooted trees (RT).

(a) Prove: For any rooted ternary tree (RTT) T, $\text{size}(T) \le (3^{\text{height}(T)+1} - 1)/3$. Find such a bound for the size of a rooted tree (RT) in terms of its height or explain why there isn't one.
(b) Prove: For any rooted ternary tree (RTT), $\text{size}(T) \ge \text{height}(T) + 1$. Find such a bound for the size of a rooted tree (RT) in terms of its height or explain why there isn't one.
(c) Prove: For any rooted full ternary tree (RFTT), $\text{size}(T) \ge 3 \times \text{height}(T) + 1$.

Problem 8.28 (Kraft Inequality). In an RBT or RFBT, the depth ℓ of a vertex is its distance to the root.

(a) Give an RBT with one vertex at depth 0, two at depth 1 and 4 at depth 2. Is your tree an RFBT?
(b) A leaf is a vertex with no children. Let $\ell_1, \ldots, \ell_L$ be the depths of the leaves in an RFBT. Prove that $\sum_{\ell_i} 2^{-\ell_i} = 1$.
(c) Prove, more generally, that in an RBT, $\sum_{\ell_i} 2^{-\ell_i} \le 1$. (For the empty tree ε, this sum is empty and equals 0.)

Problem 8.29 (Tree Merging). Start with n isolated trees: ① ② ⋯ ⓝ, each just a root (a collection of trees is a forest). Merging two trees gives a new tree with one root a child of the other root. Here is a sequence of merges:

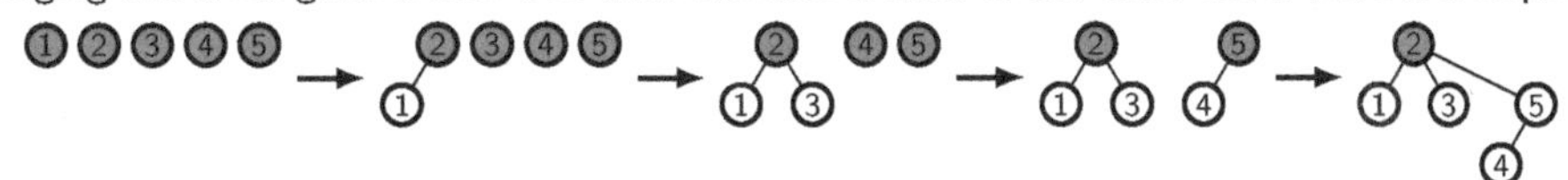

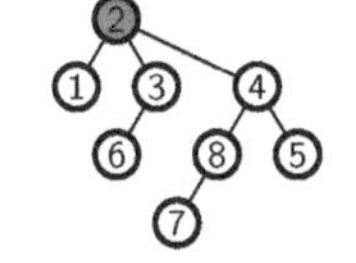

(a) Start with 8 roots ① ② ⋯ ⑧ and construct the tree on the right using merges.
(b) Start with n roots. Let T_k be the number of disjoint trees in the forest after k merges. What is T_0? Show that $T_k = n - k$.
(c) Prove that any tree with n vertices can be obtained from n roots using $n-1$ merges.

Problem 8.30 (Rooted Short Trees, RST). Merging (Problem 8.29) is used in the constructor to get "short" trees, where the smaller tree's root becomes a child of the smaller tree's root. The size of a tree is the number of vertices it has. Here is the recursive definition of RST.

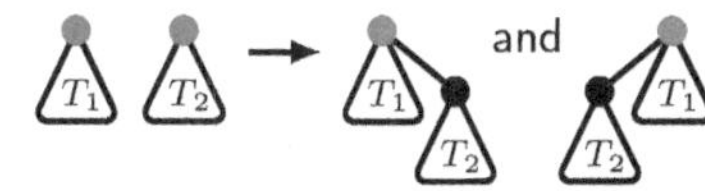

① A single root-node ● is in RST.
② Let T_1, T_2 be disjoint RSTs with roots r_1 and r_2 and $\text{size}(T_1) \ge \text{size}(T_2)$. Then making r_2 a child of r_1 gives another RST with root r_1.

(a) Is every tree in RST a rooted tree? Is RST $\subseteq$ RBT? Which of these trees are in RST?

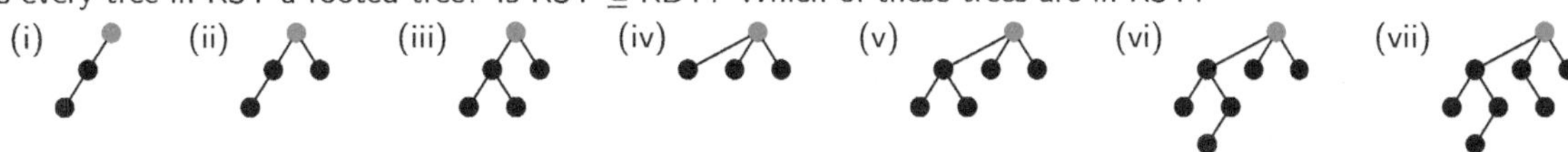

(b) Report size and height for each tree in (a). The height is the longest path-length from the root to a leaf.
(c) Prove: for every RST T, height(T) $\le \log_2$(size(T)). (Hence short tree. Union-find algorithms use short trees.)

Problem 8.31. This problem requires knowledge of matrices. Let $\text{A} = \left[\begin{smallmatrix} 1 & 1 \\ 1 & 0 \end{smallmatrix}\right]$.

(a) Prove that $\text{A}^n = \begin{bmatrix} F_{n+1} & F_n \\ F_n & F_{n-1} \end{bmatrix}$, where F_n are the Fibonacci numbers with $F_0 = 0$.
(b) Take the determinant of A^n and hence prove: $F_{n+1}F_{n-1} - F_n^2 = (-1)^n$.

Problem 8.32 (Computing Fibonaccis). Algorithm `F(n)` computes the nth Fibonacci number for $n \in \mathbb{N}$.

```
out=F(n)
 if(n<3) out=1;
 else
  out=F(n-1)+F(n-2);
```

(a) Let T_n be the time to compute $F(n)$. Get a recurrence for T_n.
(b) Show that $T_n \ge cF(n)$ for a constant c. Is this runtime impressive? Explain.
(c) Give another algorithm with linear runtime, $T_n \le Cn$.
(d) Find an algorithm with logarithmic runtime, $T_n \le C \log_2 n$. Prove the correctness and runtime of your algorithm. *[Hint: Problems 8.31, 7.44.]*

Problem 8.33. You start at $x = 0$ and at step i you can move up or down i. So a possible path is $0, 1, 3, 0, 4$.

(a) Prove that every $n \in \mathbb{N}$ can be reached.

(b) Let $T(n)$ be the minimum number of steps to reach n. Prove that $T(n) \le 3\sqrt{2n}$.

Problem 8.34 (Nested roots). Define the sequence of nested roots $\sqrt{m}$, $\sqrt{m+\sqrt{m}}$, $\sqrt{m+\sqrt{m+\sqrt{m}}}$, ... by the recurrence $x_1 = \sqrt{m}$ and $x_{n+1} = \sqrt{m + x_n}$ for $n \ge 1$. Prove that $x_n < \sqrt{m+1/4} + 1/2$. Evaluate the upper bound for $m = 1$ and $m = 6$ and compare with the actual limits (you may numerically estimate the limits).

Problem 8.35. Let $A_0, A_1, A_2, \ldots$ be a sequence. The differencing operator for sequences is like differentiation for functions. The kth difference is recursively defined as follows:

$$\Delta^{(0)} A_n = A_n; \qquad \Delta^{(k)} A_n = \Delta^{(k-1)} A_n - \Delta^{(k-1)} A_{n-1}, \text{ for } k \ge 1.$$

Show that $\Delta^{(1)} A_n = A_n - A_{n-1}$ and $\Delta^{(2)} A_n = A_n - 2A_{n-1} + A_{n-2}$. For what n are $\Delta^{(1)} A_n$ and $\Delta^{(2)} A_n$ defined?

Problem 8.36. For two sequences A_n and B_n and the differencing operator in Problem 8.35.

(a) Prove by induction on k that $\Delta^{(k)}$ is linear, $\Delta^{(k)}(aA_n + bB_n) = a\Delta^{(k)} A_n + b\Delta^{(k)} B_n$.

(b) Prove by induction on k (and using (a)) that $\Delta^{(k)} A_n = \Delta^{(1)}(\Delta^{(k-1)} A_n)$.

Problem 8.37. In this problem you analyze how the differencing operator affects polynomials.

(a) Let $A_n = n^k$. Show that $\Delta^{(1)} A_n$ is a polynomial of degree $k - 1$.

(b) If $A_n = a_0 + a_1 n + a_2 n^2 + \cdots + a_k n^k$ is a degree k polynomial in n, show that $\Delta^{(1)} A_n$ has degree $k - 1$.

(c) Prove by induction on i that if A_n is a degree k polynomial in n, then $\Delta^{(i)} A_n$ has degree $k - i$, for $0 \le i \le k$.

(d) Show that if A_n is a polynomial in n of degree k, $\Delta^{(k)} A_n$ is a constant. (This justifies the method of differences.)

Problem 8.38 (Hadamard Matrices). This problem requires knowledge of matrices. The Sylvester-Walsh recursive definition for a set of matrices $\mathcal{H} = \{\mathrm{H}_0, \mathrm{H}_1, \mathrm{H}_2, \ldots\}$ is given by

$$\mathrm{H}_0 = [1]; \qquad \mathrm{H}_k = \frac{1}{\sqrt{2}} \begin{bmatrix} \mathrm{H}_{k-1} & \mathrm{H}_{k-1} \\ \mathrm{H}_{k-1} & -\mathrm{H}_{k-1} \end{bmatrix} \qquad \text{for } k \ge 1.$$

(a) What are H_1 and H_2? Prove that H_k is a symmetric $2^k \times 2^k$ matrix with all entries $\pm 2^{-k/2}$.

(b) Prove that $\mathrm{H}_k \mathrm{H}_k^{\mathrm{T}} = \mathrm{I}$, where I is the $2^k \times 2^k$ identity matrix and $\mathrm{trace}(\mathrm{H}_k) = 0$ for $k \ge 1$.

Problem 8.39. The Hadamard matrix in Problem 8.38 is used in the Hadamard transform (signal processing, fast-matrix-algorithms, coding theory, quantum computing, etc). Let $\mathbf{x}$ be a vector of length 2^k. This problem investigates an efficient algorithm for computing the matrix vector product $\mathbf{y} = \mathrm{H}_k \mathbf{x}$. Let $n = 2^k$ be the size of $\mathbf{x}$.

(a) Show that standard matrix multiplication uses n^2 multiplications and $n(n-1)$ additions to compute $\mathbf{y}$.

(b) Partition $\mathbf{x}$ $\mathbf{y}$ into top and bottom halves. So $\mathbf{x} = \left[\begin{smallmatrix} \mathbf{x}_1 \\ \mathbf{x}_2 \end{smallmatrix}\right]$ and $\mathbf{y} = \left[\begin{smallmatrix} \mathbf{y}_1 \\ \mathbf{y}_2 \end{smallmatrix}\right]$. Show that

$$\begin{aligned} \mathbf{y}_1 &= \mathrm{H}_{k-1}\mathbf{x}_1 + \mathrm{H}_{k-1}\mathbf{x}_2 \\ \mathbf{y}_2 &= \mathrm{H}_{k-1}\mathbf{x}_1 - \mathrm{H}_{k-1}\mathbf{x}_2 \end{aligned}$$

(c) Let T_k be the number of operations (multiplies and adds) to compute $\mathrm{H}_k \mathbf{x}$. Show that

$$T_0 = 1 \qquad \text{and} \qquad T_k = 2T_{k-1} + 2^k \qquad \text{for } k \ge 1.$$

(d) Show that $T_k = n(1 + \log_2 n)$. (Multiplication by a Hadamard is fast compared to general matrix multiplication.)

Problem 8.40 (Change of Variable). A recursion can be easier to solve after you change variables from A_n to $B_n = f(A_n)$, providing the recursion for B_n is easy to solve and $f(\cdot)$ is easy to invert so you can solve for $A_n = f^{-1}(B_n)$.

(a) Solve each recursion using an appropriate change of variable.

  (i) $A_1 = 1$, $A_n = 10A_{n-1} + 1$ for $n > 1$. (Change variable to $B_n = A_n + 1/9$.)

  (ii) $A_1 = 1$, $A_n = nA_{n-1}/(n-1) + n$. (Divide both sides by n and change variable.)

  (iii) $A_1 = 1$, $A_n = 10nA_{n-1}/(n-1) + n$.

(b) Suppose $A_1 = a$, $A_n = g(A_{n-1})$ for $n > 1$. Change variable to $B_n = f(A_n)$ and show that B_n satisfies

$$B_1 = f(a), \qquad B_n = f \circ g \circ f^{-1}(B_{n-1}) \text{ for } n > 1.$$

Use this formula to obtain recursions for each change of variable you made in part (a).

Problem 8.41 (Generating Functions). Generating functions are useful for deriving formulas for complicated recursions, instead of guessing formulas to prove by induction. Let $T_0, T_1, T_2, \ldots$ be the infinite sequence produced by the recurrence $T_0 = 0$ and $T_n = T_{n-1} + 2n - 1$ for $n \ge 1$. The generating function $G(s)$, for the sequence $T_0, T_1, T_2, \ldots$, is defined by the "formal" power series

$$G(s) = T_0 s^0 + T_1 s^1 + T_2 s^2 + \ldots = \sum_{i=0}^{\infty} T_i s^i.$$

(a) Let $G^{(n)}(s)$ be the nth derivative of G. Show that $T_n = G^{(n)}(0)/n!$.
(b) Show $G(s) = \sum_{i=0}^{\infty} T_i s^i = s \cdot \sum_{i=1}^{\infty} T_{i-1} s^{i-1} + 2\sum_{i=1}^{\infty} is^i - \sum_{i=1}^{\infty} s^i$. Show that the first sum is $sG(s)$.
(c) Prove by induction that $\sum_{i=1}^{n} is^i = s(1 + ns^{n+1} - (n+1)s^n)/(1-s)^2$. What is $\sum_{i=1}^{\infty} is^i$ for $0 < s < 1$?
(d) Show that $G(s) = (1-s)^{-1} - 3(1-s)^{-2} + 2(1-s)^{-3}$.
(e) Compute $G^{(1)}(s)$, $G^{(2)}(s)$, $G^{(3)}(s)$ and conjecture a formula for $G^{(n)}(s)$. Prove it.
(f) Compute a formula for $T_n = G^{(n)}(0)/n!$. Prove it by induction.

We met the sum of the odd numbers many times. You can guess the solution and prove it by induction, so generating functions are overkill here. But when there is no easy guess, generating functions are the powertool of choice.

Problem 8.42. Find a formula for T_n where $T_0 = 1, T_1 = 4$ and $T_{n+2} = 4T_{n+1} - 4T_n$. In Problems 7.25, we guessed the solution. Generating functions remove the guesswork.
(a) Show that $G(s) = 1 + 4s + \sum_{n=2}^{\infty} T_n s^n$.
(b) Use the recurrence to show that $\sum_{n=2}^{\infty} T_n s^n = 4sG(s) - 4sT_0 - 4s^2G(s)$.
(c) Hence, show that $G(s) = (1-2s)^{-2}$.
(d) Show that $G^{(k)}(s) = 2^k(k+1)!(1-2s)^{-(k+2)}$ (the kth derivative).
(e) Use Problem 8.41(a) to show that $T_n = (1+n)2^n$.

Problem 8.43. Use generating functions to derive the formula for the Fibonacci numbers F_n in Problem 7.19(b). Recall that $F_1 = 1, F_2 = 1$ and $F_n = F_{n-1} + F_{n-2}$ for $n \geq 3$. Define the generating function

$$G(s) = F_1 s + F_2 s^2 + F_3 s^3 + \cdots = \sum_{n=1}^{\infty} F_n s^n.$$

(a) Use the recursion $F_n = F_{n-1} + F_{n-2}$ for $n \geq 3$ to show that

$$\sum_{n=3}^{\infty} F_n s^n = s \sum_{n=2}^{\infty} F_n s^n + s^2 \sum_{n=1}^{\infty} F_n s^n.$$

(b) Use (a) to show $(1 - s - s^2)G(s) = s$ and hence $G(s) = s/(1-s-s^2)$.
(c) Use the methods in Problem 8.44 or 8.45 to prove the formula $F_n = \frac{1}{\sqrt{5}}\left(\left(\frac{1+\sqrt{5}}{2}\right)^n - \left(\frac{1-\sqrt{5}}{2}\right)^n\right)$.

Problem 8.44. Let $G(s) = (1-s-s^2)^{-1}$. For $|s| < (\sqrt{5}-1)/2 \approx 0.618$, the Taylor series for $G(s)$ converges,

$$G(s) = A_0 + A_1 s + A_2 s^2 + A_3 s^3 + A_4 s^4 + \cdots = \sum_{k=0}^{\infty} A_k s^k.$$

(a) Show that $G(s) = 1 + s(1+s) + s^2(1+s)^2 + s^3(1+s)^3 + \cdots + s^i(1+s)^i + \cdots$.
(b) Show that the coefficients in the series expansion of $G(s)$ are $A_n = \sum_{i=\lceil n/2 \rceil}^{n} \binom{i}{n-i}$.
(c) Compute $A_0, \ldots, A_6$. Show $A_k = A_{k-1} + A_{k-2}$ for $k \geq 2$, and hence $A_k = F_{k+1}$ (F_n are the Fibonacci numbers).
(d) Why are Fibonacci numbers in the leading digits of $1/0.9899 = 1.01020305081321345 5\cdots$?

The function $G(s) = (1-s-s^2)^{-1}$ is related to the generating function for the Fibonacci numbers.

Problem 8.45. One can analyze $G(s) = (1-s-s^2)^{-1}$ in Problem 8.44 by using partial fractions. Show:

$$G(s) = \frac{1}{1-s-s^2} = \frac{1}{\phi_-\sqrt{5}} \cdot \frac{1}{1-s/\phi_-} - \frac{1}{\phi_+\sqrt{5}} \cdot \frac{1}{1-s/\phi_+},$$

where $\phi_\pm = -(1 \pm \sqrt{5})/2$. ($\phi_\pm$ are the roots of the quadratic $1-s-s^2$.) Using $1/(1-x) = 1 + x + x^2 + \cdots$, show:

$$G(s) = \frac{1}{\sqrt{5}}\left[1 \cdot \left(\frac{1}{\phi_-} - \frac{1}{\phi_+}\right) + s \cdot \left(\frac{1}{\phi_-^2} - \frac{1}{\phi_+^2}\right) + s^2 \cdot \left(\frac{1}{\phi_-^3} - \frac{1}{\phi_+^3}\right) + s^3 \cdot \left(\frac{1}{\phi_-^4} - \frac{1}{\phi_+^4}\right) + \cdots\right].$$

Hence, prove that the A_n in Problem 8.44 are given by $A_n = (\rho_+^{n+1} - \rho_-^{n+1})/\sqrt{5}$, where $\rho_\pm = (1 \pm \sqrt{5})/2$.

Problem 8.46. Solve these recurrences and give a formula for A_n. Tinker. The techniques available to you are: guess and prove; methods for linear recurrences, Problems 7.22–7.25; generating functions, Problems 8.44–8.42.
(a) $A_0 = 0$ and $A_n = A_{n-1} + n$.
(b) $A_0 = 1$ and $A_n = \alpha A_{n-1} + \beta$.
(c) $A_0 = 1$ and $A_n = \alpha A_{n-1} + \beta n$.
(d) $A_0 = 1$ and $A_n = 2nA_{n-1}$.
(e) $A_1 = 1; A_2 = 3/4$ $A_n = A_{n-1}/2 + A_{n-2}/4$.
(f) $A_0 = 3; A_1 = 8$ and $A_n = 5A_{n-1} - 6A_{n-2}$.
(g) $A_0 = 3; A_1 = 5; A_2 = 17$ and $A_n = 2A_{n-1} - 4A_{n-3}$.
(h) $A_0 = 2; A_1 = 2$ and $A_n = 2A_{n-1} - 2A_{n-2}$.
(i) $A_0 = 1; A_1 = -1$ and $A_n = 2A_{n-1} - 3A_{n-2}/4$.
(j) $A_0 = 2; A_1 = 6$ and $A_n = 4A_{n-1} - 4A_{n-2}$.

Problem 8.47. Solve the following challenging recurrence without guessing. $P_0 = 1$, $P_n = 1 - P_{n-1}/2$ for $n > 0$.
(a) Use generating functions to derive a formula for P_n. *[Hint: Use partial fractions to analyze the generating function.]*
(b) Write $P_n = a_n/b_n$ and use the methods from Problem 7.40 to solve the joint recursion for a_n, b_n.

Problem 8.48 (Catalan Numbers). Let C_n be the number of RBTs with n vertices. Find a formula for C_n.

(a) What are C_0, C_1, C_2, C_3, C_4? Is there any obvious pattern?
(b) Show the recursion $C_n = \sum_{i=0}^{n-1} C_i C_{n-1-i}$, for $n \geq 1$. Compute C_5 and C_6.
(c) Show that the generating function satisfies $G(s) = 1 + \sum_{n=1}^{\infty} (\sum_{i=0}^{n-1} C_i C_{n-1-i}) s^n$.
(d) Show that $\sum_{n=1}^{\infty} \sum_{i=0}^{n-1} f(n, i) = \sum_{i=0}^{\infty} \sum_{n=i+1}^{\infty} f(n, i)$. (Assume absolute convergence.)
(e) Show that $G(s) = 1 + sG(s)^2$. Solve the quadratic and show $G(s) = (1 - \sqrt{1-4s})/2s$.
(f) Let a_k be the kth derivative of $\sqrt{1-4s}$ at $s = 0$. Show that $a_k = -2^k \times 1 \cdot 3 \cdot 5 \cdot (2k-3)$.
(g) Explain why $C_n = a_{n+1}/2(n+1)!$ and hence derive $C_n = (2n)!/n!(n+1)!$.
(h) Prove by induction that $C_n = (2n)!/n!(n+1)!$. C_n are known as the Catalan numbers.

Problem 8.49. [Principle of structural induction] Define a recursive set $\mathcal{S}$ as follows:

① **[Base case]** $s_1 \in \mathcal{S}$.
② **[Constructor]** $s, s' \in \mathcal{S} \to f(s, s') \in \mathcal{S}$.

The constructor f combines s and s' to create $f(s, s') \in \mathcal{S}$. For predicate $P(s)$, suppose

$$P(s_1) \text{ is true and } P(s) \wedge P(s') \to P(f(s, s')).$$

(a) What is s_2, the second string in $\mathcal{S}$? What are the next three strings s_3, s_4, s_5?
(b) For $s \in \mathcal{S}$, define the depth $\delta(s)$ to be the minimum number of uses of the constructor needed to derive s. What are the depths of s_1, s_2, s_3, s_4, s_5? Why is depth well defined.
(c) Is there any string other than s_1 with a depth less than 1?
(d) To prove $P(s)$ is true for all $s \in \mathcal{S}$, assume there is some $s \in \mathcal{S}$ for which $P(s)$ is false.
    (i) Let s_* be a string of minimum depth for which $P(s)$ is false. Why must s_* exist? Show that $\delta(s_*) > 0$.
    (ii) Consider any derivation of s_* with depth $\delta(s_*)$. The last step constructs s_* from two strings s', s'' which appear earlier in the derivation, $s_* = f(s', s'')$. Prove that $\delta(s') < \delta(s_*)$ and $\delta(s'') < \delta(s_*)$.
    (iii) Show that $s_* \in \mathcal{S}$, a contradiction.

(A "natural" ordering of a recursive set is by increasing depth. The same proof idea works for more complicated sets.)

> Far better an approximate answer to the right question, which is often vague, than an exact answer to the wrong question. – **John Tukey**
>
> When a man tells you he knows the exact truth about anything, you are safe in inferring that he is an inexact man. – **Bertrand Russell**
>
> The art of being wise it the art of knowing what to overlook. – **William James**

Chapter 9

Sums and Asymptotics

1: Computing Sums.
2: Comparing functions: Big-Theta, Big-Oh, Big-Omega, little-oh, little-omega.
3: The integration method.

Analyzing algorithm runtime and accuracy is much of the discrete math in computer science. Consider the maximum substring sum of a sequence of numbers, the largest sum of contiguous terms in the sequence. For the sequence below, the underlined substring has the maximum possible substring-sum of 12.

$$1 \quad -1 \quad -1 \quad \underline{2 \quad 3 \quad 4 \quad -1 \quad -1 \quad 2 \quad 3} \quad -4 \quad 1 \quad 2 \quad -1 \quad -2 \quad 1$$

The general formulation of the problem for input to a computer program is a sequence of numbers

$$a_1 \quad a_2 \quad a_3 \quad a_4 \quad \cdots \quad a_{n-1} \quad a_n,$$

and the output should be the maximum substring sum. The input is characterized by a size, in this case the number of elements, n. A simple algorithm to compute the max-substring-sum is to iterate over the left and right endpoints of the substring and compute the substring sum using a loop from the left endpoint to the right (3 nested loops). Loops involve repeated operations resulting in a runtime which involves summations. The runtime of this algorithm is $T_1(n)$, shown below in (9.1). The runtimes $T_2(n), T_3(n), T_4(n)$ of three other max-substring algorithms are also shown (see Problems 9.69-9.72 for details, only if you are curious):

$$T_1(n) = 2 + \sum_{i=1}^{n}\left[2 + \sum_{j=i}^{n}\left(5 + \sum_{k=i}^{j} 2\right)\right]. \tag{9.1}$$

$$T_2(n) = 2 + \sum_{i=1}^{n}\left(3 + \sum_{j=i}^{n} 6\right). \tag{9.2}$$

$$T_3(n) = \begin{cases} 3 & n = 1; \\ 2T_3(\frac{1}{2}n) + 6n + 9 & n > 1 \text{ and even}; \\ T(\frac{1}{2}(n+1)) + T(\frac{1}{2}(n-1)) + 6n + 9 & n > 1 \text{ and odd}. \end{cases} \tag{9.3}$$

$$T_4(n) = 5 + \sum_{i=1}^{n} 10. \tag{9.4}$$

Don't panic. We can handle such nasty runtime sums and recurrences (the algorithm for T_3 is recursive).

> **Pop Quiz 9.1 [The Σ Notation for Sums.]**
>
> Recall that $\sum_{i=1}^{n} f(i)$ means $f(1) + f(2) + \cdots + f(n)$. Note, $f(i)$ can be a sum. Compute $\sum_{i=1}^{3} f(i)$ when:
>
> (a) $f(i) = 1$. (b) $f(i) = i$. (c) $f(i) = \sum_{j=1}^{3} 1$. (d) $f(i) = \sum_{j=1}^{i} 1$.

Tinker. Write a program to compute the runtimes for $n = 1, 2, \ldots$ in (9.1)–(9.4) and verify the table below.

n	1	2	3	4	5	6	7	8	9	10
$T_1(n)$	11	29	58	100	157	231	324	438	575	737
$T_2(n)$	11	26	47	74	107	146	191	242	299	362
$T_3(n)$	**3**	27	57	87	123	159	195	231	273	315
$T_4(n)$	15	**25**	**35**	**45**	**55**	**65**	**75**	**85**	**95**	**105**

Which algorithm is best? The situation is muddy. Algorithm 1 clearly loses to Algorithm 2. The race between Algorithms 2,3 & 4 is not so clean. T_3 starts well, then loses to T_2 and T_4 and eventually regains the lead over T_2 at $n = 8$. T_4 starts out worst (initial overhead), but from $n = 2$ and onward is the clear winner. We need:

1. Tools to compute sums and solve recurrences, so we can get simple formulas for runtimes like T_1, T_2, T_3, T_4.
2. Ways to compare runtimes and capture the essence of an algorithm without overcomplicating things.

9.1 Computing Sums

Tool 1 (Constant rule). A few basic tools go a long way. Here are three (easy) sums.

$$S_1 = \sum_{i=1}^{10} 3 = 3+3+3+3+3+3+3+3+3+3 \qquad 3 \times 10$$

$$S_2 = \sum_{i=1}^{10} j = j+j+j+j+j+j+j+j+j+j \qquad j \times 10$$

$$S_3 = \sum_{i=1}^{10} i = 1+2+3+4+5+6+7+8+9+10 \qquad \tfrac{1}{2} \times 10 \times (10+1)$$

The index of summation is i. In S_1 and S_2 the summand is a constant independent of the summation index i, so the sum is just the number of terms multiplied by the constant. This is not the case with S_3.

A constant not depending on the summation index can be taken outside the sum.

$$S_1 = \sum_{i=1}^{10} 3 = 3\sum_{i=1}^{10} 1 = 3 \times 10 \qquad S_2 = \sum_{i=1}^{10} j = j\sum_{i=1}^{10} 1 = j \times 10.$$

Pop Quiz 9.2
Show that $T_4(n) = 5 + 10n$.

Tool 2 (Addition rule). Consider this sum with two terms added together in the summand,

$$S = \sum_{i=1}^{5} (i + i^2).$$

In full, $S = (1+1^2) + (2+2^2) + (3+3^2) + (4+4^2) + (5+5^2)$. After rearranging the terms,

$$S = (1+2+3+4+5) + (1^2+2^2+3^2+4^2+5^2) = \sum_{i=1}^{5} i + \sum_{i=1}^{5} i^2.$$

The sum of terms added together is the addition of the individual sums.

$$\sum_i (a(i) + b(i) + c(i) + \cdots) = \sum_i a(i) + \sum_i b(i) + \sum_i c(i) + \cdots$$

Tool 3 (Common sums). Sums recur in algorithm analysis. Keep the repeat offenders at your fingertips.

Common Sums. Prove these sums by induction on n. Please do it!

1. $\sum_{i=k}^{n} 1 = n+1-k$
2. $\sum_{i=1}^{n} f(x) = nf(x)$
3. $\sum_{i=0}^{n} r^i = \frac{1-r^{n+1}}{1-r}$ $(r\neq 1)$
4. $\sum_{i=1}^{n} i = \frac{1}{2}n(n+1)$
5. $\sum_{i=1}^{n} i^2 = \frac{1}{6}n(n+1)(2n+1)$
6. $\sum_{i=1}^{n} i^3 = \frac{1}{4}n^2(n+1)^2$
7. $\sum_{i=0}^{n} 2^i = 2^{n+1}-1$
8. $\sum_{i=0}^{n} \frac{1}{2^i} = 2-\frac{1}{2^n}$
9. $\sum_{i=1}^{n} \log i = \log n!$

Exercise 9.3

Compute a formula for the sum $S(n) = \sum_{i=1}^{n}(1+2i+2^{i+2})$.

Tool 4 (Nested Sum Rule). Here are two sums which look similar.

$$S_1 = \sum_{i=1}^{3}\sum_{j=1}^{3} 1; \qquad S_2 = \sum_{i=1}^{3}\sum_{j=1}^{i} 1.$$

Let us write out these sums. We add up the summand for each possible value of i.

$$S_1 = \underset{(i=1)}{\sum_{j=1}^{3} 1} + \underset{(i=2)}{\sum_{j=1}^{3} 1} + \underset{(i=3)}{\sum_{j=1}^{3} 1} = 3 + 3 + 3 = 9 \qquad S_2 = \underset{(i=1)}{\sum_{j=1}^{1} 1} + \underset{(i=2)}{\sum_{j=1}^{2} 1} + \underset{(i=3)}{\sum_{j=1}^{3} 1} = 1 + 2 + 3 = 6.$$

In S_2, the summand depends on i, but not so in S_1. The results are quite different. Nested sums are often tricky. You will usually escape unscathed if you adhere to a simple rule:

To compute a nested sum, start with the innermost sum and proceed outward.

Let us use this rule for S_1 and S_2. In S_1, the inner sum is $\sum_{j=1}^{3} 1 = 3$. We now replace the inner sum with 3 to get the new summand for the outer sum,

$$S_1 = \sum_{i=1}^{3}\left(\sum_{j=1}^{3} 1\right) = \sum_{i=1}^{3} 3 = 3\sum_{i=1}^{3} 1 = 3\cdot 3 = 9.$$

In S_2, the inner sum is $\sum_{j=1}^{i} 1 = i$. Replacing the inner sum with i, we get

$$S_2 = \sum_{i=1}^{3}\left(\sum_{j=1}^{i} 1\right) = \sum_{i=1}^{3} i = \tfrac{1}{2}\cdot 3\cdot(3+1) = 6.$$

In the next example, we use these techniques to compute $T_2(n)$.

Example 9.1. $T_2(n) = 2 + \sum_{i=1}^{n}\left(3 + \sum_{j=i}^{n} 6\right)$. We start with the inner sum,

$$\sum_{j=i}^{n} 6 = 6\sum_{j=i}^{n} 1 = 6(n+1-i) \qquad \text{(common sum)}$$

Now, in the outer sum, replace the inner sum with the expression we just computed,

$$\sum_{i=1}^{n}\left(3+\sum_{j=i}^{n} 6\right) = \sum_{i=1}^{n}(3+6(n+1-i)) = 3\sum_{i=1}^{n} 1 + 6\sum_{i=1}^{n}(n+1-i). \tag{9.5}$$

In the last step, we used the addition rule. The first sum in (9.5) is $3n$. We can compute the second sum by using the addition rule, but here is a trick. When $i = 1$, $n+1-i = n$, and when $i = n$, $n+1-i = 1$, so

$$\sum_{i=1}^{n}(n+1-i) \;=\; n+(n-1)+(n-2)+\cdots+1 \;=\; 1+2+3+\cdots+n \;=\; \tfrac{1}{2}n(n+1).$$

Formally, this is a change of summation index in the sum, like a change of variable in integration. Define a new index variable $j = n+1-i$. So $i \geq 1$ means $j \leq n$, and $i \leq n$ means $j \geq 1$. The sum becomes

$$\sum_{i\geq 1}^{i\leq n}(n+1-i) \;=\; \sum_{j\leq n}^{j\geq 1} j \;=\; \sum_{j=1}^{n} j \;=\; \tfrac{1}{2}n(n+1).$$

Putting everything together in (9.5), $T_2(n) = 2+3n+3n(n+1) = 2+6n+3n^2$. □

Example 9.2. To practice, let us compute $\sum_{i=1}^{n}\sum_{j=1}^{i} ij$. Start with the inner sum, $\sum_{j=1}^{i} ij$. Since i is a constant independent of the summation index j, apply the constant rule and a common sum to get

$$\sum_{j=1}^{i} ij = i\sum_{j=1}^{i} j = i \times \tfrac{1}{2}i(i+1) = \tfrac{1}{2}i^2(i+1).$$

Now replace the inner sum with $\frac{1}{2}i^2(i+1)$ to get

$$\begin{aligned}
\sum_{i=1}^{n}\sum_{j=1}^{i} ij &= \sum_{i=1}^{n}\tfrac{1}{2}i^2(i+1) && \text{(replace inner sum)}\\
&= \sum_{i=1}^{n}(\tfrac{1}{2}i^3+\tfrac{1}{2}i^2) && \text{(algebra)}\\
&= \tfrac{1}{2}\sum_{i=1}^{n} i^3 + \tfrac{1}{2}\sum_{i=1}^{n} i^2 && \text{(constant and addition rule)}\\
&= \tfrac{1}{8}n^2(n+1)^2 + \tfrac{1}{12}n(n+1)(2n+1). && \text{(common sums)}
\end{aligned}$$

If you are up for it, you can further simplify to $\frac{1}{12}n + \frac{3}{8}n^2 + \frac{5}{12}n^3 + \frac{1}{8}n^4$. □

Exercise 9.4

(a) Show that $T_1(n)$ from (9.1) is $2 + 2\sum_{i=1}^{n} 1 + 5\sum_{i=1}^{n}\sum_{j=i}^{n} 1 + 2\sum_{i=1}^{n}\sum_{j=i}^{n}\sum_{k=i}^{j} 1$.

(b) Show that $\sum_{k=i}^{j} 1 = j+1-i$.

(c) Show that $\sum_{j=i}^{n}(j+1-i) = \sum_{\ell=1}^{n+1-i}\ell = \frac{1}{2}(n+1-i)(n+2-i)$.

(d) Show that $\sum_{i=1}^{n}(n+1-i)(n+2-i) = \sum_{i=1}^{n} i^2 + \sum_{i=1}^{n} i$.

(e) Use (b)–(d) to show that $\sum_{i=1}^{n}\sum_{j=i}^{n}\sum_{k=i}^{j} 1 = \frac{1}{12}n(n+1)(2n+1) + \frac{1}{4}n(n+1)$.

Exercise 9.4 analyzes the triple-nested summation in $T_1(n)$. You may compute the other sums in $T_1(n)$, collect terms and simplify (see Problem 9.69), to arrive at

$$T_1(n) = 2 + \tfrac{31}{6}n + \tfrac{7}{2}n^2 + \tfrac{1}{3}n^3.$$

With considerable effort, we have computed $T_1(n)$, $T_2(n)$ and $T_4(n)$. What about $T_3(n)$? If you are feeling Herculean, you may try to solve the recurrence in (9.3). I won't envy you. Even though we can't solve the recurrence, we can get good lower and upper bounds for $T_3(n)$ (see Problem 9.69):

$$3n(\log_2 n + 1) - 9 \leq T_3(n) \leq 12n(\log_2 n + 3) - 9.$$

The runtimes are now simplified to formulae. Here is a summary of what we know for $T_1, \ldots, T_4$.

Algorithm 1: $\boldsymbol{T_1(n)} = 2 + \frac{31}{6}n + \frac{7}{2}n^2 + \frac{1}{3}n^3$
Algorithm 2: $\boldsymbol{T_2(n)} = 2 + 6n + 3n^2$
Algorithm 3: $3n(\log_2 n + 1) - 9 \le \boldsymbol{T_3(n)} \le 12n(\log_2 n + 3) - 9$
Algorithm 4: $\boldsymbol{T_4(n)} = 5 + 10n$

Which algorithm is best? How should we compare runtimes of computer algorithms?

9.2 Asymptotics: Big-Theta, Big-Oh and Big-Omega

As you see from the runtime-table on page 114, the best algorithm depends on the input size n. Yet, you must deliver just one algorithm to a client. What n should you use to compare the algorithms?

Computers solve big problems, so we compare algorithms on big n, asymptotic in n. The runtimes of our algorithms divided by the input size n are shown in Figure 9.1. Even my pet monkey says T_4 is best. We divided runtime by the input size n because one likes to know how runtime scales with input. The most sought after algorithms scale linearly – runtime doubles when n doubles. Algorithm 4 has linear scaling because $T_4(n)/n$ approaches a constant, see Figure 9.1.

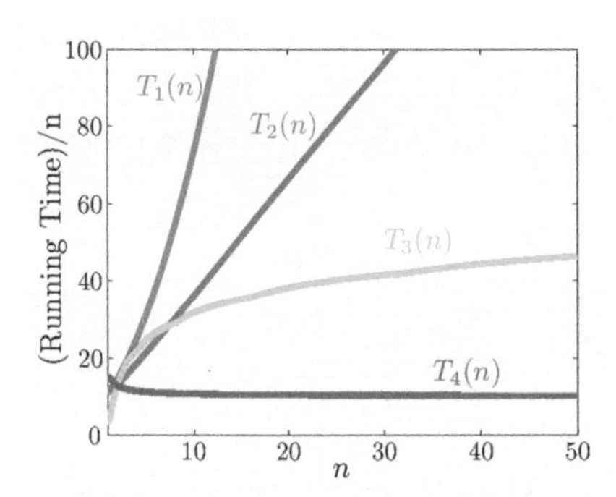

Figure 9.1: Runtimes $T_1, \ldots, T_4$.

Your fierce coder friend improved our algorithm and reduced the number of operations in the `for-loop` from 10 to 8. Their runtime was $T_4'(n) = 50 + 8n$, which is faster than T_4 for large n. At some point, we don't care about such minutia and its time to move on.

- Inputs in CS are BIG! We compare runtimes asymptotically in the input size n. That is $n \to \infty$.
- We ignore additive and multiplicative constants (minutia).

Ignoring additive and multiplicative constants highlights the growth rate of the runtime as n grows. Using growth rates to distinguish good from bad algorithms has withstood the test of time. Let us formally define the functions that are asymptotically linear, i.e. different from n by only additive or multiplicative constants.

Big-Theta. We use "big-Theta-of-n" to say a runtime is linear. The notation $T \in \Theta(n)$ is read "T is in big-Theta of n" and means $T(n)$ is asymptotically linear in n. The set $\Theta(n)$ contains the "linear" functions.

$T \in \Theta(\boldsymbol{n})$, if there are positive constants c, C for which $c \cdot \boldsymbol{n} \le T(n) \le C \cdot \boldsymbol{n}$.

In practice, we just verify $T(n)/n \to$ constant > 0.[1] The following functions of n are linear and in $\Theta(n)$,

$$2n+7, \qquad 2n + 15\sqrt{n}, \qquad 10^9 n + 3, \qquad 3n + \log n, \qquad 2^{\log_2 n + 4}.$$

The following functions of n are not linear and not in $\Theta(n)$,

$$10^{-9}n^2, \qquad 10^9\sqrt{n} + 15, \qquad n^{1.0001}, \qquad n^{0.9999}, \qquad n\log n, \qquad \frac{n}{\log n}, \qquad 2^n.$$

Let's justify some of these examples. The function $10^9 n + 3$ is certainly much bigger than n but we classify it as asymptotically linear and belonging to $\Theta(n)$ because the limit is a constant, albeit a big constant,

$$\frac{10^9 n + 3}{n} = 10^9 + \frac{3}{n} \xrightarrow[n\to\infty]{} 10^9 = \text{constant}.$$

The function $2n + 15\sqrt{n}$ is not a linear function, yet it is asymptotically linear. Look at the limit,

$$\frac{2n + 15\sqrt{n}}{n} = 2 + \frac{15}{\sqrt{n}} \xrightarrow[n\to\infty]{} 2 = \text{constant}.$$

[1] When the limit of $T(n)/n$ does not exist (e.g. see Problem 9.36), we use lim sup and lim inf.

The $15\sqrt{n}$ term eventually becomes negligible in comparison to $2n$, and so the function is effectively linear. Formally, we can give linear upper and lower bounds: $2n \le 2n + 15\sqrt{n} \le 17n$. It is in this sense that the function is "linear". Here are limits for some of the functions not in $\Theta(n)$ (prove the limits):

$$\frac{n^{1.0001}}{n} \to \infty; \qquad \frac{n^{0.9999}}{n} \to 0; \qquad \frac{n \log n}{n} \to \infty; \qquad \frac{10^9\sqrt{n} + 15}{n} \to 0.$$

When $T \notin \Theta(n)$, the limit is either 0 or ∞. If the limit is 0, $T(n)$ is "smaller" than n and we write $T \in o(n)$ read "T is in little-oh of n." The set $o(n)$ contains all functions whose growth rate is smaller than linear. When the limit is ∞, $T(n)$ is "larger" than n and we write $T \in \omega(n)$ read "T is in little-omega of n." The set $\omega(n)$ contains the functions whose growth rate is larger than linear. Intuitively, $\Theta(\cdot)$, $o(\cdot)$ and $\omega(\cdot)$ are the comparison operators $=, <$ and $>$ for functions. Here are some growth rates from practice, in order of best to worst runtime. Problem 9.12 asks you to plot them.

log	linear	loglinear	quadratic	cubic	superpolynomial	exponential	factorial	BAD
$\log n$	n	$n \log n$	n^2	n^3	$n^{\log n}$	2^n	$n!$	n^n

We can define Θ, o, ω with respect to any function $f(n)$, not just linear:

$$\frac{T(n)}{f(n)} \xrightarrow[n\to\infty]{} \begin{cases} \infty & T \in \omega(f); \\ \text{constant}>0 & T \in \Theta(f); \\ 0 & T \in o(f). \end{cases}$$

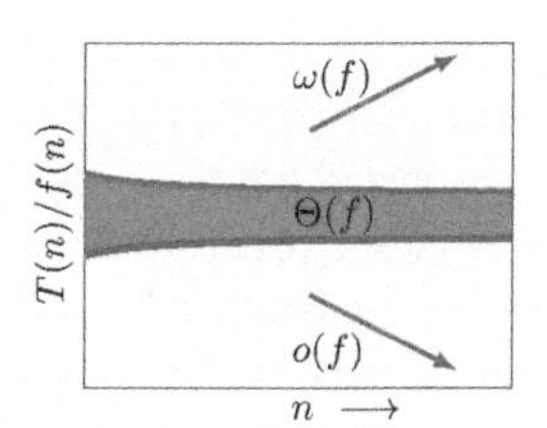

More formally, $T \in \Theta(f)$ if and only if $cf(n) \le T(n) \le Cf(n)$.

Big-Oh. To show that an algorithm is fast, having at most (say) quadratic runtime, we use big-Oh. The set $O(f)$ read "big-Oh of f" contains all functions "less than or equal to f," i.e., those in $\Theta(f)$ that "equal f" as well as those in $o(f)$ that are "less than f". Mathematically, you only need to upper bound $T(n)$,

$$T \in O(f) \quad \leftrightarrow \quad T(n) \le Cf(n).$$

Big-Omega. Similarly, to claim a runtime is slow, e.g. at least quadratic, use big-Omega. The set $\Omega(f)$ read "big-Omega of f" contains all functions "greater than or equal to f," i.e., those in $\Theta(f)$ that "equal f" as well as those in $\omega(f)$ that are "greater than f". Mathematically, you must show the lower bound,

$$T \in \Omega(f) \quad \leftrightarrow \quad cf(n) \le T(n).$$

Asymptotic notation gives 5 ways to compare functions, just as the comparison operators do for numbers,

$T \in o(f)$	$T \in O(f)$	$T \in \Theta(f)$	$T \in \Omega(f)$	$T \in \omega(f)$
"$T < f$"	"$T \le f$"	"$T = f$"	"$T \ge f$"	"$T > f$"

For polynomial runtimes, the growth rate is the polynomial's order (highest power). All these are in $\Theta(n^2)$,

$$2n^2, \qquad n^2 + n\sqrt{n}, \qquad n^2 + \log^{256} n, \qquad n^2 + n^{1.99}\log^{256} n, \qquad \sum_{i=1}^{n} i, \qquad \sum_{i=1}^{n}\sum_{j=1}^{i} 1.$$

However, $n^2 \log n \notin \Theta(n^2)$ even though the highest power of n is quadratic.

Pop Quiz 9.5
Which of $o(f)$, $O(f)$, $\Theta(f)$, $\Omega(f)$, $\omega(f)$ do the runtimes T_1, T_2, T_3, T_4 belong to (top of page 117)?
(a) $f(n) = n$. (b) $f(n) = n \log n$. (c) $f(n) = n^2$. (d) $f(n) = n^3$.

Sums with polynomial summands have polynomial growth rates. Here is a rule of thumb that often works.

Rule of Thumb. You can quickly determine the growth rate of a nested sum as
growth rate of nested sum = number of nestings + order of the summand.

The sum $\sum_{i=1}^{n}\sum_{j=1}^{i} ij$ has 2 nestings and ij is 2nd-order, so the rule of thumb gives growth rate $2+2=4$,

$$\sum_{i=1}^{n}\sum_{j=1}^{i} ij \in \Theta(n^4).$$

(The exact formula is in Example 9.2, page 116.)

Be careful if the summand is not a pure polynomial. For example $\sum_{i=1}^{n}\sum_{j=1}^{i} i\log j \in \Theta(n^3\log n) \neq \Theta(n^3)$.

Exercise 9.6

Familiarize youself with "order notation". Practice, practice. (All functions are positive and monotonic.)

(a) Show that $f+f$ and $f+f+f$ are in $\Theta(f)$. What about $f+\cdots+f$ (n terms)?
(b) For a constant $c>0$, show that $c\cdot f\in\Theta(f)$.
(c) Let $\epsilon, k>0$. Show that $\log^k n\in o(n^\epsilon)$
(d) Let $\epsilon, k>0$. Show that $n^k\in o(n^{\epsilon\log n})$ and $n^k\in o(2^{\epsilon n})$.
(e) For a constant $k>0$, show that $\log n^k\in\Theta(\log n)$.
(f) Show that $(1+\sqrt{n})/n\in o(1)$.
(g) Show that $n^{-1}+5n^{-2}\in\Theta(1/n)$.
(h) Show that $\log n!\in\Theta(n\log n)$.
(i) Show: if f is a polynomial of order a constant k, then $f\in\Theta(n^k)$.
(j) Let $f(n)=1+2+3+\cdots+n$. Is f a polynomial in n? What is the highest power of n appearing? Reconcile this problem with the previous problem.
(k) How do you show that $n^2\notin O(n)$. Show it. *[Hint: Contradiction.]*
(l) Suppose $f\in\Theta(r)$ and $g\in\Theta(s)$. Show: (i) $f+g\in\Theta(r+s)$. (ii) $f\cdot g\in\Theta(r\cdot s)$.
(m) Suppose $f\in\Theta(g)$. (i) Is $2^f\in\Theta(2^g)$? (ii) Is $\log f\in\Theta(\log g)$?
(n) Answer true or false, with explanations.
  (i) $f\in\Theta(g)\to f\in O(g)$ (ii) $f\in O(g)\to f\in\Theta(g)$ (iii) $f\in\Theta(g)\to g\in\Theta(f)$?
(o) Show that $O(n)\subset O(n^2)$. Is $\Theta(n)\subset\Theta(n^2)$?
(p) Show the transitivity properties:
  (i) If $f\in\Theta(g)$ and $g\in\Theta(h)$, then $f\in\Theta(h)$.
  (ii) If $f\in o(g)$ and $g\in o(h)$, then $f\in o(h)$.
  (iii) If $f\in O(g)$ and $g\in O(h)$, then $f\in O(h)$.
  (iv) If $f\in\omega(g)$ and $g\in\omega(h)$, then $f\in\omega(h)$.
  (v) If $f\in\Omega(g)$ and $g\in\Omega(h)$, then $f\in\Omega(h)$.
(q) Show that $O(f+g)=O(\max(f,g))$ and $\Theta(f+g)=\Theta(\max(f,g))$.
  (Recall that two sets A and B are equal if and only if $A\subseteq B$ and $B\subseteq A$.)
(r) Suppose $f\in\Theta(g)$. Show that $\sum_{i=1}^{n} f(i)=\Theta(\sum_{i=1}^{n} g(i))$.

For the problems below, two algorithms have runtime functions T_1, T_2. Which algorithm do you prefer?

(s) $T_1\in\Theta(n^2)$ and $T_2\in\Theta(n^3)$.
(t) $T_1\in\Theta(n^2)$ and $T_2\in O(n^3)$.
(u) $T_1\in\Theta(n^2)$ and $T_2\in o(n^3)$.
(v) $T_1\in\Theta(n^2)$ and $T_2\in\omega(n^2)$.
(w) $T_1\in\Theta(n^2)$ and $T_2\in\Omega(n^2)$.
(x) $T_1\in\Theta(n^2)$ and $T_2\in\Omega(n)$.
(y) $T_1\in\Theta(n^2)$ and $T_2\in O(n\log_2^{400} n)$.
(z) $T_1(n)=2n^2+n$ and $T_2(n)=15n\log_2^{400} n+25n$.

9.3 Approximation via Integration

Asymptotic analysis (big-Theta, etc.) says ignore constants and compare runtimes using growth rates. Approximate runtimes often suffice to get growth rates and integration is one way to approximate a sums. Since sums are everywhere, this is a powerful technique for getting growth rates. Warning: calculus heavy.

An integral or area under a curve is a limit of a sum of rectangles, a Riemann sum. We can approximate this Riemann sum by the integral. The rectangles in the next figure all have width 1, so the sum of their areas is $f(1)+f(2)+\cdots+f(n)$. On the left, the Riemann sum overestimates the integral by the red shaded area. On the right, the Riemann sum underestimates the integral by the red shaded area.

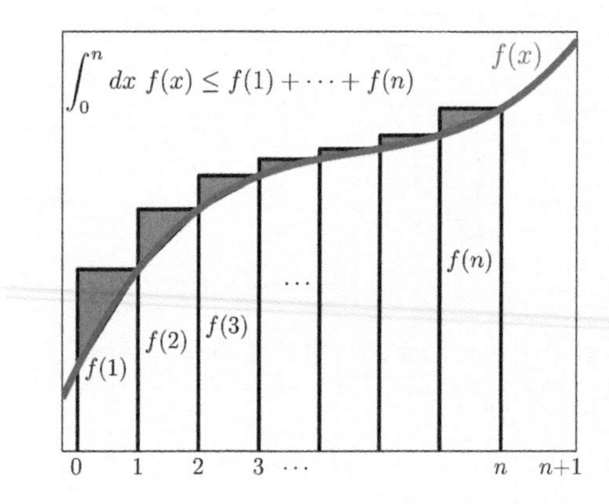

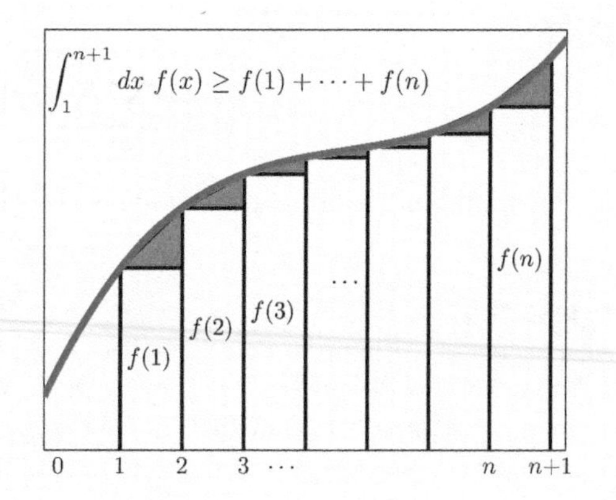

It is not hard to generalize the pictures to sum from $f(m)$ to $f(n)$, and obtain the next theorem.

Theorem 9.3. Let f be a monotonically increasing function. Then,

$$\int_{m-1}^{n} dx\ f(x) \le \sum_{i=m}^{n} f(i) \le \int_{m}^{n+1} dx\ f(x).$$

If the function f is monotonically decreasing instead, then the inequalities are reversed.

In a nutshell, you can estimate $\sum_{i=1}^{n} f(i)$ using $\int_0^n dx\ f(x)$. For a well behaved f that doesn't increase too fast, as is often the case in practice, $\sum_{i=1}^{n} f(i) \in \Theta\left(\int_0^n dx\ f(x)\right)$. Let's put the integration method to work.

Sum of integer powers: To get the sum of the integers raised to a power k, set $f(x) = x^k$. Then,

$$\sum_{i=1}^{n} i^k \approx \int_0^n dx\ x^k = \frac{n^{k+1}}{k+1} \in \Theta(n^{k+1}).$$

Exercise 9.7

To appreciate integration, plot the ratio $\sum_{i=1}^{n} i^4 \big/ (n^5/5)$ versus n, for n up to 1000. What is the limit?

Harmonic Sum: $H_n = 1 + 1/2 + 1/3 + \cdots + 1/n = \sum_{i=1}^{n} 1/i$. Use $f(x) = 1/x$ to get that

$$H_n = 1 + \sum_{i=2}^{n} \frac{1}{i} \le 1 + \int_1^n dx\ \frac{1}{x} = 1 + \ln n.$$

The inequality is reversed because $1/x$ is decreasing. To get a lower bound, we can use the integral of $1/x$ from 1 to $n+1$, which gives $\ln(n+1) \le H_n$. So,

$$\ln(n+1) \le H_n \le 1 + \ln n.$$

In fact, $H_n \to \ln n + \gamma$ where the constant $\gamma \approx 0.577$ is the famous Euler-Mascheroni constant.

Stirling's formula for $n!$. Since $\ln n! = \ln(1 \times \cdots \times n) = \ln 1 + \cdots + \ln n$, set $f(x) = \ln x$ to get

$$\ln n! = \sum_{i=1}^{n} \ln i \le \int_1^{n+1} dx\ \ln x = (n+1)\ln(n+1) - n.$$

Exponentiating both sides, and using $n! = e^{\ln n!}$ and $e^{(n+1)\ln(n+1)-n} = (n+1)^{n+1}e^{-n}$, we get

$$n! \le (n+1)^{n+1}e^{-n} \tag{9.6}$$

Stirling's approximation is better: $n! = n^n e^{-n}\sqrt{2\pi n}\cdot(1+\varepsilon(n))$, where $\varepsilon(n) \in \Theta(1/n)$. Why is our bound much looser? Integration actually gives a good approximation to $\ln n!$. Indeed, $\ln n!/((n+1)\ln(n+1) - n) \to 1$. The problem is with the exponentiation at the end, which magnifies errors (see also Exercise 9.6(m)).

Analyzing Recurrences. Let us analyze a fairly complicated recurrence,

$$T_1 = 1; \qquad T_n = T_{n-1} + n\sqrt{n} - \ln n.$$

To use the integration method, we first unfold the recursion as follows:

$$\begin{aligned}
T_n &= \cancel{T_{n-1}} + n\sqrt{n} - \ln n \\
\cancel{T_{n-1}} &= \cancel{T_{n-2}} + (n-1)\sqrt{n-1} - \ln(n-1) \\
\cancel{T_{n-2}} &= \cancel{T_{n-3}} + (n-2)\sqrt{n-2} - \ln(n-2) \\
&\vdots \\
\cancel{T_3} &= \cancel{T_2} + 3\sqrt{3} - \ln 3 \\
\cancel{T_2} &= \cancel{T_1}^{\,1} + 2\sqrt{2} - \ln 2 \\
\hline
+ \quad T_n &= 1 + 2\sqrt{2} + \cdots + n\sqrt{n} - (\ln 2 + \ln 3 + \cdots + \ln n) \\
&= \sum_{i=1}^{n} i\sqrt{i} - \sum_{i=1}^{n} \ln i
\end{aligned}$$

The cancellations occur when we sum the left and right hand sides and equate the sums. We already have approximations for both sums on the right,

$$\sum_{i=1}^{n} i^{3/2} \approx \frac{2}{5} n^{5/2}; \qquad \sum_{i=1}^{n} \ln i = \ln n! \approx (n+1)\ln(n+1) - n.$$

We conclude that

$$T_n \approx 2n^2\sqrt{n}/5 - (n+1)\ln(n+1) + n \in \Theta(n^2\sqrt{n}).$$

The analysis is rough, but that is exactly what we need to quickly estimate the growth rate of a sum or a recurrence. Constants are of no importance and get washed away in the asymptotic analysis.

Exercise 9.8

Use the integration method to get upper and lower bounds for these sums. Then determine the "simplest" function $f(n)$ for which the sum is in $\Theta(f(n))$.

(a) $\sum_{i=1}^{n}(1+i)^2$ (b) $\sum_{i=1}^{n} 2^i$ (c) $\sum_{i=1}^{n} i2^i$ (d) $\sum_{i=1}^{n} \frac{1}{1+i^2}$ (e) $\sum_{i=1}^{n} \frac{i}{1+i^2}$ (f) $\sum_{i=1}^{n} i2^{i^2}$

Exercise 9.9

Exercise 9.8(c) is a common geometric-like sum. Compute $S(n) = \sum_{i=1}^{n} i2^i$ using the following approach. (For another approach see Problem 19.61)

(a) Show: $S(n) = 1\cdot 2^1 + 2\cdot 2^2 + 3\cdot 2^3 + 4\cdot 2^4 + \cdots + n2^n$

(b) Show: $2S(n) = 1\cdot 2^2 + 2\cdot 2^3 + 3\cdot 2^4 + \cdots + (n-1)2^n + n2^{n+1}$

(c) Show: $S(n) = n2^{n+1} - \sum_{i=1}^{n} 2^i$

(d) Show: $S(n) = (n-1)2^{n+1} + 2$

Exercise 9.10 [Refining the approximation of $n!$]

Refine the approximation $n! \le (n+1)^{n+1}e^{-n}$. Use $\ln n! = \sum_{i=2}^{n} \ln i$ and the hint in the figure to show

$$n! \ge n^n e^{-n}\sqrt{n}e(2/3)^{3/2}\left(\tfrac{n+1/2}{n}\right)^{n+1/2} \approx n^n e^{-n}\sqrt{n}(2e/3)^{3/2}.$$

Our constant is $(2e/3)^{3/2} \approx 2.44$; Stirling's is $\sqrt{2\pi} \approx 2.51$.

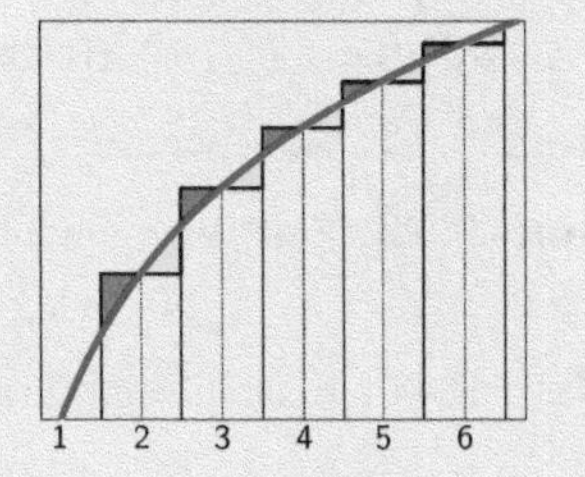

9.4 Problems

For all problems, assume basic operations take 1 time-unit ($+, -, \times, \div, \lfloor \cdot \rfloor, \lceil \cdot \rceil$, assign, compare, max, min).

Problem 9.1. Compute the following sums.

(a) $\sum_{i=1}^{5} 1$ (b) $\sum_{i=1}^{5} i$ (c) $\sum_{i=1}^{5} i^2$ (d) $\sum_{i=1}^{5}(4-i)$

(e) $\sum_{i=1}^{5} 2$ (f) $\sum_{i=1}^{5} 2^i$ (g) $\sum_{i=1}^{5}(2^i)^2$ (h) $\sum_{i=1}^{5} 2^{i^2}$

(i) $\sum_{i=1}^{5} \ln i$ (j) $\sum_{i=1}^{5} \ln i^2$ (k) $\sum_{i=1}^{5}(\ln i)^2$ (l) $\sum_{i=1}^{5} 2^{\log_2 i}$

(m) $\sum_{i=1}^{3}\sum_{j=1}^{3} 2$ (n) $\sum_{i=1}^{3}\sum_{j=1}^{3}(i-j)$ (o) $\sum_{i=1}^{3}\sum_{j=1}^{i} 2$ (p) $\sum_{i=1}^{3}\sum_{j=1}^{i}(i-j)$

(q) $\sum_{i=1}^{3}\sum_{j=1}^{3}\sum_{k=1}^{3} 2$ (r) $\sum_{i=1}^{3}\sum_{j=1}^{3}\sum_{k=1}^{3} 2^{i+j+k}$ (s) $\sum_{i=1}^{3}\sum_{j=1}^{3}\sum_{k=1}^{3}(i+j)$ (t) $\sum_{i=1}^{3}\sum_{j=1}^{3}\sum_{k=1}^{3} ijk$

Problem 9.2. Tinker and then compute formulas that do not contain a sum for the following:

(a) $\sum_{i=1}^{n} 3i$ (b) $\sum_{i=1}^{n}(3i+2j)$ (c) $\sum_{i=1}^{2n}(1+2i)$ (d) $\sum_{i=1}^{n}(3i+2i^2)$ (e) $\sum_{i=1}^{n}(i+1)^2$ (f) $\sum_{i=0}^{n} 2^{3+i}$ (g) $\sum_{i=1}^{n} ij$ (h) $\sum_{i=0}^{n}(i+j)^2$ (i) $\sum_{i=1}^{n}(-1)^i i$ (j) $\sum_{i=0}^{n}(-1)^i i^2$

Problem 9.3. Compute formulas that do not contain a sum for the following:

(a) $\sum_{i=1}^{n}\sum_{j=1}^{m}(i+j)$ (b) $\sum_{i=1}^{n}\sum_{j=1}^{i}(i+j)$ (c) $\sum_{i=0}^{n}\sum_{j=0}^{n}(2^i+2^j)^2$

(d) $\sum_{i=1}^{n}\sum_{j=1}^{i}(i+j)^2$ (e) $\sum_{i=0}^{n}\sum_{j=0}^{m} 2^{i+j}$ (f) $\sum_{i=0}^{n}\sum_{j=0}^{i}(2^i+2^j)^2$

(g) $\sum_{i=0}^{n}\sum_{j=0}^{i} 2^{i+j}$ (h) $\sum_{i=0}^{n}\sum_{j=i}^{n}(i+j)$ (i) $\sum_{i=0}^{n}\sum_{j=0}^{i}(2^j+i)^2$

(j) $\sum_{i=0}^{n}\sum_{j=0}^{i} 2^i$ (k) $\sum_{i=0}^{n}\sum_{j=0}^{i} i2^j$ (l) $\sum_{i=1}^{n}\sum_{j=1}^{n}\ln(ij)$

Problem 9.4. Compute a formula for: (a) $\sum_{i=0}^{n}(2^i)^2$ (b) $\sum_{i=0}^{n} i2^i$ (c) $\sum_{i=0}^{n} i^2 2^i$.

Problem 9.5. Compute a formula for $\sum_{n=0}^{\infty}\sum_{i=0}^{n} y^n x^i$. You may assume $|x|, |y| < 1$.

Problem 9.6. Compute formulas for (a) $\sum_{i=1}^{n}\sum_{j=1}^{n}\sum_{k=1}^{n}(i+j+k)$ (b) $\sum_{i=1}^{n}\sum_{j=1}^{i}\sum_{k=1}^{j}(i+j+k)$.

Problem 9.7. Compute a formula for the sum $4+44+444+4444+\cdots+44\cdots4$ (the last term has n fours).

Problem 9.8. Estimate these sums. (a) $\sum_{i=1}^{10}\sum_{j=1}^{20} 2^{i+j}$ (b) $2^1 \times 2^2 \times 2^3 \times \cdots \times 2^{20} = \prod_{i=1}^{20} 2^i$.

Problem 9.9. Let $\boldsymbol{a} = [1, 2, 3, 4, \ldots]$ and $\boldsymbol{b} = [1, 2, 4, 8, \ldots]$. Compute $\sum_{i=1}^{20}\sum_{j=1}^{10} a_i b_j$.

Problem 9.10. Here are errors in the use of asymptotic notation. Explain why they are errors.

(a) $2n^2 + n = \Theta(n^2)$.

(b) $4^n \in \Theta(2^n)$ because 4 is a constant factor bigger than 2, and we ignore constants.

(c) $O(1) + O(1) = O(1)$.

(d) Look! Your runtime $T \in O(n^2)$, so your algorithm is slower than linear.

(e) Look! My runtime $T \in o(n^3)$, so my algorithm is super fast (linear).

(f) $f \in O(g)$ (i.e. "$f \le g$"). Taking exponents on both sides, we conclude $2^f \in O(2^g)$.

Problem 9.11. Someone said $f = O(n)$ means "f equals $O(n)$". Why is this bad?

Problem 9.12. Plot these functions on a log-log plot to get a feeling for their behavior.

$\log n$ n $n\log n$ n^2 n^3 $n^{\log n}$ 2^n $n!$ n^n

Problem 9.13. Explain what $T(n) \in \Theta(1)$, $T(n) \in O(1)$ and $T(n) \in \Omega(1)$ mean.

Problem 9.14. Determine which of these functions is in $\Theta(n)$, in $\Theta(n^2)$, or neither.

(a) 10 (b) $3n+9$ (c) $\lfloor n \rfloor$ (d) $\lceil n/2 \rceil$ (e) n^2+n+1 (f) $\lfloor n \rfloor \cdot \lceil n/2 \rceil$ (g) $5n\log n$ (h) 2^n (i) n^2+3n (j) $n^2\log n$ (k) $3^{\log_2 n}$ (l) $4^{\log_2 n}$

Problem 9.15. Determine the order-relationships between 2^{n+1}, 2^n, 2^{2n}, 2^{n^2}, e^n, $n!$.

Problem 9.16. Determine the order-relationship between $\ln n$, $\ln(n^2+1)$, $\ln(2n)$.

Problem 9.17. Order these functions so that each is in big-Oh of the next. (F_n are the Fibonacci numbers and H_n are the Harmonic numbers.)

$F_n,\ H_n,\ n^{n^2},\ (1.5)^n,\ \sqrt{n},\ n^{100},\ n!,\ 2^n,\ (\ln n)^n,\ n^{\ln n},\ \ln^3 n,\ n^2,\ n\ln n,\ n^3,\ n^2 2^n,\ n^{2^n},\ F^2_{\lceil H_n \rceil},\ H_{F_n}.$

Problem 9.18. Answer true or false.

(a) $\sqrt{n}\ln n \in O(n)$ (b) $2n^2+1 \in O(n^2)$ (c) $\sqrt{n} \in O(\ln n)$ (d) $\ln n \in O(\sqrt{n})$ (e) $3n^3+\sqrt{n} \in \Theta(n^3)$
(f) $\ln n \in \Theta(\log_2 n)$ (g) $2^{n+1} \in O(2^n)$ (h) $2^{2n} \in O(2^n)$ (i) $3^n \in O(2^n)$ (j) $3n^3(1+\sqrt{n}) \in \Theta(n^3)$
(k) $\ln n^2 \in \Theta(\ln n)$ (l) $2^n \in \Theta(3^n)$ (m) $\ln^2 n \in \Theta(\ln n)$ (n) $2^n \in O(3^n)$ (o) $\ln(2^n) \in \Theta(\ln(3^n))$
(p) $2^{2\log_2 n} \in \Theta(n^2)$ (q) $2^{2\ln n} \in \Theta(n^2)$ (r) $2^{2\ln n} \in O(n^2)$ (s) $n! \in \Theta(n^n)$ (t) $n! \in O(n^n)$
(u) $\sum_{i=1}^{n} i^2 \in \Theta(n^3)$ (v) $\sum_{i=1}^{n} \sqrt{i} \in \Theta(n^2)$ (w) $\sum_{i=1}^{n} 2^i \in \Theta(2^n)$ (x) $\sum_{i=1}^{n} 3^i \in \Theta(3^n)$ (y) $\sum_{i=1}^{n} 3^i \in \Theta(2^n)$

Problem 9.19. For each expression $f(n)$, give as simple a function $g(n)$ as you can for which $f(n) \in \Theta(g(n))$.

(a) $3n^2+\sqrt{n}$ (b) $2^{3n}+4^n$ (c) $\ln(n^2)+\ln^2 n$ (d) $(0.9)^n+n^2$ (e) $(1.1)^n+n^{17}$ (f) $n+n\ln n+\sqrt{n}$
(g) $\sum_{i=1}^{n} i^3$ (h) $\sum_{i=1}^{n} \sqrt{i}$ (i) $\sum_{i=1}^{n} 1/i$ (j) $\sum_{i=1}^{n} 2^i$ (k) $\sum_{i=1}^{n}(2^i+5^i)$ (l) $(n+n^2)(1+2^n)$
(m) $\ln n!$ (n) $\ln^2 n!$ (o) $\ln 3^n$ (p) $\ln^2 2^n$ (q) $\ln 2^{n^2}$ (r) $(1+n)(1+n^2)$
(s) $\ln(2^n)^2$ (t) 2^{n^2+2n} (u) $\ln(2^{n^2+2n})$ (v) $\sum_{i=1}^{n} \ln i$ (w) $n^2(1+\sqrt{n})$ (x) $(n+a)^b,\ a,b>0$

Problem 9.20. Prove: (a) $\dfrac{n^3+2n}{n^2+1} \in \Theta(n)$ (b) $(n+1)! \in \Theta(n!)$ (c) $n^{1/n} \in \Theta(1)$ (d) $(n!)^{1/n} \in \Theta(n)$.

Problem 9.21. Let $f(n) = \sum_{i=1}^{n} i$. How is $f(n)$ asymptotically related to n, n^2, n^3?

Problem 9.22. For a positive integer k, show that $1^k + 2^k + \cdots + n^k \in \Theta(n^{k+1})$.

Problem 9.23. Prove by contradiction: (a) $n^3 \notin O(n^2)$ (b) $2^n \notin \Theta(3^n)$ (c) $3^{\lfloor \log_2 n \rfloor} \notin \Theta(n)$.

Problem 9.24. Show that $n^1 + n^2 + n^3 + \cdots + n^n = \sum_{i=1}^{n} n^i \in \Theta(n^n)$.

Problem 9.25. You write 1,2,3,...,n. How many digits are written? For example 1,2,3,4,5,6,7,8,9,10 is eleven digits.

Problem 9.26. Moore's law says CPU capability doubles every two years. In 2015, a standard desktop executes 10^9 operations per second (multiplications and additions). Let T_n be the runtime (number of operations) on a computing problem of size n. Complete the table below, which shows the maximum sized problem that can be solved in a second.

year	Maximum sized problem solvable given an algorithm's runtime					
	$T_n = 10^5 n$	$T_n = 10^4 n\log_2 n$	$T_n = 10n^2$	$T_n = n^3$	$T_n = 2^n$	$T_n = n!$
2015	$n_{\max} = 10^4$	?	?	?	?	?
2025	$n_{\max} \approx 3\times 10^5$	?	?	?	?	?
2035	$n_{\max} \approx 10^7$	?	?	?	?	?

Problem 9.27 (Estimate). Estimating properties of your algorithms is a fine art. Asymptotic analysis is very useful for quick and dirty sanity-checks. Practice your mental-math estimation skills (no electronic devices allowed).

(a) Are there more than a million pages in all the books of your library? What about the Library of Congress?
(b) How many hours in one million seconds. What about days? What about Years?
(c) Your algorithm sorts one thousand numbers in 1 second. How long does it take for one million numbers if the runtime is in (i) $\Theta(n)$, (ii) $\Theta(n\log_2 n)$, (iii) $\Theta(n^2)$? Give your answers in seconds, days and years.
(d) For the US, estimate the number of: (i) Cities. (ii) Gas stations. (iii) Miles of road. (iv) Miles driven per year.
(e) How many instructions can your 2GHz CPU execute in one year? What about arithmetic operations?

Problem 9.28. $f(0)=1$; $f(n)=nf(n-1)$. Compare $f(n)$ with: (a) 2^n (b) n^n.

Problem 9.29. $f(0) = 0$; $f(n) = f(n-1) + \sqrt{n}$. Compare $f(n)$ with (a) n (b) $n\sqrt{n}$ (c) n^2.

Problem 9.30. Compare these functions: $n^{1/\log_2 n}$; $n^{2/\log_2 n}$; $n^{1/\log_3 n}$; $n^{1/2^{\log_2 \log_2 n}}$; $n^{1/2^{2\log_2 \log_2 n}}$.

Problem 9.31. Give the asymptotic big-Theta behavior of the runtime T_n, where

(a) $T_0 = 1$; $T_n = T_{n-1} + n^2$ for $n \geq 2$.

(b) $T_0 = 1$; $T_1 = 2$; $T_n = 2T_{n-1} - T_{n-2} + 2$ for $n \geq 2$.

(c) $T_0 = 1$; $T_n = 2T_{n-1} + 1$ for $n \geq 1$.

(d) $n = 2^k$ and $T_1 = 1$; $T_n \leq 2T_{n/2} + n$ for $k \geq 1$. *[Hint: Prove $n \log_2 n \leq T_n \leq 2n \log_2 n$.]*

Problem 9.32. In each case, give the most accurate order relation between T_n and (i) n; (ii) 2^n; (iii) $2^{n!}$.

(a) $T_1 = 2$; $T_n = T_{n-1}^2$ for $n > 1$.

(b) $T_1 = 2$; $T_n = 2 + 2T_{n-1}$ for $n > 1$.

(c) $T_1 = 2$; $T_n = 2nT_{n-1}$ for $n > 1$.

(d) $T_1 = 2$; $T_n = (T_{n-1})^{1+2^{-n}}$ for $n > 1$.

(e) $T_1 = 2$; $T_n = (T_{n-1})^{1+1/n}$ for $n > 1$.

(f) $T_1 = 2$; $T_n = (T_{n-1})^{\sqrt{n}}$ for $n > 1$.

Problem 9.33. A postage machine has 4¢ and 7¢ stamps. Give algorithms with $O(1)$ runtime to solve these tasks.

(a) A user inputs postage n. Determine if the postage n can be dispensed (yes or no), and

(b) If yes, compute numbers n_4 and n_7 for which $n = 4n_4 + 7n_7$. That is, compute how to dispense the postage.

Problem 9.34. At an internet startup must engage users and convince them to create accounts. The 1-minute user gets bored after 1 minute and leaves. Similarly, there's the 2-minute, 3-minute, etc. users. There are half as many 2-minute users as 1-minute; half as many 3-minute users as 2-minute; and so on. The boss says you must tailor the webpage exclusively to the 1-minute user: focus on converting as many 1-minute users into accounts. Explain why.

Problem 9.35. Give order relationships between the pairs of functions. (a) $n^2!$ and $(n!)^2$ (b) $\ln(n^2!)$ and $(\ln n!)^2$.

Problem 9.36. Let $T(n) = 2^{\lfloor \log_2 n \rfloor}$.

(a) Is $T(n)$ monotonic? Plot n, $n/2$ and $T(n)$ versus n.

(b) Show that the limit of $T(n)/n$ as $n \to \infty$ does not exist.

(c) Show that there are constants c, C for which $c \cdot n \leq T(n) \leq C \cdot n$, for $n \geq 1$.

Problem 9.37. A recursive algorithm has a runtime $T(n)$ that depends only on n, the input of size. $T(1) = 1$ and for an input-size n, the algorithm solves two problems of size $\lfloor n/2 \rfloor$ and does extra work of n to get the output.

(a) Argue that $T(n)$ satisfies the recursion $T(n) = 2T(\lfloor n/2 \rfloor) + n$.

(b) Prove $T(n) \in \Theta(n \log n)$. *[Hint: Induction to show $n \log_2 n \leq T(n) \leq 2n \log_2 n$ for $n = 2^k$ and monotonicity.]*

Problem 9.38. For $f(n)$ in (a)–(f) and $g(n)$ in (i)–(v), determine if $f \in O(g)$, $g \in O(f)$, both, or neither.

	(a) n^3	(b) 2^n	(c) $n!$	(d) $\sum_{i=1}^{n} i^2$	(e) $\sum_{i=1}^{n}\sum_{j=1}^{n} 2^{i+j}$	(f) $\sum_{i=1}^{n} i\sqrt{i}$
(i)	$n^2 \log_2^2 n$	3^n	n^n	n^2	2^n	n^2
(ii)	$n^3 + n^2$	$2^{\sqrt{n}}$	$n^{n/2}$	$n^2 \log_2 n$	2^{2n}	$n^2 \log_2 n$
(iii)	$n^{3.5}$	2^{2n}	$(n+1)!$	n^3	2^{3n}	$n^{3\sin(n\pi/2)}$
(iv)	$2^{2+3\log_2 n}$	$2^{n+\log_2 n}$	$2^{n \log_2 n}$	$4^{\log_2 n}$	2^{n^2}	$4^{\log_2 n}$
(v)	$2^{\log_2^2 n}$	$2^{n+4} + 2^{\sqrt{n}}$	2^{n^2}	$8^{\log_2 n}$	$\sum_{i=1}^{n}\sum_{j=1}^{i} 2^{i+j}$	$8^{\log_2 n}$

Problem 9.39. Use the rule of thumb for nested sums on the bottom of page 118 to obtain the asymptotic growth rate for the following sums, and verify by exact computation. If the rule does not work, why not?

(a) $\sum_{i=1}^{n}\sum_{j=1}^{i} j$. (b) $\sum_{i=1}^{n}\left(i^2 + \sum_{j=1}^{n} j\right)$. (c) $\sum_{i=1}^{n}\sum_{j=1}^{n}\sum_{j=1}^{n}(i^2 + ijk)$. (d) $\sum_{i=1}^{n}\sum_{j=1}^{i^2} j$.

Problem 9.40. Give rough and dirty asymptotic analysis (growth rates) of these nested sums using big-Oh notation. The rule of thumb for nested sums on the bottom of page 118 won't work, but modified versions of the rule can work.

(a) $\sum_{i=1}^{n}\sum_{j=1}^{\lfloor\sqrt{i}\rfloor} i^3 j^2$. (b) $\sum_{i=1}^{n}\sum_{j=1}^{i^2} i^3 j^2$. (c) $\sum_{i=1}^{n}\sum_{j=1}^{i^2} i \log_2 j^3$. (d) $\sum_{i=1}^{n}\sum_{j=1}^{i^2} i^2 2^j$.

Problem 9.41 (Bounding Terms). Let $f(x)$ be a positive increasing function.

(a) Show that $\sum_{i=1}^{n} f(i) \le nf(n)$. Use this to get an upper bounds on (i) $\sum_{i=1}^{n} i^k$. (ii) $\sum_{i=1}^{n} 2^i$.

(b) Show that $\sum_{i=1}^{n} f(i) \ge (k+1)f(n-k)$ for $0 \le k < n$. Use this to get a lower bounds on (i) $\sum_{i=1}^{n} i^k$. (ii) $\sum_{i=1}^{n} 2^i$.

(c) Refine the bound in (a) and show $\sum_{i=1}^{n} f(i) \le (n-r)f(n-r)+rf(n)$, for $0 \le r \le n$. Show that $\sum_{i=1}^{n} 2^i \in O(2^n \log n)$.

Problem 9.42. Suppose $f(x)$ is positive and $f(i+1)/f(i) \le r$, where $0 < r < 1$. Show that $\sum_{i=1}^{n} f(i) \in \Theta(1)$.

Problem 9.43. You can use techniqes for sums to compute products. Show that

$$\log\Big(\prod_{i=1}^{n} f(i)\Big) = \sum_{i=1}^{n} \log f(i), \qquad \text{and} \qquad \log\Big(\prod_{i=1}^{n}\prod_{j=1}^{m} f(i,j)\Big) = \sum_{i=1}^{n}\sum_{j=1}^{m} \log f(i,j).$$

Compute the products: (a) $\prod_{i=0}^{n} 2^i$ (b) $\prod_{i=1}^{n} 2^{2i-1}$ (c) $\prod_{i=0}^{n} i2^i$ (d) $\prod_{i=0}^{n}\prod_{j=0}^{m} 2^{i+j}$ (e) $\prod_{i=0}^{n}\prod_{j=0}^{m} 2^i 3^j$.

Problem 9.44. Use integration to estimate $S_n = \sum_{i=1}^{n} r^i$. Compare with the exact formula.

Problem 9.45. Give upper and lower bounds and the asymptotic (big-Theta) behavior for

(a) $\sum_{i=1}^{n} \dfrac{i^2}{i^3+1}$. (b) $\sum_{i=1}^{n} i \ln i$. (c) $\sum_{i=1}^{n} ie^{2i}$ *[Hint: Integration by parts.]*

Problem 9.46. Use integration to get upper and lower bounds for $S_n = \sum_{i=1}^{n} \dfrac{1}{1+i^2}$.

(a) How tight are your bounds for S_{1000} (tightness is |upper bound − lower bound|).

(b) Write $S_{1000} = \sum_{i=1}^{10} \dfrac{1}{1+i^2} + \sum_{11}^{1000} \dfrac{1}{1+i^2}$. Compute the left sum. Bound the right sum with integration. What are your new bounds. How tight are they?

(c) Generally, for $n > k$, $S_n = \sum_{i=1}^{k} \dfrac{1}{1+i^2} + \sum_{k+1}^{n} \dfrac{1}{1+i^2}$. Use integration to bound the right sum. Show that the tightness of the bound is in $O(1/k^2)$.

Problem 9.47. Approximate $\sum_{i=1}^{\infty} i^{-3/2}$ to within $1/100$ using the integration method.

Problem 9.48. Give upper and lower bounds for $\dfrac{(2n)!}{(2^{2n} \times (n!)^2)}$. *[Hint: Use upper and lower bounds for $n!$.]*

Problem 9.49. Use integration to compute tight upper and lower bounds on $\sum_{i=0}^{n}\sum_{j=0}^{n} 2^{ij}$, so that the sum $\in \Theta(\text{bound})$.

Problem 9.50. Use integration to bound $\dfrac{(2i-1)!!}{(2i)!!} = \dfrac{1}{2}\cdot\dfrac{3}{4}\cdot\dfrac{5}{6}\cdots\dfrac{2i-1}{2i} = \prod_{i=1}^{n}\dfrac{2i-1}{2i}$. Compare with Problem 6.4.

Problem 9.51. For $f(x) = e^x \cdot e^{e^x}$, show

$$\sum_{i=1}^{n} f(i) \in \omega\Big(\int_0^n f(x)\Big) \qquad \text{and} \qquad \sum_{i=1}^{n} f(i) \in o\Big(\int_1^{n+1} f(x)\Big).$$

This function grows too quickly for the integration method. If your algorithm's runtime is $T(n) = e^n \cdot e^{e^n}$, good luck!

Problem 9.52. Show that $\sum_{i=1}^{n}\sum_{j=1}^{n} i = \sum_{i=1}^{n}\sum_{j=1}^{n} j$. What about $\sum_{i=1}^{n}\sum_{j=1}^{i} i = \sum_{i=1}^{n}\sum_{j=1}^{i} j$?

Problem 9.53. For any function f show these equalities between two sums.

(a) $\sum_{i=1}^{n} f(i) = \sum_{i=0}^{n-1} f(i+1)$ (b) $\sum_{i=0}^{n} f(i) = \sum_{i=0}^{n} f(n-i)$ (c) $\sum_{i=1}^{n}\sum_{j=1}^{n} f(i)f(j) = \Big(\sum_{i=1}^{n} f(i)\Big)^2$

Problem 9.54. Show that: (a) $\sum_{i=1}^{n}\sum_{j=1}^{i} f(j) = \sum_{i=1}^{n}\sum_{j=i}^{n} f(i) = \sum_{i=1}^{n} f(i)(n+1-i)$ (b) $\sum_{i=1}^{n}\sum_{j=1}^{i} f(i,j) = \sum_{i=1}^{n}\sum_{j=i}^{n} f(j,i)$.

Problem 9.55. Recall $H_n = 1 + 1/2 + 1/3 + \cdots + 1/n = \sum_{i=1}^{n} 1/i$. Let $S_n = \sum_{i=1}^{n} H_i$.

(a) Use the integration method to approximate S_n.

(b) Show that $S_n = \sum_{i=1}^{n}\sum_{j=1}^{i} 1/j$, and use Problem 9.54 to show that $S_n = \sum_{i=1}^{n}\sum_{j=i}^{n} 1/i$.

(c) Compute a formula for the double sum in (b) and compare it to your approximation.

(d) Prove your formula by induction.

Problem 9.56. Show that $\sum_{i=0}^{n-1} \frac{i}{n-i} = \sum_{i=1}^{n} \frac{n-i}{i}$. Hence, show $\frac{0}{n} + \frac{1}{n-1} + \frac{2}{n-2} + \cdots + \frac{n-2}{2} + \frac{n-1}{1} = nH_n - n$.

Problem 9.57. For any function f, show that $\sum_{i=1}^{n}\sum_{j=1}^{i} f(i,j) = \sum_{j=1}^{n}\sum_{i=j}^{n} f(i,j)$. Hence, compute these Harmonic sums.

(a) $\sum_{i=1}^{n} H_i$. (b) $\sum_{i=1}^{n} iH_i$. (c) $\sum_{i=1}^{n} i^2 H_i$.

Problem 9.58. Let $S(n) = \sum_{i=1}^{n} \frac{1}{2i-1}$. Show $S(n) = H_{2n} - \frac{1}{2}H_n$, and hence $S(n) \approx \frac{1}{2}(\ln 4n + \gamma)$, where $\gamma \approx 0.577$.

Problem 9.59 (Telescoping). Compute $\sum_{i=1}^{n}(f(i+1) - f(i))$ and $\prod_{i=1}^{n} f(i+1)/f(i)$, for any function f.

Problem 9.60. Find a formula in each case. *[Hints: Partial fractions; telescoping sum/product.]*

(a) $S(n) = \sum_{i=1}^{n} \frac{1}{i(i+1)}$

(b) $S(n) = \sum_{i=1}^{n} \frac{1}{i(i+1)(i+2)}$

(c) $S(n) = \sum_{i=1}^{n} \frac{i}{(i+1)!}$

(d) $S(n) = \sum_{i=1}^{n} \frac{1}{(3i-1)(3i+2)}$

(e) $\Pi(n) = \prod_{i=1}^{n} \left(1 + \frac{k}{i}\right)$

(f) $\Pi(n) = \prod_{i=2}^{n} \left(1 - \frac{1}{1+2+\cdots+i}\right)$

Problem 9.61. Differentiation can be used to compute sums.

(a) Give the formula for the geometric sum, $G(r) = \sum_{i=0}^{n} r^i$, and compute its derivative $\frac{dG}{dr}$.

(b) Show that $\frac{dG}{dr} = \sum_{i=0}^{n} ir^{i-1}$ and hence that $\sum_{i=0}^{n} ir^i = \frac{r}{(1-r)^2}(1 + nr^{n+1} - (n+1)r^n)$.

(c) Use the second derivative $\frac{d^2G}{dr}$ to prove the formula below for the sum $\sum_{i=0}^{n} i^2 r^i$

$$\sum_{i=0}^{n} i^2 r^i = \frac{r(1+r)}{(1-r)^3} + \frac{(2n^2+2n-1)r^{n+2} - n^2 r^{n+3} - (n+1)^2 r^{n+1}}{(1-r)^3}.$$

(d) When $-1 < r < 1$, use the result in part (c) to give formulas for the infinite sums $\sum_{i=0}^{\infty} ir^i$ and $\sum_{i=0}^{\infty} i^2 r^i$.

Problem 9.62. Use differentiation to show that $\sum_{i=1}^{\infty} 2^{-i}/i = \ln 2$.

(a) Let $S(\lambda) = \sum_{i=1}^{\infty} 2^{-\lambda i}/i$. Get a formula for $\frac{d}{d\lambda}S(\lambda)$. *[Hint: Derivative and sum commute.]*

(b) Get a formula for $S(\lambda)$ by integrating $\frac{d}{d\lambda}S(\lambda)$. For the constant of integration, try $\lambda \to \infty$.

(c) What should you set for λ in $S(\lambda)$ to get $\sum_{i=1}^{\infty} 2^{-i}/i$. What's the answer? What is $\sum_{i=1}^{\infty} 3^{-i}/i$?

Problem 9.63 (Abel's Summation by Parts). Analogous to integration by parts, $\int f dg = fg - \int g df$, prove the formula for summation by parts:

$$\sum_{i=m}^{n} f_i(g_{i+1} - g_i) = (f_n g_{n+1} - f_m g_m) - \sum_{i=m+1}^{n} g_i(f_i - f_{i-1}).$$

(a) For $\sum_{i=0}^{n} i2^i$, show that $f_i = i$ and $g_i = 2^i$. Hence show that $\sum_{i=0}^{n} i2^i = (n-1)2^{n+1} + 2$.

(b) Use summation by parts to compute a formula for $\sum_{i=0}^{n} i^2 2^i$.

(c) Using summation by parts, show $\sum_{i=1}^{n} H_i = (n+1)H_n - n$. *[Hint: $H_i = H_i \times 1$.]*

(d) Use summation by parts to show $\sum_{i=1}^{n} \frac{H_{i+1}}{i(i+1)} = 2 - \frac{1 + H_{n+1}}{n+1}$. Hence show that $\sum_{i=1}^{\infty} \frac{H_{i+1}}{i(i+1)} = 2$.

Problem 9.64.(Basel Problem) Compute exactly $\sum_{i=1}^{\infty} 1/i^2 \approx 1.645$. (Basel is the hometown of Euler who announced this sum in 1735. 100 years later, Weierstrass prove Euler's method rigorous.) Follow in Euler's steps.

(a) Use the Taylor series for $\sin x$ to give an infinite polynomial expansion for $(\sin x)/x$.

(b) What are the roots of $(\sin x)/x$? Show that $(\sin x)/x = A \cdot \prod_{i=1}^{\infty}(1 - x^2/\pi^2 i^2)$. What is A?

(c) Compare the coefficient of the x^2 term in (a) and (b) and deduce the value of $\sum_{i=1}^{\infty} 1/i^2$.

(d) Compute $\sum_{i=1}^{\infty} 1/(2i-1)^2$.

Problem 9.65 (Taylor Series and Infinite Sums). What is the Taylor series for $-\ln(1-x)$? Compute:

(a) $\sum_{i=1}^{\infty} \frac{(-1)^i}{i}$. (b) $\sum_{i=1}^{\infty} \frac{(-1)^i}{i+1}$. (c) $\sum_{i=1}^{\infty} \frac{r^{3i}}{i}$, where $0 < r < 1$.

Problem 9.66. Sharpen your canines on these tricky sums. Tinker. Find patterns. Guess. Use induction if needed.

(a) Get a formulas for these sums. (i) $\sum_{i=1}^{n} i\sqrt{2^i}$. (ii) $\sum_{i=1}^{n} i \ln\left(1 + \frac{1}{i}\right)$.

(b) Get a formula for $\binom{n}{0} + \frac{1}{2}\binom{n}{1} + \frac{1}{3}\binom{n}{2} + \cdots + \frac{1}{n+1}\binom{n}{n}$, where $\binom{n}{i} = \frac{n!}{i!(n-i)!}$.

(c) Get a formula for $\cos\theta + \cos 2\theta + \cos 3\theta + \cdots + \cos n\theta$. *[Hint:* $e^{i\theta} = \cos\theta + i\sin\theta$.*]*

(d) Show that: $\frac{1}{\log_2 k} + \frac{1}{\log_3 k} + \frac{1}{\log_4 k} + \cdots + \frac{1}{\log_n k} = \frac{1}{\log_{n!} k}$.

(e) Get a formula for $\binom{m}{0} + \binom{m}{1}\cos\theta + \binom{m}{1}\cos 2\theta + \cdots + \binom{m}{m}\cos m\theta$. *[Hint:* $e^{i\theta}$*; Binomial Theorem.]*

(f) Get a formula for $\sum_{1}^{n} iF_i = F_1 + 2F_2 + 3F_3 + \cdots + nF_n$. ($F_n$ are the Fibonacci numbers,)

(g) Get a formula for $\sum_{1}^{n} i^2 F_i = F_1 + 4F_2 + 9F_3 + \cdots + n^2 F_n$. ($F_n$ are the Fibonacci numbers,)

(h) Get a formula for this sum of ratios of Fibonacci numbers: $\sum_{i=2}^{\infty} \frac{F_i}{F_{i-1}F_{i+1}}$. *[Hint: Telescoping, see Problem 9.59.]*

(i) Using summation by parts, show $\sum_{i=1}^{n} \frac{H_i}{i} = \frac{1}{2}H_n^2 + \frac{1}{2}\sum_{i=1}^{n} \frac{1}{i^2}$. (Problem 6.6 proves this by induction).

(j) Get a formula involving the Harmonic numbers for the sum $\sum_{k=1}^{n} \frac{1}{(2k-1)(k+1)}$.

(k) Get a formula involving the Harmonic numbers for $\sum_{i=1}^{n} \frac{1}{1+1/i}$.

(l) Compute the infinite sum $\sum_{i=2}^{\infty} \frac{1}{i^4 - i^2}$. *[Hint: Partial fractions and telescoping. Basel problem.]*

(m) Compute the sum $S(n) = \sum_{i=1}^{n} \frac{3i+8}{i(i+2)} \cdot \left(\frac{1}{2}\right)^i$ and $\lim_{n\to\infty} S(n)$. *[Hint: Partial fractions and telescoping.]*

Problem 9.67 (Accelerating convergence). Let $a_i = (-1)^{i+1}/i$ for $i = 1, 2, \ldots$ and $S_n = \sum_{i=1}^{n} a_i$. The partial sums S_n converge to $S = 1 - 1/2 + 1/3 - 1/4 + 1/5 - \cdots$. Use a Taylor expansion of $\ln(1+x)$ to guess S.

(a) Compute the partial sum S_{20} and compare with the value of the full infinite sum S.

(b) The Shank transform $S^{(1)} = \Phi(S)$ is given by $S_i^{(1)} = (S_{i-1}S_{i+1} - S_i^2)/(S_{i-1} - 2S_i + S_{i+1})$. One can iterate the Shank transform and define $S^{(2)} = \Phi(S^{(1)})$, $S^{(3)} = \Phi(S^{(2)})$, and so on. Compute $S_{10}^{(4)}$ and compare with S.

(c) What values of a_i are needed to compute $S_{10}^{(4)}$ versus S_{20}. What is the conclusion?

(d) Justify the Shank transform as a way to accelerate the convergence of the sequence using the model $S_n = S + aB^n$.

Problem 9.68 (Divergent sums). Consider the sum $S = 2^0 + 2^1 + 2^2 + 2^3 + \cdots$.

(a) [Analytic Continnuation] Let $\phi(z) = \sum_{i=0}^{\infty} 2^i z^i$. When does the sum converge?
(i) Give a closed form for $\phi(z)$. (ii) Is the closed form defined at $z = 1$? (iii) What does this imply about S? (It's bizzare to evaluate this sum as negative. You need a course in complex analysis to see why it's okay.)

(b) [Axiomatic summation] Define a sum operator $\Phi(\mathbf{a})$ which assigns a value to an infinite sequence $\mathbf{a} = (a_1, a_2, \ldots)$ that we would like to interpret as the infinite sum. Any such operator should be incremental and linear,

$$\Phi(a_1, a_2, a_3, \ldots) = a_1 + \Phi(a_2, a_3, a_4, \ldots) \quad \text{and} \quad \Phi(\beta a_1, \beta a_2, \beta a_3, \ldots) = \beta\Phi(a_1, a_2, a_3, \ldots).$$

Let $x = \Phi(1, 2, 4, 8, \ldots)$. Show that $x = 1 + 2x$ and hence $x = -1$. An infinite sum of positives is negative!? ☺

Problem 9.69. Array $[a_1, \ldots, a_n]$ is input to the MaxSubstringSum algorithm below.

```
MaxSum ← 0;
for i, j = 1 to n do
  CurSum ← 0;
  for k = i to j do
    CurSum ← CurSum + a_k;
  MaxSum ← max(CurSum, MaxSum);
return MaxSum;
```

For $i \le j$, the algorithm considers all starting points i and ending points j, and computes the sum of the terms from a_i to a_j in CurSum. MaxSum is the maximum such sum. This algoirthm is known as "exhaustive brute force": consider all possible substrings $[i, j]$ and find the one with maximum sum.

Show that the runtime $T(n) = 2 + \sum_{i=1}^{n}\left[2 + \sum_{j=i}^{n}\left(5 + \sum_{k=i}^{j} 2\right)\right]$. Hence, show $T(n) = 2 + \frac{31}{6}n + \frac{7}{2}n^2 + \frac{1}{3}n^3$.

Problem 9.70. Here is a more efficient algorithm than the one in Problem 9.69.

```
MaxSum ← 0;
for i = 1 to n do
  CurSum ← 0;
  for j = i to n do
    CurSum ← CurSum + a_j;
    MaxSum ← max(CurSum, MaxSum);
return MaxSum;
```

The algorithm in Problem 9.69 repeats a lot of computation. The innermost loop (over k) computes a sum from i to j; this sum was available earlier when the sum from $i - 1$ to j was computed. We can get all substring sums starting from i in one pass from i to n.

(It helps to implement and test this and the brute-force algorithm from the previous problem on some sample sequences.)

Show that the runtime is $T(n) = 2 + \sum_{i=1}^{n}\left(3 + \sum_{j=i}^{n} 6\right)$. Hence, show $T(n) = 2 + 6n + 3n^2$.

Problem 9.71. Here is an algorithm for MaxSubstringSum based on recursion.

```
function S(ℓ, r)
if ℓ = r, return max(0, a_ℓ);
mid = ⌊(ℓ + r)/2⌋;
(LMax, RMax) = (S(ℓ, mid), S(mid + 1, r));
MidL, MidLmax ← a_mid;
for i = mid − 1 to ℓ do
  MidL ← MidL + a_i;
  MidLmax ← max(MidLmax, MidL);
MidR, MidRmax ← a_mid+1;
for j = mid + 2 to r do
  MidR ← MidR + a_j;
  MidRmax ← max(MidRmax, MidR);
return max(LMax, RMax, MidLmax + MidRmax);
```

The idea is to identify 3 cases for the max-substring: it lies entirely within the left half of the sequence (LMax); the right half of the sequence (RMax); or, it crosses over from the left to the right (MidMax). The final output is the maximum of the three cases.

The function computes the max-substring-sum from $[a_\ell, \ldots, a_r]$, so the desired max-substring sum is $S(1, n)$.

Let $T(n)$ be the running time on a sequence of size n. Show that $T(1) = 3$.

(a) If n is even, show that $T(n) = 2T(\frac{1}{2}n) + 21 + \sum_{i=1}^{\texttt{mid}-1} 6 + \sum_{i=\texttt{mid}+2}^{n} 6 = 2T(\frac{1}{2}n) + 6n + 9$.

(b) If n is odd, show that $T(n) = T(\frac{1}{2}(n + 1)) + T(\frac{1}{2}(n - 1)) + 6n + 9$.

(c) Tinker and compute $T(n)$ for $n = 1, 2, 3, 4, \ldots, 10$ to verify the table (you need to fill in the value for 10):

n	1	2	3	4	5	6	7	8	9	10
$T(n)$	3	27	57	87	123	159	195	231	273	?

(d) Use induction to prove that $T(2^n) = (6n + 12) \cdot 2^n - 9$.

(e) Prove that $3n(\log_2 n + 1) - 9 \le T(n) \le 12n(\log_2 n + 3) - 9$ and compare the bounds with your table in part (c). *[Hint: Argue by monotonicity that $T(2^{\lfloor \log_2 n \rfloor}) \le T(n) \le T(2^{\lceil \log_2 n \rceil})$.]*

Problem 9.72. Here is a very efficient MaxSubstringSum algorithm.

```
CumSum, CumMin, MaxSum ← 0;
for i = 1 to n do
  CumSum ← CumSum + a_i;
  CumMin ← min(CumSum, CumMin);
  MaxSum ← max(MaxSum, CumSum − CumMin);
return MaxSum;
```

The algorithm computes the cumulative sum CumSum from $i = 1$ to n. The max-substring-sum ending at i is CumSum(i) minus the minimum cumulative sum up to i, CumMin (CumMin starts at 0, the sum of the empty sequence). The algorithm maintains CumSum, CumMin and the maximum of (CumSum − CumMin).

Show that the running time is $T(n) = 5 + \sum_{i=1}^{n} 10$. Compute the sum and show $T(n) = 5 + 10n$.

> Babies can ask questions that grown-ups can't answer – **Paul Erdős.**
>
> Pray tell us, what's your favorite number?
> Shiva jumped up to the board, uninvited, and wrote 10,213,223.
> And pray, why would this number interest us?
> It is the only number that describes itself when you read it, "One zero, two ones, three twos, two threes" – **Abraham Verghese**

Chapter 10

Number Theory

1: Division, GCD, primes and the Fundamental Theorem of Arithmetic.
2: Modular arithmetic and cryptography.

Numbers have fascinated the great mathematicians since antiquity.[1] Six is perfect because it is the sum of its proper divisors. Is there a perfect odd number? Ten is a sum of two primes. Is every non-prime even number a sum of two primes? We can't answer these simple questions. Who cares? The great mathematical analyst, number theorist and consummate pacifist Harold Hardy, in *A Mathematician's Apology*, took pains to say:

> "No discovery of mine has made ... for good or ill, the least difference to the amenity of the world."

To Hardy, the beauty of number theory was its inapplicability to the real world. Number theory is the diamond forged in the pursuit of this beauty, for beauty's sake.[2] Ironically, just thirty years after Hardy died, RSA cryptography was born, facilitating secure internet banking, online shopping, e-mail, encoded communication during war, etc. The foundation of RSA is deep within number theory. What a blockbuster "difference to the amenity of the world." To learn this stuff, you must do the quizzes and exercises. Let us begin with division.

Pop Quiz 10.1
For $n = 27$ and $d = 7$, what is the minimum non-negative remainder r such that $n = qd + r$ for a $q \in \mathbb{Z}$?

Every highschooler knows that when n is divided by d, a non-negative remainder less than d is always possible. For example $27/6 = 4$ remainder 3, or equivalently, $27 = \mathbf{4} \times 6 + \mathbf{3}$. 4 is the quotient and 3 is the remainder.

Theorem 10.1 (Quotient-Remainder Theorem). Given $n \in \mathbb{Z}$ and $d \in \mathbb{N}$, there is a unique quotient $q \in \mathbb{Z}$ and remainder r with $0 \leq r < d$, such that $n = qd + r$. See Problem 10.1 for a proof.

We write $r = \text{rem}(n, d)$. If the remainder is zero, $n = qd$ for some $q \in \mathbb{Z}$ and d divides n, written $d|n$.

Definition 10.2 (Primes). A number $p \geq 2$ is prime if and only if its only positive divisors are 1 and p. The set of primes is $\mathrm{P} = \{2, 3, 5, 7, 11, 13, 17, 19, \ldots\}$. Note that 1 is not a prime.

Exercise 10.2
Prove the following familiar properties about divisibility.
(a) $d|0$.
(b) If $d|m$ and $d'|n$, then $dd'|mn$.
(c) If $d|m$ and $m|n$, then $d|n$.
(d) If $d|n$ and $d|m$, then $d|n+m$.
(e) If $d|n$, then $xd|xn$ for $x \in \mathbb{N}$.
(f) If $d|m+n$ and $d|m$, then $d|n$.

Exercise 10.3
(a) Show that every number greater than 1 is divisible by a prime. Use strong induction.
(b) Prove there are infinitely many primes. *[Hints: Contradiction. $n!+1$ is not divisible by $2, 3, 4, 5, \ldots, n$.]*

---

[1] Paul Erdős, loved only numbers. The prodigy Srinivasa Ramanujan was personal friends with everyone in $\mathbb{N}$, says Littlewood.
[2] It was Archimedes who said "Mathematics reveals its secrets only to those who approach it with pure love, for its own beauty."

10.1 Greatest Common Divisor

The divisors of 30 are $\{1,2,3,5,6,15,30\}$ and of 42 are $\{1,2,3,6,7,14,21,42\}$. The divisors common to 30 and 42 are $\{1,2,3,6\}$, and the greatest common divisor or GCD is 6. All common divisors of 30 and 42 divide the GCD 6. This is no accident. Try to prove it. We'll give a short proof later.

Definition 10.3 (GCD). Let m and n be two integers not both zero. The greatest common divisor $\gcd(m,n)$ is the largest integer that divides both m and n. Any other common divisor, dividing both m and n, is smaller than $\gcd(m,n)$. That is, (i) $\gcd(m,n)|m$ and $\gcd(m,n)|n$ and (ii) $d|m$ AND $d|n \to d \leq \gcd(m,n)$.

Definition 10.4 (Relatively Prime). If $\gcd(m,n)=1$, then m,n are relatively prime.

Clearly, $\gcd(m,n)=\gcd(n,m)$. Let $n=qm+r$. We prove the important fact that $\gcd(m,n)=\gcd(r,m)$,

$$\gcd(m,n)=\gcd(\text{rem}(n,m),m).$$

Proof. We prove it in two steps: (i) Show $\gcd(m,n)\leq\gcd(r,m)$ and (ii) Show $\gcd(m,n)\geq\gcd(r,m)$.

(i) $\gcd(m,n)$ divides $r=n-qm$ because it divides n and m (the RHS). Therefore, $\gcd(m,n)$ is a common divisor of r and m, which means $\gcd(m,n)\leq\gcd(r,m)$.

(ii) $\gcd(r,m)$ divides $n=qm+r$ because it divides m and r (the RHS). Therefore, $\gcd(r,m)$ is a common divisor of m and n, which means $\gcd(r,m)\leq\gcd(m,n)$. ■

Our proof is typical of "GCD-proofs". To show $\gcd(m,n)=\gcd(a,b)$,

(i) Show that $\gcd(m,n)$ is a common divisor of a and b, hence $\gcd(m,n)\leq\gcd(a,b)$.

(ii) Show that $\gcd(a,b)$ is a common divisor of m and n, hence $\gcd(m,n)\geq\gcd(a,b)$.

Conclude $\gcd(m,n)=\gcd(a,b)$.

Pop Quiz 10.4
What are $\gcd(n,0)$, $\gcd(0,0)$, $\gcd(n,n)$, $\gcd(n,1)$ and $\gcd(n,p)$ where p is a prime?

Euclid's GCD-algorithm, known to the Greeks over 3000 years ago, is based on $\gcd(m,n)=\gcd(\text{rem}(n,m),m)$. To illustrate the algorithm, we compute $\gcd(42,108)$. The first step is $\gcd(42,108)=\gcd(\text{rem}(108,42),42)$

$$\begin{aligned}
\gcd(42,108) &= \gcd(24,42) && 24=\text{rem}(108,42)=\mathbf{108}-2\cdot\mathbf{42}\\
&= \gcd(18,24) && 18=\text{rem}(42,24)=42-24=42-(108-2\cdot42)=3\cdot\mathbf{42}-\mathbf{108}\\
&= \gcd(6,18) && 6=\text{rem}(24,18)=24-18=(108-2\cdot42)-(3\cdot42-108)=2\cdot\mathbf{108}-5\cdot\mathbf{42}\\
&= \gcd(0,6) && 0=\text{rem}(18,6)=18-3\cdot6\\
&= 6 && \gcd(0,n)=n
\end{aligned}$$

Each remainder in Euclid's algorithm is an integer linear combination of the initial numbers 42 and 108. In particular, $\gcd(42,108)=6=2\times\mathbf{108}-5\times\mathbf{42}$. Euclid's algorithm allows us to write $\gcd(m,n)$ as an integer linear combination of m and n, see also Problem 10.26.

Exercise 10.5
Use Euclid's algorithm to express $\gcd(34,55)$ as an integer linear combination of 34 and 55.

Exercise 10.6
For $m=6$, $n=15$ list some positive linear combinations $mx+ny$ for $x,y\in\mathbb{Z}$. What is the smallest positive linear combination you can get? What is $\gcd(m,n)$?

From Euclid's algorithm, the GCD of m,n is an integer linear combination of m,n. Can any smaller positive number be an integer linear combination of m and n? Suppose $z>0$ is a linear combination of m,n,

$$z=mx+ny>0, \qquad \text{where } x,y\in\mathbb{Z}.$$

The RHS $mx+ny$ is divisible by $\gcd(m,n)$ because m and n are divisible by $\gcd(m,n)$. So, z is divisible by $\gcd(m,n)$, which means $z\geq\gcd(m,n)$. Our discussion amounts to Bezout's identity.

Theorem 10.5 (Bezout's Identity). The GCD of m and n is the smallest positive linear combination of m and n with integer coefficients. For some $x, y \in \mathbb{Z}$, $\gcd(m,n) = mx + ny$.

Proof. Let ℓ be the smallest positive integer linear combination of m and n, which exists by well-ordering,

$$\ell = mx + ny \qquad \text{for } x, y \in \mathbb{Z}.$$

Since $\gcd(m,n) | mx + ny$ for all $x, y \in \mathbb{Z}$, $\gcd(m,n)|\ell$ and so $\ell \geq \gcd(m,n)$. To show $\ell \leq \gcd(m,n)$, we show that ℓ is a common divisor of m, n, i.e. $\text{rem}(m,\ell) = \text{rem}(n,\ell) = 0$.

By the quotient-remainder theorem, $m = q\ell + r$ where $0 \leq r < \ell$. Then,

$$r = m - q\ell = m - q(mx + ny) = m(1 - qx) - n(qy).$$

If $r > 0$, then r is a positive linear combination of m, n which is less than ℓ, a contradiction, because ℓ was the smallest. Therefore $r = 0$ and $\ell|m$. Similarly, if $n = q'\ell + r'$, then $r' = 0$ and $\ell|n$. ■

Example 10.6. Number theory has been in the movies. In the third *Die Hard* installment, *Die Hard: With a Vengeance* in 1995, the diabolical Simon Gruber asks John McClane & Zeus Carver to use 3 and 5-gallon jugs to measure 4 gallons, or else a bomb explodes. Here is an idea for solving this problem.

1: Repeatedly fill the 3-gallon jug, whenever it gets empty.
2: Pour as much as you can from the 3-gallon jug to the 5-gallon jug, without exceeding the 5-gallon capacity.
3: If ever the 5-gallon jug is full, empty it by discarding the water.

Does this scheme work for our heroes? Let (a_3, a_5) denote the amount of water in the 3 and 5-gallon jugs, the state of the system. The start state is $(0,0)$. Here is what happens.

$$(0,0) \xrightarrow{1:} (3,0) \xrightarrow{2:} (0,3) \xrightarrow{1:} (3,3) \xrightarrow{2:} (1,5) \xrightarrow{3:} (1,0) \xrightarrow{2:} (0,1) \xrightarrow{1:} (3,1) \xrightarrow{2:} \mathbf{(0,4)} \checkmark$$

The annotation above the arrow identifies the instruction number in the algorithm. The final state solves the problem for McClane and Carver, with 4 gallons in the 5-gallon jug.

After the 3-gallon jug has just been completely emptied into the 5-gallon jug, the state is $(0,\ell)$ for $\ell \geq 0$. Suppose, to this point, the 3-gallon jug has been emptied into the 5-gallon jug $x \geq 0$ times and the 5-gallon jug has been emptied out $y \geq 0$ times. So, the amount of water left in the 5 gallon jug is

$$\ell = 3x - 5y. \qquad (*)$$

This is a linear combination of $m = 3$ and $n = 5$. Here, x and y are non-negative integers. In Bezout's identity, $\gcd(m,n) = mx + ny$ and either coefficient x or y could be negative. We can make x positive and y negative by adding a multiple of n to x and subtracting the same multiple of m from y. Indeed,

$$\gcd(m,n) = mx + ny = m(x + \alpha n) + n(y - \alpha m) = mx' - ny',$$

where $x' = x + \alpha n$ and $y' = \alpha m - y$. If α is large enough, both x' and y' become positive. In our jug problem $m = 3$ and $n = 5$, and $\gcd(3,5) = 3x - 5y$ for positive x and y, as can be verified by setting $x = 2$ and $y = 1$,

$$\gcd(3,5) = 1 = 3 \cdot 2 - 5 \cdot 1.$$

Comparing with $(*)$, after the 3-gallon jug has been emptied twice and the 5-gallon jug emptied once, we have $\ell = 1$ gallon left in the 5-gallon jug. But, we need 4 gallons. No problem. Just multiply by 4:

$$4 = 3 \cdot 8 - 5 \cdot 4.$$

After the 3-gallon jug is emptied 8 times and the 5-gallon jug emptied 4 times, you have 4 gallons left. We got there faster because it is also true that $4 = 3 \cdot 3 - 5 \cdot 1$. Suppose the movie used 3 and 6-gallon jugs, whose GCD is 3. Then, our heroes can only measure multiples of 3 because ℓ, the amount left in the 5-gallon jug, is a linear combination of 3 and 6 and hence divisible by $\gcd(3,6)$. Measuring four gallons is impossible. The bomb explodes, the heroes die and there is no 4th sequel, phew! □

Bezout's identity is a power-tool. The identity $\gcd(m,n) = mx + ny$ is almost a formula for the GCD. Though we don't know specific values of x and y, we can manipulate this equation like a formula. We claimed that any common divisor divides the GCD. You will appreciate this "one line" proof. By Bezout's identity,

$$\gcd(m,n) = mx + ny, \qquad \text{for some } x, y \in \mathbb{Z}.$$

A common divisor of m and n divides the RHS, therefore it must divide the LHS. We collect in a box, for emphasis, some important facts about the GCD.

GCD facts:

(i) $\gcd(m,n) = \gcd(\text{rem}(n,m), m)$.

(ii) Every common divisor of m, n divides $\gcd(m,n)$.

(iii) For $k \in \mathbb{N}$, $\gcd(km, kn) = k \cdot \gcd(m,n)$.

(iv) IF $\gcd(l,m) = 1$ AND $\gcd(l,n) = 1$, THEN $\gcd(l, mn) = 1$.

(v) IF $d|mn$ AND $\gcd(d,m) = 1$, THEN $d|n$.

The GCD facts (i) and (ii) were proved earlier. Here are "quick" proofs of (iii)–(v) using Bezout's identity.

(iii) Consider $\gcd(km, kn)$, the minimum positive linear combination of km and kn:

$$\gcd(km, kn) = kmx + kny = k(mx + ny).$$

Since $k > 0$, $mx + ny$ must be the minimum positive linear combination of m and n, which means that $mx + ny = \gcd(m,n)$. This proves $\gcd(km, kn) = k \cdot \gcd(m,n)$.

(iv) Suppose $\gcd(\ell, m) = 1$ and $\gcd(\ell, n) = 1$. Then, for some $x, y, x', y' \in \mathbb{Z}$,

$$1 = \ell x + my; \qquad 1 = \ell x' + ny'.$$

Multiplying the LHS and RHS of each equation, we get a positive linear combination of ℓ and mn:

$$1 = (\ell x + my)(\ell x' + ny') = \ell \cdot (\ell x x' + nxy' + myx') + mn \cdot (yy').$$

This is a minimum positive linear combination, for you can't get smaller than 1. Hence, $\gcd(\ell, mn) = 1$.

(v) Since $\gcd(d, m) = 1$, there are $x, y \in \mathbb{Z}$ for which $dx + my = 1$. Multiplying by n,

$$dnx + mny = n.$$

The LHS is divisible by d because dnx is divisible by d and, by assumption, mn is divisible by d, so mny is divisible by d. If the LHS is divisible by d, then the RHS must also be divisible by d.

Exercise 10.7

For practice, prove these facts about GCDs and relatively prime numbers.

(a) IF $d|mn$, THEN $d|\gcd(m,d) \cdot n$.

(b) Let d, d' be relatively prime. If $d|n$ and $d'|n$, then $dd'|n$.

(c) If m, n are relatively prime, then $\gcd(mn, \ell) = \gcd(m, \ell) \cdot \gcd(n, \ell)$. *[Hint: Let $D = \gcd(m, \ell)$ and $D' = \gcd(n, \ell)$. Use Bezout to show $\gcd(mn, \ell) \le DD'$. Show DD' divides both mn and ℓ.]*

(d) $\gcd(\ell, mn) = 1$ if and only if $\gcd(\ell, m) = 1$ and $\gcd(\ell, n) = 1$.

(e) $\gcd(\gcd(\ell, m), n) = \gcd(\ell, \gcd(m, n))$.

10.2 Fundamental Theorem of Arithmetic

Prime factorization is at the heart of number theory, for primes are the atomic units of all other numbers.

Every integer $n \ge 2$ can be written *uniquely* as a product of primes.

We proved that every $n \geq 2$ is a product of primes using two cases: (i) n is a prime and there is nothing to prove. (ii) n is composite, so $n = \ell m$ where ℓ and m are products of primes (strong induction), and so n is a product of these two prime-products. To prove uniqueness up to reordering, we need Euclid's Lemma:

Lemma 10.7 (Euclid's Lemma). Let p be prime. If $p|mn$ then $p|m$ or $p|n$.

Euclid's Lemma specializes GCD fact (v) on page 132 to d being a prime p. Suppose $p|mn$. Either $p|m$, or $\gcd(p, m) = 1$ as the only other divisor of p is 1. GCD fact (v) on page 132 then gives $p|n$. Let p, q_1, q_2 be primes. By Euclid's Lemma, if $p|q_1q_2$ then either $p|q_1$ and $p = q_1$ since q_1 is prime, or $p|q_2$ and $p = q_2$.

Exercise 10.8 [Euclid's Lemma Generalized]

Let $p, q_1, \ldots, q_n$ be primes. Prove that if $p|q_1q_2 \cdots q_n$, then p equals one of the q_i.

We prove uniqueness using well-ordering. Let n_* be the smallest number which is a product of primes in at least two different ways ($n_* > 2$). Then,

$$\begin{aligned} n_* &= p_1p_2 \cdots p_n \\ &= q_1q_2 \cdots q_k \end{aligned}$$

Clearly $p_1|n_*$, therefore $p_1|q_1q_2 \cdots q_k$ and so p_1 equals one of the q_i (Exercise 10.8). By rearranging the order of the q_i (without changing the product), we can set $q_1 = p_1$ and we have:

$$\begin{aligned} n_* &= p_1p_2 \cdots p_n \\ &= p_1q_2 \cdots q_k, \end{aligned}$$

where $\{p_2, \ldots, p_n\}$ and $\{q_2, \ldots, q_k\}$ are different sets of primes, because these are two different ways to write n_* as a product of primes. Now consider the integer n_*/p_1:

$$\begin{aligned} n_*/p_1 &= p_2 \cdots p_n \\ &= q_2 \cdots q_k. \end{aligned}$$

Since n_*/p_1 is a product of primes in two different ways and $n_*/p_1 < n_*$ because $p_1 \geq 2$, it means n_* was not the smallest counter-example. This contradiction proves there is no n_*. ■

Pop Quiz 10.9

Show that every $n \geq 2$ is a product of prime powers, $n = 2^{a_1}3^{a_2}5^{a_3}7^{a_4}11^{a_5}\cdots$, where $a_i \geq 0$ are unique.

10.3 Modular Arithmetic and Cryptography

We touted number theory as the foundation of secure communication, a subject whose history is intertwined with WWII in a shroud of secrecy. The setup is simple. Alice wants to securely communicate the location of Charlie's surprise party to Bob. The message is a string of bits M, a binary integer which we may assume is prime, for if not Alice separately sends the unique prime factors of M. Charlie eavesdrops. Nevertheless, Alice and Bob must hide the message from Charlie. So, Alice sends a disguised message M_* instead of M.

Alice must securely send the prime M to Bob.
Charlie eavesdrops.
So, Alice sends M_* instead of M.
Both Bob and Charlie see M_*.
Bob recovers M from M_*. Charlie shouldn't.

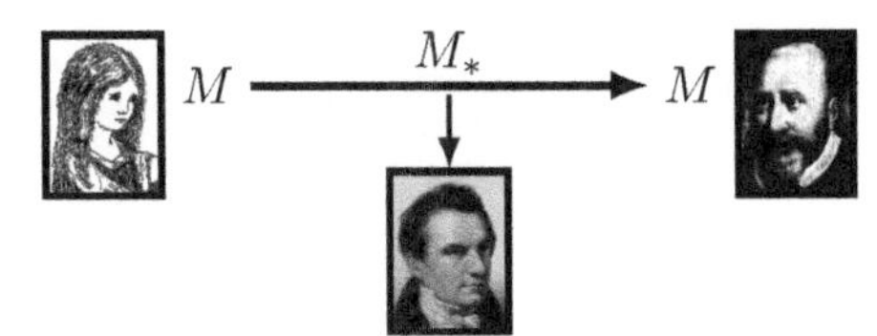

Here is one way for Alice and Bob to succeed. At an earlier time, they agree on a private key k, a large prime which they keep secret. Alice disguises M by multiplying it with k, to create the encrypted message M_*,

$$M_* = M \cdot k.$$

Alice sends the message M_* to Bob. Bob has the secret key k, and recovers M after dividing M_* by k,

$$M_*/k = (M \cdot k)/k = M.$$

The eavesdropper Charlie also hears M_*, but he does not have k. Charlie can factor M_* uniquely as a product of primes (Fundamental Theorem of Arithmetic), obtaining the factors M and k. Charlie infers that the message is M or k, and only one will usually make sense as a bit-string. So, Charlie effectively knows the message M. How is the communication between Alice and Bob secure? The key step for Charlie is to factor M_* into primes. If the message M and the key k are huge primes, then M_* is huge. We can't factor huge numbers efficiently. So, Charlie can access the message M, but only after a very long time. The surprise party would have come and gone, and the information will be useless to Charlie.

The communication is secure because, as far as we know, prime factorization is inefficient.

The problem with our first attempt at cryptography is that Alice can use the secret key k to send only one message. Suppose Alice encrypts and sends two messages M_1 and M_2:

$$M_{1*} = M_1 \cdot k \qquad \text{and} \qquad M_{2*} = M_2 \cdot k.$$

Now, Charlie can discover the secret k and decode both messages. The exercise shows why.

Exercise 10.10
Suppose M_1, M_2, k are different primes, show that $\gcd(M_{1*}, M_{2*}) = k$.

Euclid's algorithm (page 130) efficiently computes the GCD, even for huge numbers. Given M_{1*} and M_{2*}, Charlie discovers the secret key k by computing $\gcd(M_{1*}, M_{2*})$, and then recovers M_1 and M_2. A better way to disguise M is using modular arithmetic, a creation of the great Gauss, a giant among mathematical giants.

Two numbers a and b are equal or congruent modulo d if they have the same remainder when divided by d, or equivalently, $a - b$ is divisible by d. We write $a \equiv b \pmod{d}$ and d is called the modulus. To summarize:

$$a \equiv b \pmod{d} \qquad \text{if and only if} \qquad d|(a-b),$$

or, $a - b = kd$ for $k \in \mathbb{Z}$. For example, $41 \equiv 79 \pmod{19}$ because $41 - 79 = -38 = -2 \cdot 19$. The next exercise asks you to show that modular addition and multiplication are similar to regular arithmetic.

Exercise 10.11 [Modular Equivalence Properties]
Suppose $a \equiv b \pmod{d}$ and $r \equiv s \pmod{d}$. Prove:
(a) $ar \equiv bs \pmod{d}$. (b) $a + r \equiv b + s \pmod{d}$. (c) $a^n \equiv b^n \pmod{d}$.

Example 10.8. What is the last digit of 3^n, the remainder when divided by 10? Let's tinker:

n	1	2	3	4	5	6	7	8	9	10
3^n	3	9	27	81	243	729	2187	6561	19683	59049
last digit	3	9	7	1	3	9	7	1	3	9

Do you see a pattern? The last digit cycles between $\{3, 9, 7, 1\}$. The pattern is even simpler if you note that $7 \equiv -3 \pmod{10}$ and $9 \equiv -1 \pmod{10}$. The last digits are $\{3, -1, -3, 1, 3, -1, -3, 1, \ldots\} \pmod{10}$. This cycling results from the key fact that

$$3^2 \equiv -1 \pmod{10}.$$

This fact is useful because it is easy to raise -1 to a power. By part (c) of Exercise 10.11,

$$3^{2k} \equiv (-1)^k \pmod{10} \qquad (n = 2k \text{ is even}).$$

Also, since $3 \equiv 3 \pmod{10}$, using part (a) of Exercise 10.11 with $a = 3^{2k}$ and $r = 3$,

$$3^{2k+1} \equiv (-1)^k \cdot 3 \pmod{10} \qquad (n = 2k+1 \text{ is odd}).$$

The four cases for the final answer depend on n being even or odd and $k = \lfloor n/2 \rfloor$ being even or odd:

$$3^n \equiv \begin{cases} 1 & \text{if } n \text{ is even and } \lfloor n/2 \rfloor \text{ is even;} \\ -1 & \text{if } n \text{ is even and } \lfloor n/2 \rfloor \text{ is odd;} \\ 3 & \text{if } n \text{ is odd and } \lfloor n/2 \rfloor \text{ is even;} \\ -3 & \text{if } n \text{ is odd and } \lfloor n/2 \rfloor \text{ is odd.} \end{cases} \pmod{10}$$

To get the last digit, add 10 if the answer above is negative: the last digit is 9 if $3^n \equiv -1 \pmod{10}$, and 7 if $3^n \equiv -3 \pmod{10}$. For example, the last digit of 3^{2015} is 7 because 2015 and $\lfloor 2015/2 \rfloor$ are both odd. □

Pop Quiz 10.12
Compute the remainder when 5^{2015} is divided by 3.

Not all the rules of arithmetic apply to modular arithmetic. You can't always divide both sides of a modular equation by a non-zero number. Here are three examples. The cancellation only works in two of the cases.

$15 \cdot \not{6} \equiv 2 \cdot \not{6} \pmod{13}$	$15 \cdot \not{6} \equiv 13 \cdot \not{6} \pmod{12}$	$7 \cdot \not{8} \equiv 22 \cdot \not{8} \pmod{15}$
$15 \equiv 2 \pmod{13}$ ✓	$15 \not\equiv 13 \pmod{12}$ ✗	$7 \equiv 22 \pmod{15}$ ✓

The first case with prime modulus 13 works. The second case with composite modulus 12 fails. The rules of arithmetic essentially carry over to modular arithmetic with prime modulus. The third case works even though the modulus 15 is not prime. However, cancelation with modulus 15 does not always work: you cannot cancel the 5 from both sides of $20 \cdot 5 \equiv 8 \cdot 5 \pmod{15}$ because $20 \not\equiv 8 \pmod{15}$. What matters is the GCD of the modulus and the term you want to cancel. Let's state it as a theorem.

Theorem 10.9. Suppose $ac \equiv bc \pmod{d}$ and $\gcd(c, d) = 1$. Then, $a \equiv b \pmod{d}$

Proof. Since $ac \equiv bc \pmod{d}$, $d | c(a - b)$. By GCD fact (v) on page 132, $d | a - b$ because $\gcd(c, d) = 1$. ■

For a prime modulus p, $\gcd(c, p) = 1$ as long as c is not a multiple of p, and you can cancel c from both sides of a congruence. Modular arithmetic with prime modulus is very similar to regular arithmetic.

10.3.1 Modular Multiplicative Inverse

In our first crypto-scheme, Bob recovers M after dividing $M_* = Mk$ by k, because the multiplicative inverse of k is $1/k$, which means divide by k. The multiplicative inverse of x, denoted x^{-1} and read "x-inverse", satisfies

$$x^{-1}x = xx^{-1} = 1.$$

In the real numbers, as long as x is not zero, x has a multiplicative inverse equal to its reciprocal $1/x$. So $2^{-1} = 0.5$. For matrices, a matrix A has a multiplicative inverse A^{-1} as long as the determinant of A is non-zero, in which case $\mathrm{A}^{-1}\mathrm{A} = \mathrm{A}\mathrm{A}^{-1} = \mathrm{I}$. In modular arithmetic, things are a little complicated. First we fix a modulus d. Then, for integer k, the modular multiplicative inverse k^{-1} satisfies $1 \leq k^{-1} < d$ and

$$k^{-1} \cdot k \equiv 1 \pmod{d}.$$

For modulus $d = 6$, $35^{-1} = 5$ because $5 \cdot 35 = 175 \equiv 1 \pmod{6}$. Unlike the multiplicative inverse which exists when $x \neq 0$, the modular inverse may not exist for all $k \neq 0$.

Exercise 10.13
Show that 15 does not have a multiplicative inverse for modulus 6.

Theorem 10.10. The inverse of k exists modulo d if and only $\gcd(k, d) = 1$.

Proof. Suppose $k^{-1}k \equiv 1 \pmod{d}$. Then, $k^{-1}k - 1 = d \cdot \ell$, or $k^{-1}k - d\ell = 1$. A linear combination of k and d equals 1, the minimum possible positive number. By Bezout's identity, $\gcd(k, d) = 1$.

Suppose $\gcd(k, d) = 1$. By Bezout's identity, $kx + dy = 1$ for $x, y \in \mathbb{Z}$, which means $kx = 1 - dy$. By the quotient remainder theorem, $x = qd + r$, where $0 \leq r = x - qd < d$. We claim $k^{-1} = r$. Indeed,

$$kr = k(x - qd) = kx - kqd = 1 - dy - kqd = 1 - d(y + kq).$$

So, $kr - 1 = -d(y + kq)$. That is $d | (kr - 1)$, or $kr \equiv 1 \pmod{d}$ and so $r = k^{-1}$ the modular inverse. ■

When $\gcd(k,d) = 1$, one can efficiently compute k^{-1}. First use the remainders from Euclid's algorithm for $\gcd(k,d)$ to compute any x for which $kx + dy = 1$ (Bezout's identity). Then, $k^{-1} = \text{rem}(x,d)$. Let us compute 12^{-1} with modulus $p = 17$. First we use Euclid's algorithm to compute $\gcd(12,17)$.

$$\begin{aligned}
\gcd(12,17) &= \gcd(5,12) & \text{rem}(17,12) = 5 &= -12 + 17 \\
&= \gcd(2,5) & \text{rem}(12,5) = 2 &= 12 - \mathbf{5} \cdot 2 \\
& & &= 12 - (17 - 12) \cdot 2 \\
& & &= 12 \cdot 3 - 17 \cdot 2. \\
&= \gcd(1,2) = 1 & \text{rem}(5,2) = 1 &= \mathbf{5} - \mathbf{2} \cdot 2 \\
& & &= -12 + 17 - (12 \cdot 3 - 17 \cdot 2) \cdot 2 \\
& & &= 12 \cdot (-7) + 17 \cdot 5.
\end{aligned}$$

Therefore, $12^{-1} = \text{rem}(-7,17) = 10$, and indeed $12 \cdot 10 = 120 \equiv 1 \pmod{17}$. For a prime modulus, Fermat's Little Theorem gives a formula for the multiplicative inverse.

Exercise 10.14 [Fermat's Little Theorem]

(a) For a prime p, prove that $k^p \equiv k \pmod{p}$.
   (i) Show that if $k = 0$ or k is a multiple of p then the claim is trivially true.
   It remains to show the claim for k not a multiple of p.
   (ii) Show that if $i \in \{1, 2, \ldots, p-1\}$, then ik is not a multiple of p.
   (iii) Show that if $ik \equiv jk \pmod{p}$ then $i \equiv j \pmod{p}$.
   (iv) Let $\text{rem}(ik, p) = \alpha_i$, so $ik \equiv \alpha_i \pmod{p}$. Show that $\prod_{i=1}^{p-1} \alpha_i = (p-1)!$.
   (v) Show $k^{p-1}(p-1)! \equiv (p-1)! \pmod{p}$, and hence $k^{p-1} \equiv 1 \pmod{p}$, which proves Fermat's Little Theorem (why?). *[Hint: What is $\gcd((p-1)!, p)$?]*

(b) Use (a) to show that $k^{-1} \equiv k^{p-2} \pmod{p}$, when k is not a multiple of p.

(c) Compute 8^{-1} for modulus $p = 19$ (i) Using Bezout's identity. (ii) Using (b).

Armed with modular arithmetic, Alice can use use modular multiplication instead of plain vanilla multiplication to disguise her message M. Alice and Bob still need a secret key k and a large prime p (the prime need not be secret). The message M must be less than p. This can be accomplished by breaking a large message into smaller ones. To disguise the message, Alice computes Mk, and then the remainder when divided by p:

$$M_* \equiv Mk \pmod{p}.$$

Bob gets M_*, and since Bob knows about modular multiplicative inverses, to recover M, Bob simply computes the remainder when $M_* k^{-1}$ is divided by p. Indeed,

$$\begin{aligned}
M_* k^{-1} &\equiv Mkk^{-1} \pmod{p} \\
&\equiv M \pmod{p}.
\end{aligned}$$

The last equivalence is because $kk^{-1} \equiv 1 \pmod{p}$, so multiplying both sides by M gives $Mkk^{-1} \equiv M \pmod{p}$. Charlie cannot access M from M_*. Even with multiple encoded messages, $M_{1*}, M_{2*}, \ldots$, Charlie cannot discover k. We won't formally prove this. There is a scenario in which Charlie can crack the crypto. Suppose Charlie knows M_1 and M_{1*}, e.g. Charlie guesses the location of the party, and knows that M_{1*} is that location, then Charlie can discover the secret k and decipher all the remaining messages $M_{2*}, M_{3*}, \ldots$. This is called a known plain-text attack. In WWII, Alan Turing and company at Bletchly Park in Britain used German weather reports that were in both plain text and encrypted form to crack Hitler's Enigma machine. It's a good thing the Germans did not know about public key cryptography.

Exercise 10.15 [Known Plain Text Attack]

If Charlie has both M and $M_* \equiv Mk \pmod{p}$, prove that $M^{p-2} M_* \equiv k \pmod{p}$, and so Charlie can discover the secret key k and decode all future messages.

10.3.2 RSA Public Key Cryptography

The need to share a private key is a burden. How do Alice and Bob exchange the private key securely? In 1977, Rivest, Shamir and Adleman (RSA) found an elegant and secure way for Alice and Bob to communicate without a shared secret k. RSA has withstood decades of attacks and no significant vulnerabilities are known. The general idea for Alice is the same: disguise the message M to M_* so that Bob can recover M from M_* while the eavesdropper Charlie cannot. Let n be a very large number. Alice computes the encrypted message

$$M_* \equiv M^e \pmod{n}$$

The message M is disguised by raising it to the power e (repeated multiplication), modulo the divisor n. Let us work with an example. The message $M = 241$, the modulus $n = 391$ and the power $e = 225$.

$$M_* \equiv 241^{225} \pmod{391}.$$

Alice can use a halving algorithm and Exercise 10.11(c) to compute M_* efficiently:

$$\begin{array}{rcl} \multicolumn{3}{c}{\text{Halving the power}} \\ \hline 241^{225} &\equiv& 241 \cdot (241^{112})^2 \\ 241^{112} &\equiv& (241^{56})^2 \\ 241^{56} &\equiv& (241^{28})^2 \\ 241^{28} &\equiv& (241^{14})^2 \\ 241^{14} &\equiv& (241^{7})^2 \\ 241^{7} &\equiv& 241 \cdot (241^{3})^2 \\ 241^{3} &\equiv& 112 \end{array} \quad \rightarrow \quad \begin{array}{rcl} \multicolumn{3}{c}{\text{Substituting back}} \\ \hline 241^{3} &\equiv& \mathbf{112} \\ 241^{7} &\equiv& 241 \cdot 112^2 \equiv \mathbf{283} \\ 241^{14} &\equiv& 283^2 \equiv \mathbf{325} \\ 241^{28} &\equiv& 325^2 \equiv \mathbf{55} \\ 241^{56} &\equiv& 55^2 \equiv \mathbf{288} \\ 241^{112} &\equiv& 288^2 \equiv \mathbf{52} \\ 241^{225} &\equiv& 241 \cdot 52^2 \equiv 258 \end{array} \quad \pmod{391}$$

The last step on the left is because $241^3 = 35799 \times 391 + 112$. The halving on the left brings the exponent down to something manageable which we can compute directly. Now successively plug this result back into the higher exponent until we finally arrive at $M_* = 258$ on the right.

How does Bob recover the original message M from M_*? Bob has a private key $d = 97$. To recover M, Bob performs a similar exponentiation as Alice did, computing $M_*^d \pmod{391}$ as follows:

$$\begin{array}{rcl} \multicolumn{3}{c}{\text{Halving the power}} \\ \hline 258^{97} &\equiv& 258 \cdot (258^{48})^2 \\ 258^{48} &\equiv& (258^{24})^2 \\ 258^{24} &\equiv& (258^{12})^2 \\ 258^{12} &\equiv& (258^{6})^2 \\ 258^{6} &\equiv& (258^{3})^2 \\ 258^{3} &\equiv& 10 \end{array} \quad \rightarrow \quad \begin{array}{rcl} \multicolumn{3}{c}{\text{Substituting back}} \\ \hline 258^{3} &\equiv& \mathbf{10} \\ 258^{6} &\equiv& 10^2 \equiv \mathbf{100} \\ 258^{12} &\equiv& 100^2 \equiv \mathbf{225} \\ 258^{24} &\equiv& 225^2 \equiv \mathbf{186} \\ 258^{48} &\equiv& 186^2 \equiv \mathbf{188} \\ 258^{97} &\equiv& 258 \cdot 188^2 \equiv 241 \end{array} \quad \pmod{391}$$

A miracle. Bob has recovered $M = 241$. Does Bob always recover M? Yes! This is the magic of RSA.

Exercise 10.16
For $n = 391, e = 225, d = 97$ and $M = 2, \ldots, 10$, verify that Bob always recovers M. Run Alice's algorithm to encrypt M into M_*, and then Bob's algorithm to decrypt M_*.

You should be convinced from Exercise 10.16 that Bob always recovers M. In our first scheme where Alice encodes to $M_* = M \times k$ and Bob decodes using M_*/k, Bob also always recovers M. Now, on Alice's side, k is replaced with e and instead of multiplication by k, Alice performs $e - 1$ repeated multiplications by M. On Bob's side, k is replaced by d. Instead of dividing by k, Bob does $d - 1$ repeated multiplications by M_*.

To start the whole process, Alice needs the modulus n and the encrypting power e. These are created by Bob and sent publicly to Alice. The numbers n and e are called public keys. When Bob sends n and e to Alice, Charlie learns them too. But so what? This just means that Charlie can encode messages and send them to Bob. Similarly, when Alice encodes and sends M_* to Bob, Charlie sees M_*. Again, so what? To decode the message, Charlie needs d. But, Bob does not need to share the private key d with anyone. Bob keeps d to himself and uses it to decode any incoming message. Here are the details of RSA:

1: Bob first creates n as the product of two **huge** primes, $n = pq$.
2: From p and q, Bob creates e and d:
   e is any large number relatively prime to $(p-1)(q-1)$;
   d is the modular inverse of e for modulus $(p-1)(q-1)$.
3: Bob distributes the public keys n and e to the world (Alice and Charlie).
4: Bob keeps the private key d secret.
5: Alice uses the public keys to encrypt M into M_* before sending to Bob,

$$M_* \equiv M^e \pmod{n}.$$

Only Bob knows d and can decode M_* to get back $M \equiv M_*^d \pmod{n}$.

There is a relationship between $n = pq$, e and d. Knowing n and e, why can't Charlie recover d and hence decrypt Alice's message? To get d, Charlie needs to compute the modular inverse of e for modulus $(p-1)(q-1)$, where p and q are the prime factors of n. Without p and q, Charlie cannot compute $(p-1)(q-1)$. RSA is secure because it is hard for Charlie to factor n into p and q. Even the great Gauss beat his head invain to come up with an efficient factoring algorithm. Instant fame awaits if you can achieve this.

The communication is one-way. Anyone can communicate with Bob using his public keys, but Bob can't send messages out because nobody else has the private key d for decoding. If Alice broadcasts her own public keys, then Bob can use those to send messages to Alice, but only Alice. Also, the known plain text attack is not an issue. In fact, anyone can encode any message with the public keys. That does not help them determine d. Lastly, there is no secret key that Alice and Bob need to share. Alice encodes with Bob's *public keys*.

Exercise 10.17 [Mathematics of RSA]

RSA works because $M \equiv M_*^d \pmod{n}$ for any M. Show this is true. Let p and q be primes, and $n = pq$. Choose e relatively prime to $(p-1)(q-1)$ and d as the inverse of e with modulus $(p-1)(q-1)$:

$$\gcd(e, (p-1)(q-1)) = 1; \qquad ed \equiv 1 \pmod{(p-1)(q-1)}.$$

Prove $M^{ed} \equiv M \pmod{pq}$, i.e., Bob can recover M from M_* using $M \equiv M_*^d \pmod{pq}$.

(a) For some integer k, show that $ed - 1 = k(p-1)(q-1)$.
(b) Suppose p does not divide M. Show that p divides $M^{ed-1} - 1$ by showing:
  (i) $M^{ed-1} = M^{k(p-1)(q-1)}$.
  (ii) $M^{ed-1} = (1 + \alpha p)^{k(q-1)}$ for an integer α. *[Hint: Fermat's Little Theorem.]*
  (iii) $M^{ed-1} = 1 + \beta p$, for an integer β. *[Hint: Binomial Theorem.]*
  (iv) Conclude that $M^{ed-1} - 1$ is divisible by p.
(c) Prove p divides $M^{ed} - M$ and similarly that q divides $M^{ed} - M$.
(d) Conclude that $M^{ed} - M$ is divisible by pq. *[Hint: Exercise 10.7(b).]*
(e) Prove that $M^{ed} \equiv M \pmod{pq}$.

Practical Note. A deficiency with vanilla RSA is that if Alice sends the same message many times, Charlie will know this by observing the same M_* many times. Even this can be hidden. The solution is remarkably simple. Pad the message M with (say) 10 random bits (to know what random means, stay tuned for the chapters on Probability). Now, after Bob decodes, he just throws away the first 10 bits to get M.

10.4 Problems

Problem 10.1. Prove the quotient-remainder theorem. Given n, d. Let R be the possible non-negative remainders:

$$R = \{x | x = n - qd;\ q \in \mathbb{Z};\ q \leq n/d\}.$$

(a) Is R empty? Show that R has a minimum element $r = n - qd$ with $0 \leq r < d$. *[Hint: If $r \geq d$, then $r - d \in R$.]*

(b) Show uniqueness. Suppose $n = q_1 d + r_1$ and $n = q_2 d + r_2$, with $0 \leq r, r_2 < d$. Prove that $q_1 = q_2$. *[Hint: $(q_1 - q_2)d = r_2 - r_1$. Is the RHS divisible by d?]*

Problem 10.2. Kilam has 72 red and 90 blue crayons which he distributes in packets to children (with no crayons left over). Each packet has crayons of one color and must be as large as possible. How many children can get a packet?

Problem 10.3. What is the smallest positive multiple of 7 that has remainder 1 when divided by 2, 3, 4 and 5.

Problem 10.4. Kiliam exercises every 12 days and Liamsi every 8 days. Kilam and Liamsi both exercised today. How many days will it be until they exercise together again?

Problem 10.5. What are the possible remainders when a square n^2 is divided by 3? What about 4?

Problem 10.6. Prove that $2^{50}3^{100}5^{25} - 1$ is not prime.

Problem 10.7. What natural numbers are relatively prime to 2, 3 and 6?

Problem 10.8. How many zeros are at the end of 1000!?

Problem 10.9. For any $m, n, x \in \mathbb{Z}$, prove that $\gcd(m, n) = \gcd(m, n - mx)$.

Problem 10.10. Use Euclid's algorithm and the remainders generated to solve these problems.

(a) Compute $\gcd(1200, 2250)$ and find $x, y \in \mathbb{Z}$ for which $\gcd(1200, 2250) = 1200 \cdot x + 2250 \cdot y$.

(b) Find x, y as in (a), but with the additional requirement that $x \leq 0$ and $y \geq 0$.

Problem 10.11. Use Euclid's GCD algorithm to compute $\gcd(356250895, 802137245)$ and express the GCD as an integer linear combination of the two numbers. Show your work.

Problem 10.12. Let $d = \gcd(m, n)$, where $m, n > 0$. Bezout gives $d = mx + ny$ where $x, y \in \mathbb{Z}$. Prove or disprove:

(a) It is always possible to choose $x > 0$.

(b) It is always possible to choose $x < 0$.

(c) It is possible to find another $x, y \in \mathbb{Z}$ for which $0 < mx + ny < d$.

(d) It is always possible to find $a, b \in \mathbb{Z}$ for which $ax + by = 1$.

Problem 10.13. How can you make \$6.27 using 5¢ and 8¢ stamps, using the maximum number of 8¢ stamps?

Problem 10.14. Prove.

(a) For $m, n > 0$, $\gcd(m, n) = \gcd(m, n - mx)$ for $x \in \mathbb{Z}$.

(b) If a divides bc and $\gcd(a, b) = 1$ then a divides c.

(c) For prime p if $p | a_1 a_2 \cdots a_n$ then p divides one of the a_i.

(d) The gap between consecutive primes can be arbitrarily large. *[Hint: Is $n! + 2$ prime?]*

Problem 10.15. Prove, for $n, q \in \mathbb{N}$, $2^{qn} - 1$ is divisible by $2^n - 1$.

Problem 10.16. Prove $\gcd(2^a, 2^b - 1) = 1$ for $a, b \geq 1$ by finding $x, y \in \mathbb{Z}$ for which $2^a \cdot x + (2^b - 1) \cdot y = 1$. *[Hints: If $a \leq b$, the problem is easy (let $x = 2^{b-a}$). If $a > b$, what is $2^a + 2^{b-a}(2^b - 1)$? How is this helpful?]*

Problem 10.17. The Fibonacci numbers are: $F_1 = F_2 = 1$ and $F_n = F_{n-1} + F_{n-2}$ for $n > 2$.

(a) Prove that $\gcd(F_n, F_{n+1}) = 1$. (Consecutive Fibonacci numbers are relatively prime.)

(b) Prove that for $n \geq 1$, $F_m | F_{mn}$.

(c) Prove that $F_{m+n} = F_m F_{n+1} + F_{m-1} F_n$.

(d) Prove that for $m, n \geq 1$, $\gcd(F_m, F_n) = F_{\gcd(m,n)}$.

Problem 10.18. Let $\ell > 0$ be an integer linear combination of m and n. Prove that ℓ is a multiple of $\gcd(m, n)$.

Problem 10.19. Let $m, n, d > 0$ and suppose d is a common divisor for m, n, so $d | m$ and $d | n$. Suppose also that for some $x, y \in \mathbb{Z}$, $d = mx + ny$. Prove that $d = \gcd(m, n)$.

Problem 10.20. The GCD of three numbers m, n, k is their largest common divisor.

(a) Prove that $\gcd(m, n, k) = \gcd(\gcd(m, n), k)$.

(b) Prove a Bezout Theorem: $\gcd(m, n, k) = mx+ny+kz$ is the smallest positive integer linear combination possible.

Problem 10.21. You may find Bezout's identity useful for answering these questions.

(a) Prove that consecutive integers n and $n+1$ are relatively prime.

(b) For which positive n are the pair n and $n+2$ relatively prime? Prove your answer.

(c) Let p be a prime. For which positive n are the pair n and $n+p$ relatively prime. Prove your answer. *[Hint: If n is not a multiple of p then* $\gcd(n,p) = 1$.*]*

(d) For $k \in \mathbb{Z}$, prove that $2k+1$ and $9k+4$ are relatively prime.

(e) As a function of $k \in \mathbb{Z}$, compute $\gcd(2k-1, 9k+4)$.

Problem 10.22. Suppose x^2 is a multiple of y for integers $x, y > 1$. Show that $\gcd(x, y) > 1$.
Prove it in two ways: (a) Use Bezout's identity. (b) Use prime factorization.

Problem 10.23. Use well-ordering to prove a stronger version of Bezout's identity. For $m, n > 0$, there are $x, y \in \mathbb{Z}$ with $0 \le x < n$ for which $\gcd(m, n) = mx + ny$.

Problem 10.24. In each case, prove or disprove.

(a) $\mathbb{Z} \subseteq \{2x + 3y \mid x, y \in \mathbb{Z}\}$. (b) $\mathbb{Z} \subseteq \{2x + 3y \mid x, y \in \mathbb{Z}, x > 0\}$. (c) $\mathbb{Z} \subseteq \{4x + 6y \mid x, y \in \mathbb{Z}\}$.

Problem 10.25. In each case, prove or disprove whether infinitely many integer pairs $(x, y) \in \mathbb{Z}^2$ are a solution to:

(a) $3x + 4y = 5$. (b) $12x + 18y = 4$. (c) $12x + 18y = 6$.

Problem 10.26. Build an efficient algorithm to compute Bezout coefficients for $m, n > 0$. Bezout coefficients are any $x, y \in \mathbb{Z}$ for which $\gcd(m, n) = mx + ny$.

(a) Let $r_0 = n$ and $r_1 = m$. Euclid's gcd-algorithm starts by computing $r_2 = \text{rem}(n, m)$. Show that $r_2 = r_0 - \lfloor r_0/r_1 \rfloor r_1$ and $\gcd(m, n) = \gcd(r_1, r_0) = \gcd(r_2, r_1)$.

(b) As Euclid's algorithm computes remainders $r_2, r_3, r_4, \ldots$. Let $q_i = \lfloor r_{i-2}/r_{i-1} \rfloor$. Show that $r_i = r_{i-2} - q_i r_{i-1}$ and $\gcd(m, n) = \gcd(r_i, r_{i-1})$ for $i \ge 2$. (Induction)

(c) Give the sequence of remainders $r_0, r_1, r_2, r_3, \ldots$, when $m = 14$ and $n = 10$.

(d) Suppose the first remainder which is 0 is r_{k+1}. What is $\gcd(m, n)$?

(e) Compute Bezout coefficients x_i, y_i for each remainder r_i. That is express $r_i = x_i m + y_i n$.

(i) What are x_0, y_0 and x_1, y_1?

(ii) For $i \ge 2$, show that $x_i = x_{i-2} - q_i x_{i-1}$ and $y_i = y_{i-2} - q_i y_{i-1}$, where $q_i = \lfloor r_{i-2}/r_{i-1} \rfloor$.

(iii) For $m = 14, n = 10$ compute the Bezout coefficients $x_0, x_1, \ldots$ and $y_0, y_1, \ldots$ and verify $r_i = mx_i + ny_i$.

(iv) Program an efficient algorithm that, given m, n, computes $\gcd(m, n)$ and Bezout coefficients x, y. (Your need to use r_i, x_i, y_i.) Compute the GCD and Bezout coefficients for $m = 49{,}332{,}470$ and $n = 172{,}535{,}181$.

This algorithm that also computes Bezout coefficients is called the extended Euclid Algorithm.

Problem 10.27. The Extended Euclid Algorithm (Problem 10.26) gives remainders $r_0, r_1, r_2, \ldots$. Prove $r_i \le r_{i-2}/2$ for $i > 2$. *[Hints: For $i > 2$, show $r_{i-1} \le r_{i-2}$, and consider $r_{i-1} \le r_{i-2}/2$ and $r_{i-1} > r_{i-2}/2$ separately.]*
(If you are so inclined, use this fact to prove that the runtime of Euclid's algorithm is in $O(\log_2 m + \log_2 n)$.)

Problem 10.28. Solve each measuring problem, or explain why it can't be done. (You have unlimited water.)

(a) Using 6 and 15 gallon jugs, measure (i) 3 gallons (ii) 4 gallons (iii) 5 gallons.

(b) Using 5 and 11 gallon jugs, measure (i) 6 gallons (ii) 7 gallons.

Problem 10.29. Suppose the distinct primes $p_1, \ldots, p_k$ divide $n \in \mathbb{N}$. Prove that $\prod_{i=1}^{k} p_i \le n$.

Problem 10.30. Show that 2^a and $2^b - 1$ are relatively prime using their prime factorizations.

Problem 10.31. For $k \in \mathbb{N}$, show that $2^k - 1$ and $2^k + 1$ are relatively prime.

Problem 10.32. Prove by induction that $2^{2^n} - 1$ has at least n distinct primes as factors, for $n \ge 1$.

Problem 10.33. Prove that $\gcd((a^p - 1)/(a-1), a-1) = \gcd(p, a-1)$. What happens when p is prime? *[Hint: $a^p - 1 = (a-1)(1 + a + a^2 + \cdots + a^{p-1})$ and $a^k = (1 + a - 1)^k = 1 + \alpha a$ (what is α?).]*

Problem 10.34. Let $n = \prod_{p_i} p_i^{a_i}$. Prove: the number of divisors of n is $\tau(n) = \prod_{p_i}(1 + a_i)$.

Problem 10.35.[Least Common Multiple (LCM)] The least common multiple $\text{lcm}(m, n)$ is the smallest positive integer that is divisible by both m and n. Assume $m, n > 0$.

(a) Compute the LCM for the pairs: $(2, 3)$; $(3, 5)$; $(6, 8)$.
(b) Compute $\gcd(12, 16)$, $\text{lcm}(12, 16)$, $\gcd(12, 16) \times \text{lcm}(12, 16)$, 12×16.
(c) Prove the $\text{lcm}(m, n) \cdot \gcd(m, n) = mn$.
  (i) Let $m = k \cdot \gcd(m, n)$ and $n = k' \cdot \gcd(m, n)$. Prove $\text{lcm}(m, n) \leq kk' \gcd(m, n)$.
  (ii) Prove $mn | \text{lcm}(m, n) \gcd(m, n)$, hence $\text{lcm}(m, n) \gcd(m, n) \geq mn$. *[Hint: Bezout.]*
  (iii) Use (i) and (ii) to prove $\text{lcm}(m, n) = kk' \gcd(m, n)$ and $\text{lcm}(m, n) \cdot \gcd(m, n) = mn$.

Problem 10.36. Let $n = \prod_{p_i} p_i^{a_i}$ and $m = \prod_{p_i} p_i^{b_i}$. Show:

(a) $\gcd(m, n) = \prod_{p_i} p_i^{\min(a_i, b_i)}$ and $\text{lcm}(m, n) = \prod_{p_i} p_i^{\max(a_i, b_i)}$.
(b) Compute 72×108 and $\gcd(72, 108) \times \text{lcm}(72, 108)$. Show that $mn = \gcd(m, n)\text{lcm}(m, n)$ for $m, n > 0$.

(Euclid's method is more efficient as an algorithm, but (a) gives a "formula" for GCD which is useful in derivations.)

Problem 10.37 (Generating Primes: Sieve of Erasothenes). The algorithm gives a method to output all the primes up to n.

(a) Use the algorithm to output all primes up to 50.
(b) Prove that every number output is prime.
(c) Prove that every prime up to n is output.

Efficiently implementing the sieve is not trivial. Nearly linear time is possible.

```
1: List 1, ..., n and delete 1.
2: while numbers remain on the list do
3:     Let x be the smallest.
4:     Output x as prime.
5:     Delete x and its multiples.
```

Problem 10.38. Prove or disprove.

(a) $\gcd(m^k, n^k) = \gcd(m, n)^k$.
(b) $m^{-1} \equiv n^{-1} \to m \equiv n \pmod{d}$.
(c) $\gcd(m, n) = 1 \wedge \gcd(n, k) = 1 \to \gcd(m, k) = 1$.
(d) $\gcd(m, n) \neq 1 \wedge \gcd(n, k) \neq 1 \to \gcd(m, k) \neq 1$.

Problem 10.39. Generalize GCD-fact (v) on page 132. Prove $xk \equiv yk \pmod{d} \to x \equiv y \pmod{d/\gcd(k, d)}$.

Problem 10.40. Prove:

(a) $a \equiv b \pmod{d}$ and $b \equiv c \pmod{d} \to a \equiv c \pmod{d}$. (b) $a \equiv b \pmod{d} \to \gcd(a, d) = \gcd(b, d)$.

Problem 10.41. Use modular arithmetic to solve these problems.

(a) Compute the remainder when: (i) 2200^{2200} is divided by 3 (ii) 2014^{2014} is divided by 5.
(b) What is the last digit of: (i) $3^{2016} + 4^{2016} + 7^{2016}$ (ii) $3^{1000} \times 5^{2000} + 7^{3000} \times 9^{4000}$ (iii) $2^{70} + 3^{70}$?
(c) Prove that $2^{70} + 3^{70}$ is divisible by 13.
(d) What is the last digit of 102^{1211}. What is the second last digit?
(e) Prove that $102^{1211} - 3^{1211}$ is divisible by 99.
(f) A number x after multiplying by 7 and adding 5 has a remainder 2 when divided by 11. What is $\text{rem}(x, 11)$?
(g) What is the remainder when (i) $5^n + 2 \cdot 11^n$ is divided by 3? (ii) $4^{2n+1} + 5^{2n+1} + 6^{2n+1}$ is divided by 15?

Problem 10.42. It's now 3pm. Where is the hour hand after: (a) 233 hours (b) 14×233 hours (c) 233^{233} hours.

Problem 10.43. Ayfos counts from 1 to n using her five left-fingers. Label her fingers T, F, M, R, L (thumb, fore, middle, ring, little). She starts by calling T one, then F two, M three, R four, L five. She then retraces calling R six, M seven, F eight, T nine. Then F ten, and so on. What finger will Ayfos be on when she reaches (a) 1,000 (b) 10^{2015}?

Problem 10.44. Prove that 3 divides n if and only if 3 divides the sum of n's digits. Does the same hold for divisibility by 9? *[Hint: First show that $10^k \equiv 1 \pmod{3}$ for $k \geq 1$.]*

Problem 10.45. Prove there is no square in the sequence $11, 111, 1111, 11111, \ldots$. *[Hint: $x^2 \equiv ?? \pmod{4}$.]*

Problem 10.46. Let p be a prime. Prove: $x^2 \equiv y^2 \pmod{p}$ IF AND ONLY IF $x \equiv y \pmod{p}$ or $x \equiv -y \pmod{p}$. Give a counter-example to the claim when p is not prime.

Problem 10.47. Use the Fundamental Theorem of Arithmetic to prove that for every $n \in \mathbb{N}$, if $\sqrt{n} \notin \mathbb{N}$ then $\sqrt{n}$ is irrational. (There is no irreducible fraction whose square is an integer.)

Problem 10.48. For any prime p and $a \in \mathbb{N}$, prove that $a^{p^j} \equiv a \pmod{p}$ for $j \geq 1$. (Use Fermat's Little Theorem.)

Problem 10.49. Use Fermat's Little Theorem (or explain why you can't) to help calculate these remainders.

(a) $\text{rem}(3^{2015}, 7)$ (b) $\text{rem}(2^{2015}, 23)$ (c) $\text{rem}(2^{2015}, 13)$ (d) $\text{rem}(7^{81}, 15)$.

Problem 10.50. Prove: $(n-1)^2|n^{n-1}-1$. *[Hint: $n^k = (n-1+1)^k$; Binomial Theorem.]*

Problem 10.51. Compute these modular inverses, or explain why you can't.

(a) $6^{-1} \pmod 7$ (b) $6^{-1} \pmod 8$ (c) $5^{-1} \pmod{12}$ (d) $12^{-1} \pmod 5$ (e) $1265^{-1} \pmod{88179}$ (f) $31870410^{-1} \pmod{58642669}$

Problem 10.52. Find all solutions for x in each case. If there aren't any, explain why.

(a) $1 \equiv (x \times -17) \pmod 4$ (b) $x \equiv -17 \pmod 4$ (c) $1 \equiv (x \times -12) \pmod 4$ (d) $x \equiv -12 \pmod 4$
(e) $84x - 38 \equiv 79 \pmod{15}$ (f) $7x \equiv 12 \pmod{13}$ (g) $341x \equiv 2941 \pmod 9$ (h) $20x \equiv 23 \pmod{14}$
(i) $4x \equiv 5 \pmod 6$ (j) $6x \equiv 3 \pmod 9$ (k) $x^2 \equiv 2 \pmod 4$ (l) $x^2 \equiv 2 \pmod 7$

Problem 10.53. Let $b_n = 1^1 + 2^2 + \cdots + n^n = \sum_{i=1}^{n} i^i$. Prove that $b_n \equiv b_{n+100} \pmod{10}$. That is, the last digit of b_n is periodic, with period 100.

Problem 10.54. Prove there are infinitely many primes of the form $3n+2$ for $n \ge 1$.

(a) Suppose $x_i \equiv 1 \pmod 3$ for $i = 1, \ldots, k$. Prove $x_1 x_2 \cdots x_k \equiv 1 \pmod 3$.
(b) Let $p_i = 3n_i + 2$ for $i = 1, \ldots, k$ and $n_i \ge 1$. Let $N = 3p_1 \cdots p_k + 2$. Prove that N is not divisible by 2 or 3 and that $N \equiv 2 \pmod 3$.
(c) Prove there is a prime factor q of N of the form $q = 3n + 2$ for $n \ge 1$. *[Hint: Part (a).]*
(d) Prove by contradiction that there are infinitely many primes of the form $3n + 2$ for $n \ge 1$.

Problem 10.55. Use the ideas in Problem 10.54 to prove that there are infinitely many primes of the form $4n - 1$. *[Hint: For primes $p_1, \ldots, p_k$ show that $N = 4p_1p_2 \cdots p_k - 1$ cannot have all its prime factors of the form $4p + 1$.]*

Problem 10.56 (Chineese Remainder Theorem). The Chineese Remainder Theorem states that if you specify the remainders of x modulo divisors $d_1, d_2, \ldots, d_k$ which are pairwise relatively prime, then you have uniquely specified x modulo the product of the divisors $d_1 d_2 \cdots d_k$.

(a) Find x, where $x \equiv 2 \pmod 5$ and $x \equiv 3 \pmod 7$. Give at least two solutions x_1, x_2.
(b) For your solutions x_1, x_2, compute $\text{rem}(x_i, 35)$.
(c) If x_1 and x_2 both satisfy the requirements in (a), prove that $x_1 \equiv x_2 \pmod{35}$.
(d) $x \equiv 4 \pmod 8$ and $x \equiv 1 \pmod{15}$. What is $\text{rem}(x, 120)$?

Problem 10.57. Let $d_1, d_2, \ldots, d_k$ be pairwise relatively prime, that is $\gcd(d_i, d_j) = 1$. Prove the following, which proves the Chineese Remainder Theorem.

(a) Suppose $d_1|n$, $d_2|n$. Then, $d_1 d_2|n$.
(b) Suppose that $d_i|n$ for $i = 1, \ldots, k$. Then, $d_1 d_2 \cdots d_k|n$. (Induction)
(c) The unknown x satisfies $x \equiv r_i \pmod{d_i}$ (x has remainder r_i when divided by d_i). Let x_1 and x_2 be two different solutions for x. Prove that $d_i|x_1 - x_2$ for $i = 1, \ldots, k$.
(d) For x_1, x_2 as in (c), show $x_1 \equiv x_2 \pmod{d_1 d_2 \cdots d_k}$. That is, x modulo the product of divisors $d_1 \cdots d_k$ is uniquiely determined by its remainders modulo each individual divisor.

Problem 10.58. Alice sends the location of Charlie's party to Bob. The message is: *MyHouse*

(a) Convert the message to binary using the ASCII code and evaluate the binary number to get an integer message M.
(b) How can you ensure that your message is a prime number, while allowing Bob to understand the message?

Problem 10.59 (One Time Pad). Alice and Bob have shared a private key $k = k_1 k2 \cdots k_8$ (8 bits). The message $M = m_1 m_2 \cdots m_8$ (same length as k). Alice sends the message $M_* = m_{1*} m_{2*} \cdots m_{8*}$ where each bit m_{i*} is the addition modulo 2 of the corresponding bits in k and M, $m_{i*} = m_i + k_i \pmod 2$. This is the XOR one time pad.

(a) Set $k = 11010011$. (i) $M = 10110101$, what is M_*? (ii) $M* = 11100111$, what was M?
(b) If k is random, justify the statement "There is no way to recover M from M_*."
(c) (Plain text attack) Alice uses the same key k to encode $M_1 = 10111100$ and M_2. The encoded messages are $M_{1*} = 11111111$ and $M_{2*} = 00001111$. What is M_2?
(d) (Prior attack) Alice uses the same key k to encode M_1 and M_2. The encoded messages are $M_{1*} = 11111111$ and $M_{2*} = 00001111$. Can we discern anything about M_1, M_2. As a hint, here is a visual example of this attack.

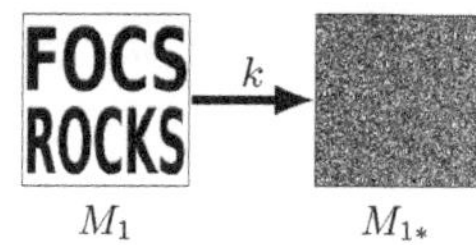

M_1 M_{1*}

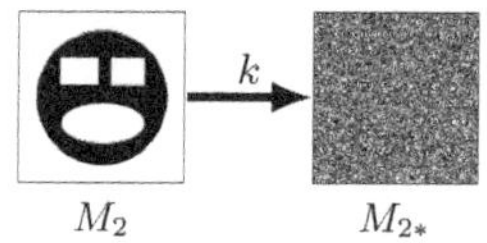

M_2 M_{2*}

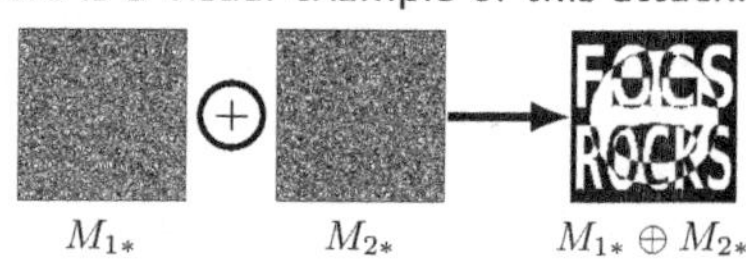

M_{1*} M_{2*} $M_{1*} \oplus M_{2*}$

Problem 10.60. Let $p = 14251$ and $q = 14519$ be two primes. Find choices for e and d in the RSA algorithm and compute the encryption M_* of the message $M = 19$. Show that your private key d decrypts M_* correctly.

Problem 10.61. For prime p, show that $p|\binom{p}{i}$ for $0 < i < p$. (Assume $\binom{p}{i} = \frac{p!}{i!(p-i)!}$ is integer, see Problem 5.43.)

Problem 10.62. For prime p and $x, y \in \mathbb{Z}$, show $(x+y)^p \equiv x^p + y^p \pmod p$. (Binomial Theorem; Problem 10.61)

Problem 10.63. Use Problem 10.62 to show that, for a prime p, if $k^p \equiv k \pmod p$, then $(k+1)^p \equiv k+1 \pmod p$. Hence, prove Fermat's Little Theorem by induction.

Problem 10.64 (Euler's Totient Function). Euler's totient function $\phi(n)$ counts the positive numbers up to n that are relatively prime to n, $\phi(n) = \sum_{d=1}^{n} [\![\gcd(n,d) = 1]\!]$. ($[\![\cdot]\!]$ is the Boolean indicator function which equals 1 if its argument is true and 0 otherwise.)

(a) Plot $\phi(n)$ versus n for $n = 1, \ldots, 20$. ($\phi(n)$ is a very erratic function.)
(b) What is $\phi(p)$ for a prime p. Show that $\phi(p^k) = p^k(1 - 1/p)$.
(c) Show that if $\gcd(m, n) = 1$ then $\phi(mn) = \phi(m)\phi(n)$.
(d) Show that $\phi(n) = n \prod_{p|n}(1 - 1/p)$. (The product is over primes which divide n.)
(e) (Due to Gauss) Compute $\sum_{d|n} \phi(d)$ for $n = 1, \ldots, 20$. Make a conjecture and prove it.
(f) Prove Euler's Extension of Fermat's Little Theorem: If $\gcd(a, n) = 1$, then $a^{\phi(n)} \equiv 1 \pmod n$.

Problem 10.65. Show: if $2^n - 1$ is prime, then n is prime. *[Hint:* $1 + 2^x + 2^{2x} + \cdots + 2^{x(y-1)} = ?$*]*
(Primes of the form $2^p - 1$ are Mersenne primes. We don't know if there are infinitely many Mersenne primes.)

Problem 10.66. Show: if $2^p - 1$ is prime then $2^{p-1}(2^p - 1)$ is perfect. *[Hint: The divisors are* $1, 2, 2^2, 2^3, \ldots, 2^{p-1}$ *and* $2^p - 1, (2^p - 1) \cdot 2, (2^p - 1) \cdot 2^2, \ldots, (2^p - 1) \cdot 2^{p-1}$. *Why?]*

Problem 10.67. Show, using the following steps, that every even perfect number has the form $2^{p-1}(2^p - 1)$ with $2^p - 1$ prime. Define $\sigma(n)$ to be the sum of the divisors of n that include n.

(a) Show: n is perfect if and only if $\sigma(n) = 2n$.
(b) Suppose $\gcd(m, n) = 1$. Show: $\sigma(mn) = \sigma(m)\sigma(n)$.
(c) Suppose x is even. Show: for some $k \geq 2$, $x = 2^{k-1}y$, where y is odd.
(d) What is $\gcd(2^{k-1}, y)$ when y is odd?
(e) Now, suppose x is an even perfect number.
  (i) Show: $2x = \sigma(x) = \sigma(y)(2^k - 1)$, and hence that $\sigma(y) = 2^k y/(2^k - 1)$.
  (ii) Show: $2^k - 1|y$ (use Euclid's lemma), hence that $y = m(2^k - 1)$.
  (iii) Show: $\sigma(y) = y + 1$ if and only if y is prime.
  (iv) Show: if $y = m(2^k - 1)$ and $\sigma(y) = 2^k y/(2^k - 1)$, then $m = 1$ and $2^k - 1$ is prime.
  (v) Conclude: $x = 2^{k-1}(2^k - 1)$ where $2^k - 1$ is prime.

(Are there infinitely many even perfect numbers? Is there an odd perfect number? We don't know.)

Problem 10.68 (Pythagorean Triples). Here is a glimpse into the type of questions asked in number theory. The Pythagorean Theorem relates the sides of a right triangle,

$$x^2 + y^2 = z^2.$$

What are all possible right triangles with integer sides? Such sides are called Pythagorean triples.

(a) Show that $(3, 4, 5)$, $(6, 8, 10)$ and $(5, 12, 13)$ are Pythagorean triples.
(b) In a primitive Pythagorean triple, $\gcd(x, y, z) = 1$. Which triples in (a) are primitive?
(c) [Euclid's formula] For $m > n$, show that $(m^2 - n^2, 2mn, m^2 + n^2)$ is a Pythagorean triple.
(d) If $\gcd(m, n) = 1$, show that Euclid's formula generates a primitive Pythagorean triple.
(e) **[Harder]** Show: every primitive Pythagorean triple can be generated by Euclid's formula.
(f) A sequence $a_1, a_2, \ldots$ is square if $a_1^2 + a_2^2 + \cdots + a_n^2$ is a square for every $n \geq 1$. Prove that there exists an infinite square sequence. *[Hint: Try starting with* $3, 4, \ldots$*.]*
(g) Now consider integral solutions to $x^3 + y^3 = z^3$. (You'll take a long time to find one ☹)

Problem 10.69. Let $\nu_p(x)$ be the largest power of prime p that divides x, so $x = \prod_{\text{primes } p} p^{\nu_p(x)}$.

(a) Show that $\nu_p(xy) = \nu_p(x) + \nu_p(y)$ and $\nu_p(x/y) = \nu_p(x) - \nu_p(y)$ (assuming y divides x).
(b) Show that $\nu_p(n!) = \sum_{i=1}^{\infty} \lfloor n/p^i \rfloor = \lfloor n/p \rfloor + \lfloor n/p^2 \rfloor + \lfloor n/p^3 \rfloor + \cdots$.
(c) In base-p, let $n = a_0 + a_1 p + a_2 p^2 + \cdots + a_k p^k$. Show that $\nu_p(n!) = (n - \sum_{i=0}^{k} a_k)/(p - 1)$.
(d) Prove that $n!$ is not divisible by 2^n.
(e) Prove that $n!$ is divisible by 2^{n-1} if and only if $n = 2^k$.

Problem 10.70. Prove that if $2n/3 < p \le n$, then $\nu_p(n!) = 1$ and $\nu_p((2n)!) = 2$. Show $\nu_p(\binom{2n}{n}) = 0$, and hence p does not divide $\binom{2n}{n}$. *[Hint: Compute $\lfloor n/p^i \rfloor$.]*

Problem 10.71. Show: $\nu_p\left(\binom{2n}{n}\right) = \nu_p((2n)!) - 2\nu_p(n!) = \sum_{i=1}^{\lfloor \log_p(2n) \rfloor} \lfloor 2n/p^i \rfloor - 2\lfloor n/p^i \rfloor \le \log_p(2n)$.

Problem 10.72. Prove that $\binom{2n}{n} \ge 4^n/(2n+1)$. *[Hint: $(1+1)^{2n} = \sum_{i=0}^{2n} \binom{2n}{i}$.]*

Problem 10.73. Prove by strong induction that $\prod_{\text{primes } p \le n} p \le 4^n$. *[Hints: In the induction, for odd $n+1$, use $\prod_{p \le 2m+1} p = (\prod_{p \le m+1} p) \times (\prod_{m+2 \le p}^{p \le 2m+1} p)$. Now show $\prod_{m+2 \le p}^{p \le 2m+1} p \le \binom{2m+1}{m}$, because if $m+2 \le$ prime $p \le 2m+1$ then p divides $\binom{2m+1}{m}$. Use the binomial expansion of $(1+1)^{2m+1}$ to show $\binom{2m+1}{m} \le 2^{2m}$.]*

Problem 10.74. Use Problems 10.69–10.73 to prove the rhyme (first proved by Chebyshev)

Chebyshev said it and I say it again,
There is always a prime between n and $2n$ —*Joseph Bertrand's Postulate*

Assume for some n there is no prime p with $n < p \le 2n$. Follow 19-year-old Paul Erdős' approach (Erdős' first paper).

(a) Show that at most $\sqrt{2n}$ prime factors of $\binom{2n}{n}$ are at most $\sqrt{2n}$, and each of these factors contributes at most $2n$ in the prime factorication of $\binom{2n}{n}$.
(b) Show that for $p \ge \sqrt{2n}$, $\nu_p(\binom{2n}{n}) \le 1$.
(c) Show that $\binom{2n}{n} \le (2n)^{\sqrt{2n}} \cdot \prod_{\sqrt{2n} \le p \le 2n/3} p \le (2n)^{\sqrt{2n}} \cdot \prod_{p \le 2n/3} p \le (2n)^{\sqrt{2n}} 4^{2n/3}$.
(d) Show that $(2n)^{\sqrt{2n}} 4^{2n/3} \ge 4^n/(2n+1)$.
(e) Show that this is impossible if $n \ge 468$. and prove Bertrand's postulate.

Problem 10.75 (Euler Product). Use Euler's method to show that $\prod_{\text{primes } p}(1 - 1/p^2) = 6/\pi^2$.

(a) Compute a formula for $1 + 1/p^2 + 1/p^4 + 1/p^6 + \cdots + 1/p^{2i} + \cdots = \sum_{i=0}^{\infty} 1/p^{2i}$.
(b) What integers x_i appear in the sum $\sum_i 1/x_i$ obtained by expanding out each product?
 (i) $(1+\frac{1}{3}+\frac{1}{3^2}+\frac{1}{3^3}+\cdots)(1+\frac{1}{7}+\frac{1}{7^2}+\frac{1}{7^3}+\cdots)$ (ii) $(1+\frac{1}{3^2}+\frac{1}{3^4}+\cdots+\frac{1}{3^{2i}}+\cdots)(1+\frac{1}{7^2}+\frac{1}{7^4}+\cdots+\frac{1}{7^{2i}}+\cdots)$
(c) Use Problem 9.64 to compute the product $\prod_{\text{primes } p}(1 - 1/p^2)$ by showing

$$\prod_{\text{primes } p} \frac{1}{1 - 1/p^2} = 1 + \frac{1}{2^2} + \frac{1}{3^2} + \frac{1}{4^2} + \frac{1}{5^2} + \frac{1}{6^2} + \cdots. \tag{10.1}$$

Problem 10.76. Here are a few famous open problems from number theory. The internet sprawls with more.

(a) The Euler-Mascheroni constant is $\gamma = \lim_{n\to\infty}(H_n - \ln n) \approx 0.5772156649$. Is γ rational or irrational?
(b) Is every even number greater than 2 a sum of two primes? (Goldbach's conjecture)
(c) Are there odd perfect numbers? Are there infinitely many even perfect numbers (or, Mersenne Primes)?
(d) Are there infinitely many twin primes, primes p where $p+2$ is also prime?
(e) (Collatz or $3n+1$ conjecture). For a number n, define $f(n) = n/2$ if n is even and $3n+1$ otherwise. Does the sequence $n, f(n), f^2(n), \ldots$ eventually become 1 for every $n \in \mathbb{N}$?
(f) A prime q is called a Sophie-Germain prime if $p = 2q+1$ is prime. The prime p is called safe. Can you find a Sophie-Germain prime larger than 100? We don't know if there are infinitely many Sophie-Germain primes.
(g) What is the exact value (in terms of known constants) of $\zeta(3) = 1 + 1/2^3 + 1/3^3 + 1/4^3 + 1/5^3 + \cdots$.
(h) **(Riemann Hypothesis)** Equation (10.1) relating primes and integers generalizes to any complex power s,

$$\prod_{\text{primes } p} \frac{1}{1 - 1/p^s} = 1 + \frac{1}{2^s} + \frac{1}{3^s} + \frac{1}{4^s} + \frac{1}{5^s} + \frac{1}{6^s} + \cdots = \zeta(s). \tag{10.2}$$

The summation is absolutely convergent for $Re(s) > 1$ and $\zeta(s)$ has a unique analytic continuation to the entire complex plane. The Riemann Hypothesis is that all zeros of $\zeta(s)$ with $0 < Re(s) < 1$ have $Re(s) = 1/2$. That's the burning question in number theory with implications to the distribution of prime numbers and more.

> The origins of graph theory are humble, even frivolous.
> – **N. Biggs, E. K. Lloyd, and R. J. Wilson**
>
> Begin at the beginning, the King said very gravely, and go on till you come to the end: then stop. – **Lewis Carroll (*Alice in Wonderland*)**

Chapter 11

Graphs

1: Basic notation: vertices, edges and isomorphism; paths and connectivity.
2: Degrees and the Handshaking Theorem.

Graphs model relationships: friendships (e.g. social networks); connectivity (e.g. cities linked by highways); conflicts (e.g. radio-towers broadcasting to the same listener); etc. An entire course on graph theory might cover just the tip of the iceberg in terms of theorems, applications and algorithms. We hope to set a modest foundation: terminology and the basics. When you see "graph," think of objects and links connecting related pairs of objects. The objects are vertices in the vertex set V and the links are edges in the edge set E. The number of vertices is $|V|$ and the number of edges is $|E|$. Here is a graph with 7 vertices and 8 edges.

Graph G

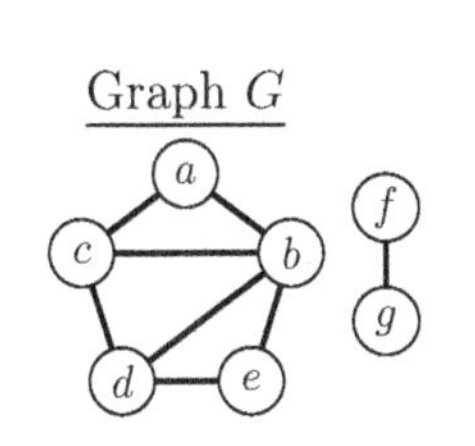

Vertices (aka nodes): ⓐ ⓑ ⓒ ⓓ ⓔ ⓕ ⓖ $\qquad V = \{a, b, c, d, e, f, g\}$.

Edges: ⓐ–ⓑ, ⓐ–ⓒ, ⓑ–ⓒ, ⓑ–ⓓ, ⓑ–ⓔ, ⓒ–ⓓ, ⓓ–ⓔ, ⓕ–ⓖ $\qquad E = \left\{ \begin{matrix} (a,b),(a,c),(b,c),(b,d), \\ (b,e),(c,d),(d,e),(f,g) \end{matrix} \right\}$.

Degree: Number of relationships $\qquad$ *e.g.*, degree$(b) = 4$.

Path: ⓐ–ⓒ–ⓑ–ⓔ–ⓓ–ⓑ $\qquad p = acbedb$.

Pop Quiz 11.1

Give the vertex and edge sets (V, E) for each graph below.

(a) 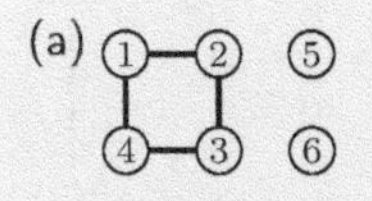
(b) 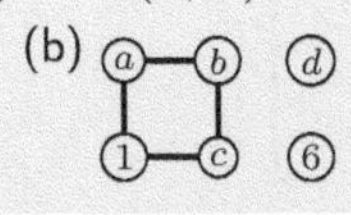
(c) 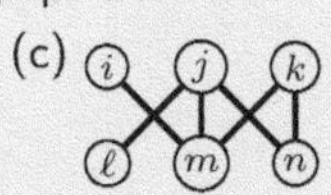
(d) 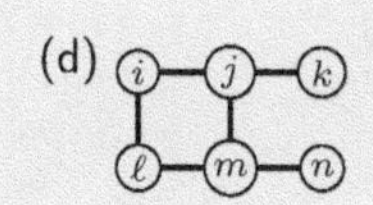

Isomorphic (Equivalent) Graphs. Vertex labels are just names. What matters are the relationships or edges. It is common to relabel the vertices to $v_1, v_2, \ldots, v_n$, which is an isomorphism. In our example, we can relabel $\{a, \ldots, g\}$ to $\{v_1, \ldots, v_7\}$ and the edges change accordingly to unordered pairs (v_i, v_j).

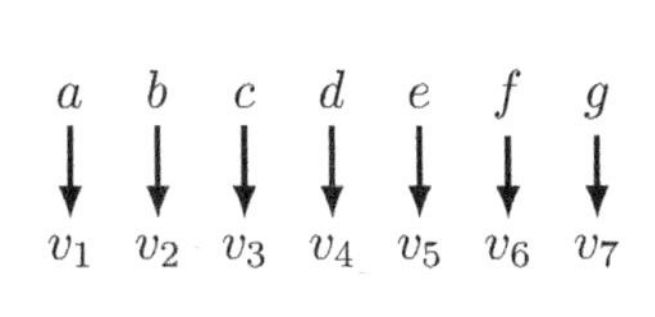

Relabeling of Graph G

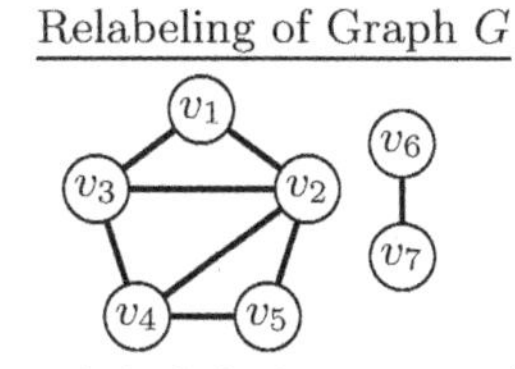

$$V = \{v_1, v_2, v_3, v_4, v_5, v_6, v_7\}.$$

$$E = \left\{ \begin{matrix} (v_1,v_2),(v_1,v_3),(v_2,v_3),(v_2,v_4), \\ (v_2,v_5),(v_3,v_4),(v_4,v_5),(v_6,v_7) \end{matrix} \right\}.$$

Two graphs are isomorphic if you can label their vertices $\{v_1, \ldots, v_n\}$ so that both graphs have the same edges.

Paths and Connectivity. A path from v_1 to v_2 is a sequence of vertices starting at v_1 and ending at v_2, with an edge between consecutive vertices. Think: v_1 is a friend of a friend ... of a friend of v_2. For example, $v_1v_3v_2v_5v_4v_2$ is a path from v_1 to v_2 with path length five, the number of edges traversed. This path revisits v_2.

A path is simple if no vertex is repeated. A cycle is a path that starts and ends at the same vertex and no edge is repeated. Vertices v_1 and v_2 are connected if there is a path from v_1 to v_2. In our graph, v_1 is connected to v_2, v_3, v_4 and v_5 but not to v_6. A graph is connected if every pair of vertices is connected. We illustrate these concepts and more in the pictures below, without giving formal definitions.

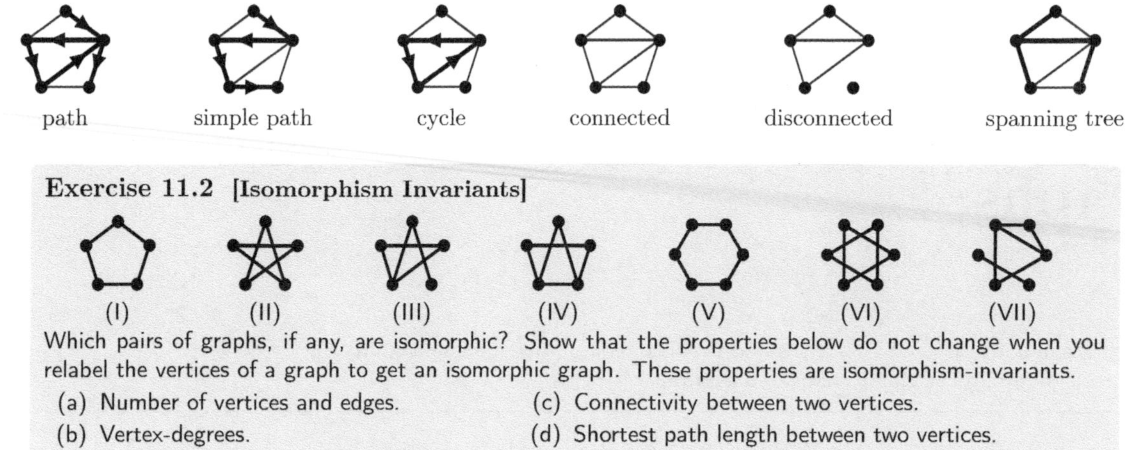

Exercise 11.2 [Isomorphism Invariants]

Which pairs of graphs, if any, are isomorphic? Show that the properties below do not change when you relabel the vertices of a graph to get an isomorphic graph. These properties are isomorphism-invariants.

(a) Number of vertices and edges.
(b) Vertex-degrees.
(c) Connectivity between two vertices.
(d) Shortest path length between two vertices.

Note: two graphs cannot be isomorphic if they differ in an isomorphism-invariant (e.g. vertex-degrees).

Adjacency Lists and Adjacency Matrices. A graph is defined once you specify the vertices V and the edges E. For computing on graphs, we need convenient representations. The two most popular, by far, are adjacency lists and the adjacency matrices. In an adjacency list, you list all the vertices as a column vector, and for each vertex in the list, you identify all its neighbors. These neighbors can be collected into a separate vector, one for each vertex in the adjacency list. A neighbor of a vertex v is any other vertex u that has an edge to v, so $(u, v) \in E$. Remember that the edges are unordered pairs so $(u, v) = (v, u)$.

The adjacency matrix A is a binary matrix with n rows and n columns. The n rows correspond to the n vertices $v_1, \ldots, v_n$ and so do the n columns. The (i, j)-entry in the adjacency matrix denoted A_{ij} (the entry in the ith row and jth column) is 1 if there is an edge connecting v_i to v_j, $(v_i, v_j) \in E$, and 0 otherwise. For our example graph, we show the adjacency list and adjacency matrix representations below.

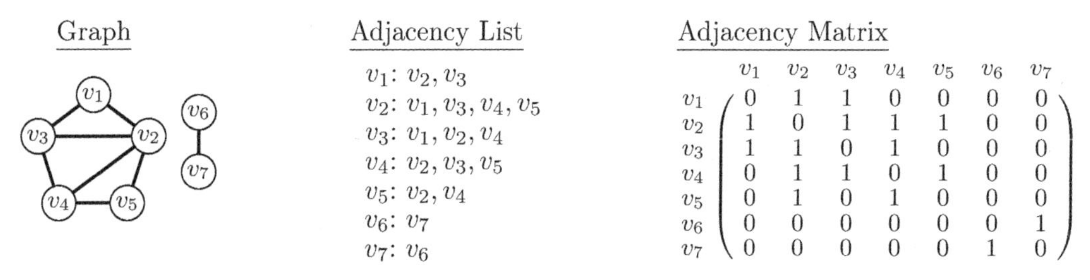

Adjacency List

v_1: v_2, v_3
v_2: v_1, v_3, v_4, v_5
v_3: v_1, v_2, v_4
v_4: v_2, v_3, v_5
v_5: v_2, v_4
v_6: v_7
v_7: v_6

Adjacency Matrix

$$\begin{array}{c|ccccccc} & v_1 & v_2 & v_3 & v_4 & v_5 & v_6 & v_7 \\ \hline v_1 & 0 & 1 & 1 & 0 & 0 & 0 & 0 \\ v_2 & 1 & 0 & 1 & 1 & 1 & 0 & 0 \\ v_3 & 1 & 1 & 0 & 1 & 0 & 0 & 0 \\ v_4 & 0 & 1 & 1 & 0 & 1 & 0 & 0 \\ v_5 & 0 & 1 & 0 & 1 & 0 & 0 & 0 \\ v_6 & 0 & 0 & 0 & 0 & 0 & 0 & 1 \\ v_7 & 0 & 0 & 0 & 0 & 0 & 1 & 0 \end{array}$$

Every edge appears twice in both representations. Consider edge (v_1, v_2). In the adjacency list, v_2 is a neighbor of v_1, and v_1 is a neighbor of v_2. Similarly, in the adjacency matrix, A_{12} and A_{21} are both 1. This observation will be very significant. Computationally, there are advantages and disadvantages of the adjacency matrix over the adjacency list. The adjacency matrix uses more memory to store unnecessary zeros, but most algorithms are faster because you can quickly determine whether any edge (v_i, v_j) is in the graph (random access).

11.1 Degree Sequence

The degree of a vertex is the number of edges it participates in. The degree δ_i of vertex v_i is the number of neighbors listed for v_i in the adjacency list, also the sum of the ith row of the adjacency matrix,

$$\delta_i = \text{number of neighbors } v_i \text{ has} = \sum_{j=1}^{n} A_{ij}.$$

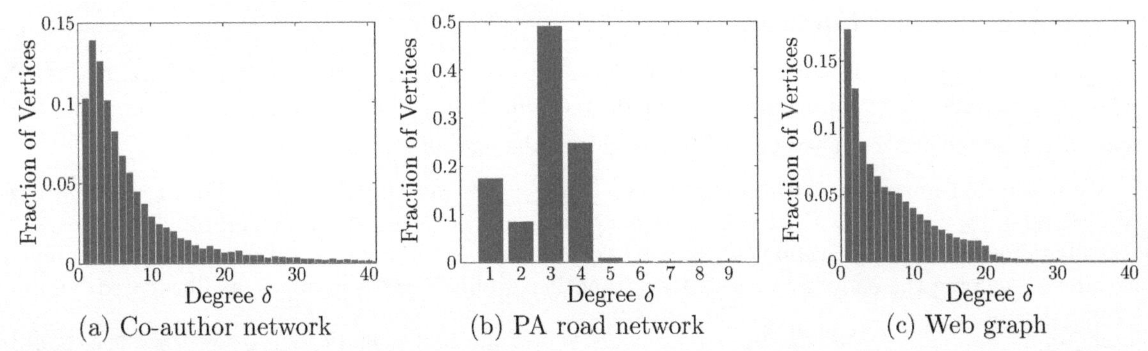

Figure 11.1: Degree histograms. (a) Co-authorship network of condensed matter papers in arXiv (1993–2003). Authors are vertices (more than 23 thousand) and links represent coauthorship (approx. 93 thousand). (b) Road network of Pennsylvania. Intersections and endpoints are vertices (more than 1 million), and roads connecting the vertices are edges (more than 1.5 million). (c) Web-graph released by Google in 2002. Web pages are vertices (approx. 900 thousand) and hyperlinks are edges (approx 5.1 million). (Data from the Stanford SNAP repository)

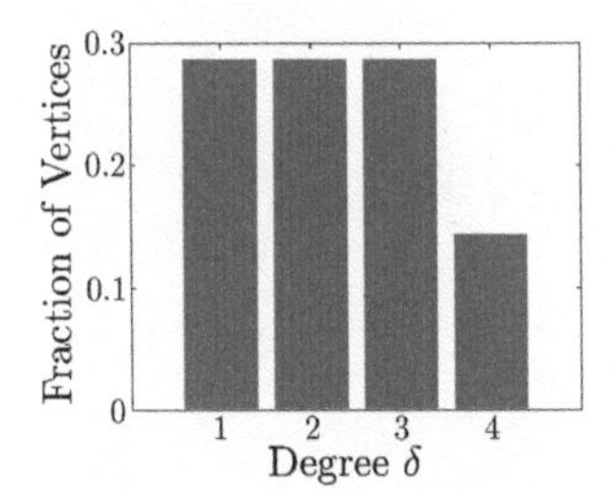

The degree sequence $\boldsymbol{\delta}$ lists all the vertex degrees in the graph, from highest to lowest. In our example graph, the degree sequence is $\boldsymbol{\delta} = [4, 3, 3, 2, 2, 1, 1]$. Another way to report the degree sequence is to list the number of vertices with degree 0, degree 1, degree 2 and so on – the degree distribution. The degree distribution can conveniently be represented as a histogram, as shown to the right. Figure 11.1 shows the degree distributions for some real-world graphs: a collaboration network; a road network; and, a world-wide-web network. The degree sequence is one of the primary signatures of a graph.

In the road network, the highest degree is 9 – imagine the chaos that could be caused by a 9-way intersection. In the collaboration network, a few vertices have a very large degree, but most vertices have small degree. The number of vertices of high degree drops quickly as the degree increases. The web-graph is similar: many low-degree vertices, and few high degree vertices; the number of vertices with high degree drops as the degree increases, but the drop is not as fast as in the collaboration network. The message is that different types of graphs arising in different applications have different degree sequences.

Exercise 11.3

Unfortunately, the degree sequence alone does not uniquely identify a graph.

(a) Give two non-isomorphic graphs which have degree sequence $[2, 2, 2, 2, 2, 2]$.
(b) Give two non-isomorphic graphs with degree sequence $[3, 3, 2, 1, 1]$.
(c) Give a graph with degree sequence $[3, 3, 3, 2, 1, 1]$.

Special Graphs. Here are some common graph patterns and their degree sequences.

Clique K_5	Bipartite $K_{3,2}$	Path/Line L_5	Cycle C_5	Star S_6	Wheel W_6
$\boldsymbol{\delta} = [4,4,4,4,4]$	$\boldsymbol{\delta} = [3,3,2,2,2]$	$\boldsymbol{\delta} = [2,2,2,1,1]$	$\boldsymbol{\delta} = [2,2,2,2,2]$	$\boldsymbol{\delta} = [5,1,1,1,1,1]$	$\boldsymbol{\delta} = [5,3,3,3,3,3]$

K_n: Complete graph, or n-clique. Each of the n vertices is linked to every other vertex.
$K_{n,\ell}$: Complete bipartite graph on n left and ℓ right vertices. Every left-vertex links to every right-vertex.
L_n: Path or Line with n vertices. Consecutive vertices are linked.
C_n: Cycle with n vertices. A path with an additional link from the last to the first vertex.
S_{n+1}: Star, with a central vertex linked to n peripheral vertices, equivalently $K_{1,n}$.
W_{n+1}: Wheel, a cycle of n vertices with a central node linked to every vertex of the cycle.

11.1.1 Handshaking Theorem

The sum of vertex-degrees is twice the number of edges because an edge (u, v) contributes 1 to degree(u) and 1 to degree(v). So every edge contributes 2 to the degree-sum, hence (degree-sum) $= 2 \times$ (number of edges).

Theorem 11.1 (Handshaking Theorem)**.** For any graph, the sum of vertex-degrees is $2|E|$, $\sum_{i=1}^{n} \delta_i = 2|E|$.

Proof. We prove that any graph with m edges has $\sum_{i=1}^{n} \delta_i = 2m$ by induction on m. For $m = 0$ (base case), every $\delta_i = 0$, so $\sum_i \delta_i = 0 = 2m$. For the inductive step, assume the claim for every graph with m edges. We prove the claim for an arbitrary graph G with $m+1$ edges. Relabel the vertices so that $e = (v_1, v_2)$ is an edge. Remove edge e, keeping the endpoints v_1, v_2, to get another graph G' with m edges, as illustrated below.

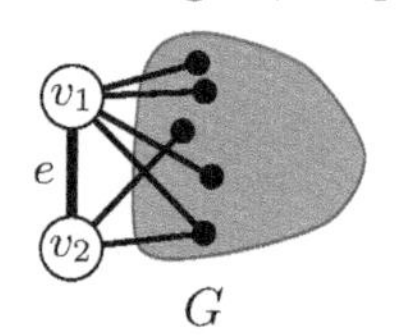

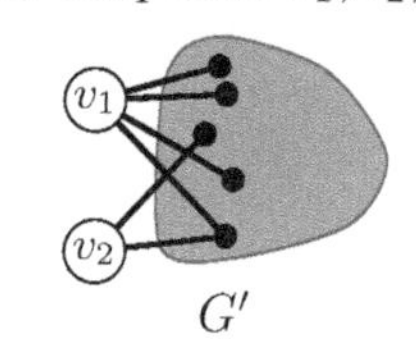

(G has $m+1$ vertices and G' has m vertices. The shaded regions represent the remaining part of the graphs which are identical for G and G' and do not affect the analysis, so we do not need their detailed structure.)

Let δ_i and δ_i' be the vertex-degrees in G and G' respectively. The edge (v_1, v_2) doesn't affect vertices $v_3, \ldots, v_n$ in the shaded region, so $\delta_i' = \delta_i$ for $i \geq 3$. By the induction hypothesis, the sum of vertex-degrees in G' is $2m$,

$$2m = \sum_{i=1}^{n} \delta_i' = \delta_1' + \delta_2' + \sum_{i=3}^{n} \delta_i' = \delta_1' + \delta_2' + \sum_{i=3}^{n} \delta_i.$$

We used $\delta_i' = \delta_i$ for $i \geq 3$. Further, $\delta_1' = \delta_1 - 1$ as v_1 lost one link to v_2. Similarly, $\delta_2' = \delta_2 - 1$. Therefore,

$$2m = (\delta_1 - 1) + (\delta_2 - 1) + \sum_{i=3}^{n} \delta_i = \sum_{i=1}^{n} \delta_i - 2.$$

Rearranging, $2(m+1) = \sum_{i=1}^{n} \delta_i$, proving the claim for G. The theorem follows by induction. ■

The proof illustrates a typical induction with graphs. You start from a *general* larger graph and remove an edge or a vertex to get a smaller graph to which you apply the induction hypothesis. A common error is to start from a general smaller graph and add a vertex or edge in a specific way, which doesn't necessarily give a general larger graph. The claim MUST be proved for a general larger graph.

Example 11.2. At a party, people shake hands. An "odd" person shakes hands with an odd number of people.

Claim: There are an even number of "odd" people.

The name "Handshaking" Theorem derives from this curious fact. We prove the claim using graphs. The n people at the party are the vertices $v_1, \ldots, v_n$ of a graph. The edge (v_i, v_j) exists if v_i and v_j shake hands. The degree δ_i is the number of handshakes v_i makes, and v_i is "odd" if δ_i is odd. Assume, to get a contradiction, that the number of "odd" people (vertices) is odd. Let's look at the sum of the degrees,

$$\sum_i \delta_i = \sum_{\delta_i \text{ even}} \delta_i + \sum_{\delta_i \text{ odd}} \delta_i = (\text{even}) + (\text{odd}) = \textbf{odd} = \textbf{2} \times \textbf{number of edges}.$$

The key step breaks the sum into two. The sum over the "even" vertices is even, a sum of even numbers. The sum over the odd number of "odd" vertices is odd, as a sum of an odd number of odd integers is odd. Even plus odd is odd, so the degree-sum is odd and equals $2|E|$ which is even. This contradiction proves the claim.

Theorem 11.3. In any graph, there are an even number of odd-degree vertices. □

Pop Quiz 11.4

Explain why you could not create a graph with the degree sequence in Exercise 11.3(c).

Exercise 11.5

(a) What is the minimum number of edges in a graph if every degree is positive?
(b) How many edges are needed to guarantee that every node has positive degree?
(c) In an r-regular graph, all vertices have degree r. Draw all 5-vertex 3-regular graphs.

11.2 Trees

A tree is a connected graph with no cycles. This is more general than the rooted binary tree on page 92. Let us build a tree by adding edges one by one to an empty graph.

step 0 step 1 step 2 step 3 step 4 step 5 step 6

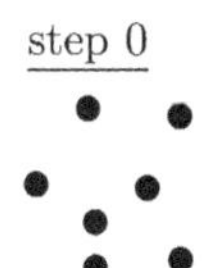
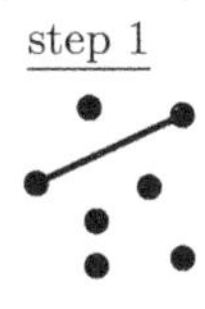
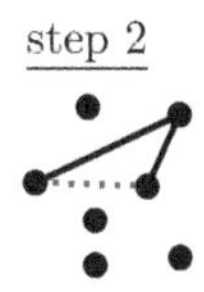
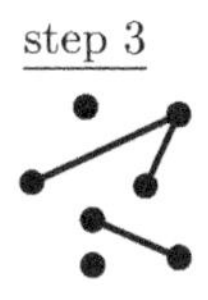
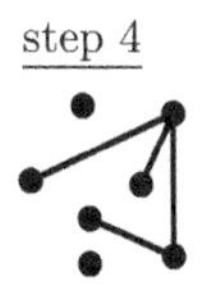
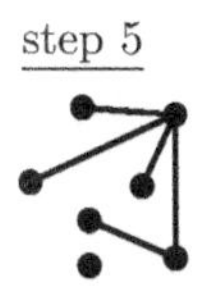
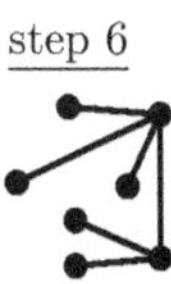

The graph in step 6 is a tree – it's connected and acyclic. Both properties, connected and acyclic, are essential to be tree. Below is a more standard drawing of this tree from step 6, with a root on top.

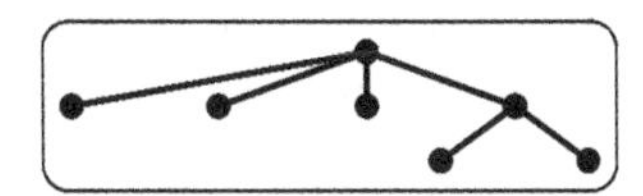

Exercise 11.6
(a) Why can't you add the dotted edge in step 2 above when we were building a tree?
(b) Why are the graphs in steps 1–5 not trees? Why can't you add edges after step 6?
(c) Prove that a graph with fewer than $n-1$ edges cannot be connected.
(d) Prove that a graph with more than $n-1$ edges must have a cycle.
(e) Prove: a connected n-vertex graph is a tree if and only if it has $n-1$ edges.

11.3 Planar Graphs

A planar graph can be drawn on a sheet of paper without edge crossings (edges need not be straight). We show three drawings of K_4. In the left one, edges cross. The right two are planar drawings of K_4.

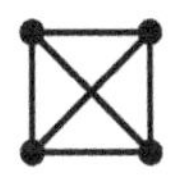

So, K_4 is planar as there is some way to draw it without edge crossings. Here are three famous examples.

Circuit Layout. Five processing units on a semi-conductor chip must be connected to each other by fine gold wire. The wires must not cross because that forms a short circuit. We tried to connect the processors, but as you see, processors 3 and 5 are yet to be connected. There is no way to connect them without wires crossing. We need a planar drawing of K_5. No matter how hard you try you will not be able to connect the processors without wires crossing. K_5 is not planar.

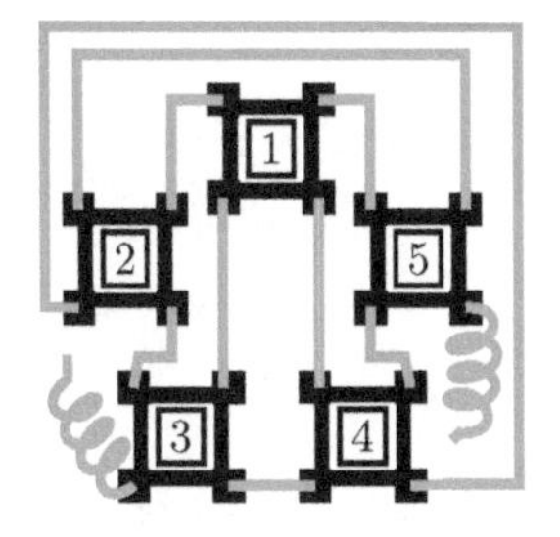

In circuit design, if you cannot make all the connections without wires crossing, you need more semi-conductor layers to get off the plane, and that's costly. Planarity plays an important role in determining how many semi-conductor layers you need. In the early days, Wozniak (cofounder of Apple) was an ace at finding planar drawings of complex circuits, to minimize the number of semi-conductor layers.

Utility Graph. Three homes need power, water and sewer. We show a layout of utility lines for this three by three utility graph. The utility lines can't cross, for we don't wish to mix water and sewer ☹. Our layout of utility lines does not satisfy this requirement. We need a planar drawing of the utility graph, which is $K_{3,3}$. No matter how hard you try, you will not be able to lay the utility lines so that they do not cross. $K_{3,3}$ is not planar.

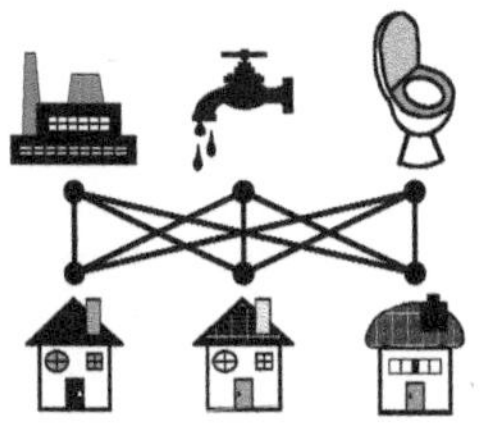

There are infinitely many ways to draw a graph. How do we know you can't draw K_5 and $K_{3,3}$ without edge crossings? We need the help of deep methods developed by the great Euler, see Exercise 11.7.

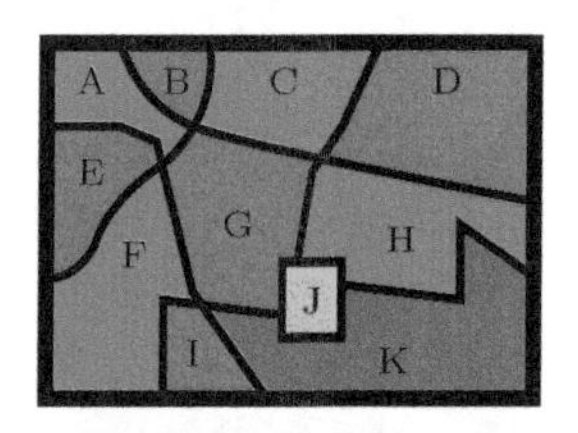

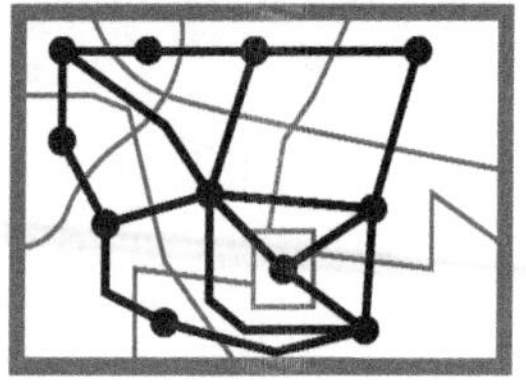

Maps and Planarity. We show a land divided into countries $A, B, \ldots, K$. Two countries are neighbors if they share a border, like A and B, but not if they share just a point, like A and F. If we place a vertex inside each country, and draw an edge between two countries that are neighbors, we get the graph illustrated below the map. Edges linking two countries go over the border between those two countries. Since none of the edges cross, the graph is planar. As long as countries are contiguous, the country graph of a map is planar (we won't prove this).

How many colors are needed to color the countries so that neighboring countries have different colors, making it easy to distinguish the countries? The Four-Color Theorem says that 4 colors suffices, and our map is colored with 4 colors.

The next exercise is a famous result due to Euler, which relates the number of edges and vertices in a planar graph. Among the applications of Euler's result are that five colors suffices to color a map and that K_5 and $K_{3,3}$ are not planar.

Exercise 11.7 [Euler's Invariant Characteristic: $F + V - E = 2$.]

Euler was fascinated by regular polyhedra. Three are shown. Vertices, edges and faces are defined in the natural way. Let V be the number of vertices, E, the number of edges and F the number of faces.

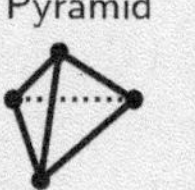

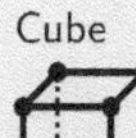
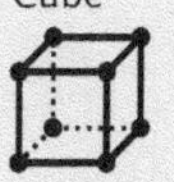

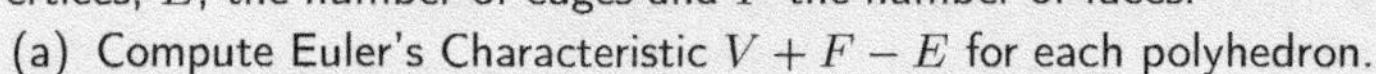

(a) Compute Euler's Characteristic $V + F - E$ for each polyhedron.

(b) Give planar drawings of the polyhedra, treating each as a graph.

(c) What do the faces of the polyhedra become in the planar graph?

Define a planar graph using intersecting lines on a plane.

- End points and intersections are vertices.
- Line segments between the vertices are edges.
- Internal faces are regions enclosed by cycles (left).
- The external face is the unbounded region not covered by internal faces (right).

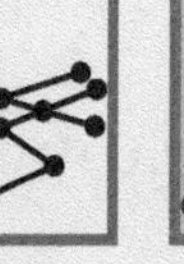
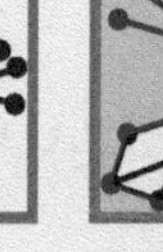

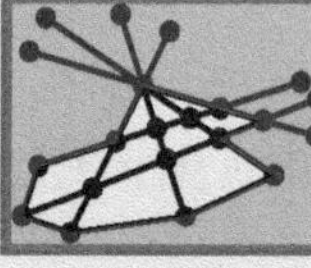

By construction, the graph is planar. Assume it is connected.

(Our discussion remains valid for general planar graphs that use intersecting piecewise linear curves.)

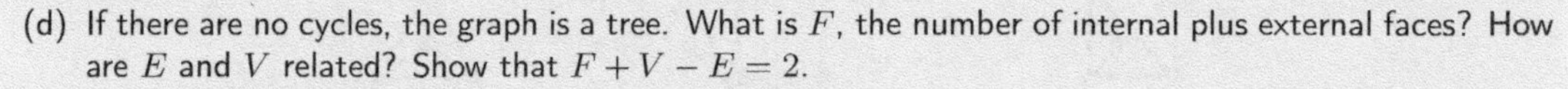

(d) If there are no cycles, the graph is a tree. What is F, the number of internal plus external faces? How are E and V related? Show that $F + V - E = 2$.

(e) Now consider a graph with cycles, having internal faces.

  (i) Remove an edge from any cycle. What is the change in $V, F,$ & E? Is the graph still connected?

  (ii) Remove one edge from a cycle at a time until there are no cycles. What is ΔV, the change in V. How are ΔE and ΔF, the changes in E and F, related?

  (iii) Prove that $F + V - E = 2$ for the original graph with cycles.

(f) Let $E(f)$ be the number of edges used to traverse the boundary of face f without lifting the pen. For the external face you may use an edge twice. In our example 24 edges are used. Show $\sum_f E(f) = 2E$.

(g) If $V \geq 3$, show $E(f) \geq 3$, and hence $E \leq 3V - 6$. Prove K_5 is not planar.

(h) If $V \geq 3$ and there are no 3-cycles, show $E \leq 2V - 4$. Prove $K_{3,3}$ is not planar.

11.4 Other Types of Graphs

We have discussed simple undirected graphs. Simple means no parallel edges or loop-edges from a vertex to itself. Undirected means the relationships are symmetric. Graphs with parallel edges or loops are multigraphs.

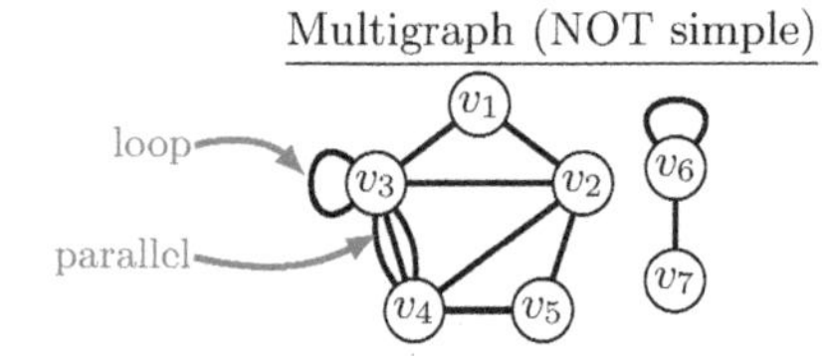

$$V = \{v_1, v_2, v_3, v_4, v_5, v_6, v_7\}.$$

$$E = \left\{ \begin{array}{l} (v_1, v_2), (v_1, v_3), (v_2, v_3), (v_2, v_4), \\ (v_2, v_5), (v_3, v_4), (v_3, v_4), (v_3, v_4), \\ (v_4, v_5), (v_6, v_7), (v_3, v_3), (v_6, v_6) \end{array} \right\}.$$

The Handshaking Theorem still holds for multigraphs because every edge contributes two to the degree-sum.

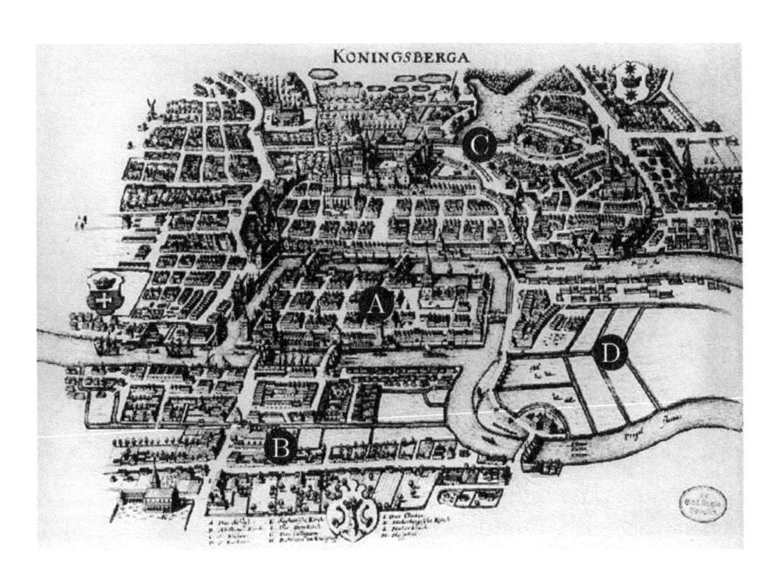

Figure 11.2: Map of Königsberg during Euler's time (now Kaliningrad) – von Merian-Erben, 1652.

Exercise 11.8 [Seven Bridges of Königsberg]

Leonhard Euler in 1736 laid the foundations of graph theory in a famous paper *"Solutio problematis ad geometriam situs pertinentis,"* that solved a problem on a multigraph. The river Pregel split Königsberg into 4 districts, see Figure 11.2 and Euler's abstraction of it below, left. Euler labeled the districts A, B, C, D. These districts were connected by seven bridges which Euler labeled a, b, c, d, e, f, g. The districts are vertices of a graph, and the bridges form edges. The resulting multigraph is shown below, right.

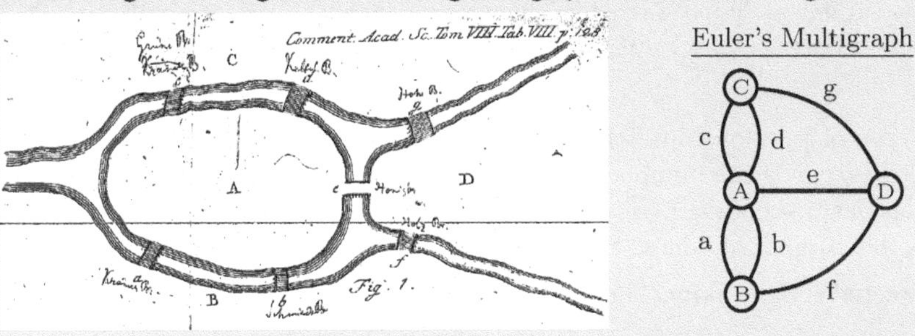

Euler's problem: Can one cross every bridge exactly once on an evening walk through Königsburg?

Weighted Graphs. Links between vertices can have a length or strength. An edge's weight captures this length or strength. In road networks, the edge-weight could be the distance between vertices. Edge-weights between routers in the internet could be the time to traverse the link. Edge-weights in social networks reflect the strength of the friendship. Graphs with edge-weights are weighted graphs and the weighted degree of a vertex is the sum of the weights on edges attached to the vertex. An edge with weight w contributes w to the weighted-degree of two vertices and $2w$ to the sum of weighted-degrees. The Handshaking Theorem becomes

Theorem 11.4 (Weighted Handshaking Theorem)**.** Sum of weighted-degrees $= 2 \times$ sum of edge-weights.

Exercise 11.9

The graph is an ISP (internet service provider) network. The vertices are ISPs. Edges connect ISPs and edge weights are packet travel times in milliseconds, e.g. the direct link between the two red ISPs takes 20ms to traverse.

How quickly can one route a packet between the red ISPs?

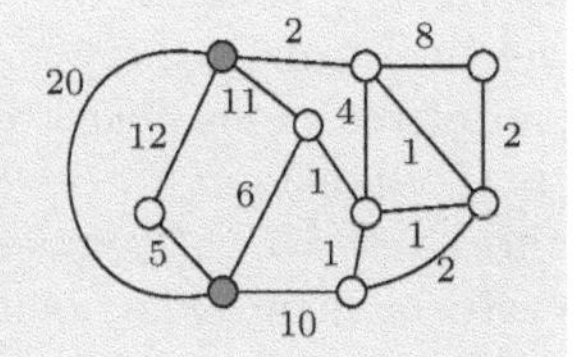

11.4.1 Directed Graphs (Digraphs)

Directed graphs represent one-way asymmetric relationships. For example one-way streets; parent-child relationships; web-hyperlinks that cannot be traversed backwards; who beats whom in a round-robin tournament.

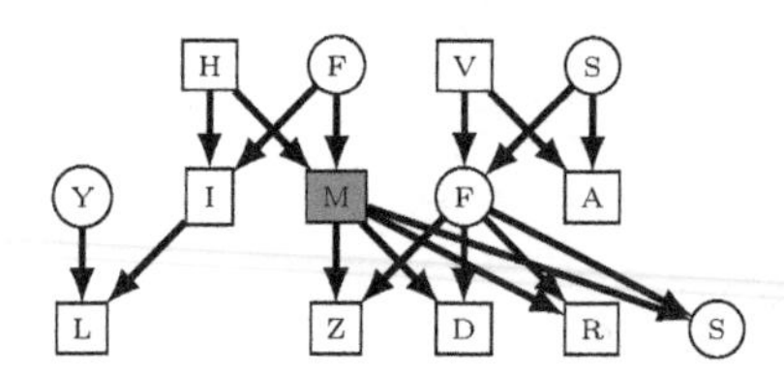

Part of the ancestry graph for the author M. A directed edge is the relation "parent of".

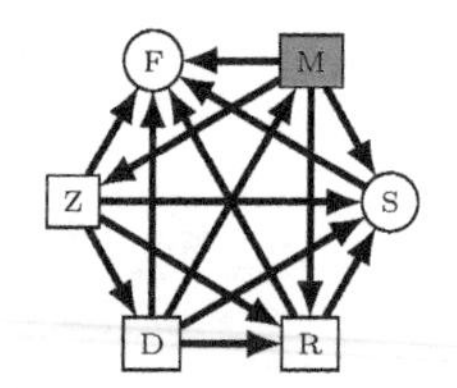

Round-robin tennis tournament in the author's family. A directed edge is the relation "beats".

Each edge $u \to v$ has a direction. The tail u is the beginning of the edge and the head v is the end, and we use the notation $(u{\to}v)$ in the edge-list. Here is a directed version of our usual example.

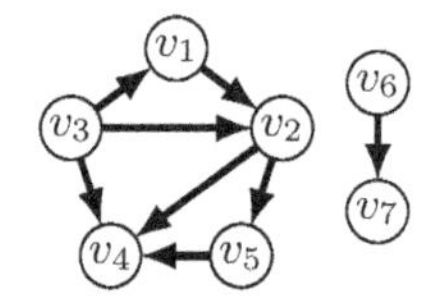

$$V = \{v_1, v_2, v_3, v_4, v_5, v_6, v_7\}.$$

$$E = \left\{ \begin{matrix} (v_1{\to}v_2), (v_3{\to}v_1), (v_3{\to}v_2), (v_2{\to}v_4), \\ (v_2{\to}v_5), (v_3{\to}v_4), (v_5{\to}v_4), (v_6{\to}v_7) \end{matrix} \right\}.$$

Pop Quiz 11.10

(a) For the graph on the right, give the vertex and edge sets.

(b) A directed path follows edges in the direction of the arrows: $v_3v_1v_2$ is a path but $v_2v_1v_3$ is not. A graph is strongly connected if there is a directed path from each vertex to every other vertex. Is the graph strongly connected?

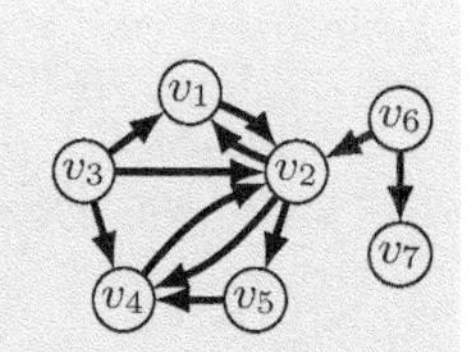

A vertex has two types of relationships: those starting at the vertex; and, those ending at the vertex. The out-degree of v_i, out-deg(v_i), is the number of relationships starting at v_i. Similarly, the in-degree, in-deg(v_i), is the number of relationships ending at v_i. Every edge contributes 1 to the in-degree of a vertex, so the sum of in-degrees equals the number of edges. Similarly, the sum of out-degrees equals the number of edges.

Theorem 11.5 (Directed Handshaking Theorem)**.** The in and out-degree sums both equal the number of edges,

$$\sum_{i=1}^{n} \text{in-deg}(v_i) = \sum_{i=1}^{n} \text{out-deg}(v_i) = |E|.$$

You should verify Theorem 11.5 for the graph in Pop Quiz 11.10. Directed graphs are good models for things that flow, e.g. sewage, traffic, internet-packets. Maximizing flow in networks is a big deal. Another application of directed graphs is to partially ordered sets.

Example 11.6 (Partial Orders)**.** The binary relation $\le$ induces a total order on integers. Any two integers m, n are comparable: either $m \le n$ or $n \le m$, or both. The relation is reflexive, i.e. $m \le m$, and transitive, i.e. $m \le n$ AND $n \le \ell$ implies $m \le \ell$. Let's define "$\le$" for 2-dimensional points,

$$(x_1, y_1) \le (x_2, y_2) \quad \text{if and only if} \quad x_1 \le x_2 \text{ and } y_1 \le y_2.$$

If (say) $x_1 \le x_2$ and $y_1 > y_2$, the two points are not comparable. Not all pairs of distinct points are comparable, so this is a partial ordering of 2-dimensional points. We show the "$\le$" relationship among 10 points in the directed graph on the right. The edge $(u{\to}v)$ means $u \le v$. These 10 points are partially ordered because not every pair of vertices is linked by an arrow. The relation is reflexive and transitive.

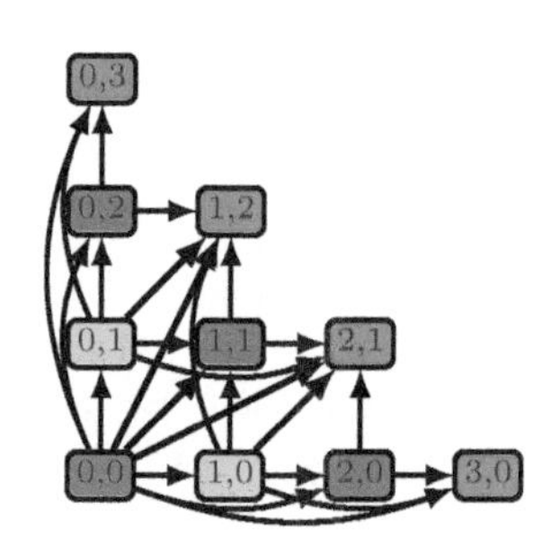

No pair of points in the set $\{(0, 2), (1, 1), (2, 0)\}$ is comparable. Such a set is an antichain. Every pair of points in the set $\{(0, 0), (1, 0), (1, 1), (1, 2)\}$ is comparable. Such a set is a chain. The points in a chain are ordered, in this case starting with the vertex $(0, 0)$ and ending with the vertex $(1, 2)$.

The largest or maximum chain has size 4. The red vertices in the set $\{(0,3),(1,2),(2,1),(3,0)\}$ are each at the end of some maximum chain. These red vertices form an antichain. This must be so, because if any two red vertices were comparable, then you could increase one of the maximum chains, which can't be possible if they really are maximum chains. Remove this antichain of red vertices. In the remaining graph, the new maximum chains have size 3 and the vertices at the end of these maximum chains, colored blue, form another antichain which is disjoint from the antichain of red vertices. Repeating this process, each time removing the vertices at the ends of maximum chains, you get the green antichain and then the purple one. We partitioned the vertices into 4 antichains. In general, if the maximum chain has size k, you can partition the vertices in this way into k disjoint antichains. That is Dilworth's Theorem. □

Exercise 11.11 [Tournament Top-Dog]

A tournament is a directed graph with a single edge between every pair of vertices. For example, the tournament on page 152 is a round-robin within the author's family in which no vertex beats every other vertex, i.e., there is no totally dominant player. Every vertex is either beaten by M or beaten by someone who is beaten by M. We call M a top-dog.

(a) List all vertices that are top-dogs in the round-robin tennis tournament on page 152?
(b) Show that every tournament has at least one top-dog.
(c) Show that it is possible to be a top-dog and yet win the fewest number of matches.

11.5 Problem Solving with Graphs

Graphs are everywhere because relationships are everywhere. However, the graph nature of a problem may be hidden at first glance. Often, the key step to unraveling a problem, is to reformulate the problem using graphs. Then, you can use all known techniques for graphs to solve the problem. Here is an example which could easily be on a CS job interview. In fact it has!

On the right is elevation data for a park. The park is a grid and grid-squares have distinct elevations. One unit of rain falls on each grid-square. Water flows from a grid-square to a neighbor of lowest elevation (neighbors can be up, down, left, right or diagonal). The arrow in the diagram indicates the water flow from the grid-square at elevation 17. We wish to provide drainage for the park. Where should we install drains and what should their capacities be? Intuition might suggest that the water will all flow to the square of lowest elevation. Hence, placing one drain of capacity 25 at the red square having lowest elevation should suffice. That's wrong! For example, the water at the square with elevation 5 cannot make it to the red square with lowest elevation.

3	2	17	11	12
4	1	18	10	7
21	22	23	16	8
20	13	5	19	9
25	24	6	14	15

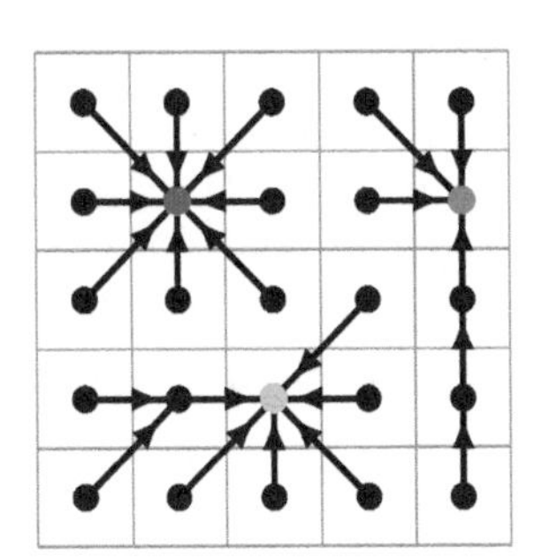

Let's model the problem as a directed graph. The grid-squares are vertices. A directed edge from u to v means that water flows from u to v. The resulting graph is shown to the right. You can recognize three disjoint trees. The red, green and blue vertices are special, because they have no outgoing arrow. These special vertices are called "sinks" into which water flows in but the water cannot flow out. We should place drains at these sinks with capacities equal to the size of the corresponding part of the graph. The capacities for the drains are blue=9 units, red=7 units and green=9 units. The solution to our problem pops out once we formulate the problem using graphs. With practice, you will see the graph in everything, and to get that practice try Problem 11.71.

11.6 Problems

Problem 11.1. Draw all graphs that have the vertex set $V = \{a, b, c\}$.

Problem 11.2. Draw pictures of K_1, K_2, K_3, K_4, K_5, K_6 and $K_{4,4}$. (Use filled in circles for vertices.)

Problem 11.3. Give the degree sequences of K_{n+1}, $K_{n,n}$, L_n, C_n, S_{n+1} and W_{n+1}.

Problem 11.4. Prove: if a graph has degree sequence $[5, 1, 1, 1, 1, 1]$, then it must be S_5.

Problem 11.5. A graph is regular if every vertex has the same degree. Which of these graphs are regular:
(a) K_6; (b) $K_{4,5}$ (c) $K_{5,5}$ (d) L_6 (e) S_6 (f) W_4 (g) W_5?

Problem 11.6. Give a graph (no loops or parallel edges) satisfying the constraints or explain why it doesn't exist.
(a) The graph has 5 vertices each of degree 3.
(b) The graph has 4 edges and vertices of degrees 1,2,3,4.
(c) The graph has 4 vertices of degrees 1,2,3,4.
(d) The graph has 6 vertices of degrees 1,2,3,4,5,5.

Problem 11.7. For graphs G and H: (i) Give adjacency lists and adjacency matrices. (ii) Give degree distributions. (iii) Determine if G and H are isomorphic.

(a) G:  H: 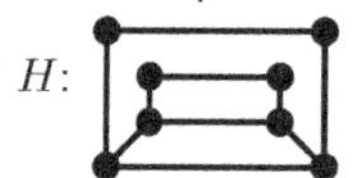 (b) G: 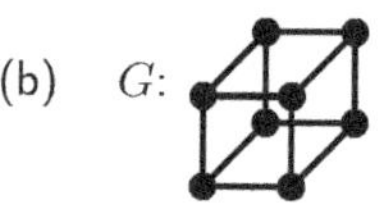 H: 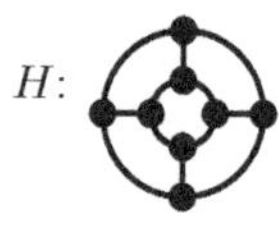

Problem 11.8. Is there a friend network with 7 friends, each of who know 3 friends?

Problem 11.9. Among 7 people, 6 have exactly 2 friends. How many friends can the 7th person have?

Problem 11.10. Give graphs with these degree distributions, or explain why you can't. Verify $2|E| = \sum_{i=1}^{n} \delta_i$.
(a) $[5, 3, 3, 2, 1]$ (b) $[3, 2, 1, 1, 1]$ (c) $[3, 3, 2, 1]$ (d) $[3, 3, 3, 3, 3]$ (e) $[3, 3, 3, 3, 3, 3]$ (f) $[3, 3, 2, 2, 2]$
(g) $[4, 4, 4, 4, 4]$ (h) $[4, 4, 3, 2, 1]$ (i) $[4, 3, 3, 2, 2]$ (j) $[3, 3, 3, 2, 2]$ (k) $[3, 3, 3, 3, 2]$ (l) $[5, 3, 2, 2, 2]$

Problem 11.11. In a graph only the two vertices u, v have odd degree. Prove there is a path from u to v.

Problem 11.12. A graph has 9 vertices, all of degree 5 or 6. Prove that at least 5 vertices have degree 6, or 6 vertices have degree 5.

Problem 11.13. Compute the number of edges in the following graphs: (a) K_n (b) $K_{n,\ell}$ (c) W_n

Problem 11.14. Model Manhattan's road network as an (n, ℓ) rectangular grid of vertices. We show a $(4, 6)$-grid.
(a) How many vertices and edges are in the $(4, 6)$-grid on the right?
(b) Compute the number of vertices and edges in the (n, ℓ)-grid.
(c) Compute the degree distribution for the (n, ℓ)-grid.
(d) How long is a shortest path from the vertex at (x, y) to the vertex at (w, z).

Problem 11.15. A graph is r-regular if every vertex has the same degree r. Show:
(a) If r is even and $n > r$, there is an r-regular graph with n vertices. (Tinker!)
(b) If r is odd and n is odd, there is no r-regular graph with n vertices.
(c) If r is odd and $n > r$ is even, there is an r-regular graph with n vertices.
(d) An r-regular graph with $4k$ vertices must have an even number of edges.

Problem 11.16. What is $|E|$ for a simple graph with degrees $[9, 5, 2, 2, 0]$. What about a multigraph?

Problem 11.17. A graph G has n vertices.
(a) What is the maximum number of edges G can have and not be connected? Prove it.
(b) What is the minimum number of edges G can have and be connected? Prove it.

Problem 11.18. At a party with 10 people, in any group of four, someone knows the other three people. Prove that someone at the party knows everyone else at the party. *[Hint: Consider the person with maximum degree.]*

Problem 11.19. Baniaz and her partner organize a party with 4 other couples. People shake hands, but no one shakes hands with their partner. Baniaz asks each of the other nine people how many people they greeted, and receives 9 different answers. How many people did Baniaz greet and how many people did her partner greet?

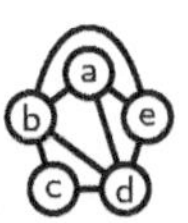

Problem 11.20 (Complement Graph). For graph G, the complement $\overline{G}$ has the same vertices, but the edges in $\overline{G}$ are the complement of the edges in G: distinct vertices u and v are adjacent in $\overline{G}$ if an only if they are not adjacent in G. Give the complements of (a) The graph shown. (b) K_n. (c) $K_{n,m}$. (d) S_{n+1}.

Problem 11.21. Answer the following questions about a graph and its complement defined in Problem 11.20.

(a) If G is regular, prove that $\overline{G}$ is also regular.
(b) Give a connected graph G for which the complement $\overline{G}$ is: (i) Connected. (ii) Not conected.
(c) Prove that either G or $\overline{G}$ must be connected.
(d) Suppose G is a tree. Give necessary and sufficient conditions for $\overline{G}$ to be connected.
(e) Give 4 and 5-vertex graphs which are isomorphic to their complement. Such graphs are self-complemetary. Show that there is no self-complementary graph with 3 or 6 vertices.
(f) Prove that there is an n-vertex self-complementary graph if and only if $n = 4k$ or $n = 4k + 1$

Problem 11.22 (Friends Paradox). Don't despair because your friends have, on average, more friends than you do. This is typical in any social network. Let δ_i be vertex v_i's degree and define vertex v_i's friend-degree κ_i as the average degree of vertex v_i's friends. Let $\overline{\delta} = (\sum_{i=1}^n \delta_i)/n$ be the average of the vertex-degrees and $\overline{\kappa} = (\sum_{i=1}^n \kappa_i)/n$ be the average of the friend-degrees. You may assume every vertex has positive degree.

(a) Compute $\overline{\delta}$ and $\overline{\kappa}$ for: K_3, $K_{2,3}$, S_5, P_4, W_5.
(b) Let $N(i)$ be the neighborhood (friends) of v_i, and δ_i the degree of v_i. Justify the steps:

$$\overline{\kappa} \overset{(i)}{=} \frac{1}{n}\sum_{i=1}^{n} \frac{1}{\delta_i}\sum_{j\in N(i)} \delta_j \overset{(ii)}{=} \frac{1}{n}\sum_{i=1}^{n} \frac{1}{\delta_i}\sum_{j\in N(i)} (\delta_j-\delta_i+\delta_i) \overset{(iii)}{=} \overline{\delta} + \frac{1}{n}\sum_{i=1}^{n}\frac{1}{\delta_i}\sum_{j\in N(i)}(\delta_j-\delta_i).$$

(c) Show that the edge (v_i, v_j) contributes $(\delta_i - \delta_j)(1/\delta_j - 1/\delta_i)$ to the double sum in the last term.
(d) Prove that $\overline{\kappa} \geq \overline{\delta}$ and characterize when $\overline{\kappa} = \overline{\delta}$. (On average, you friends have more friends than you do.)

Problem 11.23 (Graphical Sequence). A sequence $\delta_1, \delta_2, \ldots, \delta_n$ is graphical if there is a simple graph whose n vertices $v_1, v_2, \ldots, v_n$ have these degrees, $\delta_1, \delta_2, \ldots, \delta_n$.

(a) Determine if these degree sequences are graphical: (i) [4,4,2,1,1] (ii) [4,4,2,2,1,1]
(b) Suppose $\delta_1 \geq \delta_2 \geq \cdots \geq \delta_n \geq 0$ is graphical. Prove there is a graph having these degrees with its highest-degree vertex v_1 of degree δ_1 adjacent to the δ_1 next highest-degree vertices $v_2, v_3, \ldots, v_{\delta_1+1}$. *[Hint: If v_1 is not adjacent to all these vertices, "rewire" two edges so that v_1 becomes adjacent to one more of these vertices.]*
(c) **[Havel-Hakimi]** Prove: $\delta_1 \geq \delta_2 \geq \cdots \geq \delta_n \geq 0$ is graphical if and only if $\delta_2 - 1, \delta_3 - 1, \ldots, \delta_{\delta_1+1} - 1, \delta_{\delta_1+2}, \ldots, \delta_n$ is graphical. The second degree sequence corresponds to removing the highest-degree vertex (which is linked to the next highest-degree vertices).
(d) Are these sequences graphical: (i) [6,5,5,5,4,4,2,1] (ii) [8,7,6,6,5,3,2,2,2,1]

Problem 11.24 (Connected Components). For a graph G and a vertex v, the component containing v, $C(v)$, is the set of vertices which are connected to v (v is connected to itself).

(a) For the graph G on the right, give vertex and edge sets, (V, E).
(b) What are $C(b)$, $C(e)$, $C(f)$, $C(i)$? Explain why $C(a) = C(c)$.
(c) How many components are in G and what are they? The number of components is the number of distinct sets $C(v)$ for $v \in V$.
(d) How many components are in a connected graph?

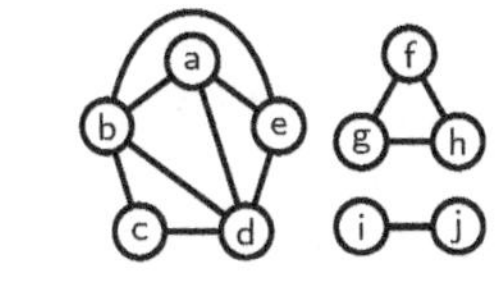

Problem 11.25. How many edges must be added to make the graph in Problem 11.24 connected? Prove: a graph with n vertices and e edges has at least $n - e$ components. Use induction on e.

Problem 11.26. A graph is 2-regular. Prove that each connected component is a cycle.

Problem 11.27. Every vertex degree in a graph is at least 2. Prove that there is at least one cycle.

Problem 11.28. Conjecture: A graph with all vertices of positive degree must be connected.

(a) You add a vertex of positive degree to a connected n-vertex graph. Is the resulting $(n+1)$-vertex graph connected?
(b) Using part (a), here is a sketch of a proof by induction that a graph with positive degrees is connected.

The base case, $n = 2$, is easy to check. Assume any n vertex graph with positive degrees is connected.
Add a vertex of positive degree to get $n + 1$ vertices. By (a), this $n + 1$ vertex graph is connected.

Give the formal proof, or disprove the claim and explain what's wrong with the induction.

Problem 11.29. The diameter of a graph is the distance between the two vertices that are furtherest apart. Compute the diameters of: (a) K_n (b) $K_{n,m}$ (c) C_n (d) P_n (e) W_n.

Problem 11.30. A standard chess-knight's move is a $(2,3)$-L, 2 squares in one direction and then 3 squares in an orthogonal direction. The knight starts at the bottom-left of a 4×4 chessboard.

(a) Give the minimum number of moves for the knight to reach each square. *[Hint: Identify squares reachable in 0 moves, then 1 move, then 2,...]*

(b) Can the knight visit every square once and return to the bottom left.

Problem 11.31. Prove the following facts of any graph $G = (V, E)$ with n vertices.

(a) There are at least two vertices with the same degree (degree twins).

(b) One can partition V into two sets so that every vertex in a set has at least half its neighbors in the other set.

(c) If every vertex has degree at least $\delta \geq 2$, there is a cycle of length at least $\delta + 1$.

(d) If every vertex has degree at least $n/2$, the graph is connected.

(e) If the degrees of non-adjacent vertices sum to at least $n - 1$, the graph is connected.

(f) If every subset S of at most $n/2$ vertices has an edge from inside S to outside, then G is connected.

Problem 11.32. Give the adjacency matrix A for the graph on the right.

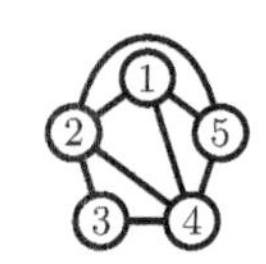

(a) For $k = 1, 2, 3$, compute matrices D_k whose (i, j) entry is the number length-k paths from i to j.

(b) Compute A^k for $k = 1, 2, 3$ and compare with D_k.

(c) For a general graph, prove by induction that $\mathrm{D}_k = \mathrm{A}^k$ for $k \geq 1$. (The kth power of A gives the number of paths of length k between vertices.)

Problem 11.33. The weighted degree of a vertex is the sum edge-weights incident to the vertex. Prove:

Theorem. The sum of the weighted degrees equals twice the sum of the edge weights.

Problem 11.34 (Euler Paths). Trace each picture by placing a pencil on a vertex and drawing over each edge once without lifting the pencil. A path using each edge once is an Euler path. Vertices can be used multiple times.

(a) 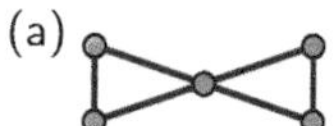 (b) 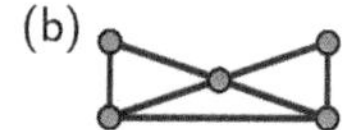 (c) 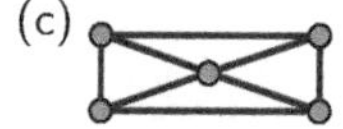 (d) 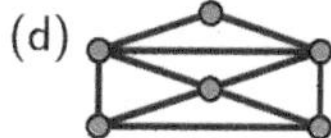 (e) 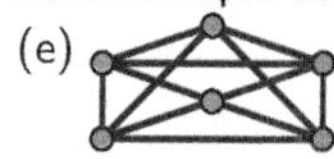

If the path starts and ends at the same vertex, it is an Euler cycle. Do any of the graphs have both an Euler path and Euler cycle? Formulate a conjecture about when a graph has an Euler path/cycle.

Problem 11.35. For a connected graph G, prove the following claims.

(a) G has an Euler cycle if and only if every vertex has even degree.

(b) G has an Euler path (not a cycle) if and only if all vertices but two have even degree.

(c) One can transform any graph G into a graph G' having an Euler cycle by adding at most one vertex and edges only from this new vertex to the other vertices. Similarly, one can get an Euler path.

Problem 11.36. For the graph shown, what is the minimum number of edges you must add so that the resulting graph has an Euler cycle (parallel edges allowed). What if parallel edges are not allowed?

Problem 11.37. For which r, s does $K_{r,s}$ have an Euler cycle?

Problem 11.38 (Hypercube). The n-hypercube H_n has 2^n vertices, one for each n-bit string $b_1 \cdots b_n$, which is the label of the vertex. There is an edge between two vertices if and only if their labels differ in just one of the bits.

(a) Give drawings of H_1, H_2 and H_3, and determine the number of edges in each graph.

(b) How many edges are in H_n and what is the degree sequence? When is there an Euler path?

Problem 11.39 (Chineese Postman). A neighborhood G has 10 streets and 7 intersections. We show the time in minutes for a postman to walk along each street.

(a) How quickly can a postman enter G at ⓐ, deliver mail along every street and exit at ⓐ?

(b) Can the time be reduced if the postman enters and exits at another intersection, e.g. ⓑ?

(c) Can the time be reduced if the postman enters and exits from different intersections?

Problem 11.40. We show the 10 dominos using pairs of numbers in $\{0, 1, 2, 3\}$ (0 is blank). We placed some of the dominos in a ring so that touching dominos meet at the same number. The ring does not include all the 10 dominos.

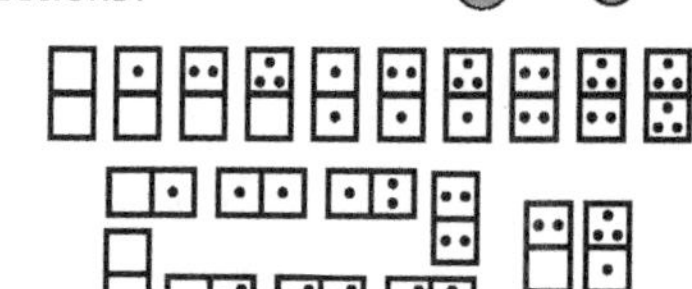

(a) Can you place all the dominos in a ring?

(b) How many dominos are there for pairs of numbers in $\{0, \ldots, n\}$?

(c) For which n can you place all the dominos in a ring? *[Hints: Make each number a vertex. Problem 11.35.]*

Problem 11.41 (Ramsey Numbers). Remarkably, a social network with 6 people must have a 3-clique or 3-war. No matter how random the network, there must be some structure. We can get more structure by increasing the size.

(a) Show that any social network with 10 people has a 4-clique or a 3-war.

(b) Show that any social network with 9 people has a 4-clique or a 3-war. *[Hints: Assume no 3-war and prove there is a 4-clique by contradiction. To get a contradiction, show that every vertex has 3 enemies and 5 friends.]*

(c) Prove Ramsey's result that any amount of structure can be guaranteed. For integers $k, s > 0$ there is a smallest number $R(k, s)$ for which any graph with $R(k, s)$ vertices has a k-clique or an s-war. $R(3, 3) \leq 6$ and $R(4, 3) \leq 9$.

(i) Prove that $R(k, s) = R(s, k)$ and $R(k, s) \leq R(k-1, s) + R(k, s-1)$. Why does this proves Ramsey's result, that there is as much structure as you wish in large enough graphs.

(ii) What is $R(k, 1)$? Prove by induction that $R(k, s) \leq (k + s - 2)!/((k-1)! \times (s-1)!)$.

Aliens give us a year to compute Ramsey(5,5) or face extinction. We could marshal the world's best minds and fastest computers, and within a year we might have the value. If, instead, the demand was Ramsey(6,6), we should preemptively attack. – Paul Erdős

Problem 11.42 (Induced Subgraph). The subgraph induced by some of the vertices is obtained by removing all other vertices and also the edges to any of those removed vertices. For the graph on the right, what are the subgraphs induced by the vertices:

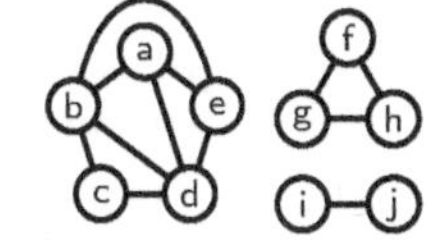

(a) $\{a, b, c\}$ (b) $\{a, b, d\}$ (c) $\{a, b, e\}$ (d) $\{a, c, e\}$ (e) $\{a, g, i\}$

Problem 11.43. A subgraph is a subset of edges and all vertices at endpoints of those edges. Note the difference between general subgraphs and induced subgraphs which are a subset of vertices and all edges linking those vertices. For the graph shown, which of these are subgraphs and which are induced subgraphs?

(a) K_3 (b) C_4 (c) P_4 (d) S_4 (e) S_5 (f) 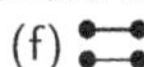

Problem 11.44. The subgraph induced by removing a vertex is a "card". An n-vertex graph has n cards. We show the 4-card "deck" of a 4-vertex graph. What are the decks of: (a) K_n (b) $K_{n,m}$ (c) C_n (d) S_{n+1}?

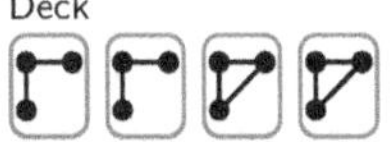

Problem 11.45. Determine the graph from its deck. (a)  (b)  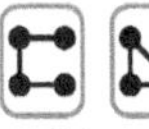 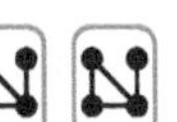

Conjecture (Kelly and Ulam): A graph with at least three vertices is uniquely specified up to isomorphism by its deck.

Problem 11.46. Prove: If $|E| \geq |V|\delta/2$, then some induced subgraph has minimum degree at least $\delta/2$.

Problem 11.47. A cut-vertex in a connected graph is a vertex whose removal results in the remaining graph being disconnected. Identify all the cut vertices in the graph on the right.

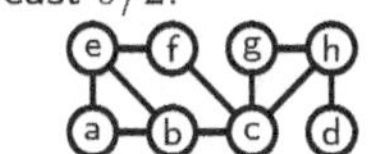

Problem 11.48. A graph has n vertices. The shortest path between two vertices u, v has length greater than $n/2$. Prove that one can disconnect u from v by removing a single other vertex. Such a vertex is called a (u, v)-cut-vertex.

Problem 11.49 (Menger's Theorem). Prove there is no (u, v)-cut-vertex (see Problem 11.48) if and only if at least two paths from u to v share no vertices other than u and v. Such paths are internally vertex-disjoint. (Menger's Theorem is a generalization: One cannot remove $k-1$ vertices and disconnect u from v if and only if there are at least k internally vertex-disjoint paths from u to v.)

Problem 11.50. Use Menger's Theorem to prove the result in Problem 11.48.

Problem 11.51. Similar to a cut-vertex, an edge e is a cut-edge in G if the removal of e disconnects G. Prove that e is a cut-edge if and only if e is not on any cycle of G.

Problem 11.52. A tree has 17 vertices. How many edges does it have. If the maximum degree is 16, draw the tree.

Problem 11.53. Prove that a tree with n vertices and maximum degree Δ has at least Δ leaves.

Problem 11.54. A tree with n vertices has diameter 2. What is the tree (give a drawing)?

Problem 11.55. Give all possible trees (up to isomorphism) that have 7 vertices with at least three vertices of degree-1 and at least two vertices of degree-3.

Problem 11.56. A graph G with n vertices and $n-1$ edges is not a tree. Show that G has at least one connected component which is a tree and at least one connected component which is not a tree.

Problem 11.57 (Spanning Tree). Is the graph on the right a tree? If not, why not?

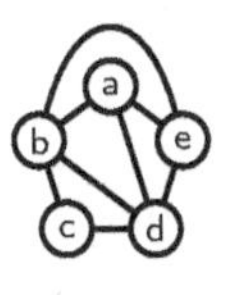

(a) Give two different trees using all vertices and a subset of the edges. Such trees are spanning trees. A spanning tree is a minimal subset of the edges which maintains connectivity.

(b) Prove that any connected graph has a spanning tree. *[Hint: If you remove an edge from a cycle in a connected graph, does it remain connected? Use induction on the number of edges.]*

(c) Which graphs have exactly one spanning tree?

Problem 11.58 (BFS-tree). Let G be connected. Start at (say) vertex ⓐ, the level-0 vertex. Draw the edges to neighbors of ⓐ, the level-1 vertices which are distance 1 from ⓐ. Now process each level-1 vertex drawing the edges to all neighbors that have not already been linked to – these are level-2 vertices. Continue processing level-2, then level-3, etc. We illustrate the steps with G.

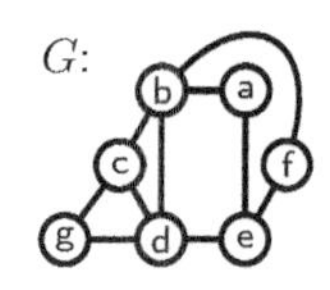

(a) Give different BFS-trees, with roots ⓐ and ⓔ.

(b) Show: when G is connected, the result is a tree with all vertices of G.

(c) Prove there are no edges of G between vertices at levels i and $(i+2)$ in the BFS-tree.

(d) Prove that the shortest path in G from the start vertex (in this case ⓐ) to any level-i vertex is i.

(e) True or False: the number of levels in the BFS-tree doesn't depend on which vertex is the root.

Building a BFS-tree for G

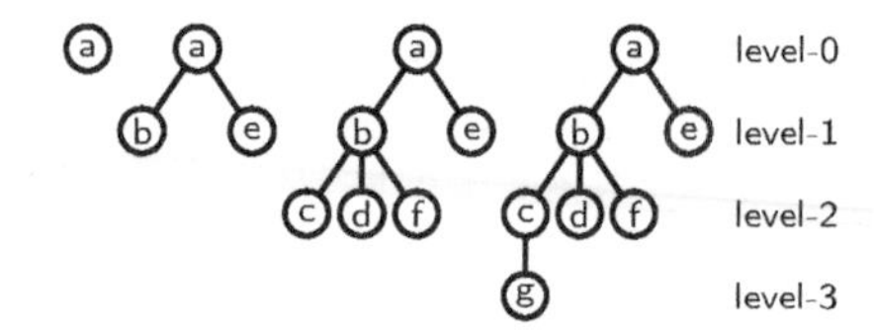

Problem 11.59. Recursively define rooted trees. Generate 3 rooted trees which are not rooted binary trees (RBTs). Give a recursive function to compute the height of a rooted tree.

Problem 11.60. Prove or disprove:

(a) A connected graph is a tree if and only if the average degree of its vertices is less than 2.

(b) Every graph with n vertices and $n-1$ edges is a tree.

(c) There is a tree with degrees $\delta_1 \geq \delta_2 \geq \cdots \geq \delta_n > 0$ if and only if $\sum_{i=1}^{n} \delta_i = 2n-2$.

Problem 11.61. Give planar drawings of these graphs and verify Euler's formula. (a) 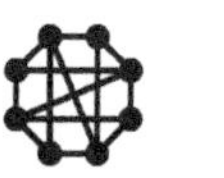 (b) 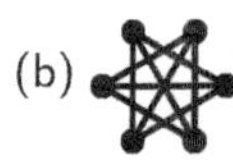

Problem 11.62. A graph G has degree sequence $[5,4,4,3,2,2]$.

(a) How many edges does G have? (b) Could G be planar? If yes, how many faces does G have. If not, why?

Problem 11.63. Prove that every subgraph of a planar graph is planar.

Problem 11.64. This problem builds on Exercise 11.7. Prove the following.

(a) If G and $\overline{G}$ are planar then $2 \leq |V| \leq 10$. *[Hint: Exercise 11.7(h).]*

(b) For a planar graph with C components, $F + V - E = 1 + C$. (Euler's invariant for disconnected graphs.)

(c) Every 5-regular graph with 10 vertices is not planar.

Problem 11.65. Euler was intrigued by regular polyhedra, convex solids bounded by finitely many polygonal faces (Platonic solids). A polyhedron is a graph whose edges are intersections between faces. The octohedron and its planar drawing are shown. (See also Exercise 11.7 on page 150.)

(a) Why is a polyhedron graph planar? *[Hint: Project onto an in-sphere.]*

(b) A polyhedron is regular if every face has the same number of sides s and every vertex is the intersection of the same number of faces d. In the octohedron, the polygons are triangles, so $s = 3$, and four triangles intersect at every vertex so $d = 4$. Show that the graph of a regular polyhedron is regular and the vertex-degree is d.

(c) Let V be the number of vertices, E the number of edges and F the number of faces of the polyhedron. Show that $Vd = 2E$ and $Fs = 2e$, hence that $Vd = Fs$.

(d) Use Euler's invariant to show: $1/s + 1/d - 1/2 = 1/E$ and hence $3 \leq s, d \leq 5$. Find all possible choices for s, d.

Problem 11.66. Color-code each country (region labeled $A, B, C, \ldots$) so that a minimum number of colors is used and countries that share a border have different color-codes.

(a) 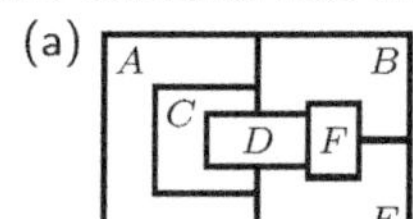

(b) 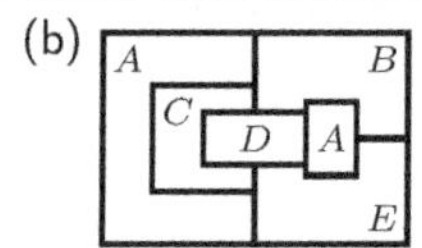

(The 4-color theorem says any map should be 4-colorable. What goes wrong in (b)? What assumption on the countries is needed?)

Problem 11.67. Subdividing an edge breaks the edge in two and adds a vertex in the middle: ●—● → ●—○—●. You can continue subdividing edges of a graph to get a subdivision of a graph.

(a) Formally define subdivision. Show that C_n can be obtained by repeated subdivision of K_3.

(b) Show that a sequence of subdivisions adds degree-2 vertices without changing other degrees.

(c) Show that a graph is planar if and only if any subdivision of the graph is planar.

(d) Can a subgraph of the Petersen graph be obtained by repteaded subdivision of $K_{3,3}$? What about K_5? Is the Petersen graph planar? Explain your answers. *[Hint: Exercise 11.7 (g,h).]*

(Kuratowski's Theorem: Every non-planar graph has a subdivision of $K_{3,3}$ or K_5 as a subgraph.)

Problem 11.68 (Topological Sort). Let G be an acyclic directed graph.

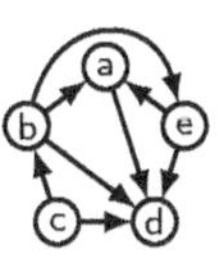

(a) Prove: there is a vertex with in-degree zero and also one with out-degree zero.

(b) For the graph on the right, order the vertices so that if u preceeds v, then there is no v-to-u path. Prove that this is always possible. Such an ordering is a topological sort.

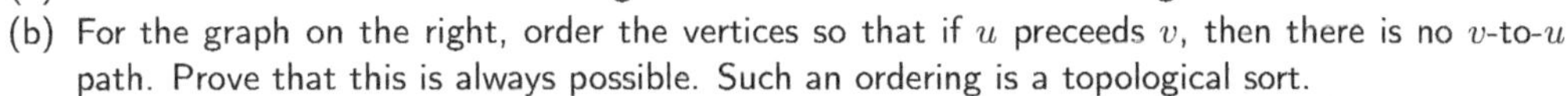

Problem 11.69. Prove that in any tournament which does not contain a cycle, some vertex beats every other vertex.

Problem 11.70. In any ordering of $[1, 2, \ldots, n^2+1]$, there is a monotonic subsequence of length $n+1$. For example, $[5, 1, 2, 4, 3]$ has the monotonic subsequences $[5, 4, 3]$, $[1, 2, 4]$ and $[1, 2, 3]$. Prove this result using directed graphs and partial orders. Let the sequence be $n^2 + 1$ vertices on a line. Add a directed edge from a number (vertex) to every higher number (vertex) on the right. We show the line of vertices for $[5, 1, 2, 4, 3]$, together with the directed edges.

(a) Show: a chain is an increasing subsequence and an antichain is a decreasing subsequence.

(b) Suppose the maximum chain has size at most n. Prove that there is an antichain of size at least $n+1$ and hence prove the result. *[Hint: Example 11.6, Dilworth's Theorem.]*

(c) Find a permutation of of $[1, 2, \ldots, n^2]$ with no monotonic subsequence of length $n+1$. (The result is tight.)

Problem 11.71. Solve each problem by first finding the appropriate graph representation.

(a) Show that you can't draw 9 line segments on the plane so that each intersects with exactly 3 others.

(b) Three cups have sizes 3,5,8 ounces. The 8 ounce cup is filled with wine. How many pours are needed to split the wine into two cups? If it can't be done, explain why. *[Hint: The start "configuration" (vertex) is $(0, 0, 8)$.]*

(c) 4 canibals and 4 pacifists must cross a river using a row-boat with space for two. If canibals outnumber pacifists on the banks or boat, pacifists are eaten. What is the minimum number of river crossings to transport the people?

(d) A queen covers a square if that square is on the same row, column or diagonal as the queen. What is the minimum number of queens required to cover the 8×8 chessboard?

(e) The friendships between seven people A, B, C, D, E, F, G are shown below Can the people sit around a circular table so that no two enemies sit next to each other? What if we add one more friendship between C and D?

	A	B	C	D	E	F	G
friends with	B, F	A, C, E	B, F, G	F, G	B, F, G	A, C, E	C, D, E

(f) Place n points on a plane so that any two points are at least distance 1 from each other. A good pair of points are distance exactly 1 from each other. Prove that there are at most $3n$ good pairs.

Problem 11.72. A chessboard is infinite in all directions. A (p, q)-knight moves $\pm p$ steps parallel to one axis and $\pm q$ steps parallel to the other axis. A standard knight is a $(2, 1)$-knight. The infinite chess-board is a graph. Each square is a vertex. Two vertices are linked if a (p, q)-knight can, in one move, reach one square from the other. For what p and q is the graph connected, e.g. is $(0, 0)$ connected to $(4, 1)$ by the $(5, 3)$-knight?

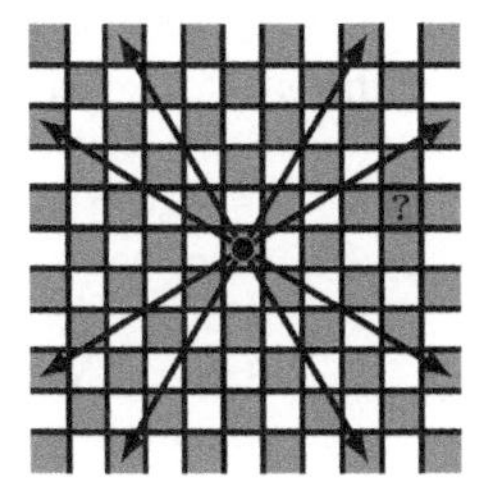

(a) What is the degree distribution (does it depend on p and q)?

(b) Prove that a $(5, 3)$-knight which starts at $(0, 0)$ can't reach $(4, 1)$, the red square.

(c) Prove the graph is connected for the $(2, 1)$-knight. (Induction)

(d) When is the graph connected for the $(p, 1)$-knight. (Induction)

(e) For what p and q is the (p, q)-knight's graph connected. *[Hints: The "obvious" necessary conditions are sufficient. Reduce the (p, q)-knight to an $(r, 1)$-knight. Prove the fact: if $\gcd(a, b) = 1$ and a is odd, then $\exists x, y \in \mathbb{N}$ for which $ax - by = 1$ with y even.]*

(f) Prove that if the infinite-in-all-directions board is connected, then the infinite-positive-quadrant board is also connected.

Problem 11.73 (Graceful Labeling). A connected graph has vertices $v_1, \ldots, v_n$ and m edges. Label vertex v_i with $\ell(v_i) \in \{0, \ldots, m\}$. The vertex labels must be distinct. An edge $e = (v_i, v_j)$ inherits the label $|\ell(v_i) - \ell(v_j)|$. The labeling is graceful if all the edge labels are different.

(a) Give graceful labelings of (i) (ii) (iii) The paths P_{10} and P_{11}. (iv) The star S_{10}.

(b) Will there always be enough vertex labels? What will the set of edge labels in any graceful labeling be?

(c) Prove that no graph with m edges can be gracefully labeled with vertex labels from $\{1, \ldots, m\}$.

The Graceful Tree conjecture due to Rosa, Ringel and Kotzig is that every tree can be gracefully labeled.

Problem 11.74 (Sperner's Lemma). Sperner's Lemma is an application of the Handshaking Theorem. We show barycentric subdivisions of a triangle with red, green and blue vertices. The task: color all other vertices, but on an outer side use only the colors at that side's end-points (there are red-green, green-blue and red-blue sides).

We show a valid coloring of a barycentric subdivision on the right. The three gray-shaded triangles are tricolored (have vertices of all three colors). Prove Sperner's Lemma.

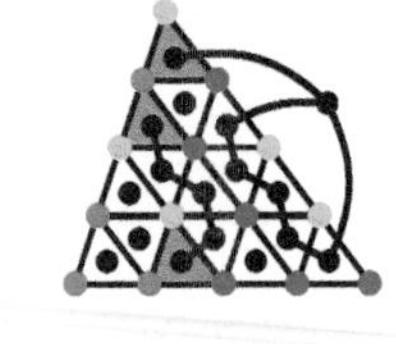

Sperner's Lemma: There is always a tricolored triangle.

Construct a graph (see figure) with vertices for subdivision triangles and an external vertex. Place edges between vertices if the boundaries of the vertex-traingles share a blue-green side.

(a) For any valid coloring of any subdivision, prove that the external vertex has odd degree.

(b) Prove that there is an odd number of odd degree vertices among the internal triangles.

(c) What are the possible degrees of internal-triangle vertices? Which triangles have odd degree?

(d) Prove Sperner's Lemma (actually you proved a stronger result than Sperner's Lemma).

(The proof works for any triangular subdivision, not just barycentric subdivisions. Sperner's Lemma generalizes to $d > 2$ dimensions: a tricolored triangle becomes a $(d+1)$-colored simplex.)

Problem 11.75 (Applications of Sperner's Lemma).

(a) **[Brouwer Fixed Point Theorem]** A map of a country is somewhere inside the country. Prove that some point on the map is directly above the point in the country that it represents. (Assume the country is triangular.) More generally, let T be a triangle, the convex hull of the vertices $\mathbf{v}_1, \mathbf{v}_2, \mathbf{v}_3$. Any continuous mapping $f : T \mapsto T$ has a fixed point $\mathbf{x}_* \in T$ for which $f(\mathbf{x}_*) = \mathbf{x}_*$.

 (i) Every $\mathbf{v} \in T$ has a unique representation $\mathbf{v} = x_1\mathbf{v}_1 + x_2\mathbf{v}_3 + x_3\mathbf{v}_3$, where $x_i \geq 0$ and $x_1 + x_2 + x_3 = 1$. (x_1, x_2, x_3) are called the barycentric coordinates of $\mathbf{v}$.

 (ii) The mapping f takes $\mathbf{x} = (x_1, x_2, x_3)$ to $(f_1(\mathbf{x}), f_2(\mathbf{x}), f_3(\mathbf{x}))$. Define the color of a point $\mathbf{v}$ as red if $f_1(\mathbf{x}) < x_1$; green if $f_1(\mathbf{x}) \geq x_1$ and $f_2(\mathbf{x}) < x_2$; and blue if $f_1(\mathbf{x}) \geq x_1$, $f_2(\mathbf{x}) \geq x_2$ and $f_3(\mathbf{x}) < x_3$. In the diagram, color v according to the color of the region into which f maps v.
 - If f does not have a fixed point, show that every $\mathbf{v} \in T$ has a well defined color.
 - What colors are the vertices of T? What colors are points on the sides of T?

 (iii) Let $\mathbf{x} = (x_1, x_2, x_3)$ and $\mathbf{y} = (y_1, y_2, y_3)$. Show that if $y_i \leq x_i$ then $\mathbf{x} = \mathbf{y}$.

 (iv) Consider a barycentric subdivision of T whose vertices are colored by f as in (ii). What can you deduce about f from a tricolored triangle as the subdivision gets finer?

 (v) Prove the Brouwer Fixed Point Theorem. Facts from calculus: T is compact so any infinite sequence has a convergent subsequence. f is continuous which means if $\mathbf{x} \to \mathbf{x}_*$ and $f_1(\mathbf{x}) < x_1$, then $f_1(\mathbf{x}_*) \leq x_{1*}$.

(b) **[Envy-Free Resource Allocation]** Users a, b, c share a resource during a time interval $[0, 1]$: the interval is split into pieces of lengths x_1, x_2, x_3; each user gets one piece. Users value pieces differently, e.g. b and c might prefer earlier and a prefers later. An example allocation is: $\underset{x_1}{b}\ |\ \underset{x_2}{c}\ |\ \underset{x_3}{a}$. Assume a piece of length 0 has no value and users value pieces in a continuous manner. Given three pieces, (x_1, x_2, x_3), a user will have a favorite piece (ties are allowed). Treat (x_1, x_2, x_3) as barycentric coordinates.

 (i) Show that one can assign an "owner" a, b or c to each vertex so that every subdivision triangle has vertices with different owners.

 (ii) Color each vertex (allocation) using its owner's favorite piece: red for x_1, green for x_2 and blue for x_3. Prove: There is always a tricolored traingle.

 (iii) Prove: There is a resource allocation with every user geting their favorite piece. Such a sharing is envy-free (no user is jealous of any other).

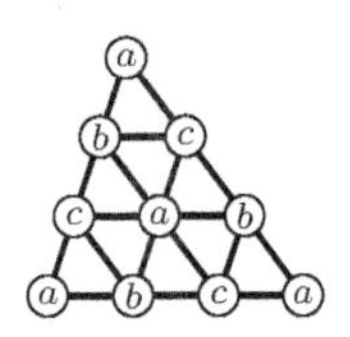

Math and I broke up two years ago, and now when we get together it's just weird and awkward for us both. – **Sariah Wilson**

Coloring outside the lines is a fine art – **Kim Nance**

A broken crayon can still color – **Unknown**

Chapter 12

Matching and Coloring

1: Bipartite graphs and stable marriage.
2: Conflict graphs and coloring.

An important class of graphs that occurs frequently in practice is the bipartite graph. To get going, we use a contentious example, sex in America.[1] The relative promiscuity of men and women is a constant source of headlines. We begin with the 1994 publication of *The Social Organization of Sexuality* which found that

- men have 74% more opposite-gender partners than women have.

You can imagine that this would cause a media sensation. What more needs to be said? Well, in 2004, A *groundbreaking* ABC News Primetime Live survey finds "a range of eye-popping sexual activities, fantasies and attitudes in this country, confirming some conventional wisdom, exploding some myths – and *venturing where few scientific surveys have gone before.*" One of the findings was that, over a lifetime,

- men have on average 20 sex-partners and women 6 (233% more for men).

The claimed margin of error in the survey is **2.5%**! Not to be outdone, the New York Times reported in 2007 that a study by the National Center for Health Statistics showed that

- men have on average 7 partners and women 4 (75% more for men).

Which survey is right? Is it about 75% or 233%? What's causing this striking asymmetry in sexual behavior?

Mathematicians should let real people run the world. Many would say that contentious examples have no place in mathematics. This is not sociology. Even worse, contentious examples might make some people uncomfortable, discouraging them from entering the beautiful world of mathematics. My thoughts?

1. There is no contentious in mathematics, only interesting and uninteresting.
2. Theorems are our facts and the case rests, not on opinion or bias, but on proof. Politicians and the media feed upon contentious issues for sensationalism, using "numbers" to suggest rigor in their message. It's our duty to remove the wool that's been pulled over the eyes of innocent victims.
3. Yes, we must teach the elegence and precision of mathematics. But, the most important message is that mathematics is the cold blooded tool for analyzing contentious real-world issues where emotions would otherwise flare. And, if we are not to teach you how to tackle contentious topics head on, then who should, and when? Just because an issue is contentious, you don't get to avoid the truth.

Let us now get to the bottom of sex in America. First, we need a model, and simple is always a good place to start tinkering. Suppose there are 10 men and 10 women in the world, and all partners are from the opposite sex. We can use a graph to represent the partner relationships between people over their lifetime. For clarity, we will use blue for men and red for women. The men are all lined up on the left, and the women on the right. An edge between a man and a woman means they were partners at some point over their lifetimes. We illustrate three worlds below: World I is monogamous; World II appears to be a world with a random set of partnerships; and, World III is extreme with two men having dated all the women. Which world is the media

[1]See also the `ocw.mit.edu` notes for 6.042J (Chapter 5 "Graph Theory," Section 5.2.1 "Sex in America").

insinuating, where men have significantly more partners on average than women? To help you, we computed the average number of partners for the men and women in each world (last row of the table, in bold).

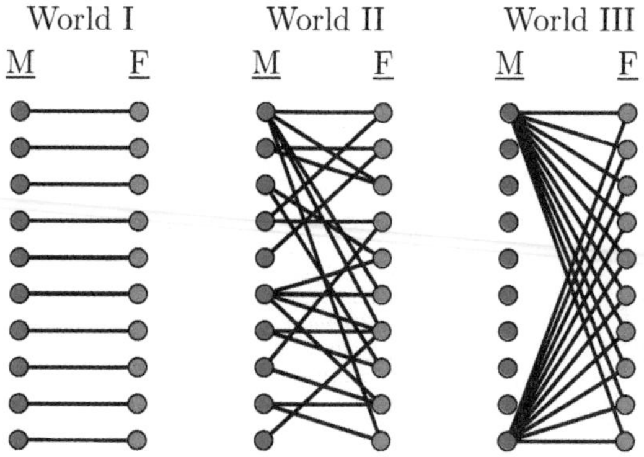

World I World II World III
M F M F M F

	World I		World II		World III	
	M	F	M	F	M	F
# partners (degree)	1	1	5	2	10	2
	1	1	2	2	0	2
	1	1	2	2	0	2
	1	1	2	2	0	2
	1	1	1	2	0	2
	1	1	4	2	0	2
	1	1	2	4	0	2
	1	1	2	2	0	2
	1	1	2	3	0	2
	1	1	1	2	10	2
average:	**1**	**1**	**2.3**	**2.3**	**2**	**2**

Hmm ... men and women have the same average number of partners in every world, no matter how relationships are organized. Behavior is irrelevant. It is a mathematical fact that the average number of partners for men must equal the average number of partners for women. Let's prove it. Each edge (relationship) contributes one partner to a man. So, the total number of partners among the men equals the number of edges $|E|$. Similarly, the total number of partners for the women equals $|E|$. The average number of partners is this total number divided by 10 for both men and women, no matter how we arrange the edges. Hoax!

The type of graph we used to model man-woman relationships is called bipartite. There are two sets of vertices, men and women, and all the edges link a vertex in one set to a vertex in the other. Bipartite graphs are a good model in many settings: students and the courses they are taking; tasks and resources needed for the task; kidney donors and recipients who match; etc.

Exercise 12.1

The conclusions of a model are accurate only if the modeling assumptions are realistic. The U.S. Census estimates that 49.2% of the population are men and 50.8% are women.

(a) For our simple model, show that the average number of partners is approximately 3.25% larger for men than women, independent of behavior, i.e., how the relationships are organized.

(b) The Census estimates approximately 1% of same-sex households. If 1% of all relationships are same-sex, show that the average number of partners is between 1.2%-5.34% larger for men than women.

You are on your own now, as to whether you believe the results of Exercise 12.1 backed by proof, or the media reports, backed by unsubstantiated claims like "going where few scientific surveys have gone before." Indeed! One last comment. The book, *The Social Organization of Sexuality* (to which the media was referring), was written by sociology researchers who did notice a problem with the data. In just the next paragraph, after the "sensational" findings of their survey, the sociologists say, and I quote:

> "...there is a basic adding up constraint that these gender differences seem to violate. Logically, men should have the same number of female sex partners as women have male sex partners. We note that this inconsistency has been found, as well, in several other surveys in recent years in the US, the UK, France, Finland and elsewhere. The inconsistency constitutes an important puzzle for which we, like others, have no good answer."

The authors propose potential answers to "the puzzle", pointing to men exaggerating and women understating as likely. Why didn't such considerations make the news? Because, there is nothing sensational about a headline "Men report more partners than women report despite having the same number on average."

12.1 Bipartite Graph Matchings

World I above is a matching. Every man on the left matches to exactly one woman on the right. We now study matchings. For a change, let's talk about tasks that must be matched to resources, not men and women. In the bipartite graphs below, the left-vertices are tasks $\{T_1, \ldots, T_4\}$ and the right-vertices are resources $\{R_1, \ldots, R_5\}$.

In (a), A gray edge links a task to a resource that can perform the task. We must perform all four tasks and each resource can be used only once. How shall we accomplish this? In (b) are 4 highlighted black edges.

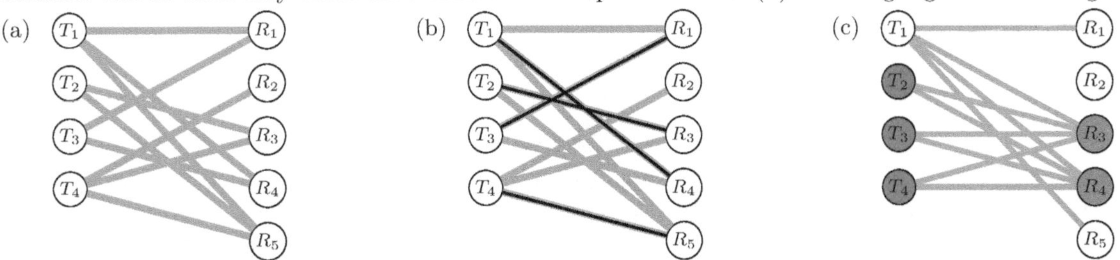

In (b) the black edges match every task to a unique resource. We can perform tasks T_1, T_2, T_3, T_4 using resources R_4, R_3, R_1, R_5 respectively. The black edges are a left-matching that covers or saturates all four left-vertices (tasks). In a matching, no two edges can share any end-points. Try to perform all tasks in (c).

Pop Quiz 12.2

In (a), find a different matching, hence a different allocation of tasks to resources.

There can be many left-matchings, or none. Hall gave a test to tell when there is at least one left-matching. The neighborhood of left-vertex x, $N(x)$, contains all right-vertices linked to x. For example, in (a) above, $N(T_1) = \{R_1, R_4, R_5\}$. The neighborhood of a set of left-vertices is the union of the neighborhoods of the individual vertices. For example, in (a) above,

$$N(\{T_1, T_2\}) = N(T_1) \cup N(T_2) = \{R_1, R_4, R_5\} \cup \{R_3, R_5\} = \{R_1, R_3, R_4, R_5\}$$

In a left-matching, any left-subset X matches to right-vertices in $N(X)$, which is impossible if $|X| > |N(X)|$ because there are more vertices to match than spots to match them with. We must have $|X| \leq |N(X)|$ for every left-subset X. There's no matching in (c) because the red vertices $\{T_2, T_3, T_4\}$ have a smaller neighborhood $\{R_3, R_4\}$. This necessary condition that $|X| \leq |N(X)|$ for every left-subset X is also sufficient.

Theorem 12.1 (Hall's Theorem). Hall's matching condition is that for every left-subset X, $|X| \leq |N(X)|$. If Hall's matching condition holds, then there is a matching which covers every left-vertex.

Proof. Let n be the number of left-vertices. We use strong induction on n. The base case is $n = 1$, one left-vertex x. Since $N(x) \geq 1$, match x to any neighbor. Assume the theorem holds when there are at most n left-vertices, and consider any bipartite graph with $n+1$ left-vertices. There are two cases.

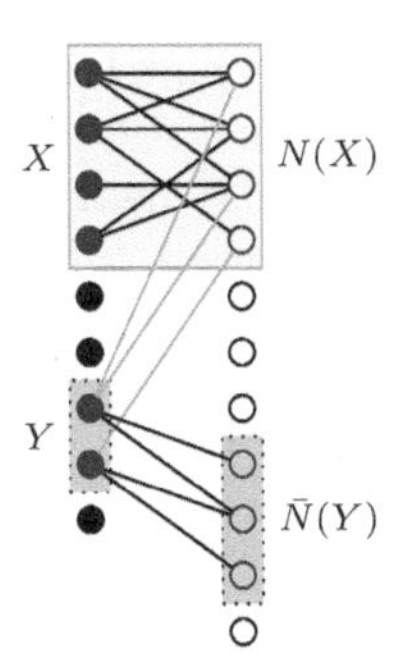

Case 1. Some proper left-subset X, with $1 \leq |X| < n+1$, has $|X| = |N(X)|$. Divide the bipartite graph into two parts as shown. The first part is X and its neighborhood $N(X)$. The second part is the rest of the graph. The neighborhood of any left-subset in X is contained in $N(X)$ and, by assumption, satisfies the matching condition. Consider any left-subset Y in the second part of the graph. The neighborhood of Y may overlap with $N(X)$ (gray edges). Let $\bar{N}(Y)$ be that part of $N(Y)$ in the second part of the graph, not overlaping with $N(X)$. From the matching condition,

$$|N(X)| + |\bar{N}(Y)| = |N(X \cup Y)| \overset{*}{\geq} |X \cup Y| = |X| + |Y|.$$

$*$ is because the full graph satisfies the matching condition. Since $|N(X)| = |X|$, we have $|\bar{N}(Y)| \geq |Y|$ and the second part of the graph satisfies the matching condition.

By the induction hypothesis, each part has a left-matching, as each has fewer than $n+1$ left-vertices and satisfies the matching condition. Combining these two left-matchings gives a left-matching for the full graph.

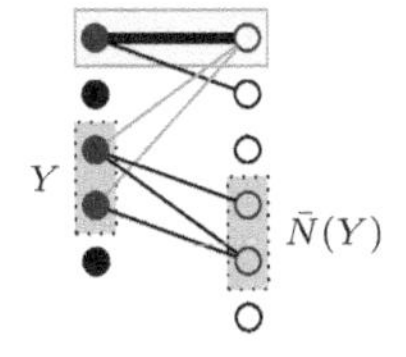

Case 2. Every proper left-subset X, with $1 \leq |X| < n+1$, has $|X| < |N(X)|$. Match the first left-vertex to any neighbor. In the remaining graph, which has n left-vertices, consider any left-subset Y and its neighborhood $\bar{N}(Y)$ in the remaining graph. Then,

$$|\bar{N}(Y)| \geq |N(Y)| - 1,$$

because $N(Y)$ contains at most one more right-vertex than $\bar{N}(Y)$. Since $|N(Y)| \geq |Y|+1$, it follows that $|\bar{N}(Y)| \geq |Y|$, and the remaining graph satisfies the matching condition.

By the induction hypothesis there is a left-matching, which we can combine with the match of the first left-vertex to get a left-matching for the full graph. In both cases, there is a left-matching which covers the $n+1$ left-vertices, which proves the theorem by induction. ■

Hall's matching condition is intuitive, but inefficient to check algorithmically, because enumerating every possible subset of left-vertices is not practical. Here is a condition that is easier to check:

$$\text{min-left-degree} \geq \text{max-right-degree}. \tag{12.1}$$

If (12.1) holds, Hall's matching condition also holds. Indeed, for any left-subset X and its neighborhood $N(X)$, let $E(X)$ be the number of edges from X to $N(X)$. Each left-vertex in X has at least min-left-degree edges, so $E(X) \geq |X| \times \text{min-left-degree} \geq |X| \times \text{max-right-degree}$. Each right-vertex in $N(X)$ has at most max-right-degree edges, so $E(X) \leq |N(X)| \times \text{max-right-degree}$. Combining the two inequalities,

$$|X| \times \text{max-right-degree} \leq E(X) \leq |N(X)| \times \text{max-right-degree} \quad \rightarrow \quad |X| \leq |N(X)|.$$

Corollary 12.2. If min-left-degree $\geq$ max-right-degree, there is a matching which covers the left-vertices.

> **Exercise 12.3**
> Prove Corollary 12.2 directly by induction, without invoking Hall's Theorem. What goes wrong? Why is Hall's Theorem, a stronger result, easier to prove?

Example 12.3 (Latin Squares). A graph problem can be hidden within an application context. Usually, once you figure out how graphs fit in, the graph problem quickly emerges.

A Latin square (the name originates from Euler) is an $n \times n$ square where each row and column is an ordering of $1, 2, \ldots, n$. A 4×4 Latin square is shown on the right. Latin squares have found application in error-correcting codes, design of board games (Kamisado) and experimental design. Our interest lies in how to construct a Latin square. We have labeled the columns " 1:" " 2:" " 3:" " 4:". How did we fill the 1st row?

1:	2:	3:	4:
3	4	2	1
4	1	3	2
1	2	4	3
2	3	1	4

We must fill each column with a number from $1, \ldots, n$ and each number can appear in just one column. If we let the columns be the left-vertices in a bipartite graph and the numbers the right-vertices, then we must find a matching in the complete bipartite graph $K_{4,4}$, because every number could be put in any column. The matching shown with black edges corresponds to our 1st row.

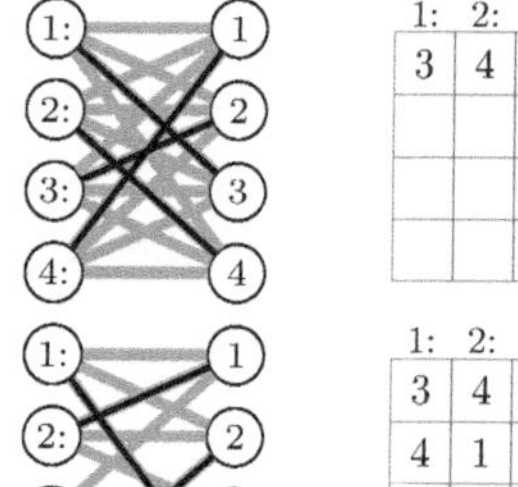

1:	2:	3:	4:
3	4	2	1

How about the 2nd row? We need another matching, but now, for example, column 1 cannot match to number 3 because 3 already appears. We need a matching in a residual graph that remains after removing the previously matched edges. The matching shown with the black edges in this new residual graph corresponds to our 2nd row.

1:	2:	3:	4:
3	4	2	1
4	1	3	2

For the 3rd row, remove the black edges and construct another matching. Repeat for the 4th row. For an $n \times n$ Latin square, the graph starts as $K_{n,n}$ and every vertex has degree n. The edges in a matching connect the left-vertices to unique right-vertices. Removing these edges decreases every left and right-vertex's degree by 1. So, all vertices continue to have the same degree. The minimum left-degree is at least the maximum right-degree and Corollary 12.2 guarantees a matching, so you can always complete the Latin square. □

12.1.1 Stable Marriage: Mathematics of Dating

People have preferences. **A**lice, **B**arb and **C**arla want to date **X**avier, **Y**ariv and **Z**ach. Everyone has a preference list, an order in which they would choose partners. In this example, Xavier's choices are Alice (top), Barb (second) and Carla (last). We show the preferences and a matching of the boys with the girls.

	X	Y	Z
1.	A	A	B
2.	B	C	A
3.	C	B	C

	A	B	C
1.	Z	Y	Z
2.	Y	X	X
3.	X	Z	Y

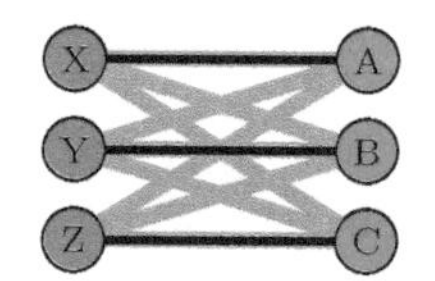

Consider the pair (Y, A) who are not matched with each other. Instead, A is matched to X, but A prefers Y. Similarly Y is matched to B, but Y prefers A. Such a pair both of who prefer each other to their current partners is volatile. If there are no volatile pairs, the matching is stable. The matching above is not stable.

Exercise 12.4
For our friends A, B, C, X, Y, Z, two matchings are given on the right.
Show that both matchings are stable.
Which matching do the girls prefer? Which matching do the boys prefer?

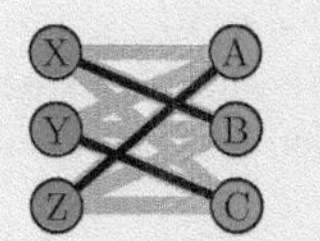

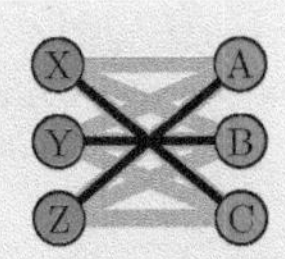

The marriages should be stable, otherwise there is potential for scandal. Can we always find a stable matching with no volatile pairs? Surprisingly, yes, and a simple iterative dating ritual works. We illustrate the steps for our six friends A, B, C, X, Y, Z. Think of a time when men wooed women as in Shakespearean romances.

Day 1. Our ladies await on balconies. Each gent serenades the top lady on his list. Here, X and Y both serenade A, Z serenades B and C is left alone to work on FOCS. A lady being wooed rejects all but her top suitor. To this favored suitor she says, "You *may* be the one, come back tomorrow."

X	Y	Z
~~A~~	A	B
B	C	A
C	B	C

A	B	C
~~X~~, Y	Z	–

A gent who is rejected cross off the lady who snubbed him from his list. Pride prevents him from accosting that lady again. Here, A rejects X and tells Y to come back, and X, not to be snubbed twice, deletes A from his list. The next day, the gents call upon whomever remains atop their respective lists.

Day 2. As instructed, Y and Z return to A and B respectively and X, who crossed off A, now goes to B's balcony. Now, it is B who has a choice, and she rejects Z who accordingly crosses B off his list. Y and X will return to court A and B again on the next day.

X	Y	Z
~~A~~	A	~~B~~
B	C	A
C	B	C

A	B	C
Y	X, ~~Z~~	–

Day 3. As instructed, Y and X return to A and B respectively. Z, who crossed off B, now goes to A's balcony. A's patience has borne fruit because A now rejects Y for her top-choice Z and Y crosses A off his list. Z and X will return to court A and B again on the next day.

X	Y	Z
~~A~~	~~A~~	~~B~~
B	C	A
C	B	C

A	B	C
~~Y~~, Z	X	–

Day 4. We have a stalemate, with at most a single suitor under each balcony. Each girl has found her boy and the dating ritual ends with the marriages

$$A\text{—}Z \qquad B\text{—}X \qquad C\text{—}Y$$

X	Y	Z
~~A~~	~~A~~	~~B~~
B	C	A
C	B	C

A	B	C
Z	X	Y

The dating ritual sounds uncannily similar to the dating practices that have evolved over the millenia. Perhaps that is no accident, because this dating ritual has nice properties that would make it evolutionarily desirable.

Theorem 12.4 (Gale-Shapely, 1962). The dating ritual has the following properties.

1. For n men and n women, the dating ritual ends after at most n^2 days of dating.
2. Every man and woman will be matched at the end.
3. The resulting set of marriages is stable, which means there are no volatile pairs.

Exercise 12.5 [Proof of Theorem 12.4]

(a) When a woman has more than one suitor, prove that some man will cross off a woman from his list. How many times can happen? Prove that at most n^2 days of dating occur before stalemate.

(b) If a woman ever gets wooed, prove that she will always get wooed on subsequent days and therefore must, at the end of the ritual, be married.

(c) At the end of the ritual assume some man m is not married. Hence, some woman w is also not married. Prove that m wooed w. Prove, by contradiction, that every man and woman get married.

(d) Suppose a man m and woman w are not married to each other at the end of the dating ritual.
  (i) Prove that if m never wooed w, m prefers his partner to w.
  (ii) Prove that if m did woo w, w prefers her partner to m
  Hence prove there are no volatile pairs at the end of the dating ritual.

Women are in control as they select their best suitor. Sadly, control doesn't mean better off. The men live happily ever after, and the women get short-changed. This is a mathematical fact that we now make precise.

Pop Quiz 12.6
In modern times, nothing stops men being on the balconies with women wooing. Run the dating ritual with the roles of men and women reversed. You should obtain the stable marriages: A—Z, B—Y and C—X.

A boy or girl who does not get their top choice experiences a regret equal to how far below their top choice they ended up. We show the regret of our friends in the table below, which you can verify.

	girls			boys		
	A	B	C	W	X	Y
Regret when girls propose and boys are on balconies	**0**	**0**	**1**	2	2	1
Regret when boys propose and girls are on balconies	0	1	2	**1**	**1**	**1**

The regret of the girls is lower when girls propose. Similarly, the regret of the boys is lower when boys propose. It is better to be the aggressor and propose than to wait timidly to be wooed. Our example is the norm. It is never worse to be the proposing side. In fact, the dating ritual gives the best possible outcome for the proposers and the worst possible outcome for the evaluators. The next Theorem is proved in Problem 12.26.

Theorem 12.5. In the dating ritual, it is better to be a proposer. More specifically:
If you are on the proposer side, your regret is the minimum you can get over all possible stable matchings.
If you are on the evaluator side, your regret is the maximum you can get over all possible stable matchings.

12.2 Coloring

Some graph problems are fundamental, and coloring is one of them. Many tasks, once appropriately modeled, reduce to coloring a graph. Here are two examples.

Task 1: Assigning Radio Frequencies

Six radio stations broadcast to different audiences determined by the geographic reach of their signals, as shown by the discs centered on the stations below.

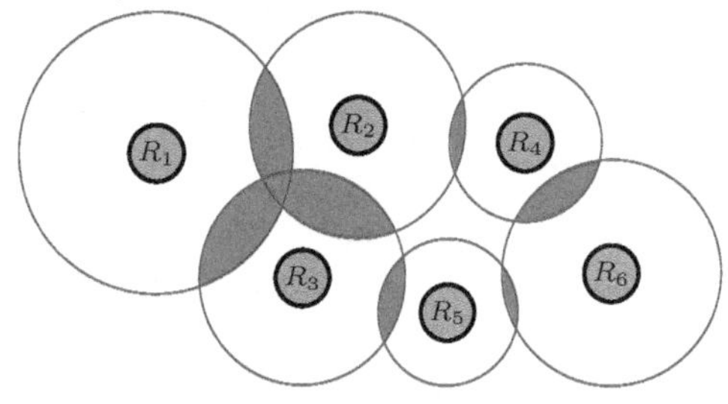

Stations with overlapping reach can broadcast to the same listener in the red areas, so they must use different frequencies, or else their signals will interfere. The task is to assign frequencies to radio stations so that no listener will hear interference. The trivial solution assigns a different frequency to each radio station. But, frequencies are in limited supply and you wish to use as few frequencies as possible. How shall we assign the frequencies to radio stations?

Task 2: Scheduling Course Exams

Students taking courses at a university can be modeled as a bipartite graph.

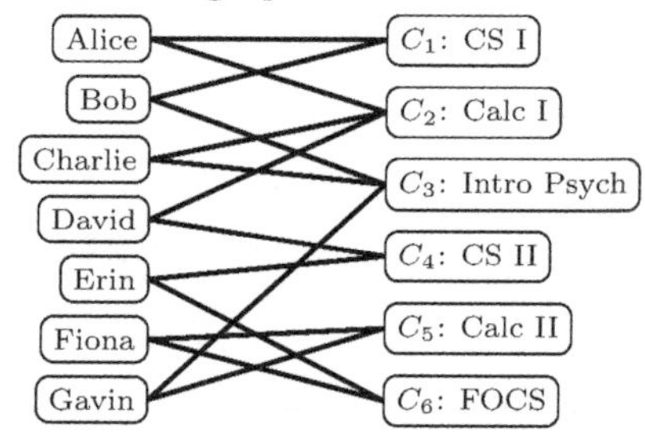

Two courses with the same student cannot have the same exam-time. For example, because of Alice, CS I and Calc I need different exam times. The task is to assign exam times to all the courses so that every student can take all their exams. Again, a trivial solution assigns each course to a different exam time. A typical university has hundreds of courses, but only 3 exam slots per day and 5 days of exams. So, you only have 15 exam slots. How do you schedule exams using the fewest exam-slots?

Solving Task 1: Radio Frequencies

If two radio stations share listeners, they conflict. Let us model these conflicts with a graph. The vertices are radio stations. There is an edge between two radio stations if their reach overlaps.

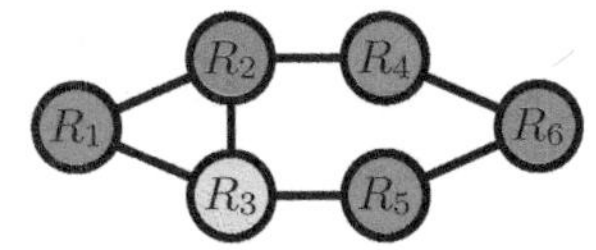

We colored each vertex with one of three colors so that vertices linked by an edge have different colors. A color corresponds to a frequency and conflicting radio stations must have different colors (frequencies). We need only three frequencies, not six.

Solving Task 2: Course Exam-times

If two courses have the same student, they conflict. Let us model the course conflicts with a graph. The vertices are courses. An edge between two courses means they have students in common.

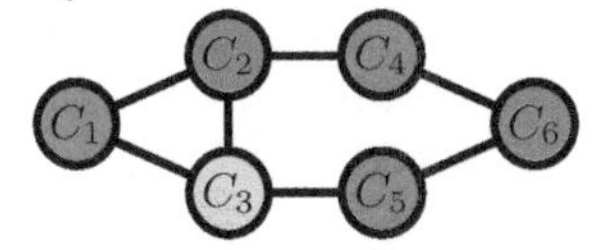

Is this familiar? Each color is an exam slot and conflicting courses linked by an edge must have different colors. We need only three exam slots. Seemingly different tasks both reduced to coloring vertices so that adjacent vertices have different colors.

Both tasks involved conflict resolution, and such problems of scheduling to avoid conflicts often reduce to graph coloring. Formally, label the vertices $v_1, \ldots, v_n$ with colors $c_1, \ldots, c_n$, where each color c_i is from a set of k colors $\{1, \ldots, k\}$. The coloring is valid or proper if adjacent vertices linked by an edge are labeled with different colors. If you use k colors, you have a k-coloring of the graph. Ideally you should use as few colors as possible. For a graph G, the minimum number of colors $\chi(G)$ for which it is possible to get a valid coloring is called the chromatic number of G. Even a 3rd-grader could understand graph-coloring, yet we can't efficiently compute the chromatic number of a general graph, let alone produce a good coloring.

Pop Quiz 12.7

(a) Prove that you need at least 3 colors to color the graph in Tasks 1 and 2 above.

(b) Graph G has n vertices. Prove that $1 \leq \chi(G) \leq n$ and give graphs that need 1 and n colors.

Greedy Coloring. Here is a simple algorithm to color the vertices in the order $v_1, \ldots, v_n$. Let the colors be $\{1, 2, 3, \ldots\}$ and let color$(v_1) = 1$. After vertices $v_1, \ldots, v_i$ are colored, color v_{i+1} with the smallest color that does not conflict with any previously colored vertex. Sequential coloring using the smallest available color is called Greedy. Here is an example. For visual effect the colors $\{1, 2, 3, 4\}$ are chosen as $\{●, ●, ○, ●\}$.

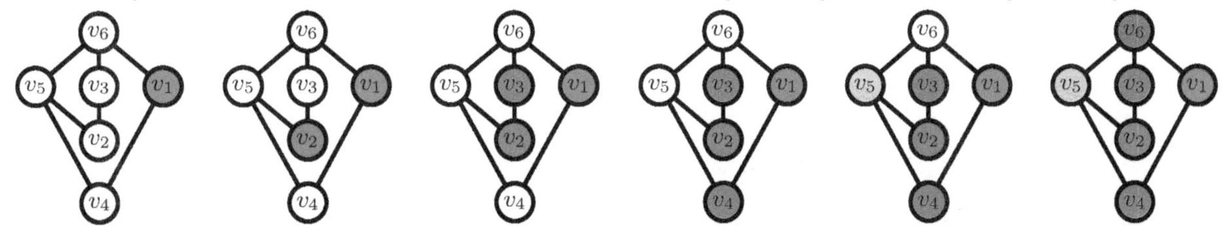

Exercise 12.8

Find a vertex-order for the graph above, for which Greedy uses just 2 colors.

There's no efficient algorithm for graph-coloring. Greedy can be unpredictable, depending heavily on the vertex-ordering. Ordering vertices by degree works well in practice. Greedy always gives small colors to low-degree vertices. Indeed, let δ_i be the degree of v_i. Greedy assigns a color to v_i that is at most $\delta_i + 1$, because the δ_i neighbors of v_i use at most δ_i colors in $\{1, 2, \ldots, \delta_i + 1\}$ leaving at least one for v_i.

Lemma 12.6. For greedy coloring using any ordering of the vertices, color$(v_i) \leq \delta_i + 1$.

Let $\Delta = \max_i \delta_i$ be the maximum degree. Lemma 12.6 implies that a greedy coloring uses no more than $\Delta + 1$ colors, which gives an upper bound on the chromatic number of a graph.

Theorem 12.7. The chromatic number $\chi(G) \leq \Delta(G) + 1$, where $\Delta(G)$ is the maximum degree in G.

(Brook's Theorem is a slight improvement of Theorem 12.7 to $\Delta(G)$ unless G is an odd cycle or K_n.)

For most graphs, $\Delta + 1$ is a gross over-estimate of the chromatic number. For example, planar graphs can have unbounded degrees but are 4-colorable. Trees are 2-colorable, and again the degrees are unbounded. For practice with induction, we prove that the chromatic number of rooted binary trees is 2.

Theorem 12.8. Rooted binary trees (RBT) can be colored using no more than two colors.

Before proving the theorem, we make a simple observation. It is always possible to color a graph in such a way that any chosen vertex has color 1. Indeed, take any coloring. If the chosen vertex has color $\ell \neq 1$, relabel the colors so that $\ell \to 1$ and $1 \to \ell$, changing all vertices with color-ℓ to color-1 and *vice versa.*

Proof. We use structural induction and the recursive definition of RBT in Section 7.3 on page 92. The claim is trivially true for the base case of an empty tree for which zero colors needed.

In the induction step, we assume that the ancestor-trees T_1 and T_2 in the constructor rule can be colored with two colors. Suppose T_1 and T_2 are non-empty. Let us use the colors {●, ●}. By our observation before the proof, T_1 can be colored using colors {●, ●} with its root vertex getting color ●. Similarly, T_2 can be colored using colors {●, ●} with its root vertex getting color ●. We now must show that the new tree obtained by applying the constructor rule to the ancestors T_1 and T_2 can be colored using the two colors {●, ●}. We keep the coloring of the ancestors and use the color ● for the root in the new tree.

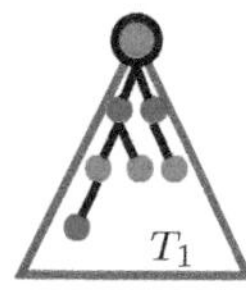

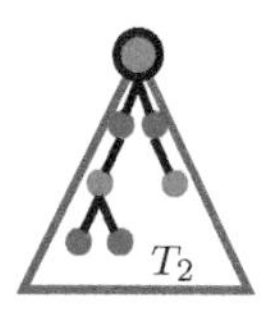

→
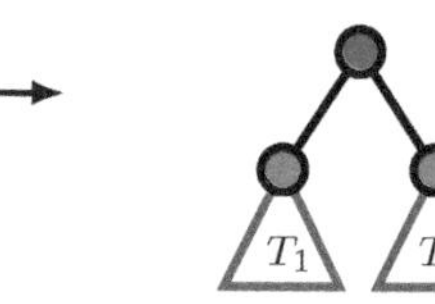

The new edges from the new root to the old roots link vertices of different color. We started with 2-colorings of T_1 and T_2, so the edges within T_1 or T_2 link vertices of different color. Therefore we have a 2-coloring of the new tree. The reader may verify the (easy) cases when T_1 or T_2 is empty. By structural induction, every RBT is 2-colorable. ■

A general rooted tree has a similar recursive definition to the RBT. The only difference is in the constructor rule where, to get a new tree, you can combine any number of trees $T_1, T_2, \ldots, T_k$ by linking their roots to a new root. The same proof above works to show that general rooted trees are 2-colorable.

If a graph is 2-colorable, let the red vertices be left-vertices and the blue vertices be right-vertices. All edges link a red to a blue vertex, so we have a bipartite graph. Conversely, any bipartite graph is 2-colorable: color left-vertices red and right-vertices blue. All edges go from left to right, connecting red to blue.

Theorem 12.9. A graph is bipartite if and only if it is 2-colorable, having a chromatic number at most 2.

Trees are 2-colorable. By Theorem 12.9, trees are bipartite.

Exercise 12.9

Prove that 6 colors suffice to color any planar graph. In Exercise 11.7(g) you proved that if $V \geq 3$, then $E \leq 3V - 6$ (a bound on the number of edges in a planar graph).

(a) Suppose that a planar graph has more than 3 vertices. Show that it must have at least one vertex of degree 5 or less. *[Hint: Use contradiction.]*

(b) Show that a planar graph remains planar if you remove a vertex and its edges.

(c) Prove that any planar graph is 6-colorable. Use induction on the number of vertices. *[Hint: In the induction step, remove a vertex of degree at most 5.]*

12.3 Whirlwind Tour of Graph Problems

We showcase a few other important graph tasks. A task can be [EASY] or [HARD], which refers to how quickly we can solve the task on a general case. We will need a model of computing to make the notions of [EASY] and [HARD] more precise, so stay tuned for the later chapters, because efficiency is an important issue in CS.

Connected Components [EASY]. You wish to virally market a song in a social network. If someone buys the song, all their friends will buy the song. Who should you market to? You would identify the connected components of the social network graph and market to one person in each component. We show the components in an example network on the right. You might go further and target "central (red)" vertices in each component.

Spanning Tree [EASY]. We show a road system which happens to be a grid. The roads are in gray. We need a minimal highway system that offers high-speed travel between any two vertices. The subset of roads used to form highways should be a spanning tree of the road network (red). A spanning tree uses a subset of the edges and all the vertices to form a tree. Every connected graph has a spanning tree.

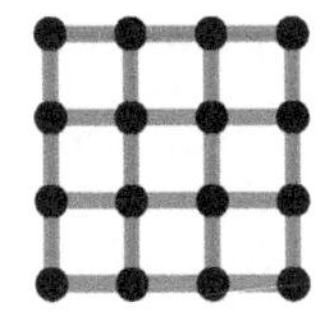

Euler Cycle [EASY]. Every winter, a northern city like Troy will get a snowfall of at least 1-foot. The city would like to deploy a snowplow to clean each road as the plow traverses the road. Ideally the plow should start at the depot, traverse every road exactly once and return to the depot. The plow needs to traverse an Euler Cycle. In the example to the right, the depot is the red vertex and the path taken by the plow is in red.

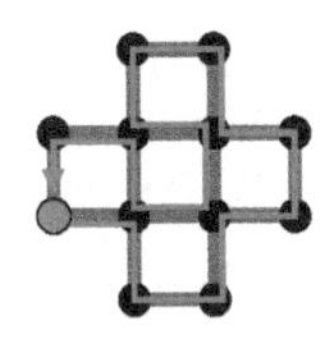

Hamiltonian Cycle [HARD]. A salesperson wishes to start in their office (red vertex) and visit every house (vertex) in the neighborhood exactly once, returning to the office. The salesperson needs to follow a Hamiltonian Cycle, shown in red.

A variant of Hamiltonian cycle is Traveling Salesperson (TSP) on a complete weighted graph where weights are distances between vertices. The task is to find a Hamiltonian cycle of minimum total distance.

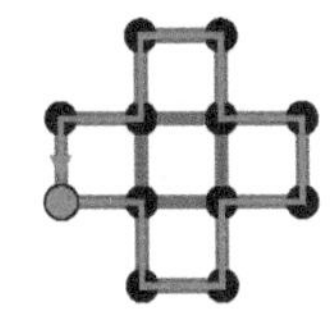

Facility Location (K-center) [HARD]. McDonalds wants to place restaurants in a road network. How should a budget of K restaurants be placed so that no customer has to drive far too reach their closest McDonalds? The task is to place the restaurants so that the furthest distance that needs to be traveled from any vertex is minimized. We show a solution for two restaurants (red vertices) in the example on the right. No vertex is further than 2 steps from a restaurant.

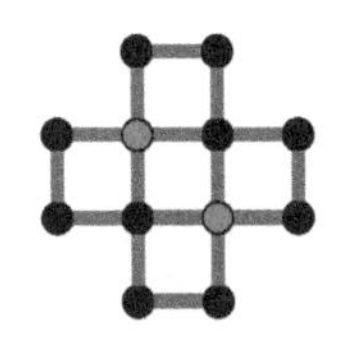

Vertex Cover [HARD]. We would like to place the minimum number of policemen at intersections in a neighborhood so that all roads can be surveiled. A policeman at an intersection can watch all roads coming to that intersection. In the example, six policemen at the red vertices suffice to "cover" all the streets. Such a set of vertices is a vertex cover. Can you do it with fewer than 6 policemen?

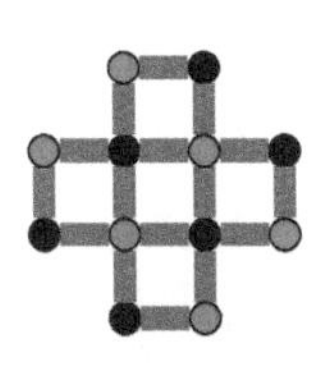

Dominating Set [HARD]. We would like to place the minimum number of hospitals at intersections (vertices) so that every intersection is either a hospital or no more than one block away from a hospital. No one need travel more than one block to get to a hospital. In the example, we show four hospitals at the red vertices that accomplish the goal. Such a set of vertices is a dominating set. Can you do it with fewer than 4 hospitals?

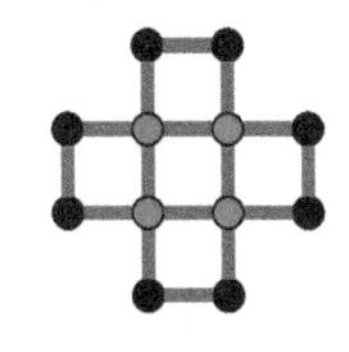

Network Flow [EASY]. A source-ISP (blue vertex) sends packets to a sink-ISP (red vertex). Each link has a capacity, a maximum number of packets that can be sent in a unit of time. What is the maximum packet transmission rate that can be achieved between the source and sink? In the example, the transmission capacity of each link is a gray edge weight. This capacity cannot be be exceeded at each link. Further, packets cannot be droped, so packets entering a vertex must exit. In the example, we show in black on each edge the capacity being used, which cannot be more than the available capacity (in gray). The total flow rate is 10, the number of packets leaving the source. Network flow is not only a stand-alone task, but also a tool for other tasks like bipartite matching.

12.4 Problems

Problem 12.1. Identify which graphs are bipartite and redraw them with left and right vertices.

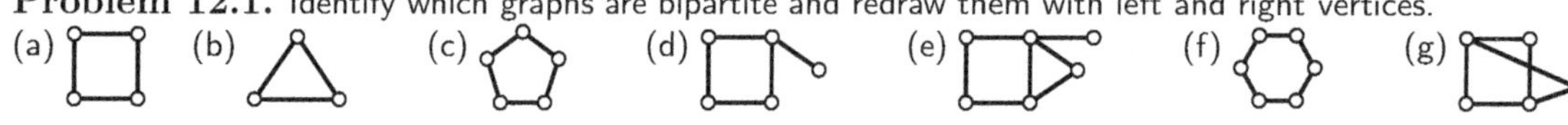

Problem 12.2. An r-regular bipartite graph G with $r \geq 1$ has left and right vertex sets V_1 and V_2. Prove $|V_1| = |V_2|$.

Problem 12.3. Bipartite matching pairs objects of one type with another type, e.g. men with women. Instead, one can match objects with each other. For example, assigning roommates when people are not compatible with everyone (one defines a compatibility graph). A perfect matching pairs up all vertices. Which graphs have perfect matchings
(a) K_n (b) C_n (c) P_n (d) S_{n+1} (e) W_{n+1}?

Problem 12.4. Show that these graphs with an even number of vertices, have no perfect matching. Show also that you can add one edge, and get a perfect matching in each case.

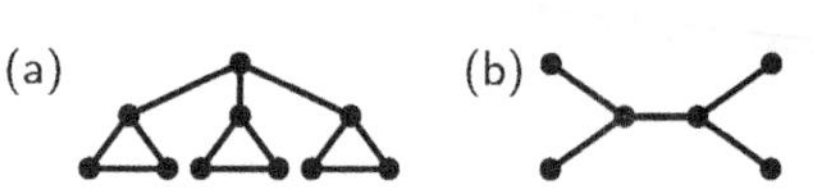

Problem 12.5. A maximum matching maximizes the number of edges in the matching. A matching is maximal if it cannot be increased by adding another edge. For each graph, find maximal and maximum matchings of the given sizes.

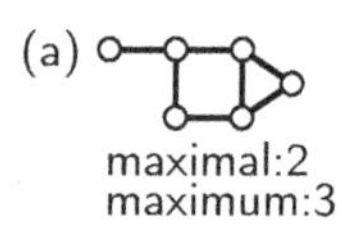

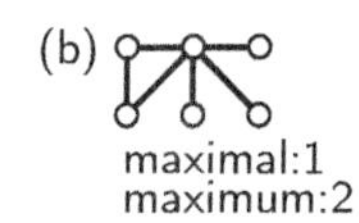

Problem 12.6. Find a maximum matching in each graph.

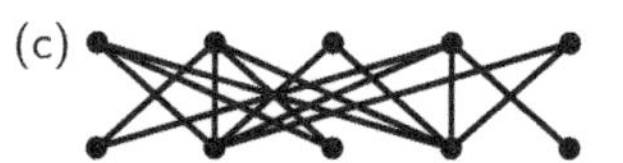

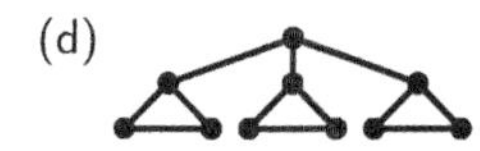

Problem 12.7. Five women A, B, C, D and E are each willing to marry a subset of the men V, W, X, Y and Z (chart on the right). Find a matching of the women to men they are willing to marry. Only one woman can marry a man. If you think it can't be done, prove it using Hall's Theorem.

A: V, W
B: V, X, Y
C: V, Z
D: W, Z
E: V, Z

Problem 12.8. A company has system admins P, Q, R, S. Admins have areas of expertise, but may only cover one area. Can the four different areas be covered? If yes, assign the admins to areas. If no, prove it using Hall's Theorem.

P: mac, wireless, email
Q: linux, wireless
R: wireless, email
S: linux, mac

Problem 12.9. In a regular bipartite graph every vertex has the same degree. Prove:
(a) The number of left and right-vertices are equal. (b) Some matching covers the left-vertices. *[Hint: Hall's theorem.]*

Problem 12.10. Prove or disprove.
(a) K_3 is bipartite.
(b) Every graph with a perfect matching is connected.
(c) Every tree has at most one perfect matching.
(d) Any maximal matching is at least half the size of a maximum sized matching.

Problem 12.11. The gray edges form a bipartite graph and the black edges are a matching.

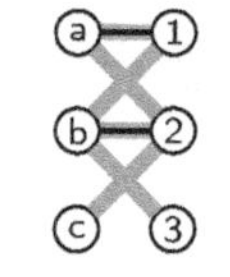

(a) Show that the matching is maximal. An augmenting path starts and ends at unmatched vertices, does not repeat vertices, and alternates between using an edge not in the matching and then one in the matching. Find an augmenting path.
(b) Prove: if there is an augmenting path, you can increase the size of the matching.

Problem 12.12. Show that a graph G is bipartite if and only if it has no cycle of odd length.
(a) Prove that if there is a cycle of odd length, the graph cannot be bipartite.
(b) Use a BFS-tree (Problem 11.58) to color even level vertices red and odd level vertices blue. Show that the 2-coloring is valid if and only if no edge connects vertices in the same level.
(c) Prove that if an edge exists between vertices in the same level, there is an odd cycle.
(d) Show that a graph has chromatic number 2 if and only if it has no cycle of odd length.

Problem 12.13. Use Problem 11.32 to prove that a bipartite graph has no cycle of odd length. *[Hint: The adjacency matrix of a bipartite graph for a suitable ordering of the vertices has the form* $\mathrm{A} = \left[\begin{smallmatrix} 0 & \mathrm{B} \\ \mathrm{B}^{\mathrm{T}} & 0 \end{smallmatrix}\right]$. *What is the form of* A^{2k+1}*?]*

Problem 12.14. Jobs $J_1, \ldots, J_n$ are performed on servers $S_1, \ldots, S_m$. Server S_i has capacity for $\ell_i \geq 0$ jobs. Each job can run on a subset of the servers. Give necessary and sufficient conditions for being able to do all the jobs.

Problem 12.15. Each of m children $\epsilon_1, \ldots, \epsilon_m$ like a subset of the camps in $\{C_1, \ldots, C_n\}$. Camp C_i has space for $c_i \geq 0$ children. Give necessary and sufficient conditions for being able to fill all the camps to capacity.

Problem 12.16. From m committees $C_1, \ldots, C_m$ we choose distinct representatives $r_1, \ldots, r_m$, one from each committee. Prove this is possible if and only if for every subset $S \subseteq \{1, \ldots, m\}$, $|\cup_{i \in S} C_i| \geq |S|$.

Problem 12.17. Two players alternately choose distinct vertices on a graph G. Player 1 starts with any vertex, and each subsequent new vertex picked must be adjacent to the previous one picked. The two players together follow a path on G. The last player to pick a vertex wins. Prove that player 2 can win if and only if G has a perfect matching.

Problem 12.18. Ayfos was born on Jan. 5,6,9 or Feb. 7,8 or Mar. 4,6 or Apr. 4,5,7. Ayfos reveals the month to Kilam and the day to Niaz. The possible birthdays are represented as a bipartite graph with months on the left and days on the right. Here is the conversation between Kilam and Niaz

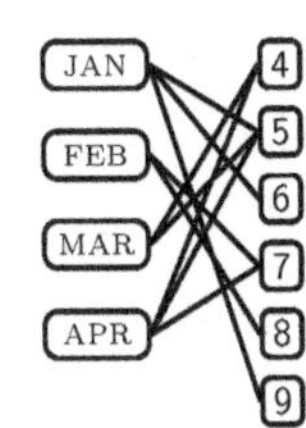

(a) *Kilam (to Niaz)*: I know that you can't figure out the month.
(b) *Niaz (to Kilam)*: Well, I can now figure out the month.
(c) *Kilam (to Niaz)*: Ahh, I can now figure out the day.

Use each statement to remove edges. Only one edge will remain. When was Ayfos born?

Problem 12.19. Matrices with row and column-sum 1 are important in probability theory.

(a) A permutation matrix is a matrix of 0s and 1s with one 1 in each column and row. Prove that a square nonnegative integer matrix is a sum of n permutation matrices if and only if every row and column sums to n. For example,

$$\begin{pmatrix} 1 & 3 & 0 \\ 2 & 1 & 1 \\ 1 & 0 & 3 \end{pmatrix} = \begin{pmatrix} 1 & 0 & 0 \\ 0 & 1 & 0 \\ 0 & 0 & 1 \end{pmatrix} + \begin{pmatrix} 0 & 1 & 0 \\ 1 & 0 & 0 \\ 0 & 0 & 1 \end{pmatrix} + \begin{pmatrix} 0 & 1 & 0 \\ 1 & 0 & 0 \\ 0 & 0 & 1 \end{pmatrix} + \begin{pmatrix} 0 & 1 & 0 \\ 0 & 0 & 1 \\ 1 & 0 & 0 \end{pmatrix}$$

(b) A doubly stochastic matrix Q is nonnegative and each row and column sums to 1. Prove, by induction on the number of non-zeros, that Q is a linear combination of permutation matrices, $Q = c_1P_1 + \cdots + c_mP_m$, where $\sum_i c_i = 1$ and $c_i > 0$. For example,

$$\begin{pmatrix} 0.5 & 0.2 & 0.3 \\ 0 & 0.3 & 0.7 \\ 0.5 & 0.5 & 0 \end{pmatrix} = \frac{3}{10}\begin{pmatrix} 0 & 0 & 1 \\ 0 & 1 & 0 \\ 1 & 0 & 0 \end{pmatrix} + \frac{1}{5}\begin{pmatrix} 0 & 1 & 0 \\ 0 & 0 & 1 \\ 1 & 0 & 0 \end{pmatrix} + \frac{1}{2}\begin{pmatrix} 1 & 0 & 0 \\ 0 & 0 & 1 \\ 0 & 1 & 0 \end{pmatrix}$$

Problem 12.20. For the given preferences of 3 boys b_1, b_2, b_3 and 3 girls g_1, g_2, g_3, find stable marriages using the dating ritual when:

(a) Boys woo and girls decide. (b) Girls woo and boys decide.

A person's regret is how far from their top choice they married (e.g. if b_1—g_3 is a marriage, then regret(b_1) $= 2$ and regret(g_3) $= 1$). Compute the regrets in (a) and (b).
(FYI: Girls have maximum regret when boys propose and minimum regret when girls propose. **Make the first move!**)

	b_1	b_2	b_3	g_1	g_2	g_3
1.	g_2	g_1	g_1	b_1	b_2	b_3
2.	g_1	g_3	g_2	b_3	b_3	b_1
3.	g_3	g_2	g_3	b_2	b_1	b_2

Problem 12.21. The dating ritual finds a stable matching in a complete bipartite graph $K_{n,n}$. If, instead, the underlying graph is complete, K_{2n}, then any pair of vertices can be matched. Each person now has a preference list over $2n-1$ people. For $n = 2$, on the right are preference lists for four friends Alice, Barb, Charlie and Dunce. **A**, **B** and **C** form a "love triangle" with **A** liking **B** who likes **C** who likes **A**. **D** is a misfit in this group. Prove there is no stable matching.

	A	B	C	D
1.	B	C	A	A
2.	C	A	B	B
3.	D	D	D	C

Problem 12.22. There is always a stable matching for any set of preferences (Gale & Shapely). Is there also always an unstable matching for any set of preferences? Prove:

Every set of preferences for n boys and n girls ($n \geq 3$) has an unstable matching.

Problem 12.23 (Greedy Matching). A greedy algorithm for stable marriage is to process the boys in an arbitrary order, giving each boy their top-choice among all available girls at the time the boy's match is made.

(a) Prove that every boy will be matched. (b) Give an example to show that the resulting matching may not be stable.

Problem 12.24. Courses $C_1, \ldots, C_k$ are available to n students. Course C_i has capacity c_i, where $\sum_i c_i = n$. Students submit preferences ranking the k courses. Each student is placed in one course. An assignment of students to courses is stable if no pair of students wish to exchange seats. Prove or disprove: The greedy algorithm which sequentially places students into their top-choice among the available courses at that time produces a stable assignment.

Problem 12.25. Ten years before the dating algorithm, the National Resident Matching Program was matching medical residents to hospitals. Each candidate submits preferences over hospitals and each hospital submits preferences over candidates. Each hospital could have multiple openings for residents. Give a dating algorithm for stable matching of residents to hospitals and prove it. *[Hint: Model a hospital with multiple openings as multiple identical hosiptals.]*

Problem 12.26 (Proof of Theorem 12.5). For the dating ritual in which boys propose and girls decide, let the resulting marriages be $M = \{b_1\text{–}g_1, \ldots, b_n\text{–}g_n\}$.

(a) For only this part, suppose the top choices of all the boys are distinct. How happy is b_1? What about g_1?

(b) Prove there is no stable matching where any b_i marries a girl he likes more than g_i.

  (i) For another stable matching with marriages $M' = \{b_1\text{—}g_1', \ldots, b_n\text{—}g_n'\}$. Suppose $b_i : [g_i' > g_i]$ (this notation means b_i prefers g_i' to g_i). Show that at some time in the dating ritual, b_i woos g_i' and gets rejected.

  (ii) Among the boys who are better off in M', let b_* be the first to be rejected by his prefered mate g_*', who rejects b_* for b (b marries g in M and g' in M'). Prove:

$$g_*' : [b > b_*]; \qquad b : [g_*' \geq g]; \text{ (Who did } b \text{ woo first?)} \qquad b : [g' > g_*'] \text{ (}M'\text{ is stable).}$$

  Therefore, prove that b is also happier in M'.

  (iii) Prove that b was rejected before b_* was rejected. Prove the claim by contradiction.

(c) Prove there is no stable matching where any g_i marries a boy she likes less than b_i. *[Hints: Contradiction. Assume g_* marries b_* in M but b in M', and $g_* : [b_* > b]$. Use stability of M' to show that b_* is happier in M' than M.]*

So, girls get short-changed and boys live happily ever after. A boy gets the best girl possible for a stable scenario.

Problem 12.27. Color C_3, C_4, C_5, C_6 using the fewest colors. Make a conjecture and prove it.

Problem 12.28. Find the minimum number of colors, $\chi(G)$, needed to color each graph.

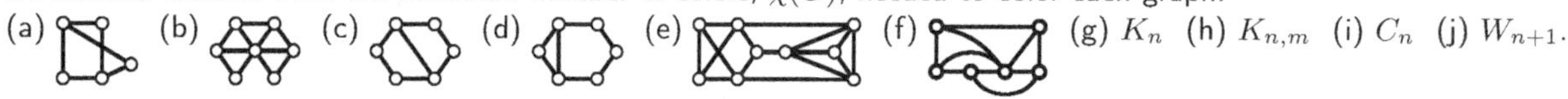

(g) K_n (h) $K_{n,m}$ (i) C_n (j) W_{n+1}.

Problem 12.29. What can you say about $\chi(G)$ if G has K_n as a subgraph?

Problem 12.30. For any graph G, show that Greedy coloring uses $\chi(G)$ colors for some vertex-ordering.

Problem 12.31. Describe a method for coloring the tree on the right using the fewest colors. Your method should work for any tree. Explain why your method works for any tree.

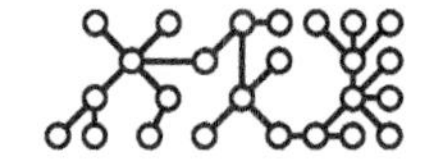

Problem 12.32. Consider Greedy coloring with the vertices ordered $1, 2, \ldots$

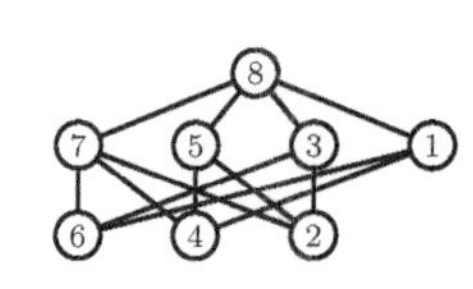

(a) How many colors does Greedy use for the graph on the right?

(b) Show that the chromatic number of the graph on the right is 2.

(c) Generalize. Show that there is a graph G with n vertices for which $\chi(G) = 2$, but Greedy uses $\Omega(n)$ colors for some vertex-order.

Problem 12.33. For any $M \geq 2$, prove that there is a tree and an ordering of its vertices for which Greedy coloring needs at least M colors. Tinker! *[Hint: O–O–O–O and recursion.]*

Problem 12.34 (4×4 Sudoko). A completed 4×4 Sudoko is shown on the right. The four 2×2 bold squares must each contain the digits $1, 2, 3, 4$. Each row and column must also contain the digits $1, 2, 3, 4$. Treating the numbers as colors, a valid solution to the Sudoko puzzle gives a 4-coloring of a particular graph. What is that graph?

2	3	1	4
1	4	2	3
3	1	4	2
4	2	3	1

Problem 12.35. A graph G with n vertices has maximum degree $\Delta \geq 1$. Prove:

(a) $\chi(G) \leq \Delta + 1$, and give a graph for which the bound cannot be improved.

(b) If at most Δ vertices have the maximum degree Δ, then $\chi(G) \leq \Delta$.

(c) If at least κ vertices have degree at most δ, then $\chi(G) \leq \max\{n - \kappa, \delta + 1\}$.

(d) If G is connected and at least one vertex has degree strictly less than Δ, then $\chi(G) \leq \Delta$.

(e) $\chi(G \setminus v) \leq \chi(G) \leq \chi(G \setminus v) + 1$, where $G \setminus v$ is G with the vertex v removed.

(f) $\chi(G)\chi(\overline{G}) \geq n$, where $\overline{G}$ is the complement graph of G.

Problem 12.36. Prove or disprove: If a graph has maximum vertex-degree k and some vertex has degree less than k, then the graph is k-colorable.

Problem 12.37. Show that every connected acyclic graph (i.e., a tree) is bipartite.

(a) Show that there is a vertex of degree 1. *[Hint: Consider an end-vertex of a longest path.]*

(b) Prove the claim by induction. *[Hint: In the induction step, remove a degree-1 vertex.]*

Problem 12.38. Computing χ and finding a χ-coloring are in a sense equivalent. A blackbox-oracle computes the chromatic number χ for any graph. Use the blackbox to find an actual coloring of a graph G with n vertices.

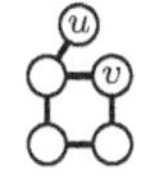

(a) For non-adjacent vertices u, v in G, the contraction $G^-_{u,v}$ merges u, v into one vertex w. All neighbors of u and v become neighbors of w. The augmentation $G^+_{u,v}$ adds the edge (u, v). Give $G^-_{u,v}$ and $G^+_{u,v}$ for the graph on the right.

(b) Show: if some optimal coloring in G gives u and v the same color, then $\chi(G) = \chi(G^-_{u,v})$. In this case, how can you get an optimal coloring of G from an optimal coloring of $G^-_{u,v}$?

(c) Show: if every optimal coloring of G gives different colors to u, v then $\chi(G) = \chi(G^+_{u,v})$. In this case, how do you get an optimal coloring of G from an optimal coloring of $G^+_{u,v}$?

(d) Show how to optimally color G using $O(n^2)$ blackbox-calls plus $O(n)$ extra work.

Problem 12.39 (5-Color Theorem). The minimum degree in a planar graph is at most 5 (Exercise 12.9). Also, K_5 is not planar (Exercise 11.7). Use these facts to prove by induction that every planar graph G with n vertices can be 5-colored. Let v be a minimum-degree vertex in G.

(a) Why can you assume that $G \setminus v$ can be 5-colored?

(b) Suppose $\deg(v) \leq 4$. Prove that G can be 5-colored.

(c) Suppose $\deg(v) = 5$. Let $v_1, \ldots, v_5$ be the neighbors of v. Prove that $G \setminus v$ can be 5-colored while using at most 4 colors for $v_1, \ldots, v_5$.

(i) Prove there are two neighbors of v who are not linked. *[Hint: Contradiction; K_5.]*

(ii) Suppose v_1 and v_2 are not linked by an edge. Merge them into a super-vertex v_1v_2 as shown on the right (every edge to v_1 or v_2 becomes an edge to the super-vertex v_1v_2). Prove that $G \setminus v$ with this super-vertex is planar and also that it can be 5-colored.

(iii) Prove that a 5-coloring of $G \setminus v$ is obtained from the 5-coloring in (ii) by giving both v_1 and v_2 the color of the supervertex v_1v_2. How many colors are used for $v_1, \ldots, v_5$?

(d) Complete the proof that G is 5-colorable.

Problem 12.40. In Section 12.3 on page 168 are the graph problems: (a) Connected components (b) Spanning tree (c) Euler cycle (d) Hamiltonian cycle (e) K-center (f) Vertex cover (g) Dominating set (h) Network flow. Give a "formal" problem specification for each task (you don't need to solve the task). Your formal specification should include:

(i) A formal specification of the input (e.g. a graph $G = (V, E)$).

(ii) A formal specifcation of the output (e.g. a subset $S \subseteq V$).

(iii) The property the output must have (e.g. S is a largest subset with pairwise adjacent vertices).

Problem 12.41. Draw a graph with chromatic number at least 6, and prove it. Make the drawing planar if you can.

Problem 12.42. Solve each problem for the graph on the right by finding the desired object.

(a) [MAXCLIQUE] A largest set of pairwise adjacent vertices.

(b) [MAXINDEPENDENTSET] A largest set of pairwise non-adjacent vertices.

(c) [MINVERTEXCOVER] A smallest vertex set such that every edge has at least one endpoint in the set.

(d) [MINDOMINATINGSET] A smallest vertex set such that every other vertex has a neighbor in the set.

If you find an efficient way to solve any of these problems on general graphs, instant fame awaits.

Problem 12.43. Solve each problem (a)–(c) for each graph (i)–(iii).

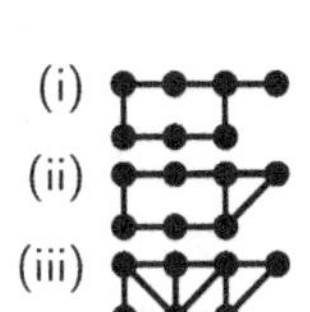

(a) Does the graph have an Euler cycle, an Euler path, both or neither?

(b) Color the graph using a minimum number of colors. What is the chromatic number?

(c) Find a minimum dominating set and a minimum vertex cover.

(d) Find a maximum clique and a maximum independent set.

Problem 12.44 (Hamiltonian Cycle). A Hamiltonian path visits every node once. A Hamiltonian cycle, in addition, returns to the start. Find Hamiltonian paths and cycles in these graphs. If you think it's impossible, explain why.

(a)  (b)  (c)  (d)  (e) 

Can a graph have both a Hamiltonian path and Hamiltonian cycle?

Problem 12.45. A tournament is a graph with a directed edge between every pair of vertices. Prove that every tournament has a directed Hamiltonian path, a path visiting every vertex once.

Problem 12.46. For what n, m does $K_{n,m}$ have (a) An Euler path/cycle (b) A Hamiltonian path/cycle?

Problem 12.47. Sir William Hamilton's "Voyage around the world" puzzle on the right is a planar drawing of a dodecahedron which represents the world with 19 cities as vertices of the dodecahedron. The puzzle is to determine whether one can start at a city and visit each city once along the edges of the dodecahedron, returning to the original city. Can you find a Hamiltonian cycle?

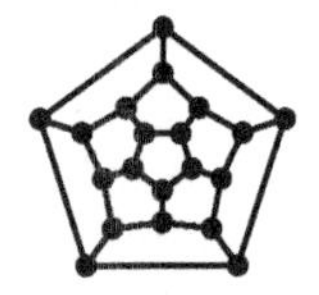

Problem 12.48. A graph has a Hamiltonian cycle. You add an edge. Must the graph continue to have a Hamiltonian cycle? Repeat for: Hamiltonian path; Euler cycle; Euler path.

Problem 12.49 (Dirac's Theorem). A graph G has $n \geq 3$ vertices and minimum degree at least $n/2$. Prove that G has a Hamiltonian cycle using the following steps.

(a) Prove that G is connected.

(b) Let $P = u_1 u_2 \cdots u_k$ be a longest path in G. Prove that all edges of u_1 and u_k are to other vertices in P.

(c) If (u_1, u_k) is an edge, then P is a cycle. If not, show that there are consecutive vertices u_j, u_{j+1} for which (u_1, u_j) and (u_{j+1}, u_k) are edges. Construct a cycle with all vertices of P.

(d) Show that the cycle in (c) is Hamiltonian (no vertex is left out). *[Hint: P is a longest path.]*

(e) Dirac's Theorem is a special case of Ore's Theorem which only requires non-adjacent vertices to have degree-sum at least n. Use the same general idea to prove Ore's Theorem.

Problem 12.50 (Petersen Graph). Give the degree sequence for the Petersen graph on the right.

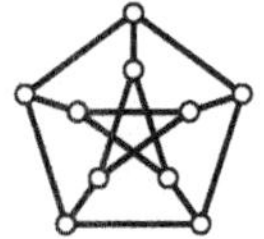

(a) Show that the Petersen graph is not bipartite and give a 3-coloring.

(b) Show that there is a Hamiltonian path, but no Hamiltonian cycle.

(c) Show that if you remove any vertex, the graph has a Hamiltonian cycle.

(d) Is there an Euler cycle or Euler path?

Problem 12.51. To virally market a product, you give it for free to sponsors – primary adopters. A sponsor convinces their friends to buy the product – secondary adopters. We show a graph in which the red sponsors convert the blue vertices, but there are some non-adopters (black). If the red sponsors can convert all the remaining vertices to blue, then the sponsors are a dominating set. Every vertex is either in the dominating set or linked to at least one vertex in the dominating set.

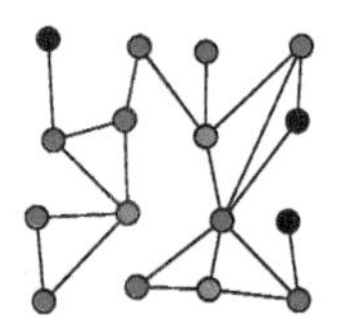

(a) Find a minimum sized set of sponsors that converts the whole network in the example, a minimum dominating set. (Finding a minimum dominating set for a general graph is [HARD].)

(b) Show that a minimum dominating set has at least $n/(\Delta+1)$ vertices. (Δ = maximum degree)

Problem 12.52. A graph has n vertices and every node has positive degree. Show that a minimum dominating set has at most $n/2$ vertices using the following approach.

(a) A weak 2-coloring is a 2-coloring such that every vertex is adjacent to at least one vertex of opposite color. Show that there exists a weak 2-coloring. *[Hint: BFS, Problem 11.58]*

(b) Show that vertices of the same color in a weak 2-coloring form a dominating set.

(c) Show that there are at least two disjoint dominating sets and complete the proof.

Problem 12.53. An independent set is maximal if you cannot increase its size by adding a vertex. Prove that any maximal independent set is a dominating set. When is the complement of a maximal independent set also dominating?

Problem 12.54. Use Problem 12.53 to show that if all vertices have positive degree, then there are two disjoint dominating sets. Hence, one has at most half the vertices. *[Hint: Largest independent set and its complement.]*

Problem 12.55. In a graph with n vertices, every group of size $\lceil n/2 \rceil$ has a common neighbor outside the group. Prove: Some vertex has degree $n-1$. *[Hint: Complement graph, contradiction and Problem 12.54.]*

Problem 12.56. Prove: S is a vertex cover if and only if its complement $\overline{S}$ is an independent set. Hence that

size(largest independent set) + size(smallest vertex cover) = number of vertices.

Problem 12.57. Prove: A graph with n vertices and max. degree Δ has an independent set of size at least $n/(\Delta+1)$.

Problem 12.58. For a graph G with n vertices, $\alpha(G)$ is the maximum size of an independent set and $\chi(G)$ is the minimum number of colors needed to color G. Prove: $\chi(G) \geq n/\alpha(G)$.

Problem 12.59. A zoo wants to place as many different species in an exhibit as possible. Two species are incompatible if they compete for food or one eats the other, which defines an incompatibility graph with species as vertices. The zoo needs a largest subset of pairwise compatible species, a maximum independent set in the incompatibility graph.

(a) If a species is incompatible with no more than Δ other species, show that you can place at least $n/(\Delta+1)$ species in the exhibit. (Δ is the maximum degree of the incompatibility graph.)

(b) (Turán) If, on average, a species is incompatible with d other species, show that you can place at least $n/(d+1)$ species in the exhibit. (The graph's average degree is d.) Use the following steps.

(i) Show that the set I created in the following way is an independent set.

1. Pick an ordering of the n vertices.
2. Place v_i into I if and only if v_i preceeds all its neighbors in the ordering.

Create an independent set for each of the $n!$ orderings $I_1, \ldots, I_{n!}$. The independent sets may not be distinct.

(ii) Show that v_i belongs to $n!/(\delta_i+1)$ of the the $n!$ independent sets $I_1, \ldots, I_{n!}$.

(iii) Show $\sum_{k=1}^{n!} |I_k| = n! \sum_{i=1}^{n} 1/(\delta_i+1)$, and thus the average size of $I_1, \ldots, I_{n!}$ is $\sum_{i=1}^{n} 1/(\delta_i+1)$.

(iv) Show that the maximum independent set has size at least $\sum_{i=1}^{n} 1/(\delta_i+1)$.

(v) Show that $\sum_{i=1}^{n} 1/(\delta_i+1) \geq n/(d+1)$. *[Hint: AM-HM inequality, see Problem 6.40.]*

Problem 12.60 (Low Stretch Spanners). Spanning trees can be highways in road networks. On the right, the thick black edges are a spanning tree highway system. The other edges are non-highways. The highway-only path between the green vertices has length 2, and there's no shorter path using all edges. For the red vertices, the shortest path-length is 1, but the highway-only path has length 3. The path-stretch is the ratio of the highway-only to shortest path-lengths. The path stretch is 1 for the green vertices and 3 for the red vertices.

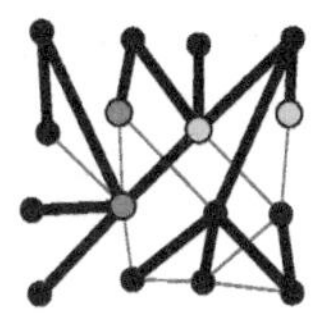

(a) The stretch is the maximum path-stretch over all vertex-pairs. Compute the stretch of the spanning tree above.

(b) Find a "best" spanning tree, having minimum stretch. (In general, this task is [HARD].)

(c) What is worst case path stretch for a minimum stretch spanning tree. *[Hint: C_n.]*

(d) Prove that the stretch of a spanning tree is at least 2 unless the graph is a already a tree.

(e) Give a minimum stretch spanning tree for K_n. What is the stretch?

Problem 12.61 (Minimum Spanning Tree, MST). In a weighted graph, it is often important to have a spanning tree whose edges have the minimum total weight, a minimum weight spanning tree, MST. In a highway system, such a tree contains the widest highways with shortest transit times.

(a) For the weighted graph shown, construct an MST.

(b) Prove or disprove. Every connected weighted graph has at least one MST.

(c) Prove or disprove. If all edge weights are distinct then all spanning trees have different total weight.

(d) Prove or disprove. If edge e has strictly minimum weight, every MST contain edge e.

Problem 12.62. In graph G, C is a vertex cover and M is a matching. Prove:

(a) If you add a vertex u to G, with some edges to u, then $C \cup \{u\}$ is a vertex cover for $G \cup \{u\}$.

(b) Each vertex in C can cover at most one edge in M.

(c) $|M| \leq |C|$. Hence prove: size(maximum matching) $\leq$ size(minimum vertex cover).

Problem 12.63 (Maximum Cut). A cut is a division of the vertices into two sets S_1 and S_2. The cut-size is the number of edges crossing from S_1 to S_2. A sad vertex doesn't have more neighbors in its own set than the other set.

(a) Show that there is a cut in which every vertex is sad. *[Hint: Consider the maximum cut.]*

(b) Show that any cut in which every vertex is sad has size at least half the size of the maximum cut.

Problem 12.64 (Line Graph). For graph G, the line graph $L(G)$ has a node for every edge in G. Two vertices in $L(G)$ are adjacent if and only if their corresponding edges in G have a common endpoint. Give the line graphs of: (a) The graph on the right. (b) K_4 (c) $K_{1,3}$ (d) C_5 (e) P_5 (f) S_5.

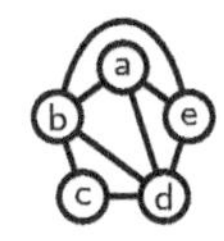

Problem 12.65. Prove the following properties about a graph G and its line graph $L(G)$.

(a) If G is connected, $L(G)$ is connected. Is the converse true?

(b) If G has an Euler cycle, $L(G)$ has a Hamiltonian cycle. Is the converse true?

(c) If G_1 and G_2 are isomorphic, $L(G_1)$ and $L(G_2)$ are isomorphic.

(d) If G has degree sequence $[\delta_1, \ldots, \delta_n]$, $L(G)$ has $\frac{1}{2}\sum_{i=1}^{n} \delta_i$ vertices and $\frac{1}{2}\sum_{i=1}^{n}(\delta_i^2 - \delta_i)$ edges.

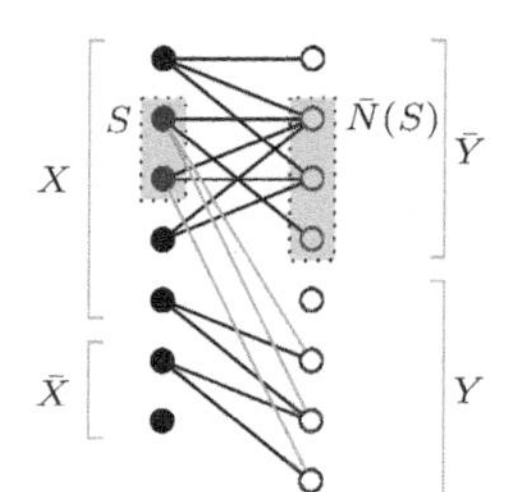

Problem 12.66 (König-Egerváry Theorem). Use Hall's Theorem to prove that the sizes of a maximum matching and minimum vertex cover are equal in bipartite graphs. Consider a bipartite graph as shown. Let Q be a minimum vertex cover with left-vertices X and right-vertices Y, so $Q = X \cup Y$. The left-vertices not in X are $\bar{X}$ and the right-vertices not in Y are $\bar{Y}$. Let $S \subseteq X$ be a subset of left-vertices in X. The neighbors of S are some vertices in Y (gray edges) and some vertices in $\bar{Y}$. Let the neighbors in $\bar{Y}$ by $\bar{N}(S)$.

(a) Prove that Q remains a vertex cover if S is replaced with $\bar{N}(S)$.
(b) Prove that $|S| \le |\bar{N}(S)|$. *[Hint: Q is a minimum vertex cover.]*
(c) Prove there is a matching from X into $\bar{Y}$ that covers X. *[Hint: Hall's Theorem.]*
(d) Similarly, prove there is a matching from $\bar{X}$ into Y that covers Y.
(e) Prove there is a matching whose size is $|Q|$ and explain why this concludes the proof.

For a direct proof of this deep result, see "A short proof of König's Theorem" by R. Rizzi, 2000.

Problem 12.67. Prove Hall's Theorem using the König-Egerváry Theorem. *[Hint: If all left-vertices can't be matched, the left-vertices not in a minimum vertex cover violate Hall's condition.]*

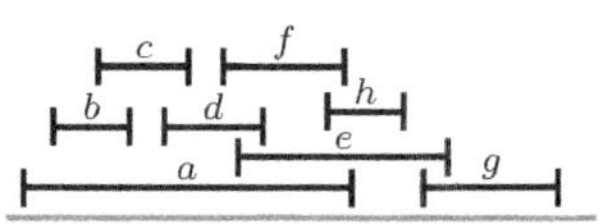

Problem 12.68 (Interval Graph). Given intervals on a line, to get the interval graph, treat intervals as vertices and add edges between intervals if they overlap. Intervals $[x_1, y_1]$ and $[x_2, y_2]$ overlap if and only if $\max(x_1, x_2) \le \min(y_1, y_2)$.

(a) Give the interval graph for the intervals $a, b, \ldots, h$ shown.
(b) The intervals are durations over which tasks $a, b, \ldots, h$ are to be performed. Only one person is available. Show that the largest number of tasks which can be performed is a largest independent set in the interval graph. What are these tasks?
(c) What is the minimum number of people needed to do all the tasks?
(d) We show the temperature range for storing a set of drugs $D_1, \ldots, D_7$ on the right.
  (i) At what temperature do you set a fridge to store the largest number of drugs? *[Hint: Formulate a graph and identify a largest clique.]*
  (ii) To store all drugs, how many fridges do you need, and at what temperatures?
(e) Which of these graphs can be an interval graph: (i) K_n (ii) C_n (iii) $K_{n,m}$ (iv) S_{n+1}.

Drug	Temp
D_1	[25,37]
D_2	[29,43]
D_3	[36,50]
D_4	[49,52]
D_5	[51,55]
D_6	[36,51]
D_7	[50,54]

Problem 12.69. From intervals $[a_i, b_i]$, $i = 1, \ldots, n$, you repeatedly choose the interval with leftmost b and throw away all intervals which overlap it. Prove that the intervals chosen are a maximum independent set in the interval graph.

Problem 12.70. In Problem 12.64, we defined the line graph. Prove that the edges in a matching of G are an independent set in the line graph $L(G)$. So, a maximum matching in G gives a maximum independent set in $L(G)$.

Problem 12.71 (Prim's Greedy Algorithm for Minimum Spanning Tree, MST). For a weighted connected graph G with n nodes, Prim's algorithm uses a greedy approach to construct a tree as follows.

1: Initialize sets S and T to empty sets. Add any vertex v_1 into S.
2: **while** $S \ne V$ **do**
3: Find a lowest weight edge $e = (u, v)$ connecting a vertex $u \in S$ to a vertex v in $\overline{S}$. Add e into T and v into S.

The tree constructed by Prim's algorithm consists of the edges in T. Let T_* be the edges of any MST.

(a) Use Prim's greedy algorithm to construct a spanning tree for the graph in Problem 12.61.
(b) Prove that the edges in T constructed by Prim's algorithm are a spanning tree for any connected graph G.
(c) Label the vertices as they are added into S as $v_1, \ldots, v_n$. The edges in T are (v_i, v_{i+1}) for $i < n$. Let (v_k, v_{k+1}) be the first edge in T that is not in T_*. Prove there is some edge $w = (v_i, v_j) \in T_*$ where $i \le k$ and $j > k$.
(d) Prove that replacing w in T_* with (v_k, v_{k+1}) gives a spanning tree with total weight no larger than weight(T_*)
(e) Prove that the spanning tree T produced by Prim's algorithm is an MST.

Problem 12.72 (Traveling Salesman and MST). A traveling salesman (red) visits 8 clients (black) and returns home (red). The salesman drives along the road network which is a grid.

(a) What order for visiting clients minimizes the distance driven? How far must the salesman drive?
(b) Prove that the distance driven is further than the weight of any minimum spanning tree of an appropriately defined graph. You must define the graph.
(c) Use a minimum spanning tree rooted at the home vertex (red) to construct a path that visits each client and uses each edge of the tree at most twice. *[Hint: Pre-order traversal.]*
(d) Prove that the tree constructed in (c) is a 2-approximation to optimal.

Problem 12.73 (Metric K-Center and Greedy). To service 10 points on the plane, are 3 warehouses, each warehouse is at a point. The roads form a grid. A point p's service distance δ_p is the distance along roads to its nearest warehouse. The maximum service distance Δ is the furthest a point is from its warehouse, $\Delta = \max_p \delta_p$. We must place the warehouses to minimize Δ.

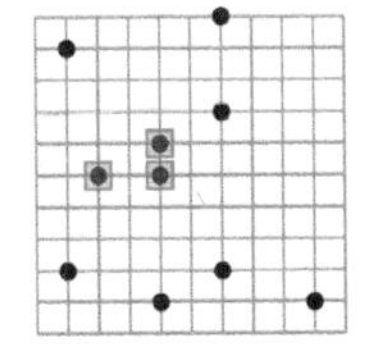

(a) Compute Δ for the 3 warehouses boxed in red.

(b) Find Δ^*, the optimal Δ by writing a program to try all choices for 3 warehouses.

(c) Here is a greedy algorithm to find k warehouses. Pick the first warehouse arbitrarily.

1: **while** number of warehouses $< k$ **do**

2: Pick the point with largest service distance to the current warehouses as the next warehouse.

Let Δ be the maximum service distance for the three warehouses returned by the greedy algorithm.

(i) Use the algorithm starting from each point. Report Δ_{best} and Δ_{worst} for the best and worst 3 warehouses found.

(ii) Show that any two warehouses is at least Δ apart and some point is at least Δ away from every warehouse.

(iii) Consider the 3 warehouses and the point which is at least Δ away from all warehouses in the optimal solution (4 points). Show that at least two of these points are serviced by the same warehouse in the optimal solution.

(iv) Show that the two points serviced by the same warehouse in the optimal solution are at most $2\Delta^*$ apart.

(v) Prove that $\Delta \leq 2\Delta^*$. That is, the greedy algorithm is a 2-approximation to optimal.

Problem 12.74. Solve each problem by first formulating it using graphs.

(a) Four knights are on a 3×3 chessboard. Using standard chess-knight moves, can one move the knights from the configuration on the left to the one on the right. If yes, show how. If no, why not?

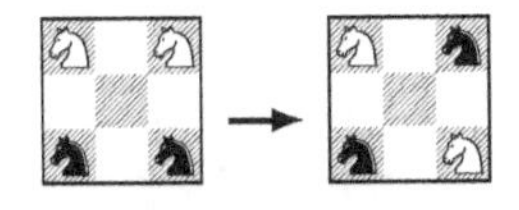

(b) In the neighborhood on the right, black regions are streets and gray regions contain houses on both sides of the streets. A mailman delivers mail to all the houses. To avoid crossing the street back and forth, he walks at least twice along every street, once on each side.

(i) Construct a path for the mailman so that each side of the street is traversed once.

(ii) Does your answer to (a) depend on the neighborhood? Explain.

(c) Six friends play each other in chess. Each game is 1 hour. At least how long will the round robin take?

(d) Radio frequencies $1, 2, \ldots$ are assigned to stations A through F. Two stations cannot be assigned the same frequency unless they are at least 100 miles apart. Pairs of stations which are within 100 miles of each other are highlighted with a red dot in the table. Assign frequencies to the stations using the minimum number of frequencies. Prove that you used the minimum number of frequencies.

	A	B	C	D	E	F
A		•			•	•
B	•		•		•	
C		•		•		
D			•			
E	•	•				•
F	•				•	

(e) Wrapping from back to front, the 3-bit substrings of 00011101 are $000, 001, 011, 111, 110, 101, 010, 100$. Find a 16 bit sequence whose 4-bit substrings are all 4-bit sequences. Is there a 2^d sequence that produces all d-bit sequences as substrings. (Efficient storage of all 2^d d-bit sequences.)

(f) Students A through F are each taking three courses indicated by blue dots in the table. The available courses are C_1 through C_8. Assign the minimum number of exam slots to the courses so that every student can take their exams. Two courses cannot have the same exam slot if a student is in both courses. Prove that you used the minimum number of exam slots.

	C_1	C_2	C_3	C_4	C_5	C_6	C_7	C_8
A	•	•	•					
B	•	•		•				
B		•	•		•			
D		•		•		•		
E			•		•		•	
F				•		•		•

(g) Four east-coast teams a, b, c, d play four west-coast teams at cities w, x, y, z over four consecutive weeks. On each week each east-coast team plays one west-coast team. An east-coast team flies round-trip into a west-coast city. While on the west-coast, the team drives around playing its matches and then drives back to its first city to take the return flight home. Teams want to minimize their driving. We show the driving distances between the west-coast cities. What cities should each team fly into and what are each teams schedules (who plays whom on each week)? *[Hint: Latin square; TSP.]*

	w	x	y	z
w	0	180	140	100
x	180	0	45	90
y	140	45	0	60
z	100	90	60	0

(h) A zoo needs habitats to house **A**ntelope, **B**aboon, **C**obra, **D**onkey, **E**lephant, **F**lamingo, **G**iraffe, **H**yena, **I**guana, **J**aguar, **K**angaroo, **L**ion and **M**onkey. But, some animals don't get along with others (shown on the right). What is the maximum number of animals that can go into one habitat? What is the minimum number of habitats you need?

1. **C** scares all but **B,E,I,M**.
2. **L,H,J** eat **A,D,K**.
3. **A,E,G** will fight for food.
4. **E,G** will trample **C,I**.
5. **F** is afraid of **E,G,H,J,L**.
6. **B,M** annoys **J,L**.

(i) Color a polyhedron's faces so that faces sharing an edge have different colors. How many colors are needed for the: (i) cube (ii) tetrahedron (iii) octahedron?

(j) A house for sale has the floorplan shown. Can a realtor who shows the house:
   (i) Start in a room and return to the room after passing through every door once?
   (ii) Start in a room and return to the room after passing through every room once?
   (iii) Remodel the house so every room has an odd number of internal doors?

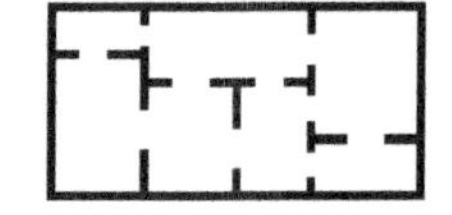

(k) Deal 52 cards of a standard deck into 13 piles of 4. Can you pick a card from each pile and get all values A,K $\cdots$ 2?

(l) We show a friendship network. The vertices are people and the edges are the friendship links. If possible, find a way for the people to be seated at a round table:
   (i) Harmoniously, so that every person has a friend to their left and their right?
   (ii) Sadistically, so that every person has an enemy to their left and their right?

(m) Color the squares on a 4×4 chess board so that a standard chess knight on any square cannot attack a square of the same color. Can you generalize to an $n \times n$ board.

Problem 12.75. Community integration is a social issue. We show a grid-community with offices (brown), parks (green) and houses (white). A house can neighbor up to 8 other houses (vertical, horizontal and diagonal). Black links show the neighbors of each house. An occupant of a house is red or blue. A house is integrated if at least half its neighbor-houses are the opposite color. The community is integrated if every house is integrated.

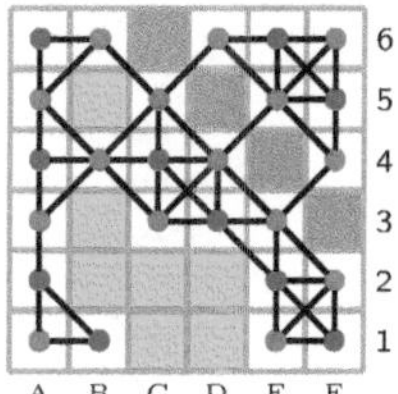

(a) We assigned colors to occupants. Identify all houses which are not integrated.
(b) **Proposition DMC23:** The community must be integrated.
   Reassign colors to houses (you may change the number of red houses) so that the community is integrated.
(c) **Opposition DMC24:** Some communities can't be integrated, depending on how parks and offices are situated. Strike down Opposition DMC24 by proving that one can always integrate a community. Prove, for any graph:

   Theorem. For any graph, one can assign red or blue to each vertex so that every vertex is integrated.

   [Hint: maximize $\sum_v$ #(opposite color neighbors of v) − #(same color neighbors of v).]
(d) Total integration requires all neighbors of every node to be the opposite color to the node. Characterize the communities that can be totally integrated.
(e) The viscinity of a vertex is its neighbors and neighbors of neighbors. Can one always ensure a node's viscinity has at least half the vertices of opposite color. *[Hint: Define a "2-hop" neighborhood graph.]*

Problem 12.76. MM is a bipartite graph. NF is a directed graph obtained by adding a source s linked it to all left-vertices, and by linking all right-vertices to a sink t. The weight (capacity) of each link is 1 (in black).

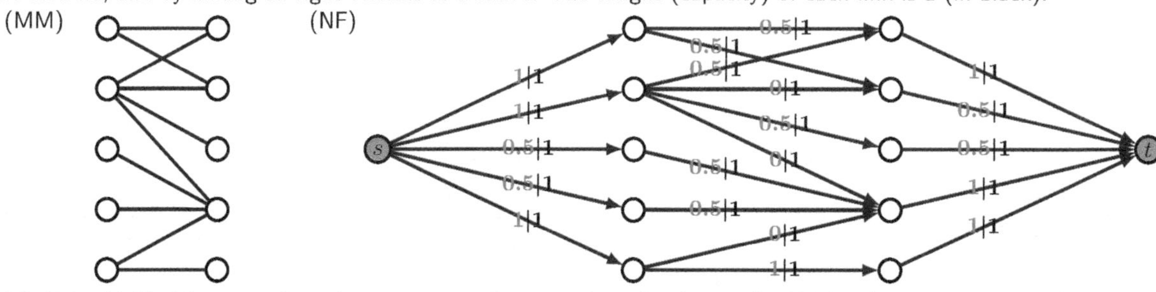

(a) Using Hall's Theorem, show there is no complete matching for the graph MM. Find a maximum matching.
(b) A flow from s to t in NF sends "stuff" from s to t along each edge. We show a flow along each edge in red, and edge capacities in black. 4 units leave s (the size of the flow). Two constraints must be satisfied:
   - [Capacity constraint] The flow on any edge cannot exceed the edge's capacity.
   - [Flow conservation] Except for s, t, everything going into a vertex must leave the vertex.

   (i) For the flow shown in red, verify that all the constraints are satisfied.
   (ii) Show that the maximum matching from (a) also corresponds to a flow.
   (iii) Show that the flow in NF is the maximum possible flow from s to t.
   (iv) Convert the flow in NF to an integral flow, with integral amounts flowing on each edge.
   (v) Show that a maximum integral flow corresponds to a maximum matching.

There is always an integral maximum flow if link capacities are integers (the Ford-Fulkerson algorithm finds one) and our example suggests that network flow can be used to find maximum matchings. This is a theme in computer science: to solve problem A, transform it into problem B and use an algorithm for problem B. Network flow has a host of such applications, from finding disjoint paths to designing surveys to airline scheduling to image segmentation.

We learned to be happy. We danced 'round the hall.
And learning to count was the key to it all. – **Sesame Street**

I have not failed. I've just found 10,000 ways that won't work.
– **Thomas Alva Edison**

Chapter 13

Counting

1: Sum rule (disjoint unions) and Product rule (counting sequences).
2: Counting one set by counting another (bijection).
3: Permutations and Combinations.

We started the book saying "Discrete mathematics deals with objects that we count." Let's count. There are three colors of candy: ◍, ●, ○. A goody-bag has 3 candies. How many different goody-bags can you make up? That's easy. Let's just manually list all the possible goody-bags. There are 10 different goody-bags:

{◍◍◍} {◍◍●} {◍◍○} {◍●●} {◍●○} {◍○○} {●●●} {●●○} {●○○} {○○○}

Only the number of candies of each color matters: {◍●○} and {◍○●} are the "same" goody-bag. You can buy bulk packs of goody-bags (so you don't need to be manually stuffing goody-bags with candy). Each bulk pack has 5 goody-bags selected from the 10 possible goody-bags. How many different bulk packs can be made? Try to solve that, it's not so easy. We will get to the answer shortly, but first we need some tools.

13.1 Counting Sequences

How many binary sequences of length n are there? A binary sequence is $b_1b_2\cdots b_{n-1}b_n$, where b_i is either 0 or 1. Every computer scientist knows that there are 2^n such sequences. Let's work it out slowly. The last bit is either 0 or 1, so there are two types of sequences, those ending in 0 and those ending in 1:

$$b_1b_2\cdots b_{n-1}\bullet 0 \quad \text{(ending in 0)} \qquad \text{and} \qquad b_1b_2\cdots b_{n-1}\bullet 1 \quad \text{(ending in 1)}.$$

Since every binary sequence falls into exactly one of these categories (ending in 0 or 1),

$$|\{b_1b_2\cdots b_n\}| = |\{b_1b_2\cdots b_{n-1}\bullet 0\}| + |\{b_1b_2\cdots b_{n-1}\bullet 1\}|,$$

We have applied the most fundamental of counting tools, the sum rule.

Sum Rule. Let N be the number of objects you are counting, and each object is one of two types: type-1 with N_1 objects and type-2 with N_2 objects. Then,

$$N = N_1 + N_2.$$

In set notation, if a set A is the union of two disjoint sets $A_1 \cup A_2$, then

$$|A| = |A_1 \cup A_2| = |A_1| + |A_2|.$$

The sum rule generalizes to more than two types of objects, by induction.

In our example, $N = |\{b_1b_2\cdots b_n\}|$, $N_1 = |\{b_1b_2\cdots b_{n-1}\bullet 0\}|$ and $N_2 = |\{b_1b_2\cdots b_{n-1}\bullet 1\}|$. The number of sequences ending in 0 equals the number of sequences $b_1b_2\cdots b_{n-1}$ of length $n-1$, since every such sequence gives a different sequence ending in 0. Also, there is no other way to get a sequence ending in 0. Similarly, the number of sequences ending in 1 is the number of sequences of length $n-1$. Therefore,

$$|\{b_1b_2\cdots b_{n-1}\bullet 0\}| = |\{b_1b_2\cdots b_{n-1}\}| \quad \text{and} \quad |\{b_1b_2\cdots b_{n-1}\bullet 1\}| = |\{b_1b_2\cdots b_{n-1}\}|.$$

We conclude that

$$|\{b_1b_2\cdots b_n\}| \;=\; |\{b_1b_2\cdots b_{n-1}\}| + |\{b_1b_2\cdots b_{n-1}\}| \;=\; 2\times|\{b_1b_2\cdots b_{n-1}\}|.$$

Repeating the argument with $|\{b_1b_2\cdots b_{n-1}\}|$, we obtain a product,

$$\begin{aligned}
|\{b_1b_2\cdots b_{n-3}b_{n-2}b_{n-1}b_n\}| &= 2\times|\{b_1b_2\cdots b_{n-3}b_{n-2}b_{n-1}\}| \\
&= 2\times 2\times|\{b_1b_2\cdots b_{n-3}b_{n-2}\}| \\
&= 2\times 2\times 2\times|\{b_1b_2\cdots b_{n-3}\}| \\
&\;\;\vdots \\
&= \underbrace{2\times\cdots\times 2\times 2}_{n \text{ of them}} \\
&= 2^n.
\end{aligned}$$

Product Rule. Let N be the number of choices for a sequence $x_1x_2\cdots x_r$.

Let N_1 be the number of choices for x_1;
Let N_2 be the number of choices for x_2 after you choose x_1;
Let N_3 be the number of choices for x_3 after you choose x_1x_2;
Let N_4 be the number of choices for x_4 after you choose $x_1x_2x_3$;
$\vdots$
Let N_r be the number of choices for x_r after you choose $x_1x_2x_3\cdots x_{r-1}$.

$$N = N_1\times N_2\times N_3\times N_4\times\cdots\times N_r.$$

For the binary sequence $b_1\cdots b_n$, set $N_1 = N_2 = \cdots = N_n = 2$ to get 2^n possible sequences.

Exercise 13.1
Use the sum rule plus induction to prove the product rule.

By carefully applying the sum and product rules, you can count most sets. Some situations recur and it is useful to know standard formulas. But, when you are feeling lost, fall back on **tinkering** and the basics. In general, the sum rule is used for case-by-case analysis, where you consider the separate cases (types) of a complex object. The product rule is used to count within one of the cases. Now for some examples.
Example (Menus): A menu has breakfast, lunch and dinner. Breakfast choices are {pancake, waffle, Doritos}, lunch choices are {burger, Doritos} and dinner choices are {salad, steak, Doritos}. I like Doritos.

How many menus are there? A menu is a "complex" object. To specify a menu, it suffices to specify the sequence BLD (breakfast, lunch, dinner). Using the product rule,

$$|\{BLD\}| = |\{B\}|\times|\{L\}|\times|\{D\}| = 3\times 2\times 3 = 18 \text{ possible menus.}$$

To count complex objects, you imagine constructing the complex object in a sequence of steps, and count the number of possible sequences. It is important that:

(i) You can construct every complex object using a sequence of steps; and,
(ii) Every sequence of steps corresponds to exactly one complex object.

Example (NY-state license plates): The NY-state license plate format is ABC-1234. How many plates are there? From the format of the license plate sequence, we infer that the first three are upper case letters of which there are 26 and the last four are digits of which there are 10. Using the product rule,

$$|\{\text{ABC-1234}\}| = 26\times 26\times 26\times 10\times 10\times 10\times 10 = 26^3\times 10^4 \approx 176 \text{ million.}$$

Example (Outcomes of a race): Ten students are running a race. The top 3 finishers will get gold, silver and bronze medals. How many outcomes are there (assignment of medals to students)? An outcome is given by FST (first, second, third). Unlike in the previous two examples, now the possible choices for S depends on who came in first, for that same person cannot also come second. However, the number of choices for S does not depend on who came in first, which is what we need to apply the product rule. After picking F, there are 9 choices for S. After picking FS, there are 8 choices for T. Therefore,

$$|\{FST\}| = 10 \times 9 \times 8 = 720.$$

Pop Quiz 13.2
If you record the finishing position of each runner, how many race outcomes are there?

Example (Counting passwords): The Unix/Linux systems administrator, the good-guy, has established some password rules. The first character must be a lower or upper-case letter. The remaining characters can be lower or upper-case letters or the digits 0,. . . ,9. Passwords must have length 6,7 or 8. Passwords are stored encrypted using a cryptographic protocol AES. A user logs in with their password. The system uses AES on the password and if the result matches what is stored in the password file, the user gains access.

You, the bad-guy, have the encrypted password file and the AES function, which the system does not secure. AES computes the encrypted password from a text password in 1 millisecond. How long will it take to crack all the passwords and access the system?

One strategy is simple brute-force. Run AES on every possible password and compare the result with the encrypted passwords. If there is a match, you have found a password. The time it takes you is 1 millisecond times the number of possible passwords. We need to count the number of passwords. A password is one of 3 types: $FS_1S_2S_3S_4S_5$ (or FS^5 for short); FS^6; and, FS^7. Here F can be one of 52 characters, and S can be one of 62 characters. We can use the product rule to compute the number of passwords of each type, and the sum rule get the total number of passwords by adding the number for each type:

$$|\{FS^5\}| + |\{FS^6\}| + |\{FS^7\}| = 52 \times 62^5 + 52 \times 62^6 + 52 \times 62^7 \approx 2 \times 10^{14}.$$

You need 2×10^{14} milliseconds$\approx$6000 years to hack in, or about 3 months on a 32,000-core super-computer. People should consider changing passwords every 3 months.

Exercise 13.3
Toss a coin and record heads H or tails T. If H, roll 2 dice and record the sum; if T, roll 4 dice and record the sum. How many outcomes can the experiment have?

Example 13.1 (Senate committees). There are 100 senators and 16 standing committees which oversee different areas (finance, foreign relations, etc.). In how many ways can a committee be selected? To construct a committee, we determine whether each senator s_i belongs to the committee ($s_i = 1$) or not ($s_i = 0$). That is, we specify the membership sequence $s_1s_2 \cdots s_{100}$. So the number of committees equals the number of binary membership sequences, $|\{s_1s_2 \cdots s_{100}\}| = 2^{100}$. If the committee cannot be empty, then the sequence $00 \cdots 0$ is not allowed and there are $2^{100} - 1$ possible non-empty committees.

A senate committee is just a subset of the senators. There is nothing special about the set of senators. The number of subsets of a 100-element set is 2^{100}. The result generalizes.

The number of distinct subsets of an n-element set is 2^n.

The relationship between subsets and binary sequences will be very useful. Here are more illustrations,

$$\begin{array}{cccccccccccccc} \{ & x_1 & x_2 & x_3 & x_4 & x_5 & x_6 & x_7 & x_8 & x_9 & x_{10} & \} & & \\ & 1 & 1 & 0 & 1 & 0 & 0 & 0 & 0 & 1 & 0 & & \longleftrightarrow & \{x_1, x_2, x_4, x_9\} \\ & 0 & 0 & 0 & 0 & 0 & 0 & 0 & 0 & 0 & 0 & & \longleftrightarrow & \varnothing \end{array}$$

On the left are binary sequences. On the right are the subsets corresponding to the sequences. □

Exercise 13.4

Regarding our senators, in how many ways can:

(a) Each senator be assigned to exactly one of the 16 "named" committees?

(b) Each senator be assigned to no more than one of the 16 "named" committees?

(c) **[Very Hard]** To illustrate the subtleties of counting and how the difficulty of a problem can drastically change if you slightly change the requirements, ponder the answers to (a) and (b) if we added the restriction that no committee can be empty. Rather than solve the full problem, we suggest you **tinker** with a smaller number of senators (say 5) and a smaller number of committees (say 2).

13.2 Build-up Counting

The number of binary sequences $b_1 \cdots b_{10}$ is 2^{10}. We add a twist. The sequence must have exactly three 1's. Now how many are there? The first thing to do is link sequences with three 1's to the sum and product rule ...**NO!** When counting, the first thing you do is **TINKER**. In this example, n is "large", $n = 10$. Its easier to tinker with smaller n, so let's start with $n = 1$. The sequence is b_1. How many such sequences have exactly three 1's. Zero. The question does not make much sense unless the number of 1's is at most n.

To help with tinkering, let's invent a notation. Let k be the number of 1's and define

$$\binom{n}{k} = \text{number binary sequences of length } n \text{ with exactly } k \text{ 1's.}$$

We need good notation because we'll use it over and over.[1] We already discovered that $\binom{n}{k}$ only makes sense when $0 \le k \le n$. When $n = 1$, the possibilities are $\binom{1}{0}$ and $\binom{1}{1}$.

$$\binom{1}{0} = \text{number binary sequences of length 1 with exactly 0 ones} = 1;$$

$$\binom{1}{1} = \text{number binary sequences of length 1 with exactly 1 one} = 1.$$

We can also compute $\binom{2}{0} = 1$, $\binom{2}{1} = 2$ and $\binom{2}{2} = 1$. Here are the binary sequences of length 3,

$$000, 001, 010, 011, 100, 101, 110, 111.$$

from which $\binom{3}{0} = 1$, $\binom{3}{1} = 3$, $\binom{3}{2} = 3$ and $\binom{3}{3} = 1$. We also list the sequences for $n = 4, 5$, and use these to build a table, called Pascal's Triangle, for different values of n and k,

Length-4 sequences:

0000 0001 0010 0011 0100 0101 0110 0111
1000 1001 1010 1011 1100 1101 1110 1111

Length-5 sequences:

00000 00001 00010 00011 00100 00101 00110 00111
01000 01001 01010 01011 01100 01101 01110 01111
10000 10001 10010 10011 10100 10101 10110 10111
11000 11001 11010 11011 11100 11101 11110 11111

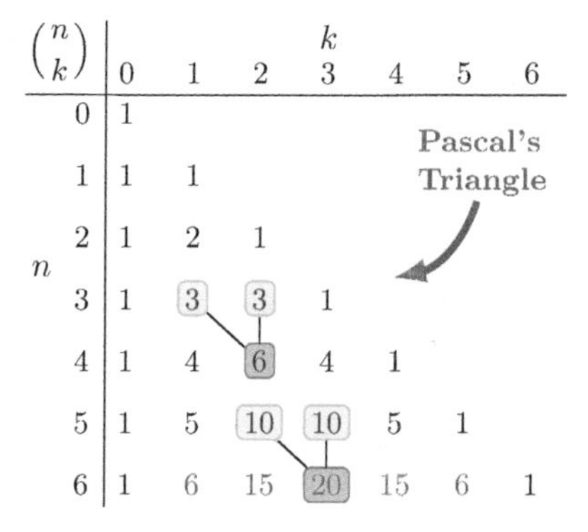

$\binom{n}{k}$	0	1	2	3	4	5	6
0	1						
1	1	1					
2	1	2	1				
3	1	3	3	1			
4	1	4	6	4	1		
5	1	5	10	10	5	1	
6	1	6	15	20	15	6	1

You should see some patterns. $\binom{n}{0} = \binom{n}{n} = 1$. To get $\binom{n}{k}$, add the above and above left entries. We filled in the entries for $n = 6$ using this pattern, without listing all the sequences.

Pop Quiz 13.5

(a) List out all the 64 length-6 sequences to verify the row for $n = 6$ above.

(b) Use the pattern to compute the number of length-10 sequences with three 1's.

The method we are developing is "build-up" counting. You build up to the complex problem from smaller problems. The pattern we observed in the table is called Pascal's Identity,

$$\binom{n}{k} = \binom{n-1}{k} + \binom{n-1}{k-1}. \tag{13.1}$$

[1] Some authors use $C(n, k)$. Other variations are ${}_nC_k$, ${}^nC_k$, C^n_k, ...

Pascal's identity is a recursion that lets you go from $n-1$ to n. Let's prove the recursion. There are two types of sequences with exactly k ones, those ending in 0 and those ending in 1. If the sequence ends in 0, the prefix is any sequence of length $n-1$ with k ones, and there are $\binom{n-1}{k}$ of these. If the sequence ends in 1, the prefix is any sequence of length $n-1$ with $k-1$ ones, and there are $\binom{n-1}{k-1}$ of these. By the sum rule, $\binom{n}{k} = \binom{n-1}{k} + \binom{n-1}{k-1}$, which is Pascal's identity. The interesting thing is that we derived Pascal's identity without using any algebraic formula for $\binom{n}{k}$. Such a derivation is a counting or combinatorial approach.

Build-up counting is a reliable workmanlike method. Start with small examples and build up to larger cases from there. Let's use build-up counting to figure out the number of ways to put the candy into goody-bags. There are three colors of candy and 3 pieces in a goody-bag. It is already too complicated, so let's tinker with a simpler problem. Suppose there is only one color ●. Well then, there is only one way to fill the goody bag, using all pieces of the color ●. Consider the other extreme, zero pieces of candy in the goody bag. There is only one goody-bag with zero pieces. Try another simple case by yourself, one piece and k colors.

Introduce a notation $Q(n,k)$ for the number goody-bags with n pieces of candy if you had k candy-colors. We know $Q(n,1) = 1$ and $Q(0,k) = 1$ (base cases). Next, reduce $Q(n,k)$ by breaking it into simpler cases, just like in recursion, and use the sum or product rule. You often need creativity here. Suppose there are i red candies ●. Since the remaining $n-i$ candies are made up of $k-1$ colors, there must be $Q(n-i,k-1)$ bags with i red candies ●. Since $i \in \{0,1,\ldots,n\}$, by the sum rule,

$$Q(n,k) = \sum_{i=0}^{n} Q(n-i,k-1) = \sum_{j=0}^{n} Q(j,k-1). \tag{13.2}$$

(Why are the two sums equal? Work it out.) This is the formula we need. Using $Q(n,k)$ for small k, we can build up to large k. Let's fill in a table, starting with the base cases $Q(n,1) = 1$ and $Q(0,k) = 1$.

$Q(n,k)$	k = 1	2	3	4	5	6	7	8	9	10	11
n = 0	1	1	1	1	1	1	1	1	1	1	1
1	1	2	3	4	5	6	7	8	9	10	11
2	1	3	6	10	15	21	28	36	45	55	66
3	1	4	10	20	35	56	84	120	165	220	286
4	1	5	15	35	70	126	210	330	495	715	1001
5	1	6	21	56	126	252	462	792	1287	2002	3003

We can now read off $Q(3,3)$, the number of goody-bags of 3 candies with 3 candy-colors, $Q(3,3) = Q(0,2) + Q(1,2) + Q(2,2) + Q(3,2) = 10$. What about bulk packets containing 5 goody-bags? A bulk packet is just like a "goody-bag" except the goodies in the bulk packet are not candies but candy 3-packs. There are 10 "colors" of 3-packs, one corresponding to each of the 10 possible 3-packs. Luckily, we extended our table for Q out to $k = 10$, and we can read off that the number of possible bulk packets is $Q(5,10) = 2002$.

The creative step in build-up counting is to link the smaller and larger problems. The rest is just application of our basic sum and product rules. Become an expert at build-up counting. There is no better way than practice and tinkering. Build-up counting is great because once you have the link from smaller problems to larger problems, you can always implement your recursion in a program. When you need a formula, good guesswork, experience and induction come in handy.

Exercise 13.6

There are many patterns in the tables for $Q(n,k)$ and $\binom{n}{k}$

(a) The green bubbles in the table suggest that $Q(n,k) = Q(n,k-1) + Q(n-1,k)$.

  (i) Prove it algebraically using the recursion for $Q(n,k)$.

  (ii) Give a counting argument, building up from two cases: (i) no ● balls; (ii) 1 or more ● balls.

(b) The dashed line in the table above illustrates a relationship between $Q(n,k)$ and $\binom{n}{k}$. Guess a formula for $Q(n,k)$ in terms of $\binom{m}{\ell}$ (i.e. what are m and ℓ).

Exercise 13.7

In each case, use the build-up method to count:

(a) The subsets of $\{1, \ldots, 20\}$ that do not contain consecutive numbers?

(b) The subsets of $\{1, \ldots, 20\}$ that contain at most one of any 3 consecutive numbers?

(c) The binary sequences of length 20 that do not contain 001?

(d) The ways to configure the first round matches of a 16-player single elimination tennis tournament?

Exercise 13.8

(a) In Exercise 13.6(b), you guessed at a relationship between $Q(n,k)$ and $\binom{m}{\ell}$. Prove it by induction using the recursions for $Q(n,k)$ and $\binom{m}{\ell}$.

(b) Prove by induction (i) $\binom{n}{k} = \frac{n!}{k!(n-k)!}$ (ii) $Q(n,k) = \frac{(n+k-1)!}{n!(k-1)!} = \binom{n+k-1}{k-1}$.

(c) Prove that the number of subsets of $\{1, \ldots, n\}$ not containing consecutive numbers is F_{n+2}. (F_k is the kth Fibonacci number. The Fibonacci numbers are $1, 1, 2, 3, 5, 8, 13, 21, \ldots$.)

(d) Prove that the number of length-n sequences not containing 001 is $F_{n+3} - 1$.

13.3 Counting One Set By Counting Another: Bijection

If every student has a seat, and every seat is occupied, the number of students and seats are equal. If there are 300 seats, there must be 300 students in lecture. We counted students by counting seats.

13.3.1 Bijection

There are 10 goody-bags with 3 candies of 3 colors. This means we can label the goody bags using $\{1, 2, \ldots, 10\}$.

{●●●}	{●●●}	{●●○}	{●●●}	{●●○}	{●○○}	{●●●}	{●●○}	{●○○}	{○○○}
$\updownarrow$	$\updownarrow$	$\updownarrow$	$\updownarrow$	$\updownarrow$	$\updownarrow$	$\updownarrow$	$\updownarrow$	$\updownarrow$	$\updownarrow$
1	2	3	4	5	6	7	8	9	10

This is a correspondence between goody-bags and the set $\{1, 2, \ldots, 10\}$, a bijection to $\{1, 2, \ldots, 10\}$. This means your set has size 10, by definition. "Counting" means establishing a bijection with a set like $\{1, 2, 3, \ldots, n\}$. A bijection between A and some other set B not $\{1, 2, 3, \ldots\}$ won't tell you the size of A, but will tell you that $|A| = |B|$, and that's useful too. Let's mathematically define a bijection between two sets.

Definition 13.2 (Bijection). A function $f : A \mapsto B$ which is 1-to-1 and onto is a bijection.

Bijection is a correspondence between the elements of two sets. A function $f : A \mapsto B$ is 1-to-1 if distinct elements of A map to distinct elements of B. A function is onto if every element of B has a pre-image in A.

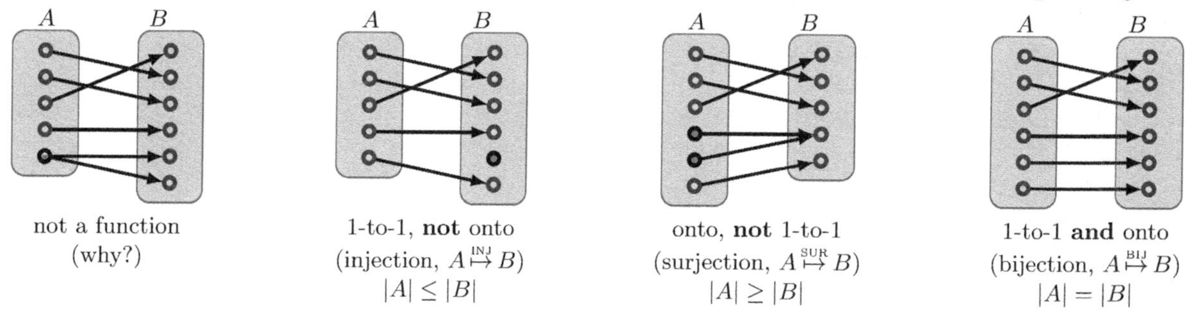

not a function (why?)

1-to-1, **not** onto (injection, $A \overset{\text{INJ}}{\mapsto} B$) $|A| \le |B|$

onto, **not** 1-to-1 (surjection, $A \overset{\text{SUR}}{\mapsto} B$) $|A| \ge |B|$

1-to-1 **and** onto (bijection, $A \overset{\text{BIJ}}{\mapsto} B$) $|A| = |B|$

We write $A \overset{\text{BIJ}}{\mapsto} B$ if there exists a bijection from A to B. A bijection can exist only if $|A| = |B|$. You can show that two sets have the same size by producing a bijection between them.

Pop Quiz 13.9

Let $A = \{1, 2, 3, 4\}$ and $B = \{2, 3, 4, 5\}$. Give functions from A to B that are:

(a) Not 1-to-1 and not onto. (b) 1-to-1 but not onto. (c) Onto but not 1-to-1. (d) 1-to-1 and onto.

13.3.2 Bijection and Counting

To count complex objects, (a) break down the complex object into cases and apply the sum rule; and, (b) within a case use a sequence of steps to create the object and apply the product rule to count sequences by multiplying the number of choices at each step. Part (b) of our strategy uses bijection between our complex objects and sequences. By counting sequences, we count the complex objects. Recall the menu-example on page 181, where we counted sequences $\{BLD\}$. For this to work,

(i) Every sequence specifies a distinct menu (1-to-1 mapping).
(ii) Every menu corresponds to a sequence (the mapping is onto).

This correspondence between sequences and menus is a bijection, therefore the number of sequences equals the number of menus. We are ready to tackle the goody-bags. Here is a way to specify the goody bag {●,●,○}. Start by listing the red candies. When you are done, place a delimiter, for example a "|" to indicate that you are done with red candies. Now list out the blue candies, placing the delimiter when you are done. Finally, list out the green candies. So, our example goody-bag would be

●●||○

There is nothing between our two delimiters because there are no blue candies. Well, once we list it this way, the color of the candy is not needed anymore. We could have listed

○○||○

We can infer the candy colors: red before the first delimiter; blue between the first and second delimiters; and, green after the second delimiter. Hmm,... Doesn't that look like the binary sequence 00110?

Pop Quiz 13.10

(a) Candies come in 3 colors: ●, ●, ○. What goody-bag corresponds to the binary sequence 00010000100?
(b) What binary sequence corresponds to the goody-bag {3●, 1●, 6○}?
(c) Show a bijection from length-$(n+2)$ binary sequences with two 1's and goody-bags with n candies.

Suppose there are 10 candies in a goody-bag and 5 colors. We use the same method to get a correspondence between binary sequences and goody-bags. We need 10 ○s for the candies and 4 delimitters to separate colors.

○○|○○○|○|○|○○○ $\leftrightarrow$ {2●, 3●, 1○, 1●, 3○}.

Every goody-bag is identified uniquely by a sequence of length 14 with four 1's. If you have k types of candies, you need $(k-1)$ delimiters, so there is a bijection between goody-bags with n candies of k colors and length $n+k-1$ sequences with $(k-1)$ ones. That is,

$$Q(n,k) = \binom{n+k-1}{k-1}.$$

We can count goody-bags if we can count sequences with a fixed number of 1's.

Exercise 13.11

(a) Candies come in 4 colors. A 10-candy goody bag is (x_1, x_2, x_3, x_4) with $x_1+\cdots+x_4 = 10$ (x_i candies of color i). Show that there are $\binom{13}{3}$ non-negative integer-solutions to $x_1+\cdots+x_4 = 10$.
(b) Show that the number of positive integer-solutions to $x_1+\cdots+x_4 = 10$ is $\binom{9}{3}$.
(c) Show that the number of non-negative integer-solutions to $x_1+\cdots+x_4 \leq 10$ is $\binom{14}{4}$.
(d) Let $S = \{x_1, \ldots, x_{10}\}$. Show a bijection from "3-subsets", the subsets of size 3, to length-10 binary sequences with 3 ones. Hence, the number of "3-subsets" is $\binom{10}{3}$.
(e) Show a bijection from 3-subsets to 7-subsets of S in part (d). Hence show: $\binom{10}{3} = \binom{10}{7}$.
(f) Show that the number of k-element subsets of an n-element set is $\binom{n}{k}$.
(g) Show that $\binom{n}{k} = \binom{n}{n-k}$ and $\sum_{i=1}^{n} \binom{n}{i} = 2^n$, without appealing to any formula for $\binom{n}{k}$.

You may have noticed something strange. The combinatorial coefficient $\binom{n}{k}$ appears all over the place, for example binary sequences, goody-bags, non-negative integer solutions, k-element subsets. Yet, we haven't derived a formula for $\binom{n}{k}$. We are counting one set by counting another, though we haven't actually counted either. All we know is that the sizes of these various sets are related to $\binom{n}{k}$.

Example 13.3. To count complex objects, we map to sequences and then count sequences.

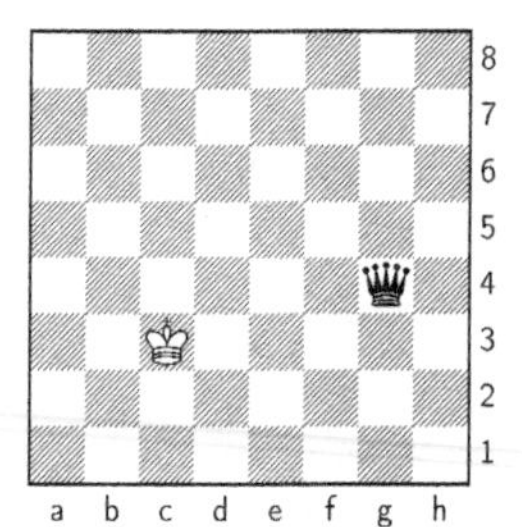

In how many ways can you place a king and queen on a chessboard so that the pieces occupy different columns and rows? A complex board position is given by the rows and columns of the king and queen, a sequence $c_K r_K c_Q r_Q$. For example, $c3g4$ is the position on the right. Every position gives a sequence with $r_k \neq r_Q$ and $c_K \neq c_Q$, and every such sequence is a unique valid position. We need to count the number of sequences with $r_k \neq r_Q$ and $c_K \neq c_Q$. There are 8 choices for c_K and 8 choices for r_K. After choosing c_K, r_K, there are only 7 choices for each of c_Q, r_Q. By the product rule, the number of sequences is $8 \times 8 \times 7 \times 7 = 3136$.

Pop Quiz 13.12
What if the pieces cannot occupy the same column, row or diagonals?

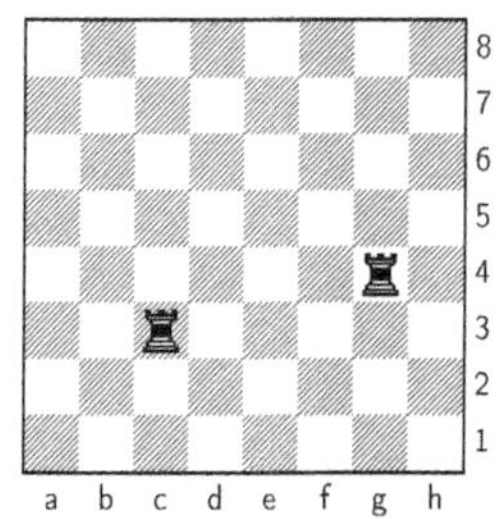

Instead of a king and queen, now place two indistinguishable castles. How many ways are there? Just as in the previous case, it looks like you need to specify the columns and rows of the two castles, $c_1r_1c_2r_2$. Consider the sequences $c3g4$ and $g4c3$. These are different sequences, but both are the same position on the right. The correspondence is not 1-to-1, so we cannot use the bijection rule. If we require the row of the first castle to be less than the row of the second one, now, the position on the right maps uniquely to $c3g4$ and we have 1-to-1 correspondence. We must count the sequences $c_1r_1c_2r_2$ with $c_1 \neq c_2$ and $r_1 < r_2$.

As before, $c_1 \neq c_2$ in 8×7 ways. Half the cases where $r_1 \neq r_2$ have $r_1 < r_2$ and the other half have $r_1 > r_2$. So, $r_1 < r_2$ in $\frac{1}{2} \times 8 \times 7$ ways. The number of valid $c_1r_1c_2r_2$ sequences is $(8 \times 7) \times (\frac{1}{2} \times 8 \times 7) = 1568$.

Another way to count positions with $r_1 < r_2$ is with cases. There are 7 cases, $r_1 = 1, \ldots, 7$ ($r_1 \neq 8$ because $r_1 < r_2$). Given r_1, r_2 can be one of the $8 - r_1$ values higher than r_1. By the sum rule,

$$\text{number of positions with } r_1 < r_2 \;=\; \sum_{r_1=1}^{7} (8 - r_1) = 7 + 6 + \cdots + 1 = \sum_{i=1}^{7} i \;=\; \tfrac{1}{2} \times 8 \times 7.$$

We avoided the case-by-case analysis because of the slick observation that the number of ways in which $r_1 < r_2$ is half the number of ways in which $r_1 \neq r_2$. Alternatively, every position for our pair of castles corresponds to two different king-queen positions, a 1-to-2 mapping. It follows that the number king-queen positions is twice the number of castle-castle positions. We summarize this general observation in the multiplicity rule.

Multiplicity Rule. If each object in A corresponds to k objects in B, then $|B| = k|A|$.

The multiplicity rule is handy because sometimes it's easier find a 1-to-k mapping instead of a 1-to-1 mapping.

Pop Quiz 13.13
In how many ways can you place 8 castles with no two on the same column or row? (Use multiplicity)

□

The trick with bijection is to map a set that is easily counted to the set you want to count and this can require creativity. Build-up counting is mundane and workmanlike, but more generally applicable.

13.4 Permutations and Combinations

One often needs k objects from a set of n. If order matters, it is a k-permutation or k-ordering. For example, the top-k finishes in a race of n students. If order does not matter, it is a k-combination or k-subset. For example, the student committees of size k from n students. For the 4-element set $S = \{1, 2, 3, 4\}$,

the twelve 2-orderings are:	the six 2-subsets are:
$\{(1,2)(1,3)(1,4)(2,1)(2,3)(2,4)(3,1)(3,2)(3,4)(4,1)(4,2)(4,3)\}$	$\{\{1,2\}\{1,3\}\{1,4\}\{2,3\}\{2,4\}\{3,4\}\}$

Now let S be an n-element set. To get a k-ordering from S, choose the first element in n ways, the second in $n-1$ ways, the third in $n-2$ ways, $\ldots$, and the k-th in $n-(k-1)$ ways. By the product rule,

$$(\text{number of } k\text{-orderings}) = n \times (n-1) \times (n-2) \times \cdots \times (n-(k-1)) = \frac{n!}{(n-k)!}.$$

The formula works for $k = n$ because $0! = 1$. Here is another way to get a k-ordering. First pick a k-subset A and then pick an order for the elements in A. By the product rule,

$$(\text{number of } k\text{-orderings}) = (\text{number of ways to pick } k\text{-subset } A) \times (\text{number of ways to order } A \text{ once picked}).$$

Exercise 13.11(f) established a bijection between k-subsets and binary sequences with k ones. The number of k-subsets of S is $\binom{n}{k}$, which is the number of ways to pick A. There are $k!$ ways to order A once picked. Therefore, (number of k-orderings) $= \binom{n}{k} \times k!$. But the number of k-orderings is $n!/(n-k)!$. Hence,

$$\frac{n!}{(n-k)!} = \binom{n}{k} \times k!$$

At last we have a formula for $\binom{n}{k}$, after rearranging. Let us highlight this very important formula in a box.

$$\boxed{(\text{number of } k\text{-subsets}) = \binom{n}{k} = \frac{n!}{k!(n-k)!}}$$

Exercise 13.14

A deck of 52 playing cards has 4 suits {♠, ♥, ♢, ♣}. Each suit has 13 values, A,K,Q,J,T,9,8,7,6,5,4,3,2. A poker hand is 5 cards (only the cards matter, not the order). Count the hands of different types:

(a) All poker hands.
(b) *4-of-a-kind*: 4 cards of one value, e.g. (♠5,♥5,♢5,♣5,♣A).
(c) *Flush*: 5 cards of the same suit, e.g. (♠A,♠T,♠8,♠5,♠2).
(d) *Full-house*: 3 cards of one value and two of another, e.g. (♠A,♢A,♣A,♠5,♥5).
(e) *3-of-a kind*: 3 cards of one value, e.g. (♠A,♢A,♠A,♥5,♢Q).
(f) *Two-pair*: 2 cards of one value and two of another, e.g. (♠A,♢A,♠5,♥5,♢Q).

Example 13.4 (Binomial Theorem). Consider the binomial $(x+y)$ cubed,

$$\begin{aligned}(x+y)^3 = (x+y)(x+y)(x+y) &= xxx + xxy + xyx + xyy + yxx + yxy + yyx + yyy \\ &= x^3 + 3x^2y + 3xy^2 + y^3.\end{aligned}$$

The expansion has all length-3 binary sequences $b_1b_2b_3$ where each $b_i \in \{x, y\}$. By the product rule, there are $2 \times 2 \times 2 = 8$ sequences. The number of these sequences which have k x's is $\binom{3}{k}$, which is the coefficient multiplying $x^k y^{3-k}$. Now consider $(x+y)^n$. There are 2^n terms, one for every length-n sequence of x's and y's. The number of sequences with k x's and $(n-k)$ y's is $\binom{n}{k}$. Each such sequence equates to $x^k y^{n-k}$. That is, $\binom{n}{k}$ is the coefficient of $x^k y^{n-k}$, which is why $\binom{n}{k}$ are called binomial coefficients. Summarizing,

$$(x+y)^n = \text{sum of all } n\text{-sequences of } x\text{'s and } y\text{'s} = \sum_{k=0}^{n} \binom{n}{k} x^k y^{n-k}.$$

□

Exercise 13.15

Use the Binomial Theorem to answer these questions.

(a) What is the constant term in the function $(2x^2 + 1/x^3)^{10}$.
(b) Which power of x has the largest coefficient in $(1+3x)^{20}$, and what is that coefficient?

13.5 Problems

It is common practice to use $[n]$ as a shorthand for the set $\{1, 2, \ldots, n\}$.

Problem 13.1. Prove: if $A_1, \ldots, A_n$ are disjoint, then $|A_1 \cup \cdots \cup A_n| = |A_1| + \cdots + |A_n|$.

Problem 13.2 (Transitivity). For finite sets A, B, C, prove that injection, surjection and bijection are transitive.

(a) Prove: IF $A \overset{\text{INJ}}{\mapsto} B$ and $B \overset{\text{INJ}}{\mapsto} C$, THEN $A \overset{\text{INJ}}{\mapsto} C$. ($\overset{\text{INJ}}{\mapsto}$ means "maps injectively to (1-to-1)")

(b) Prove: IF $A \overset{\text{SUR}}{\mapsto} B$ and $B \overset{\text{SUR}}{\mapsto} C$, THEN $A \overset{\text{SUR}}{\mapsto} C$. ($\overset{\text{SUR}}{\mapsto}$ means "maps surjectively to (onto) ")

(c) Prove: IF $A \overset{\text{BIJ}}{\mapsto} B$ and $B \overset{\text{BIJ}}{\mapsto} C$, THEN $A \overset{\text{BIJ}}{\mapsto} C$. ($\overset{\text{BIJ}}{\mapsto}$ means "maps bijectively to")

What does each transitivity statement above imply for comparing the sizes of the relevant sets.

Problem 13.3. How many 10-bit binary numbers begin with: (a) 1 (b) 1 or 01 (c) 1 or 01 or 001 (d) 000.

Problem 13.4. We show sample California (left) and West Virginia (right) license plates. Give a plausible counting-based explanation for why these states have different formats.

Problem 13.5. The choices for breakfast (B), lunch (L) and Dinner (D) are shown. You can't have two hot or cold meals in a row. How many daily menus can you create?

B $\in$ {hot sausages, hot eggs, cold cereal, cold fruit}
L $\in$ {hot pasta,hot burger, cold sandwich}
D $\in$ {hot steak,hot pizza, cold salad, cold beer}

Problem 13.6. In how many ways can 6 chess players be organized into 3 pairs for the first round of a tournament. What if the chess boards on which they play are numbered 1,2,3?

Problem 13.7. The set $A = \{1, 2, 3, 4, 5, 6\}$. How many subsets of A are there:
(a) in all (b) having $\{1, 2, 3\}$ as a subset (c) having at least 1 odd number (d) having exactly 1 even number?

Problem 13.8. A word is a 5-letter string using the characters $a, b, c, \ldots, z$. How many words
(a) in all (b) with no repeated letters (c) begin abc? (d) begin abc or end xyz (e) begin abc or end cde?

Problem 13.9. Every day, you decide whether to rest or walk a mile. After 20 days, you have walked 12 miles. In how many ways can you do this? For example, one way is to walk a mile on the first 12 days and rest on the last 8 days.

Problem 13.10. From 10 students, in how many ways can you choose a president and vice-president? What if two students are identical twins in every possible way? What if three students are identical triplets in every possible way?

Problem 13.11. Just as we counted n-bit numbers, count ternary numbers (digits are 0,1,2).
(a) (i) How many 10-trit (trinary digit) numbers are there? (ii) How many 10-trit numbers have four 1's?
(b) Explain, without explicit calculation, the equality $2^{10}\binom{10}{0} + 2^9\binom{10}{1} + 2^8\binom{10}{2} + \cdots + 2^1\binom{10}{9} + 2^0\binom{10}{10} = 3^{10}$.
(c) (i) How many 10-trit numbers have four 1's and three 2's. (ii) How many 10-trit numbers have no 2's.

Problem 13.12. We show the 28 dominos in a standard domino set. Each tile is distinct and uses two numbers from $\{0, \ldots, 6\}$. How many tiles are there if the numbers are in $\{0, \ldots, 8\}$.

Problem 13.13. An exam has 4 T/F questions; 6 four-choice questions and a long answer question whose answer is an integer between -5 and 5 inclusive. How many possible ways are there to answer the exam?

Problem 13.14. How many binary palindromes have n bits. (A palindrome is a string that equals its reversal.)

Problem 13.15. How many different functions are there which map the given domain to the given range.
(a) domain $= \{a, b, c, d\}$, range $= \{1, 2, 3, 4, 5\}$ (b) domain $= \{1, 2, 3, 4, 5\}$, range $= \{a, b, c, d\}$.

Problem 13.16. 300056400 has prime factorization $2^4 \times 3^7 \times 5^2 \times 7^3$. How many divisors does 300056400 have?

Problem 13.17. Sets A and B have sizes 3 and 8 respectively. How many functions of each type are there?
(a) 1-to-1 from A to B (b) 1-to-1 from B to A (c) Onto from A to B (d) Onto from B to A.

Problem 13.18. In each case, how many bijections are there from $\{a, b, c, d, e, f\}$ to
(a) $\{1, 2, 3, 4, 5, 6\}$ (b) $\{1, 2, 3, 4, 5, 6, 7\}$ (c) $\{1, 2, 3, 4, 5\}$?

Problem 13.19. US dollar-bills have 8 digit serial numbers, e.g. 62655681. A bill is defective if a digit repeats. What fraction of bills are defective? *[Hint: Count the non-defective bills.]*

Problem 13.20. A king is in the middle of an infinite chessboard. A move is either left, right, up, down or diagonal (8 possible moves). How many different squares can the king be on after 100 moves?

Problem 13.21. How many subsets of $X = \{x_1, \ldots, x_6\}$: (a) Contain x_1. (b) Contain x_1 and x_2 but not x_4?

Problem 13.22. Here is some information about ice-skate options.

Colors: White, Beige, Pink, Yellow, Blue. ***Sizes:*** 4,5,6,7,8. ***Extras:*** Tassels, Stripes, Bells.

How many types of skates are there if skates are sold with: (a) Exactly one extra? (b) Any number of extras?

Problem 13.23. T-shirts come in 4 colors and 5 students need to be assigned shirts.
(a) In how many ways can shirts be assigned? (Students can have the same color shirt.)
(b) What if no two students can get the same color shirt?
(c) What if the students line up, and students next to each other cannot get the same color?

Problem 13.24. 50 runners compete. How many possible outcomes are there when:
(a) We care about the order of all finishers.
(b) We are only interested in who gets gold, silver and bronze.
(c) We only care about who are in the top-10 finishers, who will qualify for the final.

Problem 13.25. Count the sleeping arrangements for 5 girls and 1 boy who stay over at a math contest in four rooms (max. two per room). Boys can't room with girls. (a) Rooms are identical? (b) Rooms are numbered $1, 2, 3, 4$?

Problem 13.26. You take two socks from a drawer with 50 different socks and put one on each foot. In how many ways can you do this? What if the drawer has 25 different *pairs* of socks?

Problem 13.27. A tennis club has 20 members who are paired up in twos for the first round of a tournament. How many ways are there of forming the first round matches?

Problem 13.28. A US Social Security number has 9 digits. The first digit may be zero.
(a) How many SS numbers are there? How many are even? How many have only even digits?
(b) How many are palindromes (e.g. 342151243)?
(c) How many have no 8? How many have at least one 8? How many have exactly one 8?

Problem 13.29. In each case, count.
(a) The stacks of 5 poker chips that can be made from 12 chips of different colors.
(b) The stacks of 5 poker chips that can be made from 3 red chips and 9 blue chips.
(c) The 7-letter words that have no two consecutive letters the same?
(d) The 2-dozen bouquets that can be formed using red, pink, peach and white roses?
(e) The subsets of $\{a, b, c, d, e, f, g\}$ that contain: (i) a and g (ii) a or g.
(f) The ways to pick 10 books to read from you collection of 100 books.
(g) The different 13-card bridge hands possible from a deck of 52 cards.
(h) The ways to choose 3 pizza toppings from 11 available toppings?
(i) The orders in which a travelling salesman can visit the 50 states?
(j) The poker hands with a card in every suit?
(k) The ways to misspell "triangle", assuming you started with "t".
(l) The cell phone numbers (ten digits not starting with 0).
(m) The graphs on the 6 vertices Ⓐ Ⓑ Ⓒ Ⓓ Ⓔ Ⓕ.
(n) The graphs on the 6 vertices Ⓐ Ⓑ Ⓒ Ⓓ Ⓔ Ⓕ which have the edges Ⓒ–Ⓓ and Ⓓ–Ⓔ.
(o) The graphs on the 6 vertices Ⓐ Ⓑ Ⓒ Ⓓ Ⓔ Ⓕ with 2 edges.
(p) The boy-girl patterns in which 2 boys and 4 girls can stand in a circle (rotations of the same pattern are identical).
(q) The ways ten distinguishible boys can join hands for a circle dance. (rotations of the same pattern are identical).
(r) The ways 6 boys and 6 girls in a dance class can be partnered into boy-girl couples.
(s) The binary 10×10 matrices in which the entries in row i sum to i.
(t) The 10×12 matrices whose entries are ± 1 and the product of the entries in every row and column is -1. What about the number of 10×11 such matrices? Tinker.

Problem 13.30. Estimate the number of possible friendship networks with 10 people. What about 100 people?

Problem 13.31. A social network has 6 people Ⓐ Ⓑ Ⓒ Ⓓ Ⓔ Ⓕ. Adding up each person's friends gives 26. How many *different* graphs could represent this social network? (Graphs differ if they don't have the same edges.)

Problem 13.32. Alice (A) and Bob (B) repeatedly play a game. A wins 4 times and B wins 3 times. In how many ways can you arrange the outcome of the games so that at some point A and B were tied?

Problem 13.33. How many quadrilaterals can be formed with vertices as the points shown? How many are: (a) squares (b) rectangles (c) parallelograms (d) trapezoids?

Problem 13.34. A school with 100 students is split into 5 teams of twenty for the intramural competitions. In how many ways can the teams be formed. *[Hint: Start by tinkering with just 5 students.]*

Problem 13.35. With 22 soccer players, in how many ways can you build two 11-person teams for a scrimmage? What if you had 32 players for an 11-on-11 scrimmage? Be careful.

Problem 13.36. Baniaz has 15 best friends from whom she must choose 6 bridesmaids one of whom will be the maid of honor. In how many ways can Baniaz do this?

Problem 13.37. A company's 5 executives and 15 employees have a golf outing.

(a) In how many ways can one choose the 1st foursome that goes out onto the golfcourse?
(b) In how many ways can one choose the 1st, 2nd, 3rd, 4th, 5th foursomes?
(c) If an executive must be in each foursome, in how many ways can one choose the 1st, 2nd, 3rd, 4th, 5th foursomes?
(d) If all that matters is who people play golf with, not when they play, in how many ways can we choose the foursomes?

Problem 13.38. An NBA team has 8 players. In how many ways can you choose 5 players to start the game?

Problem 13.39. There are 100 runners. In each case count the ways to construct the outcome.

(a) The runners run a race and we are interested in the order in which they finish.
(b) The runners run a race and we are interested in the order of the top-10 finishers.
(c) The State-team is picked as the top-10 finishers of the race.
(d) The State-team is picked as the top-10 finishers of the race with a captain and vice-captain from those top-10.
(e) 10 end-of-season awards are given to the runners (a runner may get more than one award).

Problem 13.40. How many poker hands are: (a) Straights (sequence of values, not all the same suit). (b) Straight flushes (sequence of values all the same suit).

Problem 13.41. WikiX has about 40 million articles (about 6 million in English). For a natural language processing task, you compute "edit distances" between all pairs of articles and store them in a symmetric 40million $\times$ 40million matrix of 64-bit double precision entries. About how much RAM is needed to store the distances between distinct pairs?

Problem 13.42. To determine if a graph G with 50 vertices is 3-colorable, you test all possible 3-colorings. Your computer checks a million 3-colorings per second. Estimate how long it is going to take, in the worst case.

Problem 13.43. A bank password card has 200 *different* strings of length 3 (right). Each string contains letters $A \cdots Z$ or digits $0 \cdots 9$. To login, the bank picks 4 *different* numbers (for example 1,40,22,181) and the user must input the strings corresponding to those numbers (in the example: 'AQ1' '3E9' 'D1E' 'FEX') as the password.

Password Card			
1. AQ1	**21.** 3DE	⋯	**181.** FEX
2. AAD	**22.** D1E	⋯	**182.** Q7P
⋮			
20. TR7	**40.** 3E9	⋯	**200.** 0T4

(a) Compute the number of different password *cards*.
(b) For a fixed card, how many different passwords are there:
  (i) If the strings must be input in the correct order (ii) If the strings may be input in any order?

Problem 13.44 (Counting genotypes and phenotypes). Here's a simple model for genetics. A person has two sets of 5 genes: father genes $f_1, \ldots, f_5$ and mother genes $g_1, \ldots, g_5$. A given gene-position is a trait (e.g. eye-color) and each gene can be one of four types (called alleles). For example, the eye-color gene could have alleles green, blue, brown, black. The alleles for gene 1 are $\{a_1, a_2, a_3, a_4\}$; the alleles for gene 2 are $\{b_1, b_2, b_3, b_4\}$; and so on. The entire genome is a list of 5 ordered pairs. For example, $(a_1, a_1)(b_3, b_2)(c_2, c_2)(d_2, d_3)(e_4, e_1)$ means the father-alleles are $a_1 b_3 c_2 d_2 e_4$ and the mother-alleles are $a_1 b_2 c_2 d_3 e_1$ (the father and mother genes can be the same allele). Your genes are your genotype.

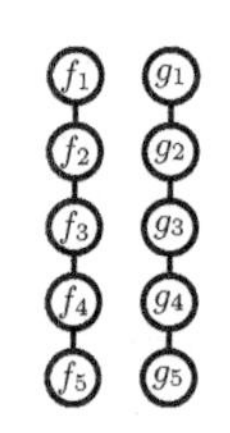

(a) How many different genotypes are there? What if a cell cannot recognize which set of genes came from the father and which set came from the mother?
(b) The phenotype are the physical traits expressed by the genotype. If a single allele of a gene is present, that allele is the trait. If two alleles are present, the trait is a combination of the two, and it *does not* depend on which allele is the father's and which is the mother's. For example: the trait for (a_1, a_1) is a_1; the trait for (a_1, a_2) and (a_2, a_1) are the same (some mix of traits a_1 and a_2, depending on the biology; it could even be just one trait if that is a "dominant" trait). How many different phenotypes are there?

Problem 13.45. There are 7 flavors of donut and you must pick a dozen. There is a bijection between packages of 12 donuts and binary sequences of length 18 with ?fill in? 1's. More generally, for k types of donuts, there is a bijection between packages of n donuts and binary sequences of length ?fill in? with ?fill in? 1's.

Problem 13.46. There are 10 sundae toppings from which you select 4. How many sundaes are possible if:
(a) You do not repeat a topping and the order in which the toppings are added does not matter to you?
(b) You do not repeat a topping and the order in which the toppings are added matters to you?
(c) You may repeat toppings and the order in which the toppings are added does not matter to you?
(d) You may repeat toppings and the order in which the toppings are added matters to you?

Problem 13.47. Count the ways to split 20 identical \$1-bills among 3 children? What if each child gets at least \$2?

Problem 13.48. In Yahtzee you roll five 6-sided dice. How many possible rolls are possible (order does not matter)?

Problem 13.49. Unlike a set, a multiset may contain the same element many times (order does not matter). Using the numbers $\{1, \ldots, 20\}$, in how many ways can you form: (a) A *set* of size 5? (b) A *multiset* of size 5?

Problem 13.50. How many 7-digit phone-numbers are non-decreasing (each digit is not less than the previous one.)

Problem 13.51. How many functions $f : \{1, \ldots, 5\} \mapsto \{1, \ldots, 10\}$ are: (a) Strictly increasing? (b) Non-decreasing?

Problem 13.52. How many integer solutions are there to $x_1 + x_2 + x_3 + x_4 = 10$ if
(a) x_i are positive? (b) x_i are non-negative? (c) $x_1 \geq -3, x_2 \geq -2, x_3 \geq 1, x_4 \geq 2$?

Problem 13.53. Solve with build-up counting. Tinker, tinker. Invent appropriate notation.
(a) How many 20-bit binary strings contain 00 as a substring. *[Hint: Count strings not containing 00.]*
(b) How many 10-digit numbers do not have 3 consecutive digits the same. *[Hint: Let $Q(n)$ count n digit numbers starting with a 0 which do not have 3 consecutive digits the same.]*
(c) A valid word has a vowel (a,e,i,o,u) and cannot have consecutive vowels. How many 10 letter words are there?
(d) How many of the 6 digit numbers 000000 through 999999 have digits which sum to 27?

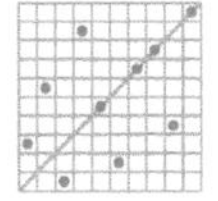

(e) In how many ways can 10 non-attacking castles be placed symmetrically about the diagonal on a 10×10 board. Castles are non-attacking if no pair is on the same row or column. In a symmetric arrangement, if there is a castle at (x, y) there must be one at (y, x).
(f) How many outcomes of the roll of 4 distinguishible dice have a sum 16?
(g) How many 10-vertex rooted binary trees (RBT) are there? (1 vertex: one; 2 vertices: two; 3 vertices: five)
(h) The streets in a neighborhood form a rectangular grid. A child starts at home and walks to school which is 10 blocks east and 10 blocks north. How many shortest paths are there?

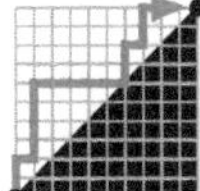

(i) On a grid, how many "diagonally dominant" up-and-right paths are there from $(0, 0)$ to $(10, 10)$. A diagonally dominant path never drops below the line $y = x$, e.g. red path. Such paths remain in the white region of the grid, never dropping into the black region.
(j) Integers z_1, z_2, z_3 satisfy $0 \leq z_1 \leq z_2 \leq z_3 \leq 10$. How many such sequences are there?
(k) How many 20-bit binary strings have six 1's and at least four consecutive 0's.
(l) A binary string is prefix-heavy if every prefix has *more* 1s than 0s. How many 20-bit strings are prefix-heavy?
(m) How many ways can 20 be represented as a sum of: (i) 5 non-negative integers. (ii) 5 positive integers.
(n) Starting at $(0, 0)$ on a grid, you keep rolling two dice. If the roll is (i, j), you move i steps right and j steps up. In how many ways can you reach the point $(10, 12)$?

Problem 13.54 (Stirling Numbers of the Second Kind). Let $A = \{a, b, c, d, e\}$.
(a) In how many ways can one partition A into (i) two sets labeled S_1, S_2 (ii) three sets labeled S_1, S_2, S_3?
(b) How many of the partitions in (a) have all sets in the partition being non-empty?
(c) The ordered Stirling number $\left[{n \atop k}\right]$ is the number of ways to partition n elements into k non-empty subsets labeled $S_1, \ldots, S_k$. What are: (i) $\left[{1 \atop k}\right]$ (ii) $\left[{n \atop 1}\right]$ (iii) $\left[{n \atop n}\right]$ (iv) $\left[{5 \atop 2}\right]$ (v) $\left[{5 \atop 3}\right]$ (vi) $\left[{n \atop 2}\right]$?
(d) Show $\left[{n \atop k}\right] = k\left(\left[{n-1 \atop k}\right] + \left[{n-1 \atop k-1}\right]\right)$. *[Hint: Consider the cases element x_1 is on its own and not on its own.]*
(e) Repeat (a) and (b) for unlabeled (identical) subsets. So, $\{a, b\}\{c, d, e\}$ and $\{c, d, e\}\{a, b\}$ are the same partition.
(f) The unordered Stirling number $\left\{{n \atop k}\right\}$ is the number of ways to partition n elements into k unlabeled (identical) sets. What are: (i) $\left\{{1 \atop k}\right\}$ (ii) $\left\{{n \atop 1}\right\}$ (iii) $\left\{{n \atop n}\right\}$ (iv) $\left\{{5 \atop 2}\right\}$ (v) $\left\{{5 \atop 3}\right\}$ (vi) $\left\{{n \atop 2}\right\}$?
(g) How is $\left\{{n \atop k}\right\}$ related to $\left[{n \atop k}\right]$. Use the relationship to show $\left\{{n \atop k}\right\} = k\left\{{n-1 \atop k}\right\} + \left\{{n-1 \atop k-1}\right\}$.
(h) Use build-up counting to compute the number of ways to partition 10 senators into 5 non-empty named committees.

Problem 13.55. In Example 13.3 on page 186, the King and Queen occupy different rows and columns. If we relax that restriction, how many positions are possible? Here are two arguments.

(i) There are 64 choices for the King and then 63 for the Queen. The product rule gives $64 \times 63 = 4032$ positions.

(ii) We count the sequences $c_K r_K c_Q r_Q$ as in Example 13.3, but now without the restriction that $c_Q \neq c_K$ and $r_Q \neq r_K$. By the product rule there are $8 \times 8 \times 8 \times 8 = 4096$ positions.

Which reasoning is correct? What is wrong in the other reasoning? How are the two answers related?

Problem 13.56. Here are some counting problems on chessboards.

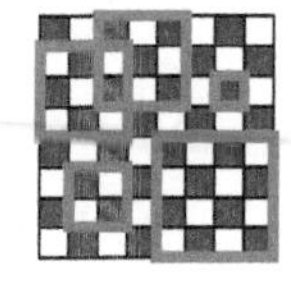

(a) We highlighted different squares (at different locations or of different sizes) on an 8×8 chess board. How many squares are there? What if it was an $n \times n$ board.

(b) In how many ways can m identical castles be placed on an $n \times n$ board so that no two are on the same row or column?

Problem 13.57. The Towers of Hanoi puzzle (Problem 7.60, page 99) has n disks on 3 bases A, B, C. Valid configurations have the disks on a base ordered from smallest on top to largest on the bottom. How many valid configurations are possible for:

(a) Distinguishable bases A, B, C. (b) Unlabeled, indistinguishible, bases.

Problem 13.58. List the 2 and 3 element subsets of $\{1, 2, 3, 4, 5\}$. Pair each 2-subset with its complement (a 3-subset) to verify that there are an equal number of 2 and 3-subsets.

Problem 13.59. Here is an application of counting to bank security. A bank has 5 VPs and no pair of VPs should be able to access the vault. However, any subset of 3 VPs should be able to access the vault. What is the minimum number of locks required on the vault and how should the keys to those locks be distributed among the VPs?

(a) How many different pairs of 2 VPs are there? Call this number m

(b) Suppose ℓ locks $L_1, \ldots, L_\ell$ suffice, with each person getting some subset of the ℓ keys. Prove that $\ell \geq m$.

 (i) Consider the VP-subsets $S_1, \ldots, S_m$. Prove that if the VPs in subset S_i combined their keys, they must be missing the key to at least one lock, call it $L(S_i)$. If they are missing the keys to multiple locks, pick one.

 (ii) Prove that the mapping $S_i \mapsto L(S_i)$ is 1-to-1. *[Hint: Contradiction: any 3 VPs can access the vault.]*

(c) Prove that m locks suffice by showing how to distribute keys of the locks to the 5 VPs.

(d) Generalize to n VPs where no subset of k has access to the vault but every subset of $k+1$ can access the vault.

Problem 13.60. Determine these Binomial expressions without the formula. Instead, reason about their meaning.
(a) $\binom{6}{0}$ (b) $\binom{6}{9}$ (c) $\binom{6}{6}$ (d) $\binom{6}{1}$ (e) $\binom{6}{5}$ (f) $\binom{6}{4} - \binom{6}{2}$ (g) $\binom{10}{2}\binom{8}{4} - \binom{10}{4}\binom{6}{2}$ (h) $\binom{10}{6}\binom{6}{2} - \binom{10}{2}\binom{8}{4}$.

Problem 13.61. Prove the Binomial Theorem by induction. (Example 13.4 used counting.)

(a) Prove $(1+x)^n = \sum_{i=0}^{n} \binom{n}{i} x^i$ by induction on n. Hence, prove $(x+y)^n = \sum_{i=0}^{n} \binom{n}{i} x^i y^{n-i}$. *[Hint: Pascal's identity.]*

(b) Expand $(1+1)^n$ and $(1-1)^n$ and show (i) $\sum_{i=1}^{n} \binom{n}{i} = 2^n$ (ii) $\sum_{i=1}^{n} (-1)^i \binom{n}{i} = 0$.

Problem 13.62. What is the coefficient of x^3 in: (a) $(1+x)^6$. (b) $(3-2x)^6$. (c) $(2x+1)^{10} - (3-2x)^5$.

Problem 13.63. What are the coefficients of x^3, x^4, x^5, x^6, x^7 in the expansion of $(\sqrt{x} + 2x)^{10}$?

Problem 13.64 (Binomial Sums). Identify the valid ranges for the variables and prove each "Binomial Identity" using the formula for the Binomial coefficient, $\binom{n}{k} = n!/k!(n-k)!$. Use induction where appropriate.

(a) Symmetry: $\binom{n}{k} = \binom{n}{n-k}$

(b) Pascal's Identity: $\binom{n}{k} = \binom{n-1}{k} + \binom{n-1}{k-1}$

(c) Absorbtion: $k\binom{n}{k} = n\binom{n-1}{k-1}$

(d) Absorbtion: $\binom{k}{i}\binom{n}{k} = \binom{n}{i}\binom{n-i}{k-i}$

(e) Sum: $\sum_{k=0}^{n} \binom{n}{k} = 2^n$

(f) Alternating sum: $\sum_{k=0}^{n} \binom{n}{k}(-1)^k = 0$

(h) First moment: $\sum_{k=0}^{n} k\binom{n}{k} = n2^{n-1}$

(i) Upper sum: $\sum_{k=m}^{n} \binom{k}{m} = \binom{n+1}{m+1}$

(j) Diagonal sum: $\sum_{k=0}^{n} \binom{m+k}{k} = \binom{m+n+1}{n}$

(k) Vandermonde Convolution: $\sum_{k=0}^{\ell} \binom{n}{k}\binom{m}{\ell-k} = \binom{m+n}{\ell}$

(l) Exponential Upper-Lower Sum: $\sum_{k=0}^{n} \binom{n+k}{k} 2^{-k} = 2^n$

Problem 13.65 (Combinatorial proofs). One can derive combinatorial relationships without using the factorial formula for $\binom{n}{k}$, but rather by counting objects in two different ways and equating the answers. Combinatorial proofs shed insight on the counting problem which are missing from from an algebraic proof using formulae. Here is a classic example of a combinatorial proof. A k-subset of n elements uniquely determines its complement subset with $n-k$ elements. This 1-to-1 correspondence between k-subsets and $(n-k)$-subsets establishes $\binom{n}{k} = \binom{n}{n-k}$ without any formula for $\binom{n}{k}$. Give combinatorial proofs for these identities which you proved algebraically in Problem 13.64.

(a) $\binom{n}{k} = \binom{n-1}{k} + \binom{n-1}{k-1}$. (To get a k-subset you either pick the first element or not.)

(b) $\sum\limits_{i=0}^{n} \binom{n}{i} = 2^n$. (To get all subsets of an n-set, count subsets of size $0, 1, \ldots, n$.)

(c) $\sum\limits_{i=k}^{n} \binom{i}{k} = \binom{n+1}{k+1}$. (To choose $k+1$ objects from $n+1$, let the last object chosen be at position $i+1$, where $i \in \{k, k+1, \ldots, n\}$.)

(d) $\sum\limits_{i=0}^{n} (-1)^i \binom{n}{i} = 0$. (For $S \subseteq X = \{x_1, \ldots, x_n\}$, let $f(S) = S \cup x_1$ if $x_1 \notin S$ and $S \setminus x_1$ otherwise. Show that f is a bijection from even to odd-sized subsets.)

(e) $k\binom{n}{k} = n\binom{n-1}{k-1}$. (To choose a k-committee with a head: (i) Choose the committee and a head from within; or, (ii) Choose the head plus $k-1$ other members.)

(f) $\binom{k}{i}\binom{n}{k} = \binom{n}{i}\binom{n-i}{k-i}$. (Generalize (e) to a k-committee with i executive members.)

(g) $\binom{n}{i}\binom{n-i}{k} = \binom{n}{k}\binom{n-k}{i}$. (From n objects choose i to color red and k to color blue.)

(h) $\sum\limits_{k=0}^{\ell} \binom{n}{k}\binom{m}{\ell-k} = \binom{m+n}{\ell}$. (Choose ℓ hats from m red and n blue hats? Consider separately 1 blue or 2 blue or, ..., or ℓ blue hats.)

Problem 13.66. Give a combinatorial proof that $k\binom{n}{k} = n\binom{n-1}{k-1}$. Hence show $\binom{n}{k} = \frac{n\times(n-1)\times(n-2)\times\cdots\times(n-k+1)}{k\times(k-1)\times(k-2)\times\cdots\times 2\times 1}$.

Problem 13.67. Consider the k-subsets of $x_1, \ldots, x_n$ where the ℓth element of the k-subset is x_i (the first $\ell-1$ elements are from $x_1, \ldots, x_{i-1}$ and the remaining $k-\ell$ elements are from $x_{i+1}, \ldots, x_n$).

(a) What are the possible cases for i? For a given i, how many such constrained k-subsets are there?

(b) Prove the combinatorial identity $\sum_{i=\ell}^{n+\ell-k} \binom{i-1}{\ell-1}\binom{n-i}{k-\ell} = \binom{n}{k}$, for $1 \le \ell \le k$.

Problem 13.68. Give a combinatorial proof for the summation in Problem 13.64(g), $\sum\limits_{k=1}^{n} k\binom{n}{k} = n2^{n-1}$.

(a) Show that the number of length-n sequences of 0s, 1s and a single x is $n2^{n-1}$.

(b) Show that $k\binom{n}{k}$ sequences from (a) have $(k-1)$ 0s. Sum over $k = 1, \ldots, n$ to prove the claim.

Problem 13.69. The ith factorial power is $k^{\underline{i}} = k(k-1)\cdots(k+1-i) = k!/(k-i)!$. Prove: $\sum_{k=i}^{n} k^{\underline{i}}\binom{n}{k} = n^{\underline{i}}2^{n-i}$. Give the explicit formulas for $i = 1, 2$. *[Hint: Problems 13.65(e),(b).]*

Problem 13.70. Use a counting argument to prove the result in Problem 13.69 as follows.

(a) How many n-trit (trinary digit) strings have k ones? How many n-trit strings have k ones and j twos?

(b) Show that $\binom{n}{k}2^{n-k} = \sum_{j=0}^{n-k} \binom{n}{j}\binom{n-j}{k}$. Show that this equivalent to the result in Problem 13.69.

Problem 13.71. Prove that $\sum_{i=0}^{m} i^{\underline{k}}\binom{n+i}{i} = k!\binom{n+k}{n}\binom{n+m+1}{m-k}$, where the factorial power $i^{\underline{k}} = i!/(i-k)!$. Give explicit formulas for $k = 0, 1, 2$. *[Hint: Show $i^{\underline{k}}\binom{n+i}{i} = k!\binom{n+k}{n}$ and use the diagonal sum in Problem 13.64(j).]*

Problem 13.72. Let $A_1, \ldots, A_n$ be subsets of $X = \{1, 2, \ldots, M\}$ with no A_i a subset of another. Let $|A_i| = \ell_i$ and let E_i be the orderings of X in which the first ℓ_i elements are in A_i.

(a) Let $M = 4$, $A_1 = \{1, 4\}$ and $A_2 = \{1, 2\}$. What are E_1 and E_2? Show that $E_i \cap E_j = \varnothing$.

(b) Show that $|E_i| = \ell_i!(M-\ell_i)!$, and hence that $\sum_{i=1}^{n} \ell_i!(M-\ell_i)! \le M!$.

(c) Prove the Lubell-Yamamoto-Meshalkin inequality: $\sum_{i=1}^{n} 1/\binom{M}{\ell_i} \le 1$, and that it's tight.

Problem 13.73. Give three proofs that the product of n consecutive natural numbers is divisible by $n!$.

(a) Induction. (b) Use the binomial coefficient $\binom{n+k}{k}$. (c) Using the number of times a prime p divides $x!$.

Problem 13.74. The generalized Binomial coefficient $\binom{r}{k}$ allows the upper index r to be any real number and the lower index k to be any non-negative integer,

$$\binom{r}{k} = \frac{r(r-1)\cdots(r-k+1)}{k(k-1)\cdots 1} = \frac{r^{\underline{k}}}{k!} \qquad \text{(for integer } k \ge 0 \text{ and 0 otherwise).}$$

(a) When r is a positive integer, show that you recover the regular Binomial coefficient $\binom{n}{k}$.

(b) When r is negative, prove the negation formula, $\binom{r}{k} = (-1)^k\binom{k-r-1}{k}$.

(c) Which identities in Problem 13.64 still hold for generalized Binomial coefficients?

Problem 13.75 (Parity of $\binom{n}{k}$). Prove that $\binom{n}{k} \equiv 0 \pmod 2$ if n is even, k is odd and $\binom{n}{k} \equiv \binom{\lfloor n/2 \rfloor}{\lfloor k/2 \rfloor} \pmod 2$ otherwise. *[Hint: Consider the 4 cases for n and k being even/odd.]*

Problem 13.76. A set of integers X sums to s. Let ℓ be the number of subsets of X with sum less than $\frac{1}{2}s$; let e be the number of subsets of X whose sum equals $\frac{1}{2}s$. Show that $\ell + \frac{1}{2}e = 2^{|X|-1}$. *[Hint: Bijection from subsets with sum $> \frac{1}{2}s$ to those with sum $< \frac{1}{2}s$.]*

Problem 13.77. How many rolls of 4 distinguishible dice sum to 6? *[Hint: Bijection to 9-bit sequences.]* What if the sum is 7? *[Hint: Sum rule.]* What if the dice are indistinguishible?

Problem 13.78. How many possible rolls are there for n distinguishible k-sided dice. What if the dice are indistinguishible? *[Hint: Bijection to binary sequences; see also Problem 5.66.]*

Problem 13.79. Show a bijection between 20-bit binary sequences with 10 ones and shortest paths on a grid from $(0,0)$ to $(10,10)$. Hence, compute the number of shortest paths from $(0,0)$ to $(10,10)$. Compare with Problem 13.53(e).

Problem 13.80. Let $P(m,n)$ be the number of shortest paths on a grid from $(0,0)$ to (m,n).

(a) Show: $P(m,n) = P(m-1,n) + P(m,n-1)$ for $m,n > 0$. What are $P(m,0)$ and $P(0,n)$?
(b) Give a bijection between the shortest paths and binary sequences of a particular type.
(c) Use your bijection to give a formula for the number of shortest paths from $(0,0)$ to (m,n).
(d) Prove, by induction, that your formula solves the recurrence derived in (a).

Problem 13.81. In the grid, ● is home, ● is work and ○ is the grocery. Two shortest paths from ● to ● are in bold, one through the grocery and one not. All shortest paths from ● to ● make 8 steps.

(a) How many different shortest paths are there from ● to ●?
(b) How many shortest paths from ● to ● use ○? How many avoid ○?
(c) Repeat (a),(b) if ● moves to m steps right and n steps north of ●

Problem 13.82. Prove that $\binom{n}{0}^2 + \binom{n}{1}^2 + \binom{n}{2}^2 + \cdots + \binom{n}{n-1}^2 + \binom{n}{n}^2 = \binom{2n}{n}$ in three different ways.

(a) Induction on n. *[Hint: Prove the stronger statement $\sum_i \binom{n}{i}\binom{n}{r-i} = \binom{2n}{r}$. Why is this stronger?]*
(b) Use $(1+x)^{2n} = (1+x)^n(1+x)^n$, and consider the coefficient of x^n on both sides.
(c) Count shortest paths on a grid from $(0,0)$ to (n,n) going through $(n,0)$ or $(n-1,1)$ ... or $(1,n-1)$ or $(0,n)$.

Problem 13.83. Tickets have 6 digit codes (000000 through 999999). How many codes have the sum of their first 3 digits equal to the sum of their last 3 digits? *[Hint: Bijection with codes that sum to 27. Problem 13.53(d).]*

Problem 13.84. A sequence is non-decreasing if $0 \le z_1 \le z_2 \le \cdots \le z_k \le n$. Count non-decreasing sequences using a bijection to non-negative solutions of $x_1 + x_2 + \cdots + x_k \le n$.

Problem 13.85. How many different rectangles are on a 5×4 grid (we shaded two).

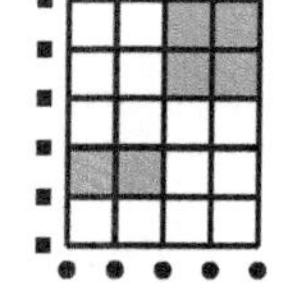

(a) Carefully count the rectangles as a summation and evaluate your sum.
(b) We show 6 squares arranged vertically along the y-axis and 5 circles arranged horizontally along the x-axis. Show a bijection between sets containing two distinct squares and two distinct circles and the rectangles on the grid. Hence compute the number of rectangles and verify with (a).
(c) Give a formula for the number of different rectangles in the $m \times n$ grid.

Problem 13.86. How many seating patterns does King Arthur have for n knights on his round table. (Rotations of the same pattern are equivalent).

Problem 13.87. In how many ways can you choose k students from n students in a line in such a way that between every pair of choosen students, there are at least 2 students left behind. *[Hint: Bijection to binary sequences. Tinker.]*

Problem 13.88. A composition of n is a *sequence* of *positive* integers adding to n, e.g., $(6,4)$, $(4,6)$ and $(2,4,2,2)$ are different compositions of 10. Count the compositions of n.

(a) Tinker. If you see a pattern, make a guess and prove it by induction.
(b) Use a bijection between compositions and binary sequences to get the answer.
  (i) Consider the 9-bit sequence 001110100. Start a number at 1 and process the sequence from left to right. When you encounter a 0, start a new number at 1; when you encounter a 1, add 1 to the current number. We get the sequence $(1,1,4,2,1,1)$. Show that this procedure gives a composition of 10 for any 9-bit sequence.
  (ii) Prove that the procedure in (i) gives a composition of n for any $(n-1)$-bit sequence. Prove that the procedure is a bijection, and determine the number of compositions of n.

Problem 13.89 (Superpermutation). The sequence $s = aba$ is a superpermutation for the two distinguishible objects $\{a, b\}$ because every permutation of $\{a, b\}$ occurs in s as a substring.

(a) Give superpermutations of shortest length for: (i) $\{a, b, c\}$ (length 9). (ii) $\{a, b, c, d\}$ (length 33).

(b) Prove that the shortest superpermutation of n objects has length between $n! + n - 1$ and $n \times n!$.

Problem 13.90. In Problem 13.53(g), you counted diagonally dominant shortest paths from $(0, 0)$ to $(10, 10)$. The number of diagonally dominant paths from $(0, 0)$ to (n, n) is the nth Catalan number C_n. Use bijection to compute C_n as follows. On the left we show a path p which is *not* diagonally dominant. Such a path must touch the $y = x - 1$ line. We highlight the first point of contact with $y = x - 1$ in the middle figure (green dot).

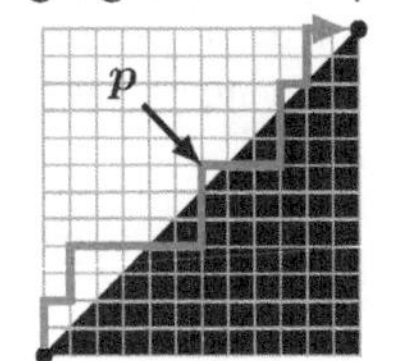

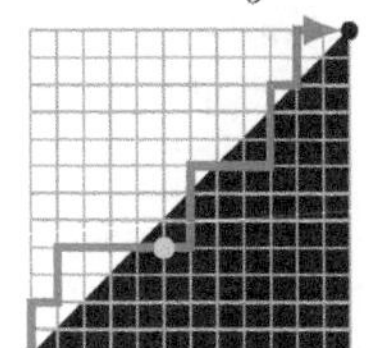
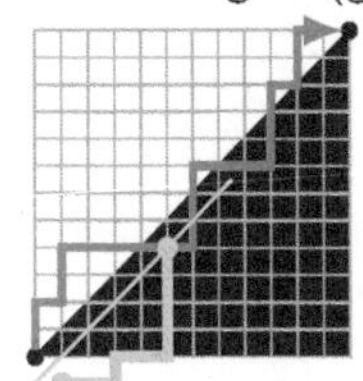
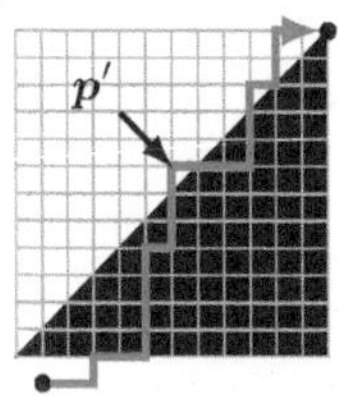

Refelect the path p *up to* the green dot using $y = x - 1$ as mirror (green) and then continue along p after the green dot, to get the path p' (rightmost figure). This path p' is a shortest path from $(1, -1)$ to (n, n).

(a) Prove that our construction that maps p to the reflected p' is a bijection between non-diagonally dominant paths from $(0, 0)$ to (n, n)) shortest paths from $(1, -1)$ to (n, n).

(b) How many shortest paths are there from: (i) $(0, 0)$ to (n, n)? (ii) $(1, -1)$ to (n, n)?

(c) Show that the number of diagonally dominant paths from $(0, 0)$ to (n, n) is $C_n = \binom{2n}{n} - \binom{2n}{n-1} = \frac{1}{n+1}\binom{2n}{n}$.

(d) Compute $C_1, C_2, \ldots, C_{10}$ and compare with Problem 13.53(g).

Problem 13.91. Let C_n be the number of ways to match n pairs of parentheses in the usual arithmetic sense (you never close an unopened parenthesis). For example "()()" and "(())" are matched but "())(" is not.

(a) Compute C_3 and C_4, listing all the corresponding sequences of matched parentheses.

(b) Prove: C_n is the nth Catalan number. *[Hint: Map to diagonally dominant paths: "(" moves up, ")" moves right.]*

Problem 13.92. Let C_n be the number of rooted binary trees on n vertices.

(a) Compute C_3 and C_4, listing all the corresponding trees.

(b) Prove: C_n is the nth Catalan number (cf. Problem 8.48). *[Hint: Use depth first search to map rooted binary trees to matched parentheses: when DFS moves down, open a parenthesis; when DFS moves up, close a parenthesis.]*

Problem 13.93 (Counting Walks). A walker at $(0, 0)$ takes n steps right. At each step he also moves either up or down. A river runs horizontally at $y = -1$ (blue forbidden region). If the walker hits the river, he drowns. (The river is an absorbing barrier). Compute $Q(n)$, the number of paths that do not get absorbed.

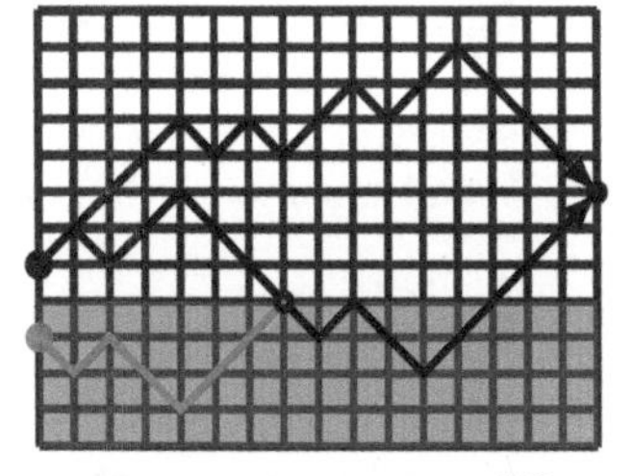

We show two paths (black) ending at $(n, 2)$. One is absorbed. The We reflected the absorbed path about the barrier $y = -1$ up to the first absorbtion point into the blue forbidden region (red). The red path together with the rest of the absorbed path gives a path from $(0, -1)$ to the same end point $(n, 2)$.

(a) What is the smallest k_* for which there is a non-absorbed path to (n, k_*). How many up moves i_* are made?

(b) How many paths are there from $(0, 0)$ to (n, k_*) in total (ignoring the absorbing river).

(c) How many paths are there from $(0, -2)$ to (n, k_*) in total (ignoring that these paths start in the river).

(d) Prove a bijection between absorbed paths from $(0, 0)$ to (n, k_*) and all paths from $(0, -2)$ to (n, k_*).

(e) Show that the number of non-absorbed paths ending at (n, k_*) is $\binom{n}{i_*} - \binom{n}{i_*+1}$.

(f) Show that the number of non-absorbed paths is $Q(n) = \binom{n}{\lceil n/2 \rceil} = n!/(\lceil n/2 \rceil! \lfloor n/2 \rfloor!)$.

(g) Generalize to a barrier at $-b$. Show that $Q(n, b) = \binom{n}{x} + \binom{n}{x+1} + \cdots + \binom{n}{x+b-1}$, where $x = \lceil \frac{1}{2}(n - b + 1) \rceil$.

Problem 13.94. Counting walks with absorbing barriers, Problem 13.93, has many applications. In each case find a link between the objects in question and paths on a grid with an absorbing barrier. Then apply Problem 13.93.

(a) Show that the number of n-bit sequences that are prefix-heavy (*more* 1s in every prefix) is $T_n = \binom{n-1}{\lceil \frac{n-1}{2} \rceil}$.

(b) Show that the number of n-bit prefix-heavy sequences ending in k zeros is $F_{n,k} = \binom{n-k-1}{\lceil \frac{n-1}{2} \rceil}$, for $k \geq 1$.

(c) Show that the number of ways to match n pairs of parentheses (Problem 13.91) is $C_n = \frac{1}{n+1}\binom{2n}{n}$.

(d) Alice (A) and Bob (B) repeatedly play a game n times. A wins more times than B. In how many ways can you arrange the outcome of the games so that: (i) At some point A and B were tied? (ii) A is always ahead of B?

Problem 13.95. Compute h_n, the number of perfect matchings in K_{2n}.

(a) Show $h_n = (2n-1)!! = (2n-1) \times (2n-3) \times \cdots \times 3 \times 1$. *[Hint: Show $h_n = (2n-1)h_{n-1}$.]*

(b) Construct a matching using consecutive pairs of vertices in a permutation of $1, \ldots, 2n$.

(i) Show that $2^n n!$ different permutations give the same matching.

(ii) Show $h_n = (2n)!/2^n n!$, and that this matches with (a). *[Hint: Multiplicity rule.]*

Problem 13.96. In how many ways can you choose a k-tuple of sets $\mathcal{S} = (S_1, S_2, \ldots, S_k)$, where $S_i \subseteq \{x_1, \ldots, x_n\}$ and $S_1 \cap S_2 \cap \cdots \cap S_k = \varnothing$. *[Hint: In how many ways can x_1 be placed into the sets? What about x_2? Product rule.]*

Problem 13.97. Prove Fermat's Little Theorem: when p is prime, $p|(a^p - a)$. For $a = 4$, $p|(4^p - 4)$. Consider a length-p sequence using 4 symbols a, b, c, d, e.g., $ababacd$ ($p = 7$). Joining the ends of a sequence gives a necklace. Multiple sequences can give the same necklace up to rotation. For $ababacd$, the duplicates are:

$ababacd$ $\quad dababac$ $\quad cdababa$ $\quad acdabab$ $\quad bacdaba$ $\quad abacdab$ $\quad babacda$

(All 7 sequences give the same necklace. Each successive sequence is obtained by removing the last symbol and adding it to the front)

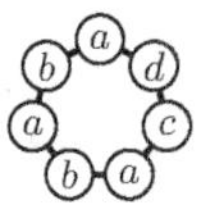

(a) Show that the number of sequences which contain more than one symbol is $4^p - 4$.

(b) You get up to p distinct sequences by repeatedly rotating the last symbol to the front. If you get fewer than p distinct sequences, show that one of the sequences is an integer repetition of some shorter sequence.

(c) Can a sequence with prime length and more than one symbol be repetitions of a shorter sequence? Explain.

(d) Prove that every distinct necklace with more than one symbol is created by p distinct sequences and hence there are $(4^p - 4)/p$ distinct necklaces with more than one symbol.

(e) Explain why you have proved Fermat's Little Theorem for $a = 4$. Generalize to arbitrary a.

Problem 13.98. In how many ways can 10 boys and 13 girls form a circle? (Rotations of the same pattern are equivalent.) *[Hint: $10 + 13$ is prime. The methods from Problem 13.97 might be useful.]*

Problem 13.99 (Cayley's formula and Prüfer codes). We show a labeled tree. Repeatedly remove the leaf with the lowest label, listing the labels of the removed leaf's neighbor.

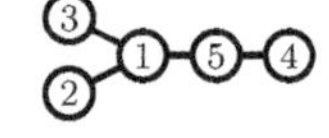

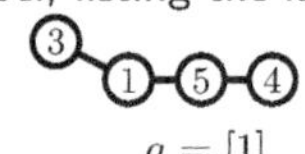

$a = [1]$

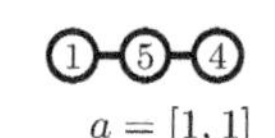

$a = [1, 1]$

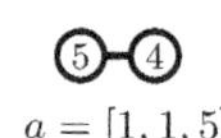

$a = [1, 1, 5]$

⑤ $a = [1, 1, 5, 5]$

The sequence of neighbors, $a = [1, 1, 5, 5]$, is the Prüffer code for the tree.

(a) Prove that the last entry in the Prüffer code must be n.

(b) Prove you can reconstruct b, the sequence in which nodes are removed ($(b[i], a[i])$ are the edges). Here is a hint: start with $b = a$ and replace $b[1]$ with the smallest label not in b; then replace $b[2]$ with the smallest label not in b; and so on up to $b[n-1]$:

$$[1, 1, 5, 5] \quad \rightarrow \quad [2, 1, 5, 5] \quad \rightarrow \quad [2, 3, 5, 5] \quad \rightarrow \quad [2, 3, 1, 5] \quad \rightarrow \quad [2, 3, 1, 4].$$

(c) Prove that there are n^{n-2} labeled trees on n vertices. *[Hint: Bijection to Prüffer codes.]*

Problem 13.100. Show: there are $(n+1)^{n-1}$ labeled rooted forests on n vertices. *[Hint: Bijection from labeled trees on $n+1$ vertices to labeled rooted forests on n vertices and Cayley's formula. Remove vertex $n+1$ from a labeled tree on $n+1$ vertices; make its neighbors roots.]*

Problem 13.101 (Parking Functions). There are n parking spots $1, \ldots, n$ in a row and n cars $C_1, \ldots, C_n$ arrive in sequence. Car C_i prefers parking spot a_i, will drive up to spot a_i, park there if the spot is available or else park in the next available spot if one exists. The sequence $(a_1, \ldots, a_n)$ is a *parking function* if every car finds a spot. List all parking functions for $n = 2, 3$. Prove that the number of parking functions is $(n+1)^{n-1}$ as follows.

(a) Instead of parking in a row, consider the parking algorithm on a circle with one additional spot $n+1$, also allowing $a_i = n+1$. Now all n cars can park for any $(a_1, \ldots, a_n)$ and there will be one empty spot. Prove that $(a_1, \ldots, a_n)$ is a parking function for the original row with n spots if and only spot $n+1$ is left empty on the circle.

(b) Prove, for the circle, that if $(a_1, \ldots, a_n)$ results in C_i parking at space p_i, then $(a_1 + j, \ldots, a_n + j) \pmod{n+1}$ results in C_i parking in space $p_i + j \pmod{n+1}$.

(c) For $i = 0, \ldots, n$, and any $(a_1, \ldots, a_n)$, prove that exactly one of $(a_1 + i, \ldots, a_n + i) \pmod{n+1}$ is a parking function for the row. That is, every row-parking function maps to $n+1$ distinct circle parking functions.

(d) How many circle parking functions are there? Prove the claim.

A good disguise should not reveal a person's height.
– **Shafi Goldwasser, Silvio Micali**

. . . a good idea comes to you when you are not looking for it. Through an improbable combination of coincidence, naivete and lucky mistakes.
– **Kary Mullis**

Chapter 14

Advanced Counting

1: Sequences with repetition: multinomials.
2: Counting with cases that overlap: inclusion–exclusion.
3: Pigeonhole principle.

Form a length-n sequence with candy of r different colors. There are $r \times r \times \cdots \times r = r^n$ ordered sequences. On the other hand, if order does not matter you're making goody bags, and there are $Q(n, r) = \binom{n+r-1}{r-1}$ choices. Fix the number of candies of each color to k_1 of color-1, k_2 of color-2,. . . , k_r of color-r. Now how many length-n sequences are there, where $n = k_1 + k_2 + \cdots + k_r$? Here order matters, but the number of each color is fixed. Denote the number of such sequences by $\binom{n}{k_1,k_2,\ldots,k_r}$, read n-choose-$(k_1, k_2, \ldots, k_r)$. For example, the are 20 sequences of 3 red candies, 1 blue candy and 1 green candy as shown below.

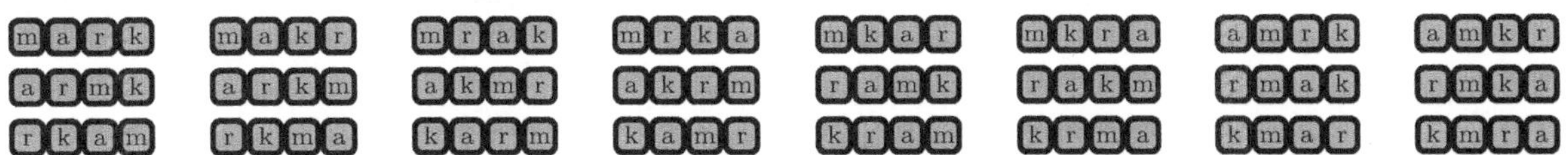

In the example above, $n = 5$, $k_1 = 3$, $k_2 = 1$ and $k_3 = 1$, and $\binom{5}{3,1,1} = 20$.

Example 14.1 (Anagrams)**.** In the game scrabble, you have some letters which you must arrange to make words – anagrams. For the tiles mark, there are $4! = 24$ distinct arrangements, giving the "words":

mark makr mrak mrka mkar mkra amrk amkr
armk arkm akmr akrm ramk rakm rmak rmka
rkam rkma karm kamr kram krma kmar kmra

Now consider the tiles anna. There are only 6 different arrangements of the letters:

aann anan anna naan nana nnaa

There are many fewer arrangements of anna due to repetition. Treat each letter of the alphabet as a color. anna is a length-4 sequence with two "colors" of tile, a and n. So, $n = 4$ and $k_1 = k_2 = 2$, as there are two of each letter (color). The number of arrangements of anna is $\binom{4}{2,2}$. For mark, there are four "colors" m, a, r and k. The sequence has 4 tiles, but now one of each "color", so the number of arrangements of mark is $\binom{4}{1,1,1,1}$. We conclude that $\binom{4}{2,2} = 6$ and $\binom{4}{1,1,1,1} = 24$. □

Example 14.2 (Binary strings)**.** The number of 10-bit strings with 4 ones is $\binom{10}{4}$. These are length-10 sequences with two types of objects, 4 ones and 6 zeros. So $n = 10$, $k_1 = 4$, $k_2 = 6$ and the number of such sequences, by definition, is $\binom{10}{4,6}$. We conclude $\binom{10}{4,6} = \binom{10}{4} = \frac{10!}{4!6!}$. That is $\binom{n}{k}$ is short for $\binom{n}{k,n-k}$. □

Is there a general formula for $\binom{n}{k_1,\ldots,k_r}$? Yes. We will give two proofs of the important formula

$$\binom{n}{k_1, k_2, \ldots, k_r} = \frac{n!}{k_1! \times k_2! \times k_3! \cdots \times k_r!} = \frac{(k_1 + k_2 + \cdots + k_r)!}{k_1! \times k_2! \times k_3! \cdots \times k_r!}. \tag{14.1}$$

Proof using multiplicity. Label the objects $1, 2, \ldots, n$ with k_1 of color-1, k_2 of color-2,..., k_r of color-r. There are $n!$ label sequences. Fix an object sequence. There are $k_1!$ ways to permute the color-1 objects while keeping them in place. Every such permutation gives the same object sequence but a different label sequence. Similarly, each of the $n_2!$ permutations of the color-2 objects gives the same object sequence but a different label sequence. And so on for the color-3 up to color-k objects. We illustrate with anna.

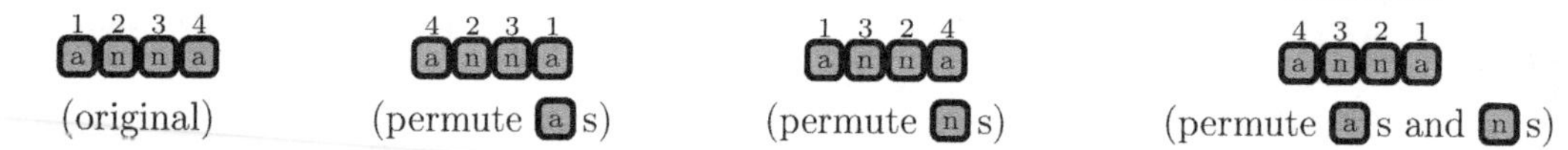

(original) (permute a s) (permute n s) (permute a s and n s)

The labels are shown above the tile. All four label sequences are the same object sequence. By the product rule, we can permutate the color-1 objects and the color-2 objects ... and the color-k objects in $k_1! \times k_2! \cdots \times k_r!$ ways. Each such permutation gives the same object sequence but a different label sequence. The correspondence between label sequences and object sequences is $(k_1! \times k_2! \cdots \times k_r!)$-to-1, so there are $(k_1! \times k_2! \cdots \times k_r!)$-times as many label sequences as there are object sequences. That is,

$$n! = k_1! \times k_2! \cdots \times k_r! \times \binom{n}{k_1, k_2, \ldots, k_r}.$$

■

Proof by sequentially choosing subsets. Treat the sequence of objects as n slots to be filled with k_1 of color-1, k_2 of color-2, and so on up to k_r of color-r. Here is an example with 12 objects, 5 are red, 4 are blue and 3 are green. Starting with red, we place the objects into 12 slots in three steps.

1: Pick 5 slots for red objects: (from 12 slots) — slots 1 2 3 4 5 6 7 8 9 10 11 12 — subset for color-1 $s_1 = \{1, 3, 4, 7, 11\}$ $\leftarrow \binom{12}{5}$ possible s_1

2: Pick 4 slots for blue objects: (from 7 remaining slots) — slots 1 2 3 4 5 6 7 8 9 10 11 12 — subset for color-2 $s_2 = \{2, 5, 6, 10\}$ $\leftarrow \binom{7}{4}$ possible s_2

3: Pick 3 slots for green objects: (from 3 remaining slots) — slots 1 2 3 4 5 6 7 8 9 10 11 12 — subset for color-3 $s_3 = \{8, 9, 12\}$ $\leftarrow \binom{3}{3}$ possible s_3

By the product rule, the number of ways to choose subsets s_1 then s_2 given s_1 and then s_3 given (s_1, s_2) is

$$\binom{12}{5} \times \binom{7}{4} \times \binom{3}{3} = \frac{12!}{5! \times 7!} \times \frac{7!}{4! \times 3!} \times \frac{3!}{3! \times 0!} = \frac{12!}{5! \times 4! \times 3!}.$$

Generalizing, there are $\binom{n}{k_1}$ ways to place color-1 in a subset of slots s_1. Fix s_1. For color-2, there are $\binom{n-k_1}{k_2}$ ways to choose a subset s_2 from the $n - k_1$ free slots. Fix (s_1, s_2). This leaves $n - k_1 - k_2$ empty slots, and hence $\binom{n-k_1-k_2}{k_3}$ possible subsets s_3 for color-3. And so on, up to $\binom{n-k_1-k_2-\cdots-k_{r-1}}{k_r}$ ways to choose s_r for color-r. By the product rule, the number of ways to choose $s_1 s_2 s_3 \cdots s_r$ is

$$\begin{aligned} \binom{n}{k_1, k_2, \ldots, k_r} &= \binom{n}{k_1} \cdot \binom{n-k_1}{k_2} \cdot \binom{n-k_1-k_2}{k_3} \cdot \cdots \cdot \binom{n-k_1-k_2-\cdots-k_{r-1}}{k_r} \\ &= \frac{n!}{k_1!(n-k_1)!} \cdot \frac{(n-k_1)!}{k_2!(n-k_1-k_2)!} \cdot \frac{(n-k_1-k_2)!}{k_3!(n-k_1-k_2-k_3)!} \cdot \frac{\cdots}{\cdots} \cdots \frac{\cdots}{\cdots} \cdot \frac{k_r!}{k_r!0!} \\ &= \frac{n!}{k_1! \times k_2! \times \cdots \times k_r!} \end{aligned}$$

■

Example 14.3 (Multinomial Theorem). Consider the multinomial $x + y + z$ cubed,

$$\begin{aligned} (x+y+z)^3 &= (x+y+z)(x+y+z)(x+y+z) \\ &= xxx + xxy + xxz + xyx + xyy + xyz + xzx + xzy + xzz + \\ &\quad\ yxx + yxy + yxz + yyx + yyy + yyz + yzx + yzy + yzz + \\ &\quad\ zxx + zxy + zxz + zyx + zyy + zyz + zzx + zzy + zzz \\ &= x^3 + 3x^2y + 3x^2z + 3xy^2 + 6xyz + 3xz^2 + y^3 + 3y^2z + 3yz^2 + z^3 \end{aligned}$$

Each term in the expansion, e.g. xxz, is of the form $t_1t_2t_3$ where $t_i \in \{x, y, z\}$ and t_1 comes from the first multinomial, t_2 from the second and t_3 from the third. The number of terms is $3 \times 3 \times 3 = 27$. Collecting terms equal to $x^iy^jz^k$ for $i + j + k = 3$ gives all sequences with i x's, j y's and k z's. The number of such sequences is $\binom{3}{i,j,k}$, which is the coefficient of $x^iy^jz^k$. Hence $(x+y+z)^3 = \sum_{i+j+k=3} \binom{3}{i,j,k} x^iy^jz^k$. Generalizing,

$$(x+y+z)^n = \sum_{i+j+k=n} \binom{n}{i,j,k} x^iy^jz^k. \tag{14.2}$$

For example, the coefficient of $x^3y^2z^3$ in $(x+y+z)^8$ is $\binom{8}{3,2,3} = \frac{8!}{3!2!3!} = 560$. □

Summary: selecting k objects from r types (colors):

	no repetition	with repetition
k-sequence (order matters)	$\dfrac{r!}{(r-k)!}$	r^k
k-subset (order does not matter)	$\binom{r}{k}$	$\binom{k+r-1}{r-1}$
$(k_1, k_2, \cdots, k_r)$-sequence (k_1 of color-1,..., k_r of color-r)		$\binom{k_1+\cdots+k_r}{k_1, k_2, \ldots, k_r}$

Exercise 14.1
In each case, count the objects specified.
(a) 8 letter words that are composed of the letters a a r d v a r k.
(b) Bouquets with three-dozen roses (rose colors are red, pink, yellow and white).
(c) A fraternity has 25 students. Every week, 5 are assigned to cook, 5 to clean bathrooms, 5 to laundry, 5 to entertainment and 5 to groceries. In how many ways can this be done if (i) No student has more than 1 task? (ii) Students can have more than 1 task? (Estimate the order of magnitude.)

Exercise 14.2
(a) Find the coefficients of: (i) x^5 in $(1+x)^9$. (ii) x^4y^3 in $(2x+3y)^7$. (iii) x^5y^8 in $(x+x^2+y^2)^7$.
(b) $(x+y)^3 = x^3+3x^2y+3xy^2+y^3$ is a sum of 4 different monomials. How many different monomials are in the expansion of $(x+y)^n$ and $(x+y+z)^n$.
(c) Prove a general multinomial theorem: $(a_1+a_2+\cdots+a_k)^n$ = sum of monomials.
(d) Prove that $\sum_{i_1+i_2+\cdots+i_k=n} \binom{n}{i_1,i_2,\ldots,i_k} = k^n$. Specialize to $k=2$.
(e) How many different monomials are in the multinomial expansion of $(a_1+a_2+\cdots+a_k)^n$?

14.1 Inclusion-Exclusion

The sum rule $|A \cup B| = |A| + |B|$ is for disjoint sets. To count complex objects, you consider the disjoint cases, count each case, and add. This helps because it is often easier to count the smaller sets in each case.

What if A and B are not disjoint? Then $A \cup B$ has three regions: $A \cap \overline{B}$ of size $|A| - |A \cap B|$; $A \cap B$; and, $\overline{A} \cap B$ of size $|B| - |A \cap B|$. Adding these three sizes,

$$|A \cup B| = |A| + |B| - |A \cap B|.$$

$A\cap\overline{B}$ $A\cap B$ $\overline{A}\cap B$

This formula helps because it also breaks the complex set $A \cup B$ into smaller sets.

Example 14.4. How many numbers from 1 to 1000 are divisible by 6 or 10? Let A_6 be the numbers divisible by 6 and A_{10} those divisible by 10. We want $|A_6 \cup A_{10}|$. The numbers divisible by d that are at most n are $d, 2d, 3d, \ldots, kd$, where $k = \lfloor n/d \rfloor$. The floor function $\lfloor x \rfloor$ is the largest integer less-equal-to x. So, $|A_6| = \lfloor 1000/6 \rfloor$ and $|A_{10}| = \lfloor 1000/10 \rfloor$. A number is divisible by 6 and 10 if and only if it is divisible by their least common multiple, which is 30. So, $|A_6 \cap A_{10}| = \lfloor 1000/30 \rfloor$. Therefore,

$$\big|\{\text{numbers in 1 to 1000 divisible by 6 or 10}\}\big| = \lfloor 1000/6 \rfloor + \lfloor 1000/10 \rfloor - \lfloor 1000/30 \rfloor = 233.$$ □

14.1.1 Union of More than Two Sets

Men are studs, smart or nice. The Venn diagram advertises Batman™ as the only smart, nice stud. The Venn diagram breaks men into seven sets,

$$\text{men} = \text{only smart} + \text{only nice} + \text{only stud} + \text{smud} + \text{smice} + \text{stice} + \text{Batman}^{\text{TM}}.$$

As you can verify from the Venn diagram,

$$\begin{aligned} \text{only smart} &= \text{smart} - \text{smud} - \text{smice} - \text{Batman}^{\text{TM}} \\ \text{only nice} &= \text{nice} - \text{stice} - \text{smice} - \text{Batman}^{\text{TM}} \\ \text{only stud} &= \text{stud} - \text{stice} - \text{smud} - \text{Batman}^{\text{TM}} \end{aligned}$$

Substituting these expressions back into the break down of men, we get,

$$\text{men} = \text{smart} + \text{nice} + \text{stud} - \text{smud} - \text{smice} - \text{stice} - 2 \cdot \text{Batman}^{\text{TM}}$$

Again, from the Venn diagram, we get

$$\begin{aligned} \text{smud} &= \{\text{smart} \cap \text{stud}\} - \text{Batman}^{\text{TM}}, \\ \text{smice} &= \{\text{smart} \cap \text{nice}\} - \text{Batman}^{\text{TM}}, \\ \text{stice} &= \{\text{stud} \cap \text{nice}\} - \text{Batman}^{\text{TM}}. \end{aligned}$$

Using these expressions, we finally arrive at

$$\text{men} = \text{smart} + \text{nice} + \text{stud} - \{\text{smart} \,\&\, \text{stud}\} - \{\text{smart} \,\&\, \text{nice}\} - \{\text{nice} \,\&\, \text{stud}\} + \text{Batman}^{\text{TM}}$$

Let us reformulate our final result for general sets A_1, A_2, A_3:

$$|A_1 \cup A_2 \cup A_3| = |A_1| + |A_2| + |A_3| - |A_1 \cap A_2| - |A_1 \cap A_3| - |A_2 \cap A_3| + |A_1 \cap A_2 \cap A_3|.$$

Here is a formal derivation of the RHS using set-operations.

$$\begin{aligned} |A_1 \cup A_2 \cup A_3| &\overset{(a)}{=} |A_1 \cup A_2| + |A_3| - |(A_1 \cup A_2) \cap A_3| \\ &\overset{(b)}{=} |A_1| + |A_2| + |A_3| - |A_1 \cap A_2| - |(A_1 \cap A_3) \cup (A_2 \cap A_3)| \\ &\overset{(c)}{=} |A_1| + |A_2| + |A_3| - |A_1 \cap A_2| - (|A_1 \cap A_3| + |A_2 \cap A_3| - |A_1 \cap A_3 \cap A_2 \cap A_3|) \\ &\overset{(d)}{=} |A_1| + |A_2| + |A_3| - |A_1 \cap A_2| - |A_1 \cap A_3| - |A_2 \cap A_3| + |A_1 \cap A_2 \cap A_3|. \end{aligned}$$

Pop Quiz 14.3
Justify (a)–(d) in the derivation above. How many integers in $[1, 1000]$ are not divisible by any of $\{4, 6, 10\}$?

We might guess a pattern for the union of n sets $A_1, A_2, \ldots, A_n$.

$$\begin{aligned} |A_1 \cup A_2 \cup \cdots \cup A_n| = &+(|A_1| + |A_2| + \cdots + |A_n|) \\ &-(|A_1 \cap A_2| + |A_1 \cap A_3| + \cdots + |A_{n-1} \cap A_n|) \\ &+(|A_1 \cap A_2 \cap A_3| + |A_1 \cap A_2 \cap A_4| + \cdots + |A_{n-2} \cap A_{n-1} \cap A_n|) \\ &\vdots \\ &(-1)^{k+1} \cdot (\text{sum of all } k\text{-way intersection-sizes}) \\ &\vdots \\ &(-1)^{n+1}|A_1 \cap A_2 \cap \cdots \cap A_n| \end{aligned}$$

Principle of Inclusion-Exclusion (PIE) for Union of n Sets

$$|A_1 \cup A_2 \cup \cdots \cup A_n| = \sum_{k=1}^{n} (-1)^{k+1} \cdot (\text{sum of all } k\text{-way intersection-sizes})$$

The inclusion-exclusion formula is a sum over k. The summand for a particular k involves the size of each k-way intersection formed by k sets from $\{A_1, \ldots, A_n\}$. There are $\binom{n}{k}$ such intersections. Let's prove the formula. To illustrate the proof idea, consider a three set union and an element x which is in A_1 and A_3.

$$|A_1 \cup A_2 \cup A_3| = |A_1| + |A_2| + |A_3| - |A_1 \cap A_2| - |A_1 \cap A_3| - |A_2 \cap A_3| + |A_1 \cap A_2 \cap A_3|.$$

Each red term has a contribution of 1 from x, for a nett of $1+1-1=1$. Every element in the union contributes 1 to the RHS, and so the RHS counts the elements in the union.

Proof. Let x be in the union $A_1 \cup A_2 \cup \cdots \cup A_n$, and suppose x is in r of the sets. An intersection of k sets contains x only if each of the k sets is one of the r-sets containing x. There are $\binom{r}{k}$ ways to pick k sets exclusively from the r sets that contain x, and these are precisely the k-way intersections to which x belongs. The contribution of x from these k-way intersections to the inclusion-exclusion sum is therefore $(-1)^{k+1}\binom{r}{k}$. The total contribution of x to the inclusion-exclusion sum is therefore

$$\binom{r}{1} - \binom{r}{2} + \binom{r}{3} - \cdots + (-1)^{r+1}\binom{r}{r} = \sum_{k=1}^{r}(-1)^{k+1}\binom{r}{k} = 1 + \sum_{k=0}^{r}(-1)^{k+1}\binom{r}{k} = 1$$

The last equality is because, by the Binomial Theorem, $0 = (1-1)^r = \sum_{k=0}^{r}(-1)^k\binom{r}{k}$. So, x contributes 1 to the inclusion-exclusion sum. Since x was arbitrary, every element in the union contributes 1 to the inclusion-exclusion sum, which means the inclusion-exclusion sum counts the elements in the union. ■

Exercise 14.4

(a) Derive the inclusion-exclusion formula for $|A_1 \cup A_2 \cup A_3 \cup A_4|$ using 2 and 3-set inclusion-exclusion.
(b) How many numbers from 1 to 2015 are not divisible by any of $\{2, 3, 5, 7\}$?
(c) In how many ways can four girls get their hats from a hat-check so that no one gets their own hat?
(d) Prove the general inclusion-exclusion formula by induction.

Example 14.5. We solve Exercise 14.4(c) for 10 girls with 10 hats. How many ways are there to give the wrong hat to every girl? First let's tinker with smaller values. You should verify these simpler cases by hand:

number of girls n	1	2	3	4	...
number of ways to give all girls the wrong hat	0	1	2	9	...

(Build Up Counting.) Call the number of permutations with n girls all getting the wrong hat D_n. These are called derangements. Can we get D_5 without tediously listing out all the 120 permutations and knocking out all the ones that don't work? In a derangement, let $k \neq 1$ be the hat person 1 gets (there are $n-1$) choices for k. We need to determine the number of ways to assign the remaining $n-1$ hats and use the product rule. There are two cases depending on who gets hat ①.

ⓚ 1 2 3 ··· k ··· n

ⓚ ① 1 2 3 ··· k ··· n — Case 1: k gets ①

ⓚ 1 2 3 ··· k ··· n — Case 2: k does not get ①

Treat person k as the new owner of hat ①. In case 1, person-k gets hat ① ("her" hat); the remaining $n-2$ hats must be a derangement for the remaining $n-2$ people, which can be done in D_{n-2} ways. In case 2 person-k does not get hat ①, so all the remaining $n-1$ people don't get "their" hats. This can be done in D_{n-1} ways. By the sum rule, there are $D_{n-1} + D_{n-2}$ ways to assign the remaining $n-1$ hats. By the product rule,

$$D_n = (n-1)(D_{n-1} + D_{n-2}).$$

We can now compute $D_5 = 4(D_4 + D_3) = 4 \times 11 = 44$. By continuing to fill our table in this way, we get D_{10}.

n	1	2	3	4	5	6	7	8	9	**10**	...
D_n	0	1	2	9	44	265	1854	14833	133496	**1334961**	...

(Inclusion-Exclusion.) We can get a formula for D_n as a sum. Define the set

$$A_i = \{\text{the permutations of hats where person } i \text{ gets her own hat}\}.$$

The union $A_1 \cup A_2 \cup \cdots \cup A_n$ contains all permutations where someone gets their own hat, therefore the number of permutations where no one gets their own hat is

$$D_n = n! - |A_1 \cup A_2 \cup \cdots \cup A_n|.$$

A k-way intersection of the A_i are the permutations where k specific girls get their hats, leaving $(n-k)!$ ways to permute the other $n-k$ hats. So the size of any k-way intersection is $(n-k)!$, and there are $\binom{n}{k}$ k-way intersections. So, (sum of sizes of all k-way intersections) $= \binom{n}{k}(n-k)!$. By inclusion-exclusion,

$$\begin{aligned}|A_1 \cup A_2 \cup \cdots \cup A_n| &= \sum_{k=1}^{n}(-1)^{k+1} \cdot \text{(sum of sizes of all } k\text{-way intersections)} \\ &= \sum_{k=1}^{n}(-1)^{k+1}\binom{n}{k}(n-k)! \\ &= \sum_{k=1}^{n}(-1)^{k+1}\frac{n!}{k!}.\end{aligned}$$

Since $n! = (-1)^0 n!/0!$ and $D_n = n! - |A_1 \cup A_2 \cup \cdots \cup A_n|$, we conclude that D_n is given by

$$D_n = n!\sum_{k=0}^{n}\frac{(-1)^k}{k!} \approx \frac{n!}{e}.$$

(The last approximation uses $1/e = 1 - \frac{1}{1!} + \frac{1}{2!} - \frac{1}{3!} + \frac{1}{4!} - \cdots$.) You may prove the formula for D_n by induction using the recursion $D_n = (n-1)(D_{n-1} + D_{n-2})$. □

Inclusion-exclusion is a sophisticated technique. You must first figure out how inclusion-exclusion plays a role in your problem, by identifying the correct union of sets to analyze. That done, the inclusion-exclusion analysis itself can be tough. Practice! Use inclusion-exclusion to solve these tough problems.

Exercise 14.5

(a) A password is a permutation of 0123456789, but it cannot contain 12 or 24 (your birthday is Dec. 24). How many valid passwords are there?

(b) Sets A and B have sizes n and m with $n \geq m$. How many functions from A to B are onto (surjective)?

(c) How many integer solutions satisfy $x_1 + x_2 + x_3 = 30$ with $0 \leq x_1 \leq 10$, $0 \leq x_2 \leq 15$, $0 \leq x_3 \leq 20$?

(d) Suppose n is divisible by the primes $p_1, \ldots, p_m$. Let $\varphi(n)$ count the non-negative integers less than n which are relatively prime with n ($\varphi(n)$ is Euler's totient function). Prove that

$$\varphi(n) = n\prod_{i=1}^{m}(1 - 1/p_i).$$

[Hint: count numbers not relatively prime to n.]

14.2 Pigeonhole Principle

When it comes to counting, nothing could be simpler than the pigeonhole principle. It stands to reason that if you have more guests than spare rooms, then some guests will have to share. That's the pigeonhole priciple.

If there are more pigeons than pigeonholes, then at least one pigeonhole must have two or more pigeons.

The pigeonhole principle is a restatement of how we use 1-to-1 functions to compare the sizes of sets. Illustrated above on the right is the set of pigeons being mapped to the set of pigeonholes. The mapping places pigeons in pigeonholes. Let A be the pigeons and B the pigeonholes. Let $f : A \mapsto B$ be the mapping of pigeons to pigeonholes. If f is 1-to-1, then $|A| \leq |B|$. Equivalently the contrapositive states if $|A| > |B|$, then f cannot be 1-to-1 and two pigeons of A must map to the same pigeonhole of B. To prove the pigeonhole principle, we prove the contrapositive. If there is at most one pigeon per pigeonhole, then the number of pigeons is not more than the number of pigeonholes. Let x_i be the number of pigeons in pigeonhole i. If $x_i \leq 1$, then

$$\text{number of pigeons} = \sum_i x_i \leq \sum_i 1 = \text{number of pigeonholes.}$$

The pigeonhole principle is simple and self-evident, yet its consequences can be profound. Indeed, the pigeonhole principle will be instrumental in exposing deficiencies in certain models of computing. But, before that, let's tackle a few simpler applications.

Example 14.6 (Social Twins). Two nodes in a social network are social twins if they have the same number of friends. There are social twins in any social network, as long as there are at least two vertices.

Proof. If every vertex-degree is at least 1, there are n vertices with degrees in $\{1, 2, \ldots, n-1\}$. Make pigeonholes $1, 2, \ldots, n-1$, one for each possible vertex-degree. There are $n-1$ pigeonholes. Each vertex is a pigeon. Place each vertex into the pigeonhole for its degree. We illustrate with a small graph,

v_1 v_2 v_6 v_3 v_4 v_5 — v_6 v_2 v_3 v_5 v_1 v_4
degree: 1 2 3 4 5
$\leftarrow$ (Pigeonholes are the degree bins. Pigeons are the vertices.)

For the graph above, vertices v_2 and v_3 are in the same degree-bin, and so are social twins. Must there always be two vertices in the same bin. Yes. Because there are only $n-1$ bins (pigeonholes), but there are n vertices (pigeons). By the pigeonhole principle, at least one bin contains more than one vertex.

If one vertex has degree 0, the other $n-1$ vertices have degrees in $\{1, \ldots, n-2\}$. The same pigeonhole argument applies to these $n-1$ vertices. (What if two or more vertices have degree 0?) ■

That there are always social twins is not so easy to prove without the insight to use pigeonhole. Though the proof is quite simple, all the main ingredients of a proof by the pigeonhole principle are there. Typically the pigeonhole principle is used to prove the existence of something, in this case social twins. The creative insight is to identify the pigeons and the pigeonholes in such a way that:

1. You can show there are strictly more pigeons than pigeonholes.
2. A pigeonhole with more than one pigeon implies the existence of whatever you seek.

Pigeonhole proofs are often non-constructive. You prove something exists without finding it. Our proof of social-twin-existence sheds no light on who the social twins are. We just know they exist. Lastly, let us mention that this result on social twins is a general property of graphs.

Theorem 14.7. Any simple graph has two vertices of the same degree. □

A proof being non-constructive is often viewed as a deficiency, but sometimes such proofs are essential, especially in cryptography (e.g. see Problem 17.39). To appreciate the value of non-constructive proof, let's go back in time. I grew up with a game called "I spy with my little eye something beginning with ...", a search game that entertains 4-year-olds. The child's task is to find some object in a complex scene. We give an instance of "I-Spy" in Figure 14.1, together with a target object (a black cat), which you must find.

The street-smart 4-year old asks: "How do I know the cat is in the picture? You're just sending me on a wild-goose-chase!" An interesting challenge arises, to convince the 4-year old that the cat is indeed in the picture without revealing the cat's location, because if you reveal the location, the task is no longer a challenge.

Imagine that we cover the picture with an endless black cloth and are able to move around a zoom lens which will only reveal what is under the lens, and nothing else. In the figure on the right is the image you see when we place the lens on top of the cat. This is our attempt to prove to the 4-year old that the cat is indeed in the picture, without revealing its actual location. And, indeed, there should no longer be any doubt

Find the cat.

Figure 14.1: The task is to find the black cat in the complex picture on the left. Enjoy!

that the cat exists in the picture. But, unfortunately, our proof has revealed critical additional information, for example the little bit of green next to the cat. It is the 4-year old who got the better of us, tricking us into revealing hints about the cat's location. We needed a "zero-additional-knowledge" non-constructive proof.

Example 14.8 (Subset Sums)**.** We end this chapter with a non-constructive pigeonhole proof. The proof shows that what we seek exists, without giving the game away. Our proof won't give any hints whatsoever as to how to actually find that object. Other than knowing the object exists, you gain zero-additional-knowledge.

Here is a set of 10 numbers, each between 1 and 100: $\{2, 3, 4, 8, 16, 32, 64, 65, 71, 99\}$. I claim there are two distinct subsets which have the same sum. Here is a proof. The two subsets are $\{2, 65\}$ and $\{3, 64\}$. That is a constructive proof because I actually found the two subsets for you. You might say my set was carefully picked to ensure there were two subsets with the same sum. Not so. I challenge you to pick any 10 numbers between 1 and 100, and there will be two subsets which have the same sum. Here is why. Say you pick $x_1 < x_2 < \ldots < x_{10}$. (Why are we ignoring the case where two numbers are equal?). The maximum possible subset sum occurs when the subset is all 10 numbers,

$$\text{maximum-sum} = x_1 + x_2 + \cdots + x_{10} < 100 + 100 + \cdots + 100 = 10 \times 100 = 1000.$$

So, there are at most 1,000 possible subset sums $0, 1, \ldots, 999$. Let us create a pigeonhole or bin for each possible subset-sum. There are $1,000$ bins, one for each of the possibilities $0, 1, 2, \ldots, 999$. Every subset of our ten numbers is a pigeon. Place each subset into the bin that matches the subset's sum.

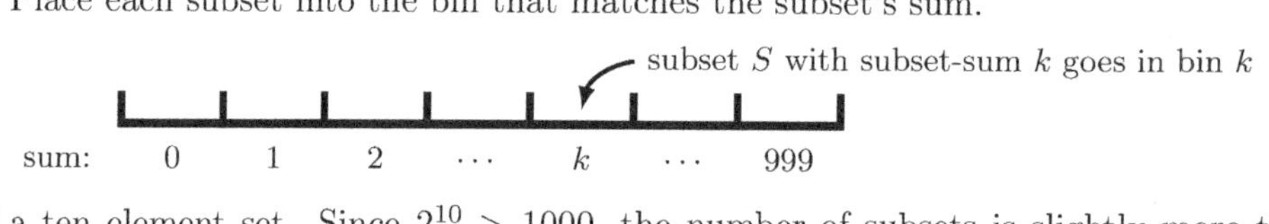

There are 2^{10} subsets of a ten element set. Since $2^{10} > 1000$, the number of subsets is slightly more than the number of bins. By the pigeonhole principle, at least one bin will have more than one subset. Those two subsets in the same bin have the same sum. This proof is non-constructive. We proved that two subsets with the same sum exist without actually finding them. We didn't even know the numbers $x_1, \ldots, x_{10}$.

Exercise 14.6

In Problem 1.44 was a set of one hundred 27-digit positive numbers. Here are some of those numbers.

1: 5719825393567961346558155629
2: 5487945882843158696672157984
⋮
32: 4332859486871255922555418653
33: 2428751582371964453381751663
34: 6738481866868951787884276161

35: 8794353172213177612939776215
36: 2989694245827479769152313629
⋮
66: 3161518296576488158997146221
67: 1917611425739928285147758625
68: 3516431537343387135357237754

69: 7549684656732941456945632221
70: 2397876675349971994958579984
⋮
100: 3414339143545324298853248718

The task was to find two different subsets of this set of hundred numbers having the same subset-sum. Prove that this is not a futile task. Show that two such subsets which have the same subset-sum must exist.

The diligent student, after some hours grinding at Problem 1.44, like the 4-year old, might suspect a ruse. The sadist professor has sent the student on a wild goose chase. Exercise 14.6 redeems the professor. Using pigeonhole you proved a solution exists without in any way revealing the solution. That is pretty impressive, that you can prove that a task is solvable without actually demonstrating the solution. You proved the "cat" exists without revealing where. To top-off your weekend, please reconsider Problem 1.44, but now armed with the knowledge that a solution must exist. It is a quest worthy of the mightiest of swords. ☺ □

The pigeonhole principle is a powerful tool when you need to show that two of something must exist. If you look over the proofs, you will agree that each proof is not too hard once you realize what the pigeonholes are and what the pigeons are – that's the hard, creative part.

Exercise 14.7

Use the pigeonhole principle for these exercises. Make sure to clearly identify what corresponds to pigeons and what corresponds to pigeonholes.

(a) Show: at a party, two guests have the same number of enemies among the guests.
(b) Show: in New York City, at least two people have the same number of head-hairs.
(c) 17 kings are on distinct squares of an 8×8 chessboard. Show that two kings attack each other.
(d) Show: among $k+1$ numbers, there is a pair whose difference is divisible by k.
(e) How many guests do you need at a party to ensure that two are born on the same day of the week? What about to ensure that two are born on a Monday?
(f) Let $x_1, x_2, \ldots, x_{n^2+1}$ be a sequence n^2+1 distinct numbers. Show that there is monotonic subsequence of length $n+1$. Specifically, assume the longest increasing subsequence has length at most n and show there is a decreasing subsequence of length at least $n+1$.
  (i) Show a generalized pigeonhole principle: if there are n pigeons and k pigeonholes, then at least one pigeonhole contains at least $\lceil n/k \rceil$ pigeons. ($\lceil z \rceil$, the ceiling function, rounds up.)
  (ii) Let ℓ_i be the length of the longest increasing subsequence that ends with x_i. Show that at least $n+1$ of the ℓ_i are equal.
  (iii) Show: if $\ell_{i_1}, \ldots, \ell_{i_k}$ are equal, then $x_{i_1}, \ldots, x_{i_k}$ are a decreasing subsequence. Use this result to finish your proof.
(g) Show: any 17 playing cards must contain a 5-card flush. (A flush is cards of the same suit).
(h) There are 51 baskets of apples. If each basket contains no more than 24 apples, show that at least 3 baskets have the same number of apples.
(i) Show: if 13 unit squares are inside a circle of radius 2, then 2 squares overlap. *[Hint: Do not use pigeonhole. Instead, think about how we proved pigeonhole.]*

14.3 Problems

It is common practice to use $[n]$ as a shorthand for the set $\{1, 2, \ldots, n\}$.

Problem 14.1. How many different words can you form using the letters: (a) ABC (b) AAA (c) AARDVARK?

Problem 14.2. How many different words can you form using the letters:
(a) REARRANGE (b) BOOKKEEPER (c) DISCRETE (d) PARALLEL (e) SUCCESS (f) MISSISSIPPI.

Problem 14.3. Using the letters in the word PEPPERONI, how many different words are there:
(a) In all? (b) That begin and end with P? (c) That have all three P's together?

Problem 14.4. The word MISSISSIPPI is scrambled into two possibly nonsensical words, e.g. IPIM SSISSIP. How many such two word anagrams are there? The order of the two words matters.

Problem 14.5. In each case, determine the number of ways the task can be performed.
(a) 10 identical candies must be distributed among 4 children.
(b) A 15-letter sequence must be made up of 5 A's, 5B's and 5C's.
(c) 10 identical rings must be placed on your 10 fingers.
(d) 3 red, 3 green and 3 blue flags are to be arranged in some order along the street for the parade.

Problem 14.6. For each word, alphabetically sort all words that can be formed from the letters. Give the word's rank (x out of y) in this alphabetic list. (a) TURING. (b) JACKASS.

Problem 14.7. Find the coefficients of x^3 and x^{17} in: (a) $(1 + \sqrt{x} + x + x^2)^{10}$ (b) $(x^{1/2} + x^{3/2} + x^{7/2})^{10}$.

Problem 14.8. What is the coefficient of x^i in $(1 + 1/x + x)^n$? How is your answer related to $T_{n,i}$ in Problem 8.3?

Problem 14.9. In how many ways can you arrange 100 books and 8 bookshelves if:
(a) The order of the books on each bookshelf matters. (A bookshelf can hold all 100 books.)
(b) The order of the books on each bookshelf does not matter.
(c) Repeat (a) and (b) if in addition each bookshelf must have at least one book.

Problem 14.10. A class has 25 boys and 25 girls. How many groups of 25 students have more girls than boys? What if there are 50 boys and 50 girls, how many groups of 50 have more girls than boys?

Problem 14.11. There are 10 pizza toppings. You can place any combination of toppings you wish on a pizza. In how many ways can you make 3 pizzas?
(a) Show that there are 2^{10} different pizzas you can make.
(b) Your friend informs you that there are $(2^{10})^3/3!$ ways to make 3 pizzas. He argues as follows: each pizza has 2^{10} choices. So the choices for our 3 pizzas is, by the product rule, $(2^{10})^3$. Since the order of the 3 pizzas does not matter, we divide by $3!$ to get the final answer. You smelled a rat because you know about modular arithmetic, and computed the remainder when $(2^{10})^3$ is divided by 6. What is the remainder and why is something wrong?
(c) Explain in words what is wrong with your friends argument and correctly compute the number of ways to make up the 3 pizzas. Your answer will be $x/3!$. Show that x is divisible by $3!$.

Problem 14.12. In each case, count the number of objects/arrangements of the given type:
(a) n-letter words, if letters are used at most once. (26 letter alphabet.)
(b) n-letter words, if letters can be reused. (26 letter alphabet.)
(c) m different colored balls are in n distinguishible urns (an urn can have 0 to m balls).
(d) m identical balls are in n distinguishible urns (an urn can have 0 to m balls).
(e) m different colored balls are in n distinguishible urns, with at most one ball in each urn.
(f) US Social-Security numbers (see Problem 13.28) with digits in strictly increasing order.
(g) US Social-Security numbers with digits in non-decreasing order.

Problem 14.13. A campus with four majors has M students of which: 1,000 are in each major; 100 are in each double-major; 10 are in each triple-major; and, 1 is in all majors. What is M?

Problem 14.14. At XYZ-College, every student takes either the SAT or the ACT. If 79.7% of students take the SAT and 41% of students take the ACT, what percentage of students take both?

Problem 14.15. Consider the binary strings consisting of 10 bits.
(a) How many contain fewer 1's than 0's?
(b) How many contain (i) 5 or more consecutive 1's (ii) 5 or more consecutive 0's?
(c) How many contain 5 or more consecutive 0's OR 5 or more consecutive 1's?

Problem 14.16. Two proof-readers A and B read a document. A finds a typos and B finds b typos. There were c typos in common. How many typos in all were found?

Problem 14.17. How many of the numbers 1,2,. . . ,1,000,000 are:
(a) Divisible by 2 or 5? (b) Not divisible by 2,3 or 5? (c) Divisible by 4 or 6?

Problem 14.18. How many 8-bit sequences (a) begin or end in 1? (b) begin in 1 or have 101 starting at position 4?

Problem 14.19. A 5-card poker hand is monochromatic if all cards are the same color; it is a flush if all cards are the same suit. How many hands are either a flush or monochromatic?

Problem 14.20. Sets A, B, C have sizes $2, 3, 4$. What are the min and max for $|A \cup B \cup C|$?

Problem 14.21. $|A_1| = 115$, $|A_2| = 125$, $|A_3| = 120$, $|A_1 \cap A_2| = 70$, $|A_1 \cap A_3| = 75$, $|A_2 \cap A_3| = 80$, $|A_1 \cap A_2 \cap A_3| = 40$. Compute the number of elements: (a) Only in A_1. (b) Only in A_2. (c) Only in A_3. (d) In all.

Problem 14.22. Determine whether the following statements are true and if so, give proofs.
(a) $|A \cup B| = |A| + |B|$ if and only if $A \cap B = \varnothing$.
(b) $|A \cup B \cup C| = |A| + |B| + |C|$ if and only if $A \cap B \cap C = \varnothing$.
(c) $|A \cup B \cup C| = |A| + |B| + |C|$ if and only if $A \cap B = \varnothing$ and $A \cap C = \varnothing$ and $B \cap C = \varnothing$.

Problem 14.23. Write out in full the inclusion-exclusion expansion of $|A_1 \cup A_2 \cup A_3 \cup A_4 \cup A_5|$.

Problem 14.24. Of 41 students in Algebra, Bio or Chem., the number failing each combination of courses is shown. How many passed all three courses?

A	B	C	AB	AC	BC	ABC
12	5	8	2	6	3	1

Problem 14.25. How many 7-digit telephone numbers are non-monotonic. A telephone number is monotonic if it's digits are either non-decreasing or non-increasing.

Problem 14.26. How many of the billion numbers $0, \ldots, 999999999$ contain a 1? Solve this problem in three ways:
(a) Compute how many do not contain a 1 and subtract from ___?___?
(b) Compute how many contain 1 one, 2 ones, . . . , 9 ones and then ___?___?
(c) Let $A_i = \{$numbers in which the ith digit is one$\}$. Compute $|A_1 \cup A_2 \cup A_3 \cup \cdots \cup A_9|$.

Problem 14.27. There are 10^k k-digit strings (repetition is allowed). How many of those strings use each digit at least once? *[Hint: How many do not contain 1? How many do not contain 1 and 2?]*

Problem 14.28. You list the numbers from 0 to 9999999. How many times does a 1 appear in the list?

Problem 14.29. Count the integer solutions to $\sum_{i=1}^{6} x_i = 27$ which satisfy, for all i, $0 \le x_i \le 9$.
(a) Find the number of solutions satisfying $x_i \ge 0$.
(b) Let A_i be the solutions with $x_i \ge 10$. How is the answer you seek related to part (a) and $|A_1 \cup A_2 \cup A_3 \cup \cdots \cup A_6|$.
(c) Compute $|A_1 \cup A_2 \cup A_3 \cup \cdots \cup A_6|$ using inclusion-exclusion and solve the problem. *[Hint: Show $|A_1 \cup A_2 \cup A_3| = 0$.]*
(d) How is your answer related to Problem 13.53(d).

Problem 14.30. Use inclusion-exclusion to count the integer solutions to $x_1 + x_2 + x_3 = 20$ where we impose the constraints $-2 \le x_1 \le 10$, $2 \le x_1 \le 8$ and $0 \le x_1 \le 15$.

Problem 14.31. w, x, y, z are non-negative integers satisfying $w + x + y + z \le 100$.
(a) How many possible solutions are there for w, x, y, z? (b) How many of those solutions have $x > 1$ OR $y > 1$?

Problem 14.32. McDonald's $1 menu has 3 items. In how many ways can you spend $10? What if you do not get more than four of any item?

Problem 14.33. Use inclusion-exclusion to count the number of integers in $[2015] = \{1, \ldots, 2015\}$ which are not divisible by any of $\{8, 12, 20\}$. *[Hint: Count the number divisible by at least one of $\{8, 12, 20\}$.]*

Problem 14.34. Consider all permutations of $\{1, 2, 3, 4, 5, 6\}$. A permutation is good if any of the sub-sequences 12, 23 or 56 appear. How many good permutations are there?

Problem 14.35. How many numbers in $[1000]$ are divisible by (a) 2 or 4? (b) 2 or 5?

Problem 14.36. Pokemon have 4 digit serial numbers, e.g. 0255. A pokemon is defective if a digit is repeated (e.g. 0255 is defective). Approximate the fraction of defective serial numbers?

Problem 14.37. A path moves up or right. We show a path from the $(0,0)$ to $(4,4)$ (white nodes). Compute the number of different paths from $(0,0)$ to $(4,4)$.

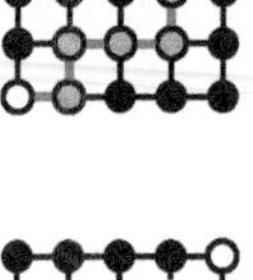

(a) Use build up counting. Let $P(n,m)$ be the number of paths from $(0,0)$ to (n,m). Show that $P(n,m) = P(n-1,m) + P(n,m-1)$.
(b) What are $P(0,m)$ and $P(n,0)$?
(c) Using (a),(b) compute $P(4,4)$, the number of paths from $(0,0)$ to $(4,4)$.
(d) Explain why $P(n,m) = \binom{n+m}{n}$.

A terrorist attack has taken out the two nodes $(1,2)$ and $(3,3)$, as shown.

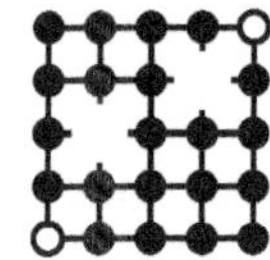

(e) How does your build up counting method need to be modified? Compute the number of paths from $(0,0)$ to $(4,4)$ that remain in the defective grid.
(f) Use inclusion-exclusion to show that the number of paths remaining equals:

$$\binom{8}{4} - \binom{3}{1}\binom{5}{2} - \binom{6}{3}\binom{2}{1} + \binom{3}{1}\binom{3}{1}\binom{2}{1}$$

Problem 14.38. You roll 8 distinguishible dice. In each case, how many outcomes are there?
(a) Not containing a 1. (b) Not containing a 1 or 2. (c) Containing all 6 numbers.*[Hint: Inclusion-exclusion.]* How is your answer to (c) related to the onto functions from $[8]$ to $[6]$?

Problem 14.39. How many permutations of $\{1,\ldots,6\}$ keep: (a) One element fixed? (b) Two elements fixed?

Problem 14.40 (Derangements). The n people who checked in their hats each left with someone else's hat. Show that this can be done in: $D_n = n!\sum_{i=0}^{n}(-1)^i/i!$ ways. *[Hint: Use inclusion-exclusion for $|B_1 \cup B_2 \cup \cdots \cup B_n|$ where B_i contains the arrangements for which person i has his hat. The answer is $n! - |B_1 \cup B_2 \cup \cdots \cup B_n|$, why?]* Recall the recursion for derangements: $D_1 = 0; D_2 = 1$ and $D_n = (n-1)(D_{n-1} + D_{n-2})$. Prove by induction that the formula for D_n satisfies this recursion.

Problem 14.41. Recall the number of dearrangements of n objects, $D_n = n!\sum_{i=0}^{n}(-1)^i/i!$. Let $D_{n,k}$ be the number of arrangements of n objects so that k are in their correct position.
(a) Prove that $\sum_{k=0}^{n} D_{n,k} = n!$.
(b) Show that $D_{n,k} = \binom{n}{k}D_{n-k}$, hence $\sum_{k=0}^{n}\binom{n}{k}D_{n-k} = n!$. (A combinatorial proof.)
(c) Show $\sum_{k=0}^{n}\binom{n}{k}D_k = n!$. *[Hint: Show $\sum_{k=0}^{n}\binom{n}{k}D_{n-k} = \sum_{k=0}^{n}\binom{n}{k}D_k$. Note $D_{n-k} \neq D_k$.]*
(d) Use (a) and (b) to show that $\sum_{k=0}^{n}\sum_{\ell=0}^{n-k}(-1)^\ell/(k!\ell!) = 1$. (A combinatorial proof.)
(e) Prove (d) by induction. *[Hint: Show $\sum_{k=0}^{n}\sum_{\ell=0}^{n-k}(-1)^\ell/(k!\ell!) = 1 + \sum_{s=1}^{n} 1/s! \sum_{k=0}^{s}\binom{s}{k}(-1)^k$.]*

Problem 14.42. Joey Gotitwrong gave the following combinatorial argument. To choose a k-subset from n elements, choose an r-subset (in $\binom{n}{r}$ ways), $r \geq k$, then a k subset from the r-subset (in $\binom{r}{k}$ ways). By the product rule the number of ways to choose a k-subset, is $\binom{n}{k} = \binom{n}{r}\binom{r}{k}$. Explain Joey's error. Give a combinarorial proof of the correct identity, $\binom{r}{k}\binom{n}{r} = \binom{n}{k}\binom{n-k}{r-k}$. *[Hint: Choose a team of r with k starters from n players in two ways: choose the team, then the starters; choose the starters, then the rest of the team. Explain why your proof works.]*

Problem 14.43. Prove that $(n!)^n$ divides $(n^2)!$. Prove it: algebraically (induction); combinatorially (multinomial coefficient); number theoretically *[Hint: number of times prime p divides $x!$]*.

Problem 14.44. For a prime p, prove that $(n_1 + n_2 + \cdots + n_k)^p \equiv n_1^p + n_2^p + \cdots + n_k^p \pmod{p}$.
[Hints: Multinomial theorem. Show that, when p is prime, p divides $\binom{p}{i_1,i_2,\ldots,i_k}$ if $i_1, i_2, \ldots, i_k$ are all less than p.]

Problem 14.45. Use the Binomial Theorem and the identity $(1+x)^m(1+x)^n = (1+x)^{m+n}$ to prove the Vandermonde convolution identity in Problem 13.64(k), $\sum_{k=0}^{\ell}\binom{n}{k}\binom{m}{\ell-k} = \binom{m+n}{\ell}$.

Problem 14.46. A drawer has 10 red and 10 blue socks. What is the minimum number of socks must you pull out to guarantee: (a) getting a pair of the same color? (b) getting a pair of blue socks?

Problem 14.47. How many guests ensure that two are born in: (a) The same month? (b) May?

Problem 14.48. ID-card numbers at a school start with an uppercase letter, followed by a 2-bit binary string followed by another uppercase letter followed by two decimal digits, e.g. $J01E38$.

(a) How many possible ID-numbers are there?

(b) 40,000 students get IDs. At least how many of the student IDs must satisfy each criterion:
(i) Have the same first letter? (ii) Have the same first letter and last digit? (iii) Start with J?

Problem 14.49. Pick any 51 different numbers from 1,...,100. Prove that two are consecutive.

Problem 14.50. For any 11 numbers, prove that two have a difference that is divisible by 10.

Problem 14.51. Bridge, Hearts and Majong each require 4 players to play. Ten students each know to play one of these three games. Prove that at least one of the games can be played.

Problem 14.52. You have 10 numbers $x_1, \ldots, x_{10}$ where $x_i \in [0, 100]$. Show that there are two distinct subsets of the numbers that have the same subset sum.

Problem 14.53. A comparison scale which you can use at most twice can only compare weights.

(a) You have 9 balls. One is heavier. Show how to determine which ball is heavier.

(b) If you had 10 balls (one being heavier), prove that you cannot guarantee finding the heavier ball.

Problem 14.54. Let S be a set of $n+1$ distinct numbers chosen from the set $\{1, 2, \ldots, 2n\}$.

(a) Estimate the number of ways to choose S when $n = 100$. *[Hint:* $\log n! = \sum_{i=1}^{n} \log i$.*]*

(b) Show that there are two numbers $x, y \in S$ with $\gcd(x, y) = 1$. *[Hint:* $\gcd(k, k+1) = 1$.*]*

Problem 14.55. Solve these problems using the pigeonhole principle, by identifying the right pigeons and pigeonholes.

(a) The points on the plane are colored red or blue. Prove that there are two points of the same color which are exactly 1 mile apart. *[Hint: Equilateral triangle.]*

(b) Let $n \in \mathbb{N}$. Some multiple of n has only the digits 0 and 5. *[Hint:* $5, 55, 555, \ldots \pmod n$.*]*

(c) 25 castles are placed on an 8×8 chessboard. Prove that 4 do not attack each other (castles on the same row or column attack each other). Arrange 24 castles so that no 4 are mutually non-attacking (prove it).

(d) Prove that if you pick any 101 numbers from the set $[200]$, some number is a multiple of another. *[Hint: Any number x has a unique representation $x = 2^k y$ where y is odd.]* (For a proof by induction, see Problem 5.47.)

(e) A shape having area greater than 1 can be translated so that it will cover at least two of the lattice points in the standard Cartesian coordinate system.

(f) For any set of n integers, there is a subset whose sum is divisible by n.

(g) Twelve points in a 5×4 grid are colored green. Show that some rectangle has four green vertices.

(h) In a friendship network with more than 200 people, everyone has at least 1 friend and no one has more than 100 friends. Show that at least 3 people have the same number of friends.

(i) Six points are placed on a unit circle. Show that two are a distance at most 1 apart.

(j) Using a comparison scale, you wish to measure any integer number of pounds of sugar from $1, 2, \ldots, M$. Prove that with k weights, $M \le (3^k - 1)/2$. (Problem 5.52 shows how to achieve this bound.)

(k) A dad has 10 kids. A candy machine has candy in many colors: 1 of color C_1, 2 of color C_2, ..., 20 of color C_{20}. Candies come out randomly. How many candies must dad be ready to buy if all kids are to get the same color?

Problem 14.56. Show: there is no bijection $f : \mathbb{N} \mapsto \mathbb{N}$ for which $f(n) \le n$ for all n, with strict inequality for some n. *[Hint: Well-ordering plus pigeonhole.]* (This is a "No-free-lunch" for file compression: if a lossless file compression scheme strictly compresses some files, it must expand some other files. ☹)

Problem 14.57. Prove a generalization of the pigeonhole principle: the maximum of any finite set of numbers is at least the average. Show how this implies the pigeonhole principle.

Problem 14.58. Let $S = \{1, 2, \ldots, 2n\}$ and let $L \subset S$ be a subset of size $n+1$.

(a) In how many ways can you select L. Simplify your answer using Stirling's approximation.

(b) Show that every choice for L contains two numbers that are relatively prime. *[Hint:* $(1,2)(3,4)\cdots(2n-1, 2n)$.*]*

(c) Show that every choice for L contains two numbers with one being a multiple of the other.

Problem 14.59 (Bins with Capacities). Let $F(n, k, m)$ count ways to place n balls into k bins where each bin can hold at most m balls ($n \le mk$). The balls are indistinguishible, so you only care about the number of balls in each bin. Use inclusion-exclusion to show:

$$F(n, k, m) = \sum_{i=0}^{\lfloor k/(m+1) \rfloor} (-1)^i \binom{k}{i} \binom{n - i(m+1) + k - 1}{k-1}.$$

[Hint: If A_i are ways for bin i to have more than m, $F(n, k, m) = \binom{n+k-1}{k-1} - |A_1 \cup A_2 \cup \cdots \cup A_k|$.*]*

Problem 14.60. How many k-digit numbers have a digit-sum s? This problem guides you through a powerful solution method that uses generating functions.

(a) Think of picking each digit as picking a term from the polynomial $(x^0 + x^1 + \cdots + x^9)$. Let
$$G(x) = (x^0 + x^1 + \cdots + x^9)^k.$$
Prove that the coefficient of x^s is the solution to the problem.

(b) Show that $G(x) = (1 - x^{10})^k (1 - x)^{-k}$.

(c) Show that $(1 - x^{10})^k = \sum_{i=0}^{k} (-1)^i \binom{k}{i} x^{10i}$ and $(1 - x)^{-k} = \sum_{j=0}^{\infty} \binom{k+j-1}{j} x^j$, hence that
$$G(x) = \Big(\sum_{i=0}^{k} (-1)^i \binom{k}{i} x^{10i}\Big) \cdot \Big(\sum_{j=0}^{\infty} \binom{k+j-1}{j} x^j\Big).$$

(d) A term x^s in (c) is obtained by taking a term i in the first sum and a term $s - 10i$ in the second. Hence, show that the coefficient of x^s is
$$\sum_{i=0}^{\lfloor s/10 \rfloor} (-1)^i \binom{k}{i} \binom{k + s - 10i - 1}{k - 1}.$$

(e) How is the formula in (d) related to Problem 14.59?

(f) Use the formula in (d) with $k = 6$ and $s = 27$. Compare with Problems 14.29 and 13.53(d).

Problem 14.61. Count the number of integer solutions to $x_1 + x_2 + x_3 = 30$ where $0 \le x_1 \le 10$, $0 \le x_2 \le 15$ and $0 \le x_3 \le 20$. Generating functions are a powerful tool for such problems.

(a) Think of picking x_1 as picking a term from the polynomial $(x^0 + x^1 + \cdots + x^{10})$, similarly picking x_2 is picking a term from the polynomial $(x^0 + x^1 + \cdots + x^{15})$ and picking x_3 is picking a term from the polynomial $(x^0 + x^1 + \cdots + x^{20})$. These polynomials are the generating functions for x_1, x_2, x_3. The generating function for the sum is the product,
$$G(x) = (x^0 + x^1 + \cdots + x^{10})(x^0 + x^1 + \cdots + x^{15})(x^0 + x^1 + \cdots + x^{20}).$$
Prove that the coefficient of x^{30} in $G(x)$ is the solution to the problem we seek.

(b) Prove that $G(x) = (1 - x^{11})(1 - x^{16})(1 - x^{21})(1 - x)^{-3}$.

(c) Let c_k be the coefficient of x^k in the expansion of $(1 - x)^{-3}$. Show that $c_k = (k + 1)(k + 2)/2$.

(d) Prove that the coefficient of x^{30} in $G(x)$ is $c_{30} - c_{19} - c_{14} - c_9 + c_3$. (Cf. Exercise 14.5(c))

(e) Solve the same problem with the constraints $-3 \le x_1 \le 7$, $2 \le x_2 \le 17$ and $1 \le x_3 \le 21$.

Problem 14.62. A walker at $(0, 0)$ takes n steps right. At each step she moves up, down or stays at the same level (trinomial walk). Contrast this with the (binomial) walker in Problem 13.93 who only moves up or down. The walker ends at position (n, i), $-n \le i \le n$? Hany different paths are possible? How is your answer related to Problem 14.7.

Problem 14.63. Here are some counting problems on graphs to challenge you.

(a) How many simple undirected graphs are there with n vertices?

(b) How many directed graphs are there with n vertices? (No self loops.)

(c) How many tournaments are there with n vertices?

(d) How many tournaments with n vertices have no cycles? *[Hint: Problem 11.69.]*

(e) Show that the number of Hamiltonian cycles in K_n is $(n - 1)!$.

(f) How many perfect matchings are there in $K_{n,n}$?

(g) How many Hamiltonian cycles are in $K_{n,n}$?

(h) Show that the number of spanning trees in K_n is n^{n-2}.

(i) How many spanning trees are in $K_{2,n}$? How many spanning trees are in $K_{n,m}$?

The probable is what usually happens. – **Aristotle**

No man ever wetted clay and then left it, as if there would be bricks by chance and fortune. – **Plutarch**

It is probable to see something improbable in a lifetime.

Chapter 15

Probability

1: The mathematics of uncertainty.
2: How to compute a probability: the sample space, outcome-tree and events.

Chances of rain tomorrow are 40%. What does the probability "40%" mean? It either rains or not. We will not indulge in philosophy, except to give you a flavor for the ongoing debate. One side views the 40% as a subjective degree of belief. A more practical group are the frequentists: if you re-live tomorrow 100 times, on about 40 of the days it will rain. Short of a time-machine, how do you re-live tomorrow? Did I say more practical? 🙂 Here is a repeatable experiment that we can do: toss a coin. If you repeat 100 times, for practical purposes, the tosses are identical and you should see approximately 50 heads. This hypothetical ideal experiment corresponds to the abstract statement: a fair coin flip will be heads with probability $\frac{1}{2}$.

Pop Quiz 15.1
How do you interpret these statements?
(a) John Smith, diagnosed with liver disease, has a 30% chance of living to seventy.
(b) An internet packet has a 99.99% chance of reaching its destination.
(c) Chances are 50-50 that I make it to Washington for your wedding.

Our focus is "mechanical" probability, which finds application in physics (statistical and quantum mechanics), economics and game theory, biology and sociology, financial markets, machine learning from big data,. . . , and very importantly computing. Probability is a fundamental tool at the heart of modern computer science, for example primality testing, hashing, internet protocols, sampling, evolutionary algorithms. Probability allows you to reason about experiments whose outcomes are uncertain. Ponder these two questions.

1. You toss a fair coin 3 times. How many heads will you get?
2. You keep tossing a fair coin until you get a head. How many tosses will you make?

Instead of classical axiomatic probability, due to Kolmogorov, we discuss the mechanical rules for computing probabilities. The main ideas can be absorbed when the possible outcomes are discrete. For more general sets of outcomes, things get technical, e.g. measure theory. Let's develop a framework for computing probabilities.

15.1 Computing Probabilities

Mathematical probability was born in a 1654 correspondence between Blaise Pascal and Pierre de Fermat when Antoine Gombaud, Chevalier de Méré, asked Pascal whether to bet even money on at least one 'double-six' during 24 rolls of a pair of dice. Here are two simpler games. Which game you prefer?

1. Toss two coins. You win if the coins match: HH or TT.
2. Roll a pair of dice. You win if the first roll is less than the second.

We outline 6 steps for using probability to pick the better game. Step 1, make sure that probability is relevant.

1. You are analyzing an experiment or game whose outcome is uncertain.

Consider tossing the two coins. Is the outcome uncertain? Yes. Now identify the set of *possible* outcomes. As we did with counting, treat the experiment as a sequence of precisely defined steps. Every step in the experiment produces a branching of the possible outcomes, resulting in a tree of possible outcome sequences.

2. Identify all possible outcomes using a tree of outcome sequences.

The experiment begins at •, the root of the outcome-tree. The first branch is the first toss, H or T, which is a partial outcome of the experiment. After the first toss are two possibilities for the second toss, H or T. A path from the root to a leaf is an outcome. There are four outcomes. We labeled each outcome by the path leading to the outcome, for example HH means coin 1 is heads and coin 2 is heads. We have four outcome sequences {HH, HT, TH, TT}.

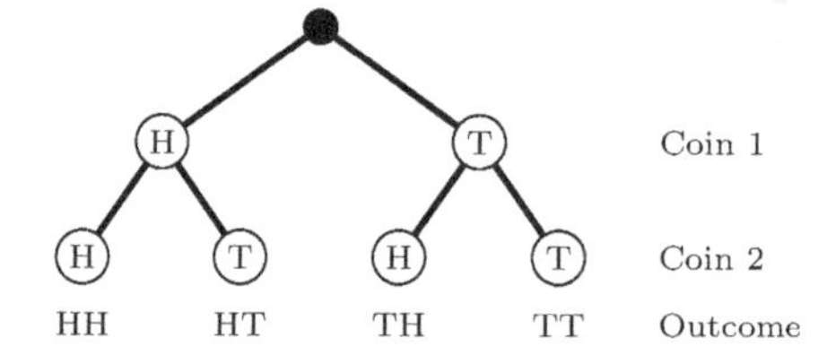

Identifying the outcomes is like counting, remember that. Each outcome is a complex object determined by a sequence of steps. When counting, we wanted the number of objects. Now, we are interested in the actual objects, the specific outcomes of the experiment. So far, there is no mention of probability. Probabilities specify how steps in the experiment are implemented. How do you determine the outcome of the first coin? By toss coin 1, we usually mean toss it randomly, which means each option has equal probability.

3. Fill in the edge probabilities. If there are k edges (options) from a vertex, and an option is chosen randomly then each edge has probability $1/k$.

There are two edges out of each vertex, so each edge-probability is $\frac{1}{2}$. A coin is a randomization device that picks one of two outcomes randomly, each with equal probability $\frac{1}{2}$. If you tossed the coin many times, about half the outcomes would be H and the other half would be T. Follow the red path. You first randomly picked H and then T to end at outcome HT. The outcome-probability is the product of the edge-probabilities along the path leading to the outcome HT,

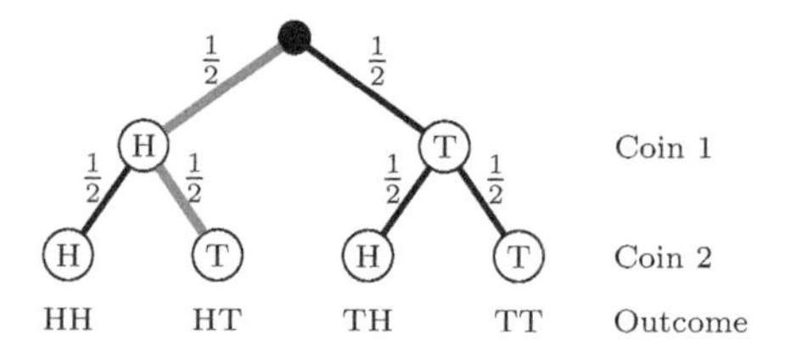

$$P(\text{HT}) = \text{outcome-probability for HT} = 1/2 \times 1/2 = 1/4.$$

4. Multiply edge-probabilities to compute every outcome-probability.

Once you get all outcomes and their outcome-probabilities, you have the probabilistic specification of the experiment (right). Enumerating outcomes and computing outcome-probabilities is purely mechanical. What use are these mechanical probabilities? Do they help us reason about the game, or are they just fictitious abstract numbers?

The probabilities are abstract, but there is a concrete link to the game. Imagine playing 100 games. Of these 100 games, in about half of them, that is 50 games, coin 1's toss will be H. For half of these 50 games where coin 1's toss is H, coin 2's toss will be T and the outcome will be HT. The outcome HT occurs about 25 times $= 100 \times 1/4$:

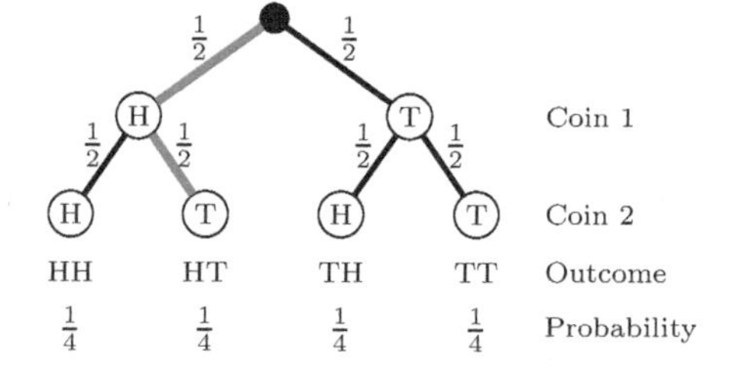

$$\text{number of times an outcome occurs} \approx \text{number of games played} \times P(\text{outcome}).$$

The outcome-probability reflects the frequency of an outcome, the fraction of times it occurs if the experiment is repeated many times. This is the frequency interpretation of a probability.

15.1.1 The Event of Interest

To determine how often you win, you identify the outcomes where you win. The subset of outcomes where you win is the event of interest. The event is usually a set of outcomes that provides an answer to a question.

Question: When do you win? → **Event:** Subset of outcomes where you win.

> **5. Determine the event of interest, a subset of the outcomes.**
> **6. Compute the event-probability by summing its outcome-probabilities.**

You win when the two coins match. The outcomes where you win are highlighted in green. Adding up the outcome-probabilities for the event of interest gives the event-probability, denoted by $\mathbb{P}$,

$$\mathbb{P}[\text{"Win"}] = 1/4 + 1/4 = 1/2.$$

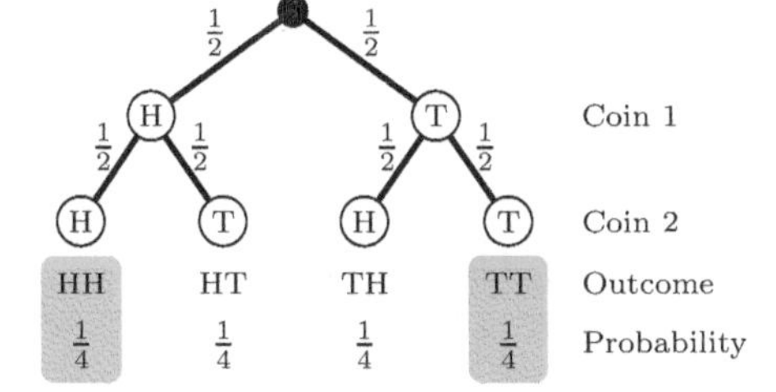

The event-probability tells you how often an outcome in the event occurs. You win 50% of the games. Note, the sum of all outcome-probabilities is 1 or 100% because some outcome must occur. Here is a summary of our probabilistic analysis.

> **1.** You are analyzing an experiment whose outcome is uncertain.
> **2.** Identify possible outcomes using a tree of outcome sequences.
> **3.** Compute the edge-probability for each edge in the outcome-tree.
> **4.** Multiply edge-probabilities to obtain outcome-probabilities.
> **5.** Determine the event of interest $\mathcal{E}$, a subset of the outcomes.
> **6.** Compute the event's probability by summing its outcome-probabilities.
>
> $$\mathbb{P}[\mathcal{E}] = \sum_{\text{outcomes } \omega \in \mathcal{E}} P(\omega).$$
>
> You interpret $\mathbb{P}[\mathcal{E}]$ as the frequency that one of the outcomes in the event of interest will occur, if you repeated the experiment many times.

Memorize this 6-step process and analyze the dice game in the next Pop Quiz. We will then do more examples.

Pop Quiz 15.2
You roll a pair of dice and win if the first roll is less than the second. Give the outcome-tree with edge-probabilities and compute the probability to win. Do you prefer the coin or dice game? Explain.

Example 15.1 (Let's Make A Deal). The Monty Hall puzzle is from the TV game show *Let's Make a Deal*. There are three doors, 1, 2, 3. The contestant is at door 1 and a prize is randomly placed behind a door. Monty *must* reveal one of the other doors which is empty. Here, he opens door 2 and you now get to switch to door 3, if you wish. You win if the prize is behind your final door. This seems like a 50-50 proposition. Either the prize is behind your current door or the other door.

To switch or not? The Monty Hall problem gained fame when Marilyn Mach (*aka* Marilyn vos Savant) told readers of her NY-Times column *Ask Marilyn* that your odds of winning double if you switch. The backlash was fierce. Even professional mathematicians accused Marilyn of misleading a math-challenged public. Marilyn was right and her critics were wrong. Let's use the 6-step process to analyze the game.

Steps 1,2 and 3: outcome-tree and edge probabilities. To determine if one should switch, let us set up the outcome-tree with edge-probabilities. The game has 3 stages. First, the contestant stands at door 1. Then, the prize-door is picked randomly from 3 doors[1], with edge-probabilities 1/3. Lastly, the host opens an

[1] To pick one among k options randomly, each having probability $1/k$, you need a randomizing device that picks each option roughly once in k tries. Most computing platforms have a built in function such as `random()` for this task.

empty door. Here is a summary of the game with the outcome-tree drawn horizontally.

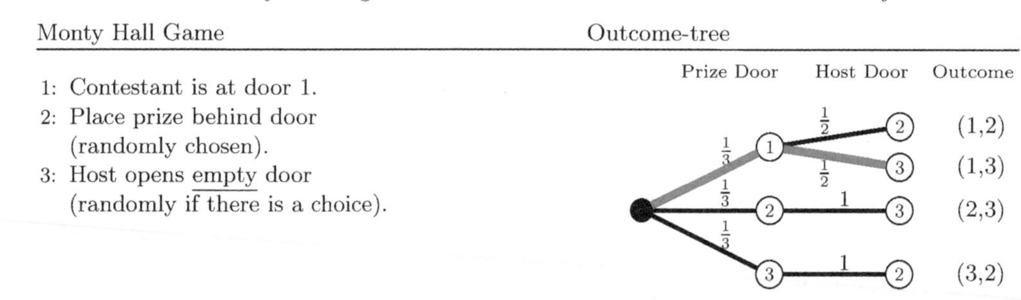

An outcome, e.g., (1,3) means (prize at door 1, host opens door 3). Intermediate vertices on a path to an outcome are partial outcomes which have edges to each option available at that stage of the game.

Pop Quiz 15.3

Why is there one edge from the partial outcome with prize-door ② but two edges from prize-door ①?

Step 4: Outcome-probabilities. Follow the red path to outcome $(1,3)$. Multiplying the edge-probabilities gives the outcome-probability $P(1,3) = 1/3 \times 1/2 = 1/6$. We can compute all outcome-probabilities,

$$P(1,2) = 1/6; \qquad P(1,3) = 1/6; \qquad P(2,3) = 1/3; \qquad P(3,2) = 1/3.$$

Step 5: Event of interest. To determine whether to switch doors, we must identify the event of interest.

Question: When does switching win? $\rightarrow$ **Event:** Outcomes where you win by switching.

The winning outcomes if you switch are (2,3) and (3,2), when the prize-door is 2 or 3. The event of interest is $\{(2,3),(3,2)\}$. The outcome-tree with outcome-probabilities and the event of interest highlighted in green is:

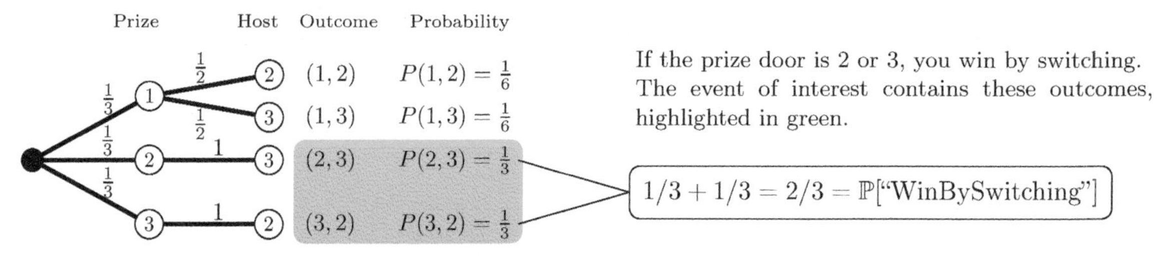

6. Compute the event-probability, the sum of the event's outcome-probabilities (in green). The probability to win if you switch is $\frac{2}{3}$. The complementary event, where you win by staying is also interesting.

$$\mathbb{P}[\text{"WinBySwitching"}] = 1/3 + 1/3 = 2/3 \qquad \mathbb{P}[\text{"WinByStaying"}] = 1/6 + 1/6 = 1/3.$$

If you always switch, in the long run you win about twice as many games as you lose. Intuitively, the prize is equally likely to be behind door 1, 2 or 3 and in two of the three prize doors you win by switching.

Pop Quiz 15.4

(a) Determine if it is still better to always switch in the Monty Hall game if:
   (i) The contestant is allowed to choose the door at the beginning.
   (ii) Monty picks door 3 with probability $\frac{2}{3}$ (not $\frac{1}{2}$) at partial outcome (1).
(b) Compute the probability to win if the contestant randomly decides to switch or stay.
(c) Analyze the Monte hall game with four doors. Compute $\mathbb{P}[\text{"WinBySwitching"}]$ and $\mathbb{P}[\text{"WinByStaying"}]$.

Probability can trap even great mathematicians. You can escape unscathed by checking your answer with a Monte-Carlo simulation. There is no need to imagine playing the Monty Hall game. You can actually play the game virtually. There is nothing fictitious or abstract about the experiment in Exercise 15.5.

Exercise 15.5 [Monte-Carlo Simulation of The Mondy Hall Game]

The algorithm on the right simulates the Monty Hall game n times. The variable count contains the number of times each outcome occurs: count[1] for (3,2); count[2] for (2,3); count[3] for (1,2); count[4] for (1,3). The variable prize is where the prize is, and host is the door opened (only needed if the prize is behind door 1). The crucial object in this pseudocode is the function rand() which generates a random real number in the interval $[0,1]$. The function rand() is a randomizing device. Most programming languages have such a built in function. The design of such randomizing devices is a complex, nevertheless crucial task in probability theory. Implement the algorithm in your favorite programming language.

```
1: count=[0,0,0,0];
2: for i=1 to n do
3:   prize=⌈rand() * 3⌉;
4:   if prize=3 then
5:     add 1 to count[1];
6:   else if prize=2 then
7:     add 1 to count[2];
8:   else
9:     host=1+⌈rand() * 2⌉;
10:    if host=2 then
11:      add 1 to count[3];
12:    else
13:      add 1 to count[4];
14: return count;
```

(a) Simulate 120 games. Report how many times the outcomes occur and how many times prize=1,2,3. Explain you observations.
(b) If your strategy is to switch doors, how many times did you win.
(c) Which strategy is better, to switch or not to switch doors?
(d) Repeat (a)–(c) for 1,200 and 12,000 games. Report the win/loss ratio for switching.

□

Example 15.2 (Non-transitive dice). Here is an amusing way to show your history-major friend Ayfos why he should major computer science instead. We show the faces of 3 dice.

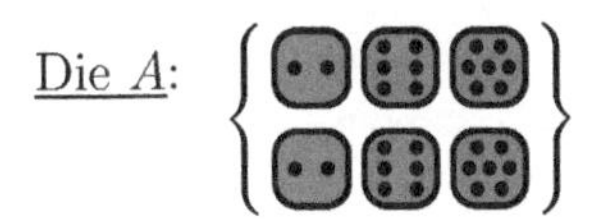

Some faces on a die have the same number of spots. There's nothing wrong with that. Here is the script.

You: "How about some fun? We each pick one die and roll. The loser pays the winner \$1."
Tiny Ayfos: "Hmm, sounds fishy. What's the catch?"
You: "To put you at ease, you can pick first. I'll even let you change your die as often as you want."
Tiny Ayfos: "Hmm, ok, I guess that sounds fair. After all, if my die is losing I can take yours."

Alas, the dice battle begins,... and 1,000 rolls later, Ayfos is down about \$100 despite his many psychic tactics. You better pay for dinner, for your strategy was simple but sly. If Ayfos picks die C, you pick B; if he picks B, you pick A; and, if he picks A you pick C. Probability will help us see why this strategy works. Consider die A versus B. Imagine an experiment which rolls die A, then die B. Each die-face is equally likely. Since each die has two faces for each value, each value on a die is equally likely. Let's use the outcome-tree.

Die A versus B. The first branch in the outcome-tree is for the possible rolls of die A. For each roll of die A, the second branch gives the possible rolls of die B. Is die A is better than die B? We highlighted in green the outcomes where die A wins. These outcomes define the event

$$\mathcal{E} = \text{“Die}A\text{Beats}B\text{”}$$

The event-probability is the sum of outcome-probabilities,

$$\mathbb{P}[\text{“Die}A\text{Beats}B\text{”}] = 5/9.$$

Since die A wins more than half the time, we prefer die A to B. Please perform the same analysis for die A versus C and die B versus C. You will appreciate that we need shortcuts to make life easier. Notice that the outcome-probabilities always sum to 1. For this experiment, all the outcome-probabilities equal 1/9. This special case is a uniform probability-space, because the outcome-probabilities are uniform – all the same.

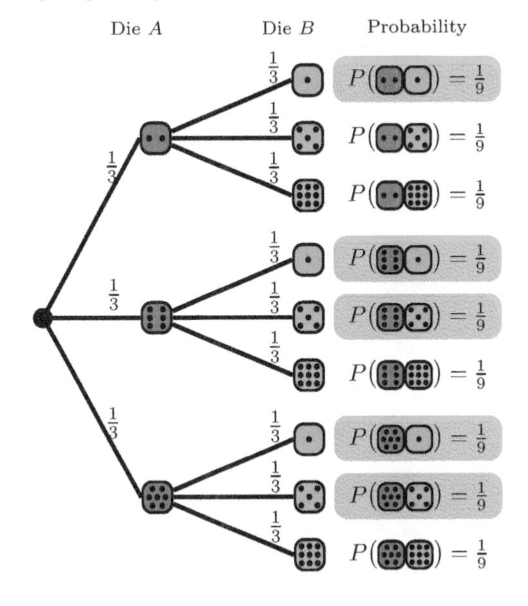

For uniform probability spaces, computing event-probabilities simplifies. Let P be the probability of an outcome. Since the sum of the outcome-probabilities equals 1,

$$1 = P \times \text{Number of possible outcomes} \qquad \to \qquad P = \frac{1}{\text{Number of possible outcomes}}.$$

In our example, the number of outcomes is 9 so $P = 1/9$. Adding outcome-probabilities in an event $\mathcal{E}$ gives

$$\mathbb{P}[\text{event } \mathcal{E}] = P \times \text{Number of outcomes in } \mathcal{E} = \frac{\text{Number of outcomes in } \mathcal{E}}{\text{Number of possible outcomes}}.$$

This formula holds for events in a uniform probability space and says that to get an event-probability you need only count the number of outcomes in the event. There are 5 outcomes where die A beats B, so $\mathbb{P}[\text{"Die}A\text{Beats}B\text{"}] = 5/9$. Our life is now a lot easier. Let's compare die A with C. As with A versus B, there are 9 outcomes with uniform probabilities all equal to $1/9$. The event "Die$C$Beats$A$" contains five outcomes,

"Die$C$Beats$A$" = {…} $\to$ $\mathbb{P}[\text{"Die}C\text{Beats}A\text{"}] = 5/9$.

Similarly, the event "Die$B$BeatsC" contains 5 outcomes,

"Die$B$Beats$C$" = {…} $\to$ $\mathbb{P}[\text{"Die}B\text{Beats}C\text{"}] = 5/9$.

Die A beats B, B beats C and C beats A. Whichever die Ayfos picks, you can win 5/9 of the games. Your edge is 11%. The conclusion that the dice are not transitive is peculiar. Probability is counter-intuitive.

Exercise 15.6

(a) Use Monte-Carlo to simulate 1000 rolls of a battle between each pair of dice in Example 15.2. Report the number of games won by each die in each battle.

(b) In Example 15.2, roll each die twice. The higher sum wins. Now, what is your strategy against Ayfos. Use Monte-Carlo to verify your conclusions. (Probability continues to rear its counter-intuitive head!)

(c) Change die A to have the six faces {…}.

  (i) Redo the analysis in Example 15.2. How often does each die win in pairwise battles. Use Monte-Carlo to verify your results. *[Hint: The outcome-probabilities involving die A are not uniform.]*

  (ii) What is Ayfos' optimal strategy, and how many of 1000 games will he win?

□

15.2 Probability and Sets

We now define a probability space formally. A probability space has two parts:

1. **Sample Space Ω.** The sample space $\Omega = \{\omega_1, \omega_2, \ldots\}$ is the set of possible outcomes.
2. **Probability Function $P(\cdot)$.** The probability function assigns a non-negative number $P(\omega)$ to each possible outcome $\omega \in \Omega$. The probability function is normalized, so that all probabilities sum to 1,

$$0 \le P(\omega) \le 1 \qquad \text{and} \qquad \sum_{\omega \in \Omega} P(\omega) = 1.$$

Any sample space and probability function form a valid probability space. In our experiments, the 6-step outcome-tree method gave the probability spaces below. Notice that outcome-probabilities sum to 1.

Tossing two coins:

ω	HH	HT	TH	TT
$P(\omega)$	1/4	1/4	1/4	1/4

Monty Hall game:

ω	(1, 2)	(1, 3)	(2, 3)	(3, 2)
$P(\omega)$	1/6	1/6	1/3	1/3

Die A versus B:

ω	…	…	…	…	…	…	…	…	…
$P(\omega)$	1/9	1/9	1/9	1/9	1/9	1/9	1/9	1/9	1/9

Outcomes in a probability space can look complex. Don't fret. A probability space just abstractly represents an experiment when the outcome of the experiment is uncertain.

Pop Quiz 15.7

For the battle between die A from Exercise 15.6(c) and die B from Example 15.2, show that the probability space has the same outcomes with different outcome-probabilities:

Ω									
$P(\omega)$	1/6	1/6	1/6	1/18	1/18	1/18	1/9	1/9	1/9

Pop Quiz 15.8

Which of these are valid probability spaces?

(a)

ω	H	HT
$P(\omega)$	1/4	3/4

(b)

ω	H	HT
$P(\omega)$	π	$1-\pi$

(c)

ω	a	b	c	d
$P(\omega)$	1/2	1/3	1/4	1/5

Events. An event $\mathcal{E}$ is any subset of outcomes, $\mathcal{E} \subseteq \Omega$. In practice, an event is expressed in words:

"When is it better to switch in the Monty Hall game?"

The corresponding subset is $\{(2,3),(3,2)\}$. A crucial step in analyzing the "plain English" question is to convert it into an appropriate subset. The event-probability is the sum of its outcome-probabilities.

$$\mathbb{P}[\mathcal{E}] = \sum_{\omega \in \mathcal{E}} P(\omega) = \text{probability that some outcome in } \mathcal{E} \text{ occurs.}$$

Two simple events are the empty event $\varnothing$ and Ω itself, and $\mathbb{P}[\varnothing] = 0$ and $\mathbb{P}[\Omega] = 1$. Let's clarify the notation $P(\cdot)$ versus $\mathbb{P}[\cdot]$. The outcome-probability function $P(\cdot)$ is for atomic outcomes $\omega \in \Omega$. The event-probability function $\mathbb{P}[\cdot]$ is for sets of outcomes. The input to $\mathbb{P}[\cdot]$ is a set of outcomes. For example,

$$P(\omega) = \mathbb{P}[\{\omega\}].$$

We use $\mathbb{P}[\mathcal{E}]$ to distinguish an event-probability from an outcome-probability $P(\omega)$.

An event is just a set. We can use set operations to construct more complex events from simpler ones. For the die A versus die B probability space, define three events,

"$A > B$" $\quad \mathcal{E}_1 = \{\ldots\}$

"Sum > 8" $\quad \mathcal{E}_2 = \{\ldots\}$

"$B < 9$" $\quad \mathcal{E}_3 = \{\ldots\}$

We can combine these events using the logical connectors OR, AND, NOT, IF...THEN, which, for sets, corresponds to union, intersection, complement, subset. For example,

"$A > B$" OR "Sum > 8" $\quad \mathcal{E}_1 \cup \mathcal{E}_2 = \{\ldots\}$

"$A > B$" AND "Sum > 8" $\quad \mathcal{E}_1 \cap \mathcal{E}_2 = \{\ldots\}$

NOT("$A > B$") $\quad \overline{\mathcal{E}_1} = \{\ldots\}$

IF "$A > B$" THEN "$B < 9$" $\quad \mathcal{E}_1 \subseteq \mathcal{E}_3$

Exercise 15.9

Here are some student statistics: 50% have black hair; 30% have blonde hair; 60% have brown eyes.

(a) You pick a student randomly. Describe the probability space.
(b) What is $\mathbb{P}$["student has either black hair or blonde hair"]?
(c) What is $\mathbb{P}$["student has neither black hair nor blonde hair"]?
(d) What is $\mathbb{P}$["student has either black hair or brown eyes"]?
(e) What is $\mathbb{P}$["student has black hair and brown eyes"]?

Probability behaves very similarly to the size of a set. Each element of a set contributes 1 to the size. When it comes to probability, each outcome in a set contributes a weight between 0 and 1 to the total probability. The probability of a set is a "soft" version of size. Hence, the behavior of the probability when you combine sets is very similar to the behavior of the size when you combine sets. For example, the sum rule for adding probabilities of disjoint sets, inclusion-exclusion, etc. The next exercise is very instructive.

Exercise 15.10 [Set properties of probabilities]

(a) **(Sum Rule)** If events $\mathcal{E}_1$ and $\mathcal{E}_2$ cannot occur together, $\mathcal{E}_1 \cap \mathcal{E}_2 = \varnothing$, and they are mutually exclusive or disjoint. For disjoint events, prove that $\mathbb{P}[\mathcal{E}_1 \cup \mathcal{E}_2] = \mathbb{P}[\mathcal{E}_1] + \mathbb{P}[\mathcal{E}_2]$.

(b) Use (b) to show that for any event $\mathcal{E}$, $\mathbb{P}[\overline{\mathcal{E}}] = 1 - \mathbb{P}[\mathcal{E}]$.

(c) **(Inclusion-Exclusion)** Pove that $\mathbb{P}[\mathcal{E}_1 \cup \mathcal{E}_2] = \mathbb{P}[\mathcal{E}_1] + \mathbb{P}[\mathcal{E}_2] - \mathbb{P}[\mathcal{E}_1 \cap \mathcal{E}_2]$. In terms of logic connectors, $\mathbb{P}[p \text{ OR } q] = \mathbb{P}[p] + \mathbb{P}[q] - \mathbb{P}[p \text{ AND } q]$.

(d) **(Union Bound/Boole's Inequality)** Prove: $\mathbb{P}[\mathcal{E}_1 \cup \mathcal{E}_2] \le \mathbb{P}[\mathcal{E}_1] + \mathbb{P}[\mathcal{E}_2]$.

(e) **(Implication bound)** Suppose $p \to q$. Prove that $\mathbb{P}[p] \le \mathbb{P}[q]$.
(IF "It's raining", THEN "It's cloudy." Thus, $\mathbb{P}$["It's raining"] $\le \mathbb{P}$["It's cloudy"].)

(f) Prove that $\mathbb{P}[\mathcal{E}_1 \cap \mathcal{E}_2] \le \mathbb{P}[\mathcal{E}_1]$ (in terms of logic connectors, $\mathbb{P}[p \text{ AND } q] \le \mathbb{P}[p]$).

You should get the feeling that the probability of an event is a "soft" version of an event's size.

15.3 Uniform Probability Spaces

In a uniform probability space, every outcome in the sample space has the same probability. For every $\omega \in \Omega$, $P(\omega) = P$, a constant. Since $1 = \sum_{\omega \in \Omega} P(\omega) = P \times |\Omega|$, it follows that

$$P(\omega) = \frac{1}{|\Omega|} \text{ for every } \omega \in \Omega.$$

The probability of event $\mathcal{E}$ is $\mathbb{P}[\mathcal{E}] = \sum_{\omega \in \mathcal{E}} P(\omega) = P \times |\mathcal{E}|$, and we conclude that

$$\mathbb{P}[\mathcal{E}] = \frac{|\mathcal{E}|}{|\Omega|} = \frac{\text{number of outcomes in } \mathcal{E}}{\text{number of possible outcomes in } \Omega}.$$

For a uniform probability space, computing a probability reduces to counting the number of outcomes in the event. Let us consider the first question at the beginning of this chapter:

"You toss a fair coin 3 times. How many heads will you get?"

The outcome is uncertain. We don't know how many heads you will get, but we can compute the probability to get (say) 2 heads. Let's first obtain the outcome-tree and probability space.

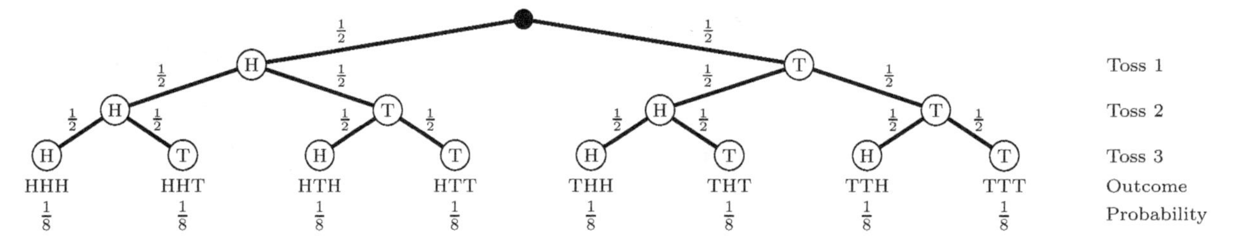

Every edge-probability equals $\frac{1}{2}$ because the coin is fair, H and T are equally likely in each toss. This is a uniform probability space. A sequence with H and T is like a binary sequence with H corresponding to 1 and T to 0. We are now experts at counting and know that the number of sequences with two heads is $\binom{3}{2}$, so

$$\mathbb{P}[\text{"2 heads"}] = \frac{\text{number of sequences with 2 heads}}{\text{number of possible sequences in } \Omega} = \frac{\binom{3}{2}}{8} = \frac{3}{8}.$$

Example 15.3. Randomly deal a 5-card poker hand from a 52-card deck (see Exercise 13.14). What are the chances of a full house and a flush? We take "randomly deal a 5-card poker hand" to mean that every hand is equally likely. This is a uniform probability space where the outcomes are the $\binom{52}{5}$ possible hands. Therefore,

$$\mathbb{P}[\text{"FullHouse"}] = \frac{\text{number of full houses}}{\binom{52}{5}} \qquad \mathbb{P}[\text{"Flush"}] = \frac{\text{number of flushes}}{\binom{52}{5}}.$$

We must count full houses and flushes, a task solved in Exercise 13.14. Here is a recap. To get a full house,

1: pick 1st rank; 13 ways **2:** pick 3 cards from 1st rank; $\binom{4}{3}$ ways **3:** pick 2nd rank; 12 ways **4:** pick 2 cards from 2nd rank. $\binom{4}{2}$ ways

By the product rule, the number of full houses is $13 \times \binom{4}{3} \times 12 \times \binom{4}{2}$. To get a flush,

1: pick suit; 4 ways **2:** pick 5 cards from suit. $\binom{13}{5}$ ways

By the product rule, the number of flushes is $4 \times \binom{13}{5}$. So, for the probabilities, we have

$$\mathbb{P}[\text{"FullHouse"}] = \frac{13 \times \binom{4}{3} \times 12 \times \binom{4}{2}}{\binom{52}{5}} \approx 0.00144; \qquad \mathbb{P}[\text{"Flush"}] = \frac{4 \times \binom{13}{5}}{\binom{52}{5}} \approx 0.00198.$$

In poker, full-house beats flush because it is rarer. In this example, we can't list the probability space or draw the outcome-tree. Nevertheless, we can compute probabilities because it is a uniform probability space. □

Exercise 15.11
(a) You roll a pair of regular dice. What is the probability that the sum is 9?
(b) You toss a fair coin ten times. What is the probability that you obtain 4 heads?
(c) You roll die A from Example 15.2 ten times. What is the probability that you roll:
(i) 4 sevens? (ii) 4 sevens and 3 sixes? (iii) 4 sevens or 3 sixes?
(d) Which randomly dealt poker hand should win: Two-pair or Three-of-a-kind?
(e) What is the probability that a randomly dealt 13-card bridge hand has an Ace?

15.4 Infinite Probability Spaces

Now consider the question:

"You keep tossing a fair coin until you get a head. How many tosses will you make?"

Again, we don't know how many tosses you will make, but we can compute the probability that you make (say) 5 tosses. Let's try to construct the probability space. You keep tossing as long as you get tails. You stop when you get heads. Let us start by trying to draw the outcome-tree.

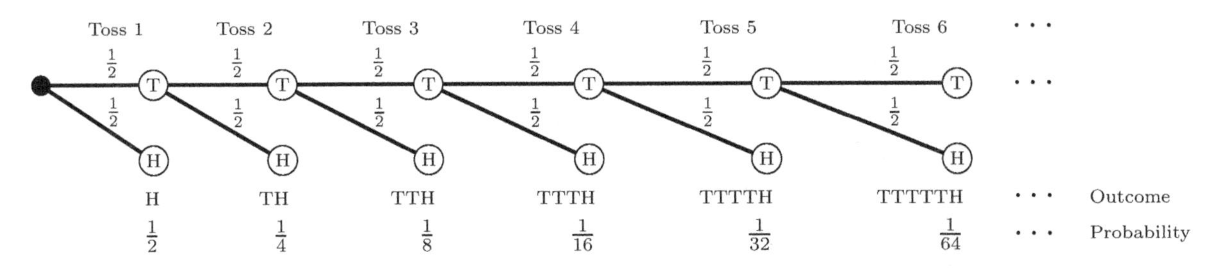

The possible outcomes never end. It is possible to get an arbitrarily long run of tails followed by a head. The outcome-tree and sample space are infinite. Let us write $\mathrm{T}^{\bullet i}$ to denote a sequence of i tails. We use $(\cdot)^{\bullet i}$ to distinguish concatenation i times from raising to the ith power. You should see a pattern in the probabilities. Our infinite probability space is

Ω	H	TH	$\mathrm{T}^{\bullet 2}\mathrm{H}$	$\mathrm{T}^{\bullet 3}\mathrm{H}$	$\mathrm{T}^{\bullet 4}\mathrm{H}$	$\mathrm{T}^{\bullet 5}\mathrm{H}$	...	$\mathrm{T}^{\bullet i}\mathrm{H}$	...
$P(\omega)$	$\frac{1}{2}$	$(\frac{1}{2})^2$	$(\frac{1}{2})^3$	$(\frac{1}{2})^4$	$(\frac{1}{2})^5$	$(\frac{1}{2})^6$	...	$(\frac{1}{2})^{i+1}$	...

You make k tosses if the first $k-1$ are T and the kth is H. The probability that you make k tosses is $(\frac{1}{2})^k$. The sum of the probabilities for all outcomes in the sample space is 1, as it should be:

$$\frac{1}{2}+\left(\frac{1}{2}\right)^2+\left(\frac{1}{2}\right)^3+\left(\frac{1}{2}\right)^4+\cdots=\sum_{i=1}^{\infty}\left(\frac{1}{2}\right)^i=\frac{\frac{1}{2}}{1-\frac{1}{2}}=1.$$

Note: This is not a uniform probability space. An infinite sample space cannot be uniform, because the sum of the constant outcome-probabilities would be infinite, not 1.

Example 15.4. You and Ayfos take turns tossing the coin. The first person to toss heads wins \$1 from the other player. Let's compute your probability to win. The sample space is the infinite one we have been discussing where you keep tossing a coin until the first arrival of heads – whoever got the heads wins. We need to identify the event of interest, the subset of outcomes where you win. You win if there were an odd number of tosses (since you go first). So, the event of interest is

$$\mathcal{E}=\{\text{H},\text{T}^{\bullet 2}\text{H},\text{T}^{\bullet 4}\text{H},\text{T}^{\bullet 6}\text{H},\ldots\}.$$

To get the probability that you win, we add the outcome probabilities in this event, which is an infinite sum.

$$\begin{aligned}\mathbb{P}[\text{"YouWin"}]=\mathbb{P}[\mathcal{E}] &= P(\text{H})+P(\text{T}^{\bullet 2}\text{H})+P(\text{T}^{\bullet 4}\text{H})+P(\text{T}^{\bullet 6}\text{H})+\cdots\\ &=\frac{1}{2}+\left(\frac{1}{2}\right)^3+\left(\frac{1}{2}\right)^5+\left(\frac{1}{2}\right)^7+\cdots\\ &=\frac{1}{2}\sum_{i=0}^{\infty}\left(\frac{1}{4}\right)^i\\ &=\frac{\frac{1}{2}}{1-\frac{1}{4}}=\frac{2}{3}.\end{aligned}$$

Again, you got the better of Ayfos. You win with probability 2/3, which means Ayfos wins with the remaining probability 1/3. You win twice as often. It's more honorable to let Ayfos toss first. □

The next two exercises give you lots of practice with infinite probability spaces involving coin tossing. By the end, you might appreciate the value of Monte-Carlo simulation.

Exercise 15.12

Ayfor and Liamsi take turns tossing a coin. Ayfos starts. The winner is the player who tosses the second head. Compute the probability each player wins. Verify your answer with Monte-Carlo simulation.

Exercise 15.13

You pick a 3-sequence of heads and tails, and your friend picks a different one. You keep tossing a fair coin until one of the two sequences appears. If your sequence appears first, you win \$1 from your friend. Otherwise you pay \$1 to your friend.

(a) You pick HHT and your friend THH. What is the probability that you win?
(b) You pick HHT and your friend HTH. What is the probability that you win?
(c) You pick HHT and your friend THT. What is the probability that you win?
(d) Use Monte-Carlo simulation to verify your answers above.
(e) If your friend must pick first, how high is your probability of winning?

15.5 Problems

Problem 15.1. In the context of this chapter, define, as carefully as you can:
(a) Experiment. (b) Sample Space. (c) Probability Space. (d) Event. (e) Probability.

Problem 15.2. A sample space Ω has four outcomes: $\omega_1, \omega_2, \omega_3, \omega_4$. What is x in each case?
(a) $P(\omega_1) = P(\omega_2) = P(\omega_3) = \frac{1}{10}, P(\omega_4) = x$. (b) $P(\omega_i) = i \times x$.

Problem 15.3. Which of these numbers cannot be a probability?
(a) 0 (b) 1 (c) 0.5 (d) $\frac{2}{3}$ (e) $\frac{3}{2}$ (f) -10^{-10} (g) 10^{-10} (h) 21% (i) 100% (j) π (k) $\frac{1}{\pi}$ (l) $\frac{1}{\sqrt{2}}$ (m) $\sqrt{2}-1$.

Problem 15.4. The mathematician D'Alembert was asked: "In two coin tosses, what are the chances an H appears?" He reasoned: if the first toss is H, stop; otherwise toss again. In two of the three possible outcomes in $\{\text{H}, \text{TH}, \text{TT}\}$ an H appears, so his answer was $\frac{2}{3}$. What is wrong with D'Alembert's reasoning. What is the correct probability?

Problem 15.5 (Galton's Paradox). Flip 3 coins. What is the probability that all three coins match?

We argue that at least two coins *must* match (pigeonhole principle). The remaining coin is equally likely to be H or T, and so will match the two matching coins half the time. Hence, all three coins match half the time. Do you agree?

Problem 15.6. You roll a pair of fair dice. Compute these probabilities:
(a) $\mathbb{P}$[sum exceeds 6]
(b) $\mathbb{P}$[sum does not exceeds 6]
(c) $\mathbb{P}$[sum is even]
(d) $\mathbb{P}$[sum is not even]
(e) $\mathbb{P}$[sum exceeds 6 AND is even]
(f) $\mathbb{P}$[sum does not exceed 6 AND is even]
(g) $\mathbb{P}$[sum exceeds 6 AND is not even]
(h) $\mathbb{P}$[sum does not exceed 6 AND is not even]
(i) $\mathbb{P}$[sum exceeds 6 OR is even]
(j) $\mathbb{P}$[sum does not exceed 6 OR is even]
(k) $\mathbb{P}$[sum exceeds 6 OR is not even]
(l) $\mathbb{P}$[sum does not exceed 6 OR is not even]

Problem 15.7. In Problem 15.6, What is the relationship between the answers to part (g) and part (j)? Use sets to explain why this relationship holds. Which other parts are related this way?

Problem 15.8. Roll two dice. Compute the probability of: (a) One 6 (b) A sum of 6 (c) A sum divisible by 3.

Problem 15.9. Roll 3 dice. Compute the probability of: (a) No 1. (b) No 2. (c) No 1 or 2. (d) At least one 1.

Problem 15.10. Flip a fair coin 4 times. Compute the probabilities of these events:
(a) $A = \{\text{Equal number of H and T}\}$. (b) $B = \{\text{First 2 flips are H}\}$. (c) A AND B. (d) A OR B.

Problem 15.11. You and a friend each toss two *fair* coins. Compute $\mathbb{P}$[you get *more* heads].

Problem 15.12. Roll a 6-sided die 5 times. What is the probability: (a) some number repeats (b) you get no sixes?

Problem 15.13. How may times should you roll a 6-sided die so that the chances of repeating a number is at least:
(a) 30% (b) 50% (c) 100%.

Problem 15.14. Over 1,000 days, 600 had rain, 400 had sunshine and 800 had either rain or sunshine. On a random day, find the chances of: (a) Rain and sunshine. (b) Rain but no sunshine. (c) Neither rain nor sunshine.

Problem 15.15. Among 400 students, 150 are in math, 120 are in bio and 50 are math-bio duals. What are the chances a random student is in: (a) math or bio (b) bio and not math (c) neither math nor bio?

Problem 15.16. A box contains 10 coins. 9 are *fair* and 1 has *two heads*. You pick a coin at random and toss it three times. What is the probability of tossing three heads (HHH)?

Problem 15.17. Two dice have probabilites $p_1, \ldots, p_6$ to roll $1, \ldots, 6$. Show: $\mathbb{P}[\text{doubles}] \geq \frac{1}{6}$.

Problem 15.18. A bag has 2 blue, 2 red, 2 green and 2 pink balls. You randomly pick 4 balls. What is the probability that the number of different colors you get is (a) 4 (b) 3 (c) 2 (d) 1.
Repeat your calculations when you pick with replacement: after you pick each ball you replace it back into the bag.

Problem 15.19. Randomly throw 4 balls into 4 buckets. Each bucket can hold up to 2 balls. What is the probability that the number of non-empty buckets is: (a) 4 (b) 3 (c) 2 (d) 1. Use Monte-Carlo to verify your answers.

Problem 15.20. Three graduates throw their hats in the air. The hats fall randomly back to the graduates. Compute the probability that no graduate gets their hat back. What about if there were four graduates?

Problem 15.21 (Gift Exchange). Four guests place gifts for each other under the tree. The gifts are randomly assigned to guests. Compute the probability that: (a) No guest gets their gift back. (b) One guest gets their gift back.

Problem 15.22. Six cups are placed randomly on six saucers (two each of red, blue and green). What is the probability that no cup is upon a saucer of the same color?

Problem 15.23. Three biased coins have a value on each side with corresponding probabilities to flip each value:

$$\text{coin } A = \begin{Bmatrix} 10 & 2 \\ 0.6 & 0.4 \end{Bmatrix}, \qquad \text{coin } B = \begin{Bmatrix} 5 & 4 \\ 0.6 & 0.4 \end{Bmatrix}, \qquad \text{coin } C = \begin{Bmatrix} 3 & 20 \\ 0.6 & 0.4 \end{Bmatrix}. \qquad \begin{matrix} \leftarrow \text{values} \\ \leftarrow \text{probabilities} \end{matrix}$$

You and a friend each pick different coins and toss. The higher value wins. Do you want to pick first or second?

Problem 15.24. A class has 10 boys and 5 girls. Three children are picked randomly, one after another. Compute the probabilities: (a) The first two are boys. (b) Both sexes are represented.

Problem 15.25. In 6-shooter Russian water-bullet-roulette do you prefer to go first or second if:
(a) The bullet wheel is not respun for each shot. (b) The bullet wheel is respun for each shot.

Problem 15.26. An urn has m blue balls and n red balls. You randomly pick the balls one by one and lay them in a line. What is the probability that the last ball is red?

Problem 15.27. In the grid shown, ● is home, ● is work and ○ is the grocery. Two shortest paths from ● to ● are in red, one goes through the grocery and one does not. All shortest paths from ● to ● have length 8. You randomly choose one of the shortest paths from ● to ●, with each shortest path being equally likely. What is the probability that you will be able to pick up groceries on your way home from work?

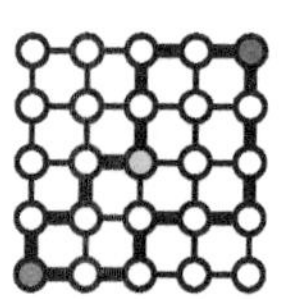

Problem 15.28. Answer Chevalier de Méré's 1654 problem: "Should you bet even money on the occurence of at least one 'double-six' during 24 rolls of a pair of dice?" What about 25 rolls?

Problem 15.29. Show that at least one 6 in 4 dice rolls is more likely than not. A pair of sixes in two dice rolls is 6-times less likely than a six in one roll. Cardano's ($\sim$1525) *rule of proportion* says you need k times as many tries to get at least one success if your odds drop by a factor k. This is how de Méré got the number 24. Justify Cardano's rule and explain why it failed de Méré?

Problem 15.30. 13-cards are dealt randomly from a standard 52-card deck. Compute probabilities to get one, two, three and four Aces. Use Monte Carlo to corroborate your answers.

Problem 15.31. Which randomly dealt 5-card poker hand (see Exercise 13.14 and Problem 13.40) should win:
(a) Four-of-a-kind or straight-flush? (b) Straight or Three-of-a-kind?

Problem 15.32. Draw two cards randomly from a 52-card deck. Compute the probabilities:
(a) The first is a K and the second a picture (A, K, Q, J). (b) At least one card is a picture.

Problem 15.33. Draw two cards randomly from a 52-card deck. Compute the probabilities:
(a) Both are ♠. (b) One is ♠. (c) One is ♠ and one is ♥. (d) One is ♠ or one is ♥.

Problem 15.34. On the internet, the chances a packet transmission is successful (reaches the destination) is 60%. Compute the probability that more than 10 tries are needed to send a packet.

Problem 15.35. Eight pawns are placed randomly on different squares of a chessboard.
(a) Compute the probability they are in a straight line (including diagonals).
(b) Compute the probability no two are in the same row or column.

Problem 15.36. If you take a monthly Malaria profilactic, the chances of Malaria that month in the Congo is 5%. You are stationed for 2 years in the Congo. What are the chances you will get Malaria sometime during your stay?

Problem 15.37. A bag contains 10 identical envelopes each with some money. You and a friend randomly draw different envelopes. Do you want to go first or second, or does it not matter?

Problem 15.38. In a bag are 12 balls, 2 balls in each of 6 colors. You randomly pick 5 balls without replacement. Compute $\mathbb{P}[i]$, the probability that you get i colors in your sample, for $i = 1, \ldots, 6$.

Problem 15.39. Give the probability space for the outcome of each of these "experiments."

(a) A fair coin is tossed and a fair die is rolled.
(b) Pick a random lower-case letter from all written English text. What if you always pick the first letter of a word?
(c) A bag contains numbers 1,...,20. 5 numbers are randomly drawn without replacement.
(d) A bag contains numbers 1,...,20. 5 numbers are randomly drawn with replacement.
(e) A pair of red and blue socks are in a drawer. You pick two socks out at random.
(f) Six cups are placed randomly on six saucers (two each of red, blue and green).
(g) A random 10-bit sequence is picked.
(h) A 10-bit sequence is picked by randomly picking the first bit and repeating that bit 9 times.
(i) A biased coin (probability p of H) is tossed 3 times.
(j) A biased coin (probability p of H) is tossed until a H is tossed.
(k) You randomly pick from $1,\ldots,20$: (i) A number. (ii) An odd number. (iii) A prime number.
(l) You roll a pair of identical dice. What if one die is red and the other is blue? What if you just record the sum?
(m) An unfair die rolls 6 with probability $\frac{1}{2}$ and the other values $1,\ldots,5$ are equally likely.
   (i) You roll the die once. (ii) You roll the die twice and record the sum.
(n) You flip a coin until you get H. What if you only counted the number of flips?
(o) There are 10 pizza toppings. You pick 3 toppings randomly for your pizza. Consider these cases.
   (i) A topping can be reused. (ii) A topping can't be reused (iii) Repeat if the order of toppings matters.
(p) A knock-out tournament (e.g. Wimbledon) begins with 2^n players and has n rounds. The initial table of draws is specified: in the first round, player $2i-1$ draws player $2i$ for $i=1,\ldots,2^{n-1}$. The outcome of a match is random. Consider two cases: (i) Only the tournament winner matters. (ii) The outcome of every match matters.
(q) Each pair from {Adam, Barb, Charlie, Doris} randomly decides whether or not to be friends.

Problem 15.40. For a probability space (Ω, P) and any two events A and B, show:

(a) If $A \subseteq B$ then $\mathbb{P}[A] \le \mathbb{P}[B]$.
(b) $\mathbb{P}[A \cup \overline{A}] = 1$ and $\mathbb{P}[A \cap \overline{A}] = 0$.
(c) $\mathbb{P}[A \cap B] + \mathbb{P}[A \cap \overline{B}] = \mathbb{P}[A]$.
(d) $\mathbb{P}[A \cap B] \le \min(\mathbb{P}[A], \mathbb{P}[B])$.
(e) $\mathbb{P}[A \cup B] + \mathbb{P}[A \cap B] = \mathbb{P}[A] + \mathbb{P}[B]$.
(f) $\mathbb{P}[A \cup B] \le \mathbb{P}[A] + \mathbb{P}[B]$.
(g) If $\mathbb{P}[A] > \frac{1}{2}$ and $\mathbb{P}[B] \ge \frac{1}{2}$, then $\mathbb{P}[A \cap B] > 0$.
(h) $\mathbb{P}[A \text{ OR } B \text{ but not both}] = \mathbb{P}[A] + \mathbb{P}[B] - 2\,\mathbb{P}[A \cap B]$ (EXCLUSIVE-OR)

Problem 15.41. For events A and B, $\mathbb{P}[A] = \frac{3}{4}$ and $\mathbb{P}[B] = \frac{1}{3}$. Show that $\frac{1}{12} \le \mathbb{P}[A \cap B] \le \frac{1}{3}$. Give examples to show that both extremes are possible. Find corresponding bounds for $\mathbb{P}[A \cup B]$.

Problem 15.42 (Gossip). The probability space in Problem 15.39(q) defines friendships of 4 people. If someone hears a rumor, they tell it to their friends. Adam got a juicy piece of gossip. What are the chances Barb hears it?

Problem 15.43 (Random Permutation). On the right is an experiment, a randomized algorithm run on a list (a_1, a_2, a_3) which is initialized to $(1,2,3)$.

(a) Give the probability space for this experiment.
(b) Generalize the algorithm to a list of size n.
(c) Prove that the probability space is uniform over the permutations of $1,\ldots,n$.

1: **for** $i = 1,\ldots,3$ **do**
2: Randomly pick list position j from $\{i, i+1, \ldots, 3\}$.
3: Swap a_i with a_j.

Problem 15.44. A fair coin is tossed 20 times giving a sequence of H and T. Compute these probabilities:
(a) The first H is at toss 20. (b) The number of H and T are equal. (c) Exactly two H. (d) At least two H.

Problem 15.45. You and a friend take turns rolling an n-sided die. The first to roll 1 wins. Compute your probability to win (as a function of n) if you roll first?

Problem 15.46. A drunk leaves the bar at position 1, and takes random steps: left (L) with probability $\frac{2}{3}$ or right (R) with probability $\frac{1}{3}$. What is the probability the drunk reaches home (at position 0) before reaching the lockup (at position 3)?

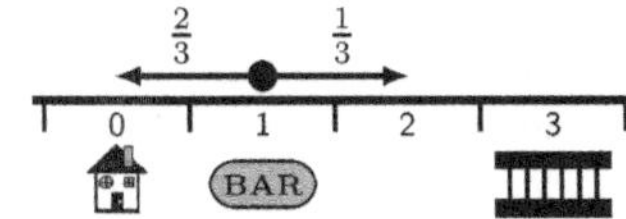

Problem 15.47. Three monkeys A, B, C have a 6-shooter pistol loaded with 2 bullets. Starting with A, each spins the bullet-wheel and shoots their foot. Compute probabilities p_A, p_B, p_C for each monkey to be the first shot.

Problem 15.48. Repeatedly toss a fair coin. Show that any fixed sequence of H and T occurs with probability 1.

Problem 15.49. You randomly throw 4 balls into 4 buckets. If a bucket has more than 2 balls, empty the buckets and restart. If all buckets have at most 2 balls, you stop. What is the probability that the number of non-empty buckets is:
(a) 4 (b) 3 (c) 2 (d) 1. (Use Monte-Carlo simulation to verify your answers.)

Problem 15.50. You and a friend repeatedly roll a die. You win if two 5s are rolled before four even numbers are rolled, and otherwise you lose. What is the probability you win?

Problem 15.51. A random cut on a circular pizza picks two random points on the circumference and cuts along the chord joining the two points. You make two random cuts. What is the probability to get 4 pieces of pizza?

Problem 15.52. An urn has m blue and n red balls. Randomly pick balls one by one and lay them in a line. Show that the probability the first k balls are blue and the $(k+1)$st ball is red is

$$\binom{m+n-k-1}{n-1} \Big/ \binom{m+n}{n}.$$

(a) Prove the answer by justifying these steps:

(i) In the outcome tree, $\mathbb{P}[\text{ball-1 is blue}] = m/(m+n)$ and $\mathbb{P}[\text{ball-1 is red}] = n/(m+n)$.

(ii) We are only concerned with the branch where ball-1 is blue.

(iii) From the "ball-1-blue" branch, $\mathbb{P}[\text{ball-2 is blue}] = (m-1)/(m+n-1)$.

(iv) Continuing, the probability that the first k balls are blue and the $(k+1)$st ball is red is

$$\frac{m}{m+n} \times \frac{m-1}{m+n-1} \times \frac{m-2}{m+n-2} \cdots \times \frac{m-k+1}{m+n-k+1} \times \frac{n}{m+n-k}.$$

(v) Show that the answer in (iv) equals the desired answer.

(b) Use a uniform probability space. Label the blue balls $b_1, \ldots, b_m$ and the red balls $r_1, \ldots, r_n$.

(i) Show that the number of ordrings of the labeled balls is $(m+n)!$

(ii) Show that the number of ways to choose the first k balls from $b_1, \ldots, b_m$, the $(k+1)$st ball from $r_1, \ldots, r_n$, and finally an ordering of the remaining balls is

$$\frac{m!}{(m-k)!} \times n \times (m+n-k-1)!.$$

(iii) Hence, show the answer is $(m! \times n \times (m+n-k-1)!)/((m-k)! \times (m+n)!)$, as desired.

(c) Obtain the answer directly, again using a uniform probability space.

(i) Show the number of arrangements of m blue and n red balls is $\binom{m+n}{n}$.

(ii) Fix the first $k+1$ balls to k blue and 1 red. Show that the number of arrangements of the remaining $m+n-k-1$ balls is $\binom{m+n-k-1}{n-1}$ and conclude the anwer.

Problem 15.53. A bag has mk balls of k colors (m of each color). Randomly pick $n \le mk$ balls without replacement. Show that the probability to get ℓ different colors ($\ell \le \min(n,k)$) is

$$P(n,k,m,\ell) = \binom{k}{\ell} \frac{(m!)^\ell}{(mk)!} \sum_{\substack{n_1+\cdots+n_\ell=n \\ 1 \le n_i \le m}} \binom{mk-n}{\delta_{n_1}, \delta_{n_2}, \ldots, \delta_{n_\ell}} \binom{n}{n_1, n_2, \ldots, n_\ell}$$

where $\delta_{n_i} = m - n_i$. Compute $P(n,k,m,\ell)$ for picking $n=5$ balls when there are $k=6$ colors and $m=3$ balls of each color. Use Monte-Carlo simulation to verify your answer.

Problem 15.54. (Inclusion-Exclusion) Derive a formula for the probability of a union (similar to size of a union):

$$\mathbb{P}\left[\bigcup_{i=1}^n \mathcal{E}_i\right] = \sum_{k=1}^{n} (-1)^{k+1} \cdot (\text{sum of probabilities of all } k\text{-way intersections})$$

Problem 15.55. In the outcome-tree, we multiply edge probabilities to get the outcome-probabilities. Prove by induction that the resulting outcome-probabilities are a valid probability space (the probabilities sum to 1).

Problem 15.56. (Principle of Restricted Choice) Suppose there are two choices A, B. Someone is to pick A or B in one of three situations (you don't know which).

Case 1. Their choice is *unrestricted* and he will pick randomly.

Case 2. Their choice is restricted to A.

Case 3. Their choice is restricted to B.

If option A is picked, restricted choice says that: (a) Case 3 can't be (obvious); (b) Case 2 becomes more likely (relative to case 1). Not picking B suggests their choice was restricted to A. Use restricted choice to explain why switching is better in the Monty Hall game. (See also Problem 16.70. Restricted choice applies when some random action *may* have been under a constraint. If the action is consistent with the constraint, then the odds tilt toward the constraint being true.)

> Good judgement comes from experience. Experience comes from bad judgement. – **Jim Horning**
>
> I have [travelled this country and] talked with the best people, and I can assure you that data processing is a fad that won't last out the year. – **Editor, Prentice-Hall, 1957**
>
> If we have data, let's look at data. If all we have are opinions, let's go with mine. – **Jim Barksdale**

Chapter 16

Conditional Probability

1: New information changes a probability.
2: The Law of Total Probability and Bayes' Theorem.

Conditioning be the pith of probability, the soul of statistics.[1] A keen reasoner updates conclusions when new data arrives. Conan Doyle's Sherlock Holmes would say, "When you have excluded the impossible, whatever remains, however improbable, must be so." Conditional probability takes us into this land of the improbable, where new information can shift probabilities, rendering the likely impossible and the near-impossible a certainty. Conditional probability is the framework for handling uncertainty when new information arrives.

Example 16.1. During the flu season (70 days in the winter), 10% of people get infected, and about 1% of those cases end up hospitalized due to complications. Needless to say, hospitalization is traumatic.

1. The probability that a random person on a random day has the flu is about 0.01 (or 1%).[2] This is called the prior probability, before you know any additional information.
$$\text{Probability of flu}, \mathbb{P}[\text{flu}] \approx 0.01.$$
2. You, a random person, have a slight fever, a common symptom of flu. This new information increases your probability of a flu, from 1% to (say) 40%. Be vigilant: hydrate and rest. The posterior probability is higher because of the new information. Translate posterior as "After you get the new information."
$$\text{Probability of flu given fever}, \mathbb{P}[\text{flu} \mid \text{fever}] \approx 0.4.$$
$\mathbb{P}[A \mid B]$ is the updated conditional probability of A, given the new information B.
3. Also, your roommie has a flu. That's additional new information. Now it is near-certain that you have a flu. Take counter-measures. You might even schedule a medical visit.
$$\text{Probability of flu given fever and roommie flu}, \mathbb{P}[\text{flu} \mid \text{fever AND roommie flu}] \approx 1.$$

Pop Quiz 16.1
(a) Estimate $\mathbb{P}$[There is a living Human tomorrow] and $\mathbb{P}$[Sun does not rise tomorrow].
(b) Estimate $\mathbb{P}$[There is a living Human tomorrow | Sun does not rise tomorrow].

□

16.1 Definition

For two events or sets A and B, the notation $\mathbb{P}[A \mid B]$ denotes conditional probability,
$$\mathbb{P}[A \mid B] = \text{Conditional probability of an outcome in } A \text{ given that it is in } B.$$

[1] Statistics deals with estimating probabilities from data.
[2] Flu lasts about a week. So, on a random day, about $7/70 = 10\%$ of all the cases are active, and 10% of 10% is 1%.

The probability $\mathbb{P}[A]$ is the fraction of times an outcome from A occurs when you repeat the experiment. The conditional probability $\mathbb{P}[A \mid B]$ is the updated probability, the fraction of times the outcome is in A when you already know it is in B. Let's take an example. A school with 5,000 students has 1,000 CS majors, 100 MATH majors and 80 dual MATH-CS majors. Pick a random student:

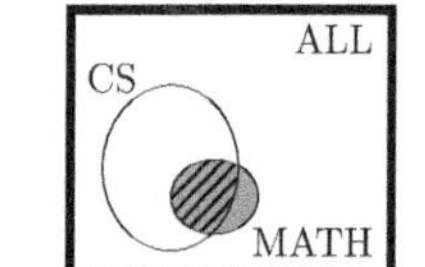

$$\begin{aligned}\mathbb{P}[\text{CS}] &= 1000/5000 = 0.2;\\ \mathbb{P}[\text{MATH}] &= 100/5000 = 0.02;\\ \mathbb{P}[\text{CS AND MATH}] &= 80/5000 = 0.016.\end{aligned}$$

What is $\mathbb{P}[\text{CS} \mid \text{MATH}]$? The information that the student is in MATH shrinks the possible outcomes from all students to MATH majors (shaded). Effectively, we are picking a random student from MATH. The probability of a CS student is the striped area $|\text{CS} \cap \text{MATH}|$ divided by size of the new sample space $|\text{MATH}|$.

$$\mathbb{P}[\text{CS} \mid \text{MATH}] = \frac{|\text{CS} \cap \text{MATH}|}{|\text{MATH}|} = \frac{80}{100} = 0.8.$$

MATH students are 4 times more likely to be CS majors than a random student.

For a non-uniform probability space, we need to deal with new information more carefully. We are interested in how often an outcome in A occurs when you know the additional information that the outcome is in B.

$\mathbb{P}[A \mid B]$ = frequency of outcomes known to be in B that are also in A.

When you repeat an experiment n times, suppose, n_B outcomes are known to be in event B. The number of these that are also in event A is the number of outcomes in both A and B, $n_{A\cap B}$. So, the fraction of outcomes known to be in B that are also in A is $\mathbb{P}[A \mid B] = n_{A\cap B}/n_B$. This is the frequency interpretation of $\mathbb{P}[A \mid B]$. Now, by the frequency interpretation of the probabilities $\mathbb{P}[B]$ and $P[A \cap B]$,

$$\mathbb{P}[B] = \frac{n_B}{n}, \qquad \text{and} \qquad \mathbb{P}[A \cap B] = \frac{n_{A\cap B}}{n}.$$

Dividing $\mathbb{P}[A \cap B]$ by $\mathbb{P}[B]$ gives $n_{A\cap B}/n_B$, which is the conditional probability we want. We conclude that

$$\mathbb{P}[A \mid B] = \frac{n_{A\cap B}}{n_B} = \frac{\mathbb{P}[A \cap B]}{\mathbb{P}[B]} = \frac{\mathbb{P}[A \text{ AND } B]}{\mathbb{P}[B]}$$

This formula defines conditional probability using regular probabilities. It updates $\mathbb{P}[A]$ to $\mathbb{P}[A \mid B]$ when you know that the outcome is in B. Conditional probability is defined for any event A, but only when $\mathbb{P}[B] \neq 0$.

Exercise 16.2

(a) Using the definition of $\mathbb{P}[A \mid B]$, what are $\mathbb{P}[\text{CS} \mid \text{MATH}]$ and $\mathbb{P}[\text{MATH} \mid \text{CS}]$?

(b) What are: (i) $\mathbb{P}[A \mid A]$? (ii) $\mathbb{P}[A \mid A\cap B]$? (iii) $\mathbb{P}[A\cap B \mid B]$? (iv) $\mathbb{P}[A\cup B \mid B]$? (v) $\mathbb{P}[A \mid A\cup B]$?

(c) Fix an event B. Show that $P_B(\omega) = \mathbb{P}[\{\omega\} \mid B]$ is a valid probability function for Ω:

(i) Show that $P_B(\omega) = P(\omega)/\,\mathbb{P}[B] \geq 0$ if $\omega \in B$ and $P_B(\omega) = 0$ otherwise.

(ii) Show that $\sum_{\omega\in\Omega} P_B(\omega) = 1$.

16.2 Examples

Conditional probability rears its head in sneaky ways. Let's work through some examples.

Rain in NY. It's cloudy one in five days and rains one in seven. What are the chances of rain on a cloudy day? The crucial first step is to realize we want a conditional probability $\mathbb{P}[\text{Rain} \mid \text{Clouds}]$,

All Days
Cloudy
Rainy

$$\mathbb{P}[\text{Rain} \mid \text{Clouds}] = \frac{\mathbb{P}[\text{Rain} \cap \text{Clouds}]}{\mathbb{P}[\text{Clouds}]}.$$

It can't rain without clouds, that is $\{\text{Rainy}\} \subseteq \{\text{Cloudy}\}$. Hence, $\mathbb{P}[\text{Rain} \cap \text{Clouds}] = \mathbb{P}[\text{Rain}]$.

Since $\mathbb{P}[\text{Rain}] = 1/7$ and $\mathbb{P}[\text{Clouds}] = 1/5$, we have that

$$\mathbb{P}[\text{Rain} \mid \text{Clouds}] = \frac{\mathbb{P}[\text{Rain} \cap \text{Clouds}]}{\mathbb{P}[\text{Clouds}]} = \frac{\mathbb{P}[\text{Rain}]}{\mathbb{P}[\text{Clouds}]} = \frac{1/7}{1/5} = \frac{5}{7}.$$

The chances of rain on a cloudy day are about 71% □

A Pair of Dice. You roll a pair of fair dice. You know that both dice are odd. How likely is it that the sum is 10? First, let's identify the conditional probability that we want:

$$\mathbb{P}[\text{Sum is 10} \mid \text{Both are Odd}] = \frac{\mathbb{P}[(\text{Sum is 10}) \text{ AND } (\text{Both are Odd})]}{\mathbb{P}[\text{Both are Odd}]}$$

We can compute the regular probabilities using the outcome-tree method. We show the probability space as a grid of possible rolls for die 1 and die 2. Please do the accompanying Pop Quiz.

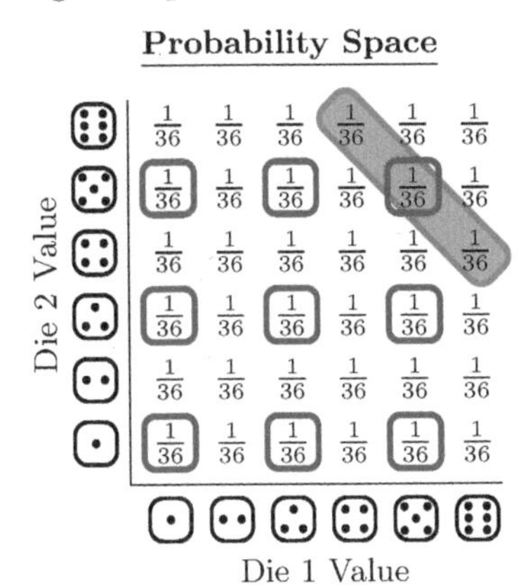

Pop Quiz 16.3

For the experiment where you roll a pair of fair dice:

(a) Show that the probability space $(\Omega, P(\cdot))$ is

$$\Omega = \{(i,j) \mid 1 \le i,j \le 6\},$$
$$P(i,j) = 1/36.$$

(b) Show that $\mathbb{P}[\text{Sum is 10}] = 1/12$. (Red shaded event.)

(c) The event "Both are Odd" contains the outcomes in blue boxes. Show that $\mathbb{P}[\text{Both are Odd}] = 1/4$.

(d) Show: $\mathbb{P}[(\text{Sum is 10}) \text{ AND } (\text{Both are Odd})] = 1/36$.

(e) Show: $\mathbb{P}[\text{Sum is 10} \mid \text{Both are Odd}] = 1/9$.

(f) What is $\mathbb{P}[\text{Both are Odd} \mid \text{Sum is 10}]$?

Summary: Computing a Conditional Probability.

1: Identify that you need a conditional probability $\mathbb{P}[A \mid B]$.
2: Determine the probability space $(\Omega, P(\cdot))$ using the outcome-tree method.
3: Identify the events A and B appearing in $\mathbb{P}[A \mid B]$ as subsets of Ω.
4: Compute $\mathbb{P}[A \cap B]$ and $\mathbb{P}[B]$.
5: Compute $\mathbb{P}[A \mid B]$ as the ratio $\mathbb{P}[A \cap B] / \mathbb{P}[B]$.

Conditional probability is no harder than regular probability. The hard part is precisely defining what conditional probability you need. Often, you will need to interpret the new information. □

Monty Hall Revisited. To contrast conditional with unconditional probability, consider a modified Monty Hall game (page 213) in which Monty prefers door 3. When the prize is behind door 1, Monty chooses to open door 3 with a higher probability 2/3 and door 2 with probability 1/3. The new probability space is on the right. You should still switch, winning when the outcome is (2,3) or (3,2) with probability

$$\mathbb{P}[\text{WinBySwitching}] = 2/3.$$

Prize	Host	Probability
1 ($\frac{1}{3}$)	2 ($\frac{1}{3}$)	$P(1,2) = \frac{1}{9}$
1 ($\frac{1}{3}$)	3 ($\frac{2}{3}$)	$P(1,3) = \frac{2}{9}$
2 ($\frac{1}{3}$)	3 (1)	$P(2,3) = \frac{1}{3}$
3 ($\frac{1}{3}$)	2 (1)	$P(3,2) = \frac{1}{3}$

Interestingly, if Monty opens door 2 your spirits should rise. Why? Monty prefers door 3, so why did he open door 2? It suggests the prize is at door 3 and you will surely win by switching! We can quantify this rising of your spirits by looking at the conditional probability of winning given the additional information that Monty opened door 2.

$$\mathbb{P}[\text{Win} \mid \text{Monty opens Door 2}] = \frac{\mathbb{P}[\text{Win AND Monty opens Door 2}]}{\mathbb{P}[\text{Monty opens Door 2}]}.$$

For the probabilities on the RHS: (i) Identify the event of interest; (ii) Sum outcome-probabilities to get the event-probability. The event {Win AND Monty opens Door 2} contains the single outcome (3,2), so

$$\mathbb{P}[\text{Win AND Monty opens Door 2}] = 1/3.$$

The event {Monty opens Door 2} contains the outcomes $\{(3,2),(1,2)\}$, so

$$\mathbb{P}[\text{Monty opens Door 2}] = 1/3 + 1/9 = 4/9.$$

Therefore, the probability to win given that Monty opens door 2 is $\frac{1}{3}/\frac{4}{9} = 3/4$,

$$\mathbb{P}[\text{Win} \mid \text{Monty opens Door 2}] = 3/4.$$

Wow! Your chances went up almost 10% just because Monty opened door 2. Similarly,

$$\mathbb{P}[\text{Win} \mid \text{Monty opens Door 3}] = \frac{\mathbb{P}[\text{Win AND Monty opens Door 3}]}{\mathbb{P}[\text{Monty opens Door 3}]} = \frac{1/3}{1/3 + 2/9} = \frac{3}{5}.$$

Initially the unconditional probability of winning is 2/3. As the game unfolds, the new information changes your odds. If Monty opens door 2, your odds improve to $3/4 > 2/3$, otherwise your odds worsen to $3/5 < 2/3$.

Exercise 16.4

Monty opens door 2. What is the probability that you win by switching when:

(a) Monty always picks door 3 if it is available?

(b) Monty randomly opens door 2 or 3 and restarts the game if he accidentally reveals the prize?

□

A Pair of Boys. Your friends Ayfos, Ifar, Need and Niaz have two children each.

1. Ayfos has at least one boy.
2. Ifar's older child is a boy.
3. One day you met Need on a walk with a son.
4. Niaz practices Clingon, an aggressive culture in which fathers will always take a son on a walk if possible. One day, you met Niaz on a walk with a boy, presumably his son.

For each friend, what is the probability that they have two boys? It's the same question in each case, but with slightly different additional information. We need conditional probabilities.

1. (The case of Ayfos.) Consider the outcome-tree of possibilities for the two children.

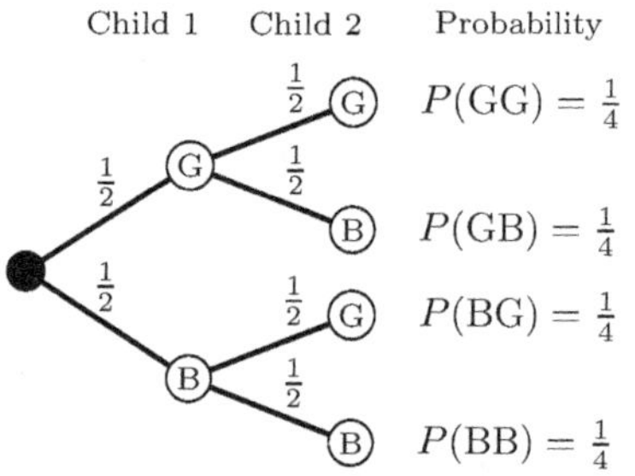

Child 1 Child 2 Probability

$P(\text{GG}) = \frac{1}{4}$

$P(\text{GB}) = \frac{1}{4}$

$P(\text{BG}) = \frac{1}{4}$

$P(\text{BB}) = \frac{1}{4}$

Using the notation G=girl and B=boy, the probability space is:

Ω	GG	GB	BG	BB
$P(\omega)$	1/4	1/4	1/4	1/4

Ayfos has at least one boy, so the outcome is one of {GB, BG, BB}. We are conditioning on this event. We want the probability of two boys, the event {BB}. We need the conditional probability

$$\mathbb{P}[\{\text{BB}\} \mid \{\text{GB},\text{BG},\text{BB}\}]$$

Given the events in the conditional probability, the rest is mechanical: compute probabilities for the intersection and conditioned event by summing outcome-probabilities, and take the ratio.

$$\mathbb{P}[\{\text{BB}\} \mid \{\text{GB},\text{BG},\text{BB}\}] = \frac{\mathbb{P}[\{\text{BB}\} \cap \{\text{GB},\text{BG},\text{BB}\}]}{\mathbb{P}[\{\text{GB},\text{BG},\text{BB}\}]} = \frac{1/4}{1/4+1/4+1/4} = \frac{1}{3}.$$

The probability that Ayfos has two boys is 1/3.

2. (The case of Ifar.) The probability space is the same, the extra information isn't. Ifar's first child is a boy, which is the event {BG, BB}. We want the conditional probability $\mathbb{P}[\{\text{BB}\} \mid \{\text{BG},\text{BB}\}]$,

$$\mathbb{P}[\{\text{BB}\} \mid \{\text{BG},\text{BB}\}] = \frac{\mathbb{P}[\{\text{BB}\} \cap \{\text{BG},\text{BB}\}]}{\mathbb{P}[\{\text{BG},\text{BB}\}]} = \frac{1/4}{1/4+1/4} = \frac{1}{2}.$$

The probability that Ifar has two boys is 1/2.

3. (The case of Need.) The probability space is not quite the same as before, because we now need to take into account whether you met a boy or girl in the experiment.

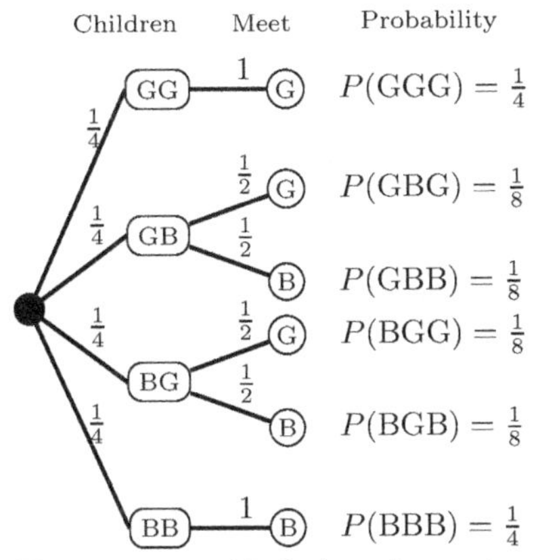

As with Ayfos, the sample space starts with the 4 possible cases for the two children. Then, the tree branches depending on who you met on the walk. We assume that Need randomly picks a child to take on a walk. In the partial outcome BB (GG), you can only meet a boy (girl) on the walk. The event "MetBoy" is {BBB, BGB, GBB}, so $\mathbb{P}[\text{TwoBoys} \mid \text{MetBoy}]$ is

$$\mathbb{P}[\{\text{BBB}\} \mid \{\text{BBB}, \text{BGB}, \text{GBB}\}] = \frac{\mathbb{P}[\{\text{BBB}\} \cap \{\text{BBB}, \text{BGB}, \text{GBB}\}]}{\mathbb{P}[\{\text{BBB}, \text{BGB}, \text{GBB}\}]} = \frac{1/4}{1/4 + 1/8 + 1/8} = \frac{1}{2}.$$

The probability that Need has two boys is 1/2.

Having a son (Ayfos) and meeting a son in a chance encounter (Need) are different. Meeting a son is more likely with two boys, which is why Need is more likely to have two boys than Ayfos.

4. (The case of Niaz.) The sample space is the same as with Need, the probabilities are different. When Niaz has the choice of a boy or girl, he always takes the boy on a walk. The edge-probabilities (GB)—(G) and (BG)—(G) become 0. The edge-probabilities (GB)—(B) and (BG)—(B) become 1. The probability space becomes

Ω	GGG	GBG	GBB	BGG	BGB	BBB
$P(\omega)$	1/4	0	1/4	0	1/4	1/4

We need the same conditional probability $\mathbb{P}[\{\text{BBB}\} \mid \{\text{BBB}, \text{BGB}, \text{GBB}\}]$,

$$\mathbb{P}[\{\text{BBB}\} \mid \{\text{BBB}, \text{BGB}, \text{GBB}\}] = \frac{\mathbb{P}[\{\text{BBB}\} \cap \{\text{BBB}, \text{BGB}, \text{GBB}\}]}{\mathbb{P}[\{\text{BBB}, \text{BGB}, \text{GBB}\}]} = \frac{1/4}{1/4 + 1/4 + 1/4} = \frac{1}{3}.$$

With Niaz, meeting a boy in essence just tells you he has at least one boy, similar to the case of Ayfos.

Shine your headlights back over these four cases of "A Pair of Boys." You should appreciate how a subtle change in the information you know affects a probability. You'll survive as long as you precisely state how you interpret any new information and then update your probabilities accordingly. □

Exercise 16.5
You play a best of three set tennis match against an inferior opponent. You win the first set with probability 2/3. A player who wins a set wins the next set with probability 3/4. Compute the probabilities that
(a) You win the match.
(b) (i) You win the match if you win the first set. (ii) You won the first set if you won the match.
Part (b)(ii) is a valid question though it may seem strange. The match is over and you won. Yet, we are asking for the probability that you won the first set even though the first set has already taken place.

16.3 Conditional Probability Traps

There are several traps that lay in wait and sucker you into using the wrong probability. Don't be fooled. The following four probabilities are all different, and apply in different situations:

$$\mathbb{P}[A] \qquad \mathbb{P}[A \mid B] \qquad \mathbb{P}[B \mid A] \qquad \mathbb{P}[A \text{ AND } B].$$

16.3.1 Sampling Bias

Sampling bias occurs when you confuse $\mathbb{P}[A]$ with $\mathbb{P}[A \mid B]$, a common mistake because conditioning is subtle. Be on the lookout to update probabilities when you get new information. An embarrassing case of sampling bias arose in the 1948 US presidential election between Truman and Dewey. George Gallup had introduced quota sampling (the Gallup poll) where interviewers sample voters according to quotas: so many women, men, blacks, whites, under 40, over 40, etc. The most convenient means at that time to identify subjects was the telephone directory. The Gallup poll's results on how people voted were:

Candidate	Dewey	Truman	Others
Poll percentage voting for candidate	50%	44%	6%

Dewey's huge lead plus impending printing press strikes prompted the Chicago Tribune to prematurely tout the headline "**DEWEY DEFEATS TRUMAN.**" That mistake haunts them to this day, because Truman easily won. The Tribune incorrectly thought the Gallup poll measures $\mathbb{P}[\text{random person votes for Dewey}] \approx 0.5$. Wrong! The table below shows that the Gallup poll systematically over-estimates the Republican's chances.

Election Year	1936	1940	1944	1948
Gallup Poll (Rep. Candidate)	44%	48%	48%	50%
Actual (Rep. Candidate)	38%	45%	46%	45%

The crucial bit of additional information is how the subjects were found, using the telephone directory.

$$\text{Gallup \% for Dewey} \approx \mathbb{P}[\text{random person votes for Dewey} \mid \text{person has a telephone}].$$

Back then, only the wealthy had a telephone, which created a bias in the sample toward Republicans. The conditional probability captures this bias. Naturally, if you polled only Republicans, Dewey would win,

$$\text{Gallup \% for Dewey} \gg \mathbb{P}[\text{random person votes for Dewey}].$$

Exercise 16.6

(a) The course review asks students to voluntarily rate the course as good or bad. We use the ratings to estimate $\mathbb{P}[\text{student likes the course}]$. Is there a sampling bias?

(b) During WWII, Abraham Wald surveyed the returning war-planes and observed that most of the damage was in the middle of the plane. After deep thought, Wald, a very good statistician, decided to add armor reinforcements to the tail and nose of the planes. Explain why Wald came to this conclusion.

16.3.2 Transposed Conditional

The fallacy of the transposed conditional is when you confuse $\mathbb{P}[A \mid B]$ with $\mathbb{P}[B \mid A]$. A beautiful illustration occurred in an 1835 report by Lombard titled "De l'influence des professions sur la durée de la vie," a study on how profession affects lifespan. Here are some professions and, according to Lombard's study, their lifespan.

Profession	Mortician	Chocolatier	Professor	Soldier	Dancer	Stonemason	Student
Lifespan (years)	75.0	73.6	66.6	48.4	42.9	34.4	**20.2**

Wow! Being a student is risky business. Don't pull out of college quite yet, at least not before we explain what is going on. The study is claiming to get at your lifespan given your profession, a quantity like

$$\mathbb{P}[\text{lifespan} \leq 20 \mid \text{profession}].$$

To measure this, you should follow people of different professions around and see how long they live. Instead, Lombard did the more convenient thing and surveyed death records, tabulating profession and lifespan upon death. There is a serious problem with Lombard's study. His data was for the transposed conditional,[3]

$$\mathbb{P}[\text{profession} \mid \text{lifespan} \leq 20].$$

Pop Quiz 16.7

What are the likely professions recorded at time of death for people who die before 20?

[3]Even if Lombard followed students and doctors around, there is still a subtle conditioning issue. You become a student at age (say) 17, but a doctor at age (say) 25. Some 17-year-olds won't make it to 25☹. Doctors live longer simply because they already lived longer (Problem 16.63). It's better to ask how many more years will you live after starting a profession.

Medical Testing. A school in NY has a test to screen for onset of **L**oud **A**nd **M**ostly **E**rroneous (LAME) behavior. One in a hundred people are LAME. If you are LAME, the test is wrong in only 10% of cases – the false negative rate when the test says NO even though you are LAME. If you are not LAME, the test is wrong in only 5% of cases – the false positive rate when the test says YES even though you are not LAME. Gru tested positive for LAME. What are the chances Gru is LAME? Let us argue as follows. Suppose Gru is not LAME.

$$\mathbb{P}[\text{test says YES} \mid \text{Gru is not LAME}] = 0.05,$$

which is extremely unlikely, therefore Gru is likely to be LAME. This is a sort-of "probabilistic proof by contradiction". There is no such thing. Indeed, this is the opposite of a correct argument, another fallacy of the transposed conditional. The test says YES, so we actually want

$$\mathbb{P}[\text{Gru is not LAME} \mid \text{test says YES}].$$

Let's compute this conditional probability using the out-come tree method.

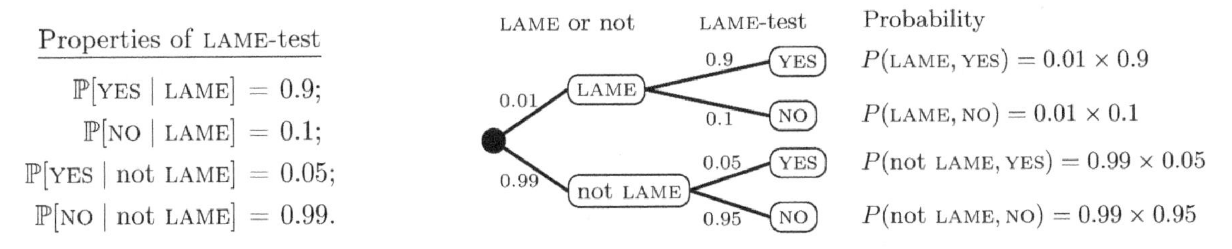

On the left is a summary of LAME-test using conditional probabilities. On the right, is the outcome-tree. First, you are either LAME or not. Second, the test says YES or NO.

$$\mathbb{P}[\text{not LAME} \mid \text{YES}] = \frac{\mathbb{P}[\text{not LAME AND YES}]}{\mathbb{P}[\text{YES}]} = \frac{0.99 \times 0.05}{0.99 \times 0.05 + 0.9 \times 0.01} \approx 85\%.$$

The test says YES, yet chances are 85% that Gru is not LAME! What is going on? The test is overwhelmed by a vast majority of non-LAME people. When the test says YES, either you are LAME (rare) plus the test was right (likely); or, you are not LAME (very likely) plus the test got it wrong (rare). In this case, the latter wins.

Pop Quiz 16.8
When does the conditional $\mathbb{P}[A \mid B]$ equal the transposed conditional, $\mathbb{P}[B \mid A]$?

16.4 Law of Total Probability

We saw proofs that used an exhaustive case-by-case analysis. In probability, the analog of case-by-case analysis is the law of total probability. Rewrite the definition of conditional probability as

$$\mathbb{P}[A \cap B] = \mathbb{P}[A \text{ AND } B] = \mathbb{P}[A \mid B] \times \mathbb{P}[B]. \tag{16.1}$$

The joint probability $\mathbb{P}[A \cap B]$ that events A and B jointly occur is the product of the conditional $\mathbb{P}[A \mid B]$ and $\mathbb{P}[B]$. Consider an event A. The outcomes in A are either in the event B, shaded green, or not in B, i.e. in $\overline{B}$, shaded red. Using the sum rule for disjoint sets (see Exercise 15.9(b) on page 217),

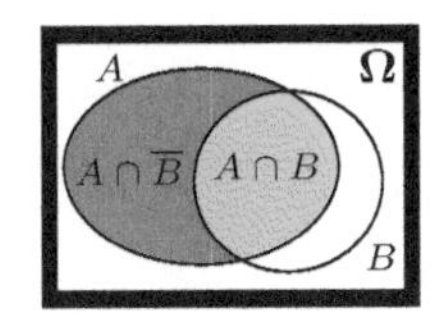

$$\begin{aligned} \mathbb{P}[A] &= \mathbb{P}[A \cap B] + \mathbb{P}[A \cap \overline{B}], \\ &= \mathbb{P}[A \mid B] \times \mathbb{P}[B] + \mathbb{P}[A \mid \overline{B}] \times \mathbb{P}[\overline{B}]. \end{aligned} \tag{16.2}$$

In the last step, we used (16.1) for $\mathbb{P}[A \cap B]$ and $\mathbb{P}[A \cap \overline{B}]$. The sum in (16.2) is the law of total probability.

Law of Total Probability

$$\mathbb{P}[A] = \mathbb{P}[A \mid B] \times \mathbb{P}[B] + \mathbb{P}[A \mid \overline{B}] \times \mathbb{P}[\overline{B}].$$

The law of total probability gives a case-by-case decomposition of the probability of A. To compute $\mathbb{P}[A]$, condition on each of the two cases $\{B, \overline{B}\}$, weight each case by its probability and add. You can use more than 2 cases provided exactly one of the cases must occur

Example 16.2. A box contains two fair coins and one two-headed coin. You pick a coin at random and flip. What is the probability to flip heads? We can use the law of total probability with the two cases:

$$\begin{aligned}\text{Case 1, } B &: \text{ You picked one of the fair coins}\\ \text{Case 2, } \overline{B} &: \text{ You picked the two-headed coin}\end{aligned}$$

There are two fair coins and one two-headed, so $\mathbb{P}[B] = 2/3$ and $\mathbb{P}[\overline{B}] = 1/3$. In case 1 you picked a fair coin, so $\mathbb{P}[\text{H} \mid B] = 1/2$. In case 2 you picked the two-headed coin, so $\mathbb{P}[\text{H} \mid \overline{B}] = 1$. Therefore,

$$\mathbb{P}[\text{H}] = \mathbb{P}[\text{H} \mid B]\,\mathbb{P}[B] + \mathbb{P}[\text{H} \mid \overline{B}]\,\mathbb{P}[\overline{B}] = \frac{1}{2} \times \frac{2}{3} + 1 \times \frac{1}{3} = \frac{2}{3}.$$

You can solve this problem using the outcome-tree method. The law of total probability is quicker. □

Example 16.3 (Fair "toss" from biased coin)**.** A biased coin has unknown probability of heads p. Can one get a fair "flip", which means output H with probability 1/2 and T with probability 1/2? One idea is to flip twice and say heads or tails based on the two tosses in such a way that you will say heads half the time. This idea is implemented in the following algorithm.

The algorithm corresponding to the tree on the right makes two tosses. Lower case 'h' and 't' denote the outcomes of a coin toss. If the two tosses are 'ht', output H; if they are 'th' output T; otherwise RESTART. Keep tossing until an H or T is output. There is a symmetry in the algorithm because $P(\text{'ht'}) = P(\text{'th'}) = p(1-p)$. This suggests that an H is as likely as a T.

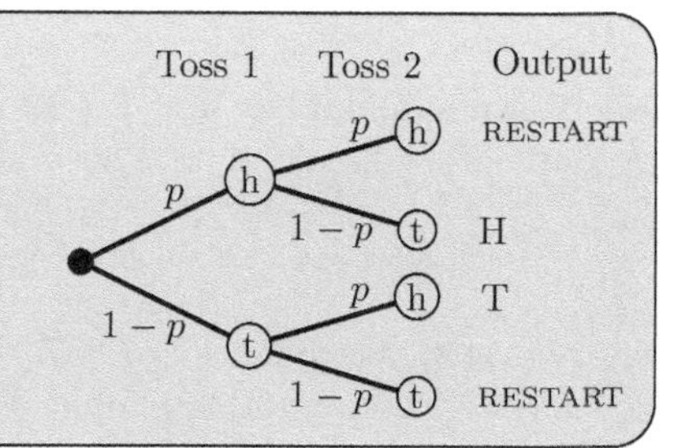

Let us compute the probability the algorithm outputs H. For our probabilistic case-by-case analysis, there are three cases for how the algorithm begins: RESTART, 'ht' or 'th'. By the law of total probability,

$$\mathbb{P}[\text{H}] = \mathbb{P}[\text{H} \mid \text{RESTART}] \times \mathbb{P}[\text{RESTART}] + \mathbb{P}[\text{H} \mid \text{'ht'}] \times \mathbb{P}[\text{'ht'}] + \mathbb{P}[\text{H} \mid \text{'th'}] \times \mathbb{P}[\text{'th'}].$$

Using the outcome-tree, we can compute the non-conditional probabilities,

$$\mathbb{P}[\text{RESTART}] = p^2 + (1-p)^2 \qquad \mathbb{P}[\text{'ht'}] = p(1-p) \qquad \mathbb{P}[\text{'th'}] = p(1-p)$$

For the cases 'ht' and 'th', the output is known so $\mathbb{P}[\text{H} \mid \text{'ht'}] = 1$ and $\mathbb{P}[\text{H} \mid \text{'th'}] = 0$. In the case where you restart from scratch, the probability to output H is exactly what we are trying to compute, namely $\mathbb{P}[\text{H}]$. So,

$$\mathbb{P}[\text{H} \mid \text{RESTART}] = \mathbb{P}[\text{H}].$$

Putting all this together,

$$\mathbb{P}[\text{H}] = \mathbb{P}[\text{H}] \times (p^2 + (1-p)^2) + 1 \times p(1-p) + 0 \times p(1-p).$$

Rearranging this equation gives $\mathbb{P}[\text{H}] \times (1 - p^2 - (1-p)^2) = p(1-p)$, or

$$\mathbb{P}[\text{H}] = \frac{p(1-p)}{1 - p^2 - (1-p)^2} = \frac{p(1-p)}{2p(1-p)} = \frac{1}{2}.$$

Summary. Though we don't know p, we can still get a fair toss! Our analysis of the algorithm used the law of total probability to write $\mathbb{P}[\text{H}]$ in terms of itself. By solving the resulting equation, we obtained $\mathbb{P}[\text{H}] = 1/2$.

We could also have used our loyal outcome-tree method to analyze the algorithm. It is convenient to combine the outcomes 'hh' and 'tt' into a single outcome which we label R for restart. We have that $P(\text{R}) = p^2 + (1-p)^2$. With this new merged outcome, our algorithm, after two flips, produces H, T or R. In the case of R, the algorithm continues flipping. As a result, our algorithm could continue flipping for ever. Hence, we get an the infinite outcome-tree even though the algorithm is asked to produce just one H or T. The infinite outcome-tree is shown below.

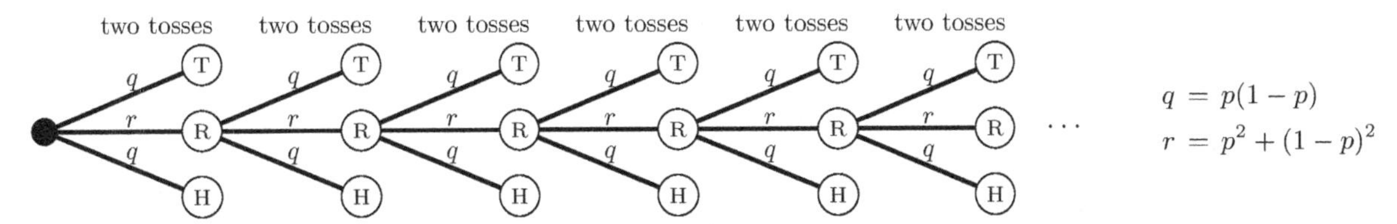

Each outcome in the tree above corresponds to two tosses of the coin. The edge-probabilities above are $q = p(1-p)$ and $r = p^2 + (1-p)^2 = 1 - 2q$. We are interested in the event that you get a heads. We show the outcomes in this event of interest and the correpsonding probabilities below,

outcomes	H	RH	RRH	RRRH	$\cdots$	$\text{R}^{\bullet i}\text{H}$	$\cdots$
probability	q	rq	r^2q	r^3q	$\cdots$	r^iq	$\cdots$

Adding the event's outcome-probabilities to get the event-probability, we get:

$$\mathbb{P}[\text{H}] = q(1 + r + r^2 + r^3 + \cdots) = \frac{q}{1-r} = \frac{q}{1-1+2q} = \frac{1}{2}.$$

All correct paths lead to the same answer. The law of total probability is a sleek approach. The brute force outcome-tree method may be tedious, but it works. □

Exercise 16.9

(a) Prove the formula below, and generalize it to n events $A_1, \ldots, A_n$.

$$\mathbb{P}[A_1 \text{ AND } A_2 \text{ AND } A_3] = \mathbb{P}[A_1 \mid A_2 \text{ AND } A_3] \times \mathbb{P}[A_2 \mid A_3] \times \mathbb{P}[A_3].$$

(b) Explain why edge-probabilities in the outcome-tree are conditional probabilities. Using (a), justify multiplying edge-probabilities to obtain outcome-probabilities

Exercise 16.10 [Craps]

The popular Las Vegas gambling game Craps is summarized in the algorithm to the right.

(a) For $x \in \{2, \ldots, 12\}$ compute the probability to roll x before 7. (x is called the point.)

(b) Compute the probability to win at craps.

1: Roll two fair dice. Let x be the sum.
2: If $x \in \{7, 11\}$, you win. STOP
3: If $x \in \{2, 3, 12\}$, you lose. STOP
4: Continue to roll the dice until a sum of 7 or x. If x is first, you win. If 7 is first, you lose.

Exercise 16.11 [Bayes' Theorem]

Bayes' Theorem links a conditional probability to the transposed conditional probability. Show that

$$\mathbb{P}[A \mid B] = \frac{\mathbb{P}[B \mid A] \times \mathbb{P}[A]}{\mathbb{P}[B]} = \frac{\mathbb{P}[B \mid A] \times \mathbb{P}[A]}{\mathbb{P}[B \mid A] \times \mathbb{P}[A] + \mathbb{P}[B \mid \overline{A}] \times \mathbb{P}[\overline{A}]}$$

Election voting in NY state suggests that about 40% of voters are Republican, of which 70% oppose raising taxes, and 60% are Democrat, of which 50% oppose raising taxes.

(a) Use the law of total probability to compute $\mathbb{P}$[Voter opposes higher taxes].

(b) Using Bayes' theorem, compute $\mathbb{P}$[Republican | Voter opposes higher taxes].

Exercise 16.12 [Two consecutive heads before two consecutive tails]

A biased coin with probability p of heads is flipped until either two consecutive H or two consecutive T are obtained. Compute the probability to get two consecutive H before two consecutive T.

(a) Use the outcome-tree method and infinite probability spaces. (b) Use the law of total probability.

16.5 Problems

Problem 16.1. What is $\mathbb{P}$[Heads | Coin is flipped fairly]? (The conditional probability is "obvious", yet not computable from the definition because the probabilities in its definition are not obvious. One can formally develop probability starting from conditional probability and then defining regular probability. We started with regular probability and defined conditional probability.)

Problem 16.2. Planes are safer than cars: 5 deaths per billion miles driven versus 0.08 deaths per billion miles flown. Use conditioning to suggest ways to improve your driving odds.

Problem 16.3. Researchers can easily fall into conditional probability traps. An IZA Institute of Labor Economics article "Health, Height and the Household at the Turn of the 20th Century" found that:

> In a study of British army recruits, the average height of British men (of average age of 20), was about 5 feet 6 inches (168 centimeters) at the turn of the century (1911), whereas British army recruits now (2014) stand on average at about 5 feet 10 inches (178 cm). The increase of 10cm can be attributed, most likely, to improved nutrition, health services and hygiene,...

You may assume that British army recruits are men and tend to be taller members of society.

(a) What conditional probability trap did the researchers fall into? Be specific.

(b) For fixed army size and a larger population, will the average height of army recruits be larger or smaller?

(c) For fixed population size, and a larger army, will the average height of the army recruits be larger or smaller?

(d) The male population of England and Wales in 1911 was about 17,000,000 and in 2014 it was about 29,000,000. Meanwhile, the British armed forces dropped from about 500,000 in the 1900s to about 180,000 in 2014. Can you explain the results in the quoted study without relying on nutrition, health and hygeine.

(e) Assume men have random heights from 140cm to 180cm (a better model would use a Bell curve). Use Monte Carlo to build a population of 17,000,000 men for 1911 and a separate population of 29,000,000 men for 2014. Build an army by starting from the tallest person and accepting them into the army with probability 5%, continuing with the next tallest person and so on until you get an army of the desired size.

  (i) Why do you start from the tallest person?

  (ii) Report the average height in each population and the average height of each army.

Conditioning killeth. BEWARE of convenient data in statistical studies rather than correct randomly sampled data.

Problem 16.4. Two worlds have 1 million birds each. World 1 has 100 black ravens and the rest are other birds. World 2 has 1000 black ravens, 1 white raven and the rest are other birds. You enter a randomly picked world.

(a) What are the chances that all ravens are black in your world?

(b) You see a random bird and it's a black raven. Now, what are the chances that all ravens are black in your world? (In this case, observing a black raven decreases your belief that "ALL ravens are black." See also Problem 3.58)

Problem 16.5. There are **5,000** students: **1,000** CS; **100** MATH; and, **80** dual CS-MATH. A randomly picked student is in CS or MATH. Compute the probability the student is in CS.

Problem 16.6. Chances are 6% a random day is a rainy Sunday. Today is Sunday. What are the chances of rain?

Problem 16.7. A bag has 3 red and 4 blue marbles. You draw two marbles.

(a) What are the chances the second marble is red?

(b) One of the marbles is red. What are the chances the second marble is red?

(c) The first marble, it's red. What are the chances the second marble is red?

Problem 16.8. An urn has 10 black balls. A random number of balls are painted white.

(a) Randomly pick two balls with replacement. What are the chances both are white?

(b) Randomly pick a ball. The ball is white. Replace the ball. What are the chances the next randomly picked ball is white? What if the first ball was black?

(c) Randomly pick a ball with replacement until it is white. It took two tries. Replace the ball and randomly pick a new ball. What is the probability it is white? What is your best guess for the number of white balls in the urn?

(d) Describe Monte Carlo simulations you could run to verify your answers to (a), (b) and (c).

Problem 16.9. In "Let's Make a Deal," Monty prefers door-3 and will always open it when possible. If Monty opens door-3, should you switch or stay? What about if he opens door 2?

Problem 16.10. Flip 3 fair coins. At least one flip is heads. What is the probability at least two flips are heads?

Problem 16.11 (Galton's paradox). You fliped 3 fair coins. Two flips match. The remaining flip matches those two matching flips with probability $\frac{1}{2}$, hence $\mathbb{P}$[3match | 2 match] $= \frac{1}{2}$. Do you agree? What is $\mathbb{P}$[3 match | 2 match]?

Problem 16.12. Draw cards from a shuffled 52-card deck. What are the chances the 5th card drawn is the ♠A.

Problem 16.13. For events A and B, prove: (a) $\mathbb{P}[A \mid A \cup B] \geq \mathbb{P}[A]$ (b) $\mathbb{P}[A \mid A \cap B] = 1$.

Problem 16.14. Prove or disprove.
(a) $\mathbb{P}[\overline{A} \mid B] = 1 - \mathbb{P}[A \mid B]$. (b) $\mathbb{P}[A \mid \overline{B}] = 1 - \mathbb{P}[A \mid B]$. (c) $\mathbb{P}[A \cup B] = 1 - \mathbb{P}[\overline{A} \mid \overline{B}]\, \mathbb{P}[\overline{B}]$.

Problem 16.15. Prove or disprove: $\mathbb{P}[A \mid B] = 1$ if and only if $B \subseteq A$.

Problem 16.16 (Conditioning and Inclusion-Exclusion). Prove or disprove.
(a) $\mathbb{P}[A \cup B \mid C] = \mathbb{P}[A \mid C] + \mathbb{P}[B \mid C] - \mathbb{P}[A \cap B \mid C]$. (b) $\mathbb{P}[A \mid B \cup C] = \mathbb{P}[A \mid B] + \mathbb{P}[A \mid C] - \mathbb{P}[A \mid B \cap C]$.

Problem 16.17. Bag 1 has two black balls, Bag 2 has a black and a white ball. Randomly pick a bag and randomly take a ball from it. The ball is black. What are the chances the second ball in the same bag is black?

Problem 16.18. Compute the probability the sum of two fair dice is even given the dice have different values.

Problem 16.19. We show the number of students taking various extracurriculars.
(a) What are the chances Ayfos (a random student) is doing Ballet?
(b) What are the chances Ayfos is a 6th grader?
(c) Ayfos is a 7th grader. What are the chances Ayfos is doing
  (i) Skating? (ii) Ballet or Skating?
(d) Baniaz is doing chess. What are the chances she's a 6th grader?

Grade	Chess	Ballet	Skating
6th	65	55	30
7th	85	55	70
8th	60	75	45

Problem 16.20. We show weekly texting patterns (number of students).
(a) What are the chances Niaz has 21 or more texts?
(b) What are the chances Niaz is in 11th grade?
(c) Niaz is in 11th grade. What are the chances he has 50 or fewer texts?
(d) Need has 50 or fewer texts. What are the chances he is in 11th grade?

	Number of texts		
Grade	$0-20$	21-50	Over 50
9th	25	55	30
10th	5	60	50
11th	1	40	70

Problem 16.21. We show blood groups versus race. O can donate blood to anyone; A can donate to A or AB; B can donate to B or AB; and, AB can donate only to AB. (O is a universal donor and AB a universal recipient.) You (a random person) are travelling in a land (Caucasia, Africa, Asia or South Asia) and are involved in an accident. You need a blood transfusion. A random local donor is picked.

Race	O	A	B	AB
Caucasian	9.5%	9%	2%	1%
African	9%	6.5%	4.5%	1.5%
Asian	13.5%	8%	5.5%	1.5%
South Asian	8%	6%	11.5%	3%

(a) What are your chances of survival?
(b) Give a table of your survival chances depending on your land of origin and the land you are travelling in.

Problem 16.22. A box has 6 fair and 4 two-headed coins. You pick a random coin, flip it, and get H. What is the probability you picked a fair coin, $\mathbb{P}[\text{fair coin} \mid \text{you got H}]$?

Problem 16.23. One-in-20 men are color blind and one-in-400 women are color blind. There are an equal number of men and women. You draw a person at random.
(a) What is the probality that the person is color blind?
(b) The person is color blind. What is the probability that the person is male?

Problem 16.24. Niaz must place 50 red and 50 blue marbles into two jars in any way he wishes, as long as both jars are non-empty. Baniaz will pick a jar randomly and then pick a marble from that jar. Niaz wins if Baniaz picks a red marble. How should Niaz distribute the marbles into the jars, and what is the probability that Niaz wins?

Problem 16.25. Kilam throws two darts at the center of a dartboard. The second dart lands farther from the center than the first. Kilam now throws a third dart. What is the probability that the third throw is worse (farther from the center) than his first? (Kilam's skill stays constant.)

> Ayfos argues: Kilam throws 3 independent darts and the 3rd dart will be closer than the first only when the third dart is the best throw. Each dart has an equal chance of being the best throw, so the probability for the third dart to be the best throw is $\frac{1}{3}$. Therefore the third dart will be worse than the first with probability $\frac{2}{3}$.
>
> Niaz argues: We don't care about the second dart. All that matters is the first and third darts. The third dart has a 50-50 shot at beating the first one. So, the third dart will be worse than the first with probability $\frac{1}{2}$.

It's easy to come up with seemingly intuitive but wrong arguments. When in doubt, use the outcome-tree. Compute the correct probability and determine which (if any) of Ayfos and Niaz are correct. Give an intuition for your answer.

Problem 16.26. Randomly draw 5 cards from a 52-card deck and reveal one. Compute the probability of two aces if the revealed card is: (a) ♥A (b) an Ace (c) ♥K (d) not an Ace?

Problem 16.27 (Spam). Spam is 40% of email. "Great deal" is in the subject of 1% of spam emails and 0.2% of non-spam emails. What are the chances an email with "great deal" in the subject is spam. *[Hint: Bayes Theorem.]*

Problem 16.28. FOCS has sections A (20 female, 14 male) and B (18 male, 14 female).
(a) What are the chances a random FOCS student is female?
(b) What are the chances a random student picked from a random FOCS section is female?
(c) What are the chances a randomly picked FOCS student who is female is in section A?

Problem 16.29. A storm produces hail 20% of the time. One-in-1000 storms is a super-storm, producing hail 80% of the time. It is hailing. What are the chances that it's a super-storm?

Problem 16.30. It rains half the time. If it's rains, chances of heavy traffic are 75% but otherwise 25%. In heavy traffic I am late for work, otherwise I'm late 50% of the time. I was late for work. What are the chances it's raining?

Problem 16.31. Randomly draw two balls from a bag with 3 black and 3 white balls. Compute these probabilities.
(a) Ball 1 is black. (b) Ball 2 is black. (c) Balls 1 and 2 are black. (d) Ball 2 is black if ball 1 is black.

Problem 16.32. A household has two kids. When you knock on the front door, it is opened by a girl. What are the chances the household has two girls?

Problem 16.33. Sally has two children. One is a son Mag. What are the chances Mag has a brother? Susie also has two children. You randomly meet one in the super-market, his name is Tom. What are the chances Tom has a brother?

Problem 16.34. Niaz, who has two children, either goes alone on a walk with probability $\frac{1}{2}$ or takes a random child. You met him walking with a boy. What are the chances he has two boys?

Problem 16.35. Baniaz has two kids. What are the chances both are girls in each of the situations below?
(a) Baniaz confirms that one of her children is a girl.
(b) Baniaz confirms one of her children is a girl named Leilitoon (a rare name, assuming names are randomly picked).
(c) Baniaz confirms one of her children is a girl who was born on a Sunday.

Problem 16.36. A parent picks a boy's name as Beta with probability $0 < \beta < 1$. Baniaz has two children with different names. What is the probability Baniaz has two boys if:
(a) Baniaz has a boy (b) Baniaz has a boy named Beta (c) Baniaz does not have a boy named Beta?

Problem 16.37. There are two beavers, brown and black. What are the chances both are male? What if you know:
(a) one is male (b) one is male and one is born on a Tuesday (c) one is a male born on a Tuesday?
Verify answers with Monte Carlo simulation. How strange, the birthday of a beaver changes the probability of two males.

Problem 16.38. Analyze the following version of the Monty Hall game with 4 doors. You are at door 1. Monty chooses a door to open as follows: he starts at door 2, tosses a fair coin and opens the door if the door is empty AND the toss is heads. If he does not open the door, he moves up one door and repeats the coin toss (from door 4, he moves to door 2). Monty continues until he open a door. You only see the final door opened (not the whole process). Determine the optimal strategy and probability to win. (The strategy depends on the door opened.)

Problem 16.39. A bag has 3 coins: a 2-headed coin, a 2-tailed coin and a regular fair coin. Randomly pick a coin and place it on the table. You can see a heads facing up. What is the probability the side facing down is heads?

Problem 16.40. Cards with distinct values $v_1, \ldots, v_m$ are dealt in random order. The k'th card is largest among the cards already dealt. What is the probability it is the largest in the pack?

Problem 16.41. Cards are drawn randomly from a 52-card deck until a ♠ is drawn. What are these probabilities?
(a) No ♥ have been drawn? (b) No ♥ or ♢ have been drawn? (c) No ♥, ♢ or ♣ have been drawn?
Verify your answers using a Monte Carlo. Report the exact and Monte Carlo results.

Problem 16.42. Five out of 100 coins are two-headed. You randomly pick a coin and flip it "fairly" twice (each side is equally probable). What is the probability to get (a) 2 heads (b) 2 tails (c) matching tosses?

Problem 16.43. A box has 6 fair coins and 4 two-headed coins. You pick a coin randomly. What are the chances you picked a fair coin if (a) You flip and get H. (b) You flip again and get H. (c) You flip yet again and get H.

Problem 16.44. A box has three coins: fair, two-headed and two-tailed. You pick a random coin. What are the chances you have the two-headed coin if (a) You flip it and get H? (b) You flip the same coin again and get H?

Problem 16.45. Alice, Bob and Carol take turns rolling a die in the order $A, B, C, A, B, C, \ldots$.

(a) Compute the probability that A gets a 6 first, B second and C third.

(b) Compute the probability that A gets the first 6, B the second and C the third.

Problem 16.46. A class has 10 boys and 5 girls. Three children are selected one after another. Compute the probability that the first two are boys if both sexes are represented.

Problem 16.47. A cab was in a hit and run accident at night. Two companies, Green and Yellow, operate cabs.

- 85% of the cabs in the city are Green and 15% are Yellow.
- A witness identified a Yellow cab. In dim light, a witness correctly identifies cab-color 80% of the time.

With no additional evidence, which cab company do you think is responsible and why?

Problem 16.48. A patron in a NY-City bar supports the NY-Yankees. The probability a random person in a bar was born in Manhattan is $1/50$. Three in four people born in Manhattan support the Yankees. One in ten non-Manhattanites support the Yankees. What are the chances the bar-patron supporting the Yankees is born in Manhattan?

Problem 16.49. Students understand 80% of the material. On a 5-choice problem, a student who understands the topic gets it correct 95% of the time, and otherwise guesses correctly 20% of the time. Compute the probability that:

(a) A student answers correctly? (b) A student who answers correctly understands the topic?

Problem 16.50. A box has 10 coins, 9 are fair and 1 is two-headed. You pick a coin at random, toss it three times and get HHH. What is the probability that the coin you picked is fair?

Problem 16.51. One out of n coins is 2-headed. A random coin is picked and flipped k times. All flips were H.

(a) What is the probability that the coin flipped is 2-headed.

(b) For $n = 10^6$, how high should one pick k to be 99.9% sure the 2-headed coin was flipped?

Problem 16.52. Kilam and Liamsi are taking an oral exam. There are 20 questions in a hat. Kilam knows the answer to 10 questions. Each student draws a question from the hat (without replacement) and if they answer correctly they get an A. Kilam argues vehemently with the professor that he must draw from the hat first because then he has highest chances of getting a question he knows – if he draws second, then Liamsi might have already drawn one of the "easy" questions that he knows. Explain to Kilam why he is wrong using two techniques:

(a) Use a uniform probability space to compute Kilam's probability to get an A if he draws second.

(b) Use total probability with two cases: Liamsi gets an "easy" question; and Liamsi gets a "hard" question.

(The professor says none of this matters: students should be prepared to answer to all questions.)

Problem 16.53. Adam, Barb, Charlie and Doris each choose a random number in $\{1, 2, 3, 4, 5\}$. What are the chances that some pair chooses the same number? What if there are k people and n numbers?

Problem 16.54. In June 2015, 23 Fortune 500 companies listed women CEOs (4.6%). Since about 50% of people are women, this is evidence of gender bias in the workplace, when it comes to promoting women to CEO. That is,

$$\mathbb{P}[\text{NamedCEO} \mid \text{Woman}] \ll \mathbb{P}[\text{NamedCEO} \mid \text{Man}].$$

What is wrong with this reasoning? What is the correct reasoning?

Problem 16.55 (Clinical tests). Chances are 80% that an untreated person gets acne during a month's observation. Chances are 40% an acne drug works. If the drug works, 90% of acne cases are suppressed. Patients arrive (one per month), are randomly either given the drug (treated group) or not (control group), and then observed for a month.

(a) What are the chances the first patient to develop acne is a control patient?

(b) What are the chances the drug is effective if the first patient to develop acne is a control patient?

(c) What are the chances the drug is effective if the first patient to develop acne is a treated patient?

Problem 16.56. In the random gossip network of Problem 15.42, what is the probability that Barb will hear Adam's gossip if Charlie and Doris are not friends?

Problem 16.57. 1 in 1000 drivers is driving drunk. The breathalyzer never fails to detect a drunk person, but is wrong 5% of the time on a sober person. On New Year's eve, there is a random sobriety checkpoint at which drivers are stopped randomly and given the breathalyzer. What are the chances that a driver who fails the brethalyzer is drunk? Is the brethalyzer test doomed? Explain why/how it's not so bad in practice.

Problem 16.58. Three monkeys A, B, C have a 6-shooter pistol loaded with two bullets. Starting with A, each takes turns spinning the bullet-wheel and shooting their foot. Compute:

(a) The probabilities p_A, p_B, p_C that each monkey escapes unscathed.

(b) The probabilities q_A, q_B, q_C that each monkey is the first to be injured.

Problem 16.59. A biased coin is tossed repeatedly. How like is a run of m heads before a run of n tails?

Problem 16.60. Randomly pick a card from a well shuffled deck. What is the probability that:

(a) The card is a king given it is a spade. (b) The card is a spade given it is a king.

Problem 16.61. You randomly deal a 5-card poker hand from a 52-card deck (Exercise 13.14). What is the probability of a full house if the first two cards are queens? What if the first two cards are ♠Q and ♥Q?

Problem 16.62. A plane has n seats assigned to n passengers, who randomly choose an available seat on boarding. What is the probability the last passenger gets her assigned seat? What if the first passenger chooses the wrong seat?

Problem 16.63. The Social-Security Administration publishes probabilities that a random newborn lives to a given age. This is called a survival curve (shown here for US males).

Age (years)	10	20	30	40	50	60	70	80	90	100	110	120
% Survivors	99.2	98.7	97.5	95.9	92.8	86.0	73.5	50.3	17.4	0.9	0.001	0

For example, 86% of newborn males live to 60. For random 10, 30 and 50 year-olds,

(a) Compute the probability that each lives to 80.

(b) Compute the probability that each dies between 70 to 80 .

(c) For any survival curve, prove: $\mathbb{P}$[live till 80 | lived till 17] $<$ $\mathbb{P}$[live till 80 | lived till 25].

Problem 16.64. About 1 in a 1000 people have Coeliac disease. The test for Coeliac makes a mistake on 1 in 10 people who have it (90% accuracy if you have Coeliac) and on 1 in 100 people who do not have it (99% accuracy if you do not have Coeliac). You got tested, and the result was positive. What are the chances that you have Coeliac?

Problem 16.65 (Texas Holdem Poker). In Texas Holdem you get two cards first, and then 5 more (for a total of 7 cards). You choose a hand of 5-cards from these seven cards. Your first two cards are the same rank. What are the chances you'll be able to make: (a) a flush? (b) a full house? (c) a four-of-a-kind? (d) a straight? What are the chances if, instead, your first two cards are of the same suit?

Problem 16.66 (Positive Predictive Value, PPV). The PPV of a medical test is the probability a random person has the condition if the test says YES. PPV quantifies how much you can trust the test.

$$\text{PPV} = \mathbb{P}[\text{person has medical condition} \mid \text{test says YES}].$$

Suppose a fraction p of the population has the condition and let $\gamma = p/(1-p)$ be the ratio of people with the condition to people without the condition. The true positive rate TP is the probability the test says YES if you have the condition; the false positive rate FP is the probability the test says YES if you do not have the condition. Show that

$$\text{PPV} = \frac{1}{1 + (\frac{FP}{TP})/\gamma}.$$

The population's γ is not under your control. For a test to be useful, you need $\frac{FP}{TP} \ll \gamma$. Doctors typically do not tell a patient what the PPV of a test is. Make sure you ask.

Problem 16.67 (Prosecutor's Fallacy). In a small town of 10,000 people, a crime is committed by one person. Everyone will be subjected to the lie-detector. One person, Liamsi, is identified by the lie-detector as having committed the crime. Here are the properties of the lie-detector. If you are guilty, you will be found out 90% of the time. If you are not guilty you will pass the lie-detector test 99.9% of the time. Prosecutor Paul argues:

"Were Kilam innocent, he fails the lie detector **0.1%** of the time. So, beyond a reasonable doubt, he's guilty!"

(a) What conditional probability trap did the prosecutor fall into?

(b) Explain to Prosecutor Paul why he should compute $\mathbb{P}$[Person found is guilty | One person is found by lie-detector].

(c) Compute the conditional probability in (b) using the following steps.

  (i) Show that $\mathbb{P}$[One person is found by lie-detector] $= 0.9 \times (0.999)^{9999} + 0.1 \times 9999 \times 0.001 \times (0.999)^{9998}$.

  (ii) The sum in (i) has two terms. Show that the left term in the sum is the probability that the person found is guilty AND one person is found by lie-detector.

  (iii) Show that $\mathbb{P}$[Person found is guilty | One person is found by lie-detector] $\approx 47\%$. That's reasonable doubt! The one person found as guilty is more likely to be innocent.

(d) Repeat part (c) for a town with 100,000 people.

Moral: If you search for something among many, e.g. 10,000, be careful when you find what you seek.

Problem 16.68 (Meiosis). Recall the genetics model in Problem 13.44. In sexual reproduction, during meiosis, a single set of genes (a gamete) is produced from the father and mother-genes. Think of a biological robot or enzyme (blue square) which randomly picks one set of genes and one-by-one replicates each gene as it iterates through the set. The robot can get confused and randomly "crossover" to the other gene-set after transcribing k genes in the starting gene-set ($k = 1, \ldots, 5$). After crossing-over, the enzyme continues by transcribing the genes in the other gene-set. In the example, the crossover happens after f_2 and the resulting gamete is $f_1 f_2 g_3 g_4 g_5$.

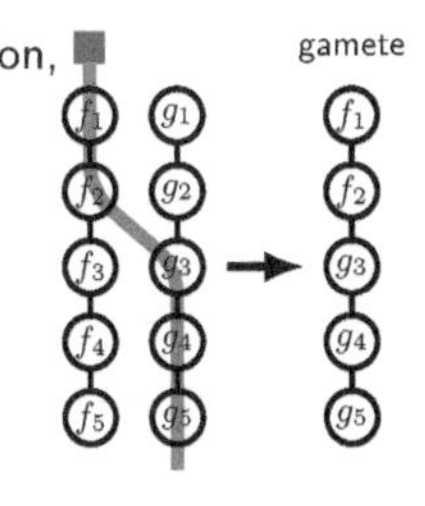

(a) Assume a single crossover at a random location. Give the probability space.
(b) What are $\mathbb{P}[f_1 \in \text{gamete}]$, $\mathbb{P}[f_2 \in \text{gamete}]$ and $\mathbb{P}[f_1 \in \text{gamete} \mid f_2 \in \text{gamete}]$?

Problem 16.69 (Simpson's Paradox). Simpsons paradox arises when you analyze a conditional probability by breaking it down into cases. At a famous university, renowned for science and engineering, an investigation into gender asymmetry in graduate admissions, produced this (approximate) data.

	Science/Engineering		Languages/Humanities	
	# Applicants	#Admitted	# Applicants	#Admitted
Male	825	533	273	16
Female	108	81	352	34

For a randomly picked applicant:
(a) Compute $\mathbb{P}[\text{Admitted} \mid \text{Male}]$ and $\mathbb{P}[\text{Admitted} \mid \text{Female}]$. Is there a case for gender bias in admissions?
(b) Now consider the disciplines separately and compute

$\mathbb{P}[\text{Admitted} \mid \text{Male and Applied to Science/Engineering}]$
$\mathbb{P}[\text{Admitted} \mid \text{Male and Applied to Languages/Humanities}]$
$\mathbb{P}[\text{Admitted} \mid \text{Female and Applied to Science/Engineering}]$
$\mathbb{P}[\text{Admitted} \mid \text{Female and Applied to Languages/Humanities}]$

Is there a case for gender bias in admissions?

(The full and by-discipline conditional probabilities lead to opposite conclusions. Extreme care must be taken when approaching high-octane issues with conditional probabilities. Though our numbers are approximate, the conclusions match the real-life investigation. The critical issue that must be understood is why significantly fewer female students apply to science & engineeding.)

Problem 16.70 (Principle of Restricted Choice). Suppose there are two choices A, B. Someone is to pick A or B in one of three situations (you don't know which).

1. His choice is unrestricted and he will pick randomly. (*A priori* probability p_1 for case 1.)
2. His choice is restricted to A. (*A priori* probability p_2 for case 2.)
3. His choice is restricted to B. (*A priori* probability p_3 for case 3.)

Suppose that he picks option A. Prove that the *a posteriori* probabilities are given by

$$p_1' = \frac{p_1}{p_1 + 2p_2}; \qquad p_2' = \frac{2p_2}{p_1 + 2p_2}; \qquad p_3' = 0.$$

In words: (a) Situation 3 could not have occurred and (b) Situation 2 becomes two times more likely relative to situation 1 than it was *a priori* (that is $p_2'/p_1' = 2p_2/p_1$).

Problem 16.71. Use restricted choice to explain the difference between the cases of Ayfos and Need on page 228

Problem 16.72. A box has 6 fair coins and 4 biased coins with probability of heads $\frac{2}{3}$.
(a) Pick a single random coin and flip it 3 times. What is $\mathbb{P}[2 \text{ heads}]$?
(b) Flip 3 times, each time fliping a random coin and then replacing it. What is $\mathbb{P}[2 \text{ heads}]$?

Problem 16.73. A randomly shuffled 52-card deck is face down. At each step, you may take the top card (before seeing it) or reveal and discard it. If one card remains, you must take it. The game stops when you decide to take a card. You win if your card is red (otherwise you lose).
(a) If you decide to take the 1st card, what is the probabilty that you win?
(b) Prove that no strategy wins with higher probability. *[Hint: Prove a more general claim: with k red and ℓ black cards, the maximum win probability is $k/(k+\ell)$ (use induction).]*

Problem 16.74 (First Ballot Theorem (Bertrand, 1887)). Voters sequentialy vote randomly for A or B. Assume that an $n = 2k + 1$ votes are cast (odd number). Show that the probability A was always ahead of B is:
(a) Δ/n if A wins by Δ votes. *[Hint: Problems 13.93 and 13.94(d).]* (b) $2^{-2k}\binom{2k}{k} \approx 1/\sqrt{k}$ if A wins.

Problem 16.75. Alice, Barb and Claire each toss a fair die in that order until someone gets a 6 and wins. Compute the probabilities each player wins. Generalize to n players. Compute the probabilities $p_1, \ldots, p_n$ that each player wins.

Problem 16.76. A jar has one amoeba. Every minute, every amoeba turns into 0, 1, 2, or 3 amoebae, each with probability $\frac{1}{4}$ (dies, does nothing, splits into 2, or splits into 3). Assume that amoebae act independently. Compute the probability that the amoeba population eventually dies out. You may assume that the probability is strictly less than 1.

Problem 16.77 (More efficient fair toss from biased coin). Recall Example 16.3 on page 232. We show another algorithm to get a fair toss from a biased coin. The algorithm may: output a result after 2, 3, or 4 tosses; or, in some cases, after 4 tosses it restarts. Lower case 'h' and 't' denote the outcomes of the biased coin, with the probability of 'h' being p. The algorithm keeps tossing until the output is either H or T. Show that

$$\mathbb{P}[\mathrm{H}] = \tfrac{1}{2}.$$

(a) Use the law of total probability.
(b) Sum probabilities on an infinite outcome-tree.

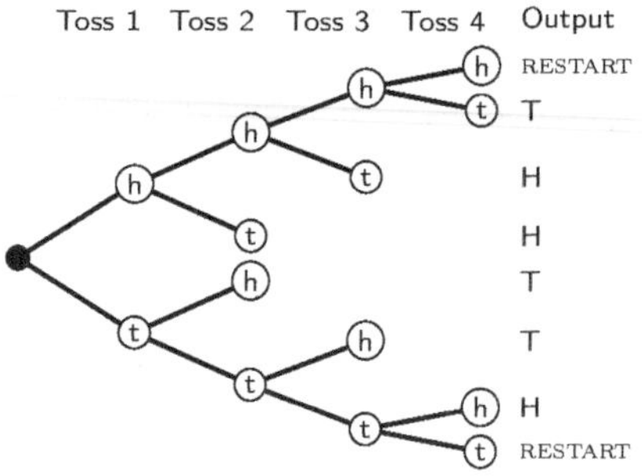

Toss 1 Toss 2 Toss 3 Toss 4 Output

h h h h RESTART
h h h t T
h h t H
h t H
t h T
t t h T
t t t h H
t t t t RESTART

Problem 16.78. Alice and Bob take turns answering questions. The probability of a correct answer is α for Alice and β for Bob. Show that the probability Alice is first to answer correctly is

(a) $\alpha/(\alpha+\beta-\alpha\beta)$ if Alice goes first. (b) $\alpha(1-\beta)/(\alpha+\beta-\alpha\beta)$ if Bob goes first.

In both cases, give two derivations of your answer using:

(i) The outcome-tree method (infinite probability space). (ii) The law of total probability.

Problem 16.79. Alice and Bob play a tennis game. Alice wins a point with probability α. The first person to win at least 4 points with a margin of at least 2 points wins the game. What is the probability that Alice wins the game? Verify your result with Monte Carlo for $\alpha \in \{\frac{1}{3}, \frac{2}{5}, \frac{3}{7}, \frac{4}{9}\}$. Report the fraction of wins in simulation for Alice.

Problem 16.80 (Monte Carlo Roulette). A roulette wheel has a zero 0 (green) and the numbers $1, \ldots, 36$ half of which are red and the other half are black. You bet on red and the wheel is spun coming to rest on a number. The game is summarized in the algorithm to the right. Use the law of total probability to compute the probability that you win.

1: Spin: red wins; black loses; 0 goes to HOLD.
2: If you're in HOLD, spin:
red wins; black loses; 0 goes to JAIL.
3: If you're in JAIL, spin:
red goes back to hold (step 2); black or 0 loses.

Problem 16.81. You have a fair 5-sided die which can generate one of the numbers $\{1,2,3,4,5\}$ with probability $\frac{1}{5}$ each. You wish to simulate a fair 7-sided die which generates a number in $\{1,2,3,4,5,6,7\}$ with probability $\frac{1}{7}$ each. Give an algorithm to do so, and prove it.

Problem 16.82. You continually toss a biased coin with $p = \mathbb{P}[H]$. Show that the probability for the first head to occur on an even numbered toss is $(1-p)/(2-p)$.

(a) Use the outcome-tree method (infinite probability space). (b) Use the law of total probability.

Problem 16.83. A king wishes to fairly decide who of his three children A, B, C will inherit his throne. The king tosses a fair coin until either HH or TT appear. If HH appears on an even toss, A inherits. If TT appears on an even toss, B inherits. If HH or TT appear on an odd toss, C inherits. Is the king's process is fair?

Problem 16.84. Show that to get a single fair "toss", the process in Example 16.3 on page 232 makes $2k$ tosses for $k \geq 1$ with probability $2p(1-p)(p^2+(1-p)^2)^{k-1}$.

Problem 16.85. You toss a biased coin twice with probability of heads is p. If the outcome is: HH, you win; TT, you lose; and, otherwise, you restart. Compute the probability to win.

Problem 16.86. Dirty Harry and Ugly Sam play two-bullet Russian Roulette: a 6-cylinder revolver is randomly loaded with two bullets and the cylinder is spun. Ugly Sam and Dirty Harry take turns shooting their big-toe until someone gets hurt. This is what you do if you fail FOCS and drop out. The cylinder moves one shell forward after each shot.

(a) What is the probability that Ugly Sam is shot on the first trigger-pull?
(b) What is the probability that Dirty Harry is shot on the second trigger-pull?
(c) What is the probability that Ugly Sam is the one to get hurt.
(d) The bullets are loaded into consecutive shells before spinning. Repeat parts (a)-(c).

Problem 16.87. Let P_n be the probability of at least 2 heads in n fair coin tosses.

(a) What is P_2? What is the probability of no heads in n coin tosses?

(b) Use the law of total probability to show that $P_n = \frac{1}{2}P_{n-1} + \frac{1}{2} - \frac{1}{2^n}$ for $n > 2$.

(c) Prove by induction that $P_n = 1 - (n+1)2^{-n}$. (Binomial distribution, see Chapter 18).

Problem 16.88 (Total Probability for More than 2 Cases). Events $C_1, \ldots, C_k$ are a partition of Ω if no two can co-occur and at least one must occur ($\cup_{i=1}^k C_i = \Omega$ and $C_i \cap C_j = \varnothing$).

(a) If $C_1, \ldots, C_k$ are a partition of Ω, show that $C_1 \cap A, \ldots, C_k \cap A$ are a partition of A.

(b) Prove the Law of Total Probability for the k "cases" in a partition $C_1, \ldots, C_k$ of Ω:

$$\mathbb{P}[A] = \sum_{i=1}^k \mathbb{P}[A \mid C_i] \cdot \mathbb{P}[C_i] = \mathbb{P}[A \mid C_1] \cdot \mathbb{P}[C_1] + \cdots + \mathbb{P}[A \mid C_k] \cdot \mathbb{P}[C_k].$$

Problem 16.89. Use the law of total probability to solve these problems.

(a) Repeatedly roll two fair dice. What is the probability to roll a sum of 6 before a sum of 8. Give some intuition.

(b) Repeatedly roll two fair dice. What is the probability to roll a sum of 6 before a sum of 10.

(c) Repeatedly roll two fair dice. What is the probability to roll a sum of 12 before rolling two consecutive sums of 7.

(d) Repeatedly flip a biased coin with probability of heads p. Show that the probability to observe two consecutive H before two consecutive T is $p^2(2-p)/(1-p(1-p))$.

Problem 16.90. Prove formulas for a "conditional" law of total probability,

(a) $\mathbb{P}[A \cap C \mid B] = \mathbb{P}[A \mid B \cap C] \cdot \mathbb{P}[C \mid B]$

(b) Suppose $C_1, \ldots, C_k$ are a partition of Ω. Prove that

$$\mathbb{P}[A \mid B] = \mathbb{P}[A \mid B \cap C_1] \cdot \mathbb{P}[C_1 \mid B] + \cdots + \mathbb{P}[A \mid B \cap C_k] \cdot \mathbb{P}[C_k \mid B].$$

(Weight each of k cases C_i and B by the probability of C_i given B and add.)

Problem 16.91. Suppose $C_1, \ldots, C_k$ are a partition of Ω. Prove or disprove:

$$\begin{aligned}\mathbb{P}[A] &= \mathbb{P}[A \mid B \cap C_1] \cdot \mathbb{P}[C_1 \cap B] + \cdots + \mathbb{P}[A \mid B \cap C_k] \cdot \mathbb{P}[C_k \cap B].\\ \mathbb{P}[A \mid B] &= \mathbb{P}[A \mid B \cap C_1] \cdot \mathbb{P}[C_1 \cap B] + \cdots + \mathbb{P}[A \mid B \cap C_k] \cdot \mathbb{P}[C_k \cap B].\\ \mathbb{P}[A \text{ AND } B] &= \mathbb{P}[A \mid B \cap C_1] \cdot \mathbb{P}[C_1 \cap B] + \cdots + \mathbb{P}[A \mid B \cap C_k] \cdot \mathbb{P}[C_k \cap B].\end{aligned}$$

Build-up Probability. When it's hard to get a formula, you can often compute a probability by starting simple and building up just as we did in build-up counting.

Problem 16.92. Let $Q(n)$ be the probability of an even number of heads in n coin flips with probability p of heads.

(a) What are $Q(1), Q(2), Q(3)$? Show that $Q(n+1) = p + (1-2p)Q(n)$.

(b) When $p = \frac{1}{2}$, what is the solution to this recurrence?

(c) Prove by induction that $Q(n) = \frac{1}{2} + \frac{1}{2}(1-2p)^n$. (To solve recurrences, see for example Problem 8.41.)

Problem 16.93. Compute the probability that when you toss a fair coin 20 times you do not see the pattern HH. As a first step, let $Q(n)$ be the probability to not see HH in n coin tosses.

(a) What are $Q(1), Q(2), Q(3)$ and $Q(4)$? Show that $Q(n) = \frac{1}{2}Q(n-1) + \frac{1}{4}Q(n-2)$.

(b) Use the recurrence to compute $Q(20)$. How is the answer related to Problem 13.53(a)?

(c) Prove that $Q(n) = (\phi_+^n - \phi_i^n + \frac{1}{4}(\phi_+^{n-1} - \phi_-^{n-1}))/(\phi_+ - \phi_-)$, where $\phi_\pm = \frac{1}{4}(1 \pm \sqrt{5})$.
[Hints: Induction. For the induction step, show first that $4\phi_\pm^2 = 2\phi_\pm + 1$.]

(d) Generalize these results to the case when the coin is biased with probability p of H.

Problem 16.94. Let $B(n,k)$ be the probability of k heads in n tosses of a biased coin with probability p of heads.

(a) What are $B(1,0), B(1,1), B(2,0), B(2,1), B(2,2)$?

(b) Show that $B(n,k) = pB(n-1,k-1) + (1-p)B(n-1,k)$. Use this recursion to construct a triangle like Pascal's Triangle for $B(n,k)$ with $p = \frac{1}{3}$. What is $B(10,4)$ for $p = \frac{1}{3}$?

(c) When $p = \frac{1}{2}$, what is the solution to this recurrence?

(d) Prove by induction that $B(n,k) = \binom{n}{k}p^k(1-p)^{n-k}$. (Binomial distribution, see Chapter 18).

Problem 16.95. A coin with with probability p of heads is tossed until you get TT (two consecutive tails). Compute P_n, the probability that you toss the coin n times.

(a) What are P_2 and P_3? Use total probability to show: $P_n = pP_{n-1} + p(1-p)P_{n-2}$ for $n > 2$.

(b) Solve the recurrence and show $P_n = a(\phi_+^{n-1} - \phi_-^{n-1})$. (What are a, ϕ_+, ϕ_-?) Verify with Monte Carlo simulation.

Problem 16.96. You keep flipping a coin and score 1 point for each H and 2 points for each T. Compute the probability that you will at some point have a total score of 20.

(a) Let P_n be the probability that your score will hit n. What are P_0, P_1, P_2?
(b) Explain why $\mathbb{P}[\text{score} = n \text{ OR score} = n+1] = 1$.
(c) Use (b) to show that $1 = P_n + P_{n+1} - \mathbb{P}[\text{score} = n \text{ AND score} = n+1]$, and hence prove $P_{n+1} = 1 - \frac{1}{2}P_n$.
(d) Compute P_{20}, and verify with Monte Carlo simulation.
(e) Solve the recursion and obtain a formula for P_n, and verify with Monte Carlo simulation. *[Hint: Problem 8.47].*

Problem 16.97. Start with $5 and flip a biased coin up to 20 times (probability of H is p). On each flip, you may bet an integer number of dollars up to how much money you have. On the first flip you may bet $0, 1, \ldots, 5$ dollars. If you flip H, you win the amount bet. If you flip T, you lose the amount bet. You target is $20 and hence you wish to maximize the probability to have at least $\$20$ at the end. What is your first bet when:
(a) $p = 0.5$ (b) $p = 0.7$ (c) $p = 0.3$?

Problem 16.98. On Mars, boys are twice as likely as girls. A Martian couple has children until they have two boys in a row. Compute the probability the couple will have 10 children.

(a) Let $Q(n)$ be the probability to have n children. What are $Q(2)$ and $Q(3)$?
(b) Show taht $Q(n) = \frac{1}{3}Q(n-1) + \frac{2}{9}Q(n-2)$ for $n > 3$ and hence compute $Q(n)$.
(c) Get a formula for $Q(n)$ and prove it by induction.

Problem 16.99. A three-sided die has face-values 1,2,3. Roll the die 10 times and compute the sum. What is the probability the sum is 15. *[Hint: Let $Q(n, s) = \mathbb{P}[\text{sum of } s \text{ in } n \text{ rolls}]$.]*

Problem 16.100. Toss a biased coin 25 times. Suppose the probability of heads is $\frac{1}{3}$. Compute the probability that the number of heads is divisible by 3.

(a) Relate $A(n), B(n), C(n)$ to $A(n-1), B(n-1), C(n-1)$ and compute $A(25)$, where:

$$\begin{aligned} A(n) &= \mathbb{P}[\text{number of heads has remainder 0 when divided by 3}] \\ B(n) &= \mathbb{P}[\text{number of heads has remainder 1 when divided by 3}] \\ C(n) &= \mathbb{P}[\text{number of heads has remainder 2 when divided by 3}] \end{aligned}$$

(b) Use Monte Carlo to estimate the probability and compare with your answer in (a).

Problem 16.101. Solve the recurrences in Problem 16.100 to get a formula for the probability that 3 divides the number of heads in n coin flips, with probability p of heads. *[Hint: Adapt Problem 7.40 on page 97.]*

Problem 16.102. Three friends A, B, C each have tokens a, b, c. At every step a random pair swaps whatever tokens they currently have. If the first pair picked is (A, B) and then (A, C), the token are distributed c, a, b.

(a) After 10 swaps, compute the probability that each friend has their own token.
(b) After 11 swaps, compute the probability that each friend has their own token.
(c) Tinker further and make a conjecture for the probability that each friend has their own token after n swaps.
(d) Prove your conjecture by induction.
(e) Repeat parts (a)-(d) if initially the tokens are distributed randomly to the friends.

Problem 16.103. On day 0 there is a single amoeboid. Each day, a living amoeboid dies or splits into two amoeboids. The probability to split is $p = \frac{3}{4}$.

(a) Compute the probability the species is extinct on day 10. *[Hint: Let $Q(n, t) = \mathbb{P}[n \text{ amoeboids on day } t]$.]*
(b) Compute the probability the species goes extinct.

> Today expect something good to happen to you no matter what occurred yesterday. – **Sarah Breathnach**
>
> My mother told me to be a lady. And for her, that meant be your own person, be independent. – **Ruth Bader Ginsburg**
>
> Independence? That's middle class blasphemy. We are all dependent on one another, every soul of us on earth. – **George Bernard Shaw**

Chapter 17

Independent Events

1: Independence is a simplifying assumption.
2: Computing probabilities of complex events: the birthday problem and hashing.

Two events are independent if knowing something about one event does not tell you anything about the other. In other words, the events have nothing to do with each other.

- Kilam's first child is a boy. Does this tell you anything about the sex of Kilam's second child? The prevailing medical opinion is no. The sex of Kilam's children are independent.
- Kilam's first child has blue eyes. It's a good guess Kilam's second child has blue eyes too, for both children share Kilam's genes. The eye color of Kilam's children are not independent. Liamsi, who is not related to Kilam, has a child Kit. Can you guess Kit's eye color. Not likely because Kit's eye color has nothing to do with Liamsi's kids' eyecolors. Eyecolors of unrelated people are independent.
- You toss a fair coin and got heads. You toss the coin again. Your first toss does not help you guess the second toss? The two coin tosses are independent.
- It's raining. Is it cloudy? Yes! Cloudy weather and rainy weather are not independent.

Pop Quiz 17.1
A biased coin has unknown probability p of heads. Your flip the coin and get H. Does the first toss help you predict the second toss? Are the two coin tosses independent?
Suppose $p = \frac{1}{3}$. Does the first toss being H help you predict the second toss?

You need to think about the context to determine whether events are independent.

Independence is an assumption.

What does independence mean mathematically? Consider tossing two independent coins 100 times. Coin 1 will flip H about 50 times. So too will coin 2. How often will you get HH? This is where the independence comes in. Take the 50 cases where coin 1 is H. Coin 2 is not affected by the coin 1 being H, so coin 2 will be H in about 25 of the 50 cases where coin 1 is H. Using the frequency interpretation of a probability,

$$\mathbb{P}[\text{coin 1=H AND coin 2=H}] = 25/100 = 1/4.$$

Because $\mathbb{P}[\text{coin 1=H}] = \frac{1}{2}$ and $\mathbb{P}[\text{coin 2=H}] = \frac{1}{2}$, we can write

$$\mathbb{P}[\text{coin 1=H AND coin 2=H}] = 1/4 = 1/2 \times 1/2 = \mathbb{P}[\text{coin 1=H}] \times \mathbb{P}[\text{coin 2=H}].$$

Another example. It rains 1 in 7 days, $\mathbb{P}[\text{rain}] = 1/7$. It is cloudy 1 in 5 days, $\mathbb{P}[\text{clouds}] = 1/5$. How often is it raining and cloudy? What is $\mathbb{P}[\text{rain AND clouds}]$? It rains 1 in 7 days, so in 35 days it rains about 5 times. It is cloudy 1 in 5 days, so of these 5 rainy days, it should be cloudy once. Thus, it rains and is cloudy 1 in 35 days. Wrong! We are reasoning as though rain and clouds are independent, as with the coin tosses. Everyone knows that when it rains, it must be cloudy. Every one of the 1 in 7 days with rain are also cloudy:

$$\mathbb{P}[\text{rain AND clouds}] = 1/7 \gg 1/35 = \mathbb{P}[\text{rain}] \times \mathbb{P}[\text{clouds}].$$

Independence relates the AND event to the individual events:

$$\mathbb{P}[\text{coin 1=H AND coin 2=H}] = \mathbb{P}[\text{coin 1=H}] \times \mathbb{P}[\text{coin 2=H}]; \quad \leftarrow \text{independent}$$
$$\mathbb{P}[\text{rain AND clouds}] \neq \mathbb{P}[\text{rain}] \times \mathbb{P}[\text{clouds}]. \quad \leftarrow \text{not independent}$$

Independence. Events A and B are independent if

$$\mathbb{P}[A \text{ AND } B] = \mathbb{P}[A \cap B] = \mathbb{P}[A] \times \mathbb{P}[B].$$

In general, $\mathbb{P}[A \cap B] = \mathbb{P}[A \mid B] \times \mathbb{P}[B]$. Independence means that

$$\mathbb{P}[A \mid B] = \mathbb{P}[A].$$

$\mathbb{P}[A \mid B] = \mathbb{P}[A]$ mathematically states the intuition that independent events "have nothing to do with each other." Knowing the outcome is in B, i.e. given B occurs, the probability the outcome is in A does not change.

Exercise 17.2
For independent A and B, $\mathbb{P}[A \cap B] = \mathbb{P}[A] \cdot \mathbb{P}[B]$. For general dependent A and B, prove or disprove:
(a) $\mathbb{P}[A \cap B] \geq \mathbb{P}[A] \cdot \mathbb{P}[B]$ (b) $\mathbb{P}[A \cap B] \leq \mathbb{P}[A] \cdot \mathbb{P}[B]$ (c) $\mathbb{P}[A \cap B] \leq \min(\mathbb{P}[A], \mathbb{P}[B])$.

Independence is a non-trivial assumption, and you can't always assume it. You must think carefully about the context and whether independence holds. When it does, computing probabilities is a lot easier, so whenever possible you should look for and exploit independence.

Example 17.1. In 1961, Frank Drake developed the Drake equation to estimate how many alien civilizations are out there. In 2010, Peter Backus adapted the Drake equation to estimate how many women are "out there" for him to date, in a paper "Why I don't have a girlfriend." The famous physicist Enrico Fermi popularized this technique to answer complex questions like "How many dateable girls are out there?" Fermi's method is to break down the question into several little questions whose answers you can estimate and then combine to get an approximate answer to the complex question. This works because little errors in the little answers typically cancel because sometimes you overestimate and sometimes you underestimate.

First, you need to identify the smaller events that combine to give the complex event. In this case the complex event is A = "Dateable girl". Identifying the smaller events amounts to setting your criteria for what "dateable" means. Here are the criteria Backus used (you may have different criteria):

A_1 = "Lives nearby"; A_2 = "Right sex"; A_3 = "Right age"; A_4 = "Single";
A_5 = "Educated"; A_6 = "Attractive"; A_7 = "Finds me attractive"; A_8 = "We get along".

You want to compute $\mathbb{P}[A]$. At a minimum, all the reasonable criteria above must be satisfied. This means

$$\mathbb{P}[A] = \mathbb{P}[A_1 \cap A_2 \cap A_3 \cap A_4 \cap A_5 \cap A_6 \cap A_7 \cap A_8].$$

We need the probability of a huge AND. If the criteria are independent, the probability simplifies to a product,

$$\mathbb{P}[A] = \mathbb{P}[A_1] \cdot \mathbb{P}[A_2] \cdot \mathbb{P}[A_3] \cdot \mathbb{P}[A_4] \cdot \mathbb{P}[A_5] \cdot \mathbb{P}[A_6] \cdot \mathbb{P}[A_7] \cdot \mathbb{P}[A_8].$$

We can estimate the probabilities of these simpler events separately for (say) a 25-year-old heterosexual male in NY-state, assuming that "nearby" means in-state[1], we get the following little probabilities.

$$\begin{aligned}
\mathbb{P}[\text{"Lives nearby"}] &\quad \frac{\text{number(nearby)}}{\text{number(world)}} \approx \frac{20\text{ million}}{7\text{ billion}} \approx \frac{3}{1000} \\
\mathbb{P}[\text{"Right sex"}] &\quad 1/2 \text{ because there are about 50\% male and 50\% female in the world} \\
\mathbb{P}[\text{"Right age"}] &\quad 15/100 \text{ because about 15\% of people are between 20 and 30} \\
\mathbb{P}[\text{"Single"}] &\quad 1/2 \text{ because about 50\% of people are single} \\
\mathbb{P}[\text{"Educated"}] &\quad 1/4 \text{ because about 25\% in the US have a college degree} \\
\mathbb{P}[\text{"Attractive"}] &\quad 1/5 \text{ because you find 1 in 5 people attractive} \\
\mathbb{P}[\text{"Finds me attractive"}] &\quad 1/10 \text{ because you are modest} \\
\mathbb{P}[\text{"We get along"}] &\quad 1/16 \text{ because you get along with 1 in 4 people and assume so for her}
\end{aligned}$$

Multiplying the little probabilities, we get the big probability of a dateable person,

$$\mathbb{P}[\text{"Dateable"}] = \frac{3}{1000} \times \frac{1}{2} \times \frac{15}{100} \times \frac{1}{2} \times \frac{1}{4} \times \frac{1}{5} \times \frac{1}{10} \times \frac{1}{16} \times \approx 3.5 \times 10^{-8}.$$

About 1 in 30 million people is dateable, or about 250 of the 7 billion people out there, which is 40 times fewer viable dates than alien civilizations estimated by Drake. Reducing a complex event to an AND of unrelated simpler events is powerful because it is much easier to estimate the little probabilities.

One in 30 million is slim odds. In practice, you can't expect perfect independence. For example, age, getting along and being educated are not completely unrelated, so you might tweak the probabilities to account for some conditioning. If you relax some criteria, things improve. For example, if you can move to any metro-area, your odds improve by perhaps a factor of 50. If you add more deal-breaker criteria, your odds worsen.

Exercise 17.3

In general, show that the Fermi formula for $\mathbb{P}[A]$ should be

$$\mathbb{P}[A] = \mathbb{P}[A_1] \cdot \mathbb{P}[A_2 \mid A_1] \cdot \mathbb{P}[A_3 \mid A_1 \cap A_2] \cdot \mathbb{P}[A_4 \mid A_1 \cap A_2 \cap A_3] \cdots \mathbb{P}[A_8 \mid A_1 \cap \cdots \cap A_7]$$

The order of the simpler events can make the computation easier. Use Fermi's method to estimate the number of people using a cellphone during a weekday-minute.

□

Independence of 3 Events. Consider the uniform probability space for three independent coins with 8 outcomes each of probability $\frac{1}{8}$). Three events A_1, A_2, A_3 are defined below.

ω	HHH	HHT	HTH	HTT	THH	THT	TTH	TTT
$P(\omega)$	1/8	1/8	1/8	1/8	1/8	1/8	1/8	1/8

$A_1 = \{\text{coins } 1 \,\&\, 2 \text{ match}\}$
$A_2 = \{\text{coins } 2 \,\&\, 3 \text{ match}\}$
$A_3 = \{\text{coins } 1 \,\&\, 3 \text{ match}\}$

Pop Quiz 17.4

(a) Show that $\mathbb{P}[A_1] = \mathbb{P}[A_2] = \mathbb{P}[A_3] = 1/2$.
(b) Show that $\mathbb{P}[A_1 \cap A_2] = \mathbb{P}[A_2 \cap A_3] = \mathbb{P}[A_1 \cap A_3] = 1/4$.
(c) Show that $\mathbb{P}[A_1 \cap A_2 \cap A_3] = 1/4$. Can you give an intuitive explanation?

For our three events, any pair is independent, for example $\mathbb{P}[A_1 \cap A_2] = 1/4 = \mathbb{P}[A_1] \cdot \mathbb{P}[A_2]$. Despite that, the three events together are not independent,

$$\mathbb{P}[A_1 \cap A_2 \cap A_3] = 1/4 \neq \mathbb{P}[A_1] \cdot \mathbb{P}[A_2] \cdot \mathbb{P}[A_2] = 1/8.$$

The events are pairwise or 2-way independent, but not 3-way independent, where k-way independence for n events $A_1, \ldots, A_n$ means

$$\mathbb{P}[\text{any } k\text{-way intersection}] = \text{product of the } k \text{ individual event probabilities.}$$

[1]We use demographic data from the US Census Bureau (population by age, college degree, etc).

That is $\mathbb{P}[A_{i_1} \cap A_{i_2} \cap \cdots \cap A_{i_k}] = \mathbb{P}[A_{i_1}] \cdot \mathbb{P}[A_{i_2}] \cdots \mathbb{P}[A_{i_k}]$. Let us consider another example, the probability space from rolling two independent dice.

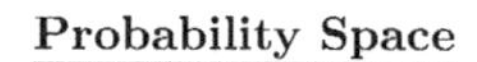

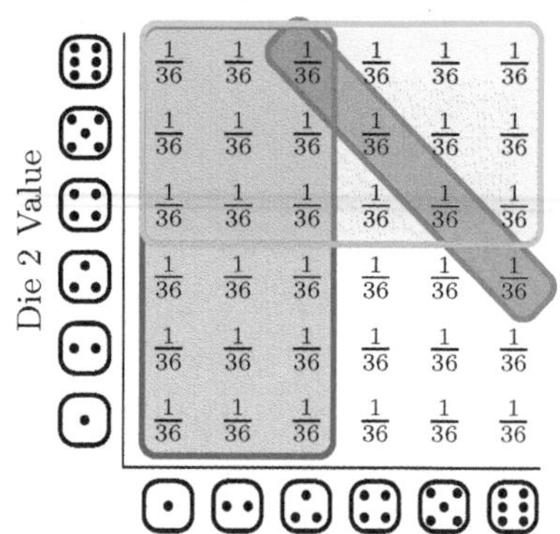

Define the three events,

$$
\begin{aligned}
A_1 &= \{\text{Die } 1 \leq 3\} && \text{(blue)} \\
A_2 &= \{\text{Die } 2 \geq 4\} && \text{(green)} \\
A_3 &= \{\text{Die } 1 + \text{Die } 2 = 9\} && \text{(red)}
\end{aligned}
$$

Pop Quiz 17.5

(a) Show that A_1, A_2, A_3 are 3-way independent,

$$\mathbb{P}[A_1] = 1/2; \quad \mathbb{P}[A_2] = 1/2; \quad \mathbb{P}[A_3] = 1/9.$$
$$\mathbb{P}[A_1 \cap A_2 \cap A_3] = 1/36 = \mathbb{P}[A_1] \cdot \mathbb{P}[A_2] \cdot \mathbb{P}[A_3].$$

(b) Show: $\mathbb{P}[A_1 \cap A_3] = 1/36$. What is $\mathbb{P}[A_1] \cdot \mathbb{P}[A_3]$?

(c) Show: $\mathbb{P}[A_2 \cap A_3] = 1/12$. What is $\mathbb{P}[A_2] \cdot \mathbb{P}[A_3]$?

(d) Are A_1, A_2, A_3 2-way independent?

Pop Quizzes 17.4 and 17.5 give events that are 2-way but not 3-way independent and events that are 3-way but not 2-way independent. For A_1, A_2, A_3 to be independent, we require both 2-way and 3-way independence. The definition generalizes to n events: $A_1, \ldots, A_n$ are independent if they are 2-way, 3-way, ..., n-way independent. That's quite a heavy requirement for independence, but our examples show they are all needed.

> $A_1, \ldots, A_n$ are **independent** if the probability of any intersection of distinct events is the product of the event-probabilities of those events,
> $$\mathbb{P}[A_{i_1} \cap A_{i_2} \cap \cdots \cap A_{i_k}] = \mathbb{P}[A_{i_1}] \cdot \mathbb{P}[A_{i_2}] \cdots \mathbb{P}[A_{i_k}].$$

Exercise 17.6

Suppose that A_1, A_2, A_3 are independent.

(a) What is $\mathbb{P}[A_3 \mid A_1 \cap A_2]$?

(b) Show that for any choice of $X = A_1$ or $\overline{A_1}$, $Y = A_2$ or $\overline{A_2}$ and $Z = A_3$ or $\overline{A_3}$,

$$\mathbb{P}[X \cap Y \cap Z] = \mathbb{P}[X] \cdot \mathbb{P}[Y] \cdot \mathbb{P}[Z]. \qquad (*)$$

(c) Show also that if $(*)$ holds for all 2^3 choices of (X, Y, Z), then A_1, A_2, A_3 are independent. This definition of independence also generalizes to n events and is equivalent to the one in the text.

17.1 Coincidence: The Birthday Paradox

In class there are 200 students. I like to look for Foundations-of-Computer-Science (FOCS) twins, two students with the same birthday. I ask students one by one for their birthday, checking if anyone else's birthday matches. Students groan, expecting the tedious game to continue forever. Indeed, every one of the 200 students could have a different birthday. Surprisingly, I find FOCS-twins by student 3 or 4. Should we be surprised? How likely is this coincidence? It is 99.5% likely that I won't ask more than 10 students, assuming:

1. Birthdays of different people are independent (no twins, triplets, ...).
2. All birthdays are equally likely (no spring-fling, January-born effects). If some birthdays are more likely, then the chances of finding FOCS-twins actually improve.

Independence is crucial. Independence means the birthdays are not adversarially coordinated to be different. Let's get into the details. There are 366 possible birthdays. Let the set of students be $S = \{s_1, \ldots, s_{200}\}$. Suppose s_1 has birthday January 1 (it could just as well be any day). Define the events:

$$A_2 = \{\text{birthday}(s_2) \neq \text{Jan 1}\}, \quad A_3 = \{\text{birthday}(s_3) \neq \text{Jan 1}\}, \quad \ldots, \quad A_{200} = \{\text{birthday}(s_{200}) \neq \text{Jan 1}\}.$$

The probability that s_1 fails to have a FOCS-twin is

$$\mathbb{P}[A_2 \cap A_3 \cap \cdots \cap A_{200}] = \mathbb{P}[A_2] \cdot \mathbb{P}[A_3] \cdots \mathbb{P}[A_{200}], \tag{17.1}$$

a product since $A_2, \ldots, A_{200}$ are independent because they relate to the birthdays of different students. If $\text{birthday}(s_2) \neq$ January 1, that leaves 365 of the 366 available birthdays for s_2, so $\mathbb{P}[A_2] = 365/366$. The same argument works for $A_3, \ldots, A_{200}$,

$$\mathbb{P}[A_2] = \mathbb{P}[A_3] = \cdots = \mathbb{P}[A_{200}] = \frac{365}{366}.$$

Using these probabilities in (17.1),

$$\mathbb{P}[s_1 \text{ has no FOCS-twin}] = \left(\frac{365}{366}\right)^{199} = \left(\frac{B-1}{B}\right)^{N-1}. \tag{17.2}$$

We took the liberty of writing the formula for the general setting with N students and B possible birthdays. If s_1 has no FOCS-twin, I move to s_2. If s_2 also fails to have a FOCS-twin, then both s_1 and s_2 don't have FOCS-twins. Let E_i be the event $\{s_i \text{ has no FOCS-twin}\}$. We want $\mathbb{P}[E_1 \cap E_2]$.

$$\mathbb{P}[E_1 \cap E_2] = \mathbb{P}[E_1] \cdot \mathbb{P}[E_2 \mid E_1].$$

We need $\mathbb{P}[E_2 \mid E_1]$, the conditional probability that s_2 doesn't have a FOCS-twin given that s_1 doesn't. Since s_1 has no FOCS-twin, no other student is born on January 1. This reduces the number of available birthdays from B to $B-1$ for the $N-1$ students $s_2, \ldots, s_N$. Using the same formula in (17.2), the probability s_2 who is one of $N-1$ students has no FOCS-twin when these $N-1$ students have $B-1$ available birthdays is

$$\mathbb{P}[E_2 \mid E_1] = \left(\frac{B-2}{B-1}\right)^{N-2} = \left(\frac{364}{365}\right)^{198}. \tag{17.3}$$

Knowing s_1 has no FOCS-twin reduces the problem for s_2 from N students with B possible birthdays to $N-1$ students with $B-1$ possible birthdays. Let us make a point about conditioning and independence. Students s_1 and s_2 are independent. This means that s_1 being born on a particular day does not affect the probabilities that s_2 is born on some day. However, the events s_1 fails to have a FOCS-twin and s_2 fails to have a FOCS-twin are not independent. Why? By symmetry, the probability s_2 fails to have a FOCS-twin is $(365/366)^{199}$, the same as the probability s_1 fails to have a FOCS-twin. But, when s_1 has no FOCS-twin, that takes care of part of the requirements for s_2 to not have a FOCS-twin, because s_1 and s_2 don't have the same birthday. Therefore, it is now a little easier for s_2 to have no FOCS-twin. Plugging in the numbers,

$$\mathbb{P}[E_2] = \left(\frac{365}{366}\right)^{199} < \left(\frac{364}{365}\right)^{198} = \mathbb{P}[E_2 \mid E_1].$$

Indeed, if there are only two students and you know s_1 has no FOCS-twin, it is certain that s_2 has no FOCS-twin. Collecting everything together,

$$\mathbb{P}[E_1 \cap E_2] = \mathbb{P}[E_1] \cdot \mathbb{P}[E_1 \mid E_2] = \left(\frac{B-1}{B}\right)^{N-1} \left(\frac{B-2}{B-1}\right)^{N-2} = \left(\frac{365}{366}\right)^{199} \times \left(\frac{364}{365}\right)^{198}.$$

We can get this result another way. The chances s_2 is not born on s_1's birthday are 365/366. The chances the other 198 students are not FOCS-twins with s_1 or s_2 are $(364/366)^{198}$. Multiplying, due of independence,

$$\mathbb{P}[E_1 \cap E_2] = \frac{365}{366} \times \left(\frac{364}{366}\right)^{198}.$$

Pop Quiz 17.7

Generalize the prior discussion. Suppose $s_1, \ldots, s_{k-1}$ do not have FOCS-twins. Compute the probability s_k has no FOCS-twin. Let E_k be the event s_k has no FOCS-twin. Show:

$$\mathbb{P}[E_k \mid E_1 \cap E_2 \cap \cdots \cap E_{k-1}] = \left(\frac{B-k}{B-k+1}\right)^{N-k}. \tag{17.4}$$

We are almost done. The probability of no FOCS-twin among the first k students is $\mathbb{P}[E_1 \cap \cdots \cap E_k]$, which is a product of conditional probabilities of the form in (17.4),

$$\begin{aligned}\mathbb{P}[E_1 \cap \cdots \cap E_k] &= \mathbb{P}[E_1] \cdot \mathbb{P}[E_2 \mid E_1] \cdot \mathbb{P}[E_3 \mid E_1 \cap E_2] \cdots \mathbb{P}[E_k \mid E_1 \cap \cdots \cap E_{k-1}] \\ &= \left(\frac{B-1}{B}\right)^{N-1} \times \left(\frac{B-2}{B-1}\right)^{N-2} \times \cdots \times \left(\frac{B-k}{B-k+1}\right)^{N-k} \end{aligned} \tag{17.5}$$

Let's plug in the numbers for $N = 200$ and $B = 366$ to get $\mathbb{P}[E_1 \cap \cdots \cap E_{10}]$,

$$\mathbb{P}[s_1, \ldots, s_{10} \text{ have no FOCS-twin}] = \left(\frac{365}{366}\right)^{199} \times \left(\frac{364}{365}\right)^{198} \times \left(\frac{363}{364}\right)^{197} \times \cdots \times \left(\frac{356}{357}\right)^{190} \approx 0.005.$$

The chances of not finding a FOCS-twin after 10 students is 0.5%. The chances are 99.5% for the complement event, that I find a FOCS-twin. Here is a table with the chances of a FOCS-twin by the kth student.

Finding a FOCS-twin by the kth student with class size 200

k	1	2	3	4	5	6	7	8	9	10	23	25
chances (%)	42.0	66.3	80.4	88.6	93.3	96.1	97.7	98.7	99.2	99.5	99.999	100

The chances are 42% that I stun the audience with a FOCS-twin on the first student!

Example 17.2 (Birthday Paradox). At a cocktail party with just 50 people, what are the chances two have the same birthday? It's the same game we played in the class, except now we ask all N people if they have a twin. This means $k = N$ in (17.5) and the probability of no social twins at the cocktail party is

$$\mathbb{P}[\text{no social twins}] = \left(\frac{365}{366}\right)^{49} \times \left(\frac{364}{365}\right)^{48} \times \left(\frac{363}{364}\right)^{47} \times \cdots \times \left(\frac{315}{316}\right)^{0} \approx 0.03.$$

Chances are about 97% that two people share a birthday at the party. In such a small gathering, you are almost guaranteed a pair of social twins. This coincidence is surprising enough to be called a paradox.

Moral. When searching for something among many options, do not be surprised to find it. We searched for social twins among 1,225 possible pairs. It's no surprise one of these many possibilities fits the bill. □

Exercise 17.8

(a) Approximate the probability of no FOCS-twins in the class of 200.

(b) Approximate the probability of no social-twins at a party with 367 people.

(c) How many people do you need at a party for the probability of a social twin to be $\geq 50\%$? Give a plot of $\mathbb{P}$[there is a social twin] versus the number of people at the party.

(d) Derive (17.5) using a uniform probability space instead of independence.

(i) How many birthday-sequences are there for N students?

(ii) What is the probability of each sequence?

(iii) How many outcomes have the first k birthdays not being repeated.

(iv) Show: $\mathbb{P}[\text{no repetition of first } k \text{ birthdays}] = \frac{1}{B^N} \times \frac{B!}{(B-k)!} \times (B-k)^{N-k}$.

(v) Show that the formula in (iv) matches the one in Equation (17.5).

(vi) For $k = N$, show that the formula becomes

$$1 \times \left(1 - \frac{1}{B}\right) \times \left(1 - \frac{2}{B}\right) \times \cdots \times \left(1 - \frac{N-1}{B}\right).$$

Derive this formula directly by multiplying conditional probabilities.

17.1.1 Hashing

We pull together some of our tools to analyze an important algorithm in Computer Science. The motivation is search. A little company which started in 1998 and whose name begins with a G makes a big living off-of search. Say no more. Hashing is fundamental to search. The basic task of a search engine is to quickly find all webpages containing a user's query-word. In the example below are three webpages and some search queries whose answers we obtained by visual inspection of the webpages. That's too slow for a billion webpages.

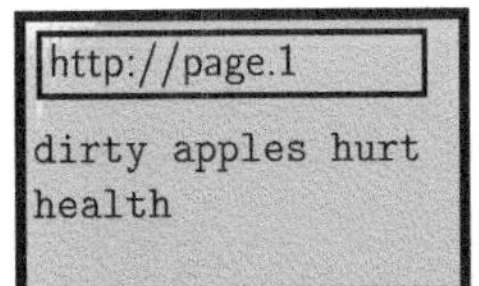

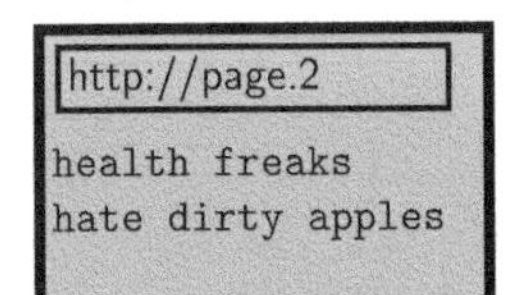

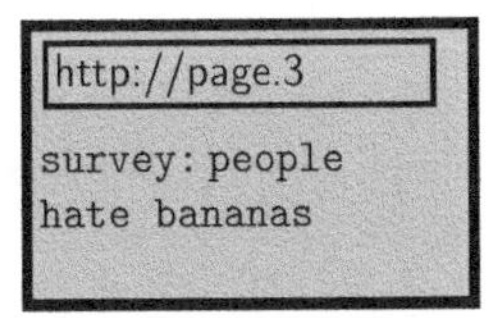

Example Search Queries

find(`apples`) = {page.1, page.2}
find(`hate`) = {page.2, page.3}
find(`bananas`) = {page.3}

Sorting approach to search. Here's an idea. Preprocess all words in the webpages to make a "telephone directory", but instead of listing telephone numbers for a word, list web-addresses. To answer a query, simply look up the word in the huge web-address directory.

The web-address directory for our three webpages is shown on the right. If you've ever looked up a phone number you know that the search is efficient because the words are sorted. Using binary search, a single query has $O(\log N)$ runtime for a directory with N sorted words. That's not good enough because humans want instant gratification. Instant gratification means $O(1)$ search. How do you search a huge directory in near-constant time, independent of N? Hashing is the solution.

Web-address Directory

`apples`	→ {page.1, page.2}
`bananas`	→ {page.3}
`dirty`	→ {page.1, page.2}
`freaks`	→ {page.2}
`hate`	→ {page.2, page.3}
`health`	→ {page.1, page.2}
`hurt`	→ {page.1}
`people`	→ {page.3}
`survey`	→ {page.3}

Hashing approach to search. A hash function HASH(w) maps a word w to an integer in $[0, B-1]$. A simple way to hash a word is to convert each letter to a number, for example $\texttt{a} \to 1, \texttt{b} \to 2, \ldots, \texttt{z} \to 26$, raise each letter to a large prime power p, for example $p = 17$, add the results and finally take the remainder with respect to another prime modulus B, for example $B = 11$. For `hate`, we have

$$\text{HASH}(\texttt{hate}) = 8^{17} + 1^{17} + 20^{17} + 5^{17} \pmod{11} = 7$$

The table on the right has B rows indexed $0, \ldots, B-1$. The entry for `hate` is stored in the table-row HASH(`hate`) $= 7$. We show the full hash-table for our simple hash function and the three webpages. To search for the query `people`, compute HASH(`people`) $= 3$. That takes you to table-row 3, where you find the webpages associated with `people`.

Our scheme has a problem if the query is `survey`. You compute HASH(`survey`) $= 9$, which takes you to table row 9, where you find `apples`. You must search within row 9 to complete the task. This is an example of a collision. The search runtime is in $O(1)$ provided

Row	Entries
0	`bananas` → {page.3}
1	
2	`hurt` → {page.1}
3	`people` → {page.3}
4	`dirty` → {page.1, page.2}
5	
6	
7	`freaks` → {page.2} `hate` → {page.2, page.3}
8	
9	`apples` → {page.1, page.2} `survey` → {page.3}
10	`health` → {page.1, page.2}

1. Computing HASH(w) for the query-word w has runtime in $O(1)$.
2. Going to table-row HASH(w) in the hash-table has runtime in $O(1)$.
3. Searching for the query w within its row of the hash-table has runtime in $O(1)$.

Using standard array-implementations, table look-up has runtime in $O(1)$. Our simple hash function takes similar words like `hurt` and `hate` and distributes them to seemingly unrelated rows. It is a sophisticated number theoretic task to construct good hash functions, which are efficient and distribute words in a randomn and independent way. We take such professional hash functions as a given without getting into the details.

If two words are mapped into the same row, they collide, for example `freaks` and `hate` in our little example. The simplest way to ensure $O(1)$ search within a table row is to have at most one entry per row. That is, we do not wish to have any collisions or hash-twins. Treat the hash of a word as its "birthday". There are B possible birthdays, which is the number of rows in the table. Let us compare hash-twins and FOCS-twins.

Words $w_1, w_2, \ldots, w_N$ and Hashing	↔	Students $s_1, s_2, \ldots, s_N$ and Birthdays
$w_1, \ldots, w_N$ HASHED to rows $0, 1, \ldots, B-1$	↔	$s_1, \ldots, s_N$ BORN on days $0, 1, \ldots, B-1$
No collisions, or HASH-twins	↔	No FOCS-twins

We are in the setting of the birthday paradox. The N words are analogous to people. The B possible hash values correspond to birthdays. Using the formula in Exercise 17.8(d)(vi),

$$\mathbb{P}[\text{no collisions}] = \left(1 - \frac{1}{B}\right) \cdot \left(1 - \frac{2}{B}\right) \cdots \left(1 - \frac{N-1}{B}\right). \tag{17.6}$$

We don't want collisions, that is we want $\mathbb{P}[\text{no collisions}]$ to be large. We need to analyze the RHS. A well known fact from calculus will be useful: $1 + x \le e^x$, for all $x \in \mathbb{R}$. Using this fact, $1 - i/B \le e^{-i}$, and so

$$\begin{aligned}\mathbb{P}[\text{no collisions}] &\le e^{-1/B} \cdot e^{-2/B} \cdots e^{-(N-1)/B}\\ &= e^{-(1+2+\cdots+(N-1))/B}\\ &= e^{-N(N-1)/2B}.\end{aligned}$$

We want $B \gg N(N-1)$ so the probability of no collision is large, approximately 1. When $B \ge 2N$, every term in the product of Equation (17.6) is of the form $1 - x$, where $x \le \frac{1}{2}$. Another bound from calculus is $1 - x \ge e^{-2x}$ for $x \le \frac{1}{2}$, which gives a lower bound on the probability of no collisions when $B \ge 2N$,

$$\begin{aligned}\mathbb{P}[\text{no collisions}] &\ge e^{-2\cdot 1/B} \cdot e^{-2\cdot 2/B} \cdots e^{-2\cdot(N-1)/B} \qquad \text{(when } B \ge 2N)\\ &= e^{-2\cdot(1+2+\cdots+(N-1))/B}\\ &= e^{-N(N-1)/B}.\end{aligned}$$

Theorem 17.3 (Collision bound). Independently place N objects randomly into $B \ge 2N$ bins. Then,

$$e^{-N(N-1)/B} \le \mathbb{P}[\text{every bin has at most one object}] \le e^{-N(N-1)/2B}.$$

Theorem 17.3 is a guide for choosing the hash-table size B. The sorting solution to search uses table size N to achieve $O(\log N)$ search time. The hashing approach uses a quadratic table size $\Theta(N^2)$ but gives faster $O(1)$ search time. Increasing speed at the expense of more memory is a recurring trade off in computer science.

Exercise 17.9

(a) For 100 objects randomly placed in 300 bins, compute upper and lower bounds on
  (i) $\mathbb{P}[\text{every bin has at most one object}]$ (ii) $\mathbb{P}[\text{some bin has more than one object}]$

(b) For 100 words, give a table size B for which you have at least 90% confidence of no collisions.

(c) If $B = N^{2+\epsilon}$ for $\epsilon > 0$, show that $\mathbb{P}[\text{no collisions}] \to 1$ as N increases.

(d) If $B = N^{2-\epsilon}$ for $1 > \epsilon > 0$, show that $\mathbb{P}[\text{no collisions}] \to 0$ as N increases.

17.2 Random Walk and Gambler's Ruin

A famous problem involves a drunk at a bar not knowing whether home is left or right. He has short term memory loss, so he randomly walks, taking independent steps left (L) and right (R). Home is at the 0, just left of the bar and the lockup is 2 steps right. Inebriated loitering is not allowed, so if the drunk happens upon the lockup, he spends the night in a cell. If he gets home first, he sleeps well in his comfy bed.

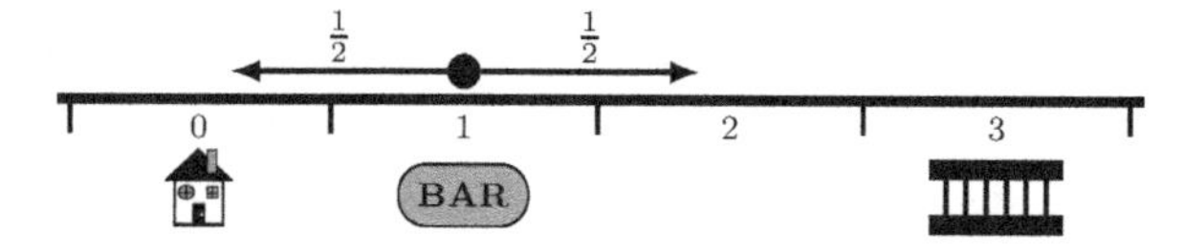

What is the probability the drunk will sleep well? One left step brings him home; if he steps right, he may step right again into the lockup or left back to the bar. Here are the sequences leading to home,

$$\text{L, RLL, RLRLL, RLRLRLL, } \ldots, (\text{RL})^{\bullet i}\text{L}, \ldots.$$

Steps are independent, so, $\mathbb{P}[(\text{RL})^{\bullet i}\text{L}] = \frac{1}{2} \times \frac{1}{2} \times \cdots = \left(\frac{1}{2}\right)^{2i+1}$ for $i = 0, 1, \ldots$. Adding the probabilities gives

$$\mathbb{P}[\text{home}] = \sum_{i=0}^{\infty} \mathbb{P}[(\text{RL})^{\bullet i}\text{L}] = \frac{1}{2} + \left(\frac{1}{2}\right)^3 + \left(\frac{1}{2}\right)^5 + \cdots = \frac{1}{2}\left(1 + \left(\frac{1}{2}\right)^2 + \left(\frac{1}{2}\right)^4 + \cdots\right) = \frac{\frac{1}{2}}{1 - \frac{1}{4}} = \frac{2}{3}.$$

A sleek approach is to use the law of total probability with three cases for how the walk starts: {L, RR, RL}. L and RR reach home and the lockup respectively. RL returns the drunk to the start, at the bar. So,

$$\begin{aligned}\mathbb{P}[\text{home}] &= \mathbb{P}[\text{L}] \times \mathbb{P}[\text{home} \mid \text{L}] + \mathbb{P}[\text{RR}] \times \mathbb{P}[\text{home} \mid \text{RR}] + \mathbb{P}[\text{RL}] \times \mathbb{P}[\text{home} \mid \text{RL}] \\ &= \frac{1}{2} \times 1 + \frac{1}{4} \times 0 + \frac{1}{4} \times \mathbb{P}[\text{home}] \\ &= \frac{1}{2} + \frac{1}{4}\mathbb{P}[\text{home}].\end{aligned}$$

We can solve this linear equation for $\mathbb{P}[\text{home}]$ to get $(1 - 1/4)\,\mathbb{P}[\text{home}] = 1/2$, or $\mathbb{P}[\text{home}] = 2/3$.

Pop Quiz 17.10

Compute $\mathbb{P}[\text{home}]$ if the bar is at position 2, instead of position 1.

Let us now consider a more general case where the lockup is at position L and the drunk has a bias, stepping left with probability p and right with probability $1 - p$.

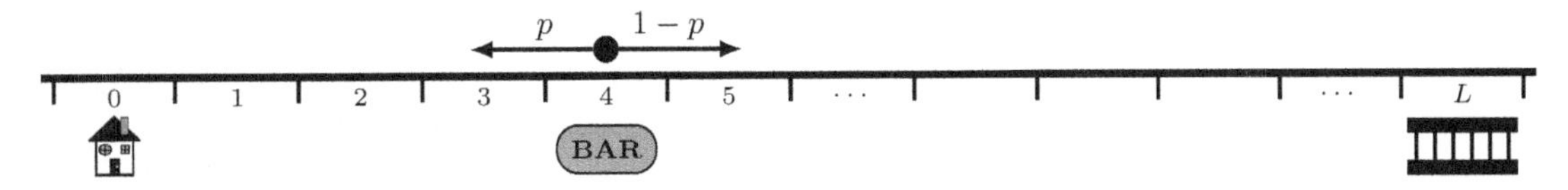

In the diagram, the bar is at position 4, the drunk's starting position. In general, suppose the drunk is at position k. Let P_k be the probability to reach home before the lockup if the starting position is k,

$$P_k = \mathbb{P}[\text{home} \mid \text{drunk's current position is } k].$$

Our goal is to compute P_k for $k = 0, 1, \ldots, L$. Let's start with some easy cases,

$$\begin{aligned} P_0 &= 1 \qquad &&\text{(Drunk has reached home)} \\ P_L &= 0 \qquad &&\text{(Drunk can't escape the lockup once there)}\end{aligned}$$

Consider P_k for $0 < k < L$. We use the law of total probability with the two cases for the first step (L or R),

$$P_k = \mathbb{P}[\text{L}] \times \mathbb{P}[\text{home} \mid \text{L}] + \mathbb{P}[\text{R}] \times \mathbb{P}[\text{home} \mid \text{R}]$$

If the drunk steps left, with probability p, he is at $k - 1$, and so $\mathbb{P}[\text{home} \mid \text{L}] = P_{k-1}$. If the drunk steps right, with probability $1 - p$, he is at $k + 1$ and $\mathbb{P}[\text{home} \mid \text{R}] = P_{k+1}$. We have

$$P_k = pP_{k-1} + (1 - p)P_{k+1}. \tag{17.7}$$

Since $P_k = pP_k + (1 - p)P_k$, (17.7) can be rewritten as

$$pP_k + (1 - p)P_k = pP_{k-1} + (1 - p)P_{k+1}.$$

Rearranging this last equation, we get $(1 - p)(P_k - P_{k+1}) = p(P_{k-1} - P_k)$. Setting $\beta = p/(1 - p)$ gives

$$(P_k - P_{k+1}) = \beta(P_{k-1} - P_k), \tag{17.8}$$

Let $P_0 - P_1 = \Delta$. Since $P_0 = 1$, $P_1 = 1 - \Delta$. We continue by setting $k = 1, 2, \ldots$ in (17.8),

$$\begin{array}{llcl} & & & P_0 = 1 \\ & & & P_1 = 1 - \Delta \\ (k=1) & P_1 - P_2 = \beta(P_0 - P_1) = \beta\Delta & \rightarrow & P_2 = 1 - \Delta - \beta\Delta. \\ (k=2) & P_2 - P_3 = \beta(P_1 - P_2) = \beta^2\Delta & \rightarrow & P_3 = 1 - \Delta - \beta\Delta - \beta^2\Delta. \\ (k=3) & P_3 - P_4 = \beta(P_2 - P_3) = \beta^3\Delta & \rightarrow & P_4 = 1 - \Delta - \beta\Delta - \beta^2\Delta - \beta^3\Delta. \\ \vdots & \vdots\ \vdots\ \vdots & & \\ (\text{general}) & P_{k-1} - P_k = \beta(P_{k-2} - P_{k-1}) = \beta^{k-1}\Delta & \rightarrow & P_k = 1 - \Delta - \beta\Delta - \beta^2\Delta - \cdots - \beta^{k-1}\Delta. \end{array}$$

The sum for P_k is just a geometric sum, which we can obtain in closed form as

$$P_k = 1 - \Delta - \beta\Delta - \beta^2\Delta - \cdots - \beta^{k-1}\Delta = \begin{cases} 1 - \Delta\dfrac{\beta^k - 1}{\beta - 1} & \beta \neq 1; \\ 1 - k\Delta & \beta = 1; \end{cases} \tag{17.9}$$

To find Δ, we set $P_L = 0$ in (17.9). This gives $\Delta = (\beta - 1)/(\beta^L - 1)$ when $\beta \neq 1$ and $\Delta = 1/L$ when $\beta = 1$.

Theorem 17.4 (Random Walk and Ruin). In a random walk let p be the probability to step closer to the goal which is k steps away. Suppose failure is $L - k$ steps away in the opposite direction. Let $\beta = p/(1-p)$. The probability to attain the goal before failure is

$$P(k, L; p) = \begin{cases} \dfrac{\beta^L - \beta^k}{\beta^L - 1} & \beta = p/(1-p) \text{ when } p \neq 1/2; \\ \dfrac{L-k}{L} & \text{when } p = 1/2. \end{cases}$$

Example 17.5 (Gambler's Ruin). A gambler enters the casino with \$50. His game is roulette. His goal is to leave with \$100 unless he goes bankrupt first, a double or nothing goal.

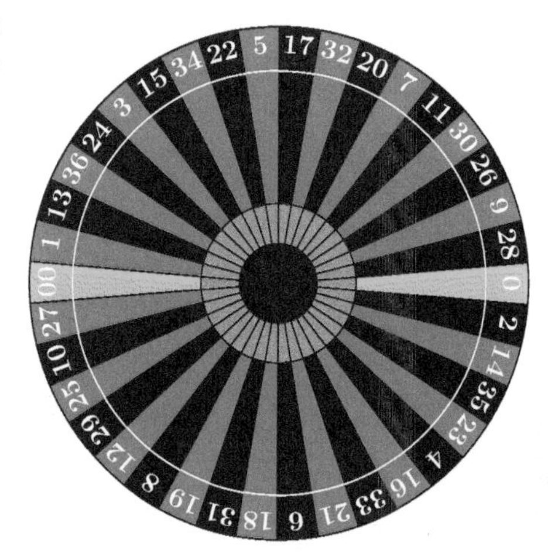

The roulette-wheel has 18 red, 18 black and 2 green numbers. The gambler bets on red, his favorite color. A ball is randomly thrown into the wheel. If the ball lands on a red number, with probability $\frac{18}{38} \approx 0.474$, the gambler wins \$1. Otherwise the gambler loses \$1. The gambler is doing a random walk with his money. If he wins the bet, with probability $p \approx 0.474$, he steps \$1 closer to his goal which is 50 steps away. So, $k = 50$. Ruin, i.e. bankruptcy, is also 50 steps away, that is $L - k = 50$ or $L = 100$. What is the probability that the gambler leaves with \$100, attaining the goal? We plug in $\beta = p/(1-p) = 0.9$ into Theorem 17.4 and obtain

$$\mathbb{P}[\text{win}] = P(50, 100; p) = \frac{0.9^{100} - 0.9^{50}}{0.9^{100} - 1} \approx 0.0051.$$

Even with nearly fair odds in roulette ($p \approx 1/2$), the chances are 99.5% that the gambler leaves bankrupt. No wonder it is the Gambler's Ruin. What if the gambler started with \$60? You can plug in the numbers and compute $P(60, 120; p)$. Here is a table with the chances of ruin as the gambler gets richer or poorer.

Initial wealth	\$10	\$20	\$30	\$40	\$50	\$60	\$70	\$80
Chances of Ruin	74.1%	89.1%	95.9%	98.5%	99.5%	99.8%	99.95%	99.98%

You might think that as you get richer, your chances of doubling up increase. Nope. As you get richer, your chances of total ruin very quickly becomes a near-certainty. A true case of riches to rags. □

Exercise 17.11

(a) The roulette-gambler starts with \$100. How likely is he to double his money?
Another strategy is to bet all the \$100 once on red. Is this a better strategy?

(b) You are in a dinner party of 15 sitting at a circular table. The bread starts with you and each person, whenever they get the bread, independently passes it left or right with equal probability. What is the probability that the person sitting diametrically opposite you is the last to get the bread?

17.3 Problems

Problem 17.1. Prove the following important facts:

(a) The events Ω and $\varnothing$ are independent of any event E.

(b) If A, B are independent events, then $\bar{A}, \bar{B}$ are independent events.

(c) If an event A is independent of *every* event E, then $\mathbb{P}[A]$ is either 0 or 1. *[Hint: A is independent of A.]*

Problem 17.2. Prove or disprove transitivity of independent events: If A & B are independent events and B & C are independent events, then A & C are independent events.

Problem 17.3. Prove or disprove: If $A \cap B = \varnothing$ then A and B are independent.

Problem 17.4. Does A and B being independent imply that $\mathbb{P}[A \cap B \mid C] = \mathbb{P}[A \mid C]\,\mathbb{P}[B \mid C]$?

Problem 17.5. For the probability space given, compute $\mathbb{P}[A]$ and $\mathbb{P}[A \mid B]$ to determine if the events are independent.

(a) $A = \{1,2,3\}$ and $B = \{2,3,4\}$.

(b) $A = \{2,3,4\}$ and $B = \{1,2,3\}$.

(c) $A = \{1,5\}$ and $B = \{1,2,5\}$.

(d) $A = \{1,2,5\}$ and $B = \{1,5\}$.

(e) $A = \{1,2,3\}$ and $B = \{1,2,3\}$.

(f) $A = \{1,2,3\}$ and $B = \{4,5\}$.

(g) $A = \varnothing$ and $B = \{1,5\}$.

(h) $A = \{1,5\}$ and $B = \varnothing$.

(i) $A = \{1,2,3,4,5\}$ and $B = \{1,2\}$.

(j) $A = \{1,2\}$ and $B = \{1,2,3,4,5\}$.

Ω	1	2	3	4	5
P	0.1	0.1	0.2	0.2	0.4

Problem 17.6. Compute the probability that a random 10-bit sequence starts with 111.

Problem 17.7. You randomly roll two independent dice. Compute these probabilities.

(a) $\mathbb{P}$[both are odd] (b) $\mathbb{P}$[one is odd] (c) $\mathbb{P}$[at least one is odd] (d) $\mathbb{P}$[sum is even].

Problem 17.8. Is the second event independent of the first? Explain.

(a) You randomly draw a card from a 52-card deck and it is an ace. You randomly draw a second card and are interested in whether it is also an ace.

(b) You randomly draw a card from a 52-card deck and it is an ace. You randomly draw a second card and are interested in whether it is a two.

(c) You randomly draw a card from a 52-card deck and it is a club. You randomly draw a second card and are interested in whether it is a spade.

(d) You randomly draw a card from a 52-card deck and it is an ace. You replace the card, randomly draw a second card and are interested in whether it is also an ace.

Problem 17.9. On a standard 8×8 chessboard (alternating black and white squares), label the rows and columns $1, \ldots, 8$. You pick a square at random. Are these events independent.

(a) $A = \{\text{white square}\}$; $B = \{\text{black square}\}$.

(b) $A = \{\text{even row}\}$; $B = \{\text{even column}\}$.

(c) $A = \{\text{white square}\}$; $B = \{\text{even column}\}$.

Problem 17.10. You have a well shuffled deck. Are the events A and B independent?

(a) One card is drawn. $A =$ "king" and $B =$ "spade".

(b) Two cards are drawn sequentially. $A =$ "both same suit" and $B =$ "both same rank".

Problem 17.11. A survey shows that 65% of children dislike vegetables. Four children are chosen at random with replacement. What is the probability that all four dislike vegetables?

Problem 17.12. For two fair dice, show that "sum is 7" and "first roll is odd" are independent.

Problem 17.13. A jar contains 10 red, 10 green and 10 blue balls. You randomly pick two balls. Are their colors independent if you pick (a) With replacement? (b) Without replacement?

Problem 17.14. A jar has 8 red, 5 green and 6 blue balls. You pick two balls. Compute $\mathbb{P}$[both balls are green] and $\mathbb{P}$[balls have different colors] if you pick (a) Without replacement. (b) With replacement.

Problem 17.15. You roll two independent dice D_1, D_2. In each case, are the events A and B independent?

(a) $A = \{D_1 \text{ is odd}\}$, $B = \{D_2 \text{ is even}\}$.

(b) $A = \{D_1 + D_2 = 10\}$, $B = \{D_1 \text{ and } D_2 \text{ are both odd}\}$.

(c) $A = \{D_1 + D_2 = 9\}$, $B = \{D_1 \leq 3, D_2 \geq 4\}$.

Problem 17.16. Use independence, when appropriate, to compute these probabilities.

(a) Toss two fair coins and two dice. What is $\mathbb{P}$[two heads and die sum of 9]?

(b) Randomly pick 10 digits independently from $\{0, 1, \ldots, 9\}$. What is $\mathbb{P}$[no 0s]?

(c) A jar contains 90 red and 10 blue balls. You pick 10 balls randomly. What is $\mathbb{P}$[all red]?

(d) Flip a fair coin 10 times. What is $\mathbb{P}$[all heads occurr at the end]?

(e) Independently pick 10 bits $b_1 b_2 \cdots b_{10}$ with probability $3/4$ for 1. What is $\mathbb{P}$[sequence is non-decreasing]?

(f) I try each of 10 keys in a random order until the door opens. What are the chances I enter by the 3rd attempt?

Problem 17.17. Ayfos has three (independent) children. Each sex is equally likely. For events:

$A = \{\text{all three of same sex}\}$ $B = \{\text{at most one boy}\}$ $C = \{\text{there's a boy and a girl}\}$,

which pairs are independent? What if each sex is not equally likely? Repeat for four children.

Problem 17.18. There are two roads from A to B, from B to C and from A to C. In winter, each road is independently blocked with snow, with probability p. Compute these probabilities:

(a) (i) There is a route from A to B. (ii) There is a route from A to C.

(b) There is a route from A to B if, from A to C: (i) There is no route. (ii) There is a route.

Problem 17.19. You are a tourist in a foreign park, where there are twice as many tourists as locals. Locals hate the tourists and will always answer a question incorrectly. Tourists are random and answer repeated questions independently, giving the correct answer with probability $2/3$. You meet a random passer by and ask whether the exit is left or right.

(a) The answer is left. What are the chances the exit is left?

(b) You ask the same person and get left again. Now, what are the chances the exit is left?

(c) You ask a 3rd time and get left again. Now, what are the chances the exit is left?

(d) You ask a 4th time. What are the chances the exit is left: (i) The answer is left? (ii) The answer is right?

Problem 17.20. I randomly pick a number x from $\{1, \ldots, n\}$, with probability p_i to pick $x = i$. I randomly pick a second number r from $\{1, \ldots, M\}$ and reveal to you $z = x + r \pmod M$.

(a) Does knowing z help you to predict x? Explain.

(b) You have access to a fair coin. Give an algorithm to produce z assuming the p_i have finite binary expansions, $p_i = \sum_{j=1}^{k} b_{ij} 2^{-j}$ and M is a power of 2, $M = 2^{\ell}$.

Problem 17.21. Los Angeles has about 6,500 miles of road and 20 million people. Estimate the chances a random person has an accident with a drunk driver in their lifetime. *[Hints: Estimate the chances of no accident. Consider only Friday's and Saturday's.]*

Problem 17.22. Use the Fermi-method to estimate:

(a) The number of piano tuners in USA.

(b) The number of passenger cars that are sold each year in the USA.

(c) The dollar amount New York state spends on K-12 education a year.

(d) The number of people airborne over the US at any given moment.

(e) The average savings per flight if airlines asked passengers to urinate before boarding.

(f) The number of correct consecutive letters from Macbeth somewhere in the typings of 1 million monkeys typing randomly on 1 million typewriters for a year.

(g) The number of insects living on planet Earth.

(h) The total amount of time spent by college students studying for finals in a semester.

(i) The computer memory usage by all college students in the USA.

(j) The number of cities in the USA with population above 10,000.

Problem 17.23. In each case, give a probability space and events that are:

(a) 2-way and 3-way independent but not 4-way independent.

(b) 3-way and 4-way independent but not 2-way independent.

Problem 17.24. Suppose that A and B are independent.

(a) Which of the following pairs of events are independent:

(i) $A, \overline{B}$ (ii) $\overline{A}, \overline{B}$ (iii) $\overline{A}, B$ (iv) $A, \overline{A} \cap B$ (v) $A, \overline{A} \cup B$

(b) Show that: (i) $\mathbb{P}[A \mid \overline{B}] = \mathbb{P}[A]$. (ii) $\mathbb{P}[\overline{A} \mid \overline{B}] = \mathbb{P}[\overline{A}]$.

(c) If A and B have positive probability, can they be disjoint events.

(d) Can $\mathbb{P}[A] = 0$?

(e) Show that $\mathbb{P}[\overline{A \cup B}] = \mathbb{P}[\overline{A}] \times \mathbb{P}[\overline{B}]$.

Problem 17.25. Projects are independent and take 1,2 or 3 days to complete, each equally likely. You and your spouse each start a project on day 1. On any night, if you and your spouse are in sync and have just finished a project that day, you will have dinner together. Otherwise, if just one of you finish a project, you will start a new project. What is the probability that the next time you have dinner with your spouse will be on the 3rd night?

Problem 17.26. A jar contains 6 red balls, 3 green balls, 5 white balls and 7 yellow balls. Two balls are chosen from the jar, with replacement. What is the probability that:
(a) Both balls chosen are green? (b) Both balls are the same color? (c) The balls are different color?

Problem 17.27. Two chips are made from transistors which fail independently with probability p. One chip has 2 transistors, and the other has 4. A chip fails if more than half its transistors fail. Data shows that both chips fail with the same probability. What are possible values of p?

Problem 17.28. A 100-sided die with faces $1,\ldots,100$ is rolled 5 times. Compute the probability that all rolls are different.

Problem 17.29. How many times must you roll a 100-sided die so that the chances of rolling some number more than once is at least: (a) 30% (b) 50% (c) 100%.

Problem 17.30. On page 248, we computed a table with the chances to find a FOCS-twin by the kth student when the class size is 200. Recompute the table for a class of size 300.

Problem 17.31. For the birthday problem with N students, we assumed all birthdays are equally likely. Show that if some days are more likely than others, then the probability of FOCS-twins goes up. Index the days $1,\ldots,B$. Let p_i be the probability of a birthday on day i. Show:

$$Q(p_1,\ldots,p_B) \stackrel{\text{def}}{=} \mathbb{P}\left[\text{student 1 fails to have a FOCS-twin}\right] \le \left(\frac{B-1}{B}\right)^{N-1}.$$

(a) Show that $Q(p_1,\ldots,p_B) = \sum_{i=1}^{B} p_i(1-p_i)^{N-1}$.

(b) Show that Q is maximized when all p_i are equal. To do so, suppose that $p_1 > p_B$ and define

$$\Delta Q(\delta) = Q(p_1-\delta, p_2, \ldots, p_{B-1}, p_B+\delta) - Q(p_1, p_2, \ldots, p_{B-1}, p_B).$$

(i) Show that $\lim_{\delta\to 0} \Delta Q/\delta = (1-p_1)^{N-1}(2p_1-1) + (1-p_B)^{N-1}(1-2p_B)$.
(ii) Show that the expression in (i) is positive.
(iii) Explain why this proves that $Q(p_1,\ldots,p_B)$ is maximized when all the p_i are equal.

Problem 17.32. The manager of a movie theater announces that one free ticket will go to the first person in line whose birthday is the same as someone who has already bought a ticket. You can get into line at any time. You don't know anyone else's birthday, and birthdays are independent, being distributed randomly throughtout the year.
(a) What position in line gives you the greatest chance of winning the free ticket?
(b) What is the probability that you will get the free ticket.

Problem 17.33. Independently generate a 10-bit binary sequence $b_1\cdots b_{10}$ with $\mathbb{P}[b_i = 0] = 1/2$. Compute the probability the sequence is sorted from low to high, e.g. 0000111111 is sorted.

Problem 17.34. 3 independent bits are sent over a channel, and $\mathbb{P}[\text{bit=1}] = 3/4$. The channel is noisy. independently flipping each bit with probability $1/4$. The signal received is 101.
(a) What are the possible values of the signal and what are the posterior probabilities.
(b) Which signal would you decode the received 101 as? What is your probability of error?
(c) Suppose we also send over the channel the number of ones in the original signal (a size hint) as a separate 2-digit binary string. For each possible size received (00,01,10,11) give the posterior probability over signals and your probability of error in decoding.
(d) What is the posterior over the 4 digit signals for message:1111 and size hint:011?
(e) Verify your results with a Monte-Carlo simulation.

Problem 17.35. You have $100 and bet $1 at a time on roulette. You goal is to win $50. Compute the probability that you reach your goal before going bankrupt.

Problem 17.36. L people at a circular table with seats $0, 1, \ldots, L-1$ numbered counter-clockwise pass bread around (see Exercise 17.11). A person passes right with probability p and left with probability $1-p$, where $0 < p < 1$. The bread starts at seat 0. What is the probability P_k that the person at seat k is the last to receive the bread?
(a) With $p = 1/3$ and $L = 10$, run a Monte-Carlo simulation to compute $P_1, \ldots, P_9$.
(b) Compute P_k for general L and p and compare with your Monte-Carlo simulation.

Problem 17.37 (Generating Functions). The gambler's ruin recurrence is

$$P_k = pP_{k-1} + (1-p)P_{k+1} \text{ for } 0 < k < L; \qquad P_0 = 1 \text{ and } P_L = 0.$$

We solved this recursion using a trick. It is a little unsettling to need tricks for solving standard problems like this. The method of generating functions is a standard tool, albeit algebraically intense.

(a) Define the polynomial $G(s) = \sum_{k=0}^{L} P_k s^k$, called the generating function for the sequence $\{P_k\}$. Define $\alpha = 1/(1-p)$ and $\beta = p/(1-p)$. Use the recursion to show that

$$G(s) = \frac{1 + (P_1 - \alpha)s + \beta P_{L-1} s^{L+1}}{1 - \alpha s + \beta s^2},$$

(b) Show that $1 - \alpha s + \beta s^2 = (1 - a_+ s)(1 - a_- s)$, where $a_\pm = \frac{1}{2}\alpha \pm \frac{1}{2}\sqrt{\alpha^2 - 4\beta}$.

(c) Show that $\dfrac{1}{1 - \alpha s + \beta s^2} = \dfrac{a_+}{(a_+ - a_-)(1 - a_+ s)} - \dfrac{a_-}{(a_+ - a_-)(1 - a_- s)}$.
(This is called an expansion into partial fractions. It works when $a_+ \neq a_-$, i.e. $p \neq \frac{1}{2}$.)

(d) P_k is the coefficient of the s^k in $G(s)$. Show, for $1 \leq k \leq L$, that

$$P_k = \frac{a_+^{k+1} - a_-^{k+1} + a_+^k(P_1 - \alpha) - a_-^k(P_1 - \alpha)}{a_+ - a_-}.$$

(e) Use $P_L = 0$ to show that $P_1 - \alpha = -(a_+^{L+1} - a_-^{L+1})/(a_+^L - a_-^L)$.

(f) Show that $P_k = (a_+^L a_-^k - a_+^k a_-^L)/(a_+^L - a_-^L)$, when $p \neq \frac{1}{2}$

(g) Show that the formula for P_k in (v) matches Theorem 17.4 on page 252. *[Hint: Induction.]*

(h) What happens when $p = 1/2$? *[Hint:* $(1-s)^{-2} = 1 + 2s + 3s^3 + \cdots + (k+1)s^k + \cdots$*].*

Problem 17.38 (Kolmogorov Zero-One Law). Let $s_1, s_2, s_3, \ldots$ be an infinite sequence of independent random signs (± 1). Define the event $A_p = \{s_1, s_2, \ldots \mid \sum_{i=1}^{\infty} s_i/i^p \text{ converges}\}$.

(a) Using Monte Carlo or otherwise, estimate $\mathbb{P}[A_p]$ for $p \in \{\frac{1}{4}, \frac{1}{2}, \frac{3}{4}, 1, 2\}$. Some creativity is required.

(b) Let B_n be any event defined using only $s_1, \ldots, s_n$. Show that $\mathbb{P}[A_p \mid B_n] = \mathbb{P}[A_p]$.
(A_p is an example of a tail-event because it is independent of any finite prefix $s_1, \ldots, s_n$.)

(c) Kolmogorov's law is that $\mathbb{P}[A_p] = 0$ or 1. Here is the intuition. Define B_n by

$$B_n = \{s_1 \cdots s_n x \mid s_1 \cdots s_n \text{ is the prefix of a sequence in } A_p \text{ and } x \text{ is any } \pm 1 \text{ sequence}\}.$$

B_n "is" A_p as $n \to \infty$. So, by (a), A_p is independent of A_p. Deduce Kolmogorov's law.

(d) Make a conjecture for $\mathbb{P}[A_p]$, depending on p. (Lookup Rademacher, Paley & Zygmund.)

The 0-1 law holds for any tail-event. The formal proof needs measure theory to define probability because the sample space is uncountable. The 0-1 law is the root of phase transitions in physical systems (water/ice; percolation/no percolation; connected/disconnected infinite graph, etc.)

> **Randomized Algorithms** are a modern tool using probability to design algorithms. An algorithm that works with some (usually large) probability is better than no algorithm.

Problem 17.39 (The "ATM"-Test). Here is an application of probability to security. You want to authenticate yourself at the ATM without revealing your password. After all, who knows what another "bank's" ATM might do with your password? We faced a similar problem in Section 14.2 on page 202, to convince you that a solution to the subset sum problem exists without revealing it. In cryptography, such proofs are called "zero-knowledge" because they do not convey any information about the solution. Here is one strategy for the ATM situation.

> **for** $t = 1, \ldots, T$ **do**
> The ATM tests you. Each test is independent.
> **if** You know the password **then**
> You answer correctly and reveal no password-information.
> **else if** You are an imposter and don't know the password **then**
> You can only answer the test correctly with probability at most $\frac{1}{2}$.
> You access the account only if you pass all T tests.

Compute T, the number tests, so that an imposter can access your account with probability at most 10^{-100}. (For a test that you can answer without revealing your password, but an imposter cannot, see Problem 29.57.)

Problem 17.40 (Approximate median). You have an array of 1000 distinct numbers. The median has rank 500. You wish to choose a number in the middle 20% with rank in $\{401, \ldots, 600\}$: good.
A deterministic approach sorts the numbers and then picks one in the middle, What is the asymptotic runtime?

(a) Pick a number randomly. What are the chances of success? What is the runtime?
(b) Continue to pick a number independently and randomly until success. What are the chances you need k draws to succeed? What is the maximum number of draws you may need?
(c) Continue to pick a number randomly without replacement until success. What are the chances you need k draws to succeed? What is the maximum number of draws you may need?

Part (a) is a Monte Carlo algorithm with a fixed runtime and some probability of failure. Parts (b) and (c) are Las Vegas algorithms which guarantee success but have a nondeterministic runtime.

Problem 17.41 (Contention Resolution). Pam and Sam try to access a database at time steps $1, 2, 3, \ldots$. If both try to access the database, both get locked out for that time step.

(a) Pam and Sam try in every time step to access the database. Will they ever succeed?
(b) Pam and Sam implement a randomized algorithm. Each independently attempts to access the database with probability p (independently at every time step). Let $P(i) = \mathbb{P}[\text{Pam gains access to the database at time step } i]$. Similarly define $S(i)$ for Sam. Let $B(i)$ be the probability that one of them gains access at time step i.
  (i) Compute $P(i)$, $S(i)$ and $B(i)$. Set p to the value that maximizes $P(i)$.
  (ii) Show that $\mathbb{P}[\text{Pam waits } k \text{ steps for access}] = (\frac{3}{4})^{k-1}\frac{1}{4}$.
  (iii) Show that $\mathbb{P}[\text{First successful access is after } k \text{ steps}] = (\frac{1}{2})^k$.
(c) Repeat the problem for three people Pam, Sam and Ram all accessing the same database.

Problem 17.42 (Min-Cut). A cut in a graph with n vertices separates the vertices into sets A and B. The cut-value, cut(A, B), is the number of edges going from A to B. The task is to find a cut with minimum value. Suppose one repeatedly merges sets of vertices until there are just two sets. Here is an example.

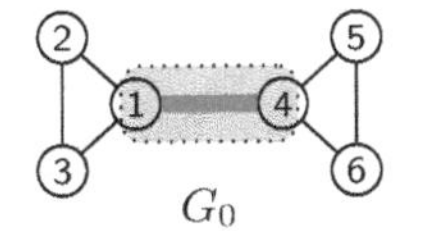

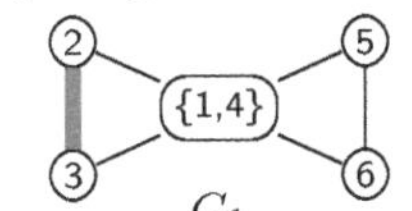

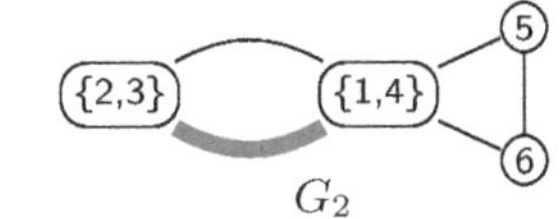

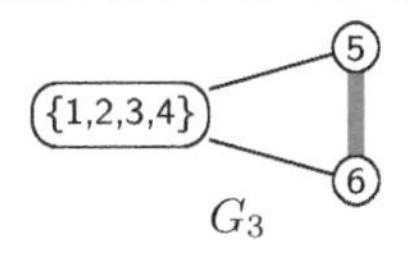

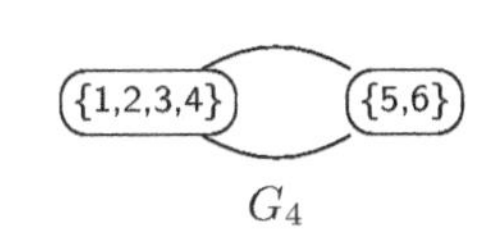

G_0 : Original graph, 1st contraction. Two vertices are contracted at the red edge into a super-vertex $\{1, 4\}$, giving G_1.
G_1 : 2nd contraction. The super-vertex maintains edges to all vertices connected to either vertex 1 or 4. The super-vertex is a set of vertices. Contract again on the red edge in G_1 to get a super-vertex $\{2, 3\}$, producing G_2.
G_2 : 3nd contraction merging super-vertices. The super-vertex $\{2, 3\}$ keeps all edges to neighbors of vertices 2 or 3: the two edges to super-vertex $\{1, 4\}$ result in a multigraph with parallel edges. Contract on the red edge to get G_3.
G_3 : 4th contraction. Contract on the red edge to get G_4.
G_4 : Only two super-vertices remain, identifying the cut $A = \{1, 2, 3, 4\}$, $B = \{5, 6\}$ with cut-value cut$(A, B) = 2$.

(a) Is the cut constructed in the example above a min-cut?
(b) Give a sequence of edge contractions that does give a min-cut.
(c) What property must every contraction-edge satisfy for the result to be a min-cut.

Randomized algorithm for min-cut: For contraction $i + 1$, choose the contraction-edge independently and randomly from all available edges in G_i, the multi-graph after contraction i. Compute the probability that this algorithm produces a min-cut. Suppose the min-cut has size k and there are M cuts $(A_1, B_1), \ldots, (A_M, B_M)$ with this minimum size.

(d) Prove that $|E(G_i)| \geq \frac{1}{2}(n - i)k$, where $|E(G)|$ is the number of edges in graph G. *[Hints: Every cut in G_i is a cut in G_0. If the min-cut size is k, can the minimum degree be less than k? Handshaking Theorem.]*
(e) Fix a min-cut, for example (A_1, B_1). Prove by induction that all the edges in the cut (A_1, B_1) remain in G_i with probability at least $(1 - \frac{2}{n})(1 - \frac{2}{n-1}) \cdots (1 - \frac{2}{n-i+1})$.
(f) Prove that $\mathbb{P}[\text{algorithm returns cut } (A_1, B_1)] \geq 2/n(n - 1)$. *[Hint: What should i be in the product of part (e)?]*
(g) Prove that $\mathbb{P}[\text{return a min-cut}] \geq 2M/n(n - 1)$. *[Hint: The algorithm returns one cut.]*
(h) Independently repeat the algorithm ℓ times and return the cut of minimum value. Show:

$$\mathbb{P}[\text{return a min-cut}] \geq 1 - \left(1 - \frac{2M}{n(n-1)}\right)^{\ell} \geq 1 - e^{-2M\ell/n(n-1)}.$$

Show that the algorithm succeeds with probability at least $1 - \epsilon$ for $2M\ell \geq n(n - 1)\log(1/\epsilon)$.

> **Probabilistic Method.** The probabilistic method is a modern technique that uses probability and independence to prove results about a deterministic setting.

Problem 17.43. The surface of a sphere is arbitrarily painted red and blue with 90% of the surface painted red. Prove that it is possible to inscribe a cube whose vertices are all red.

(a) Consider a randomly inscribed cube with vertices $v_1, \ldots, v_8$. Show that $\mathbb{P}[v_i \text{ is blue}] = 0.1$.
(b) Show that $\mathbb{P}[v_1 \text{ OR } v_2 \text{ OR } \cdots \text{ OR } v_8 \text{ is blue}] \leq 0.8$.
(c) Hence show that $\mathbb{P}[\text{all 8 vertices are red}] \geq 0.2 > 0$.
(d) What does it mean if a probability is positive?

Problem 17.44. The sets $S_1, \ldots, S_m$ are subsets of a universal set $S = \{1, \ldots, n\}$. The task is to color the vertices in S red or blue so that none of the S_i are monochromatic, i.e. contain vertices of only one color. Here is an example of a valid coloring of 5 sets $S_1, \ldots, S_5$ using vertex colors ① ② ③ ④ ⑤.

S_1 : {①②③} S_2 : {①②④} S_3 : {①③④} S_4 : {②③④} S_5 : {①②⑤}.

(a) Prove that the following collections of sets are not 2-colorable.
 (i) {①②} {①③} {②③}
 (ii) {①②③} {①③④} {②③④} {①③⑤} {②④⑤} {①④⑤} {②③⑤}
(b) When there are more elements per set, one can color more sets. Suppose each set has size $|S_i| = \ell$. Let $m(\ell)$ be the maximum number of sets one can guarantee is 2-colorable. So any collection of $m(\ell)$ sets is 2-colorable; and there is some collection of $m(\ell) + 1$ sets that is not 2-colorable. Show that $m(\ell) \geq 2^{l-1} - 1$ (Erdős, 1963).
 (i) Independently color each element randomly. Compute $P_i = \mathbb{P}[S_i \text{ is monochromatic}]$.
 (ii) Show that $\mathbb{P}[\text{any } S_i \text{ is monochromatic}] \leq \sum_i P_i$.
 (iii) If $m < 2^{l-1}$, show that $\mathbb{P}[\text{any } S_i \text{ is monochromatic}] < 1$.
 (iv) Show that $\mathbb{P}[\text{all } S_i \text{ are not monochromatic}] > 0$.
 (v) Conclude that there must be a valid 2-coloring, hence prove that $m(\ell) \geq 2^{l-1} - 1$.

(Erdős also showed $m(\ell) \in O(\ell^2 2^\ell)$. Beck (in 1978) and Spencer (in 1981) showed $m(\ell) > \ell^{\frac{1}{3} - o(1)} 2^\ell$; Radhakrishnan and Srinivasan (in 2000) improved this to $m(\ell) > c2^\ell \sqrt{\ell / 2 \ln \ell}$ for $c = 1 - o(1)$.)

Problem 17.45.

(a) Consider a cycle with n vertices. Show that the number of different min-cuts is $\frac{1}{2}n(n-1)$.
(b) Show, that no graph with n vertices can have more than $\frac{1}{2}n(n-1)$ different min-cuts. *[Hint: Problem 17.42(g) (a probability cannot be greater than 1).]*

Problem 17.46. In a tournament, every player plays every other player and wins or loses (there is directed edge between every pair). A tournament is k-dominated if every subset of k players is beaten by some other player. Show that there is a tournament with 25 players that is 2-dominated.

(a) Construct a tournament by independently and randomly choosing each edge-direction.
 (i) A set S of 2 players is dominated if another player beats everyone in S. Show that
 $$\mathbb{P}[S \text{ is not dominated}] = \left(1 - \tfrac{1}{4}\right)^{n-2}.$$
 (ii) Let $S_1, \ldots, S_M$ be the different subsets of 2 players. What is M?
 (iii) Show that $\mathbb{P}[\text{None of the } S_i \text{ are dominated}] \leq M \times (1 - \frac{1}{4})^{n-2}$.
 (iv) For $n = 25$, show that $\mathbb{P}[\text{None of the } S_i \text{ is dominated}] < 1$
 (v) Explain why there must be some tournament with 25 vertices that is 2-dominated.
(b) Show that there is a k-dominated tournament with n vertices if $2^{-k}(n-k) > \ln \binom{n}{k}$. Hence, show that there is a $(1-\epsilon)\log_2 n$–dominated tournament (asymptotic in n, for any $\epsilon > 0$). *[Hint: Show $\mathbb{P}$[no k-subset is dominated] $\leq \binom{n}{k} \times (1 - \frac{1}{2^k})^{n-k}$ and use $1 - x \leq e^{-x}$.]*

Problem 17.47. [Lubell-Yamamoto-Meshalkin inequality, Problem 13.72] $A_1, \ldots, A_n$ are subsets of $\{1, 2, \ldots, M\}$, with no A_i a subset of another and $\ell_i = |A_i|$. Use probability to prove $\sum_{i=1}^n 1/\binom{M}{\ell_i} \leq 1$. *[Hint: Let X_σ be a random permutation of X and E_i the event that A_i is a prefix of X_σ. Compute $\mathbb{P}[E_1 \cup \cdots \cup E_n]$. What is $E_i \cap E_j$?]*

> Know that everything is in perfect order whether you understand it or not.
> – **Valery Satterwhite**
>
> And those who were seen dancing were thought to be insane by those who could not hear the music.
> – **Friedrich Nietzsche**

Chapter 18

Random Variables

1: "Measuring the outcome of an experiment"
2: The distribution and cumulative distribution functions.
3: Common random variables: Bernoulli (binary); Uniform; Binomial; Waiting Times.

Randomness in the real world involves complex outcomes. The 10^{23} or so molecules in a gas are at random positions with random velocities. An outcome for the gas must specify the position and velocity of every molecule. Such fine details are just too complex to fathom. Rather, we measure aggregate properties of the molecules, like temperature (related to average speed), pressure and volume. For practical purposes, outcomes with similar temperature are equivalent from the temperature-perspective. Temperature is a random variable, a measurable property derived from the complex outcome of all the positions and velocities.

Let's move to a familiar setting. Toss 3 independent coins. Consider the "complex" outcome $\omega = \text{HHT}$. Two measurable properties of ω are the number of heads and whether or not all three tosses are the same.

$$\begin{aligned}\textsc{count}(\text{HHT}) &= 2;\\ \textsc{match}(\text{HHT}) &= 0.\end{aligned}$$

COUNT is a measurement in the traditional sense, which can be large or small. MATCH is an indicator that classifies the outcome into one of two types, 1 for matching tosses and 0 for non-matching tosses. The measurement maps an outcome to a value. We call the measurement a random variable, its value varies depending on which outcome occurs. We use big bold letters for random variables, so define $\mathbf{X}$ as the number of heads and $\mathbf{Y}$ as the indicator of whether all tosses match.

	Sample Space Ω								
ω	HHH	HHT	HTH	HTT	THH	THT	TTH	TTT	
$P(\omega)$	1/8	1/8	1/8	1/8	1/8	1/8	1/8	1/8	
$\mathbf{X}(\omega)$	3	2	2	1	2	1	1	0	← number of heads
$\mathbf{Y}(\omega)$	1	0	0	0	0	0	0	1	← matching tosses
$\mathbf{Z}(\omega)$	8	2	2	1/2	2	1/2	1/2	1/8	← ?

The random variable $\mathbf{X}$ is a function that maps ω to a real value $\mathbf{X}(\omega)$. Think of $\mathbf{X}(\omega)$ as the measurement for outcome ω. Any function that maps outcomes in the sample space to values is a random variable. We also defined the function $\mathbf{Z}(\omega)$, another random variable. Try to guess what the random variable $\mathbf{Z}$ measures.

> A random variable $\mathbf{X}$ is a function that maps outcomes to real values, $\mathbf{X} : \Omega \mapsto \mathbb{R}$.

A random variable, like $\mathbf{X}$, is neither "random" nor a "variable" and has nothing to do with probabilities. It is just a function that attaches values to outcomes. We can use a random variable to define events. For example:

$$\begin{aligned}\{\mathbf{X}=2\} &= \{\text{HHT},\text{HTH},\text{THH}\}\\ \{\mathbf{X}\geq 2\} &= \{\text{HHH},\text{HHT},\text{HTH},\text{THH}\}\\ \{\mathbf{Y}=1\} &= \{\text{HHH},\text{TTT}\}\\ \{\mathbf{X}\geq 2 \text{ AND } \mathbf{Y}=1\} &= \{\text{HHH}\}\end{aligned}$$

We often omit the parentheses and write $\mathbf{X}=2$ for the event containing the outcomes ω for which $\mathbf{X}(\omega)=2$. The probability of an event defined using random variables is, as usual, the sum of its outcome-probabilities:

$$\begin{aligned}\mathbb{P}[\mathbf{X}=2] &= 3/8 && (\tfrac{1}{8}+\tfrac{1}{8}+\tfrac{1}{8})\\ \mathbb{P}[\mathbf{X}\geq 2] &= 1/2 && (\tfrac{1}{8}+\tfrac{1}{8}+\tfrac{1}{8}+\tfrac{1}{8})\\ \mathbb{P}[\mathbf{Y}=1] &= 1/4 && (\tfrac{1}{8}+\tfrac{1}{8})\\ \mathbb{P}[\mathbf{X}\geq 2 \text{ AND } \mathbf{Y}=1] &= 1/8\end{aligned}$$

Pop Quiz 18.1

The random variables $\mathbf{X}$ and $\mathbf{Y}$ are defined in the text above.

(a) Are the two events independent (i) $\{\mathbf{X}=2\}$ and $\{\mathbf{Y}=1\}$? (ii) $\{\mathbf{X}\geq 2\}$ and $\{\mathbf{Y}=1\}$?

(b) Compute these conditional probabilities. (i) $\mathbb{P}[\mathbf{X}=2 \mid \mathbf{Y}=0]$. (ii) $\mathbb{P}[\mathbf{X}\geq 2 \mid \mathbf{Y}=0]$.

Let us examine the random variable $\mathbf{Z}$. Start with \$1. Double your money for each H and halve it for each T. For outcome HHH, you end with $\$1\times 2\times 2\times 2=\$8$; for outcome HHT, you end with $\$1\times 2\times 2\times \frac{1}{2}=\$2$; and so on. The random variable $\mathbf{Z}$ measures your final wealth. Without too much sweat, you can verify that

$$\mathbf{Z}(\omega)=2^{2\mathbf{X}(\omega)-3}.$$

We just say $\mathbf{Z}=2^{2\mathbf{X}-3}$. It's fine to define one function using another. A random variable can be defined using one or more other random variables. For example $\mathbf{W}=\mathbf{X}+\mathbf{Y}$ is the function $\mathbf{W}(\omega)=\mathbf{X}(\omega)+\mathbf{Y}(\omega)$.

Exercise 18.2

Flip four independent coins with heads-probability 2/3. Number the coins 1,2,3,4 and define random variables $\mathbf{X}_{12}$, $\mathbf{X}_{23}$ and $\mathbf{X}_{34}$ as the number of heads from coins (1,2), coins (2,3) and coins (3,4) respectively.

(a) Compute these probabilities. (i) $\mathbb{P}[\mathbf{X}_{12}\geq 2]$. (ii) $\mathbb{P}[\mathbf{X}_{12}+\mathbf{X}_{23}\geq 2]$. (iii) $\mathbb{P}[\mathbf{X}_{12}+\mathbf{X}_{34}\geq 2]$.

(b) Determine if these events are independent. (i) $\mathbf{X}_{12}\geq 2$ and $\mathbf{X}_{23}\geq 2$. (ii) $\mathbf{X}_{12}\geq 2$ and $\mathbf{X}_{34}\geq 2$.

18.1 Probability Distribution Function (PDF)

A random variable $\mathbf{X}$ transforms the sample space Ω of possible outcomes to a set $\mathbf{X}(\Omega)$ of possible measurements. For our three coin tosses where $\mathbf{X}$ is the number of heads,

$$\underbrace{\{\text{HHH},\text{HHT},\text{HTH},\text{HTT},\text{THH},\text{THT},\text{TTH},\text{TTT}\}}_{\Omega} \xrightarrow{\mathbf{X}} \underbrace{\{3,2,1,0\}}_{\mathbf{X}(\Omega)}$$

Each possible value x of the random variable $\mathbf{X}$ corresponds to an event. For every outcome in the event, the random variable $\mathbf{X}$ evaluates to x. Here are the events for every $x\in\mathbf{X}(\Omega)$,

	possible values for number of heads, $x\in\mathbf{X}(\Omega)$			
x	0	1	2	3
Event	{TTT}	{HTT, THT, TTH}	{HHT, HTH, THH}	{HHH}

To get $\mathbb{P}[\mathbf{X}=x]$ for each $x\in\mathbf{X}(\Omega)$, add the outcome-probabilities for outcomes in the event $\{\mathbf{X}=x\}$,

	possible values $x\in\mathbf{X}(\Omega)$			
x	0	1	2	3
$P_{\mathbf{X}}(x)$	1/8	3/8	3/8	1/8

(18.1)

The notation $P_{\mathbf{X}}(x)$ stands for $\mathbb{P}[\mathbf{X} = x]$. Think of the set of possible values $\mathbf{X}(\Omega)$ as a new sample space where outcomes ω are replaced by values x. The probability distribution function or PDF of $\mathbf{X}$ is $P_{\mathbf{X}}(x)$. The PDF is the probability function defined on $\mathbf{X}(\Omega)$, derived from the original outcome-probability function $P(\omega)$ defined on Ω. The subscript-$\mathbf{X}$ identifies the random variable. The probability distribution function $P_{\mathbf{X}}$ depends on $\mathbf{X}$ and the original probability space (Ω, P).

Probability Distribution Function (PDF): The PDF $P_{\mathbf{X}}(x)$ is the probability a random variable $\mathbf{X}$ has value x,

$$P_{\mathbf{X}}(x) = \mathbb{P}[\mathbf{X} = x].$$

For practical purposes, the pair $(\mathbf{X}(\Omega), P_{\mathbf{X}})$ functions as a new probability space and you can forget about the original probability space (Ω, P). The original outcomes in Ω are complex. The new "outcomes" in $\mathbf{X}(\Omega)$ are just numbers, and a convenient way to show the PDF is to plot a histogram, see Figure 18.1.

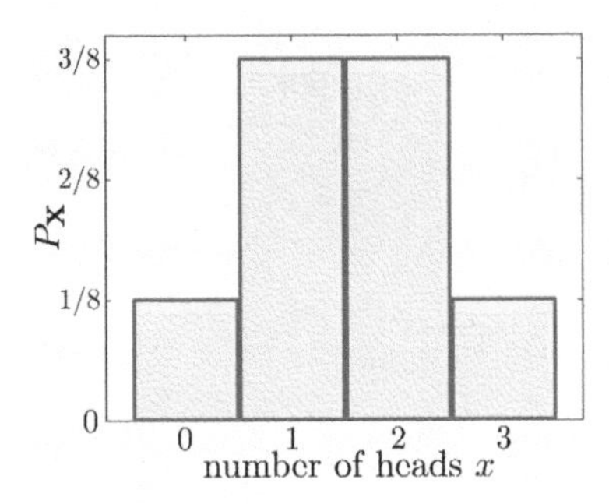

Figure 18.1: **Probability distribution.** In the histogram, each bar shows the probability of the corresponding value x. We plot the PDF of the random variable

$$\mathbf{X} = \text{number of heads}$$

for the underlying probability space Ω defined by tossing three independent fair coins.

An event defined using $\mathbf{X}$ is a set of values. For example, $\{\mathbf{X} \geq 1\} = \{1, 2, 3\}$. The probability of such an event is the sum of probabilities for each value in the event, so

$$\mathbb{P}[\mathbf{X} \geq 1] = P_{\mathbf{X}}(1) + P_{\mathbf{X}}(2) + P_{\mathbf{X}}(3) = \frac{3}{8} + \frac{3}{8} + \frac{1}{8} = \frac{7}{8}.$$

Let us consider one more example. Roll two fair dice and let $\mathbf{X}$ be the sum of the two rolls.

Probability Space

Die 2 Value						
6	$\frac{1}{36}$	$\frac{1}{36}$	$\frac{1}{36}$	$\frac{1}{36}$	$\frac{1}{36}$	$\frac{1}{36}$
5	$\frac{1}{36}$	$\frac{1}{36}$	$\frac{1}{36}$	$\frac{1}{36}$	$\frac{1}{36}$	$\frac{1}{36}$
4	$\frac{1}{36}$	$\frac{1}{36}$	$\frac{1}{36}$	$\frac{1}{36}$	$\frac{1}{36}$	$\frac{1}{36}$
3	$\frac{1}{36}$	$\frac{1}{36}$	$\frac{1}{36}$	$\frac{1}{36}$	$\frac{1}{36}$	$\frac{1}{36}$
2	$\frac{1}{36}$	$\frac{1}{36}$	$\frac{1}{36}$	$\frac{1}{36}$	$\frac{1}{36}$	$\frac{1}{36}$
1	$\frac{1}{36}$	$\frac{1}{36}$	$\frac{1}{36}$	$\frac{1}{36}$	$\frac{1}{36}$	$\frac{1}{36}$
	1	2	3	4	5	6

Die 1 Value

The probability space for the two dice experiment is shown on the left. A particular value for a sum $\mathbf{X}$ defines an event whose outcomes are along a diagonal from top-left to bottom-right. The four outcomes in the shaded event have $\mathbf{X} = 9$. It follows that

$$\mathbb{P}[\mathbf{X} = 9] = 4 \times \frac{1}{36} = \frac{1}{9}.$$

The possible values for the sum $\mathbf{X}$ are $2, 3, \ldots, 12$.

Pop Quiz 18.3

Show that $\mathbf{X}$ has the PDF given in the table below, see also Figure 18.2.

x	2	3	4	5	6	7	8	9	10	11	12
$P_{\mathbf{X}}(x)$	$\frac{1}{36}$	$\frac{2}{36}$	$\frac{3}{36}$	$\frac{4}{36}$	$\frac{5}{36}$	$\frac{6}{36}$	$\frac{5}{36}$	$\frac{4}{36}$	$\frac{3}{36}$	$\frac{2}{36}$	$\frac{1}{36}$

Exercise 18.4

A random variable $\mathbf{X}$ has PDF $P_{\mathbf{X}}(x) = Ax$ for $x \in \{1, \ldots, 10\}$. (a) What is A? (b) Compute $\mathbb{P}[\mathbf{X} \geq 5]$.

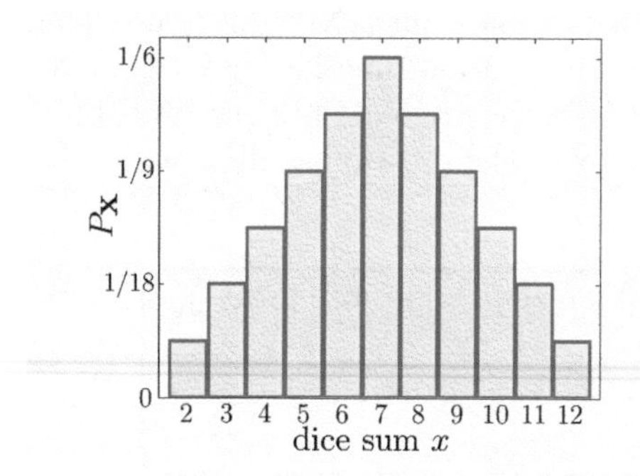

Figure 18.2: **PDF for the Sum of Two Dice.** The probabilities from Pop Quiz 18.3 are shown in the plot. Bar plots are often used to illustrate a PDF.

Example 18.1. Toss 3 independent coins with probability of heads $p = 1 - 1/\sqrt[3]{2} \approx 0.2063$. Let $\mathbf{X}$ be the number of heads. You can use the outcome-tree method to obtain the probability space below.

ω	HHH	HHT	HTH	HTT	THH	THT	TTH	TTT
$P(\omega)$	p^3	$p^2(1-p)$	$p^2(1-p)$	$p(1-p)^2$	$p^2(1-p)$	$p(1-p)^2$	$p(1-p)^2$	$(1-p)^3$
	0.00878	0.03378	0.03378	0.12996	0.03378	0.12996	0.12996	0.5
$\mathbf{X}(\omega)$	3	2	2	1	2	1	1	0

You should verify that the PDF for $\mathbf{X}$ is:

x	0	1	2	3
$P_\mathbf{X}(x)$	0.5	0.38988	0.10134	0.00878

Switch gears to a game where \$1, \$2 or \$3 is picked with probabilities 0.77975, 0.2027 and 0.01755 respectively. If a coin flip is heads, you win the money. Let $\mathbf{Y}$ be your winnings, $\mathbf{Y}$ can be \$0, \$1, \$2 or \$3. What is the PDF of $\mathbf{Y}$? For example, $\mathbb{P}[\mathbf{Y}=0] = \frac{1}{2}(0.77975 + 0.2027 + 0.01755) = 0.5$. Please verify the full PDF below,

y	0	1	2	3
$P_\mathbf{Y}(y)$	0.5	0.38988	0.10134	0.00878

Interesting, $\mathbf{X}$ and $\mathbf{Y}$ have the same PDF! The experiments are different, yet the random variables are identically distributed. From the perspective of the random variables, the experiments are equivalent. Random variables hide unnecessary details, summarizing them into the single number we care about. Once we have the PDF of $\mathbf{X}$, we're done with the underlying probability space. □

18.1.1 Joint Probability Distribution

Consider two random variables together, i.e. jointly. For example $\mathbf{X}$ and $\mathbf{Y}$ on page 259.

ω	HHH	HHT	HTH	HTT	THH	THT	TTH	TTT	
$P(\omega)$	1/8	1/8	1/8	1/8	1/8	1/8	1/8	1/8	
$\mathbf{X}(\omega)$	3	2	2	1	2	1	1	0	← number of heads
$\mathbf{Y}(\omega)$	1	0	0	0	0	0	0	1	← matching tosses

The pair $(\mathbf{X}, \mathbf{Y})$ is a joint random variable. One can use both $\mathbf{X}$ and $\mathbf{Y}$ to define events. The event $\{\mathbf{X} \geq 2$ AND $\mathbf{Y} = 0\}$ has the outcomes $\{\text{HHT}, \text{HTH}, \text{THH}\}$. The event-probability is a sum of outcome-probabilities

$$\mathbb{P}[\mathbf{X} \geq 2 \text{ AND } \mathbf{Y} = 0] = \frac{1}{8} + \frac{1}{8} + \frac{1}{8} = \frac{3}{8}.$$

The simplest event sets each random variable to a value. For example $(\mathbf{X}=0, \mathbf{Y}=0)$ is the empty event $\varnothing$, and $(\mathbf{X}=1, \mathbf{Y}=0)$ is the event $\{\text{HTT}, \text{THT}, \text{TTH}\}$. Summing outcome-probabilities,

$$\mathbb{P}[\mathbf{X}=0, \mathbf{Y}=0] = 0; \qquad \mathbb{P}[\mathbf{X}=1, \mathbf{Y}=0] = 3/8.$$

For every possibility $\mathbf{X} = x$ and $\mathbf{Y} = y$, we can compute $\mathbb{P}[\mathbf{X} = x, \mathbf{Y} = y]$. These probabilities constitute the joint probability distribution function or joint PDF for the joint random variable $(\mathbf{X}, \mathbf{Y})$,

$$P_{\mathbf{XY}}(x, y) = \mathbb{P}[\mathbf{X} = x, \mathbf{Y} = y].$$

We often drop the $\mathbf{XY}$-subscript and write $P(x, y)$. Here is $P(x, y)$ for all (x, y) as a joint PDF table,

$P(x,y)$		X = 0	X = 1	X = 2	X = 3	
Y	0	0	3/8	3/8	0	**3/4**
	1	1/8	0	0	1/8	**1/4**
		1/8	**3/8**	**3/8**	**1/8**	

(18.2)

In the table above, the shaded cell corresponds to $(\mathbf{X} = 1, \mathbf{Y} = 0)$, and $\mathbb{P}[\mathbf{X} = 1, \mathbf{Y} = 0] = 3/8$. Verify every entry in the table by identifying the outcomes in the event and suming the outcome-probabilities. We show row and column sums right of and below the table. Compare the column sums $(\frac{1}{8}, \frac{3}{8}, \frac{3}{8}, \frac{1}{8})$ with $P_{\mathbf{X}}$, the PDF of $\mathbf{X}$ in (18.1) on page 260. The column sums reproduce the PDF of $\mathbf{X}$. Let's prove this. Consider the column sum for $\mathbf{X} = x$. Using the law of total probability with the two cases $\mathbf{Y} = 0$ and $\mathbf{Y} = 1$:

$$\begin{aligned} P_{\mathbf{X}}(x) = \mathbb{P}[\mathbf{X} = x] &= \mathbb{P}[\mathbf{X} = x | \mathbf{Y} = 0]\, \mathbb{P}[\mathbf{Y} = 0] + \mathbb{P}[\mathbf{X} = x | \mathbf{Y} = 1]\, \mathbb{P}[\mathbf{Y} = 1] \\ &= \mathbb{P}[\mathbf{X} = x \text{ AND } \mathbf{Y} = 0] + \mathbb{P}[\mathbf{X} = x \text{ AND } \mathbf{Y} = 1] \\ &= P_{\mathbf{XY}}(x, 0) + P_{\mathbf{XY}}(x, 1). \end{aligned}$$

The same logic works for more than two cases, and also applies to the row sums. In general,

$$\begin{aligned} P_{\mathbf{X}}(x) &= \sum_{y \in \mathbf{Y}(\Omega)} \mathbb{P}[\mathbf{X} = x | \mathbf{Y} = y]\, \mathbb{P}[\mathbf{Y} = y] = \sum_{y \in \mathbf{Y}(\Omega)} P_{\mathbf{XY}}(x, y); \\ P_{\mathbf{Y}}(y) &= \sum_{x \in \mathbf{X}(\Omega)} \mathbb{P}[\mathbf{Y} = y | \mathbf{X} = x]\, \mathbb{P}[\mathbf{X} = x] = \sum_{x \in \mathbf{X}(\Omega)} P_{\mathbf{XY}}(x, y). \end{aligned} \quad (18.3)$$

The PDFs for $\mathbf{X}$ and $\mathbf{Y}$ are sums over the joint-$\mathbf{XY}$ PDF. That means we can recover individual PDFs from the joint PDF. The joint PDF has more information. $P_{\mathbf{X}}$ and $P_{\mathbf{Y}}$ are called marginal PDFs.

Pop Quiz 18.5

All entries in the joint-$\mathbf{XY}$ PDF table sum to 1, as do the column and row sums. Explain why.

We can get complicated probabilities, even conditional probabilities, directly from the joint PDF. To compute an event-probability, you add the probabilities in the cells of the joint-PDF table corresponding to the event.

Let's compute $\mathbb{P}[\mathbf{X} + \mathbf{Y} \leq 2]$. The $(\mathbf{X}, \mathbf{Y})$ pairs $(0,0), (1,0), (2,0), (0,1), (1,1)$ correspond to the event (gray cells in the table to the right). Adding the probabilities,

$$\mathbb{P}[\mathbf{X} + \mathbf{Y} \leq 2] = 0 + \frac{3}{8} + \frac{3}{8} + \frac{1}{8} + 0 = \frac{7}{8}.$$

		X = 0	X = 1	X = 2	X = 3
Y	0	0	$\frac{3}{8}$	$\frac{3}{8}$	0
	1	$\frac{1}{8}$	0	0	$\frac{1}{8}$

Now consider $\mathbb{P}[\mathbf{Y} = 1 \mid \mathbf{X} + \mathbf{Y} \leq 2]$,

$$\mathbb{P}[\mathbf{Y} = 1 \mid \mathbf{X} + \mathbf{Y} \leq 2] = \frac{[\mathbf{Y} = 1 \text{ AND } \mathbf{X} + \mathbf{Y} \leq 2]}{\mathbb{P}[\mathbf{X} + \mathbf{Y} \leq 2]}.$$

		X = 0	X = 1	X = 2	X = 3
Y	0	0	$\frac{3}{8}$	$\frac{3}{8}$	0
	1	$\frac{1}{8}$	0	0	$\frac{1}{8}$

To get the numerator add the cells shaded red. Thus,

$$\mathbb{P}[\mathbf{Y} = 1 \mid \mathbf{X} + \mathbf{Y} \leq 2] = \frac{1}{8} \Big/ \frac{7}{8} = \frac{1}{7}.$$

For practice, show $\mathbb{P}[\mathbf{X} + \mathbf{Y} \leq 2 \mid \mathbf{Y} = 1] = 1/2$ and $\mathbb{P}[\mathbf{X} \leq 2 \mid \mathbf{X} + \mathbf{Y} \geq 2] = 3/4$. From the definition of independence, the events $\{\mathbf{X} = x\}$ and $\{\mathbf{Y} = y\}$ are independent if

$$\mathbb{P}[\mathbf{X} = x \text{ AND } \mathbf{Y} = y] = \mathbb{P}[\mathbf{X} = x] \times \mathbb{P}[\mathbf{Y} = y].$$

That is, if the joint PDF at (x, y) is the product of the marginals at x and y,

$$P_{\mathbf{XY}}(x, y) = P_{\mathbf{X}}(x) \cdot P_{\mathbf{Y}}(y).$$

X and **Y** are independent if this holds for all pairs (x, y), a stringent requirement. As a rule of thumb, random variables that measure properties of different experiments will be independent. Here are two examples.

- **X** counts the heads in 10 coin tosses and **Y** is the sum of 2 dice. **X** and **Y** are independent because **X** depends solely on the coins and **Y** solely on the dice and these are two different experiments.
- **X** counts the heads in 10 coin tosses and **Y** is the indicator of whether the coin tosses all match. **X** and **Y** measure properties of the same experiment and in this case are not independent.

Pop Quiz 18.6
Let **X** count the heads in the first 5 coin tosses and **Y** the sum of 2 dice rolls plus the indicator of whether the last five coin tosses all match. Are **X** and **Y** are independent?

It is helpful to think about whether random variables are measuring totally unrelated quantities, but, the true demonstration of independence is to verify that the joint-PDF is always the product of the marginals.

Independent Random Variables: $P_{\mathbf{XY}}(x, y) = P_{\mathbf{X}}(x)P_{\mathbf{Y}}(y)$ for all (x, y).

Independence must hold for all $(x, y) \in \mathbf{X}(\Omega) \times \mathbf{Y}(\Omega)$, which means for all possible pairs (x, y) where $x \in \mathbf{X}(\Omega)$ and $y \in \mathbf{Y}(\Omega)$. Let's work through testing whether our random variables **X** and **Y** in (18.2) are independent. Start with the joint PDF and the marginals (column and row sums) as shown below on the left, reproduced from (18.2) on page 263. Now construct a table whose entries are the product of the marginals.

$P_{\mathbf{XY}}(x,y)$		**X** = 0	1	2	3	
Y	0	0	3/8	3/8	0	**3/4**
	1	1/8	0	0	1/8	**1/4**
		1/8	**3/8**	**3/8**	**1/8**	

$P_{\mathbf{X}}(x)P_{\mathbf{Y}}(y)$		**X** = 0	1	2	3	
Y	0	3/32	9/32	9/32	9/32	**3/4**
	1	1/32	3/32	3/32	1/32	**1/4**
		1/8	**3/8**	**3/8**	**1/8**	

Each table-entry on the right is the product of marginal probabilities. The shaded entry at $\mathbf{X} = 1, \mathbf{Y} = 0$ is $3/8 \times 3/4 = 9/32$. The table on the right should match the left exactly if **X** and **Y** were independent. The entries that do not match are in red. None of the entries match! **X** and **Y** are far from independent.

Exercise 18.7
(a) For three flips of a biased coin (probability of H is 1/3), let **X** be the number of heads and **Y** the indicator of two H in a row. Give the joint and marginal PDFs. Compute $\mathbb{P}[\mathbf{X} \le 2 \mid \mathbf{X} + \mathbf{Y} \ge 2]$.
(b) For the setting in Exercise 18.2, give the joint PDF of each pair of random variables, and determine if they are independent. (i) $\mathbf{X}_{12}$ and $\mathbf{X}_{23}$. (ii) $\mathbf{X}_{12}$ and $\mathbf{X}_{34}$. (iii) $\mathbf{X}_{12}^2$ and $\mathbf{X}_{34}^2$.
(c) Show that $\sum_{x,y} P_{\mathbf{X}}(x)P_{\mathbf{Y}}(y) = 1$, that is the product of the marginals is a valid joint-PDF.

18.1.2 Cumulative Distribution Function (CDF)

Another useful event is when a random variable is as most a value. What are the chances of at most 2 heads in 3 coin tosses, $\mathbb{P}[\mathbf{X} \le 2]$? We must accumulate probabilities for values of **X** up to 2, a cumulative probability.

x	0	1	2	3
$P_{\mathbf{X}}(x)$	1/8	3/8	3/8	1/8
$\mathbb{P}[\mathbf{X} \le x]$	1/8	4/8	7/8	1

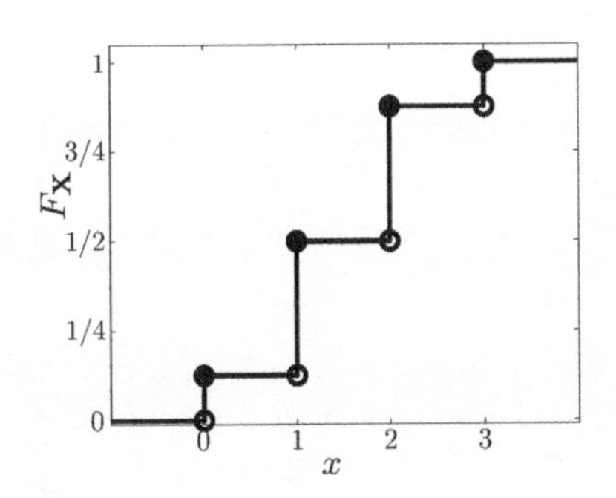

Figure 18.3: **Cumulative Distribution.** The plot shows $F_{\mathbf{X}}(x) = \mathbb{P}[\mathbf{X} \le x]$, which is non-decreasing with jumps when $P_{\mathbf{X}}(x) > 0$. The solid circles indicate which value applies at a jump. The cumulative distribution function $F_{\mathbf{X}}$ is continuous from the right, but may not be continuous from the left.

The cumulative probability is a running sum of the PDF. The PDF is zero if x can't occur. The cumulative probability can be non-zero for an arbitrary x. For example, $\mathbb{P}[\mathbf{X} \le 2.5]$ sums probabilities up to and including 2.5 which is at least the cumulative probability up to 2. See Figure 18.3 for a plot of these cumulative probabilities. The PDF and the CDF contain the same information. You can derive one from the other.

Cumulative Distribution Function (CDF). The CDF $F_{\mathbf{X}}(x)$ is the probability for the random variable $\mathbf{X}$ to be at most x,

$$F_{\mathbf{X}}(x) = \mathbb{P}[\mathbf{X} \le x].$$

Exercise 18.8

You roll a fair die twice. Let $\mathbf{X}$ be the value of the maximum roll.

(a) Use the outcome-tree method to get the PDF of $\mathbf{X}$.

(b) Compute the CDF of $\mathbf{X}$ and use the CDF to get the PDF.

(c) Compute the CDF and PDF for the maximum of 10 rolls of the die.

18.2 Bernoulli/Binary

Some random variables occur frequently, keep them at your fingertips. The simplest and most frequent is the Bernoulli or Binary random variable which indicates whether an outcome is of one type or another, for example a coin toss is H or T or a drunk's step can be left or right. We use 0 and 1 as the two possible values,

$$\mathbf{X} = \begin{cases} 1 & \text{with probability } p; \\ 0 & \text{with probability } 1-p. \end{cases}$$

Things get interesting when we combine many Bernoulli random variables. Let $\mathbf{X}_1, \mathbf{X}_2, \ldots, \mathbf{X}_n$ be the Bernoulli outcomes of n independent coin tosses, where H $= 1$ and T $= 0$. Let $\mathbf{X}$ be the total number of heads. $\mathbf{X}$ is not Bernoulli, since it can be one of $n+1$ possible values $0, 1, \ldots, n$. However, $\mathbf{X}$ is a sum of the $\mathbf{X}_i$,

$$\mathbf{X} = \mathbf{X}_1 + \mathbf{X}_2 + \cdots + \mathbf{X}_n.$$

That is, the sum of Bernoulli indicators can be used to count. In this case, the total number of heads is a sum of independent Bernoullis. For the drunk who takes n steps, each step $\mathbf{X}_i$ is a Bernoulli (right $= 1$, left $= 0$). Where is the drunk after n steps? Let $\mathbf{R}$ be the number of right steps, like number of heads. Then,

$$\mathbf{R} = \mathbf{X}_1 + \mathbf{X}_2 + \cdots + \mathbf{X}_n.$$

The number of left steps is $\mathbf{L} = n - \mathbf{R}$. Let $\mathbf{X}$ be the final position, so $\mathbf{X} = \mathbf{R} - \mathbf{L} = 2\mathbf{R} - n$:

$$\mathbf{X} = 2(\mathbf{X}_1 + \mathbf{X}_2 + \cdots + \mathbf{X}_n) - n.$$

The final position of the drunk is related to a sum of Bernoullis. The sum of n independent Bernoullis is a very important random variable, called a Binomial random variable. We will come back to it later.

18.3 Uniform

A uniform random variable has the same probability for each possible value, just as a uniform probability space has the same probability for each outcome. Assume there are n possible values $1, 2, \ldots, n$. Then, each value has probability $1/n$. A fair die roll is uniform, with $n = 6$. If $\mathbf{X}$ is uniform on n values, its PDF is

$$\mathbb{P}[\mathbf{X} = k] = P_{\mathbf{X}}(k) = 1/n, \qquad \text{for } k = 1, \ldots, n.$$

The PDF-sum is $n \times 1/n = 1$, as it must be for a valid PDF. The shorthand $\mathbf{X} \sim \mathbf{U}[n]$ means "$\mathbf{X}$ is uniform on $1, \ldots, n$." Uniform is a common assumption in practice because it is agnostic in that no value is preferred.

The uniform distribution is a powerful equalizer in games of strategy. As a meek 5th grader, I'd ride my bike to school along the road (black) or through the park (red). My "friend" GR would often meet and escort me to school, relieving me of my lunch. I choose a path and GR chooses where to wait. I win (+1) if I avoid GR and lose (−1) otherwise. I am now beefier, I know probability and can win half the battles.

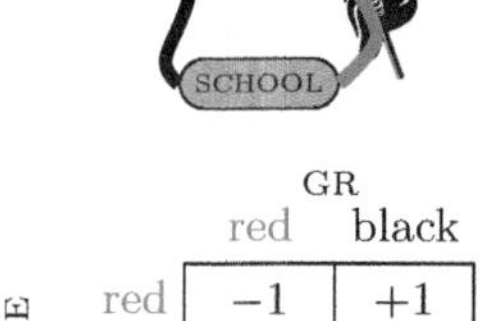

The payoff matrix to the right neatly summarizes my situation depending on the path I choose and where GR waits. This is called the matching game: if we match, GR wins; if not, I win. If I always choose red, GR can always win by choosing red, similarly if I choose black. Am I doomed? The key to this game is that neither of us knows what the other will do ahead of time. We each choose paths independently and the game plays out. If I choose a path uniformly, red with probability 1/2 and black with probability 1/2, no matter what path GR is on, I will be on the other path half the time. I win half the battles by avoidance.

ME \ GR	red	black
red	−1	+1
black	+1	−1

Example 18.2. I pick any two different numbers from $\{1, 2, \ldots, 5\}$, and randomly give you one. You must guess if my number is smaller than yours. For example, if I pick $\{2, 4\}$, you get 2 with probability 1/2 and you get 4 with probability 1/2. Here is the challenge: you must tell me your strategy **before** I pick my numbers.

> **Pop Quiz 18.9**
> (a) Your strategy is to always guess smaller. Show that $\mathbb{P}[\text{you win}] = 1/2$.
> (b) You randomly guess smaller or bigger with probability 1/2 for each. Show that $\mathbb{P}[\text{you win}] = 1/2$.
> (c) You guess bigger if you get 1, 2 or 3. What numbers will I pick? What is $\mathbb{P}[\text{you win}]$?
> (d) Is there a strategy for which $\mathbb{P}[\text{you win}] > 1/2$? Remember, I pick numbers after learning your strategy.

Since I show you a number at random, how can you possibly guess whether it is the smaller one? Surprisingly, you can. Here is an idea for a winning strategy. I choose L and H. Suppose you have an x that is in between them, i.e., $L < x < H$. Now, I randomly give you y, where y is L or H. You can compare y with x. If $x < y$, I gave you H and you win by saying smaller. If $x > y$, I showed you L and you win by saying larger. So, you must win if you have an appropriate x. All this is well and good, but how do you get this x? Guess!

Use a uniform random variable $\mathbf{X}$ with possible values $\{1\frac{1}{2}, 2\frac{1}{2}, 3\frac{1}{2}, 4\frac{1}{2}\}$ to guess x. There are two cases: (i) $L < \mathbf{X} < H$ and you win; (ii) Either $\mathbf{X} < L$ and you always say smaller or $\mathbf{X} > H$ and you always say larger. In Pop Quiz 18.9 you showed that if you always say smaller your win-probability is 1/2. The same holds if you always say larger. Let us use the law of total probability with our two cases to analyze this strategy and determine how often you win. Let $\mathcal{E}$ be the event $\{L < \mathbf{X} < H\}$. Note that $\mathbb{P}[\mathcal{E}] = (H - L)/4$.

$$\begin{aligned}\mathbb{P}[\text{you win}] &= \mathbb{P}[\mathcal{E}] \cdot \mathbb{P}[\text{you win} \mid \mathcal{E}] + \mathbb{P}[\overline{\mathcal{E}}\,] \cdot \mathbb{P}[\text{you win} \mid \overline{\mathcal{E}}\,] \\ &= \mathbb{P}[\mathcal{E}] \cdot 1 + (1 - \mathbb{P}[\mathcal{E}]) \cdot \tfrac{1}{2} \\ &= \tfrac{1}{2} + \tfrac{1}{2}\,\mathbb{P}\,[\mathcal{E}] \\ &= \tfrac{1}{2} + \tfrac{1}{8}(H - L) > \tfrac{1}{2}.\end{aligned} \tag{18.4}$$

Since $H \geq L + 1$, your probability to win is at least 5/8, which is significantly bigger than 1/2.

> **Exercise 18.10**
> (a) Verify the steps in (18.4). (b) Show that if $\mathbf{X}$ is not uniform, I can pick H and L so that $\mathbb{P}[\text{you win}] < \frac{5}{8}$.

□

18.4 Binomial

Let's get back to the number of heads in n independent coin tosses. Let $\mathbf{X}$ be the number of heads. Recall from Section 18.2 on page 265 that $\mathbf{X}$ is a sum of independent Bernoullis,

$$\mathbf{X} = \mathbf{X}_1 + \cdots + \mathbf{X}_n.$$

We derived the PDF for 3 fair coin tosses in (18.1) on page 260. The case of n coin tosses looks daunting. Rather than list the sample space, we use independence and techniques from counting. Consider the general case of n biased coin tosses with probability p of heads. Consider the outcomes contributing to $\mathbb{P}[\mathbf{X} = 3]$.

HHHTT $\cdots$ TTT,	HHTHT $\cdots$ TTT,	HHTTHT $\cdots$ TTT,	...
$p{\cdot}p{\cdot}p{\cdot}(1-p){\cdot}(1-p)\cdots(1-p)$,	$p{\cdot}p{\cdot}(1-p){\cdot}p{\cdot}(1-p)\cdots(1-p)$,	$p{\cdot}p{\cdot}(1-p){\cdot}(1-p){\cdot}p{\cdot}(1-p)\cdots(1-p)$,	...

Each outcome-probability is a product of the probabilities for each individual coin toss because the tosses are independent. So, for example,

$$P(\text{HHHTT}) = P(\text{H}) \cdot P(\text{H}) \cdot P(\text{H}) \cdot P(\text{T}) \cdot P(\text{T}) = p^3(1-p)^2.$$

Every outcome in $\{\mathbf{X} = 3\}$ has 3 heads and $n-3$ tails, so each outcome-probability is $p^3(1-p)^{n-3}$. To compute $\mathbb{P}[\mathbf{X} = 3]$, we need to know the number of outcomes with 3 heads, because we must sum the outcome-probability that many times. The number of outcomes with 3 heads equals the number of strings of length n with 3 heads and $n-3$ tails? We solved this problem when we studied counting in Chapter 13. The binomial coefficient $\binom{n}{3}$ gives the number of such strings. So,

$$\mathbb{P}[\mathbf{X} = 3] = \binom{n}{3} p^3(1-p)^{n-3} = \frac{n!}{3!(n-3)!} \cdot p^3(1-p)^{n-3}.$$

There is nothing special about $\mathbf{X} = 3$, and we could have just as easily computed $\mathbb{P}[\mathbf{X} = k]$. The number of outcomes is $\binom{n}{k}$ and the probability of each outcome is $p^k(1-p)^{n-k}$, so

$$\mathbb{P}[\mathbf{X} = k] = P_{\mathbf{X}}(k) = \binom{n}{k} p^k(1-p)^{n-k} = \frac{n!}{k!(n-k)!} \cdot p^k(1-p)^{n-k}.$$

This formula for the probability of k successes in n independent trials with success probability p is the Binomial Distribution $B(k; n, p)$. In math-speak one would say $\mathbf{X} \sim \mathbf{B}(n, p)$ to mean that $\mathbf{X}$ is a Binomial random variable with n trials and success probability p.

Binomial Distribution. Let $\mathbf{X}$ be the number of successful trials from n independent trials with success probability p. So, $\mathbf{X} = \mathbf{X}_1 + \cdots + \mathbf{X}_n$ is a sum of n independent Bernoullis, with $\mathbb{P}[\mathbf{X}_i = 1] = p$. The PDF of $\mathbf{X}$ is a Binomial distribution, $P_{\mathbf{X}}(k) = B(k; n, p)$, where

$$B(k; n, p) = \binom{n}{k} p^k(1-p)^{n-k}.$$

The name Binomial is in honor of the binomial coefficients in the formula. A fair coin corresponds to setting $p = 1/2$, in which case the probability of getting k heads is $\binom{n}{k}2^{-n}$. Using this formula, you should have no trouble reproducing the PDF in Equation (18.1) on page 260.

Exercise 18.11

(a) A multiple choice test has 20 questions with 5 answers per question. You guess randomly. Compute the probability that you pass. To pass, you must get at least 50% correct.

(b) In the world series, two teams battle to be first to win 4 games. Games are independent. A team wins a game with probability $\frac{1}{2}$. The series can end in 4, 5, 6 or 7 games. What is the probability of each?

(c) A die is rolled 100 times. What is the probability to get 20 ones and 30 fours?

(d) Plot the Binomial distribution $B(k; n, p)$ versus k for $n = 1{,}000$ and $p = 0.3$.

18.5 Waiting Time to Success

It is not unusual to keep trying until you succeed. Your router keeps trying to send an internet packet until it is received. Millions of people are trying to access the Google server. A couple might have children until they get a boy and girl. Suppose you make independent attempts at some task with a success-probability p each time. How many trials do you need till success? Let the random variable $\mathbf{X}$ be the number of attempts until success, called the waiting time to success. To compute the PDF of $\mathbf{X}$, we use the outcome-tree.

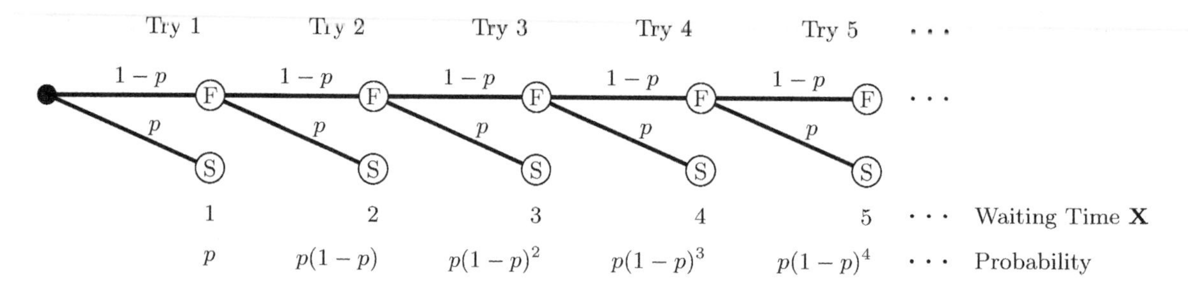

The waiting time is t when the first $t-1$ trials fail, denoted $\mathrm{F}^{\bullet t-1}$, and the t-th trial succeeds denoted S. Since the trials are independent, $\mathbb{P}[\mathrm{F}^{\bullet t-1}\mathrm{S}] = (1-p)^{t-1}p = \beta(1-p)^t$, where $\beta = p/(1-p)$,

$$P_{\mathbf{X}}(t) = \beta(1-p)^t \qquad \text{for } t = 1, 2, 3, \ldots.$$

This is a geometric waiting time distribution, where the probability to wait t steps decays exponentially with t. Figure 18.4 shows the PDFs of a uniform distribution on $\{0, \ldots, 16\}$, the Binomial distribution $B(k; 20, 0.4)$ and the exponential waiting time distribution with success-probability $p = 0.125$. As you can see, these PDFs have very different shapes. The PDFs in Figure 18.4 do share a common property. Can you guess what?

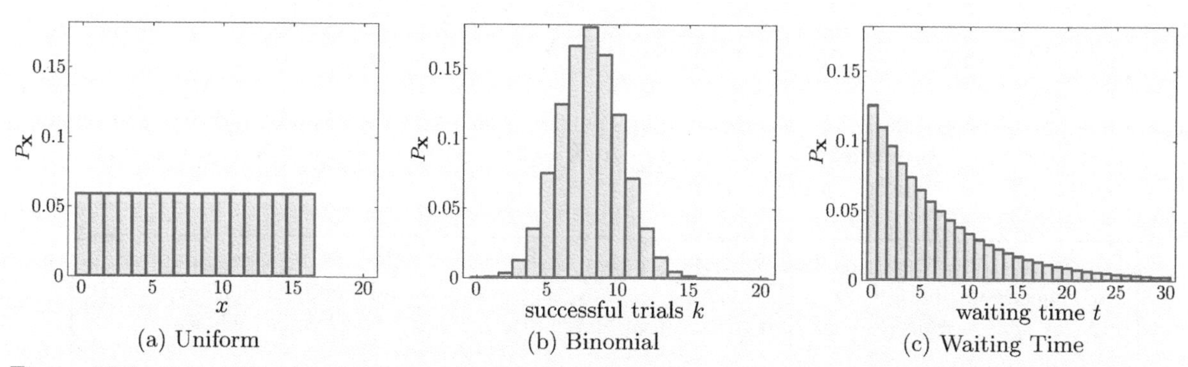

Figure 18.4: Probability distributions: (a) Uniform on $\{0, \ldots, 16\}$; (b) Binomial $B(k; 20, 0.4)$; (c) Exponential waiting time to success with success probability $p = 0.125$.

Exercise 18.12

(a) The sex of children are independent and boys are as likely as girls. Compute the probability that a couple will have at least 4 children before they have a boy.

(b) A couple wants two boys. Let $\mathbf{X}$ be the the number of children they have in order to get two boys. Compute the PDF of $\mathbf{X}$ and give a plot.

(c) The success probability for transmission of internet packets is 0.9.

  (i) Compute the probability you need at least 20 transmissions to send an email of 12 packets.

  (ii) You have 20 transmission slots and try to send a packet in each slot. What is the probability that you successfully send at least 1 packet.

18.6 Problems

Problem 18.1. $\mathbf{X}$ and $\mathbf{Y}$ are random variables on the same sample space Ω. Are $\mathbf{X}+\mathbf{Y}$, $\mathbf{XY}$ and $\min(\mathbf{X},\mathbf{Y})$ random variables? If yes, define how to compute them for an outcome $\omega \in \Omega$.

Problem 18.2. For probability space (Ω, P), is P a random variable? What about $P \ln P$?

Problem 18.3. For each PDF, show that the sum of the probabilities is 1.

(a) $P_{\mathbf{X}}(k) = 1/n$ for $k = 1, 2, \ldots, n$.
(b) $P_{\mathbf{X}}(k) = B(k; n, p)$ for $k = 0, 1, \ldots, n$.
(c) $P_{\mathbf{X}}(k) = p(1-p)^{k-1}$ for $k = 1, 2, 3 \ldots$.
(d) $P_{\mathbf{X}}(k) = e^{-\lambda}\lambda^k/k!$ for $k = 0, 1, 2, \ldots$.

Problem 18.4. For what values of a constant A are the following a valid normalized PDF.

(a) $P_{\mathbf{X}}(k) = Ak$ for $k = 0, \ldots, 5$.
(b) $P_{\mathbf{X}}(k) = Ak$ for $k = 0, \ldots, n$.
(c) $P_{\mathbf{X}}(k) = A$ for $k = 0, \ldots, \infty$.
(d) $P_{\mathbf{X}}(k) = Ak^2$ for $k = 0, \ldots, 5$.
(e) $P_{\mathbf{X}}(k) = A2^{-k}$ for $k = 0, \ldots, 5$.
(f) $P_{\mathbf{X}}(k) = A/k$ for $k = 1, \ldots, \infty$.
(g) $P_{\mathbf{X}}(k) = A/k^2$ for $k = 1, \ldots, \infty$.
(h) $P_{\mathbf{X}}(k) = A2^{-k}$ for $k = 0, \ldots, \infty$.
(i) $P_{\mathbf{X}}(k) = A/k!$ for $k = 0, \ldots, \infty$.
(j) $P_{\mathbf{X}}(k) = A\lambda^k/k!$ for $k = 1, \ldots, \infty$.
(k) $P_{\mathbf{X}}(k) = Ak\lambda^k$ for $k = 1, \ldots, \infty$.
(l) $P_{\mathbf{X}}(k) = A\lambda^k/k$ for $k = 1, \ldots, \infty$.

Problem 18.5. A random variable $\mathbf{X}$ has a PDF from Problem 18.4(a)–(l). In each case compute:
(a) $\mathbb{P}[\mathbf{X} > 1]$. (b) The most probable value of $\mathbf{X}$. (c) $\mathbb{P}[\mathbf{X}$ is even$]$.

Problem 18.6. Random variables $\mathbf{X}$ and $\mathbf{Y}$ are independent and have a uniform distribution on $\{1, \ldots, 10\}$. What is the PDF of $\mathbf{X}+\mathbf{Y}$? Give a plot of the histogram.

Problem 18.7. A biased die rolls values in $\{1,2,3,4,5,6\}$ with probabilities $p_1, p_2, p_3, p_4, p_5, p_6$ respectively. Can one choose p_i so that the PDF of the sum of two rolls is uniform on $\{2, \ldots, 12\}$?

Problem 18.8. A LAN is two disjoint networks (right), with two special nodes A, B. Randomly pick two different nodes in the network (every pair of nodes has equal probability of being picked). You add a new network link between the two nodes you picked.

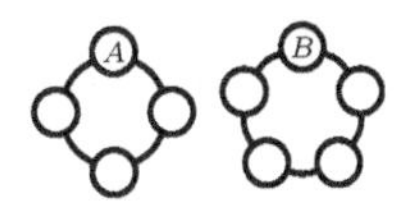

(a) Compute the probability that there will be a path from A to B.
(b) Let $d(A, B)$ be the length of the shortest path between A and B after you add the new link. If the network is not connected we say that $d(A, B) = \infty$. Give the PDF of $d(A, B)$.

Problem 18.9. Let $\mathbf{F}$ be the indicator random variable equal to 0 if a couple's first child is a boy and 1 if it is a girl. Let $\mathbf{X}$ be the number of children they have (waiting time) until they have at least 1 boy and 1 girl. Let p be the probability of a boy (different children are independent). Are $\mathbf{F}$ and $\mathbf{X}$ independent: (a) If $p = 1/2$? (b) If $p = 1/3$?

Problem 18.10. Flip a coin 10 times and define random variables $\mathbf{X}_T$, the number of tails flipped, and $\mathbf{X}_H$, the number of heads flipped. Are $\mathbf{X}_T$ and $\mathbf{X}_H$ independent?

Problem 18.11. Toss a coin until you get a given string of tosses. Let $\mathbf{X}$ be the number of tosses. For each given string, determine the PDF of $\mathbf{X}$. (a) H. (b) HH. (c) HHH. (d) HT. (e) Any string with at least 3 H's.

Problem 18.12. The independent random variables $\mathbf{X}$ and $\mathbf{Y}$ are ± 1, each with probability $1/2$. Let $\mathbf{Z} = \mathbf{XY}$. Show that $\mathbf{X}$, $\mathbf{Y}$ and $\mathbf{Z}$ are pairwise independent. Are they independent?

Problem 18.13. Toss 3 biased coins (probability $3/5$ of heads) and let $\mathbf{X}$ be the number of heads and $\mathbf{Y}$ be an indicator random variable for whether the last two tosses match.

(a) Give the joint PDF $P_{\mathbf{XY}}(x, y)$ as a joint PDF table. Are $\mathbf{X}$ and $\mathbf{Y}$ independent?
(b) Compute: $P_{\mathbf{X}}(2)$, $P_{\mathbf{Y}}(1)$ and $\mathbb{P}[\mathbf{X} = 2 \mid \mathbf{Y} = 1]$.

Problem 18.14. In a dice game, if you roll 1, the game stops and you win \$1. For any other roll, you must decide whether to stop and win the value rolled, or continue rolling. One strategy is to stop if the roll is τ or larger. For this strategy, give the PDF of your winnings for the six different choices of the threshold τ, where $\tau \in \{2, 3, \ldots, 6\}$.

Problem 18.15. Let $\mathbf{X}_1, \mathbf{X}_2, \mathbf{X}_3$ be uniform random variables on $\{1, \ldots, 10\}$. Let $\mathbf{Z}$ be the sum, $\mathbf{Z} = \mathbf{X}_1 + \mathbf{X}_2 + \mathbf{X}_3$.
(a) Give the PDF of $\mathbf{Z}$. (b) You observe $\mathbf{Z} = 10$. Give the conditional PDF for $\mathbf{X}_1$, $\mathbb{P}[\mathbf{X}_1 = x \mid \mathbf{Z} = 10]$.

Problem 18.16. $\mathbf{X}_1$ and $\mathbf{X}_2$ are independent uniform random variables on $\{1, 2, \ldots, 10\}$.

(a) Give the PDFs of: (i) The sum, $\mathbf{Y} = \mathbf{X}_1 + \mathbf{X}_2$. (ii) The maximum, $\mathbf{Z} = \max(\mathbf{X}_1, \mathbf{X}_2)$.
(b) Repeat if there are three independent uniform random variables $\mathbf{X}_1, \mathbf{X}_2, \mathbf{X}_3$.

Problem 18.17. A biased die has probability $p_i = Ai$ to roll i, for $i \in \{1, \ldots, 6\}$, where A is a constant.
(a) Give the PDF of the sum of two rolls. (b) Give the PDF of the sum of three rolls.

Problem 18.18. Let $\mathbf{X}$ and $\mathbf{Y}$ be waitings times with success probabilities p and q. Give the PDF of $\mathbf{Z} = \mathbf{X} + \mathbf{Y}$.

Problem 18.19. Let $\mathbf{X}_1, \ldots, \mathbf{X}_5$ be independent uniform random variables on $\{1, 2, \ldots, 10\}$. Give the PDFs of the minimum and maximum, $\mathbf{Y} = \min(\mathbf{X}_1, \mathbf{X}_2, \mathbf{X}_3, \mathbf{X}_4, \mathbf{X}_5)$ and $\mathbf{Z} = \max(\mathbf{X}_1, \mathbf{X}_2, \mathbf{X}_3, \mathbf{X}_4, \mathbf{X}_5)$. Use Monte Carlo simulation to verify your answer. *[Hint: Compute $\mathbb{P}[\mathbf{Y} \geq i]$ and $\mathbb{P}[\mathbf{Z} \leq i]$.]*

Problem 18.20. The independent random variables $\mathbf{X}$ and $\mathbf{Y}$ have the same PDF, $P(k) = 2^{-k}$ for $k = 1, 2, \ldots, \infty$. For $m, n \in \mathbb{N}$, compute these probabilities:

(a) $\mathbb{P}[\min(\mathbf{X}, \mathbf{Y}) \leq m]$.
(b) $\mathbb{P}[\max(\mathbf{X}, \mathbf{Y}) \leq m]$.
(c) $\mathbb{P}[\mathbf{X}$ divides $\mathbf{Y}]$.
(d) $\mathbb{P}[\mathbf{X} = \mathbf{Y}]$.
(e) $\mathbb{P}[\mathbf{X} > m\mathbf{Y}]$.
(f) $\mathbb{P}[\mathbf{X} \geq m\mathbf{Y}]$.
(g) $\mathbb{P}[m\mathbf{X} = n\mathbf{Y}]$.
(h) $\mathbb{P}[m\mathbf{X} > n\mathbf{Y}]$.
(i) $\mathbb{P}[m\mathbf{X} \geq n\mathbf{Y}]$.

Problem 18.21. The Alphas and Omegas contest a best of seven game world series. A team wins a game with probability $1/2$ and games are independent. The superstar on the Alphas is Epsilon. In a game, Epsilon can get $0, 1, \ldots, 4$ hits with probabilities $1/2, 1/8, 1/8, 1/8, 1/8$. Give the PDF for the number of hits Epsilon gets in the series.

Problem 18.22. You draw a 5 card poker hand from a shuffled 52-card deck. Give the PDF for the number of Aces.

Problem 18.23. You and a friend are randomly placed in a line with eight other people (ten people in line). Give the PDF for the number of people between you and your friend. Verify with Monte Carlo.

Problem 18.24 (Derangements). Ten graduates throw up their hats which land randomly on heads. Give the PDF for the number of graduates getting back their own hat. *[Hint: Problem 14.41.]*

Problem 18.25. Let $\mathbf{X}$ be a random variable taking values in $\{1, \ldots, n\}$ with unknown PDF. Let $\mathbf{R}$ be a uniform random variable on $\{1, \ldots, M\}$, and $\mathbf{Y} = \mathbf{X} + \mathbf{R} \pmod M$. Show that $\mathbf{X}$ and $\mathbf{Y}$ are independent.

Problem 18.26 (Secure Multi-Party Computation (MPC)). Problem 18.25 shows that you can obfuscate a random variable $\mathbf{X}$ by adding to it a uniform random variable $\mathbf{R}$. This technique can be used to privately share a sum in a multiparty computation. Suppose three parties (Alice, Bob, Charlie) wish to know their average salary without revealing their individual salaries. Effectively, they wish to privately share the sum of the salaries. Let $\mathbf{X}_1, \mathbf{X}_2, \mathbf{X}_3$ be the salaries. Let M be a sufficiently large integer, larger than the sum $\mathbf{X}_1 + \mathbf{X}_2 + \mathbf{X}_3$.

(a) Alice generates $\mathbf{R}_1$ uniformly on $\{1, \ldots, M\}$ and sends $\mathbf{Y}_1 = \mathbf{X}_1 + \mathbf{R}_1 \pmod M$ to Bob using Bob's public key. Explain why Bob cannot infer Alice's salary.
(b) Bob generates $\mathbf{R}_2$ uniformly on $\{1, \ldots, M\}$ and sends $\mathbf{Y}_2 = \mathbf{Y}_1 + \mathbf{R}_2 \pmod M$ to Charlie using Charlie's public key. Explain why Charlie cannot infer Bob or Alice's salary.
(c) Charlie generates $\mathbf{R}_3$ uniformly on $\{1, \ldots, M\}$ and sends $\mathbf{Y}_3 = \mathbf{Y}_2 + \mathbf{R}_3 \pmod M$ to Alice using Alice's public key. Explain why Alice cannot infer Bob or Charlie's salary.
(d) Now, Alice sends $\mathbf{Y}_4 = \mathbf{Y}_3 - \mathbf{R}_1$ to Bob. Can Bob infer any salaries.
(e) Bob sends $\mathbf{Y}_5 = \mathbf{Y}_4 - \mathbf{R}_2$ to Charlie. Charlie computes and sends $\mathbf{Y}_6 = \mathbf{Y}_5 - \mathbf{R}_3$ to Alice and Bob. What is $\mathbf{Y}_6$?
(f) Is Charlie better off than anyone else?

Problem 18.27.

(a) Give the CDF for the PDF:

x	0	1	2	3	4
$P_{\mathbf{X}}(x)$	0.2	0.1	0.2	0.4	0.1

(b) Give the PDF for the CDF:

x	$(-\infty, 0)$	$[0, 1)$	$[1, 2)$	$[2, 3)$	$[3, 4)$	$[4, \infty)$
$F_{\mathbf{X}}(x)$	0	0.1	0.15	0.5	0.8	1

Problem 18.28. For independent $\mathbf{X}, \mathbf{Y}$, show: (a) $P_{\mathbf{X}}(x \mid \mathbf{Y} = y) = P_{\mathbf{X}}(x)$. (b) $\mathbb{P}[\mathbf{X} \leq x, \mathbf{Y} \leq y] = F_{\mathbf{X}}(x) F_{\mathbf{Y}}(y)$.

Problem 18.29. A random cut on a circular pizza picks two random points on the circumference and cuts along the chord joining the two points. Give the PDF for the number of pieces produced when you make three random cuts.

Problem 18.30. Let $\mathbf{X}$ be the number of flips of a fair coin until H appears. Give the PDF and CDF of $\mathbf{X}$.

Problem 18.31. Give a formula for the CDF $F_{\mathbf{X}}(k)$ where the distribution of $\mathbf{X}$ is:

(a) Uniform on $\{1, \ldots, n\}$. Give a plot of $F_{\mathbf{X}}$ for $n = 20$.
(b) Binomial with n trials and success probability p (leave it as a sum). Give a plot of $F_{\mathbf{X}}$ for $n = 20, p = 0.25$.
(c) The waiting time to success with probability 0.25. Give a plot of $F_{\mathbf{X}}$.

Problem 18.32. A die roll is $\{1, 2, \ldots, 6\}$ with probabilities $\{p_1, p_2, \ldots, p_6\}$. Give the CDF for the maximum out of 10 rolls of the die. From your CDF, obtain the PDF.

Problem 18.33. Which random variables (measurements) are Binomial? The number of successes is Binomial if:

> (i) The experiment counts successes in a fixed number of binary (succeed/fail) trials.
> (ii) Each trial has a fixed probability p of success.
> (iii) The trials are independent of each other.

(a) Randomly answer 20 multiple-choice questions (5 choices each). Count the number correct.
(b) Flip a biased coin (probability p of H) and count the number of heads in 100 flips.
(c) Flip a biased coin until 2 heads appear (probability p of H) and count the number of flips.
(d) A college admissions officer randomly samples students from 1,000 applications until they find four from NY-state. Count the number of applications sampled.
(e) A college admissions officer randomly samples 100 students without replacement from 1,000 applications and counts the number of applicants from NY-state.
(f) A college admissions officer randomly samples 100 students with replacement from 1,000 applications and counts the number of applicants from NY-state.
(g) A Gallup poll randomly samples 1,000 Americans (without replacement) and asks them if they own an SUV. We count the number of SUV-owners among those polled.
(h) The number of darts you throw until you hit the bulls-eye.
(i) The number of darts hitting the bulls-eye if you throw 3 darts.
(j) Hats of 100 men are given back to the men randomly. Count how many men get their hat back.
(k) Each vertex of a graph is randomly placed into one of two sets A or B. The graph has m edges. A cut-edge has its vertices in different sets. We count the number of cut edges.
(l) Draw 10 cards from a shuffled deck and count the number of aces.
(m) You have 10 shuffled decks. Draw one card from each deck and count the number of aces.
(n) Let $\mathbf{X}$ be the number of 1s in the BITWISE-OR of two 10-bit sequences of independent random bits (1/0 are T/F). For example,0001110010 BITWISE-OR $1000111000 = 1001111010$).
(o) Toss 20 fair coins and re-toss (just once) all coins which flipped H. Count the number of: (i) Coins showing heads at the end. (ii) Heads tossed in the experiment.
(p) Your total winnings in 100 fair coin flips when you win \$2 per H and lose \$1 per T.
(q) A box has 50 bulbs in a random order, with 5 being defective. Of the first 5 bulbs, count the number defective.

Problem 18.34. Let a and b be two random 10-bit sequences, and let $c = a \oplus b$ be their BITWISE-OR, where 0 is F and 1 is T. For example, $0001110010 \oplus 1000111000 = 1001111010$. Compute $\mathbb{P}[c \text{ has five 1s}]$.

Problem 18.35. Ten biased coins are flipped, with probability of heads $3/5$. Plot the PDF of the number of heads. Use Monte-Carlo to "flip" the 10 biased coins. Repeat 10,000 times and give a histogram of the number of heads flipped. Compare the histogram with the PDF. (Look up histogram on the `WWW`.)

Problem 18.36. In a flight, airplane engines independently fail with probability p. An airplane crashes if more than half its engines fail. For what values of p is a 2-engine airplane safer than a 4 engine airplane?

Problem 18.37. Which is more likely: n sixes in $6n$ dice or $n+1$ sixes in $6(n+1)$ dice?

Problem 18.38. Flip a fair coin n times. What is the probability of an equal number of H and T? Recompute the probability given the new information that the first flip is H.

Problem 18.39. Compute these probabilities.
(a) Independently toss 5 fair coins. What is $\mathbb{P}[\text{you get 4 or more heads}]$?
(b) You roll 4 independent fair dice. What is $\mathbb{P}[\text{exactly one 2 and one 4}]$?
(c) Independently generate 4 random bits $b_1b_2b_3b_4$. Compute $\mathbb{P}[\sum_{i=1}^{4} b_i = 2]$.
(d) Independently generate 10 random bits $b_1b_2\cdots b_{10}$. What is the probability $b_1 \leq b_2 \leq \cdots \leq b_{10}$.

Problem 18.40. Roll 10 independent dice. Compute these probabilities:
(a) There's no 1. (b) There's no 2. (c) There's no 1 or 2. (d) There's at least one 1.

Problem 18.41. A 101-sided die is fair (die faces are $1, \ldots, 101$). Compute these probabilities:

(a) In 10 rolls at least one 101 is rolled.

(b) A pair of rolls match.

(c) The sum of two rolls equals k for $k \in \{2, \ldots, 202\}$.

(d) Some number is rolled more than once in n rolls.

Problem 18.42. A 101-sided die is not fair (die faces are $1, \ldots, 101$). The probability to roll 101 is 100 times the probability of any other roll. All rolls other than 101 are equaly likely.

(a) Give the PDF for: (i) A single roll. (ii) The sum of two rolls.

(b) Give the probability of: (i) At least one 101 in 10 rolls. (ii) Doubles in a pair of rolls.

(c) What is the probability for some number to be rolled more than once (i) in three rolls? (ii) in n rolls?

Problem 18.43. Recall the random process in sexual reproduction whereby a gamete is created from the father and mother-genes (see Problem 16.68). Let $\mathbf{X}$ be the number of father-genes in the gamete. Give the PDF for $\mathbf{X}$. Does $\mathbf{X}$ have a Binomial distribution? Explain why or why not.

Problem 18.44. Passengers miss flights 10% of the time. FOCS-air has 9 seats and books 10 passengers; DMC-air has 18 seats and books 20 passengers. Which flight is over-booked more often?

Problem 18.45. A town has two hospitals, one big and one small. The big hospital delivers 1000 babies and the small hospital delivers 100 babies. There's a 50/50 chance of male or female on each birth. Which hospital has a better chance of having the same number of boys as girls?

Problem 18.46. A 500 student course with 28 lectures is taught in a lecture hall with 460 seats. Students attend lecture 90% of the time. Assume students are independent and independently attend each lecture.

(a) What are the chances a student won't have a seat in the first lecture. *[Hint: Problem 18.67 may be useful.]*

(b) What are the chances that in all 28 lectures, every student has a seat.

(c) How many seats are needed for at least a 99% chance that all lectures can accomodate all students who attend.

Problem 18.47. For independent $\mathbf{X}$ and $\mathbf{Y}$, let $\mathbf{U}(\omega) = f(\mathbf{X}(\omega))$ and $\mathbf{V}(\omega) = g(\mathbf{Y}(\omega))$, where f and g are arbitrary functions. Show that $\mathbf{U}$ and $\mathbf{V}$ are independent.

Problem 18.48. $\mathbf{X}$ and $\mathbf{Y}$ are random variables.

(a) Is there a joint PDF for which $\mathbf{X}$ and $\mathbf{Y}$ are independent but $\mathbf{X}^2$ and $\mathbf{Y}^2$ are not?

(b) Is there a joint PDF for which $\mathbf{X}^2$ and $\mathbf{Y}^2$ are independent but $\mathbf{X}$ and $\mathbf{Y}$ are not?

(c) If $\mathbf{X}$ can only take on 1 value, are $\mathbf{X}$ and $\mathbf{Y}$ independent?

Problem 18.49. Let $\mathbf{X}, \mathbf{Y}$ be independent random variables. Let $\mathcal{X}$ be a subset of the possible values of $\mathbf{X}$ (an "event" of $\mathbf{X}$-outcomes). Similarly, let $\mathcal{Y}$ be a subset of the possible values of $\mathbf{Y}$. Show that the events $\mathcal{X}$ and $\mathcal{Y}$ are independent, $\mathbb{P}[\mathbf{X} \in \mathcal{X} \text{ AND } \mathbf{Y} \in \mathcal{Y}] = \mathbb{P}[\mathbf{X} \in \mathcal{X}] \times \mathbb{P}[\mathbf{Y} \in \mathcal{Y}]$.

Problem 18.50. Let $\mathbf{X}_1, \ldots, \mathbf{X}_n$ be random variables. Define joint and conditional PDFs:

$$\begin{aligned} P(x_1, \ldots, x_n) &= \mathbb{P}[\mathbf{X}_1 = x_1 \text{ AND } \mathbf{X}_2 = x_2 \text{ AND } \cdots \text{ AND } \mathbf{X}_n = x_n]; \\ P(x_i \mid x_1 \ldots, x_{i-1}) &= \mathbb{P}[\mathbf{X}_i = x_i \mid \mathbf{X}_1 = x_1, \mathbf{X}_2 = x_2, \ldots, \mathbf{X}_{i-1} = x_{i-1}] \end{aligned}$$

(a) Show that $P(x_1, \ldots, x_n) = P(x_1) \cdot P(x_2 \mid x_1) \cdot P(x_3 \mid x_1, x_2) \cdots P(x_n \mid x_1 \ldots, x_{n-1})$.

(b) Define independence for n random variables. (Relate the joint PDF to the marginals.)

Problem 18.51 (Transformations). A random variable $\mathbf{X}$ has PDF $P_{\mathbf{X}}(x)$ and CDF $F_{\mathbf{X}}(x)$.

(a) For $\mathbf{Y} = a\mathbf{X} + b$ with $a > 0$, show that $F_{\mathbf{Y}}(y) = F_{\mathbf{X}}\left((y - b)/a\right)$.

(b) For $\mathbf{Y} = \mathbf{X}^2$, show that $F_{\mathbf{Y}}(y) = F_{\mathbf{X}}\left(\sqrt{y}\right) - F_{\mathbf{X}}\left(-\sqrt{y}\right) + P_{\mathbf{X}}(-\sqrt{y})$ (assume $y \geq 0$).

Problem 18.52 (Bayes' Theorem). For two random variables $\mathbf{X}, \mathbf{Y}$, show that

$$\mathbb{P}[\mathbf{X} = x \mid \mathbf{Y} = y] = \frac{P_{\mathbf{XY}}(x, y)}{P_{\mathbf{Y}}(y)} = \frac{P_{\mathbf{XY}}(x, y)}{\sum_x P_{\mathbf{XY}}(x, y)}$$

Problem 18.53. Suppose $\mathbf{X}$ and $\mathbf{Y}$ are independent, taking values in the same set V.

(a) If $\mathbf{X}$ is a uniform random variable, show that $\mathbb{P}[\mathbf{X} = \mathbf{Y}] = 1/|V|$.

(b) If $\mathbf{X}$ and $\mathbf{Y}$ have the same marginal distribution, show that $\mathbb{P}[\mathbf{X} = \mathbf{Y}] \geq 1/|V|$.

(c) In general, $0 \leq \mathbb{P}[\mathbf{X} = \mathbf{Y}] \leq 1$. Give joint distributions that achieve both bounds.

Problem 18.54. For the guessing game in Example 18.2 on page 266, I choose L uniformly on $\{1, 2, 3, 4\}$ and set $H = L + 1$. Can you improve on the strategy in Example 18.2 (a simple enhancement gives win-probability $5/8 + 3/32$).

Problem 18.55. A hair-gene can be {a,a}, {b,b}, {a,b} or {b,a}. The option {a,a} gives blonde hair and the other three possibilities give black hair. One-third of black haired people are {b,b}. When two parents mate, half of each parent's gene is randomly selected and the two halves combine to get the offspring's gene. 100 blonde men mate with 100 black haired women. Compute the probability of k blonde children.

Problem 18.56 (Clinical Trials). Patients are placed into control and treatment groups in a clinical trial (50 controls and 100 treatments). A placebo is given to the controls and the drug to patients in the treatment-group. The probability that a patient is cured is p_c for the control group and p_t for treatment group. We don't p_c or p_t. We know:

- p_c is either 0.4, 0.5 or 0.6 and each possibility is equally likely.
- Chances are 50% the drug has no effect ($p_t = p_c$), chances are 30% of a 10% positive effect ($p_t = p_c + 1/10$), and chances are 20% of a 10% detrimental side-effect ($p_t = p_c - 1/10$).

Patients are independent. In the study, 27 in the control group are cured and 63 in the treated group are cured.

(a) Before the clinical trial, what are the probabilities of the 9 combinations for p_c, p_t.

(b) After the clinical trial, what are the probabilities of the 9 combinations for p_c, p_t.

Problem 18.57. Toss a fair coin independently 101 times. What is the probability to get:

(a) Zero heads? (b) At least 1 heads? (c) A majority of heads?

Repeat for a biased coin with probability $2/3$ of heads.

Problem 18.58. For 20 fair coin flips, define events $A = \{\text{equal number of H and T}\}$ and $B = \{\text{first 3 flips are H}\}$. Compute the probabilities: (a) A occurs. (b) B occurs. (c) A AND B occur. (d) A OR B occur.

Problem 18.59. Toss 20 fair coins. Now re-toss (just once) all coins which came up heads.

(a) Let $\mathbf{X}$ be the number of heads showing at the end. Give the PDF for $\mathbf{X}$, $P_{\mathbf{X}}$.

(b) What is the probability you end up with 5 heads showing at the end?

(c) What is the probability you tossed 5 heads in total (in both rounds of tossing)?

Problem 18.60. You drive 500 times every year (to and from work). You speed 5% of the time. When you speed, chances of a ticket are 1%. On any given year, compute the probabilities you get $0, 1, 2$ and 3 or more tickets.
In 2014 about 41 million tickets were issued. The US population was about 317 million (about half commute to work and 90% of commuters drive). Does this data reasonably match the model?

Problem 18.61. Each edge In a 10-vertex graph is independent and present with probability p.

(a) For $p \in \{0.01, 0.02, 0.03, \ldots, 0.99\}$, compute $\mathbb{P}[\text{graph has 10 edges}]$ and give a plot versus p.

(b) Use Monte Carlo to estimate the probability the graph is connected for each value of p in (a). Plot the probability to be connected versus p. (Randomly generate graphs. The fraction of connected graphs estimates the probability.)

Problem 18.62. A drunk starts a random walk (page 250) at 0 with probability $2/3$ to step left. His position $\mathbf{X} \in \{0, \pm1, \pm2, \ldots\}$ has PDFs after 1, 2 and 3 steps as shown below.

	drunk's position x										
	$\cdots$	-4	-3	-2	-1	0	1	2	3	4	$\cdots$
1 step $P_{\mathbf{X}}(x)$	$\cdots$	0	0	0	2/3	0	1/3	0	0	0	$\cdots$
2 step $P_{\mathbf{X}}(x)$	$\cdots$	0	0	4/9	0	4/9	0	1/9	0	0	$\cdots$
3 step $P_{\mathbf{X}}(x)$	$\cdots$	0	8/27	0	4/9	0	2/9	0	1/27	0	$\cdots$

Plot the PDF for the drunk's position after the drunk has taken 10 and 20 steps. Show the result of a Monte Carlo simulation to experimentally confirm your answer. *[Hint: You could solve this problem in one of two ways: Use the build up method and relate the $(k+1)$-step $P_{\mathbf{X}}$ to the k-step $P_{\mathbf{X}}$; or, relate $P_{\mathbf{X}}$ to a Binomial distribution.]*

Problem 18.63 (Noisy Channels). A message $m_1 \cdots m_n$ of n bits is sent over a link that independently flips bits with probability $1/10$. You send each bit $2k+1$ times. The receiver "decodes" the $2k+1$ received bits per message-bit by majority vote, yielding the received message $r_1 \cdots r_n$.

(a) The message is garbled if even one bit is decoded incorrectly. What is the smallest k for which you can recover the message at least 99.9% of the time?

(b) Using error correction, you can tolerate ϵn incorrect bits (constant fraction of error). If $\epsilon = 1/10$, what is the smallest k allowing message recovery at least 99.999% of the time.

Problem 18.64. A device with 100 independent components fails if four or more components fail. The failure probability is $p = 0.01$ on a given year. Compute (a) $\mathbb{P}$[device fails in year 1]. (b) $\mathbb{P}$[device lasts more than 5 years].

Problem 18.65. Let $\mathbf{X}$ be the number of successes in n independent trials and $\mathbf{Y}$ the number of successes in m additional trials (success-probability p in all trials). Let $\mathbf{Z} = \mathbf{X} + \mathbf{Y}$. Give the PDF of $\mathbf{Z}$. Hence, show that if $\mathbf{X} \sim B(n,p)$ and $\mathbf{Y} \sim B(m,p)$ are independent then $\mathbf{X} + \mathbf{Y} \sim B(n+m,p)$.

Problem 18.66 (Properties of the Binomial Distribution). Let $\mathbf{X}$ be the number of successes in n independent trials with success probability p. Compute these probabilities:

(a) $\mathbb{P}$[no successes] and $\mathbb{P}$[no failures]. Specialize to $p = 1/2$
(b) $\mathbb{P}$[at least 1 success] and $\mathbb{P}$[at least 1 failure]. Specialize to $p = 1/2$
(c) $\mathbb{P}$[even number of successes] and $\mathbb{P}$[even number of failures]. Specialize to $p = 1/2$
[Hint: Use the Binomial Theorem to expand $(x+y)^n - (y-x)^n$. See also Problem 16.92.]

Problem 18.67 (Computing Binomial Probabilities). The formula $B(k;n,p) = \binom{n}{k}p^k(1-p)^k$ is numerically unstable. For example, $B(0;1000,1/3) = (1/3)^{1000}$ which is numerically 0 on most computing platforms.

(a) Fix n and p and let $L_k = \ln B(k;n,p)$. What is L_0?
(b) Show that $L_{k+1} = L_k + \ln(p(n-k)/(1-p)(k+1))$ for $k = 0,\ldots,n-1$.
(c) For $n = 1000$ and $p = 1/3$, plot $B(k;n,p) = e^{L_k}$ versus k.

Problem 18.68. For the Binomial distribution $B(k;n,p) = \binom{n}{k}p^k(1-p)^k$, fix $p = 1/3$.

(a) For $n = 10, 20, \ldots, 100$, let k^* maximize $B(k;n,p)$. Plot k^*/n versus n. Make a guess for $k^*(n)$ and prove it.
(b) Plot the maximum probability $B(k^*;n,1/3)/\sqrt{n}$ versus n. Make a guess for $B(k^*;n,p)$ and prove it.

Problem 18.69. For the Binomial distribution $B(k;n,p) = \binom{n}{k}p^k(1-p)^k$, let $M(n,p)$ be the probability that a (strict) majority of at least $\ell = \lceil (n+1)/2 \rceil$ trials are a success.

(a) Express $M(n,p)$ as a sum. Show: (i) $M(n,p)$ is increasing in p. (ii) For $p > 1/2$, $M(n,p)$ is increasing in n.
(b) Fix $p > 1/2$ and prove:

$$1 - \frac{p}{2p-1}\binom{n}{\ell}p^{n-\ell}(1-p)^{\ell} \le M(n,p) \le 1 - \binom{n}{\ell}p^{n-\ell}(1-p)^{\ell}.$$

Problem 18.70. You and a friend independently and repeatedly try to access a wireless channel, randomly with probability p at each step. The channel is accessible if one of you (not both) try to access. Let $\mathbf{X}$ be how long you wait for a first access and $\mathbf{Y}$ how long your friend waits. Give the PDF of: (a) $\mathbf{X}$ (b) $\mathbf{Y}$ (c) $\mathbf{Z} = \mathbf{X} - \mathbf{Y}$.

Problem 18.71 (Zipf or Power Laws). Randomly pick an English word. We plot a word's probability versus its usage rank. You get close to a power law PDF, $P(\text{rank}) = \alpha/(\text{rank})^{\beta}$, which is linear on a log-log scale. Here is a simple model that could explain the power law. Randomly type letters a, b or space ␣. Everytime a space appears, you have created a new word.

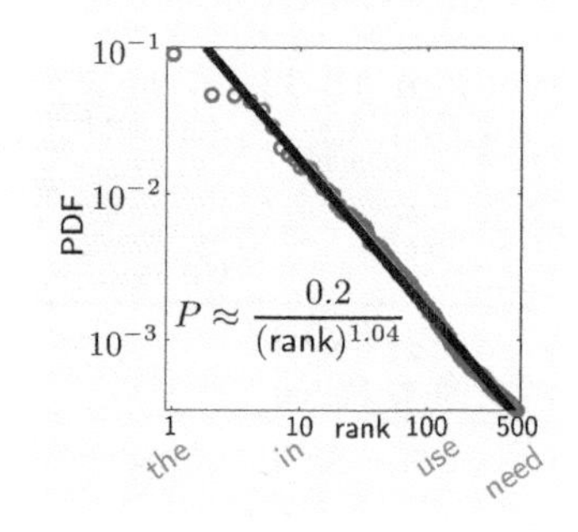

(a) Write a program to randomly type 100 million symbols. Collect the words and their frequencies and give a log-log plot of frequency versus rank.
(b) Show that words with rank around 2^i have probability about $(1/3)^i$. Get theoretical estimates of α and β and compare with the Monte Carlo in (a).
(c) Repeat for an alphabet of just one letter a and three letters a, b, c.

(Power laws are everywhere from city population distribution to wealth distribution.)

Problem 18.72 (Waiting Time is "Memoryless"). With a success-probability of p, you made τ trials with no success. Let $\mathbf{X}$ be the total trials to the first success.

(a) Compute the probability to wait an additional t trials, $\mathbb{P}[\mathbf{X} = \tau + t \mid \mathbf{X} > \tau]$.
(b) Why do we say that the waiting time is "memoryless"?

Problem 18.73 (Waiting for r Successes). Let the success-probability in a trial be p. Let $\mathbf{X}$ be the waiting time for r successes. Derive the PDF of $\mathbf{X}$, i.e. compute $\mathbb{P}[\mathbf{X} = t]$.

(a) At which step is the rth success? In how many ways can you arrange the first $r-1$ successes?
(b) Show that $P_{\mathbf{X}}(t) = \binom{t-1}{r-1}p^r(1-p)^{t-r}$.
(c) Show that (c) matches the PDF of the waiting time for one success when $r = 1$.

Problem 18.74 (Waiting for k successes and ℓ failures). Let $\mathbf{X}$ be the waiting time for k successes and ℓ failures with success probability p. Show that

$$P_{\mathbf{X}}(t) = \begin{cases} 0 & t < k+\ell; \\ \binom{t-1}{k-1} p^k (1-p)^{t-k} + \binom{t-1}{\ell-1} p^{t-\ell}(1-p)^{\ell} & t \geq k+\ell. \end{cases}$$

Use Monte Carlo to obtain the PDF for $p = 1/2, k = 2, \ell = 6$ and compare with the PDF above.

Problem 18.75 (Successes in n Trials). A trial succeeds with probability p and you have a budget of n trials. Let $\mathbf{X}$ be the number of successes. In this problem, derive the PDF for $\mathbf{X}$ in two ways, and in so doing, you will produce a combinatorial proof of a famous combinatorial summation. You must compute $P_{\mathbf{X}}(k) = \mathbb{P}[\mathbf{X} = k]$.

(a) Show that $P_{\mathbf{X}}(k) = \binom{n}{k} p^k (1-p)^{n-k}$.

(b) Use the waiting time distribution for k successes to derive $P_{\mathbf{X}}(k)$:

- (i) Show that the trial on which the kth success occurs must be one of $k, k+1, \ldots, n$.
- (ii) Where does the $(k+1)$th success occur?
- (iii) Use the law of total probability to show that

$$\mathbb{P}[\mathbf{X} = k] = \sum_{i=k}^{n} \mathbb{P}[k\text{th success at } i] \cdot \mathbb{P}[(k+1)\text{th success after } n \mid k\text{th success at } i].$$

- (iv) Show that $\mathbb{P}[(k+1)\text{th success after } n \mid k\text{th success at } i] = (1-p)^{n-i}$.
- (v) Use Problem 18.73 to show $\mathbb{P}[\mathbf{X} = k] = p^k(1-p)^{n-k} \sum_{i=k-1}^{n-1} \binom{i-1}{k-1}$.

(c) Prove the identity $\sum_{i=m}^{n} \binom{i}{m} = \binom{n+1}{m+1}$. (Upper summation of binomial coefficients.)

Problem 18.76 (Interviewing/Optimal Dating). Here is a model for dating to find an optimal spouse. You date in a random order n "job" candidates interested in you having distinct values $v_1, v_2, \ldots, v_n$. Here are the rules.

I. When you date (interview) candidate i you can determine his/her value v_i.

II. After determining v_i you must decide to accept or reject candidate i.
If you accept, you stop dating, get married and settle down.
If you reject, it too is final - no second chances.

III. You must get the best candidate (or else there is potential for scandal).

What are your chances of finding the optimal spouse, getting married, and living happily ever after? One strategy is to date the first K potential partners with no intention of settling down. During this exploration phase, you learn what's out there ("playing the field"). After K candidates, you now accept any candidate that beats all previous candidates. It turns out this type of strategy is best. What is the optimal value of K and what are your chances of success?

(a) Let $\mathbf{X}$ be the position of the best spouse. What is the PDF of $\mathbf{X}$?

(b) Fix K. Compute $\mathbb{P}[\text{success} \mid \mathbf{X} = i]$. *[Hint: Where's the best of the first $i-1$ candidates?]*

(c) For given K, let $Q(K) = \mathbb{P}[\text{success}]$. Show $Q(K) = n(H_n - H_K)/K$, where $H_n = 1 + 1/2 + \cdots + 1/n$ is the nth Harmonic number. *[Hint: Total probability.]*

(d) Let K^* maximize $Q(K)$. Show that $H_n - 1 \leq H_{K^*} < H_n - 1 + 1/K^*$. Hence, show that $K^* \to \infty$, and $H_{K^*} \to H_n - 1$ (for $n \to \infty$). *[Hint: Analyze $Q(K+1) - Q(K)$.]*

(e) Use $H_n \approx \ln n + 0.577$ and $H_{K^*} \to H_n - 1$ to show $K^* \to n/e$ and $Q(K^*) \to 1/e$ (for $n \to \infty$). (Surprisingly, chances of success with a million sequential suitors is about 37%)

(f) Assume people date "seriously" from age 20-40 years and at a uniform rate (e.g. 1 date per month). At what age should you stop "playing the field" and get ready to settle down if someone comes along who beats all others you have dated? (Census data: $\sim 35\%$ of marriages last 25 years; divorce is least likely when marriage-age is 28-32.)

Problem 18.77 (Multinomial). Pick 10 fruits independently with probabilities: pear $1/2$; apple $1/3$; orange $1/6$. Compute the probabilities to get: (a) 5 pears. (b) 5 pears and 2 apples. (c) At least 5 pears or at least 2 apples.

Problem 18.78 (Hypergeometric). A crate has 50 bulbs, 10 are defective. You randomly pick 10 bulbs without replacement. Let $\mathbf{X}$ be the number of defective bulbs in the 10 you picked. Give the PDF of $\mathbf{X}$.

Generalize to the case where there are n bulbs, m are defective and you pick k bulbs. Let $\mathbf{X}$ be the number of defective bulbs in the k you picked. Give the PDF of $\mathbf{X}$, $P_{\mathbf{X}}(x; n, m, k)$.

Problem 18.79. A lake has 600 fish. 60 have been marked by a biologist in a study. A year later, the biologist randomly caught (without replacement) 60 fish. Give the PDF for the number of marked fish in the second sample. What if there is a 10% chance of a fish dying after a year? Give the new PDF.

Problem 18.80 (Mark and Recapture). The number of fish in a lake is $\mathbf{X} \in [200, 400]$, with each value of $\mathbf{X}$ being equally likely. In a study, a biologist randomly caught, 40 fish (without replacement), marked them and replaced them in the lake. The next day the biologist caught 40 random fish and found 20 to be marked.

(a) What was the PDF of $\mathbf{X}$ before the biologist did anything?

(b) What is the updated PDF of $\mathbf{X}$ after finding that 20 fish in the new sample are marked (give a plot)?

(c) What is the most likely number of fish in the lake?

Problem 18.81. You have $\mathbf{N}$ coins in your pocket. $\mathbf{N}$ is unknown and has a Poisson PDF, $\mathbb{P}[\mathbf{N} = k] = e^{-2}2^k/k!$. You toss all the coins. What is the PDF for the number of H you get?

Problem 18.82. A die is rolled n times (independently). What is the probability to get:

(a) $n/2$ ones and $n/2$ fours? (Assume n is even.)

(b) k_1 ones, k_2 twos , k_3 threes , k_4 fours, k_5 fives and k_6 sixes, where $k_i \geq 0$ and $k_1 + k_2 + \cdots + k_6 = n$?

Problem 18.83 (Poisson PDF). Recall the Binomial distribution $B(k; n, p)$ for k successes in n trials with success probability p. Consider this PDF for $p = \lambda/n$ when n gets large. This means there are many trials, but the success probability on any given trial is very small.

(a) Show that $P_{\mathbf{X}}(k) = (\lambda^k/k!) \times (1 - \lambda/n)^{n-k} \times (n(n-1)\cdots(n-(k-1))/n^k)$.

(b) For λ, k fixed and $n \to \infty$, show that $P_{\mathbf{X}}(k) \to e^{-\lambda}\lambda^k/k!$. (The Poisson PDF which models the number of "arrivals" in many applications: helpdesk-calls in a day; gamma-rays in an hour; insurance claims in a year; traffic at an intersection.)

Problem 18.84 (Poisson-Binomial). Give the PDF for the number of successes in 10 trials when the success-probabilities in the trials: $(\frac{1}{10}, \frac{1}{10}, \frac{3}{10}, \frac{4}{10}, \frac{5}{10}, \frac{6}{10}, \frac{6}{10}, \frac{7}{10}, \frac{8}{10}, \frac{9}{10})$. Compare with the Binomial PDF for 10 trials, each having the same success-probability $\frac{1}{2}$ (equal to the average). *[Hint: Let $Q(r, k) = \mathbb{P}[r$ successes in the first k trials$]$.]*

Problem 18.85 (Banach's Matchbox). Kilam has two matchboxes, one in his left pocket and one in his right. The matchboxes start with 100 matches. Each time Kilam needs a match he is equally likely to use one from either pocket. The first time Kilam reaches for a match and finds the matchbox empty, let $\mathbf{X}$ be the number of matches in the other box. Give the PDF of $\mathbf{X}$ and verify it with Monte Carlo.

Problem 18.86. Pick random numbers from $\{1, \ldots, 100\}$ with replacement until their sum exceeds 100. Let $\mathbf{X}$ count how many numbers picked. Give the PDF for $\mathbf{X}$ and verify it with Monte Carlo. Can you generalize to numbers from $\{1, \ldots, n\}$ until the sum exceeds n?

Problem 18.87 (Random Graphs). A graph with n nodes $v_1, \ldots, v_{10}$ is a random graph if every edge (v_i, v_j) is independent and present in the graph with probability p.

(a) Compute the probability that there are k edges in the graph, as a function of n and p.

(b) Let $\mathbf{D}_i$ be the degree of node v_i. Are $\mathbf{D}_1$ and $\mathbf{D}_2$ independent?

(c) Give the joint distribution for $(\mathbf{D}_1, \mathbf{D}_2)$. You must compute $\mathbb{P}[\mathbf{D}_1 = d_1 \text{ AND } \mathbf{D}_2 = d_2]$. *[Hint: Law of total probability with the two cases: edge (v_1, v_2) is present or not.]*

Problem 18.88 (Hitting Time). A drunk starts at a bar and randomly walks left or right.

(a) His house is 10 steps to the left. Let $\mathbf{H}$ be the number of steps it takes the drunk to reach home, called the hitting time. Use Monte Carlo to estimate the PDF of $\mathbf{H}$, and give a plot.

(b) The drunk continually wanders until he comes back to the bar. Let $\mathbf{R}$ be the number of steps it takes the drunk to come back to the bar, called a return time. Use Monte Carlo to estimate the PDF of $\mathbf{R}$, and give a plot.

(c) Use the techniques from Problem 13.93 to analytically compute the PDF for the hitting time $\mathbf{H}$ and compare with your Monte Carlo simulation. *[Hint: Compute $\mathbb{P}[$hitting time $> x]$.]*

Blessed is He who expects nothing, for He shall never be disappointed.
– **Alexander Pope**

"Mom, I did infinitely better than expected on my final." "Wow son, that's great. How did you do it?" –**old haggard joke**

In all affairs it's a healthy thing now and then to hang a question mark on the things you have long taken for granted. – **Bertrand Russell**

Chapter 19

Expected Value

1: Summarizing a PDF using a "typical" or expected value.
2: Conditional expectation and the law of total expectation.

Let's take stock. We started with a probability space: complex experiments with complex outcomes. A random variable simplifies a complex outcome like HHTHTTHHH to a single measured value that you care about, like the number of heads COUNT(HHTHTTHHH) = 6. A random variable is characterized by its probability distribution function or PDF, which, for practical purposes, captures the entire experiment into the probabilities of various measured values. If you are interested in two measurable properties of the experiment, you have two random variables and a joint PDF. Once you have the random variables of interest and their joint PDF, you don't need the underlying probability space anymore.

Often, you would like to further summarize the experiment and reduce the random variable's entire PDF to a single number that captures the typical or average measured value.

Exercise 19.1

(a) Use Monte Carlo to "roll" a fair die 10 times. Report the average roll. For rolls $\{4, 1, 6, 1, 2, 3, 5, 3, 6, 3\}$, the average is 3.4. Repeat the experiment with 1,000 rolls and report the average roll.

(b) Use Monte Carlo to "toss" a fair coin 10 times. Repeat the experiment 1,000 times, each time counting the number of heads in the 10 tosses to get $\mathbf{X}_1, \ldots, \mathbf{X}_{1000}$. Report the average of the $\mathbf{X}_i$.

(c) It rains for 1 hour every morning. For that hour, independently during each minute, 1mm of rain falls with probability $1/8$ or no rain falls with probability $7/8$. Run a Monte Carlo for 1,000 days and show the daily rainfall as a plot of rain in mm versus day number. Report the average daily rainfall.

(d) 1,000 gamblers each play 1,000 Roulette games, always betting \$1 on red (Example 17.4 on page 252). Run a Monte Carlo to get the profit of each gambler and report their average profit.

If you ran the experiments in Exercise 19.1, you'll agree that the average of 1,000 fair dice rolls is about 3.5, 10 coin tosses on average yield 5 heads, the average daily rainfall is about 7.5mm and a gambler who bets \$1 on red in Roulette on average loses \$52.63 in 1,000 games. A grain of salt is called for. How can a Roulette gambler "on average" lose \$52.63, when he must win or lose \$1 in each game? It's an arithmetic fact that the average of a set of numbers may take us out of the set, e.g., the average of 1 and 2 is $1\frac{1}{2}$. Nevertheless, we still use the average to describe the set $\{1, 2\}$ at a coarse level, even though the average is not in the set.

We can't always run Monte Carlo experiments to determine averages. We need to do some arithmetic. Let's begin with the mathematical equivalent of the experimental average, called expectation. Toss two coins and repeat many times. We are interested in the random variable $\mathbf{X}$ = "number of H". We performed this experiment 24 times, tossing two coins each time and counting the number of H (shown below the outcome),

HH	TH	HT	HH	HH	TH	TT	TT	HH	TT	HT	HT	HH	HT	TT	HT	TT	HT	HT	TH	HH	TH	TT	TH
2	1	1	2	2	1	0	0	2	0	1	1	2	1	0	1	0	1	1	1	2	1	0	1

The average value of **X** is the sum of the observed values divided by the number of experiments,

$$\frac{2+1+1+2+2+1+0+0+2+0+1+1+2+1+0+1+0+1+1+1+2+1+0+1}{24} = \frac{24}{24} = 1.$$

This average is the sample average. It helps to re-order the experiments using the value of **X**,

TT	TT	TT	TT	TT	TT	HT	HT	HT	HT	HT	HT	HT	TH	TH	TH	TH	TH	HH	HH	HH	HH	HH	HH
		$n_0 = 6$									$n_1 = 12$									$n_2 = 6$			
0	0	0	0	0	0	1	1	1	1	1	1	1	1	1	1	1	1	2	2	2	2	2	2

This is helpful because there is another way to compute the sum of **X**-values. Multiply value 0 by its number of occurrences n_0 to get the contribution $n_0 \times 0$. The contributions of 1 and 2 are $n_1 \times 1$ and $n_2 \times 2$. Hence, $\text{average}(\mathbf{X}) = (6\times 0 + 12 \times 1 + 6 \times 2)/24 = 24/24$,

$$\text{average}(\mathbf{X}) = \frac{n_0 \times 0 + n_1 \times 1 + n_2 \times 2}{n} = \frac{n_0}{n} \times 0 + \frac{n_1}{n} \times 1 + \frac{n_2}{n} \times 2,$$

where n is the number of experiments. Now for the punch-line. For large n, the frequency of an outcome approximates its probability, $P_{\mathbf{X}}(x) \approx n_x/n$. We conclude that

$$\text{average}(\mathbf{X}) \approx P_{\mathbf{X}}(0)\cdot 0 + P_{\mathbf{X}}(1)\cdot 1 + P_{\mathbf{X}}(2)\cdot 2 = \sum_{x\in\mathbf{X}(\Omega)} x \cdot P_{\mathbf{X}}(x).$$

On the left is the practical quantity we can measure, the sample average. On the right is a mathematical formula, a sum, which approximates this average. When you repeat the experiment many times the mathematical sum and the experimental average will get closer. We can compute the mathematical sum without any appeal to Monte Carlo. The mathematical sum is the expected value of **X**, written $\mathbb{E}[\mathbf{X}]$.

Expected Value $\mathbb{E}[\mathbf{X}]$. The expected value of a random variable **X** is the sum of the possible outcome-values x, each weighted by its probability $P_{\mathbf{X}}(x)$:

$$\mathbb{E}[\mathbf{X}] = \sum_{x\in\mathbf{X}(\Omega)} x \cdot P_{\mathbf{X}}(x).$$

Synonyms: Expectation, Mathematical Expectation, Mean, Average.

To compute the expected value, we need the PDF of **X**. For two coin tosses, we have:

	SAMPLE SPACE Ω			
ω	HH	HT	TH	TT
$P(\omega)$	1/4	1/4	1/4	1/4
$\mathbf{X}(\omega)$	2	1	1	0

$\rightarrow$

	$x \in \mathbf{X}(\Omega)$		
x	0	1	2
$P_{\mathbf{X}}(x)$	1/4	1/2	1/4

The mathematical expectation for the number of heads in two coin tosses is

$$\mathbb{E}[\text{number of heads in two coin tosses}] = 0 \times \frac{1}{4} + 1 \times \frac{1}{2} + 2 \times \frac{1}{4} = 1.$$

Pop Quiz 19.2 [Expected Value Directly From Sample Space]

For the two coin tosses, compute $\sum_{\omega\in\Omega} \mathbf{X}(\omega)\cdot P(\omega)$. Prove, for any **X** defined on any Ω,

$$\mathbb{E}[\mathbf{X}] = \sum_{x\in\mathbf{X}(\Omega)} x \cdot P_{\mathbf{X}}(x) = \sum_{\omega\in\Omega} \mathbf{X}(\omega)\cdot P(\omega).$$

Sum of Dice. For a single roll of a fair die, the values $1, \ldots, 6$ each have probability 1/6, so

$$\mathbb{E}[\text{fair die roll}] = \frac{1}{6} \times (1+2+3+4+5+6) = \frac{21}{6} = 3\frac{1}{2}.$$

The sample average is real. The expected value is an abstract mathematical substitute for this average. The expected value of a single die roll is $3\frac{1}{2}$. If you roll a die, you "expect" to roll $3\frac{1}{2}$. That's nonsense. You can never roll a $3\frac{1}{2}$. The expected value tells you the average over many rolls. If you run an experiment once, the expected value is a summary of what might happen, not necessarily the "typical" outcome.

Pop Quiz 19.3
Use Monte Carlo to "roll" a die n times. Plot $|\text{sample average} - \mathbb{E}[\mathbf{X}]|$ vs. n up to $n = 10^6$.

For the expected sum of two dice, here are the probability space, random variable and its PDF.

Probability Space

Die 2 Value \ Die 1 Value	1	2	3	4	5	6
6	$\frac{1}{36}$	$\frac{1}{36}$	$\frac{1}{36}$	$\frac{1}{36}$	$\frac{1}{36}$	$\frac{1}{36}$
5	$\frac{1}{36}$	$\frac{1}{36}$	$\frac{1}{36}$	$\frac{1}{36}$	$\frac{1}{36}$	$\frac{1}{36}$
4	$\frac{1}{36}$	$\frac{1}{36}$	$\frac{1}{36}$	$\frac{1}{36}$	$\frac{1}{36}$	$\frac{1}{36}$
3	$\frac{1}{36}$	$\frac{1}{36}$	$\frac{1}{36}$	$\frac{1}{36}$	$\frac{1}{36}$	$\frac{1}{36}$
2	$\frac{1}{36}$	$\frac{1}{36}$	$\frac{1}{36}$	$\frac{1}{36}$	$\frac{1}{36}$	$\frac{1}{36}$
1	$\frac{1}{36}$	$\frac{1}{36}$	$\frac{1}{36}$	$\frac{1}{36}$	$\frac{1}{36}$	$\frac{1}{36}$

$\mathbf{X}$ = sum

Die 2 Value \ Die 1 Value	1	2	3	4	5	6
6	7	8	9	10	11	12
5	6	7	8	9	10	11
4	5	6	7	8	9	10
3	4	5	6	7	8	9
2	3	4	5	6	7	8
1	2	3	4	5	6	7

x	$P_{\mathbf{X}}(x)$
2	1/36
3	2/36
4	3/36
5	4/36
6	5/36
7	6/36
8	5/36
9	4/36
10	3/36
11	2/36
12	1/36

To compute the expected value, we use the formula $\mathbb{E}[\mathbf{X}] = \sum_x x \cdot P_{\mathbf{X}}(x)$,

$$\mathbb{E}[\mathbf{X}] = \frac{2\cdot 1}{36} + \frac{3\cdot 2}{36} + \frac{4\cdot 3}{36} + \frac{5\cdot 4}{36} + \frac{6\cdot 5}{36} + \frac{7\cdot 6}{36} + \frac{8\cdot 5}{36} + \frac{9\cdot 4}{36} + \frac{10\cdot 3}{36} + \frac{11\cdot 2}{36} + \frac{12\cdot 1}{36} = 7. \tag{19.1}$$

It's curious that the expected sum of two dice is twice the expected value of one die.

Pop Quiz 19.4
Let $\mathbf{D}_1$ and $\mathbf{D}_2$ be the values of the two dice. Compute $\mathbb{E}[\mathbf{D}_1 - \mathbf{D}_2]$ and $\mathbb{E}[\,|\mathbf{D}_1 - \mathbf{D}_2|\,]$.

Exercise 19.5

(a) For a uniform probability space, show that the expected value of $\mathbf{X}$ is the average of $\mathbf{X}(\omega)$ over all outcomes ω, $\mathbb{E}[\mathbf{X}] = \frac{1}{|\Omega|}\sum_{\omega\in\Omega}\mathbf{X}(\omega)$. Compute the expected sum of two dice this way.

(b) For any $\mathbf{X}$, let $\mathbf{Y} = a\mathbf{X} + b$ for constants a, b. Show that $\mathbb{E}[\mathbf{Y}] = a\,\mathbb{E}[\mathbf{X}] + b$.

(c) $\mathbf{X}_1$ and $\mathbf{X}_2$ are random variables defined on the same sample space Ω and $\mathbf{Y}$ is the sum, $\mathbf{Y} = \mathbf{X}_1 + \mathbf{X}_2$. Show that $\mathbb{E}[\mathbf{Y}] = \mathbb{E}[\mathbf{X}_1] + \mathbb{E}[\mathbf{X}_2]$.

Example 19.1 (Paying for Gamble). A game pays the value rolled on a die. You shouldn't pay more than your expected payoff to play, which is \$3.50. If you pay more, on average you lose money. □

19.1 Expected Value of Common Random Variables

We start simple. A binary random variable $\mathbf{X}$ is 1 with probability p and 0 otherwise. The expected value is

$$\mathbb{E}[\mathbf{X}] = 0\cdot(1-p) + 1\cdot p = p. \qquad \text{(same as the success probability)}$$

Theorem 19.2 (Bernoulli/Binary). A Bernoulli random variable with success probability p has expectation p.

A uniform random variable $\mathbf{X}$ takes values in $\{1, \ldots, n\}$, each with probability $1/n$. The expected value is:

$$\mathbb{E}[\mathbf{X}] = \sum_{i=1}^{n} i \times \frac{1}{n} = \frac{1}{n} \times \frac{1}{2}n(n+1) = \frac{1}{2}(n+1).$$

Theorem 19.3 (Uniform). A Uniform random variable $\mathbf{X} \sim \mathbf{U}[n]$ has expectation $\mathbb{E}[\mathbf{X}] = (n+1)/2$.

19.1.1 Binomial Distribution

Toss a coin n times and let $\mathbf{X}$ be the number of heads which is in $\{0,\ldots,n\}$. For a biased coin with probability p of heads, the PDF of $\mathbf{X}$ is a Binomial distribution, $P_{\mathbf{X}}(k) = B(k;n,p) = \binom{n}{k}p^k(1-p)^{n-k}$ (see page 267),

x	0	1	2	$\ldots$	k	$\ldots$	n
$P_{\mathbf{X}}(x)$	$(1-p)^n$	$np(1-p)^{n-1}$	$\binom{n}{2}p^2(1-p)^{n-2}$	$\ldots$	$\binom{n}{k}p^k(1-p)^{n-k}$	$\ldots$	p^n

To get the expected value, we take the columnwise product and add. Define $q = 1-p$.

$$\begin{aligned}\mathbb{E}[\mathbf{X}] &= 0\cdot q^n + 1\cdot npq^{n-1} + \cdots + k\cdot\binom{n}{k}p^kq^{n-k} + \cdots + n\cdot p^n\\ &= \sum_{k=1}^{n} k\cdot\binom{n}{k}p^kq^{n-k}. \qquad \text{(What happened to the } k=0 \text{ term?)}\end{aligned}$$

Let's work through this formidable sum for $\mathbb{E}[\mathbf{X}]$, starting with a helpful identity.

Lemma 19.4. For $n \geq k \geq 1$, $k\binom{n}{k} = n\binom{n-1}{k-1}$.

You can verify the lemma using the formula $\binom{n}{k} = n!/k!(n-k)!$. Here is a "combinatorial" proof. From n people, choose a k-committee with a leader. The k-committee can be chosen in $\binom{n}{k}$ ways and a leader from within in k ways, giving $k\cdot\binom{n}{k}$ different k-committees with a leader. Alternatively, choose the leader in n ways and the rest of the committee in $\binom{n-1}{k-1}$ ways, giving $n\cdot\binom{n-1}{k-1}$ different k-committees with a leader. Both answers must match, proving the lemma. By Lemma 19.4,

$$\mathbb{E}[\mathbf{X}] = \sum_{k=1}^{n} n\cdot\binom{n-1}{k-1}p^kq^{n-k} = np\sum_{k=1}^{n}\binom{n-1}{k-1}p^{k-1}q^{n-1-(k-1)}.$$

We pulled a constant np outside the summation, which is valid because np does not depend on k. Now, the summand depends on k only through $k-1$. Similar to a change of variables in integration, you can change the index of summation. Let $\ell = k-1$, so the summand is $\binom{n-1}{\ell}p^\ell q^{n-1-\ell}$ and since k goes from 1 to n, the new index $\ell = k-1$ goes from 0 to $n-1$, and we get

$$\mathbb{E}[\mathbf{X}] = np\sum_{\ell=0}^{n-1}\binom{n-1}{\ell}p^\ell q^{n-1-\ell} = np(p+q)^{n-1}.$$

The last expression follows from the Binomial theorem, $(x+y)^{n-1} = \sum_{\ell=0}^{n-1}\binom{n-1}{\ell}x^\ell y^{n-1-\ell}$. Since $p+q=1$,

Theorem 19.5 (Number of successes in independent trials). Let $\mathbf{X}$ be a Binomial random variable with n trials and success probability p. Then, $\mathbb{E}[\mathbf{X}] = np$.

A Binomial random variable is a sum of n independent Bernoullis, $\mathbf{X} = \mathbf{X}_1 + \cdots + \mathbf{X}_n$ (Section 18.4, page 267). Isn't it curious that the expected sum of n Bernoullis is n times the expected value of a single Bernoulli.

19.1.2 Waiting Time to Success

You make independent trials with success probability p, e.g. sending an internet packet. Let $\mathbf{X}$ be the number of trials till the first success. $\mathbf{X} \in \{1,2,\ldots\}$ and has PDF (see page 268)

t	1	2	3	$\ldots$	k	$\ldots$
$P_{\mathbf{X}}(t)$	$\beta(1-p)$	$\beta(1-p)^2$	$\beta(1-p)^3$	$\ldots$	$\beta(1-p)^k$	$\ldots$

where $\beta = p/(1-p)$. To get $\mathbb{E}[\mathbf{X}]$, take the columnwise product and add,

$$\mathbb{E}[\mathbf{X}] = \beta(1-p) + 2\beta(1-p)^2 + 3\beta(1-p)^3 + \cdots = \beta\sum_{k=1}^{\infty}k(1-p)^k. \tag{19.2}$$

(β factors out of the sum.) For infinitely many possible values, the expected value is an infinite sum. As you can see, to compute expected values, you must become good at computing sums. The expected value is a useful summary of an experiment, so you need to be familiar with the many tricks for sums like these.

Lemma 19.6. For $|a| < 1$, $\sum_{k=1}^{\infty} ka^k a + 2a^2 + 3a^3 + 4a^4 + \cdots = \frac{a}{(1-a)^2}$.

Proof. Consider the infinite geometric sum $1 + a + a^2 + a^3 + a^4 + \cdots = 1/(1-a)$. Equate the derivatives of both sides, which is allowed because when $|a| < 1$ the series absolutely converges. We get:

$$1 + 2a + 3a^2 + 4a^3 + \cdots = \frac{1}{(1-a)^2} \quad \rightarrow \quad a + 2a^2 + 3a^3 + 4a^4 + \cdots = a \times \frac{1}{(1-a)^2}.$$

Another proof: Let $S = \sum_{k=1}^{\infty} ka^k$, then $S - aS = a + a^2 + a^3 + \cdots$. You can fill in the rest. ■

We use the lemma to get the expected waiting time. Set $a = (1-p)$ in Lemma 19.6. Then,

$$\sum_{k=1}^{\infty} k(1-p)^k = \frac{1-p}{p^2} = \frac{1}{\beta p}.$$

The last step uses $\beta = p/(1-p)$. So, the expectation in (19.2) is $\mathbb{E}[\mathbf{X}] = \beta/\beta p = 1/p$.

Theorem 19.7 (Waiting time)**.** Let $\mathbf{X}$ be the waiting time with success probability p. Then, $\mathbb{E}[\mathbf{X}] = 1/p$.

Example 19.8. Boys are as likely as girls, $p = \frac{1}{2}$. So, a couple that has kids until a girl expects two kids.

If at first you don't succeed, try and try again. – Thomas H. Palmer, 1840.
See also the poem of King Bruce and the spider, Bernard Barton, 1784–1849.

Memorize the simple formula $\mathbb{E}[\mathbf{X}] = 1/p$, as you often make continued attempts at a task. □

Exercise 19.6

(a) Compute the expected number of heads from 20 fair coin tosses.
(b) A multiple choice test has 20 questions and each question has 5 possible answers. If you answer randomly, how many questions do you expect to get right?
(c) You shoot 5 darts randomly at a dart board. The bulls-eye has radius 1/10th that of the board. What is the expected number of darts that hit the bulls-eye?
(d) For a Binomial $\mathbf{X}$ with PDF $P_{\mathbf{X}}(k) = B(k; n, p)$, show $\mathbb{E}[\mathbf{X}(\mathbf{X}-1)] = n(n-1)p^2$.

Exercise 19.7

(a) You shoot darts randomly at a dart board until you hit the bulls-eye whose radius is $\frac{1}{10}$th that of the board. What is the expected number of darts you throw?
(b) EX-ultimate Pokemon cards are rare, only 1% of cards are EX. How many 5-packs of cards should you expect to buy if your goal is to get an EX-ultimate?
(c) How much should a million dollar lottery ticket cost if the chances of winning are 1 in 10 million?
(d) Compute $\mathbb{E}$[number of kids] if a couple procreates until: (i) A boy and a girl. (ii) Two boys.

19.2 Conditional Expectation

When new information arrives, you update a probability. You must also update an expected value. The updated expected value, given the new information, is a conditional expectation. Let us consider height. The average height in the US is about $66\frac{1}{2}$". If you radomly picked a person, you expect their height to be about $66\frac{1}{2}$". The PDF of the height $\mathbf{X}$ for a random individual is shown on the right. The expected height is the sum of heights weighted by their probability. A specific sub-population in the US will not conform to the overall average of $66\frac{1}{2}$". Suppose you randomly picked a person who is female. What do you expect their height to be? $66\frac{1}{2}$" is not a good guess.

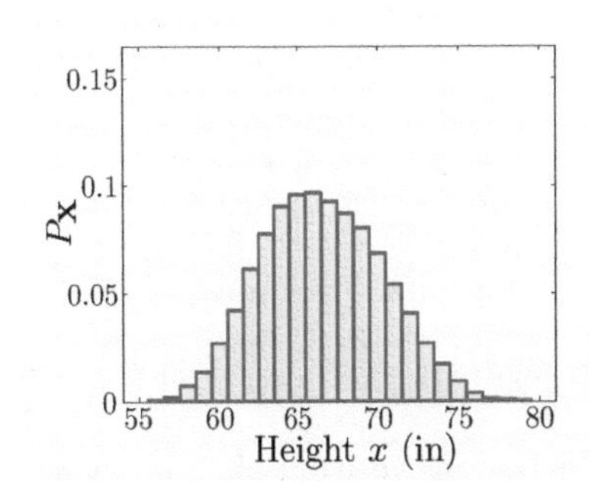

The average female height is the expected height conditioned on female. We weight each height by the probability of that height conditioned on female, and add. The probabilities for various heights conditioned on being female is the red PDF. Similarly, the blue PDF shows the probabilities for various heights conditioned on being male. The average female height is about 64" and the average male height is about about 69". The male and female PDFs are conditional PDFs,

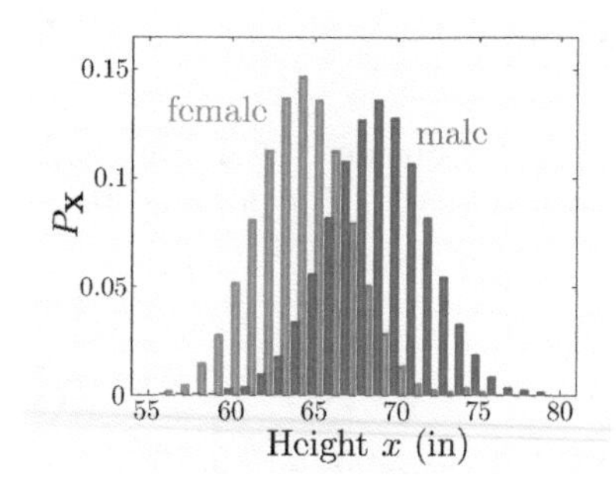

$$\begin{aligned} P_{\mathbf{X}}(x \mid \text{female}) &= \mathbb{P}[\mathbf{X} = x \mid \text{female}] \qquad \text{(red)} \\ P_{\mathbf{X}}(x \mid \text{male}) &= \mathbb{P}[\mathbf{X} = x \mid \text{male}] \qquad \text{(blue)} \end{aligned}$$

Let's define conditional expectation, the updated expectation given the new information that the outcome is in event A. For example "female" specifies an event (subset) within the sample space of all individuals.

Conditional Expected Value $\mathbb{E}[\mathbf{X} \mid A]$:

$$\mathbb{E}[\mathbf{X} \mid A] = \sum_{x \in \mathbf{X}(\Omega)} x \cdot \mathbb{P}[\mathbf{X} = x \mid A] = \sum_{x \in \mathbf{X}(\Omega)} x \cdot P_{\mathbf{X}}(x \mid A). \tag{19.3}$$

The notation $P_{\mathbf{X}}(x \mid A)$ means $\mathbb{P}[\mathbf{X} = x \mid A]$. Conditional expectation is like a regular expectation, except you weight the x-values by conditional probabilities, the conditional PDF. Let's work through two examples.

Example 19.9 (Conditional Dice). Let $\mathbf{X}$ be the sum of two dice. Find $\mathbb{E}[\mathbf{X} \mid \text{die } 1{=}4]$ and $\mathbb{E}[\mathbf{X} \mid \text{one roll is } 4]$.

To compute $\mathbb{E}[\mathbf{X} \mid \text{die } 1{=}4]$, we need the conditional probability

$$\mathbb{P}[\mathbf{X} = x \mid \text{die } 1{=}4] = \frac{\mathbb{P}[\mathbf{X} = x \text{ AND die } 1{=}4]}{\mathbb{P}[\text{die } 1{=}4]}.$$

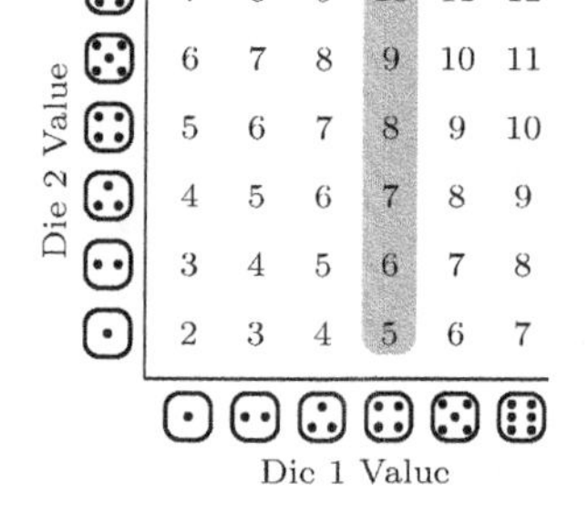

We show $\mathbf{X}$ for outcomes in the probability space. The event $\{\text{die } 1{=}4\}$ is shaded gray. Every outcome-probability is $1/36$, so $\mathbb{P}[\text{die } 1{=}4] = 1/6$. The possible sums are $5, 6, \ldots, 10$. Thus, $\mathbb{P}[\mathbf{X} = x \text{ AND die } 1{=}4] = 1/36$ for $x \in \{5, \ldots, 10\}$ and zero otherwise. We have

$$\mathbb{P}[\mathbf{X} = x \mid \text{die } 1{=}4] = \frac{1}{36} \Big/ \frac{1}{6} = \frac{1}{6} \qquad \text{for } x \in \{5, \ldots, 10\}.$$

Finally, we get

$$\mathbb{E}[\mathbf{X} \mid \text{die } 1{=}4] = \frac{1}{6} \cdot (5 + 6 + \cdots + 10) = 7\frac{1}{2}.$$

(Larger than the unconditional expectation of 7 because die 1 is larger than the expected value of one die.)

A conditional PDF is a valid PDF, with updated probabilities for each possible value of $\mathbf{X}$. A conditional expected value is the expected value with respect to these updated conditional probabilities. Conditional probabilities and conditional expectations have all the properties of their unconditional counterparts.

To compute $\mathbb{E}[\mathbf{X} \mid \text{one roll is } 4]$, we interpret "one roll is 4" to mean at least one roll is 4. An alternative interpretation is exactly one roll is 4. The event $\{\text{one roll is } 4\}$ is shaded and $\mathbb{P}[\text{one roll is } 4] = 11/36$. Please verify the conditional PDF below,

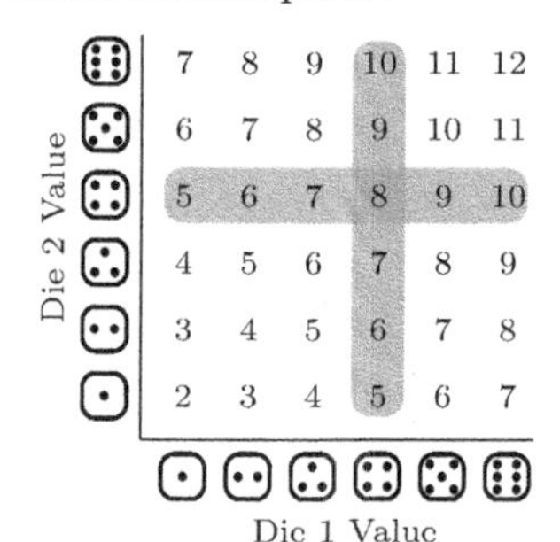

x	5	6	7	8	9	10
$\mathbb{P}[\mathbf{X} = x \mid \text{one roll is } 4]$	2/11	2/11	2/11	1/11	2/11	2/11

Computing the expected value for this conditional PDF gives

$$\mathbb{E}[\mathbf{X} \mid \text{one roll is } 4] = \frac{2}{11} \cdot (5 + 6 + 7 + 9 + 10) + \frac{1}{11} \cdot 8 = 7\frac{5}{11}.$$

If instead exactly one roll is 4, the conditional expectation is $7\frac{2}{5}$. Conditioning is subtle. □

In the above example, the event "one roll is 4" is not defined using the random variable $\mathbf{X}$. This event is defined in the underlying probability space with the two dice rolls. So, to compute conditional probabilities and conditional expectations, we had to resort to the original probability space. This takes away from the lure of the random variable and its PDF, whose promise was to rid you of any dependence on the underlying complex probability space. If you condition on an event defined using solely the random variable, then you don't have to revisit the probability space.

Example 19.10 (Number of trials to success after one failure). Let $\mathbf{X}$ be the number of trials to success with success probability p. If the first trial fails, how many trials do you expect to make? Since the first try fails, $\mathbf{X} \geq 2$, and we need the conditional expectation $\mathbb{E}[\mathbf{X} \mid \mathbf{X} \geq 2]$. In this case, we are conditioning on an event defined using the random variable itself. To begin, we need the conditional probability

$$\mathbb{P}[\mathbf{X} = t \mid \mathbf{X} \geq 2] = \frac{\mathbb{P}[\mathbf{X} = t \text{ AND } \mathbf{X} \geq 2]}{\mathbb{P}[\mathbf{X} \geq 2]}.$$

Let's tackle each term separately. First, $\mathbb{P}[\mathbf{X} = t \text{ AND } \mathbf{X} \geq 2] = \mathbb{P}[\mathbf{X} = t] = \beta(1-p)^t$ when $t \geq 2$, and zero otherwise, where $\beta = p/(1-p)$. (For the waiting time PDF, see page 280). Also, $\mathbb{P}[\mathbf{X} \geq 2] = (1-p)$, the probability to fail on the first trial. Therefore,

$$\mathbb{P}[\mathbf{X} = t \mid \mathbf{X} \geq 2] = \frac{\beta(1-p)^t}{(1-p)} = \beta(1-p)^{t-1}, \qquad \text{for } t = 2, 3, \ldots.$$

To get the conditional expectation, weight the possible values of t by their probabilities and add,

$$\mathbb{E}[\mathbf{X} \mid \mathbf{X} \geq 2] = \beta \sum_{t=2}^{\infty} t(1-p)^{t-1} = \beta \sum_{t=2}^{\infty} (t-1+1)(1-p)^{t-1}.$$

As t goes from 2 to ∞, $t-1$ goes from 1 to infinity. So, we may rewrite the sum as

$$\mathbb{E}[\mathbf{X} \mid \mathbf{X} \geq 2] = \beta \sum_{t=1}^{\infty} (t+1)(1-p)^t = \beta \sum_{t=1}^{\infty} t(1-p)^t + \beta \sum_{t=1}^{\infty} (1-p)^t.$$

The first sum is the unconditional expectation $\mathbb{E}[\mathbf{X}]$, which equals $1/p$ (Theorem 19.7 on page 281). The second sum is the sum of the waiting time PDF probabilities which must equal 1. So,

$$\mathbb{E}[\mathbf{X} \mid \mathbf{X} \geq 2] \;=\; 1 + 1/p.$$

We can interpret the result above as follows. Given the first failure, the waiting process "restarts" and you expect to make $1/p$ more trials in addition to that first failure, for a total of $1 + 1/p$. □

Exercise 19.8

(a) Compute the expected sum of a pair of dice rolls given the sum is at least 4.

(b) You toss a fair coin 20 times. Compute the expected number of heads given:
 (i) The number of heads is even. (ii) The number of heads is at least 8.

(c) Let $\mathbf{X}$ be a uniform random variable on $\{5, 6, \ldots, 15\}$. Compute $\mathbb{E}[\mathbf{X}^2 \mid \mathbf{X} \text{ is prime}]$.

(d) Compute $\mathbb{E}[\text{number of trials to success} \mid k \text{ initial failures}]$ when the success probability is p.
 (For this reason, the exponential PDF is a memoryless distribution. ☺)

Exercise 19.9

At birth, a random person lives to an age $\mathbf{X}$. The PDF $P_{\mathbf{X}}$ is shown on the right (this "survival" data is from the US Social Security Administration). Kilam is 25 years old; Liamsi is 17. Show that Kilam expects to live to an older age than Liamsi (in general, the older you are, the older you expect to live till). You must show that:

$$\mathbb{E}[\mathbf{X} \mid \mathbf{X} \geq 25] > \mathbb{E}[\mathbf{X} \mid \mathbf{X} \geq 17].$$

(Assume the PDF is non-zero for ages 1-110.)

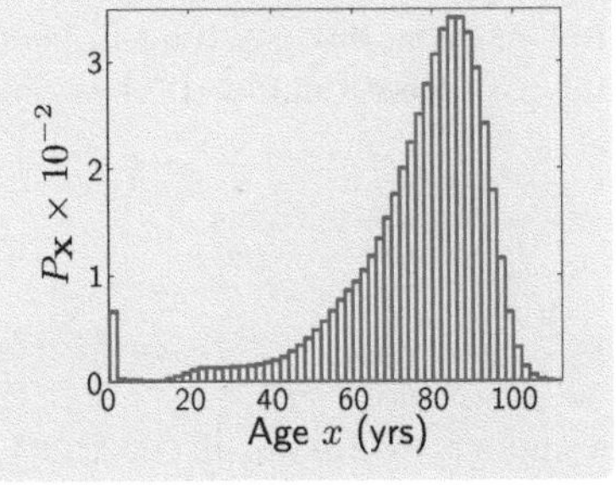

19.2.1 Law of Total Expectation

The law of total probability allows us to compute a probability by considering different cases for the outcome and using conditional probabilities. The law of total expectation is similar. One can compute an expectation by considering different cases and using conditional expectations. Master this simple but powerful tool.

Law of Total Expectation

$$\mathbb{E}[\mathbf{X}] = \mathbb{E}[\mathbf{X} \mid A] \times \mathbb{P}[A] + \mathbb{E}[\mathbf{X} \mid \overline{A}] \times \mathbb{P}[\overline{A}].$$

The law says compute conditional expectations for the two cases $\{A, \overline{A}\}$, weight by the probability of each case and add. You can use more than 2 cases provided exactly one case must occur (Problem 19.46). The law of total expectation follows from the law of total probability.

$$\begin{aligned}
\mathbb{E}[\mathbf{X}] &\overset{(a)}{=} \sum_x x \cdot \mathbb{P}[\mathbf{X} = x] && \text{expected value} \\
&\overset{(b)}{=} \sum_x x \cdot \big(\mathbb{P}[A]\,\mathbb{P}[\mathbf{X} = x \mid A] + \mathbb{P}[\overline{A}]\,\mathbb{P}[\mathbf{X} = x \mid \overline{A}]\big) && \text{total probability} \\
&\overset{(c)}{=} \mathbb{P}[A] \sum_x x \cdot \mathbb{P}[\mathbf{X} = x \mid A] + \mathbb{P}[\overline{A}] \sum_x x \cdot \mathbb{P}[\mathbf{X} = x \mid \overline{A}] && \text{rules for sums} \\
&\overset{(d)}{=} \mathbb{P}[A] \times \mathbb{E}[\mathbf{X} \mid A] + \mathbb{P}[\overline{A}] \times \mathbb{E}[\mathbf{X} \mid \overline{A}] && \text{conditional expectation}
\end{aligned}$$

Pop Quiz 19.10
Justify each of the steps (a) – (d) in the derivation above.

Total expectation helps because the conditional expectations can be easier to compute than the unconditional expectation. Now for some examples to demonstrate the awesome power of total expectation.

Example 19.11 (Average height in the US)**.** We begin with the example that got us started on conditional expectation. About 51% of the population is female. Females have average height 64"and males have average height 69". We can use the law of total expectation to compute the average height:

$$\begin{aligned}
\mathbb{E}[\text{height}] &= \mathbb{E}[\text{height} \mid \text{female}] \times \mathbb{P}[\text{female}] + \mathbb{E}[\text{height} \mid \text{male}] \times \mathbb{P}[\text{male}] \\
&= 0.51 \times 64" + 0.49 \times 69" \approx 66\tfrac{1}{2}".
\end{aligned}$$

□

Example 19.12 (Different types of coins)**.** A box has two fair coins and a biased two-headed coin. You pick a coin randomly and toss it n times. What is the expected number of heads? Let $\mathbf{X}$ be the number of heads, we want $\mathbb{E}[\mathbf{X}]$. We use total expectation with two cases: you either pick a fair coin or the biased coin. If the coin that is picked has probability p of heads, then $\mathbb{E}[\mathbf{X} \mid p] = np$.

$$\begin{aligned}
\mathbb{E}[\mathbf{X}] &= \underbrace{\mathbb{E}[\mathbf{X}|\text{fair}]}_{n/2} \times \underbrace{\mathbb{P}[\text{fair}]}_{2/3} + \underbrace{\mathbb{E}[\mathbf{X}|\text{biased}]}_{n} \times \underbrace{\mathbb{P}[\text{biased}]}_{1/3} \\
&= \frac{n}{2} \times \frac{2}{3} + n \times \frac{1}{3} = \frac{2}{3}n.
\end{aligned}$$

It's tempting to argue that $\mathbb{E}[p] = \frac{1}{2} \times \frac{2}{3} + 1 \times \frac{1}{3} = \frac{2}{3}$, so the expected number of heads is $n \times \mathbb{E}[p] = \frac{2}{3}n$. This works in this case, but is wrong in general. For instance, suppose you toss the coin until the first H. Let $\mathbf{Y}$ be the number of tosses made. If the coin has probability p of heads, then $\mathbb{E}[\mathbf{Y} \mid p] = 1/p$:

$$\begin{aligned}
\mathbb{E}[\mathbf{Y}] &= \underbrace{\mathbb{E}[\mathbf{Y}|\text{fair}]}_{2} \times \underbrace{\mathbb{P}[\text{fair}]}_{2/3} + \underbrace{\mathbb{E}[\mathbf{Y}|\text{biased}]}_{1} \times \underbrace{\mathbb{P}[\text{biased}]}_{1/3} \\
&= 2 \times \frac{2}{3} + 1 \times \frac{1}{3} = 1\frac{2}{3}.
\end{aligned}$$

You get the wrong answer if you use $1/\,\mathbb{E}\,[p] = 1\frac{1}{2}$. □

Example 19.13 (Toss a coin to determine number of dice). Toss a biased coin and if H roll a die or if T roll two dice. Let $\mathbf{X}$ be the sum of the dice rolled. As an exercise in masochism, find the PDF for $\mathbf{X}$ and from there compute $\mathbb{E}[\mathbf{X}]$. We get it much more quickly using the law of total expectation and two cases H or T:

$$\mathbb{E}[\mathbf{X}] = \mathbb{E}[\mathbf{X} \mid \text{H}] \times \mathbb{P}[\text{H}] + \mathbb{E}[\mathbf{X} \mid \text{T}] \times \mathbb{P}[\text{T}]$$

When the coin flip is H, you roll one die, so $\mathbb{E}[\mathbf{X}|\text{H}]$ is the expected roll of one die which is 3.5. Similarly when the coin flip is T, you roll two dice so $\mathbb{E}[\mathbf{X}|\text{T}] = 7$. Letting $p = \mathbb{P}[\text{H}]$,

$$\begin{aligned}\mathbb{E}[\mathbf{X}] &= 3.5p + 7(1-p) \\ &= 7 - 3.5p.\end{aligned}$$

□

Example 19.14 (Sum of 3 Dice Rolls). Let $\mathbf{X}$ be the sum of 3 fair dice. Let $\mathbf{X}_1$ be the first die and $\mathbf{X}_2$ the sum of the other two dice. Using total expectation with 6 cases for $\mathbf{X}_1$,

$$\begin{aligned}\mathbb{E}[\mathbf{X}] &= \mathbb{E}[\mathbf{X} \mid \mathbf{X}_1 = 1] \times \mathbb{P}[\mathbf{X}_1 = 1]\, \mathbb{E}\,[\mathbf{X} \mid \mathbf{X}_1 = 2] \times \mathbb{P}[\mathbf{X}_1 = 2] + \cdots + \mathbb{E}[\mathbf{X} \mid \mathbf{X}_1 = 6] \times \mathbb{P}[\mathbf{X}_1 = 6] \\ &= \mathbb{E}[\mathbf{X} \mid \mathbf{X}_1 = 1] \times \frac{1}{6}\, \mathbb{E}\,[\mathbf{X} \mid \mathbf{X}_1 = 2] \times \frac{1}{6} + \cdots + \mathbb{E}[\mathbf{X} \mid \mathbf{X}_1 = 6] \times \frac{1}{6}.\end{aligned}$$

We need the expected sum given the first roll is i. The values $\mathbf{X}$ can take are $i + x$, where $x \in \{2, \ldots, 12\}$ and $\mathbb{P}[i + x] = P_{\mathbf{X}_2}(x)$, the PDF for the sum of two dice. Therefore,

$$\begin{aligned}\mathbb{E}[\mathbf{X} \mid \mathbf{X}_1 = i] &= \sum_x (i + x) P_{\mathbf{X}_2}(x) \\ &= i \sum_x P_{\mathbf{X}_2}(x) + \sum_x x P_{\mathbf{X}_2}(x).\end{aligned}$$

The first sum is 1 because every PDF sums to 1. The second sum is 7 because it is just the expected sum of 2 dice rolls, which we computed in (19.1). Therefore $\mathbb{E}[\mathbf{X} \mid \mathbf{X}_1 = i] = i + 7$. Intuitively, the first die does not affect the expected outcome of the second two. We finally arrive at our result,

$$\mathbb{E}[\mathbf{X}] = \frac{1}{6} \times ((1+7) + (2+7) + \cdots + (6+7)) = 10\frac{1}{2}.$$

It is curious that the expected sum of 3 dice rolls is 3 times the expectation of a single roll. □

Example 19.15 (Waiting time). Let $\mathbf{X}$ be the waiting time to success with success probability p. On page 281 we computed $\mathbb{E}[\mathbf{X}]$ using an infinite sum. Let's use total expectation with two cases for the first trial.

We can represent the infinite outcome-tree on page 268 compactly as shown on the right. With probability p, you succeed and the process ends. With probability $1 - p$, you fail and the process "restarts" with you still waiting for your success, except you have used up a trial.

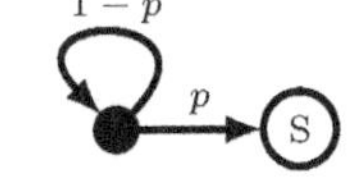

$$\begin{aligned}\mathbb{E}[\mathbf{X}] &= \underbrace{\mathbb{E}[\mathbf{X} \mid \text{S}]}_{1} \times \underbrace{\mathbb{P}[\text{S}]}_{p} + \mathbb{E}\,[\mathbf{X} \mid \text{F}] \times \underbrace{\mathbb{P}[\text{F}]}_{1-p} \\ &= 1 \times p + \mathbb{E}[\mathbf{X} \mid \text{F}] \times (1-p).\end{aligned}$$

In case of failure, the expected number of trials is 1, for the failure, plus an additional $\mathbb{E}[\mathbf{X}]$ because you effectively go back to the begining of the process, and your expected wait to a success is the unconditional expectation. Therefore, $\mathbb{E}[\mathbf{X} \mid \text{F}] = 1 + \mathbb{E}[\mathbf{X}]$ and

$$\begin{aligned}\mathbb{E}[\mathbf{X}] &= p + (1 + \mathbb{E}[\mathbf{X}])(1-p) \\ &= 1 + (1-p)\,\mathbb{E}\,[\mathbf{X}].\end{aligned}$$

Solving this equation for $\mathbb{E}[\mathbf{X}]$ gives $\mathbb{E}[\mathbf{X}] = 1/p$. We obtained this result earlier by summing an infinite series. The law of total expectation is easier and works well when the conditional expectations can be either computed easily or related to the unconditional expectation. You treat the required expectation as an unknown and at the end you have to solve an equation for that unknown. □

Example 19.16 (Waiting for two boys). How many children do you expect to have to get two boys? Let p be the probability of a boy and $\mathbf{X}$ the number of children. The process of getting two boys is shown on the right. With probability $1-p$ you initially fail, restarting the process. With probability p you get the first boy and now await the second boy for whom you expect to wait $1/p$ more trials.

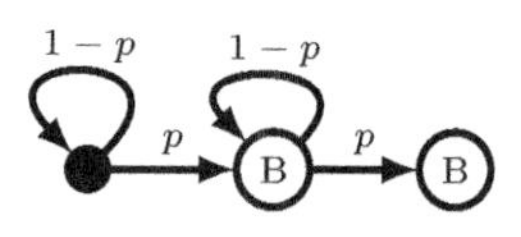

Using the law of total expectation with the two cases boy or girl for the first child,

$$\begin{aligned}\mathbb{E}[\mathbf{X}] &= \mathbb{E}[\mathbf{X} \mid \mathrm{B}] \times \underbrace{\mathbb{P}[\mathrm{B}]}_{p} + \underbrace{\mathbb{E}[\mathbf{X} \mid \mathrm{G}]}_{1+\mathbb{E}[\mathbf{X}]} \times \underbrace{\mathbb{P}[\mathrm{G}]}_{1-p} \\ &= \mathbb{E}[\mathbf{X} \mid \mathrm{B}] \times p + (1+\mathbb{E}[\mathbf{X}]) \times (1-p).\end{aligned}$$

We used $\mathbb{E}[\mathbf{X} \mid \mathrm{G}] = 1 + \mathbb{E}[\mathbf{X}]$ because the process restarts if the first child is a girl. This means you already had one try, and you now expect to wait just as long as you did from the very beginning, which is $\mathbb{E}[\mathbf{X}]$. If the first child is a boy, then the expected number of children is 1 (the boy) plus however long you expect to wait for the next boy, which is $1/p$. That is, $\mathbb{E}[\mathbf{X} \mid \mathrm{B}] = 1 + 1/p$. Therefore,

$$\begin{aligned}\mathbb{E}[\mathbf{X}] &= (1+1/p) \times p + (1+\mathbb{E}[\mathbf{X}]) \times (1-p) \\ &= 2 + (1-p)\,\mathbb{E}\,[\mathbf{X}].\end{aligned}$$

Solving this equation for $\mathbb{E}[\mathbf{X}]$ gives $\mathbb{E}[\mathbf{X}] = 2/p$. Curious. The expected wait for two boys is twice that for one boy. In Exercise 19.7(d), you computed this expectation from the PDF using an infinite sum. Here, we used total expectation which is quick and easy. □

Exercise 19.11

Use the law of total expectation to compute the expected value of $\mathbf{X}$ in each case.

(a) A jar has m fair coins and k biased two-headed coins. Pick a random coin.
   (i) Flip the coin n times and let $\mathbf{X}$ be the number of heads.
   (ii) Flip the coin until you get a H and let $\mathbf{X}$ be the number of flips.
(b) Boys and girls are equally likely and $\mathbf{X}$ is the number of children until you get a boy and a girl.
(c) Girls are twice as likely as boys and $\mathbf{X}$ is the number of children until you get a boy and a girl.
(d) $\mathbf{X}$ is the sum of 4 fair dice.
(e) $\mathbf{X}$ is the sum of 2 fair dice if a coin flips H or the sum of 3 fair dice if the flip is T.
(f) $\mathbf{X}$ is the square of the waiting time to success with success probability p.

Exercise 19.12 [Expected runtime of Quicksort]

Quicksort is a popular sorting algorithm which sorts a list recursively. Given the list $8,2,1,4,9,3,5,7,6$, randomly pick a "pivot" element, for example 4 and partition the elements into those smaller than the pivot on the left and those larger on the right:

$$[8,2,1,4,9,3,5,7,6] \to [2,1,3,4,8,9,5,7,6].$$

Now recursively sort the left and the right parts. Assume it takes $n+1$ time steps to partition a list with n elements into the left and right part, no matter which pivot is picked. Compute the expected runtime of Quicksort on a list of n distinct numbers.

(a) Let T_n be the expected runtime on a list of n numbers, with $T_1 = 1$. Show that

$$T_n = n + 1 + \frac{2}{n}\sum_{i=1}^{n-1} T_i \qquad \text{for } i > 1.$$

(b) Show that $T_2 = 4$ and for $n > 2$, $T_n = \left(1 + \frac{1}{n}\right) T_{n-1} + 2$.
(c) **[Hard]** Prove that $T_n \le 2H_n e^{H_n}$, where H_n is the nth Harmonic number.
   (Since $H_n \approx \ln n$, the expected runtime of Quicksort is about $2n \ln n$.)

19.3 Problems

Problem 19.1. Which best describes the expected value of a random variable $\mathbf{X}$?
(a) It is the typical observed value of $\mathbf{X}$ in an experiment.
(b) It is the most likely value of $\mathbf{X}$ to be observed in an experiment.
(c) It is just one of the possible values of $\mathbf{X}$ that can be observed in an experiment.
(d) None of the above. If so, how do you explain the expected value to a lay-person?

Problem 19.2. Give examples of a random variable $\mathbf{X}$ (its PDF) with the following properties.
(a) $\mathbb{E}[\mathbf{X}] > 1$ but $\mathbb{P}[\mathbf{X} > 1] \approx 0$. (b) $\mathbb{E}[\mathbf{X}] = 1$ but $\mathbb{P}[\mathbf{X} = 1] = 0$.

Problem 19.3. Suppose $\mathbb{E}[\mathbf{X}] = \mu$. Show that $\mathbb{P}[\mathbf{X} \geq \mu] > 0$ and therefore, there must be an outcome ω for which $\mathbf{X}(\omega) \geq \mu$. Similarly, there must be an outcome ω for which $\mathbf{X}(\omega) \leq \mu$.

Problem 19.4. You roll a loaded 6-sided die (values 1,. . . ,6). Each even roll is twice as likely as each odd roll. What is the expected value of a single roll of this loaded die?

Problem 19.5. Let $\mathbf{X}$ and $\mathbf{Y}$ be two independent dice rolls. Define $\mathbf{Z} = \mathbf{X} + 2\mathbf{Y}$. Give the PDF of $\mathbf{Z}$ and $\mathbb{E}[\mathbf{Z}]$.

Problem 19.6. Compute the expected value of a random variable having each PDF in Problem 18.4.

Problem 19.7. Compute the expected value for each PDF in Figure 18.4 on page 268.

Problem 19.8. Roll a pair of fair dice until you get a sum of 6. What is the expected number of rolls?

Problem 19.9. Roll a die until you get a number greater than 1. Let $\mathbf{X}$ be the final roll.
(a) How many rolls do you expect to make? (b) What is $\mathbb{E}[\mathbf{X}]$?

Problem 19.10. Flip a fair coin. If it is H you pay \$10. If it is T, flip again: if the second flip is H you pay \$10, and if T you get \$40. Compute the expected gain. How much would you pay to play this game?

Problem 19.11. An artwork's value $\mathbf{X}$ is uniformly distributed on $\{\$100, \$101, \ldots, \$200\}$. If you bid b, you get the artwork if $b \geq \mathbf{X}$, and its value value doubles, so your profit is $2\mathbf{X} - b$. What bid maximizes your expected profit?

Problem 19.12. A game costs $\$x$ to play. You toss 4 fair coins. If you get more heads than tails, you win $\$10 + x$ for a profit of \$10. Otherwise, you lose and get nothing back, so your loss is $\$x$. What is your expected profit?

Problem 19.13. A die is rolled 3 times. After each roll, you may accept the value rolled as payoff and leave, or continue to the next roll. How much would you pay to play this game?

Problem 19.14. In a gamble, your payoff is the maximum of three fair dice rolls. How much would you pay to play?

Problem 19.15. In a dice game, if you roll 1, the game stops and you win \$1. For any other roll, you must decide whether to stop and win the value rolled, or continue rolling. Your strategy is to stop if the roll is τ or larger (you may choose $\tau \in \{2, \ldots, 6\}$). How much will you pay to play? (See also Problem 18.14.)

Problem 19.16. A drive fails on year t with probability $f(t) = 2^{-t}$. The hard-drive survived to year 2. What is the expected lifetime of the drive? What if $f(t) = t^{-1}/H_{10}$ for $t \in \{1, \ldots, 10\}$? (H_{10} is the 10th Harmonic number.)

Problem 19.17. 10% of drives are defective. A test for identifying defective drives has accuracy 90%. You tested 1000 drives and 150 failed the test. What is the expected number of defective drives among the 1000?

Problem 19.18. Children are independent and both sexes are equally likely. A randomly selected child in a family is male. Do you expect him to have an equal number of brothers and sisters?

Problem 19.19. A royal family has children until it has a boy or three children, whichever comes first. Children are independent and each sex is equally likely. Find the expected number of princes and the expected number of princesses.

Problem 19.20. A keychain has 10 similar keys. You are fumbling in the dark trying each key in a random order to open your appartment door . What is the expected number of keys you try before you unlock the door?

Problem 19.21. You randomly guess every answer on a multiple choice exam with 50 questions and 4 possible answers per question. What is the expected number of questions you answer correctly?

Problem 19.22. What is the expected number of rolls of a 6-sided die until you roll a 6?

Problem 19.23. How many children do you expect to sample until you find someone born on December 25th?

Problem 19.24. You may invest in a particular project. There is a 35% chance to lose $30,000, a 40% chance to break even, and a 25% chance to make $55,000. Based solely on this information, what should you do?

Problem 19.25. A bag has 2 red and 3 blue balls. You randomly pick balls without replacement. You win $1 for each red ball and lose $1 for each blue ball. You may stop picking at any time. How much would you pay to play?

Problem 19.26. In a race with 3 horses, horse i wins with probability $\frac{i}{6}$. You start with $1 and bet b_i on horse i. If horse i wins, you get back $b_i o_i$. (o_i is the payoff-odds for horse i.)

(a) If horse i wins, show that your wealth increases by $b_i o_i - \sum_{i=1}^{3} b_i$.

(b) If $(o_1, o_2, o_3) = (5, 4, 2)$, show how to guarantee a profit. In general, show this if $\sum_i 1/o_i < 1$.

(c) Let $(o_1, o_2, o_3) = (4, \frac{7}{2}, 2)$. How will you place bets to maximize the expected profit.

(d) For (c), how will you place bets to maximize the expected return, where return $= \ln(\text{profit})$.

Problem 19.27. In a lottery, for $1 you pick any 5 different numbers from {1,. . . ,75}. Now 5 different numbers are randomly picked from {1,. . . ,75}. If your numbers match those drawn in any order, you win $15,000,000. Compute the probability to win and your expected winnings.

Problem 19.28. A lottery runs every month. For $1, you pick an 8-digit number, e.g. 03312014. The lottery takes 10% of the $1 and the remainder goes into the jackpot. The lottery picks a random 8-digit string and all matching tickets evenly split the jackpot. The jackpot grows until someone wins. Every month, 100 million people play the lottery.

(a) Assume everyone bets a random 8-digit number.

  (i) What is your expected winning on the first month of the lottery?

  (ii) Nobody wins on the first month. What is your expected winning on the second month?

  (iii) After how many months of unclaimed jackpot is it "profitable" to play the lottery?

(b) Assume everyone bets a valid date (birthday, anniversary, etc.) `mmddyyyy`, e.g. 03312014.

  (i) What strategy will you use to pick a number and why?

  (ii) What is your expected winning on the first month of the lottery?

  (iii) Nobody wins on the first month. What is your expected winning on the second month?

  (iv) After how many months of unclaimed jackpot is it "profitable" to play the lottery?

Problem 19.29. A drunk starts at 0 and takes independent steps left with probability $1/3$ and right with probability $2/3$. What is the expected position of the drunk after 100 steps?

Problem 19.30. You bet $1 on a fair coin toss: if H, you double your money; if T, you lose your bet. If you lose, you double your bet and play again. Compute your expected profit if:

(a) You continue betting until you win or have made n coin tosses.

(b) You continue betting until you win with no limit on the number of tosses.

Problem 19.31. You got all heads in 10 flips of a random coin from a jar with 9 fair coins and 1 two-headed coin. Compute the expected number of heads in another 100 flips of the same coin.

Problem 19.32. Toss 9 fair coins. Toss another 9 coins if and only if you got more heads than tails. Let $\mathbf{X}$ be the total number of heads you toss. What is $\mathbb{E}[\mathbf{X}]$?

Problem 19.33. Compute $\mathbb{E}$[number of 1s] in the BITWISE-OR of two 10-bit sequences of independent random bits (1/0 are T/F). E.g.,0001110010 BITWISE-OR 1000111000 = 1001111010).

Problem 19.34. A big hospital delivers 100 babies per day and a small hospital delivers 20 babies per day. A day is unusual if more than 60% or more of births are one sex. In a year, what is the expected number of unusual days in a big hospital versus a small hospital?

Problem 19.35. A bag has 3 white and 1 black ball and another 1 white and 3 black balls. Pick a random bag (probability $1/2$ for each bag) and a random ball from that bag (probability $1/4$ for each ball). The ball is white. Let $\mathbf{X}$ be the number of white balls in the other bag. What is $\mathbb{E}[\mathbf{X}]$? (The **information** that the ball is white is crucial.)

Problem 19.36. It rains 1 in 7 days and is cloudy 1 in 5 days. Assume a year has 366 days.

(a) What is the expected number of rainy days in a year?

(b) On a year with 100 cloudy days, what is the expected number of rainy days?

(c) On a year with at least 50 cloudy days, what is the expected number of rainy days?

Problem 19.37. A box has 6 fair coins and 4 two-headed coins. You picked a coin randomly and made 10 independent flips. Let $\mathbf{X}$ be the number of heads you get. What is $\mathbb{E}[\mathbf{X}]$?

Problem 19.38. A box has 1024 fair and 1 two-headed coin. You pick a coin randomly, make 10 flips and get all H.
(a) You flip the same coin you picked 100 times. What is the expected number of H?
(b) You flip the same coin you picked unitl you get H. What is the expected number of flips you make?

Problem 19.39. Pick random numbers from $\{1,\ldots,100\}$ with replacement until their sum exceeds 100. How many numbers do you expect to pick. Can you generalize to numbers from $\{1,\ldots,n\}$ until the sum exceeds n?

Problem 19.40. A password must be a permutation of $\{0,1,\ldots,9\}$. Your birthday is 12/24 (Dec. 24), so for security reasons, your password can't contain the substrings 12, 24 (e.g., 0213456789 is ok, but none of {0123456789, 0132456789, 987654321, 0113456789, 0312456789} are ok).
(a) How many possible passwords can you set?
(b) If you pick passwords using independent random permutations, with each permutation being equally likely, what is the expected number of tries before you get an acceptable password.
(c) If you pick passwords using independent random 10-digit strings, with each string being equally likely, what is the expected number of tries before you get an acceptable password.
(d) You generated your password as in (b). A hacker can test 100,000 passwords per second. What is the expected time for a hacker to get into your account if:
 (i) The hacker randomly generates a permutation to test, each time independently.
 (ii) The hacker randomly generates the digits of a 10-digit string to test each time.
 (iii) The hacker picks a random ordering of all valid passwords (permutations without 12 and 24) and systematically tries each one from the first to the last in this ordering.
 (iv) The hacker picks a random ordering of all passwords (permutations) and systematically tries each one from the first to the last in this ordering.
 (v) The hacker picks a fixed but random ordering of all 10-digit strings and systematically tries each one from the first to the last in this ordering.

Problem 19.41. For two dice rolls $\mathbf{D}_1$ and $\mathbf{D}_2$, let $\mathbf{X}=\mathbf{D}_1+\mathbf{D}_2$ and $\mathbf{Y}=\mathbf{D}_1-\mathbf{D}_2$.
(a) Show that $\mathbb{E}[\mathbf{XY}]=\mathbb{E}[\mathbf{X}]\,\mathbb{E}[\mathbf{Y}]$. (b) Are $\mathbf{X}$ and $\mathbf{Y}$ independent?

Problem 19.42 (Moment Generating Function). Let $\mathbf{X}$ be the waiting time to success with success-probability p. Let $\mathbf{Z}=e^{s\mathbf{X}}$ and let $M(s)=\mathbb{E}[\mathbf{Z}]=\mathbb{E}[e^{s\mathbf{X}}]$.
(a) Show that $M(s)=p/(e^{-s}-1+p)$ within a certain range of s. What is that range for s?
(b) Let $M^{(k)}(s)=\frac{d^k}{ds^k}M(s)$. Show that $\mathbb{E}[\mathbf{X}^k]=M^{(k)}(0)$. $\mathbb{E}[\mathbf{X}^k]$ is the kth moment of $\mathbf{X}$ The derivatives of $M(s)$ at $s=0$ give the moments of $\mathbf{X}$. For this reason, $M(s)$ is called the moment generating function of $\mathbf{X}$.)
(c) Use the moment generating function to compute $\mathbb{E}[\mathbf{X}]$, $\mathbb{E}[\mathbf{X}^2]$ and $\mathbb{E}[\mathbf{X}^3]$.
(d) Let $\mathbf{X}$ and $\mathbf{Y}$ be independent random variables. Let $\mathbf{Z}=\mathbf{X}+\mathbf{Y}$ be the sum. Show that the moment generating function for $\mathbf{Z}$, when it exists, is the product of the moment generating functions for $\mathbf{X}$ and $\mathbf{Y}$, when they exist.

Problem 19.43. A random variable $\mathbf{X}$ takes values in $\{0,1,2,\ldots\}$. Let $G_\mathbf{X}(x)=\mathbb{P}[\mathbf{X}>x]$.
(a) Show that $G_\mathbf{X}(x)=1-F_\mathbf{X}(x)$. ($F_\mathbf{X}$ is the CDF) (b) Show that $\mathbb{E}[\mathbf{X}]=\sum_{x=0}^{\infty}G_\mathbf{X}(x)$.

Problem 19.44. A random variable $\mathbf{X}$ takes values in $\{0,1,\ldots,n\}$ and has CDF $F_\mathbf{X}$.
(a) Show that $\mathbb{E}[\mathbf{X}]=(n+1)-\sum_{x=0}^{n}F_\mathbf{X}(x)$.
(b) Show that this result is consistent with Problem 19.43(b).
(c) What happens here when $n\to\infty$? Why does Problem 19.43(b) still work?

Problem 19.45. Prove the following properties of expectations.
(a) (i) $\mathbf{X}\ge t\to\mathbb{E}[\mathbf{X}]\ge t$. (ii) $\mathbb{E}[\mathbf{X}]\ge t\to\mathbb{P}[\mathbf{X}\ge t]>0$. (iii) $\mathbf{X}\ge\mathbf{Y}\to\mathbb{E}[\mathbf{X}]\ge\mathbb{E}[\mathbf{Y}]$.
(b) If $a\le\mathbf{X}\le A$ then $a\,\mathbb{E}[\mathbf{Y}]\le\mathbb{E}[\mathbf{XY}]\le A\,\mathbb{E}[\mathbf{Y}]$ for any random variable $\mathbf{Y}$.
(c) **[Markov Inequality]** Suppose $\mathbf{X}$ is non-negative, $\mathbf{X}\ge 0$. Then, $\mathbb{E}[\mathbf{X}]\ge t\,\mathbb{P}[\mathbf{X}\ge t]$ for any $t\ge 0$.
 (i) Consider a random variable $\mathbf{Y}=\begin{cases}0 & \mathbf{X}<t;\\ t & \mathbf{X}\ge t.\end{cases}$ Show that $\mathbf{X}\ge\mathbf{Y}$ and compute $\mathbb{E}[\mathbf{Y}]$.
 (ii) Prove Markov's Inequality using part (a)(iii).

Problem 19.46 (Total Expectation with Many Cases). Suppose $C_1, \ldots, C_k$ are events that partition Ω. This means no two events can co-occur and at least one event must occur, $\cup_{i=1}^{k} C_i = \Omega$ and $C_i \cap C_j = \varnothing$. Prove:

$$\mathbb{E}[A] = \sum_{i=1}^{k} \mathbb{E}[A \mid C_i] \cdot \mathbb{P}[C_i] = \mathbb{E}[A \mid C_1] \cdot \mathbb{P}[C_1] + \cdots + \mathbb{E}[A \mid C_k] \cdot \mathbb{P}[C_k].$$

Problem 19.47 (Expected value from joint PDF). Let $\mathbf{Z} = f(\mathbf{X}, \mathbf{Y})$ be a function defined using random variables $(\mathbf{X}, \mathbf{Y})$ with joint PDF $P_{\mathbf{XY}}(x, y)$. The expectated value is defined from the probability space by

$$\mathbb{E}[\mathbf{Z}] = \sum_{\omega \in \Omega} Z(w) \cdot P(\omega) = \sum_{\omega \in \Omega} f(\mathbf{X}(\omega), \mathbf{Y}(\omega)) \cdot P(\omega).$$

Show that the expected value can be computed from the joint-PDF using a sum over all possible x and y:

$$\mathbb{E}[\mathbf{Z}] = \sum_{x \in \mathbf{X}(\Omega)} \sum_{y \in \mathbf{Y}(\Omega)} f(x, y) \cdot P_{\mathbf{XY}}(x, y).$$

Problem 19.48. Let $\mathbf{X}$ and $\mathbf{Y}$ have joint distribution $P_{\mathbf{XY}}(x, y)$. Let $\mathbf{Z} = f(\mathbf{X}, \mathbf{Y})$. Prove that

$$\mathbb{E}[\mathbf{Z}] = \sum_{x \in \mathbf{X}(\Omega)} P_{\mathbf{X}}(x) \sum_{y \in \mathbf{Y}(\Omega)} P_{\mathbf{Y}}(y \mid \mathbf{X} = x) f(x, y) = \sum_{x \in \mathbf{X}(\Omega)} P_{\mathbf{X}}(x)\, \mathbb{E}_{\mathbf{Y}}\left[f(x, \mathbf{Y}) \mid \mathbf{X} = x\right].$$

Problem 19.49 (Expected Hitting Time). Compute the expected number of steps for this scenario. A drunk leaves the bar at position 1, and takes independent steps: left (L) with probability 2/3 or right (R) with probability 1/3. The drunk stops if he reaches home (at position 0) or the lockup (at position 3).
(Home and the lockup are "barriers". The time to reach a barrier is called the hitting time.)

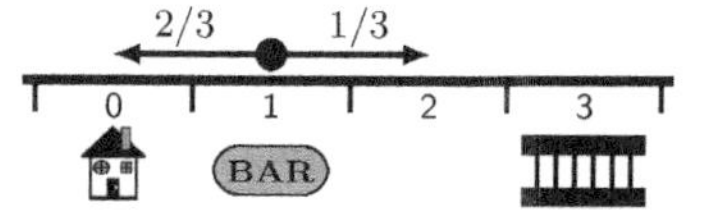

Problem 19.50. In Problem 19.49, compute the expected number of steps conditioned on the drunk making it home (conditional expectation).

Problem 19.51. Generalize the expected hitting time in Problem 19.49 to p being the probability to move left and L the position of the lockup. Let E_k be the expected number of steps when starting at position k. Let $\beta = p/(1-p)$.

(a) What are E_0 and E_L? Show that for $0 < k < L$, $E_k = 1 + pE_{k-1} + (1-p)E_{k+1}$.

(b) Use (a) to show: $E_k = \dfrac{\beta+1}{\beta-1}\left(k - L\dfrac{\beta^k - 1}{\beta^L - 1}\right)$. *[Hint:* $\sum_{i=0}^{n} i\beta^i = (n\beta^{n+1} - (n+1)\beta^{n+1} + \beta)/(\beta-1)^2$.*]*

Problem 19.52. A gambler walks into a casino with \$50 and plays roulette. The gambler bets \$1 on red (probability 18/36 to win) and keeps betting until either going bankrupt or doubling his money. If it takes about 1 minute to play one game of roulette, how many hours of entertainment does the gampler expect to have. *[Hint: Problem 19.51.]*

Problem 19.53 (Least-Squares Fit). You summarize a random variable $\mathbf{X}$ using a single number h. The squared error h makes in approximating $\mathbf{X}$ is $(h - \mathbf{X})^2$. Define the quality of h by its expected error, err$(h) = \mathbb{E}[(h - \mathbf{X})^2]$.

(a) Show that err$(h) = h^2 - 2h\,\mathbb{E}[\mathbf{X}] + \mathbb{E}[\mathbf{X}^2]$.

(b) Show that $h^* = \mathbb{E}[\mathbf{X}]$ is optimal, i.e. minimizes err(h), and that h^* has expected squared error $\mathbb{E}[\mathbf{X}^2] - \mathbb{E}[\mathbf{X}]^2$.

(This is a famous result: $\mathbb{E}[\mathbf{X}]$ is the estimator of $\mathbf{X}$ with minimum expected squared error.)

Problem 19.54. The expected value summarizes a random variable $\mathbf{X}$. Another popular summary of $\mathbf{X}$ is a median, which is a "midpoint" of the PDF. We say a midpoint because the median may not be unique. The median is any value m for which at least half of the probability of $\mathbf{X}$ is at or below m and at least half is at or above m,

$$\mathbb{P}[\mathbf{X} \leq m] \geq 1/2 \qquad \text{and} \qquad \mathbb{P}[\mathbf{X} \geq m] \geq 1/2.$$

x	0	1	2	3
$P_{\mathbf{X}}(x)$	1/8	3/8	1/4	1/4

(a) Give all the medians for a random variable with PDF on the right.

(b) Give all medians of the waiting time with success probability 1/5.

(c) Give all medians of a Binomial with 20 trials and success probability 1/5

Problem 19.55 (Least-Absolute-Error Fit). You wish to summarize random variable $\mathbf{X}$ with PDF $P_{\mathbf{X}}$ using a number h, as in Problem 19.53. The error h makes in approximating $\mathbf{X}$ is the absolute error $|h - \mathbf{X}|$. The quality of h is the expected absolute error, err$(h) = \mathbb{E}[|h - \mathbf{X}|]$. Show that to minimize err(h) you should pick h as a median of $\mathbf{X}$. (This is a famous result: the least-absolute-error or robust regression estimator of $\mathbf{X}$ is a median of $\mathbf{X}$.)

Problem 19.56. Toss two coins. Roll 6 dice for each H tossed. Compute the expected number of sixes.

Problem 19.57. A Martian couple has children until they have 2 males (sexes of children are independent). Compute the expected number of children the couple will have if, on Mars, males are:
(a) Half as likely as females. (b) Just as likely as females. (c) Twice as likely as females.

Problem 19.58. A Martian couple has children until they have 2 males *in a row* (sexes of children are independent). Compute the expected number of children the couple will have if, on Mars, males are:
(a) Half as likely as females. (b) Just as likely as females. (c) Twice as likely as females.

Problem 19.59. A team is equally likely to win or lose its first game. In each following game, the previous result is twice as likely as the opposite result. What is the expected number of games played to get two wins.

Problem 19.60.(Hard) Couples have children (at least 1) until they get an equal number of boys and girls (balance). Let $\mathbf{X}$ be the number of children a couple has. Use these steps to compute $\mathbb{E}[\mathbf{X}]$:
(a) Show that $\mathbb{P}[\mathbf{X} > k+1] = 2^{-k}\binom{k}{k/2}$ for k even and $\mathbb{P}[\mathbf{X} > k+1] = 2^{-k}\binom{k}{(k-1)/2}$ for k odd.
(b) Show that $4^k/\sqrt{4k} \le \binom{2k}{k} \le 4^k/\sqrt{3k+1}$ and use Problem 19.43 to show that $\mathbb{E}[\mathbf{X}] = \infty$.
(c) Compute $\mathbb{E}[\mathbf{X}]$ if there is a cap of N on the number of children?

Problem 19.61 (Derivatives and Sums). Differentiating "under" the summation is a useful technique for computing sums, which is important because expectations involve sums.
(a) Show that $a\frac{\partial}{\partial a}\sum_{k=0}^{n}\binom{n}{k}a^k b^{n-k} = \sum_{k=0}^{n} k\cdot\binom{n}{k}a^k b^{n-k}$.
(i) Show that $\sum_{k=0}^{n} k\cdot\binom{n}{k}a^k b^{n-k} = na(a+b)^{n-1}$.
(ii) Use a similar approach to show that $\sum_{k=0}^{n} k^2\cdot\binom{n}{k}a^k b^{n-k} = (nab+n^2a^2)(a+b)^{n-2}$.
(b) Show that $a\frac{\partial}{\partial a}\sum_{k=0}^{n} a^k = \sum_{k=0}^{n} ka^k$.
(i) Show that $\sum_{k=0}^{n} ka^k = \dfrac{a+na^{n+2}-(n+1)a^{n+1}}{(1-a)^2}$.
(ii) Use a similar approach to show that

$$\sum_{k=0}^{n} k^2a^k = \frac{a(a+1)-(n+1)^2a^{n+1}+(2n^2+2n-1)a^{n+2}-n^2a^{n+3}}{(1-a)^3}.$$

(iii) For $|a|<1$, prove the infinite sums $\sum_{k=0}^{\infty} ka^k = \dfrac{a}{(1-a)^2}$ and $\sum_{k=0}^{\infty} k^2a^k = \dfrac{a(a+1)}{(1-a)^3}$.

Problem 19.62. Let $\mathbf{X}$ be a Binomial on n trials with success probability p.
(a) Use Problem 19.61(a)(ii) to show that $\mathbb{E}[\mathbf{X}^2] = np(1-p)+n^2p^2$.
(b) Use Exercise 19.6(b) on page 281 and (a) to show $\mathbb{E}[\mathbf{X}^2-\mathbf{X}] = \mathbb{E}[\mathbf{X}^2]-\mathbb{E}[\mathbf{X}]$.

Problem 19.63. Let $\mathbf{X}$ be the waiting time with success probability p. Compute $\mathbb{E}[\mathbf{X}^2]$ in two ways:
(a) Use the PDF of $\mathbf{X}$ (infinite sum plus Problem 19.61(b)(iii)). (b) Use the Law of Total Expectation.

Problem 19.64 (Expected Wait to r Successes). Let $\mathbf{X}$ be the waiting time for r successes with success probability p. Compute $\mathbb{E}[\mathbf{X}]$. Recall the PDF of $\mathbf{X}$ is (Problem 18.73)

$$P_{\mathbf{X}}(t) = \binom{t-1}{r-1}p^r(1-p)^{t-r}.$$

(a) Show that $\mathbb{E}[\mathbf{X}] = \sum_{t=r}^{\infty} t\cdot\binom{t-1}{r-1}\beta^r(1-p)^t = r\beta^r\sum_{t=r}^{\infty}\binom{t}{r}(1-p)^t$, where $\beta = p/(1-p)$.
(b) Show the combinatorial identity $\sum_{i=0}^{\infty}\binom{r+i}{r}\alpha^i = 1/(1-\alpha)^{r+1}$.
(i) Show that $\binom{r+i}{r}$ is the coefficient of α^i in the product of the r+1 terms:

$$(1+\alpha+\alpha^2+\cdots)(1+\alpha+\alpha^2+\cdots)\cdots(1+\alpha+\alpha^2+\cdots).$$

(ii) Show that the product is equal to $1/(1-\alpha)^{r+1}$.
(iii) Use (i) and (ii) to prove the combinatorial identity.
(c) Use the combinatorial identity to evaluate the summation and show $\mathbb{E}[\mathbf{X}] = r/p$.

Problem 19.65 (Stock-Trading). A stock has price \$1000. Every day it randomly (probability $1/2$) goes up or down by \$1. You will trade this stock using a trading strategy for 100 days.

(a) A simple "buy and hold" strategy is to buy the stock on day 0 and sell it on the 100th day.
(i) What is the expected profit? (ii) What is the probability that the profit is positive.

(b) Another strategy buys the stock if the price is \$1000. If the stock reaches \$1001, sell and wait (if the price comes back down to \$1000, buy again and repeat). On the 100th day, sell any stock owned at the current price.
(i) What is the expected profit? (ii) What is the probability that the profit is positive. Verify with Monte Carlo.

Problem 19.66 (Game Theory). A lion can prowl the plain or water-hole. An impala can graze the plain or drink at the water-hole. If both are at the water, the lion (very happy) drinks water and eats the impala (very sad). If both are on the plain, the lion (happy) eats the impala (very sad). If the lion is on the plain, and the impala at the water, the impala (happy) drinks and the lion (very unhappy) has nothing. If the lion is at the water and the impala on the plain, the impala (happy) eats and the lion drinks.

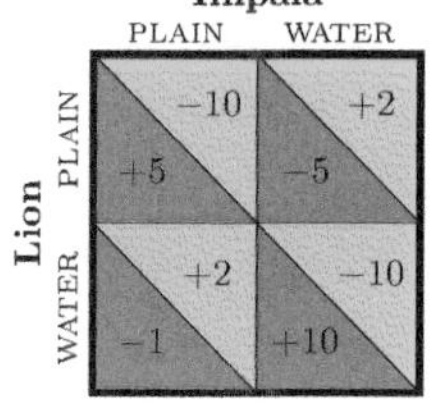

Depending on who does what, the payoffs to each animal are summarized in the payoff-matrix to the right. Each box is a pair of actions, one for the lion and one for the impala. The payoffs to the lion are in red and the impala's payoffs are in green. For example, in the PLAIN-PLAIN box (both on the plain), the lion's payoff is $+5$ and the impala's payoff is -10.

The impala is on the plain with probability p. The lion is on the plain with probability q. The animals may change their probabilities and we assume that both animals know p and q.

(a) The impala picks an action randomly, $p = 1/2$. The lion chooses q to maximize his expected payoff. What will the expected payoffs be for lion and impala? Can the impala do better, knowing the lions choice of q?

(b) The impala assumes the lion observes p and maximizes his (the lion's) expected payoff. Is there a value p^* for which the lion is indifferent between PLAIN and WATER?

(c) Similarly, the lion assumes the impala observes q and maximizes his (the impala's) expected payoff. Is there a value q^* for which the impala is indifferent between PLAIN and WATER?

(d) The impala and lion choose p^* and q^* respectively. Can either animal increase their expected payoff by unilaterally changing their probability?

The pair (p^*, q^*) is a Nash equilibrium from which neither animal gains by deviating. The Nobel prize winner John Nash proved that such equilibria always exist.

Problem 19.67. J. B. S. Haldane, after a back of the envelope calculation, pronounced "I would gladly give up my life for two brothers or eight cousins." Justify this statement using the following simple model for genetics. There are two types of a gene for an important trait: the rare (and precious) type A occuring with probability x and the common type a occuring with probability $1 - x$. Each person has two copies of the gene. When two people mate to produce a child, one copy of the gene from each parent is randomly passed on to the child. For example, if the parents have genes (mom:Aa, dad:Aa), then the child will be AA with probability $1/4$, Aa with probability $1/2$ and aa with probability $1/4$. You have the precious type A (so your genes are either AA or Aa).

(a) Compute $\mathbb{P}$[you are AA or Aa | your parents are (AA, AA)]. Repeat for your parents being (AA, Aa), (Aa, Aa), (AA, aa), (Aa, aa), (aa, aa).

(b) Compute $\mathbb{P}$[your parents are (AA, AA) | you are AA or Aa]. Repeat for your parents being (AA, Aa), (Aa, Aa), (AA, aa), (Aa, aa), (aa, aa).

(c) Show that the chances your sibling is AA or Aa if you are is $(1 + \frac{1}{4}x(1-x))/(2-x)$. As $x \to 0$ (A is rare), how many siblings would you give your life for, if the expected number of people with the A-gene mustn't decrease?

(d) By a similar analysis, show that if you have an A-gene, then your cousin has an A-gene with probability $(1+x(9 - 9x + 15x^2 - 20x^3 + 8x^5))/(8 - 4x)$, which approaches $1/8$ as $x \to 0$.

Problem 19.68. You are randomly presented one of two identical envelopes. One envelope contains twice as much money as the other. You are given the option to switch envelopes. You reason as follows:

1: My current envelope contains an amount A. The other envelope has $B = A/$ or $B = 2A$.
2: Each possibility has probability $1/2$ since I was given a random envelope, so

$$\mathbb{E}[B] = \tfrac{1}{2} \times (A/2) + \tfrac{1}{2} \times (2A) = 5A/4.$$

3: The other envelope has a higher expected value than my current amount A, so I switch.
4: I am back in the same situation as step 1, and end up switching forever. ☹

Explain what is wrong with the reasoning above and resolve the paradox.

"Data! Data! Data!" he cried, impatiently. "I can't make bricks without clay."
– **Sherlock Holmes**

Learn everything you can, anytime you can, from anyone you can; there will always come a time when you will be grateful you did. – **Sarah Caldwell**

Chapter 20

Expected Value: Sums and Other Tools

1: Linearity of expectation. Iterated expectation. Build-up expectation.
2: Sums of indicator random variables.

20.1 Linearity

Two lottery tickets for different lotteries pay off \$1 on average. It stands to reason that both will payoff \$1+\$1 on average. What if both tickets are for the same lottery? It looks complicated: when one ticket wins, the other loses, etc. Not so. You still expect to win the simple sum, \$1+\$1. In both scenarios, the key is that the total winnings is the sum of the winnings from each ticket. Whenever this is true, you expect to win the sum.

The expected value of a sum is a sum of the expected values.

This is true for any finite sum of random variables, whatever their joint distribution.[1]

Theorem 20.1 (Linearity of Expectation). Let $\mathbf{X}_1, \mathbf{X}_2, \ldots, \mathbf{X}_k$ be random variables and let $\mathbf{Z} = a_1\mathbf{X}_1 + a_2\mathbf{X}_2 + \cdots + a_k\mathbf{X}_k$ be a linear combination of the $\mathbf{X}_i$. Then,

$$\mathbb{E}[\mathbf{Z}] = \mathbb{E}[a_1\mathbf{X}_1 + a_2\mathbf{X}_2 + \cdots + a_k\mathbf{X}_k] = a_1\,\mathbb{E}[\mathbf{X}_1] + a_2\,\mathbb{E}[\mathbf{X}_2] + \cdots + a_k\,\mathbb{E}[\mathbf{X}_k].$$

Proof. The expected value is a sum of outcome-values weighted by outcome-probabilities:

$$\begin{aligned}
\mathbb{E}[\mathbf{Z}] &= \sum_{\omega\in\Omega} \mathbf{Z}(\omega)\cdot P(\omega) && \leftarrow \text{Pop Quiz 19.2}\\
&= \sum_{\omega\in\Omega} \big(a_1\mathbf{X}_1(\omega) + a_2\mathbf{X}_2(\omega) + \cdots + a_k\mathbf{X}_k(\omega)\big)\cdot P(\omega)\\
&\overset{(a)}{=} a_1\sum_{\omega\in\Omega}\mathbf{X}_1(\omega)\cdot P(\omega) + a_2\sum_{\omega\in\Omega}\mathbf{X}_2(\omega)\cdot P(\omega) + \cdots + a_k\sum_{\omega\in\Omega}\mathbf{X}_k(\omega)\cdot P(\omega)\\
&\overset{(b)}{=} a_1\,\mathbb{E}[\mathbf{X}_1] + a_2\,\mathbb{E}[\mathbf{X}_2] + \cdots + a_k\,\mathbb{E}[\mathbf{X}_k].
\end{aligned}$$

For (a) we used rules for sums. For (b) we used $\mathbb{E}[\mathbf{X}_i] = \sum_\omega \mathbf{X}_i(\omega)P(\omega)$. ■

1. Summation can be taken inside or pulled outside an expectation.
2. Constants can be taken inside or pulled outside an expectation.

$$\mathbb{E}\left[\sum_{i=1}^{k} a_i\mathbf{X}_i\right] = \sum_{i=1}^{k} a_i\,\mathbb{E}[\mathbf{X}_i]$$

[1]The same holds for an infinite sum of well behaved random variables. We won't get into those details.

Example 20.2 (Sum of dice). Let $\mathbf{X}$ be the sum of n fair dice, so $\mathbf{X} = \mathbf{X}_1 + \cdots + \mathbf{X}_n$ where $\mathbf{X}_i$ is the value rolled by die i. We know that $\mathbb{E}[\mathbf{X}_i] = 3\frac{1}{2}$, so by the linearity of expectation,

$$\mathbb{E}[\mathbf{X}] = \mathbb{E}[\mathbf{X}_1 + \cdots + \mathbf{X}_n] = \mathbb{E}[\mathbf{X}_1] + \cdots + \mathbb{E}[\mathbf{X}_n] = n \times 3\tfrac{1}{2}.$$

For example, the expected sum of 4 dice is 14. If you first compute the PDF of the sum of 4 dice (do it!) and then the expected value from the PDF, you will appreciate the one-liner above. □

Example 20.3 (Binomial). Let $\mathbf{X}$ be the number of successes in n independent trials with success probability p per trial. Recall that $\mathbf{X}$ is a sum of n independent Bernoullis, $\mathbf{X} = \mathbf{X}_1 + \cdots + \mathbf{X}_n$ (Section 18.4, page 267). By Theorem 19.2 on page 279, each Bernoulli has expected value p. By linearity of expectation,

$$\mathbb{E}[\mathbf{X}] = \mathbb{E}[\mathbf{X}_1 + \cdots + \mathbf{X}_n] = \mathbb{E}[\mathbf{X}_1] + \cdots + \mathbb{E}[\mathbf{X}_n] = n \times p.$$

For example, you expect 50 heads from 100 fair coin tosses ($n = 100, p = \frac{1}{2}$). The derivation leading up to Theorem 19.5 on page 280 involved complicated sums. This is a breeze. □

Example 20.4 (Time to n successes). Let $\mathbf{X}$ be the wait for n successes with success probability p. If you did Problem 19.64, you laboriously computed $\mathbb{E}[\mathbf{X}]$ from its PDF. On page 286 we computed $\mathbb{E}[\mathbf{X}]$ for $n = 2$ using the law of total expectation. Using linearity of expectation we compute $\mathbb{E}[\mathbf{X}]$ for arbitrary n. Unlike the dice, or the Binomial, now $\mathbf{X}$ is not explicitly a sum of random variables. We must first express $\mathbf{X}$ as a sum. The n successes can be broken into n steps: 1st success; 2nd success; and so on to the nth success.

Let $\mathbf{X}_1$ be the number of trials to the 1st success; $\mathbf{X}_2$ the number of additional trials from the 1st to the 2nd success; $\mathbf{X}_3$ the number of additional trials from the 2nd to the 3rd success; and so on up to $\mathbf{X}_n$, the number of additional trials from the $(n-1)$th to the nth success. The total number of trials, $\mathbf{X}$, equals the trials for the 1st success plus the additional trials for the 2nd success, plus the 3rd success, and so on:

$$\mathbf{X} = \mathbf{X}_1 + \cdots + \mathbf{X}_n.$$

There! $\mathbf{X}$ is a sum of random variables. Now for the key insight. Each $\mathbf{X}_i$ is a "trials to one success" random variable with success probability p: after your $(i-1)$th success, the process "restarts" and $\mathbf{X}_i$ is the time for one more success. Therefore, $\mathbb{E}[\mathbf{X}_i] = 1/p$ and

$$\begin{aligned}\mathbb{E}[\mathbf{X}] = \mathbb{E}[\mathbf{X}_1 + \cdots + \mathbf{X}_n] &= \mathbb{E}[\mathbf{X}_1] + \cdots + \mathbb{E}[\mathbf{X}_n] \\ &= n \times \frac{1}{p} = \frac{n}{p}.\end{aligned}$$

If you are waiting for 3 boys, you have to wait 3-times as long as for 1 boy. □

Exercise 20.1 [Linearity of Expectation]

Use linearity of expectation to generalize the previous results.

(a) **[General Dice]** A fair r-sided die has sides $1, \ldots, r$. Roll n fair dice each with a different number of sides: $r_1, r_2, \ldots, r_n$. The sum is $\mathbf{X}$. Show that $\mathbb{E}[\mathbf{X}] = \frac{1}{2}n + \frac{1}{2}\sum_{i=1}^{n} r_i$.

(b) **[Poisson-Binomial]** Let $\mathbf{X}$ be the number of successes on n independent trials, where trial i has its own success probability p_i. Show that $\mathbb{E}[\mathbf{X}] = \sum_{i=1}^{n} p_i$.

(c) **[General Waiting Time]** Let $\mathbf{X}$ be the number of trials till n successes, where the ith success occurs with success probability p_i. Show that $\mathbb{E}[\mathbf{X}] = \sum_{i=1}^{n} 1/p_i$.

(d) Redo (a)–(c) by getting the expectation using the PDF of $\mathbf{X}$ – just kidding. ☺

Example 20.5 (Waiting time squared). Let $\mathbf{X}$ be the waiting time to success, with success probability p. In Example 19.15 on page 285, we used the law of total expectation to show that $\mathbb{E}[\mathbf{X}] = 1/p$. Let us use total expectation and linearity of expectation to compute the expected square of the waiting time, $\mathbb{E}[\mathbf{X}^2]$.

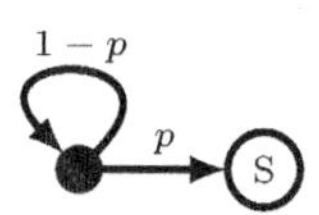

Introduce a random variable $\mathbf{Y}$, the waiting time after the first trial. The total waiting time $\mathbf{X} = 1 + \mathbf{Y}$, so by linearity of expectation, $\mathbb{E}[\mathbf{X}] = 1 + \mathbb{E}[\mathbf{Y}]$. Taking the square of $\mathbf{X}$ and using linearity again, we have:

$$\mathbb{E}[\mathbf{X}^2] = \mathbb{E}[(1+\mathbf{Y})^2] = \mathbb{E}[1 + 2\mathbf{Y} + \mathbf{Y}^2] = 1 + 2\,\mathbb{E}\,[\mathbf{Y}] + \mathbb{E}[\mathbf{Y}^2].$$

The first trial succeeds with probability p, or fails with probability $1-p$. By the law of total expectation,

$$\begin{aligned}\mathbb{E}[\mathbf{Y}^2] &= \underbrace{\mathbb{E}[\mathbf{Y}^2 \mid \text{success}]}_{0} \times p + \underbrace{\mathbb{E}[\mathbf{Y}^2 \mid \text{failure}]}_{\mathbb{E}[\mathbf{X}^2]} \times (1-p) \\ &= (1-p)\,\mathbb{E}\left[\mathbf{X}^2\right].\end{aligned}$$

The last step is because if the first trial succeeds, then $\mathbf{Y}=0$ and if the first trial fails, then the waiting process "restarts" and $\mathbf{Y}$ is a random variable with the same PDF as $\mathbf{X}$. Since $\mathbb{E}[\mathbf{Y}] = \mathbb{E}[\mathbf{X}] - 1 = 1/p - 1$,

$$\mathbb{E}[\mathbf{X}^2] = 1 + 2 \times \left(\frac{1}{p} - 1\right) + (1-p)\,\mathbb{E}\left[\mathbf{X}^2\right] \quad \rightarrow \quad \mathbb{E}[\mathbf{X}^2] = \frac{2-p}{p^2}. \tag{20.1}$$

The final expression for $\mathbb{E}[\mathbf{X}^2]$ is obtained after solving the equation on the left for $\mathbb{E}[\mathbf{X}^2]$. □

Example 20.6 (Coupon Collecting). When I was a kid in Zimbabwe, a pack of chewing-gum came with the flag of some country. There were about 169 countries with populations above $\frac{1}{2}$million. And so began a craze to chew gum and collect all 169 flags. I failed because of those last few elusive flags, Brunei comes to mind. How much gum must I chew before I collect all 169 flags, that is, how long do I expect to wait?

A trial is a purchase of chewing-gum. A success occurs if I get a flag that I don't have, and 169 successes means I got all the flags. Suppose there are n flags. Let $\mathbf{X}_1$ be the wait for the 1st success and p_1 the success-probability. The first flag must be new, so $p_1 = 1$. Let $\mathbf{X}_2$ be the additional wait for the 2nd success. After one success there are $n-1$ new flags, so the success-probability is now $p_2 = (n-1)/n$. After $i-1$ successes, let $\mathbf{X}_i$ be the additional wait for the ith success and p_i the success probability after $i-1$th successes. After $i-1$ successes, there are $n-(i-1)$ new flags, so $p_i = (n-(i-1))/n$. Let $\mathbf{X}$ be the total waiting time,

$$\mathbf{X} = \mathbf{X}_1 + \mathbf{X}_2 + \cdots + \mathbf{X}_n.$$

The success probability for $\mathbf{X}_i$ is p_i, and so $\mathbb{E}[\mathbf{X}_i] = 1/p_i$. By linearity of expectation,

$$\begin{aligned}\mathbb{E}[\mathbf{X}] &= \mathbb{E}[\mathbf{X}_1 + \cdots + \mathbf{X}_n] = \mathbb{E}[\mathbf{X}_1] + \cdots + \mathbb{E}[\mathbf{X}_n] \\ &= \frac{1}{p_1} + \frac{1}{p_2} + \cdots + \frac{1}{p_n} \\ &= \frac{n}{n-0} + \frac{n}{n-1} + \cdots + \frac{n}{n-(n-1)} \\ &= n \cdot \left(\frac{1}{n} + \frac{1}{n-1} + \cdots + \frac{1}{1}\right) = nH_n,\end{aligned}$$

where $H_n = 1 + 1/2 + 1/3 + \cdots + 1/n \approx \ln n + 0.577$.

Theorem 20.7 (Coupon Collector). In a trial you randomly receive one of n different objects. The expected number of independent trials to collect all n objects is $nH_n \approx n \ln n + 0.577n$.

You can see the ramifications. To collect all 169 flags, I expect to buy about 965 packets of gum. That's a lot of $$$ and chewing ☺. Also, that last "rare" flag is just an artifact of the process The chance of getting the nth flag is $1/n$, so it feels rare but it need not be; it's just the "unlucky" flag that came last.

Coupon collecting scams are alive and well. Think of the cereal box which contains (say) one-of-five cartoon characters. When you collect all five, you can get a $2-rebate. You expect to buy about 12 boxes to get the rebate. If a cereal box costs about $5, that's a $3\frac{1}{3}$% discount. Whoopee! □

20.2 Iterated Expectation

Iterated expectation is a special case of the law of total expectation when applied to a random variable that depends on other random variables. Let's be concrete.

> **Experiment.** Roll a die and let $\mathbf{X}_1$ be the value. Now, roll a second die $\mathbf{X}_1$ times and let $\mathbf{X}_2$ be the sum of these $\mathbf{X}_1$ rolls of the second die.

An example outcome is $(4; 2, 1, 2, 6)$ with $\mathbf{X}_1 = 4$ and $\mathbf{X}_2 = 11$. The first entry, 4, is the value of the first die, which determines the number of additional rolls and $\mathbf{X}_2$ is the sum of those additional rolls $\{2, 1, 2, 6\}$.

Pop Quiz 20.2

How large is the sample space for the experiment? Is the probability space uniform?

The price of a game with payoff $\mathbf{X}_2$ is $\mathbb{E}[\mathbf{X}_2]$, which you can compute from the PDF of $\mathbf{X}_2$. By now, we are used to faster methods. There are six cases for the first roll, $\mathbf{X}_1 \in \{1, \ldots, 6\}$. By total expectation,

$$\mathbb{E}[\mathbf{X}_2] = \mathbb{E}[\mathbf{X}_2 \mid \mathbf{X}_1 = 1] \cdot \mathbb{P}[\mathbf{X}_1 = 1] + \cdots + \mathbb{E}[\mathbf{X}_2 \mid \mathbf{X}_1 = 6] \cdot \mathbb{P}[\mathbf{X}_1 = 6]. \tag{20.2}$$

For the RHS, observe that $\mathbb{P}[\mathbf{X}_1 = i] = 1/6$ because $\mathbf{X}_1$ is a fair die roll. What about $\mathbb{E}[\mathbf{X}_2 \mid \mathbf{X}_1 = i]$? If $\mathbf{X}_1 = i$, then $\mathbf{X}_2$ is the sum of i dice rolls which has expected value $i \times 3\frac{1}{2}$. So, $\mathbb{E}[\mathbf{X}_2 \mid \mathbf{X}_1 = i] = i \times 3\frac{1}{2}$, and

$$\mathbb{E}[\mathbf{X}_2] = \frac{1}{6} \times (1 \times 3.5 + 2 \times 3.5 + \cdots + 6 \times 3.5) = 12.25.$$

Observe that $\mathbb{E}[\mathbf{X}_2]$ is a number, as is $\mathbb{E}[\mathbf{X}_2 \mid \mathbf{X}_1 = 1]$. But, what is $\mathbb{E}[\mathbf{X}_2 \mid \mathbf{X}_1 = i]$? It is a function of i, $\mathbb{E}[\mathbf{X}_2 \mid \mathbf{X}_1 = i] = i \times 3\frac{1}{2}$. Since $\mathbf{X}_1 = i$, we can write this function as

$$\mathbb{E}[\mathbf{X}_2 \mid \mathbf{X}_1] = \mathbf{X}_1 \times 3\tfrac{1}{2}.$$

The LHS is the expectation of $\mathbf{X}_2$ given the value of $\mathbf{X}_1$, whatever it be. The RHS is a function of this unknown but fixed value $\mathbf{X}_1$. We normally condition on a known event. Here, the event is unknown, determined by the value of $\mathbf{X}_1$. The result, $\mathbf{X}_1 \times 3\frac{1}{2}$, is a new random variable defined in terms of $\mathbf{X}_1$. From (20.2),

$$\mathbb{E}[\mathbf{X}_2] = \sum_{i=1}^{6} P_{\mathbf{X}_1}(i) \times \mathbb{E}[\mathbf{X}_2 \mid \mathbf{X}_1 = i].$$

The RHS is exactly the expected value of this new random variable $\mathbb{E}[\mathbf{X}_2 \mid \mathbf{X}_1]$. That is,

$$\mathbb{E}[\mathbf{X}_2] = \mathbb{E}_{\mathbf{X}_1}\left[\mathbb{E}[\mathbf{X}_2 \mid \mathbf{X}_1]\right] = \mathbb{E}_{\mathbf{X}_1}[3\tfrac{1}{2} \times \mathbf{X}_1] = 3\tfrac{1}{2} \times \mathbb{E}_{\mathbf{X}_1}[\mathbf{X}_1] = 3\tfrac{1}{2} \times 3\tfrac{1}{2} = 12\tfrac{1}{4}.$$

Note well that $\mathbb{E}[\mathbf{X}_2 \mid \mathbf{X}_1]$ is a random variable whose value depends on $\mathbf{X}_1$, hence we can take its expectation w.r.t. $\mathbf{X}_1$. ($\mathbb{E}_{\mathbf{X}_1}$ emphasizes that we are taking the expectation of a function of the random variable $\mathbf{X}_1$.)

Iterated Expectation. Let $\mathbf{Z}$ be a random variable whose value depends on $\mathbf{X}$. Then,

$$\mathbb{E}[\mathbf{Z}] = \mathbb{E}_{\mathbf{X}}[\mathbf{Z} \mid \mathbf{X}].$$

1: Compute the expectation of $\mathbf{Z}$ fixing $\mathbf{X}$ and treating it as an unknown variable.
2: The result is a function of $\mathbf{X}$, which we denote $\mathbb{E}[\mathbf{Z} \mid \mathbf{X}]$.
3: Compute the expected value of this function of $\mathbf{X}$ using the PDF of $\mathbf{X}$.

Exercise 20.3

Let $\mathbf{X}$ be randomly chosen from $\{1, \ldots, 100\}$. Now choose $\mathbf{Y}$ randomly from $\{1, \ldots, \mathbf{X}\}$.

(a) Compute the PDF of $\mathbf{Y}$, $P_{\mathbf{Y}}(y)$ and give a plot of $P_{\mathbf{Y}}(y)$. Use the PDF to compute $\mathbb{E}[\mathbf{Y}]$.
(b) Compute $\mathbb{E}[\mathbf{Y}]$ using iterated expectation.

Exercise 20.4

Let $\mathbf{X}$ be the waiting time to success. Use iterated expectation to compute $\mathbb{E}[\mathbf{X}]$ and $\mathbb{E}[\mathbf{X}^2]$. Recall we defined $\mathbf{Y}$ as the number of trials after the first one and $\mathbf{X} = 1 + \mathbf{Y}$. Introduce a third random variable $\mathbf{Z}$ that indicates whether the first trial failed, $\mathbf{Z} = 1$ with probability $1 - p$ and $\mathbf{Z} = 0$ with probability p.

(a) Show that $\mathbb{E}[\mathbf{Y} \mid \mathbf{Z}] = \mathbb{E}[\mathbf{X}] \cdot \mathbf{Z}$ and $\mathbb{E}[\mathbf{Y}^2 \mid \mathbf{Z}] = \mathbb{E}[\mathbf{X}^2] \cdot \mathbf{Z}$.
(b) Show that $\mathbb{E}[\mathbf{Y}] = (1 - p)\, \mathbb{E}[\mathbf{X}]$ and $\mathbb{E}[\mathbf{Y}^2] = (1 - p)\, \mathbb{E}[\mathbf{X}^2]$. (Iterated expectation.)
(c) Use (b) to show $\mathbb{E}[\mathbf{X}] = 1/p$ and $\mathbb{E}[\mathbf{X}^2] = (2 - p)/p^2$.

20.3 Build-up Expectation

When computing a general closed form for an expectation is too complex, starting from simpler problems and using build-up expectation can help. How many kids do you expect to have if you want at least k boys and ℓ girls? Let p be the probability of a boy, in practice $p = 1/2$. We show the PDF for the waiting time in Figure 20.1 when $k = 2, \ell = 6$. This problem is hard to analyze from the PDF (see Problems 20.40–20.42).

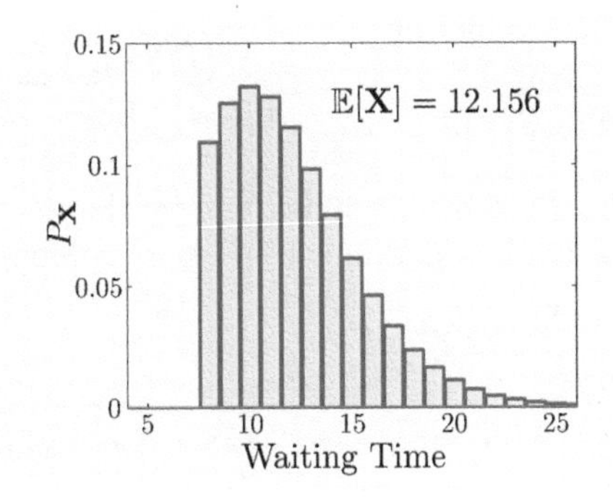

Figure 20.1: **Waiting for 2 boys and 6 girls.** The plot shows the PDF for the waiting time $\mathbf{X}$ to 2 boys and 6 girls. Don't worry, we won't need the PDF. The expected wait in this case is about 12.16, a little longer than the wait for just the 6 girls.

We can use build-up to compute the expected number of children. First, let's introduce a notation. Define:

$$W(k,\ell) = \mathbb{E}[\text{wait for } k \text{ boys and } \ell \text{ girls}].$$

The first child is either a boy or girl. After a boy, you must wait for $k-1$ boys and ℓ girls; similarly after a girl, you must wait for k boys and $\ell - 1$ girls. By total expectation,

$$\begin{aligned} W(k,l) &= \underbrace{\mathbb{E}[\text{wait} \mid \text{boy}]}_{1+W(k-1,\ell)} \times \underbrace{\mathbb{P}[\text{boy}]}_{p} + \underbrace{\mathbb{E}[\text{wait} \mid \text{girl}]}_{1+W(k,\ell-1)} \times \underbrace{\mathbb{P}[\text{girl}]}_{1-p} \\ &= 1 + pW(k-1,\ell) + (1-p)W(k,\ell-1). \end{aligned}$$

The base cases are $W(k,0) = k/p$ (wait for k boys with success probability p) and $W(0,\ell) = \ell/(1-p)$ (wait for ℓ girls with success probability $(1-p)$). Using the recurrence with $p = \frac{1}{2}$ to fill a table for $W(k,\ell)$ gives:

$W(k,\ell)$		ℓ = 0	1	2	3	4	5	6	7	⋯
k	0	0	2	4	6	8	10	12	14	⋯
	1	2	3	4.5	6.25	8.13	10.06	12.03	14.02	⋯
	2	4	4.5	5.5	6.88	8.5	10.28	12.16	14.09	⋯
	⋮	⋮	⋮	⋮	⋮	⋮	⋮	⋮	⋮	⋱

(Annotations in table: $2 \xrightarrow{\times(1-p)} 3$, $1+$, $\downarrow \times p$ from 2 to 3.)

The expected wait for 2 boys and 6 girls is about 12.16, not much more than the wait for 6 girls. Why?

20.4 Expected Value of a Product

Let $\mathbf{X}$ be the roll of a single die. What is $\mathbb{E}[\mathbf{X}^2]$? From the definition of expectation,

$$\mathbb{E}[\mathbf{X}^2] = \frac{1}{6}\cdot 1^2 + \frac{1}{6}\cdot 2^2 + \frac{1}{6}\cdot 3^2 + \frac{1}{6}\cdot 4^2 + \frac{1}{6}\cdot 5^2 + \frac{1}{6}\cdot 6^2 = \frac{91}{6} = 15\frac{1}{6}. \tag{20.3}$$

Recall that $\mathbb{E}[\mathbf{X}] = 3\frac{1}{2}$ and look at the following derivation:

$$\mathbb{E}[\mathbf{X}^2] = \mathbb{E}[\mathbf{X}\times\mathbf{X}] = \mathbb{E}[\mathbf{X}]\times\mathbb{E}[\mathbf{X}] = (3.5)^2 = 12.25. ✗$$

Wrong! The mistake is shaded out in our derivation. In general, the expected product is not the product of expectations: $\mathbb{E}[\mathbf{X}\times\mathbf{X}] \neq \mathbb{E}[\mathbf{X}]\times\mathbb{E}[\mathbf{X}]$. Now, let us consider $\mathbb{E}[\mathbf{X}_1\mathbf{X}_2]$ for two independent dice rolls $\mathbf{X}_1, \mathbf{X}_2$.

The random variable $\mathbf{X}_1\mathbf{X}_2$ is shown for our probability space on the right. Weight each value by its probability 1/36 and add to get

$$\mathbb{E}[\mathbf{X}_1\mathbf{X}_2] = 441/36 = 12.25.$$

Since $\mathbb{E}[\mathbf{X}_1] = \mathbb{E}[\mathbf{X}_2] = 3\frac{1}{2}$, in this case

$$\mathbb{E}[\mathbf{X}_1\mathbf{X}_2] = \mathbb{E}[\mathbf{X}_1] \times \mathbb{E}[\mathbf{X}_2] = (3.5)^2 = 12.25.$$

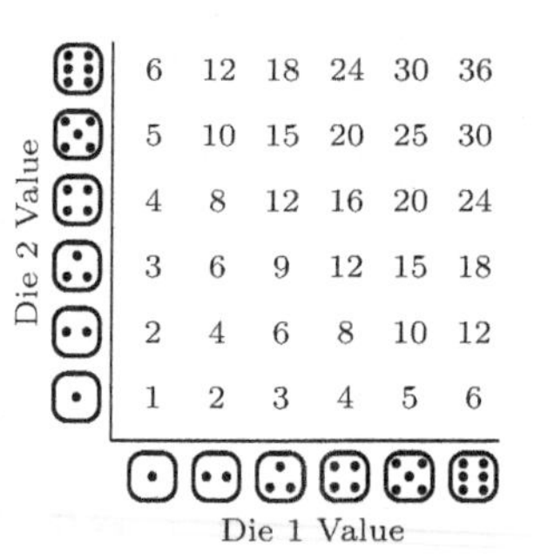

This is not an isolated incident. The expectation of a product is the product of expected values for independent random variables.

Theorem 20.8. If $\mathbf{X}$ and $\mathbf{Y}$ are independent then $\mathbb{E}[\mathbf{XY}] = \mathbb{E}[\mathbf{X}] \times \mathbb{E}[\mathbf{Y}]$.

Proof. To compute the expected value from the joint PDF, weight the possible values $x \cdot y$ by the joint probability $P_{\mathbf{XY}}(x,y)$ and sum. This is the natural extension of expected value to a joint PDF, see Problem 19.47.

$$\mathbb{E}[\mathbf{XY}] = \sum_{x\in\mathbf{X}(\Omega)}\sum_{y\in\mathbf{Y}(\Omega)} P_{\mathbf{XY}}(x,y)\cdot xy = \sum_{x\in\mathbf{X}(\Omega)}\sum_{y\in\mathbf{Y}(\Omega)} P_{\mathbf{X}}(x)P_{\mathbf{Y}}(y)\cdot xy.$$

The last expression holds because of independence, $P_{\mathbf{XY}}(x,y) = P_{\mathbf{X}}(x)P_{\mathbf{Y}}(y)$. Since $P_{\mathbf{X}}(x)\cdot x$ does not depend on y, we can pull it outside the summation with respect to y,

$$\mathbb{E}[\mathbf{XY}] = \sum_{x\in\mathbf{X}(\Omega)} P_{\mathbf{X}}(x)\cdot x \sum_{y\in\mathbf{Y}(\Omega)} P_{\mathbf{Y}}(y)\cdot y = \sum_{x\in\mathbf{X}(\Omega)} P_{\mathbf{X}}(x)\cdot x\cdot \mathbb{E}[\mathbf{Y}].$$

Finally, $\mathbb{E}[\mathbf{Y}]$ is a number, so we can pull it outside the summation with respect to x,

$$\mathbb{E}[\mathbf{XY}] = \mathbb{E}[\mathbf{Y}] \sum_{x\in\mathbf{X}(\Omega)} P_{\mathbf{X}}(x)\cdot x \ = \ \mathbb{E}[\mathbf{Y}]\cdot\mathbb{E}[\mathbf{X}].$$

■

Expected value of a product XY.
1. In general, the expected product is <u>not</u> a product of expectations.
2. For <u>independent</u> random variables, it is: $\mathbb{E}[\mathbf{XY}] = \mathbb{E}[\mathbf{X}] \times \mathbb{E}[\mathbf{Y}]$.

Here is a quick one-line proof of this result using iterated expectation,

$$\mathbb{E}[\mathbf{XY}] = \mathbb{E}_{\mathbf{X}}[\mathbb{E}[\mathbf{XY} \mid \mathbf{X}]] \overset{(a)}{=} \mathbb{E}_{\mathbf{X}}\left[\mathbf{X}\,\mathbb{E}\left[\mathbf{Y}\mid\mathbf{X}\right]\right] \overset{(b)}{=} \mathbb{E}_{\mathbf{X}}\left[\mathbf{X}\,\mathbb{E}\left[\mathbf{Y}\right]\right] \overset{(c)}{=} \mathbb{E}\left[\mathbf{Y}\right]\mathbb{E}_{\mathbf{X}}\left[\mathbf{X}\right] = \mathbb{E}[\mathbf{Y}]\,\mathbb{E}\left[\mathbf{X}\right].$$

Pop Quiz 20.5
Justify each of the steps (a)–(c) in the derivation above.

The sum and product are functions of random variables. For a function $f(\mathbf{X},\mathbf{Y})$ of two random variables $\mathbf{X},\mathbf{Y}$, we could ask when the expected value of $f(\mathbf{X},\mathbf{Y})$ equals the function evaluated at the expected values of the random variables. Mathematically, when does

$$\mathbb{E}[f(\mathbf{X},\mathbf{Y})] \overset{?}{=} f(\mathbb{E}[\mathbf{X}],\mathbb{E}[\mathbf{Y}]).$$

If f is linear, equality always holds by linearity of expectation. When f is a product, equality holds when $\mathbf{X}$ and $\mathbf{Y}$ are independent. These are two important special cases when you can take the expectation inside $f(\cdot)$.

Exercise 20.6
$\mathbf{X}_1, \mathbf{X}_2$ are independent dice rolls. Determine if the equalities hold. Explain.
(a) $\mathbb{E}[\mathbf{X}_1\mathbf{X}_2 \mid \mathbf{X}_1+\mathbf{X}_2=9] \overset{?}{=} \mathbb{E}\left[\mathbf{X}_1 \mid \mathbf{X}_1+\mathbf{X}_2=9\right] \times \mathbb{E}[\mathbf{X}_2 \mid \mathbf{X}_1+\mathbf{X}_2=9]$.
(b) (i) $\mathbb{E}\left[\frac{1}{\mathbf{X}_1}\right] \overset{?}{=} \frac{1}{\mathbb{E}[\mathbf{X}_1]}$. (ii) $\mathbb{E}\left[\frac{\mathbf{X}_1}{\mathbf{X}_2}\right] \overset{?}{=} \frac{\mathbb{E}[\mathbf{X}_1]}{\mathbb{E}[\mathbf{X}_2]}$. (iii) $\mathbb{E}\left[\frac{\mathbf{X}_1}{\mathbf{X}_2}\right] \overset{?}{=} \mathbb{E}\left[\mathbf{X}_1\right] \times \mathbb{E}\left[\frac{1}{\mathbf{X}_2}\right]$.

20.5 Sums of Indicators

A common application for linearity of expectation is to a sum of indicators. Suppose n men throw their hats up and the hats land randomly on heads. What is the expected number of hats that land on the correct head?

> **Disclaimer:** Prepare yourself for some intense algebra. If you are not up for it, you may skip forward to the green End-Disclaimer.

Let's exercise our counting and probability skills by computing the PDF of $\mathbf{X}$, the number of hats that land on a correct head. There are $n!$ permutations of the hats on heads and each is equally likely, so

$$\mathbb{P}[\mathbf{X}=k]=P_{\mathbf{X}}(k)=\frac{\text{number of ways to assign } k \text{ hats correctly}}{n!}.$$

For the numerator, there are $\binom{n}{k}$ ways to select the hats to assign correctly. The remaining $n-k$ hats must all be assigned to the remaining men as a derangement as none of these hats can go to its owner. We counted derangements in Example 14.5 on page 201. The number of derangements of the $n-k$ hats, none of which go to its owner, is $(n-k)!\sum_{i=0}^{n-k}(-1)^i/i!$. By the product rule for counting,

$$\text{number of ways to assign } k \text{ hats correctly}=\binom{n}{k}\times(n-k)!\sum_{i=0}^{n-k}\frac{(-1)^i}{i!}.$$

Dividing by $n!$ and using $\binom{n}{k}(n-k)!/n!=1/k!$, we get the PDF of $\mathbf{X}$,

$$P_{\mathbf{X}}(k)=\frac{1}{k!}\sum_{i=0}^{n-k}\frac{(-1)^i}{i!}. \tag{20.4}$$

From here, it's just summation and algebra to get $\mathbb{E}[\mathbf{X}]$. By definition, $\mathbb{E}[\mathbf{X}]=\sum_{k=0}^{n}k\cdot P_{\mathbf{X}}(k)$, so we have:

$$\begin{aligned}\mathbb{E}[\mathbf{X}] &= \sum_{k=0}^{n}k\cdot P_{\mathbf{X}}(k)=\sum_{k=1}^{n}k\cdot\frac{1}{k!}\sum_{i=0}^{n-k}\frac{(-1)^i}{i!}\\ &= \sum_{k=1}^{n}\frac{1}{(k-1)!}\sum_{i=0}^{n-k}\frac{(-1)^i}{i!}.\end{aligned}$$

Note that the sum starts at $k=1$ because the $k=0$ term makes no contribution. Instead of summing from $k=1,\ldots,n$, we can sum from $0,\ldots,n-1$ and replace every k in the summand with $k+1$. Thus,

$$\mathbb{E}[\mathbf{X}]=\sum_{k=0}^{n-1}\sum_{i=0}^{n-1-k}\frac{(-1)^i}{k!i!} = ☹ \tag{20.5}$$

What a complicated sum! We made our point: computing expectations from sums can be tough. We have better things to do, so we leave this sum as an exercise and move on.

Exercise 20.7

Prove that for $r\geq 0$, $\sum_{k=0}^{r}\sum_{i=0}^{r-k}\frac{(-1)^i}{k!i!}=1$. Hence, what is $\mathbb{E}[\mathbf{X}]$ in (20.5)?

Tinker with $r=3$. The sum as explicitly stated computes a row sum in the table (gray) and adds them for $k=0,1,\ldots,r$. An alternate way to add all the values is to consider each diagonal (blue), and add the diagonal-sums. Use the Binomial theorem to compute the diagonal-sums. A simple pattern will emerge. The identity is inevitable because the PDF in (20.4) must sum to 1.

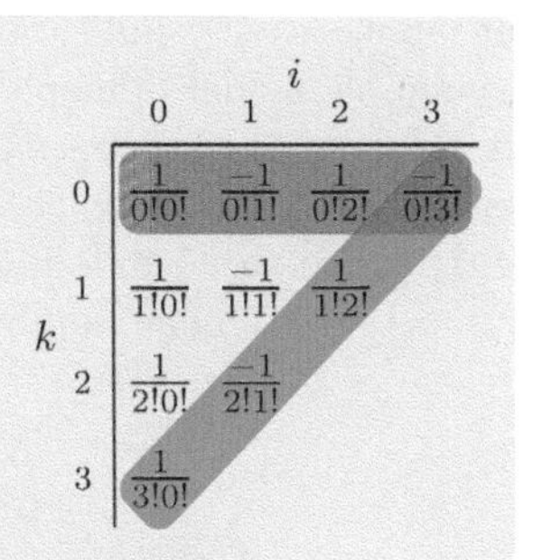

> **End-Disclaimer:** Welcome back. We now show you how to compute this expectation easily using linearity of expectation and indicators.

We want the number of men with correct hats, $\mathbf{X}$. When you must count how many times something happens, it is useful to introduce an indicator random variable which equals 1 if the thing happens and 0 if not.

Let's see this idea in action. Label the men $1, 2, \ldots, n$. We are interested in whether man i gets his hat. Let $\mathbf{X}_i$ indicate whether man i gets his correct hat, $\mathbf{X}_i = 1$ if man i gets his hat and zero otherwise. $\mathbf{X}_i$ is just a Bernoulli random variable. For example, consider this arrangement of hats:

hats:	4	2	3	1
men:	1	2	3	4

Men 1 and 4 got the wrong hats (red), and men 2 and 3 got the right hats (green), which gives the indicators

$$\mathbf{X}_1 = 0 \qquad \mathbf{X}_2 = 1 \qquad \mathbf{X}_3 = 1 \qquad \mathbf{X}_4 = 0.$$

What is $\mathbb{P}[\mathbf{X}_i = 1]$, the probability man i gets his hat? Since man i can get any one of n hats randomly, the probability he gets his own hat is $1/n$. So, $\mathbb{P}[\mathbf{X}_i = 1] = 1/n$ and $\mathbb{E}[\mathbf{X}_i] = 1/n$, the expectation of a Bernoulli. Now for the crucial observation. The sum of the indicators $\mathbf{X}_i$ is the number of men with their own hat,

$$\mathbf{X} = \mathbf{X}_1 + \mathbf{X}_2 + \cdots + \mathbf{X}_n.$$

In the example with $\mathbf{X}_1 = 0, \mathbf{X}_2 = 1, \mathbf{X}_3 = 1, \mathbf{X}_4 = 0$, the sum is 2, which indeed gives the number of correctly placed (green) hats. By linearity of expectation,

$$\mathbb{E}[\mathbf{X}] = \mathbb{E}[\mathbf{X}_1] + \mathbb{E}[\mathbf{X}_2] + \cdots + \mathbb{E}[\mathbf{X}_n] = \frac{1}{n} + \frac{1}{n} + \cdots + \frac{1}{n} = n \times \frac{1}{n} = 1.$$

Done! Here's a summary. Indicators are used to count. The total count is a sum of the indicators. If you know the expected value of each indicator, the expected total is a sum of the expected values of the indicators.

Example 20.9 (Records). People talk about records. It could be a record breaking year for high temperatures or rainfall, or some other trivia. Here are the high temperatures for January in Central Park NY,

year (18xx)	'76	'77	'78	'79	'80	'81	'82	'83	'84	'85	'86	'87	'88	'89	'90	'91	...
high (°C)	7.8	1.0	3.6	1.9	8.2	−0.2	2.3	0.1	0.8	3.2	1.0	3.2	0.1	5.5	8.6	4.7	...

A year is record-breaking if its temperature beats the previous maximum. We highlighted in red the record-breaking years for January temperature. How many times do you expect to see the record broken? Since we are counting the number of times something happens, indicator random variables spring to mind. For year t, let $\mathbf{X}_t = 1$ if that year is a record breaker, and zero otherwise. The record-breaker indicators are shown below.

year number t	1	2	3	4	5	6	7	8	9	10	11	12	13	14	15	16	...
$\mathbf{X}_t$	1	0	0	0	1	0	0	0	0	0	0	0	0	0	1	0	...

We relabeled the years $1, 2, \ldots$ because it is the number of years from the "beginning of time" that matters not the year label. A red 1 indicates the record-breaking years. How many times will the record be broken? Here is a very simple model. The observed high-temperatures $\tau_1, \tau_2, \ldots \tau_T$ over T years are distinct and randomly ordered. That is, the sequence of temperatures is a random permutation of the observed values.

The Bernoulli $\mathbf{X}_t$ is 1 when year-t's temperature is largest among years $1, 2, \ldots, t$. Since the temperatures in the first t years are randomly ordered, the maximum is equally likely to occur in any one of those t years. So, $\mathbb{P}[\mathbf{X}_t = 1] = 1/t$. The number of times the record is broken over years $1, 2, \ldots, T$ is the sum of the $\mathbf{X}_t$,

$$\mathbf{X} = \mathbf{X}_1 + \mathbf{X}_2 + \cdots + \mathbf{X}_T = \sum_{t=1}^{T} \mathbf{X}_t.$$

By linearity of expectation,

$$\mathbb{E}[\mathbf{X}] = \sum_{t=1}^{T} \mathbb{E}[\mathbf{X}_t] \stackrel{(a)}{=} \sum_{t=1}^{T} \frac{1}{t} = H_T \approx \ln T + 0.577, \tag{20.6}$$

where $H_T = 1 + \frac{1}{2} + \cdots \frac{1}{T}$ is the Tth Harmonic number. In (a) we used $\mathbb{E}[\mathbf{X}_t] = \mathbb{P}[\mathbf{X}_t = 1] = 1/t$. The number of records broken up to time T grows as the natural logarithm of T, a well known rule for "exchangeable" observations. Over 140 years of history, you expect to see $H_{140} \approx 5.52$ records broken. That seems startlingly low and indeed could be a conversation starter for us boring math-types. We better check with data.

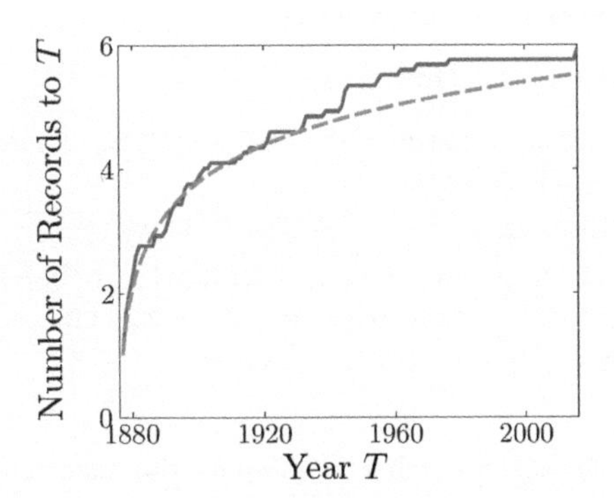

Figure 20.2: **Record-breaking.** Temperature data (blue) for 140 years from 1876–2015 shows the number of records broken averaged over 12 experiments (Jan, Feb,..., Dec) versus time T. The expected number of records broken from (20.6) is in red. Note that the average number of records broken over 140 years of history is about 6 and theory predicts 5.52.

You may argue that the model is too simple, but the data in blue corroborates the model in red. Even the shocking prediction of fewer than 6 records is validated. This is a good opportunity to embelish our standard workflow for modeling and solving problems, especially for problems involving probability.

1: Model the problem your are trying to solve using a discrete mathematical object.
2: Analyze your model to derive some new knowledge.
3: **Validate conclusions against data** and change the model if necessary.

□

Exercise 20.8

Here is another model for records. Each January's temperature is random, chosen independently and uniformly from n possible temperatures $y_1 < y_2 < y_3 < \cdots < y_n$. So, $\mathbb{P}[\text{temperature} = y_i] = \frac{1}{n}$.

(a) Let $\mathbf{X}_t$ indicate if year t is record-breaking. What is $\mathbb{P}[\mathbf{X}_1 = 1]$?. Let the random variable $\mathbf{Y}$ be year t's temperature. For $t \geq 2$, show that $\mathbb{P}[\mathbf{X}_t = 1] = \frac{1}{n}\sum_{i=1}^{n} \mathbb{P}[\mathbf{X}_t = 1 | \mathbf{Y} = y_i]$.

(b) Show that $\mathbb{P}[\mathbf{X}_t = 1 | \mathbf{Y} = y_i] = (\frac{i-1}{n})^{t-1}$, for $t \geq 2$.

(c) Show: $\mathbb{P}[\mathbf{X}_t = 1] = \frac{1}{n}\sum_{i=1}^{n-1} (\frac{i}{n})^{t-1}$.

(d) Let $\mathbf{X}$ be the number records. Use linearity of expectation to show that

$$\mathbb{E}[\mathbf{X}] = 1 + \frac{1}{n}\sum_{i=1}^{n-1} \frac{i}{n-i}\left[1 - \left(\frac{i}{n}\right)^{T-1}\right].$$

(e) When $T \to \infty$, show that the expected number of records becomes H_n.

(f) High temperatures range from about -8 to 12 in increments of 0.1 ($n \approx 200$). How many records are expected over the course of history?

(g) Explain the difference between this model and the one analyzed in Example 20.9.

Exercise 20.9

Use linearity of expectation with a sum of indicator random variables for (a) and (b).

(a) You pick m numbers independently and uniformly from the set $\{1, \ldots, n\}$. What is the expected number of distinct elements you pick?

(b) You randomly draw k balls (without replacement) from a white and b black balls. What is the expected number of white balls? (What if the draws were with replacement?)

(c) **[Very Hard]** Obtain and use the PDF to get the expectations in parts (a) and (b) .

Exercise 20.10

A random tournament has 10 vertices. An edge exists between each pair of vertices with its direction chosen randomly. A ranking is a directed path that uses each vertex once. Find the expected number of rankings.

20.6 Problems

Problem 20.1. Let $\mathbf{X}$ and $\mathbf{Y}$ be independent dice rolls, and $\mathbf{Z} = \mathbf{X} + 2\mathbf{Y}$. Compute $\mathbb{E}[\mathbf{Z}]$.

Problem 20.2. Is $\mathbb{E}[\mathbf{X}|\mathbf{Y}]$ a function of $\mathbf{X}$, of $\mathbf{Y}$, of both $\mathbf{X}$ and $\mathbf{Y}$ or of neither $\mathbf{X}$ nor $\mathbf{Y}$?

Problem 20.3. Compute the expected value of each random variable in Problem 18.33.

Problem 20.4. Use linearity to compute $\mathbb{E}[\mathbf{X}_2]$ for the experiment on page 295 where the first die roll $\mathbf{X}_1$ determines how many dice are summed to give $\mathbf{X}_2$. Write $\mathbf{X}_2$ as the sum of 6 random variables,

$$\mathbf{X}_2 = \mathbf{Z}_1 + \mathbf{Z}_2 + \mathbf{Z}_3 + \mathbf{Z}_4 + \mathbf{Z}_5 + \mathbf{Z}_6,$$

where $\mathbf{Z}_i$ is additional die roll i if that roll is made and zero otherwise. A possible outcome is $(4; 2, 1, 2, 6)$ for which the first roll was 4 and the additional rolls are $\mathbf{Z}_1, \mathbf{Z}_2, \mathbf{Z}_3, \mathbf{Z}_4$ equal to $2, 1, 2, 6$ respectively and $\mathbf{Z}_5 = \mathbf{Z}_6 = 0$.

(a) What is $\mathbb{P}[\mathbf{Z}_i = 0]$? Use total expectation with the two cases $\{\mathbf{X}_1 < i\}$ and $\{\mathbf{X}_1 \geq i\}$ to compute $\mathbb{E}[\mathbf{Z}_i]$.

(b) Use linearity of expectation to compute $\mathbb{E}[\mathbf{X}_2]$.

Problem 20.5. A box contains numbers $1, \ldots, 100$. You randomly pick 5 numbers. Compute the expected sum when you pick numbers (a) *with replacement* (b) *without replacement*. Generalize to picking k numbers from $1, \ldots, n$.

Problem 20.6. In a document with M typos, *independent* proof-readers A and B respectively find a typos and b typos, with c typos in common. Let p_A (resp. p_B) be the probability that A (resp. B) detects a specific typo.

(a) What is the expected number of typos found by: (i) A (ii) B (iii) Both A and B?

(b) The typos found were corrected. Estimate the number of typos which remain.

Problem 20.7. In a round of speed-dating (Section 1.2 on page 8), 16 people $A, B, \ldots, P$ are randomly assigned seats at four tables with four seats per table. Two people meet if they sit at the same table.

(a) Compute the probability that A will meet B during an evening with 4 rounds of speed-dating.

(b) Show that every person expects to meet 8.856 people during an evening with 4 rounds of speed-dating.

Problem 20.8. You send a random number of packets, uniform on $\{1, 2, \ldots, 10^5\}$. A packet is resent until it reaches. A packet's size is also random, uniform on $\{1, 2, \ldots, 10^5\}$. In each case, find the expected time spent sending packets.

(a) The chances a packet reaches its destination are 90% and it takes 0.01 sec. to send a packet, independent of size.

(b) The chances a packet reaches its destination are 90% and it takes $(0.01 \times \text{size})$ sec. to send a packet.

(c) A packet reaches its destination with probability $(1/\text{size})$ and it takes $(0.01 \times \text{size})$ sec. to send a packet.

Problem 20.9. A file manager stores each of 4000 files on one of 4 disks, randomly selected. The total size of all files is 500MB. Compute the expected: (a) Number of files on each disk. (b) Amount of storage used on each disk.

Problem 20.10. Let $\mathbf{X}$ be the number of trials to success with success-probability p. Use iterated expectation to compute $\mathbb{E}[\mathbf{X}^3]$. Confirm your answer from the PDF by computing an infinite sum.

Problem 20.11. Ten sailors return from shore and sleep randomly in their ten bunks (one sailor per bunk).

(a) Let $\mathbf{X}$ be the number of sailors in the correct bunk. Compute (i) $\mathbb{P}[\mathbf{X} = 10]$ (ii) $\mathbb{P}[\mathbf{X} = 9]$ (iii) $\mathbb{P}[\mathbf{X} = 8]$.

(b) Compute the expected number of sailors in the correct bunk, that is $\mathbb{E}[\mathbf{X}]$.

Problem 20.12. You visit $\mathbf{N} \in \{1, 2, \ldots\}$ shops ($\mathbf{N}$ is random). At the ith shop, you spend $\mathbf{X}_i$ for $i = 1, \ldots, \mathbf{N}$. The $\mathbf{X}_i$ are random, having the same expected value μ. In total you spend $\mathbf{X}$. Show that your expected spending is the expected number of shops you visit times the expected spending in each shop, $\mathbb{E}[\mathbf{X}] = \mathbb{E}[\mathbf{N}] \cdot \mu$.

Problem 20.13. Let $\mathbf{X}_1$ be a random variable which takes values greater than 1, $\mathbf{X}_1 > 1$. Let $\mathbf{X}_2$ be the waiting time to success with success probability $(\mathbf{X}_1 - 1)/\mathbf{X}_1$.

(a) Compute $\mathbb{E}[\mathbf{X}_2 \mid \mathbf{X}_1]$. What is it a function of? (b) Show that $\mathbb{E}[\mathbf{X}_2] = 1 + \mathbb{E}[1/(\mathbf{X}_1 - 1)]$ (iterated expectation).

Problem 20.14. A Martian couple has children until 2 males. On Mars, males are half as likely as females and children are independent. Compute the expected number of children the couple will have.

Problem 20.15. 10,000 people are to be tested for a rare disease that affects 1% of the population. (10,000 tests.)

(a) Group people into batches of 10 and do one test on all the blood in a batch. If the test is negative, all people in the batch are negative. In any positive batch, administer individual tests. What is the expected number of tests?

(b) What is the best batch-size and the corresponding expected number of tests?

(c) Can you do better than in part (b). Try to decrease the expected number of tests as much as you can.

Problem 20.16. Dangerous chemical compounds $C_1, C_2, \ldots, C_n$, $n \geq 4$, must be placed in buckets $B_1, \ldots, B_k$. Compound C_i explodes if it is in the same bucket as any of the compounds $\{C_{i-3}, C_{i-2}, C_{i-1}, C_{i+1}, C_{i+2}, C_{i+3}\}$. For example, C_3 is explosive with $\{C_1, C_2, C_4, C_5, C_6\}$ (there is no C_0). We wish to avoid any explosions by choosing the number of buckets, k, so that all the compounds can be placed in the buckets safely.

(a) Show that you need *at least* 4 buckets and *at most* n buckets, $4 \leq k \leq n$.

(b) Show that you can safely put the compounds into 4 buckets ($k = 4$ suffices) for all $n \geq 4$.

(c) Let $n = 10$ (you have 10 compounds). Suppose you *independently* place the the compounds randomly into 4 buckets with each bucket having probability $\frac{1}{4}$. Compute:

(i) The probability that C_1 is in a bucket with an explosive partner.

(ii) The probability that C_4 is in a bucket with an explosive partner.

(iii) Compute the expectated number of explosive pairs created. *[Hint: Sum of indicators.]*

Problem 20.17.

(a) A cereal box comes with one of 10 toys. You buy cereal until you collect all 10 toys. Compute:
(i) $\mathbb{P}$[you buy at most 15 boxes of cereal]. (ii) $\mathbb{E}$[number of boxes bought].

(b) Let $\mathbf{X}$ be the number of fair die rolls until all values appear. Compute: (i) $\mathbb{P}[\mathbf{X} \geq 10]$. (ii) $\mathbb{E}[\mathbf{X}]$.

(c) Find the expected sample size when you sample students until you get: (i) 40 distinct birthdays (ii) all birthdays.

Problem 20.18. A bag has 10 red balls. On each turn a random ball is painted blue if it isn't already blue, and returned to the bag. Find the expected number of turns to paint all balls blue. Generalize to n red balls.

Problem 20.19. A bag has 4 balls of different colors. At each step, pick two random balls and paint one ball the other ball's color. Replace the balls and repeat. On average, how many steps till all balls are the same color?

Problem 20.20. Solve using build-up expectation. If in doubt, verify with Monte Carlo.

(a) A couple has kids until 2 boys and 4 girls. How many children do they expect if girls are twice as likely as boys.

(b) The sequence 01001000010001010100 has seven 00's. Find the expected number of 00's in 20 random bits.

(c) A drunk starts at a bar and randomly takes independent steps left or right until reaching home or jail. Home is 20 steps to the left and jail is 20 steps to the right. Compute the expected number of steps the drunk makes.

(d) There are 100 different toys in cereal boxes and you will stop collecting toys when you have 20 of them. What is the expected number of cereal box purchases? Generalize to the case with n different toys and you stop toy-collecting when you have k of them. Show, by induction, that $n(H_n - H_{n-k})$ solves your recursion.

(e) Get a recursion for the expected number of successes in n trials with success probability p. Solve the recursion.

(f) A biased coin (probability $\frac{1}{3}$ of heads) is tossed 10 times. In a run, all consecutive flips are the same, for example HHTHTTTTHH has five runs. Compute the expected number of runs.

(g) There is a blue jar with 10 blue balls and red jar with 10 red balls. At each step, a random ball is selected from each jar and they are swapped. After 10 such swaps, compute the expected number of red balls in the red jar.

(h) Cards are drawn randomly from a 52-card deck until a spade is drawn. What is the expected number of draws?

(i) Flip a biased coin with probability $\frac{1}{3}$ of H. What is the expected waiting time to ten heads in a row?

(j) 20 kids stand in line. A random pair of *adjacent* standing kids pair up and sit. This continues until no more pairs can be formed. What is the expected number of unpaired kids?

(k) **(ESP)** A deck has 26 red and 26 black cards. At each step, you guess the color of the next card (knowing how many red and blue cards went by). What is the expected number of correct guesses?

(l) **(Banach's Matchbox)** Two matchboxes start with 100 matches. Each time Kilam needs a match he is equally likely to use one from either box. The first time Kilam reaches for a match and finds the box empty, what is the expected number of matches in the other matchbox?

(m) A 3-sided fair die is rolled until one 1, two 2s and three 3s appear. What is the expected number of rolls?

(n) There are 100 empty slots in a line. Doves, one by one, randomly pick an empty slot whose neighboring slots are also empty, until no viable slots remain. On average, how many slots have doves?

(o) You have 6 guesses to guess $\mathbf{X}$, a random integer in $[1, 1000]$. At each guess you are told if $\mathbf{X}$ is higher or lower. If you guess right, you win $\mathbf{X}$. What is the expected profit with optimal guessing. What is your first guess?

Problem 20.21. Al and Joe each randomly pick 5 restaurants from 20, and must eat at a restaurant both picked.

(a) Use indicator random variables to compute the expected number of restaurants that they can eat at.

(b) Find the PDF for the number of restaurants they can eat at, and get the expected value from the PDF.

Problem 20.22. For a fair coin, show that the expected number of flips to get n heads in a row is $2(2^n - 1)$.

Problem 20.23. Five students independently get a random number in $\{1, \ldots, 10\}$. A score is increased for every pair of student whose numbers agree. Find the expected score when:

(a) For every pair of students whose numbers agree, the score is increased by 1.
(b) For every pair of students whose numbers agree, the score is increased by the number the pair has.
(c) Generalize (a) and (b) to n students independently getting a number in $\{1, \ldots, k\}$.

Problem 20.24. A carnival game costs 50¢ to play. You roll three dice.

(a) You win $1 if at least one roll is a six. Do you wish to play?
(b) You win a dollar amount equal to the number of sixes rolled. Do you wish to play?

Problem 20.25. Flip a fair coin until you get two H in a row. Let $\mathbf{X}$ be the number of flips.

(a) Show that $\mathbb{P}[\mathbf{X} = n] = (\phi_+^{n-1} - \phi_-^{n-1})/\sqrt{20}$, where $\phi_\pm = (1 \pm \sqrt{5})/4$.
(b) Use (a) to show $\mathbb{E}[\mathbf{X}] = 6$. *[Hint: Show $\sum_{n=0}^{\infty} na^n = a/(1-a)^2$ and $\sum_{n=0}^{\infty} a^n = 1/(1-a)$.]*
(c) Use iterated expectation or total probability to show $\mathbb{E}[\mathbf{X}] = 6$.

Problem 20.26. Flip a coin until a specific sequence of heads and tails appears. Let $\mathbf{X}$ be the number of flips.

(a) What is the expected number of flips, $\mathbb{E}[\mathbf{X}]$, when the sequence: (i) TH (ii) HHH (iii) TTHH.
(b) You want a specific sequence of length k. Prove that $\mathbb{E}[\mathbf{X}] \leq k2^k$.

Problem 20.27. Sequences HHH and TTHH compete. A coin is tossed and the sequence that appears first wins.

(a) Find the expected number of flips until HHH appears. Repeat for TTHH.
(b) Find the probability that HHH wins the game.
(c) Give intuition for why TTHH wins more often against HHH, yet in isolation TTHH needs more flips to appear.

Problem 20.28. You have a fair 5-sided die which can generate one of the numbers $\{1, 2, 3, 4, 5\}$ with probability $\frac{1}{5}$ each. You wish to simulate a fair 7-sided die which generates a number in $\{1, 2, 3, 4, 5, 6, 7\}$ with probability $\frac{1}{7}$ each. Give an algorithm to do so and find the expected number of rolls of your 5-sided die to get a single "roll" of the 7-sided die. Try to minimize the expected number of rolls as much as you can.

Problem 20.29. Use linearity of expectation and indicator random variables for (a)–(d).

(a) The concierge randomly returns coats of n men. On average, how many men get their own coat?
(b) You toss m balls randomly into n bins. Let $\mathbf{X}$ be the number of bins that contain exactly k balls. What is $\mathbb{E}[\mathbf{X}]$?
(c) You randomly and independently choose a k-subset A and ℓ-subset B of $\{1, \ldots, n\}$. Let $\mathbf{X} = |A \cap B|$ and $\mathbf{Y} = |A \cup B|$. What are $\mathbb{E}[\mathbf{X}]$ and $\mathbb{E}[\mathbf{Y}]$?
(d) A street has n houses, k are red and ℓ are white. Find the expected number of neighbors painted different colors.
(e) **[Hard]** Obtain and use the PDF to get the expectation for parts (a)–(d) .

Problem 20.30. How many pairs of students in a class of 200 do you expect to have the same birthday? (Assume there are 365 birthdays and birthdays are random and independent.)

Problem 20.31. A biased coin (probability p of heads) is tossed n times. A run is a consecutive sequence of the same outcome (HHTHTTTTHH has five runs). Show that the expected number of runs is $1 + 2(n-1)p(1-p)$. *[Hint: Let $\mathbf{X}_i = 1$ if outcomes i and $i-1$ disagree.]*

Problem 20.32 (Bernoulli's diffusion model). A blue jar has n blue balls and a red jar has n red balls. At each step, a pair of random balls is swapped, one from each jar. After k such swaps, compute the expected number of red balls in the red jar. *[Hint: Let $\mathbf{X}_i = 1$ if red ball i is in the red jar. Problem 18.66]*

Problem 20.33. One hundred men check their hats and coats at a restaurant. When leaving, the hats and coats are distributed independently and randomly to the men. Compute the expected number of men who leave the restaurant:

(a) With both clothing items that are their own. (b) With at least clothing items that is their own.

Problem 20.34. There are n elderly couples and m randomly selected people expire. What is the expected number of remaining *couples*. *[Hint: $\mathbf{X}_i = 1$ if both members of couple i remain.]*

Problem 20.35. Projects are independent and take 1,2 or 3 nights to complete (each equally likely). You and your spouse have dinner and each start a project on night 1. On any night, if you and your spouse are in sync and have just finished a project, you will have dinner together. Otherwise, if just one of you finish a project, you will start a new project. What is the expected number of nights till you next dinner with your spouse?

Problem 20.36 (St. Petersburg Paradox). A coin is flipped until H and you win $\$2^t$ if t flips are made. How much do you pay for this gamble if: (a) You only care about money. (b) You get $(\log_2 \mathbf{X})^k$ in utility from $\$\mathbf{X}$.

Problem 20.37 (Sampling With vs. Without replacement). An urn has 10 white and 20 black balls. You randomly pick a ball until you get a white ball. Let $\mathbf{X}$ be the waiting time (number of balls sampled).

(a) What is the expected waiting time if you pick balls *with* replacement.

(b) Suppose you pick balls *without* replacement.

(i) Comparing to with replacement, guess whether the expected waiting time will increase or decrease, and why.

(ii) Use build-up expectation to compute the expected waiting time and compare with (a).

(iii) Find the PDF for the waiting time $\mathbf{X}$ and use it to compute the expected waiting time. *[Hint: Problem 13.71.]*

(iv) Generalize to m white and n black balls. Give a formula for the expected waiting time.

(v) Define the indicator random variable $\mathbf{B}_i = 1$ if black ball i is picked *before any white ball.* Show that $\mathbf{X} = \mathbf{B}_1 + \mathbf{B}_1 + \cdots + \mathbf{B}_{20}$ and use this to compute the expected waiting time.

Problem 20.38. Exercise 20.8 on page 301 assumed temperatures are picked uniformly from $y_1, \ldots, y_n$. Suppose y_i is picked with probability p_i. Let F_i be the cumulative probability $p_1 + p_2 + \cdots + p_i$.

(a) Show that $\mathbb{E}[\text{number of records broken to time } T] = 1 + \sum_{i=1}^{n-1} \frac{p_{i+1} F_i}{1 - F_i}(1 - F_i^{T-1})$.

(b) For the exponential distribution, $p_i = \lambda e^{-\alpha i}$. Show that $\lambda = (e^\alpha - 1)/(1 - e^{-\alpha n})$, and that

$$\mathbb{E}[\text{number of times record is broken as } T \to \infty] = 1 + \lambda e^{-\alpha} \sum_{i=1}^{n-1} \frac{1 - e^{-\alpha i}}{1 - e^{-\alpha(n-i)}}.$$

Use this to show that the expected number of records over history is in $\Theta(n)$.

Problem 20.39. For $T \ll n$ in Exercise 20.8, show that the number of records broken is logarithmic in T.

Problem 20.40. Let $\mathbf{X}$ be the waiting time to k boys and ℓ girls (see Section 20.3). Let $\mathbf{X}_b$ be the time you wait for the k boys and let $\mathbf{X}_g$ be any *additional* time you must wait to get up to ℓ girls.

(a) What are the possible values of $\mathbf{X}_b$ and $\mathbf{X}_g$. Show that $\mathbf{X} = \mathbf{X}_b + \mathbf{X}_g$. Is $\mathbf{X}_g$ independent of $\mathbf{X}_b$? Explain.

(b) Show that $\mathbb{E}[\mathbf{X}_g \mid \mathbf{X}_b] = \max(0, k + \ell - \mathbf{X}_b)/(1 - p)$.

(c) Hence show using iterated expectation, that $\mathbb{E}[\mathbf{X}] = \frac{k}{p} + \frac{1}{1-p}\mathbb{E}[\max(0, k + \ell - \mathbf{X}_b)]$.

Problem 20.41. Let $\mathbf{X}$ be the wait for k successes with success probability p. Compute $\mathbb{E}[\max(0, r - \mathbf{X})]$ for $r \geq k$.

(a) Let $\mathbf{X}$ have PDF $P_{\mathbf{X}}(i)$ for $i \geq k$. Show that $\mathbb{E}[\max(0, r - \mathbf{X})] = \sum_{i=k}^{r} (r - i) \cdot P_{\mathbf{X}}(i)$.

(b) Use Problem 18.73 to show that $P_{\mathbf{X}}(i) = \binom{i-1}{k-1} p^k (1-p)^{i-k}$.

(c) Hence, show that $\mathbb{E}[\max(0, r - \mathbf{X})] = \begin{cases} r & k = 0; \\ \sum_{i=k}^{r} (r - i)\binom{i-1}{k-1} p^k (1-p)^{i-k} & k > 0. \end{cases}$

(d) Using Problem 20.40(d), show that the expected waiting time to k boys and ℓ girls is

$$\frac{k}{p} + \frac{1}{1-p} \sum_{i=k}^{k+\ell} (k + \ell - i) \binom{i-1}{k-1} p^k (1-p)^{i-k}.$$

(e) For $p = \frac{1}{3}$ and $p = \frac{1}{2}$, compute the expected waiting time to get 2 boys and 2 girls.

(f) **[Hard]** One can further simplify (d) using a special function known as the normalized incomplete Beta function $I(x, m, n)$ which is available in most mathematical packages,

$$I(x, m, n) = \frac{\int_0^x dt\ t^{m-1}(1-t)^{n-1}}{\int_0^1 dt\ t^{m-1}(1-t)^{n-1}}.$$

(i) Show that $\sum_{i=0}^{m} \binom{n+i}{n} x^i = (1 - I(x, m+1, n+1))/(1-x)^{n+1}$.

(ii) Show that the expected wait to k boys and ℓ girls is $W(k, \ell) = \frac{k}{p} \cdot I(1 - p, \ell, k + 1) + \frac{\ell}{1-p} \cdot I(p, k, \ell + 1)$.

Two useful identities: $I(x, m, n) = I(1 - x, n, m)$;
$I(x, m, n + 1) = I(x, m, n) + \binom{m+n-1}{n} x^m (1-x)^n$.

(iii) When boys and girls are equally likely, show that the expected wait for k of each is $(1 + \binom{2k}{k} 2^{-2k}) \cdot 2k$. Give intuition for why it's about the expected time to just k boys.

Problem 20.42. Let $W(k,\ell)$ be the expected wait for k boys and ℓ girls with the probability for a boy being p.
(a) What are $W(k,0)$ and $W(0,\ell)$? Show that $W(k,\ell)$ satisfies the recursion

$$W(k,\ell) = 1 + pW(k-1,\ell) + (1-p)W(k,\ell-1) \qquad \text{(for } k>0 \text{ and } \ell>0\text{)}.$$

(b) Use build-up to compute the expected wait to 2 boys and 2 girls for $p=\frac{1}{3}$ and $p=\frac{1}{2}$.
(c) Prove by induction that the formula in Problem 20.41(d) solves the recursion in (a).

Problem 20.43. Random variables $(\mathbf{X}_1,\ldots,\mathbf{X}_k)$ have joint-PDF $P_{\mathbf{X}_1\cdots\mathbf{X}_k}(x_1,\ldots,x_k)$, where $(x_1,\ldots,x_k)$ is a k-tuple in $\mathbf{X}_1(\Omega)\times\cdots\times\mathbf{X}_k(\Omega)$. Let $\mathbf{Z}=f(\mathbf{X}_1,\ldots,\mathbf{X}_k)$. The expectation of $\mathbf{Z}$ is

$$\mathbb{E}[\mathbf{Z}] = \sum_{\omega\in\Omega} Z(w)\cdot P(\omega) = \sum_{\omega\in\Omega} f(\mathbf{X}_1(\omega),\ldots,\mathbf{X}_k(\omega))\cdot P(\omega).$$

(a) Show that $\mathbb{E}[\mathbf{Z}] = \sum_{(x_1,\ldots,x_k)} f(x_1,\ldots,x_k)\cdot P_{\mathbf{X}_1\cdots\mathbf{X}_k}(x_1,\ldots,x_k)$.
(b) Use (a) with $f(\mathbf{X}_1,\ldots,\mathbf{X}_k)=a_1\mathbf{X}_1+\cdots+a_k\mathbf{X}_k$ to prove linearity of expectation.

Problem 20.44 (Linearity of Conditional Expectation). For random variables $\mathbf{X}_1,\ldots,\mathbf{X}_n$ and event A, prove: $\mathbb{E}[\mathbf{X}_1+\cdots+\mathbf{X}_n \mid A] = \mathbb{E}[\mathbf{X}_1\mid A]+\cdots+\mathbb{E}[\mathbf{X}_n\mid A]$.

Problem 20.45. Is it generally true that $\mathbb{E}[1/\mathbf{X}] = 1/\,\mathbb{E}[\mathbf{X}]$? Is it ever true?

Problem 20.46. Let $\mathbf{X}_1$ and $\mathbf{X}_2$ be independent dice rolls. Determine if the equalities hold. Explain.
(a) $\mathbb{E}[e^{\mathbf{X}_1}] \stackrel{?}{=} e^{\mathbb{E}[\mathbf{X}_1]}$.
(b) $\mathbb{E}[e^{\mathbf{X}_1+\mathbf{X}_2}] \stackrel{?}{=} e^{\mathbb{E}[\mathbf{X}_1]}+e^{\mathbb{E}[\mathbf{X}_2]}$.
(c) $\mathbb{E}[e^{\mathbf{X}_1+\mathbf{X}_2}] \stackrel{?}{=} e^{\mathbb{E}[\mathbf{X}_1+\mathbf{X}_2]}$.
(d) $\mathbb{E}[e^{\mathbf{X}_1+\mathbf{X}_2}] \stackrel{?}{=} e^{\mathbb{E}[\mathbf{X}_1]}\cdot e^{\mathbb{E}[\mathbf{X}_2]}$.
(e) $\mathbb{E}[e^{\mathbf{X}_1+\mathbf{X}_2}] \stackrel{?}{=} \mathbb{E}[e^{\mathbf{X}_1}]\cdot\mathbb{E}[e^{\mathbf{X}_2}]$.
(f) $e^{\mathbb{E}[\mathbf{X}_1+\mathbf{X}_2]} \stackrel{?}{=} e^{\mathbb{E}[\mathbf{X}_1]}\cdot e^{\mathbb{E}[\mathbf{X}_2]}$.
(g) $\mathbb{E}[e^{\mathbf{X}_1\cdot\mathbf{X}_2}] \stackrel{?}{=} e^{\mathbb{E}[\mathbf{X}_1]}\cdot e^{\mathbb{E}[\mathbf{X}_2]}$.
(h) $\mathbb{E}[e^{\mathbf{X}_1\cdot\mathbf{X}_2}] \stackrel{?}{=} \mathbb{E}[e^{\mathbf{X}_1}]\cdot\mathbb{E}[e^{\mathbf{X}_2}]$.

Problem 20.47. Which equalities are true in general, and why? Tinker with $\mathbf{X}_1$ and $\mathbf{X}_2$ being die rolls.
(a) $\mathbb{E}[\log(\mathbf{X}_1+\mathbf{X}_2)] = \mathbb{E}[\log\mathbf{X}_1]+\mathbb{E}[\log\mathbf{X}_1]$.
(b) $\mathbb{E}[\log(\mathbf{X}_1+\mathbf{X}_2)] = \log(\mathbb{E}[\mathbf{X}_1]+\mathbb{E}[\mathbf{X}_1])$.
(c) $\mathbb{E}[\log(\mathbf{X}_1\mathbf{X}_2)] = \mathbb{E}[\log\mathbf{X}_1]+\mathbb{E}[\log\mathbf{X}_1]$.

Problem 20.48. Prove: (a) $\mathbb{E}[(\mathbf{X}+a)^2] = \mathbb{E}[\mathbf{X}^2]+2a\mathbb{E}[\mathbf{X}]+a^2$. (b) $\mathbb{E}[(a_1\mathbf{X}_1+\cdots+a_n\mathbf{X}_n)^2] = \sum_{i=1}^{n}\sum_{j=1}^{n} a_ia_j\mathbb{E}[\mathbf{X}_i\mathbf{X}_j]$.

Problem 20.49. Show $\mathbb{E}[\mathbf{X}^2] = \mathbb{E}[\mathbf{X}]^2+\mathbb{E}[(\mathbf{X}-\mathbb{E}[\mathbf{X}])^2]$, and hence that $\mathbb{E}[\mathbf{X}^2]\geq\mathbb{E}[\mathbf{X}]^2$.

Problem 20.50. Suppose $\mathbf{X}$ is a positive random variable, taking values $x_1,\ldots,x_k$. Prove $\mathbb{E}[1/\mathbf{X}]\geq 1/\,\mathbb{E}[\mathbf{X}]$.

Problem 20.51. For a positive random variable $\mathbf{X}$, taking values $x_1,\ldots,x_k$ with probabilities $p_1,\ldots,p_k$, show $\mathbb{E}[\mathbf{X}^n]\geq\mathbb{E}[\mathbf{X}]^n$, for $n\geq 1$. Use the following steps.
(a) Show the claim for $k=2$: $(p_1x_1^n+p_2x_2^n)\geq(p_1x_1+p_2x_2)^n$. *[Hint: Consider stationary points of the difference.]*
(b) Use induction on k to prove the claim for $k\geq 2$.

Problem 20.52. Show that $\mathbb{E}[\mathbf{X}^{2n}]\geq\mathbb{E}[\mathbf{X}^2]^n$. *[Hint: Problems 20.49 and 20.51.]*

Problem 20.53. For random variable $\mathbf{X}$, define $f(\lambda)=\mathbb{E}[e^{\lambda\mathbf{X}}]$. Show that $\frac{d}{d\lambda}f(\lambda)=\mathbb{E}[\mathbf{X}e^{\lambda\mathbf{X}}]$. (In general, you can take a derivitive inside or pull it outside an expectation, when all quantities are absolutely convergent.)

Problem 20.54 (Expectation and exponentiation). Let $\mathbf{X}$ be a random variable taking finitely many values.
(a) Use the Taylor series of $e^{\mathbf{X}}$ to show that $\mathbb{E}[e^{\mathbf{X}}]=\sum_{i=0}^{\infty}\mathbb{E}[\mathbf{X}^i]/i!$.
(b) Prove $\mathbb{E}[e^{\mathbf{X}}]\geq e^{\mathbb{E}[\mathbf{X}]}$ when $\mathbf{X}$ is a positive random variable. *[Hint: Problem 20.51.]*
(c) Prove $\mathbb{E}[e^{\mathbf{X}}]\geq e^{\mathbb{E}[\mathbf{X}]}$ even if $\mathbf{X}$ can be negative. *[Hint: Start with two possible values for $\mathbf{X}$. Induction.]*

Problem 20.55 (Covariance). Show that for any random variables $\mathbf{X}$ and $\mathbf{Y}$,

$$\mathbb{E}[\mathbf{XY}] = \mathbb{E}[\mathbf{X}]\cdot\mathbb{E}[\mathbf{Y}]+(\mathbb{E}[\mathbf{XY}]-\mathbb{E}[\mathbf{X}]\cdot\mathbb{E}[\mathbf{Y}]).$$

The expected product is the product of expectations when the covariance $\mathrm{Cov}(\mathbf{X},\mathbf{Y})=\mathbb{E}[\mathbf{XY}]-\mathbb{E}[\mathbf{X}]\cdot\mathbb{E}[\mathbf{Y}]=0$. Random variables with zero covariance are *uncorrelated.* Independent implies uncorrelated (independence is stronger than uncorrelated). Give random variables $\mathbf{X},\mathbf{Y}$ which are uncorrelated but dependent.

Problem 20.56 (Jensen's Inequality). A function f is convex if, for any $\alpha \in [0,1]$,

$$f(\alpha x + (1-\alpha)y) \leq \alpha f(x) + (1-\alpha)f(y)$$

(a) If $\mathbf{X}$ takes on two possible values, prove that $\mathbb{E}[f(\mathbf{X})] \geq \mathbb{E}[f(\mathbf{X})]$.
(b) Prove by induction on the number of possible values of $\mathbf{X}$ that $\mathbb{E}[f(\mathbf{X})] \geq \mathbb{E}[f(\mathbf{X})]$.
(c) Prove that $\frac{1}{x}, e^x, x^2, -\ln x$ are convex on $(0,\infty), (-\infty,\infty), [0,\infty), (0,\infty)$ respectively.
(d) Prove: (i) $\mathbb{E}[1/\mathbf{X}] \geq 1/\mathbb{E}[\mathbf{X}]$. (ii) $\mathbb{E}[e^{\mathbf{X}}] \geq e^{\mathbb{E}[\mathbf{X}]}$. (iii) $\mathbb{E}[\mathbf{X}^2] \geq \mathbb{E}[\mathbf{X}]^2$. (iv) $\mathbb{E}[\ln \mathbf{X}] \leq \ln \mathbb{E}[\mathbf{X}]$.

Problem 20.57 (Linearity and Infinite Sums). Define the betting sequence $1, 2, 4, 8, \ldots$, that is $b_t = 2^{t-1}$. At step t, a gambler bets $\$b_t$ on a fair coin flip. If the flip is H, he wins $\$b_t$; otherwise he loses $\$b_t$. If the gambler wins at step t, the game stops. Let $\mathbf{X}$ be the gambler's winnings at the end of the game.

(a) Compute the expected winnings using the waiting time distribution for when the game stops. Let P_t be the probability the gambler stops betting at step t.
 (i) Show that $P_t = 2^{-t}$ and that if the game stops at step t, the gambler's winnings is $\$1$.
 (ii) Show that the expected winnings is $\mathbb{E}[\mathbf{X}] = \sum_{t=1}^{\infty} P_t = 1$.
(b) Compute the expected winnings using linearity of expectation. At step t, the gambler wins an amount $\mathbf{X}_t$ where $\mathbf{X}_t \in \{0, 2^{t-1}, -2^{t-1}\}$, and $\mathbf{X}_t$ is zero if the game stops before step t.
 (i) Compute $\mathbb{P}[\mathbf{X}_t = 0]$, $\mathbb{P}[\mathbf{X}_t = 2^{t-1}]$ and $\mathbb{P}[\mathbf{X}_t = -2^{t-1}]$. Hence, compute $\mathbb{E}[\mathbf{X}_t]$.
 (ii) Show that $\mathbf{X} = \mathbf{X}_1 + \mathbf{X}_2 + \mathbf{X}_3 + \cdots$. Use linearity of expectation to compute $\mathbb{E}[\mathbf{X}]$.
 (iii) Explain the discrepancy between the results from (a) and (b).
(c) If the game stops after T steps, show that (a) and (b) give the same expected winnings.

Probabilistic Method. The probabilistic method is a modern technique that uses probability and expectations to prove results about a deterministic setting.

Problem 20.58 (Ramsey Numbers). Fix $k > 1$. Suppose n satisfies $2\binom{n}{k}2^{-\frac{1}{2}k(k-1)} < 1$. Prove that some graph with n vertices has neither a k-clique nor a k-war. So, you need more than n vertices to *guarantee* a k-clique or a k-war. (Recall $n = 6$ ensures a 3-clique or 3-war.)

(a) Let $S_1, S_2, \ldots, S_M$ be the distinct k-subsets of the n vertices. What is M?
(b) Generate a random graph on n vertices $v_1, \ldots, v_n$ by independently adding each edge (v_i, v_j) into the edge set with probability $\frac{1}{2}$. Show that $\mathbb{P}[S_i$ is a k-clique or k-war$] = 2 \times 2^{-\frac{1}{2}k(k-1)}$.
(c) Let $\mathbf{X}_i = 1$ if S_i is a k-clique or k-war, and 0 otherwize. What is $\mathbb{E}[\mathbf{X}_i]$.
(d) Let $\mathbf{X}$ be the total number of k-cliques or k-wars. What is $\mathbb{E}[\mathbf{X}]$?
(e) Explain why to prove the claim, it suffices that $\mathbb{E}[\mathbf{X}] < 1$.
(f) For $k \in [5, 10]$, what is the largest n for which $2\binom{n}{k}2^{-\frac{1}{2}k(k-1)} < 1$? If $ne \leq k2^{\frac{1}{2}(k-1)-\frac{1}{k}}$, prove there is an n-vertex graph with no k-clique or k-war. *[Hint: $\binom{n}{k} \leq (ne/k)^k$.]*

Problem 20.59. Prove that every graph $G = (V, E)$ has a cut of size at least $|E|/2$. (A cut partitions V into two disjoint sets A, B; its size is the number of edges crossing from A to B.)

(a) Construct the sets A, B by randomly placing vertices independently into one of the sets. Let $e = (u, v)$ be an edge in the graph. Compute $\mathbb{P}[u$ and v are in different sets$]$.
(b) Define the indicator $\mathbf{X}(e) = 1$ if u and v are in different sets. Show that the value of the cut is $\mathbf{X} = \sum_{e \in E} \mathbf{X}(e)$. Compute $\mathbb{E}[\mathbf{X}]$ and prove the claim (Problem 19.3 will help).

Problem 20.60. In Problem 20.59 you proved there is always a cut of size at least $|E|/2$. The *randomized algorithm* of independently placing each vertex into one of the two sets A or B (each with probability $\frac{1}{2}$) gives a cut with expected size $|E|/2$. Unfortunately, this algorithm will not always find a cut of size $|E|/2$, even though one exists. It is even *possible* to produce a cut of size zero, and that's unsettling. Here's one way to "derandomize" the algorithm.

(a) For vertices $v_1, v_2, \ldots, v_n$ let $\mathbf{X}_1, \mathbf{X}_2, \ldots, \mathbf{X}_n$ indicate which set each vertex is in ($\mathbf{X}_i = 1$ if $v_i \in A$ and $\mathbf{X}_i = 0$ if $v_i \in B$). Let $\mathbf{Z}$ be the cut-size. What are: $\mathbb{E}[\mathbf{Z}]$, $\mathbb{E}[\mathbf{Z} \mid \mathbf{X}_1 = 0]$ and $\mathbb{E}[\mathbf{Z} \mid \mathbf{X}_1 = 1]$?
(b) Suppose $\mathbf{X}_1, \mathbf{X}_2, \ldots, \mathbf{X}_k$ are fixed to $x_1, x_2, \ldots, x_k$. Show that

$$\mathbb{E}[\mathbf{Z} \mid x_1, \ldots, x_k] = \tfrac{1}{2}\,\mathbb{E}[\mathbf{Z} \mid x_1, \ldots, x_k, \mathbf{X}_{k+1} = 0] + \tfrac{1}{2}\,\mathbb{E}[\mathbf{Z} \mid x_1, \ldots, x_k, \mathbf{X}_{k+1} = 1].$$

So, one of the conditional expectations on the RHS is at least as large as $\mathbb{E}[\mathbf{Z} \mid x_1, \ldots, x_k]$.

(c) As in (b), suppose $\mathbf{X}_1, \mathbf{X}_2, \ldots, \mathbf{X}_k$ are fixed to $x_1, x_2, \ldots, x_k$ (the first k vertices are placed in sets A or B). Let δ_A (resp. δ_B) be the number of edges from v_{k+1} to the vertices already placed in A (resp. B). Show that

$$\mathbb{E}[\mathbf{Z} \mid x_1, \ldots, x_k, \mathbf{X}_{k+1} = 1] - \mathbb{E}[\mathbf{Z} \mid x_1, \ldots, x_k, \mathbf{X}_{k+1} = 0] = \delta_B - \delta_A.$$

Set $x_{k+1} = \begin{cases} 1 & \text{if } \delta_B \geq \delta_A \\ 0 & \text{otherwise,} \end{cases}$ and prove that $\mathbb{E}[\mathbf{Z} \mid x_1, \ldots, x_k] \leq \mathbb{E}[\mathbf{Z} \mid x_1, \ldots, x_k, x_{k+1}]$.

(d) Prove that the sequential *greedy* algorithm which deterministically places vertex v_k in the set to which v_k has fewer edges must produce a cut of size at least $|E|/2$.

This technique for derandomizing an algorithm is called the method of conditional expectations.

Problem 20.61. Consider this collection of 8 logical OR-clauses (each OR has 3 variables):

$$(x \vee y \vee z) \quad (\overline{x} \vee \overline{y} \vee z) \quad (\overline{x} \vee \overline{z} \vee w) \quad (\overline{x} \vee \overline{z} \vee w) \quad (y \vee z \vee w) \quad (x \vee \overline{y} \vee w) \quad (y \vee \overline{z} \vee \overline{w}) \quad (x \vee \overline{z} \vee \overline{w})$$

The goal is to choose T/F for each variable so that a maximum number of OR-clauses is T. The probabilistic method gives a quick proof that at least 7 clauses can simultaneously be true.

(a) Choose each variable to be T/F randomly and independently. Show: $\mathbb{P}[\text{OR-clause is T}] = \frac{7}{8}$.

(b) Let $\mathbf{X}_i = 1$ if the ith clause is satisfied and 0 otherwise. The number of satisfied clauses is $\mathbf{X} = \sum_i \mathbf{X}_i$. Compute $\mathbb{E}[\mathbf{X}]$ and prove that at least 7 clauses are simultaneously satisfiable.

(c) If there were seven (not eight) clauses, prove that one can always satisfy all seven clauses.

(d) Generalize. Suppose there are n clauses $C_1, \ldots, C_n$ and clause C_i has k_i *different* variables. Prove: One can choose T/F for each variable so that at least $\sum_i (1 - 2^{-k_i})$ clauses are T.

Problem 20.62. In Problem 20.61, by randomly picking the truth-value of each variable, on average, $\frac{7}{8}$-th of the clauses are satisfied. This randomized algorithm does not guarantee a truth-assignment with at least $\frac{7}{8}$-th of the clauses satisfied. Use the method of conditional expectations (Problem 20.60) to derandomize this algorithm. Suppose there are n variables and m clauses. Let $\mathbf{X}_1, \ldots, \mathbf{X}_n$ indicate which variables are T. Let $\mathbf{Z}$ be the number of clauses satisfied.

(a) Suppose $\mathbf{X}_1, \ldots, \mathbf{X}_k$ are fixed to $x_1, \ldots, x_k$. Show that

$$\mathbb{E}[\mathbf{Z} \mid x_1, \ldots, x_k] = \tfrac{1}{2}\,\mathbb{E}\left[\mathbf{Z} \mid x_1, \ldots, x_k, \mathbf{X}_{k+1} = \text{T}\right] + \tfrac{1}{2}\,\mathbb{E}\left[\mathbf{Z} \mid x_1, \ldots, x_k, \mathbf{X}_{k+1} = \text{F}\right].$$

So, one of the conditional expectations on the RHS is at least as large as $\mathbb{E}[\mathbf{Z} \mid x_1, \ldots, x_k]$.

(b) Fix $\mathbf{X}_1, \ldots, \mathbf{X}_k$ to $x_1, \ldots, x_k$. Set $x_{k+1} = \text{T}$ if $\mathbb{E}[\mathbf{Z} \mid x_1, \ldots, x_k, \mathbf{X}_{k+1} = \text{T}] \geq \mathbb{E}[\mathbf{Z} \mid x_1, \ldots, x_k, \mathbf{X}_{k+1} = \text{F}]$, and $x_{k+1} = \text{F}$ otherwise. Prove that

$$\mathbb{E}[\mathbf{Z} \mid x_1, \ldots, x_k] \leq \mathbb{E}[\mathbf{Z} \mid x_1, \ldots, x_k, x_{k+1}].$$

How do you determine if $\mathbb{E}[\mathbf{Z} \mid x_1, \ldots, x_k, \mathbf{X}_{k+1} = \text{T}] \geq \mathbb{E}[\mathbf{Z} \mid x_1, \ldots, x_k, \mathbf{X}_{k+1} = \text{F}]$?

(c) Use (b) to give the details of a greedy algorithm to assign truth-values that satisfy at least $\frac{7}{8}$-th of the clauses. Prove it, and give the asymptotic runtime of the algorithm.

Problem 20.63. A graph $G = (V, E)$ has n vertices, m edges, and degree sequence $\delta_1, \ldots, \delta_n$. Let the $n \times n$ adjacency matrix be A ($\text{A}_{ij} = 1$ if edge $(v_i, v_j) \in E$ and 0 otherwise). Let $x_1, \ldots, x_n$ be *any* sequence of n numbers with $x_i \in [0, 1]$. Let α be the size of a maximum independent set in G. Show that

$$\alpha \geq \sum_{i=1}^{n} x_i - \tfrac{1}{2} \sum_{i=1}^{n} \sum_{j=1}^{n} \text{A}_{ij} x_i x_j. \tag{20.7}$$

(a) Remove each vertex v_i (and its edges) independently, with probability $1 - x_i$. Let $\mathbf{X}$ be the number of vertices and $\mathbf{Y}$ the number of edges which remain in the graph. Show that:

$$\mathbb{E}[\mathbf{X}] = \sum_{i=1}^{n} x_i \qquad \text{and} \qquad \mathbb{E}\left[\mathbf{Y}\right] = \tfrac{1}{2} \sum_{i=1}^{n} \sum_{j=1}^{n} \text{A}_{ij} x_i x_j.$$

(b) After doing part (a), repeat until no edges remain: pick any edge and remove one of its vertices, the one with the largest number of incident (remaining) edges. Prove that you remove at most $\mathbf{Y}$ vertices.

(c) Prove there are at least $\mathbf{X} - \mathbf{Y}$ independent vertices remaining after (b). Hence, conclude there is an independent set of size at least $\mathbb{E}[\mathbf{X} - \mathbf{Y}]$ and prove (20.7).

(d) Suppose the x_i are a constant x. Show that $\alpha \geq nx - mx^2$. Maximize the RHS and show that there is an independent set of size at least $n/2\bar{\delta}$, where $\bar{\delta}$ is the average degree.

(e) Set $x_i = 1/\delta_i$ and prove that $\alpha \geq \frac{1}{2} \sum_{i=1}^{n} 1/\delta_i$. *[Hint:* $\frac{1}{ab} \leq \frac{1}{2}(\frac{1}{a^2} + \frac{1}{b^2})$*.]*

(f) Given the optimal $x_i^* \in [0, 1]$ that maximize (20.7), show how to derandomize the algorithm using conditional expectations (see Problems 20.60 and 20.62) to deterministically get an independent set satisfying (20.7) with x_i^*.

(g) Prove that for the optimal $x_i^* \in [0, 1]$ which maximize (20.7), you get equality in (20.7).

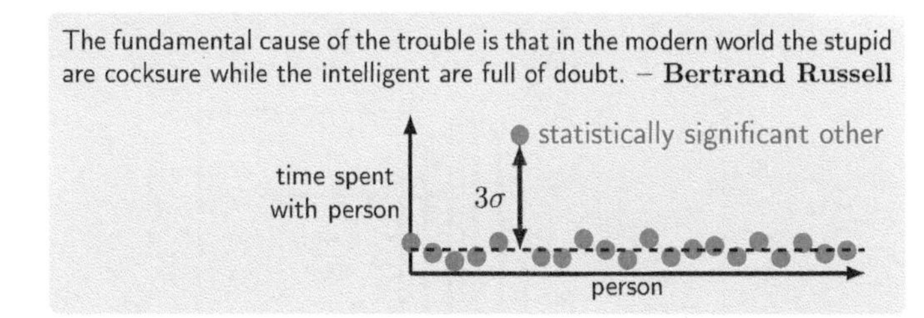

Chapter 21

Deviations from the Mean

1: Quantifying deviations from the mean: variance and the 3-sigma rule.

The mean, or expected value, summarizes a random variable. It's not the whole story.

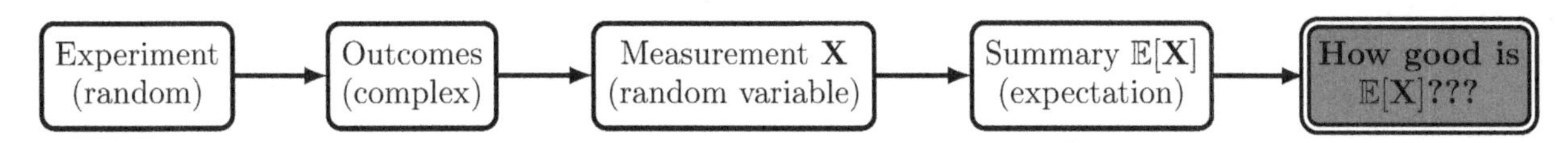

Let's do an experiment. You can do this experiment along with us at home.

Experiment. Roll n dice and compute $\mathbf{X}$, the average of the n rolls.

The expected sum of n dice is $n \times 3\frac{1}{2}$ (see page 294). By linearity of expectation,

$$\mathbb{E}[\text{average of } n \text{ dice}] = \mathbb{E}[\text{sum}/n] = \mathbb{E}[\text{sum}]/n = (n \times 3\tfrac{1}{2})/n = 3\tfrac{1}{2}.$$

The number of rolls does not matter, the expected average is $3\frac{1}{2}$. Try it with different n, see Figure 21.1.

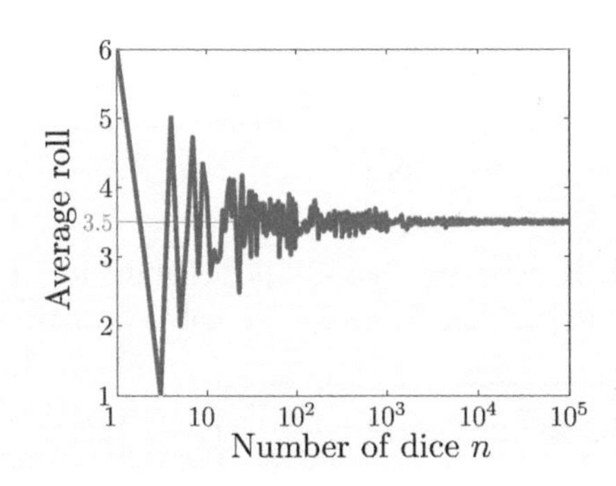

Figure 21.1: **Average of n dice rolls.** The figure shows the average of n independent dice rolls from a single experiment, plotted versus n. For small n, things vary wildly. For large n, things settle down to the expected value of $3\frac{1}{2}$. The observed average of n dice seems to depend on n, though its expected value does not.

The number of dice matters. The average of few dice fluctuates wildly, but the average of many dice "converges". The mean is more useful when the actual measurement deviates little from it.

Look at the PDFs in Figure 21.2, which compare the average for 4 dice with 100 dice. Both PDFs are centered around the same mean in red. However, for 4 dice, the distribution is much wider: the probable values for 4 dice are between 1 and 6 and the probable values for 100 dice are between 3 and 4, a much tighter range, closer to the mean. The average of 100 dice will almost never be 1 (probability $(\frac{1}{6})^{100} \approx 0$). In Figure 21.2, the arrow labeled σ describes this width. The mean is a good summary of $\mathbf{X}$ only when the width is small and the likely values of $\mathbf{X}$ are concentrated around the mean. A measure for this width is a range around the mean, mean $\pm\,\sigma$, into which $\mathbf{X}$ will fall with high probability (say) 95%. Unfortunately, this high-probability width is hard to handle mathematically. The variance is convenient and almost as good.

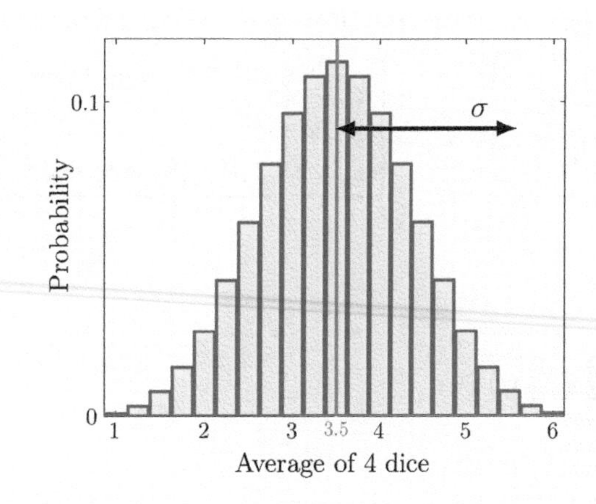

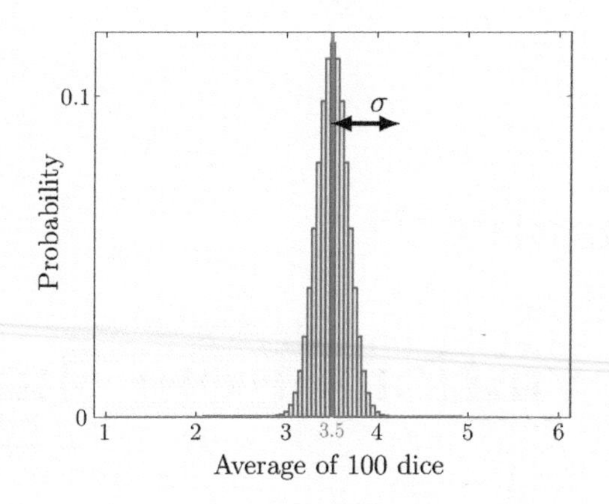

Figure 21.2: (Left) Average of 4 dice (21 possible values $1, 1\frac{1}{4}, \ldots, 6$). (Right) Average of 100 dice (501 possible values $1, 1\frac{1}{100}, \ldots, 6$). We plot (aggregated) probabilities for the average to be within a range defined by the width of the bar. The PDF's are centered on the mean of $3\frac{1}{2}$ with a "width" (or spread) indicated by the arrow labeled σ.

21.1 Variance

We refer to $\mathbb{E}[\mathbf{X}]$ by $\mu(\mathbf{X})$, or just μ (μ is the Greek letter "m", for mean). If μ is a good summary of the PDF, then $\mathbf{X}$ should not deviate much from μ. Define the deviation $\boldsymbol{\Delta}$ of the observed value $\mathbf{X}$ from its mean μ,

$$\boldsymbol{\Delta} = \mathbf{X} - \mu.$$

Remember, always, that the mean μ is just a number, a constant. The deviation $\boldsymbol{\Delta}$ is a random variable ($\mathbf{X}$ shifted by a constant μ). Consider the sum of two dice, with $\mu = 7$.

$\mathbf{X}$	2	3	4	5	6	7	8	9	10	11	12	
$\boldsymbol{\Delta}$	−5	−4	−3	−2	−1	0	1	2	3	4	5	$\leftarrow \mathbf{X} - 7$
$P_\mathbf{X}$	$\frac{1}{36}$	$\frac{2}{36}$	$\frac{3}{36}$	$\frac{4}{36}$	$\frac{5}{36}$	$\frac{6}{36}$	$\frac{5}{36}$	$\frac{4}{36}$	$\frac{3}{36}$	$\frac{2}{36}$	$\frac{1}{36}$	← Pop Quiz 18.3 (page 261)

Pop Quiz 21.1

The expected deviation, $\mathbb{E}[\boldsymbol{\Delta}]$ should be a good candidate to measure the quality of the mean μ. Compute $\mathbb{E}[\boldsymbol{\Delta}]$ for the sum of two dice. Prove that $\mathbb{E}[\boldsymbol{\Delta}] = 0$ for any random variable $\mathbf{X}$.

The expected deviation is always zero. Negative deviations when $\mathbf{X}$ is below μ cancel positive deviations when $\mathbf{X}$ is above μ. Any deviation, positive or negative is bad. By squaring the deviation we get a positive error.[1]

Variance, σ^2, is the expected value of the squared deviations,

$$\sigma^2 = \mathbb{E}[\boldsymbol{\Delta}^2] = \mathbb{E}[(\mathbf{X} - \mu)^2] = \mathbb{E}[(\mathbf{X} - \mathbb{E}[\mathbf{X}])^2]$$

When the context is clear, we just say σ^2 instead of $\sigma^2(\mathbf{X})$. Let's compute the variance for a sum of 2 dice. To compute the expected squared deviation, weight squared deviations by their probabilities and add.

$\mathbf{X}$	2	3	4	5	6	7	8	9	10	11	12	
$\boldsymbol{\Delta}^2$	25	16	9	4	1	0	1	4	9	16	25	$\leftarrow (\mathbf{X} - 7)^2$
$P_\mathbf{X}$	$\frac{1}{36}$	$\frac{2}{36}$	$\frac{3}{36}$	$\frac{4}{36}$	$\frac{5}{36}$	$\frac{6}{36}$	$\frac{5}{36}$	$\frac{4}{36}$	$\frac{3}{36}$	$\frac{2}{36}$	$\frac{1}{36}$	

[1]You could also take the absolute value, but that is mathematically less convenient.

$$\sigma^2 = \mathbb{E}[\Delta^2] = \frac{1}{36}\cdot 25+\frac{2}{36}\cdot 16+\frac{3}{36}\cdot 9+\frac{4}{36}\cdot 4+\frac{5}{36}\cdot 1+\frac{6}{36}\cdot 0+\frac{5}{36}\cdot 1+\frac{4}{36}\cdot 4+\frac{3}{36}\cdot 9+\frac{2}{36}\cdot 16+\frac{1}{36}\cdot 25$$
$$= 5\frac{5}{6}.$$

The variance measures the squared deviations, hence it is σ^2. The square-root of the variance, known as the standard-deviation, quantifies the sizes of the unsquared deviations,

$$\sigma = \sqrt{\text{variance}} = \sqrt{5\tfrac{5}{6}} \approx 2.52.$$

The standard-deviation quantifies the size of deviations from the mean. One often reports $\mu \pm \sigma$,

"The sum of two dice is 7 plus or minus 2.52," or $\mathbf{X} = 7 \pm 2.52.$

This strange way to report μ and σ suggests $\mathbf{X}$ is likely to be in the interval $[4.48, 9.52]$. We will say more on this later. The larger the standard deviation, the larger this interval and the worse μ is at summarizing $\mathbf{X}$.

Standard Deviation, σ, is the square-root of the variance,

$$\sigma = \sqrt{\mathbb{E}[\Delta^2]} = \sqrt{\mathbb{E}[(\mathbf{X}-\mu)^2]} = \sqrt{\mathbb{E}[(\mathbf{X}-\mathbb{E}[\mathbf{X}])^2]}$$

Exercise 21.2

(a) Compute the variance and standard deviation of: (i) a single die roll (ii) the average of two dice rolls.
(b) Compute the variance and standard deviation of a Bernoulli with probability p.
(c) For the sum of two dice rolls, compute the probability that $\mathbf{X} \in [\mu - \sigma, \mu + \sigma]$.

Example 21.1 (Risk). Consider these two gambles (each are free to play).

$\mathbf{X}_1$: win \$2 probability $= \frac{2}{3}$; lose \$1 probability $= \frac{1}{3}$.

$\mathbf{X}_2$: win \$102 probability $= \frac{2}{3}$; lose \$201 probability $= \frac{1}{3}$.

We leave the reader to show that $\mathbb{E}[\mathbf{X}_1] = \mathbb{E}[\mathbf{X}_2] = \$1$. In both gambles, your expected winning is \$1. In both gambles, the probability of winning is the same, significantly above $\frac{1}{2}$. Yet, I would happily take gamble $\mathbf{X}_1$. I won't take gamble $\mathbf{X}_2$ because it's too risky. The two gambles are differentiated by their variance,

$$\sigma^2(\mathbf{X}_1) = \tfrac{2}{3}\cdot(2-1)^2 + \tfrac{1}{3}\cdot(-1-1)^2 = 2;$$
$$\sigma^2(\mathbf{X}_2) = \tfrac{2}{3}\cdot(102-1)^2 + \tfrac{1}{3}\cdot(-201-1)^2 \approx 2\times 10^4.$$

The variance captures the risk: $\mathbf{X}_1 = 1 \pm \sqrt{2}$ and $\mathbf{X}_2 = 1 \pm 142$. For an expected profit of \$1, you might risk a small loss as in gamble $\mathbf{X}_1$, but not a huge loss as in gamble $\mathbf{X}_2$. □

21.1.1 Computing Variance

We now derive a formula which is usually the most practical way to compute the variance. We start from the definition of the variance, and use linearity of expectation.

$$\begin{aligned}
\sigma^2 &= \mathbb{E}[(\mathbf{X}-\mu)^2] \\
&= \mathbb{E}[\mathbf{X}^2 - 2\mu\mathbf{X} + \mu^2] && \leftarrow \text{Expand } (\mathbf{X}-\mu)^2 \\
&= \mathbb{E}[\mathbf{X}^2] - 2\mu\,\mathbb{E}[\mathbf{X}] + \mu^2 && \leftarrow \text{Linearity of expectation} \\
&= \mathbb{E}[\mathbf{X}^2] - \mu^2. && \leftarrow \mathbb{E}[\mathbf{X}] = \mu
\end{aligned}$$

To get the variance: (i) find the squared mean μ^2; (ii) Find the expected square, $\mathbb{E}[\mathbf{X}^2]$; (iii) Subtract.

Variance: $\sigma^2 = \mathbb{E}[\mathbf{X}^2] - \mu^2 = \mathbb{E}[\mathbf{X}^2] - \mathbb{E}[\mathbf{X}]^2.$

Let's see how this method works for the sum of two dice. Using the definition of $\mathbb{E}[\mathbf{X}^2]$,

$$\begin{aligned}\mathbb{E}[\mathbf{X}^2] &= \sum_{x=2}^{12} P_{\mathbf{X}}(x)\cdot x^2\\ &= \frac{1}{36}\cdot 2^2+\frac{2}{36}\cdot 3^2+\frac{3}{36}\cdot 4^2+\frac{4}{36}\cdot 5^2+\frac{5}{36}\cdot 6^2+\frac{6}{36}\cdot 7^2+\frac{5}{36}\cdot 8^2+\frac{4}{36}\cdot 9^2+\frac{3}{36}\cdot 10^2+\frac{2}{36}\cdot 11^2+\frac{1}{36}\cdot 12^2\\ &= 54\frac{5}{6}.\end{aligned}$$

Since $\mu = 7$, we have that $\sigma^2 = 54\frac{5}{6} - 7^2 = 5\frac{5}{6}$, as we got before.

Exercise 21.3
In Exercise 21.2(a) and (b), compute $\mathbb{E}[\mathbf{X}^2]$, $\mathbb{E}[\mathbf{X}]$ and verify that $\sigma^2 = \mathbb{E}[\mathbf{X}^2] - \mathbb{E}[\mathbf{X}]^2$.

For more practice, let's compute the variance of some familiar random variables.

Uniform. If $\mathbf{X} \sim \mathbf{U}[n]$, $\mathbb{E}[\mathbf{X}^2] = \frac{1}{n}(1^2 + \cdots + n^2) = \frac{1}{n} \times \frac{n}{6}(n+1)(2n+1)$, where we used the formula for the sum of the first n squares. By Theorem 19.3 on page 279, $\mathbb{E}[\mathbf{X}] = \frac{1}{2}(n+1)$. Using $\sigma^2 = \mathbb{E}[\mathbf{X}^2] - \mathbb{E}[\mathbf{X}]^2$, we get

$$\sigma^2(\text{Uniform}) = \tfrac{1}{6}(n+1)(2n+1) - (\tfrac{1}{2}(n+1))^2 = \tfrac{1}{12}(n^2-1). \quad (21.1)$$

Bernoulli. For a Bernoulli $\mathbf{X}$ with success probability p, we know that $\mathbb{E}[\mathbf{X}] = p$. For the expectation of the square, we have $\mathbb{E}[\mathbf{X}^2] = p \cdot 1^2 + (1-p)\cdot 0^2 = p$. Therefore

$$\sigma^2(\text{Bernoulli}) = \mathbb{E}[\mathbf{X}^2] - \mathbb{E}[\mathbf{X}]^2 = p - p^2 = p(1-p). \quad (21.2)$$

Binomial. For a Binomial $\mathbf{X}$, the number of successes in n trials with success probability p, we showed in Theorem 19.5 on page 280 that $\mathbb{E}[\mathbf{X}] = np$. In Exercise 19.6(b) on page 281, you laboriously showed that $\mathbb{E}[\mathbf{X}(\mathbf{X}-1)] = n(n-1)p^2$. By linearity of expectation,

$$n(n-1)p^2 = \mathbb{E}[\mathbf{X}(\mathbf{X}-1)] = \mathbb{E}[\mathbf{X}^2 - \mathbf{X}] = \mathbb{E}[\mathbf{X}^2] - \mathbb{E}[\mathbf{X}] = \mathbb{E}[\mathbf{X}^2] - np.$$

Therefore, $\mathbb{E}[\mathbf{X}^2] = n(n-1)p^2 + np$ and

$$\sigma^2(\text{Binomial}(n,p)) = \mathbb{E}[\mathbf{X}^2] - \mathbb{E}[\mathbf{X}]^2 = n(n-1)p^2 + np - n^2p^2 = np(1-p). \quad (21.3)$$

Waiting times. For the waiting time $\mathbf{X}$ with success probability p, $\mathbb{E}[\mathbf{X}] = 1/p$ (Theorem 19.7 on page 281). From (20.1) on page 295 we have that $\mathbb{E}[\mathbf{X}^2] = (2-p)/p^2$. Therefore,

$$\sigma^2(\text{Waiting Time}) = \mathbb{E}[\mathbf{X}^2] - \mathbb{E}[\mathbf{X}]^2 = \frac{2-p}{p^2} - \frac{1}{p^2} = \frac{1-p}{p^2}. \quad (21.4)$$

21.1.2 Variance is Non-Negative

For any non-negative random variable $\mathbf{X}$, $\mathbb{E}[\mathbf{X}] = \sum_\omega \mathbf{X}(\omega)P(\omega) \geq 0$, because the terms in the sum are all non-negative products. The squared deviation $\mathbf{\Delta}^2 = (\mathbf{X}-\mu)^2$ is non-negative, therefore its expected value, the variance, is non-negative. That is, $\sigma^2 = \mathbb{E}[\mathbf{\Delta}^2] \geq 0$. Since $\sigma^2 = \mathbb{E}[\mathbf{X}^2] - \mathbb{E}[\mathbf{X}]^2 \geq 0$, we conclude

$$\mathbb{E}[\mathbf{X}^2] \geq \mathbb{E}[\mathbf{X}]^2. \quad (21.5)$$

Memorize this important inequality. The expected square is larger than the square of the expectation.

Example 21.2 (The average of reciprocals is at least the reciprocal of the average)**.** We prove this result indirectly using probability. Let $x_1, \ldots, x_n$ be positive. Their average is $x_{\text{av}} = (x_1 + \cdots + x_n)/n$. We prove

$$\frac{1}{n}\sum_{i=1}^{n}\frac{1}{x_i} \geq \frac{1}{x_{\text{av}}}.$$

Our goal is to use $\mathbb{E}[\mathbf{X}^2] > \mathbb{E}[\mathbf{X}]^2$ by analyzing the mean and variance of some random variable $\mathbf{X}$. Play along as we let $\mathbf{X}$ be a random variable taking on values $1/x_1, \ldots, 1/x_n$ with probabilities $p_i = x_i/nx_{\text{av}}$. You may verify that $p_i \geq 0$ and $\sum_{i=1}^n p_i = 1$ so these are valid probabilities.

$$\mathbb{E}[\mathbf{X}^2] = \sum_{i=1}^{n} \frac{1}{x_i^2} \cdot p_i = \sum_{i=1}^{n} \frac{1}{x_i^2} \cdot \frac{x_i}{n x_{\text{av}}} = \frac{1}{n x_{\text{av}}} \sum_{i=1}^{n} \frac{1}{x_i}.$$

The expected square of $\mathbf{X}$ involves an expression we want, $\sum 1/x_i$. Let's compute $\mathbb{E}[\mathbf{X}]$,

$$\mathbb{E}[\mathbf{X}] = \sum_{i=1}^{n} \frac{1}{x_i} \cdot p_i = \sum_{i=1}^{n} \frac{1}{x_i} \cdot \frac{x_i}{n x_{\text{av}}} = \frac{1}{n x_{\text{av}}} \sum_{i=1}^{n} 1 = \frac{\cancel{n}}{\cancel{n} x_{\text{av}}} = \frac{1}{x_{\text{av}}}.$$

Since $\mathbb{E}[\mathbf{X}^2] \geq \mathbb{E}[\mathbf{X}]^2$, for any random variable $\mathbf{X}$, we conclude that

$$\frac{1}{n x_{\text{av}}} \sum_{i=1}^{n} \frac{1}{x_i} \geq \frac{1}{x_{\text{av}}^2} \qquad \text{or,} \qquad \frac{1}{n} \sum_{i=1}^{n} \frac{1}{x_i} \geq \frac{1}{x_{\text{av}}}.$$

Are you mesmerized? Where did $\mathbf{X}$ come from? We invented it. We analyzed a made-up random variable and got a deterministic fact about positive numbers. The creativity was inventing the right $\mathbf{X}$. □

21.2 Variance of a Sum

The variance does not behave like the expectation when you linearly transform a random variable. For example, let $\mathbf{X}$ be a Bernoulli random variable and $\mathbf{Y} = a + \mathbf{X}$, where a is a constant. The distribution of $\mathbf{Y}$ is

$$\mathbf{Y} = \begin{cases} a+1 & \text{with probability } p; \\ a & \text{with probability } 1-p. \end{cases}$$

The expectation transforms linearly as we expect, $\mathbb{E}[\mathbf{Y}] = p \cdot (a+1) + (1-p) \cdot a = a + p = a + \mathbb{E}[\mathbf{X}]$. That is, the expectation increases by a. The deviations for $\mathbf{Y}$ are obtained by subtracting the mean $a+p$ from $\mathbf{Y}$:

$$\mathbf{\Delta_Y} = \begin{cases} 1-p & \text{with probability } p; \\ -p & \text{with probability } 1-p, \end{cases}$$

The deviations do not depend on a. Hence, the variance or expected squared deviation won't depend on a:

$$\sigma^2(\mathbf{Y}) = p \cdot (1-p)^2 + (1-p) \cdot (-p)^2 = p(1-p) = \sigma^2(\mathbf{X}).$$

By adding a constant, we transformed $\mathbf{X}$ to get $\mathbf{Y}$, yet the variance did not change. The deviations from the mean for $\mathbf{X}$ are the same as the deviations for $\mathbf{Y}$ because both $\mathbf{Y}$ and its mean are both shifted by a:

$$\mathbf{\Delta_Y} = \mathbf{Y} - \mathbb{E}[\mathbf{Y}] = \mathbf{X} + a - (\mathbb{E}[\mathbf{X}] + a) = \mathbf{X} - \mathbb{E}[\mathbf{X}] = \mathbf{\Delta_X}.$$

The a cancels. Suppose, instead, we multiply $\mathbf{X}$ by a constant to get $\mathbf{Y} = b\mathbf{X}$,

$$\mathbf{Y} = \begin{cases} b & \text{with probability } p; \\ 0 & \text{with probability } 1-p. \end{cases}$$

The expected value transforms linearly as we expect, $\mathbb{E}[\mathbf{Y}] = p \cdot b + (1-p) \cdot 0 = pb = b\,\mathbb{E}[\mathbf{X}]$. The expected square is tricky. Since $\mathbf{Y}^2 = b^2\mathbf{X}^2$, linearity says $\mathbb{E}[\mathbf{Y}^2] = b^2\,\mathbb{E}[\mathbf{X}^2]$ and indeed this is the case,

$$\mathbb{E}[\mathbf{Y}^2] = p \cdot b^2 + (1-p) \cdot 0 = pb^2 = b^2\,\mathbb{E}[\mathbf{X}^2].$$

A simple calculation now shows that the variance is multiplied by b^2, not b:

$$\sigma^2(\mathbf{Y}) = \mathbb{E}[\mathbf{Y}^2] - \mathbb{E}[\mathbf{Y}]^2 = pb^2 - p^2b^2 = b^2 p(1-p) = b^2\sigma^2(\mathbf{X}).$$

These facts are true for any random variable, not just for a Bernoulli. We state them as a Theorem.

Theorem 21.3. Let $\mathbf{Y} = a + b\mathbf{X}$. Then, $\sigma^2(\mathbf{Y}) = b^2\sigma^2(\mathbf{X})$.

Exercise 21.4

Prove Theorem 21.3. Apply Theorem 21.3 to a drunk who steps right, $\mathbf{Y} = +1$, with probability p or left, $\mathbf{Y} = -1$, with probability $1-p$. Relate $\mathbf{Y}$ to a Bernoulli and use Theorem 21.3 to compute $\sigma^2(\mathbf{Y})$.

We now tackle the variance of a sum. Let $\mathbf{X}$ be the sum of two dice rolls $\mathbf{X}_1$ and $\mathbf{X}_2$, so $\mathbf{X} = \mathbf{X}_1 + \mathbf{X}_2$. To compute $\sigma^2(\mathbf{X})$ we use the identity $\sigma^2(\mathbf{X}) = \mathbb{E}[\mathbf{X}^2] - \mathbb{E}[\mathbf{X}]^2$ and linearity of expectation.

$$\begin{aligned}
\mathbb{E}[\mathbf{X}]^2 &= \mathbb{E}[\mathbf{X}_1 + \mathbf{X}_2]^2 \overset{(*)}{=} (\mathbb{E}[\mathbf{X}_1] + \mathbb{E}[\mathbf{X}_2])^2 &&= \mathbb{E}[\mathbf{X}_1]^2 + \mathbb{E}[\mathbf{X}_2]^2 + 2\,\mathbb{E}[\mathbf{X}_1]\,\mathbb{E}[\mathbf{X}_2]; \\
\mathbb{E}[\mathbf{X}^2] &= \mathbb{E}[(\mathbf{X}_1 + \mathbf{X}_2)^2] = \mathbb{E}[\mathbf{X}_1^2 + \mathbf{X}_2^2 + 2\mathbf{X}_1\mathbf{X}_2] &&\overset{(*)}{=} \mathbb{E}[\mathbf{X}_1^2] + \mathbb{E}[\mathbf{X}_2^2] + 2\,\mathbb{E}[\mathbf{X}_1\mathbf{X}_2].
\end{aligned}$$

In both derivations above, we use linearity in $(*)$. Subtracting,

$$\begin{aligned}
\sigma^2(\mathbf{X}) &= \mathbb{E}[\mathbf{X}^2] - \mathbb{E}[\mathbf{X}]^2 \\
&= \mathbb{E}[\mathbf{X}_1^2] + \mathbb{E}[\mathbf{X}_2^2] + 2\,\mathbb{E}[\mathbf{X}_1\mathbf{X}_2] - \mathbb{E}[\mathbf{X}_1]^2 - \mathbb{E}[\mathbf{X}_2]^2 - 2\,\mathbb{E}[\mathbf{X}_1]\,\mathbb{E}[\mathbf{X}_2] \\
&= \underbrace{\mathbb{E}[\mathbf{X}_1^2] - \mathbb{E}[\mathbf{X}_1]^2}_{\sigma^2(\mathbf{X}_1)} + \underbrace{\mathbb{E}[\mathbf{X}_2^2] - \mathbb{E}[\mathbf{X}_2]^2}_{\sigma^2(\mathbf{X}_2)} + 2\underbrace{(\mathbb{E}[\mathbf{X}_1\mathbf{X}_2] - \mathbb{E}[\mathbf{X}_1]\,\mathbb{E}[\mathbf{X}_2])}_{\text{extra term called covariance}}
\end{aligned}$$

The variance is the sum of the variances plus a third term, the (expected product – product of expectations). This third term is zero when $\mathbf{X}_1$ and $\mathbf{X}_2$ are independent because for independent random variables, the expected product equals the product of expectations (see Section 20.4 on page 297),

$$\mathbb{E}[\mathbf{X}_1\mathbf{X}_2] = \mathbb{E}[\mathbf{X}_1]\,\mathbb{E}[\mathbf{X}_2]. \qquad \leftarrow \text{independent random variables}$$

In our case, $\mathbf{X}_1$ and $\mathbf{X}_2$ are independent dice rolls, so $\sigma^2(\mathbf{X}) = \sigma^2(\mathbf{X}_1) + \sigma^2(\mathbf{X}_2)$. We computed the expected square of a die roll in (20.3) on page 297, $\mathbb{E}[\mathbf{X}_1^2] = 15\frac{1}{6}$. Therefore,

$$\sigma^2(\mathbf{X}_1) = \mathbb{E}[\mathbf{X}_1^2] - \mathbb{E}[\mathbf{X}_1]^2 = 15\tfrac{1}{6} - (3\tfrac{1}{2})^2 = 2\tfrac{11}{12}.$$

Since $\mathbf{X}_1$ and $\mathbf{X}_2$ are identical die rolls, they have the same variance. Therefore,

$$\sigma^2(\mathbf{X}) = \sigma^2(\mathbf{X}_1) + \sigma^2(\mathbf{X}_2) = 2 \times 2\tfrac{11}{12} = 5\tfrac{5}{6}.$$

We already got this same result using the PDF of $\mathbf{X}$. There no harm in getting a result using different methods.

Variance of a Sum. For independent random variables, variance(sum) = sum(variances).

Our derivation works for the sum of any number of independent random variables. Prove it as an exercise.

Theorem 21.4 (Variance of a sum). Let $\mathbf{X}_1, \ldots, \mathbf{X}_n$ be independent and let $a_1, \ldots, a_n$ be constants. Then, the variance of the weighted sum is given by a sum of variances weighted by squared weights:

$$\sigma^2(a_1\mathbf{X}_1 + \cdots + a_n\mathbf{X}_n) = a_1^2\sigma^2(\mathbf{X}_1) + \cdots + a_n^2\sigma^2(\mathbf{X}_n).$$

Theorem 21.4 is similar to linearity of expectation with two differences: (i) The constants get squared. (ii) We require independence of the random variables, whereas linearity of expectation holds for any random variables. The second difference is an important distinction between linearity of expectation and linearity of variance.

Let's apply this new tool to a Binomial random variable. Recall that a Binomial is a sum of n independent Bernoullis $\mathbf{X}_1, \ldots, \mathbf{X}_n$. The variance of each Bernoulli is $\sigma^2(\mathbf{X}_i) = p(1-p)$. By Theorem 21.4 we have

$$\sigma^2(\text{Binomial}) = \sigma^2(\mathbf{X}_1) + \cdots + \sigma^2(\mathbf{X}_n) = p(1-p) + \cdots + p(1-p) = np(1-p). \tag{21.6}$$

Be careful when the random variables are not independent. Variances do not add.

Exercise 21.5

Prove Theorem 21.4. The proof is similar to the argument we gave for $\sigma^2(\mathbf{X}_1 + \mathbf{X}_2)$.

Exercise 21.6

Compute the variance of the waiting time to 5 successes with success probability $p = \frac{1}{3}$. Use a Monte Carlo simulation to estimate σ^2 and compare the two answers.

Example 21.5. Three hats land randomly on the heads of three men. Let $\mathbf{X}$ be the number of men who get their own hat. What is $\sigma^2(\mathbf{X})$? In Section 20.5 on page 299, we wrote $\mathbf{X}$ as a sum of indicators,

$$\mathbf{X} = \mathbf{X}_1 + \mathbf{X}_2 + \mathbf{X}_3.$$

We argued that each $\mathbf{X}_i$ is a Bernoulli with probability $p = \frac{1}{3}$ and showed that $\mathbb{E}[\mathbf{X}] = 1$. Suppose the first two men get their hats, so that $\mathbf{X}_1$ and $\mathbf{X}_2$ are both 1. Then the third man must also get his hat, so $\mathbf{X}_3 = 1$. That means $\mathbf{X}_3$ is not independent of $\mathbf{X}_1$ and $\mathbf{X}_2$ and we cannot use Theorem 21.4 to get the variance.

Pop Quiz 21.7
If $\mathbf{X}_1 = 1$ and $\mathbf{X}_2 = 0$, what is $\mathbf{X}_3$? If $\mathbf{X}_1 = 0$ and $\mathbf{X}_2 = 0$, what is $\mathbf{X}_3$?

Since we have a sum of non-independent random variables, and cannot apply Theorem 21.4, we must resort to the basic definition $\sigma^2(\mathbf{X}) = \mathbb{E}[\mathbf{X}^2] - \mathbb{E}[\mathbf{X}]^2$ to compute the variance. We know $\mathbb{E}[\mathbf{X}] = 1$, so we need $\mathbb{E}[\mathbf{X}^2]$.

$$\begin{aligned}\mathbb{E}[\mathbf{X}^2] &= \mathbb{E}[(\mathbf{X}_1 + \mathbf{X}_2 + \mathbf{X}_3)^2] \\ &= \mathbb{E}[\mathbf{X}_1^2 + \mathbf{X}_2^2 + \mathbf{X}_3^2 + 2\mathbf{X}_1\mathbf{X}_2 + 2\mathbf{X}_1\mathbf{X}_3 + 2\mathbf{X}_2\mathbf{X}_3] \\ &= \mathbb{E}[\mathbf{X}_1^2] + \mathbb{E}[\mathbf{X}_2^2] + \mathbb{E}[\mathbf{X}_3^2] + 2\,\mathbb{E}\,[\mathbf{X}_1\mathbf{X}_2] + 2\,\mathbb{E}\,[\mathbf{X}_1\mathbf{X}_3] + 2\,\mathbb{E}\,[\mathbf{X}_2\mathbf{X}_3]. \qquad \leftarrow \text{linearity}\end{aligned}$$

Since $\mathbf{X}_i$ are Bernoulli, $\mathbb{E}[\mathbf{X}_i^2] = p = 1/3$. We must compute the terms like $\mathbb{E}[\mathbf{X}_1\mathbf{X}_2]$, the cross products. Observe that the product of Bernoullis is a Bernoulli, since a product of 0s and 1s can only equal 0 or 1. Therefore, $\mathbb{E}[\mathbf{X}_1\mathbf{X}_2] = \mathbb{P}[\mathbf{X}_1 = 1 \text{ AND } \mathbf{X}_2 = 1]$. There are $3! = 6$ equally likely permutations of the hats. The first two men get their hats in only one of these permutations, so $\mathbb{P}[\mathbf{X}_1 = 1 \text{ AND } \mathbf{X}_2 = 1] = \frac{1}{6}$. The analyses of $\mathbf{X}_1\mathbf{X}_3$ and $\mathbf{X}_2\mathbf{X}_3$ are identical, so $\mathbb{E}[\mathbf{X}_1\mathbf{X}_2] = \mathbb{E}[\mathbf{X}_1\mathbf{X}_3] = \mathbb{E}[\mathbf{X}_2\mathbf{X}_3] = \frac{1}{6}$. We can now compute $\mathbb{E}[\mathbf{X}^2]$,

$$\mathbb{E}[\mathbf{X}^2] \;=\; 1/3 + 1/3 + 1/3 + 2 \times 1/6 + 2 \times 1/6 + 2 \times 1/6 \;=\; 2.$$

Finally, $\sigma^2 = \mathbb{E}[\mathbf{X}^2] - \mathbb{E}[\mathbf{X}]^2 = 2 - 1^2 = 1$. The variance is 1.

Exercise 21.8
If n men are involved in the hat throwing, show that the variance is still 1.

□

21.3 Law of Large Numbers

The variance σ^2 is a tool for understanding when the mean is a good summary of a random variable. The standard deviation σ quantifies the range within which the random variable $\mathbf{X}$ is likely to fall, a probabilistic width. Specifically, $\mu \pm 3\sigma$ is a good choice for this range of a random variable, which is the 3-sigma-rule.

Theorem 21.6 (3-Sigma-Rule)**.** For any $\mathbf{X}$, $\mathbb{P}[\mu - 3\sigma < \mathbf{X} < \mu + 3\sigma] \geq 8/9 \approx 90\%$.

Chances are at least about 90% that $\mathbf{X} = \mu \pm 3\sigma$. For the sum of two dice, $\sigma = 2.42$ and $3\sigma \approx 7.25$. Since $\mu = 7$, by the 3-sigma-rule, with probability at least about 90%,

$$\text{sum of two dice} \in (-0.25, 14.25).$$

This is a pretty vacuous claim since we know that the sum of two dice has to be between 2 and 12. Though the 3-sigma-rule is true, in this particular instance it is not useful. The range provided by the 3-sigma-rule applies to all random variables with mean 7 and standard deviation 2.42. For any particular random variable, like the sum of two dice, it might be an excessive range. The next exercise is instructive.

Exercise 21.9
(a) For the sum of n independent, fair dice, show that $\sigma^2 = 35n/12$.
(b) Plot the expected sum of n dice $\mu(n)$ versus n .
(c) On the same plot show the range for the sum of n dice given by the 3-sigma-rule.
(d) For what n is the range from the 3-sigma-rule useful (strictly inside $[n, 6n]$).

The 3-sigma-rule is a special case of Chebyshev's Inequality. To prove it, we need a basic result known as Markov's Inequality. Let $\mathbf{X}$ be non-negative, and consider $\mathbb{E}[\mathbf{X}]$,

$$\mathbb{E}[\mathbf{X}] = \sum_{x\geq 0} x \cdot P_{\mathbf{X}}(x) \overset{(a)}{\geq} \sum_{x\geq\alpha} x \cdot P_{\mathbf{X}}(x)$$
$$\overset{(b)}{\geq} \sum_{x\geq\alpha} \alpha \cdot P_{\mathbf{X}}(x) = \alpha \cdot \mathbb{P}[\mathbf{X} \geq \alpha].$$

(a) is true because all terms in the sum are positive and we threw away the positive terms with $0 \leq x < \alpha$. (b) is true because $x \geq \alpha$. The derivation works for any α. Rearranging terms, we obtain Markov's Inequality,

Lemma 21.7 (Markov Inequality). For any non-negative random variable $\mathbf{X}$ and $\alpha \geq 0$, $\mathbb{P}[\mathbf{X} \geq \alpha] \leq \mathbb{E}[\mathbf{X}]/\alpha$.

Pop Quiz 21.10
100 hats land randomly on the heads of 100 men. Use Markov's Inequality to give an upper bound on the probability that at least 50 men get their own hats.

We use Markov's Inequality to prove Chebyshev's Inequality which is a generalization of the 3-sigma-rule.

Theorem 21.8 (Chebyshev Inequality). For any random variable $\mathbf{X}$ with mean μ and variance σ^2, and $t \geq 0$,

$$\mathbb{P}[\mu - t\sigma < \mathbf{X} < \mu + t\sigma] \geq 1 - \frac{1}{t^2};$$
$$\mathbb{P}[|\mathbf{X} - \mu| \geq t\sigma] \leq \frac{1}{t^2},$$

The two bounds are equivalent. Using $t = 3$ in Chebyshev's Inequality gives Theorem 21.6.

Proof. The two bounds are equivalent because

$$\mathbb{P}[\mu - t\sigma < \mathbf{X} < \mu + t\sigma] = 1 - \mathbb{P}[|\mathbf{X} - \mu| \geq t\sigma].$$

We prove $\mathbb{P}[|\mathbf{X} - \mu| \geq t\sigma] \leq 1/t^2$. The event $|\mathbf{X} - \mu| \geq t\sigma$, after squaring both sides, is exactly the event $(\mathbf{X} - \mu)^2 \geq t^2\sigma^2$. We need to bound $\mathbb{P}[(\mathbf{X} - \mu)^2 \geq t^2\sigma^2]$. Since $(\mathbf{X} - \mu)^2$ is a non-negative random variable, we can use Markov's Inequality with $\alpha = t^2\sigma^2$:

$$\mathbb{P}[(\mathbf{X} - \mu)^2 \geq t^2\sigma^2] \leq \frac{\mathbb{E}[(\mathbf{X} - \mu)^2]}{t^2\sigma^2} \overset{(a)}{=} \frac{\cancel{\sigma^2}}{t^2\cancel{\sigma^2}} = \frac{1}{t^2}.$$

(a) follows because, by definition, $\sigma^2 = \mathbb{E}[(\mathbf{X} - \mu)^2]$. ■

Pop Quiz 21.11
Use Chebyshev's Inequality to bound the probability in Pop Quiz 21.10. Compare both bounds with the exact probability (set $n = 100, k = 50$ in (20.4) on page 299).

Chebyshev's Inequality gives a quick estimate of the probability that a random variable lies within some range of its mean. The bound can be crude, i.e. loose, because it must hold for any random variable, in particular the worst behaved one. The 90% chance of being within 3σ of the mean holds for any random variable. Well behaved random variables will be within this 3σ range far more often than the Chebyshev bound.

Exercise 21.12
You toss 100 fair independent coins. Let $\mathbf{X}$ be the number of heads.
(a) What are $\mathbb{E}[\mathbf{X}]$ and $\sigma^2(\mathbf{X})$. *[Hint: $\mathbf{X} = \mathbf{X}_1 + \cdots + \mathbf{X}_n$, where $\mathbf{X}_i$ are Bernoulli.]*
(b) Compute $\mathbb{P}[40 < \mathbf{X} < 60]$.
(c) What does Chebyshev's Inequality give as a lower bound for $\mathbb{P}[40 < \mathbf{X} < 60]$.

In Exercise 21.12, the worst case general Chebyshev bound is loose. This is because $\mathbf{X}$ is special, a sum of many independent Bernoullis. The sum of many independent random variables deserves some attention.

21.3.1 Weak Law of Large Numbers

A sum of independent random variables is very special, and also common. For example: number of heads in many coin flips; position of a drunk on a random walk; profit of an insurance company from many independent policies; etc. Let $\mathbf{X}_1, \ldots, \mathbf{X}_n$ be n independent random variables, each with the same mean and variance:

$$\mathbb{E}[\mathbf{X}_i] = \mu \qquad \text{and} \qquad \sigma^2(\mathbf{X}_i) = \sigma^2.$$

To be concrete, let $\mathbf{X}_1, \ldots, \mathbf{X}_n$ be independent dice rolls with $\mu = 3\frac{1}{2}$ and $\sigma^2 = 2\frac{11}{12}$. Let $\mathbf{X} = (\mathbf{X}_1 + \cdots + \mathbf{X}_n)/n$ be the average roll. The expected value of $\mathbf{X}$ is a sum of expected values, by linearity. Since $\mathbf{X}_i$ are independent, the variance of $\mathbf{X}$ is also a sum of variances, but divided by n^2, not n (Theorem 21.4 on page 314):

$$\mathbb{E}[\mathbf{X}] = \mathbb{E}\left[\frac{\mathbf{X}_1 + \cdots + \mathbf{X}_n}{n}\right] = \frac{\mathbb{E}[\mathbf{X}_1] + \cdots + \mathbb{E}[\mathbf{X}_n]}{n} = \frac{\mu + \cdots + \mu}{n} = \mu;$$

$$\sigma^2(\mathbf{X}) = \sigma^2\left(\frac{\mathbf{X}_1 + \cdots + \mathbf{X}_n}{n}\right) = \frac{\sigma^2(\mathbf{X}_1) + \cdots + \sigma^2(\mathbf{X}_n)}{n^2} = \frac{\sigma^2 + \cdots + \sigma^2}{n^2} = \frac{\sigma^2}{n}.$$

The expected value is a constant, independent of n, as we saw when we opened this chapter. The variance, however, is decreasing with n: the 3-sigma range decreases with n. The 3-sigma range is illustrated in the figure. Note how the envelope of the 3-sigma range around the mean encloses the observed averages from Figure 21.1 on page 309, shown here in blue. The 3-sigma range can go outside the possible values, in which case it is not much use. But, eventually the 3-sigma range converges to 0. The observed average converges with high probability to the mean. That, in a nutshell, is the weak law of large numbers.

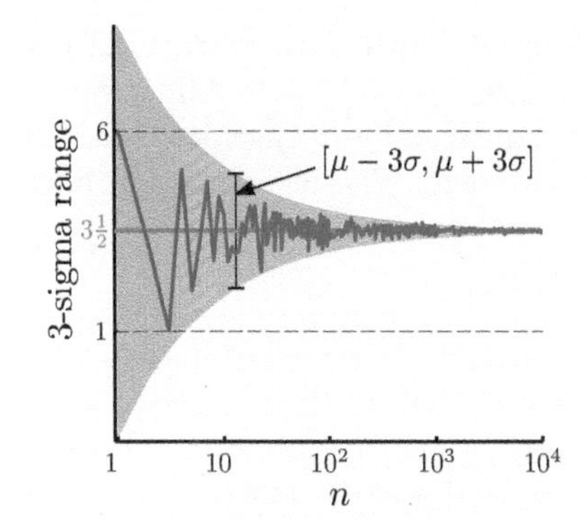

The average of independent random variables converges to the mean.

Mathematically, this follows from Chebyshev's inequality because the variance of the average decreases with n.

We can quantify the rate of convergence to the mean. Indeed, from the 3σ-rule, most of the time,

$$\mathbf{X} = \mu(\mathbf{X}) \pm 3\sigma(\mathbf{X}).$$

Since $\sigma(\mathbf{X}) = \sigma/\sqrt{n}$, the 3σ-range is shrinking like $1/\sqrt{n}$. Here is one way to formally state the weak law.

Theorem 21.9 (Weak Law of Large Numbers). Let $\mathbf{X}_1, \ldots, \mathbf{X}_n$ be n independent random variables, each with the same mean μ and variance σ^2. Let $\mathbf{X} = (\mathbf{X}_1 + \cdots + \mathbf{X}_n)/n$. Then,

$$\mathbb{P}[|\mathbf{X} - \mu| < \epsilon\sigma] \geq 1 - \frac{1}{n\epsilon^2}.$$

You pick an error-tolerance $\epsilon\sigma$ (think of ϵ as a small number). The theorem says the probability of observing an average $\mathbf{X}$ within your error-tolerance of the mean μ is nearly 1, converging to 1 as $n \to \infty$, no matter what your error tolerence. Simply put, the measured average converges to the mean, with high probability.

Proof. Apply Theorem 21.8 with $t = \epsilon\sqrt{n}$ and $\sigma(\mathbf{X}) = \sqrt{\sigma^2(\mathbf{X})} = \sqrt{\sigma^2/n} = \sigma/\sqrt{n}$. ■

21.3.2 Strong Law of Large Numbers

The average converges to the mean. The PDF of the average also converges. From the 3-sigma rule,

$$\mathbf{X} = \mu(\mathbf{X}) \pm 3\sigma(\mathbf{X}).$$

If you subtract $\mu(\mathbf{X})$ and divide by $\sigma(\mathbf{X})$, you get a scaled deviation from the mean which is likely to be in the range $[-3, 3]$. This scaled deviation from the mean is called the z-score,

$$\mathbf{Z} = \frac{\mathbf{X} - \mu(\mathbf{X})}{\sigma(\mathbf{X})}.$$

The z-score $\mathbf{Z}$, just like $\mathbf{X}$, is a random variable, and we can obtain its PDF. You can compute the PDF of $\mathbf{Z}$ from the PDF of $\mathbf{X}$, but we won't get into those details. Instead, we use Monte Carlo to approximate the

PDF of $\mathbf{Z}$. Consider the average of n dice. We roll n dice, compute their average $\mathbf{X}$ and then the z-score

$$\mathbf{Z} = \frac{\mathbf{X} - 3\frac{1}{2}}{\sqrt{35/12n}}.$$

We repeat this experiment many times and show the histograms of the z-scores for different n.

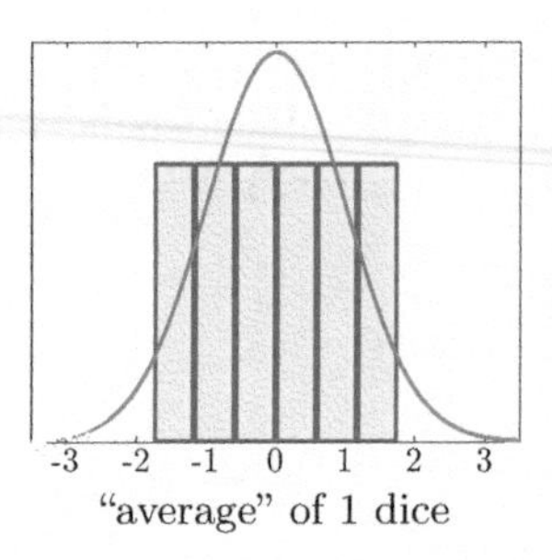

"average" of 1 dice

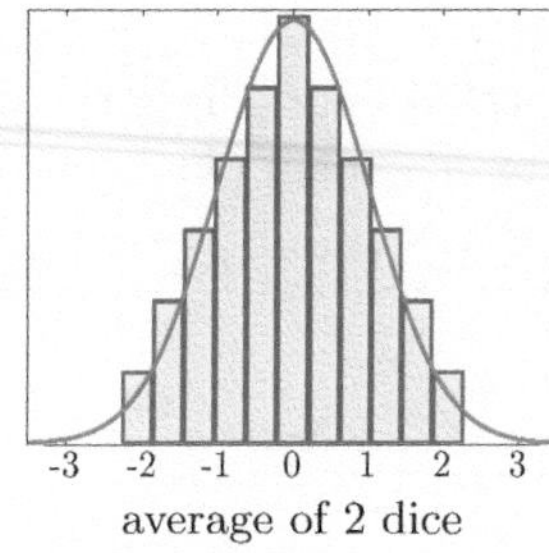

average of 2 dice

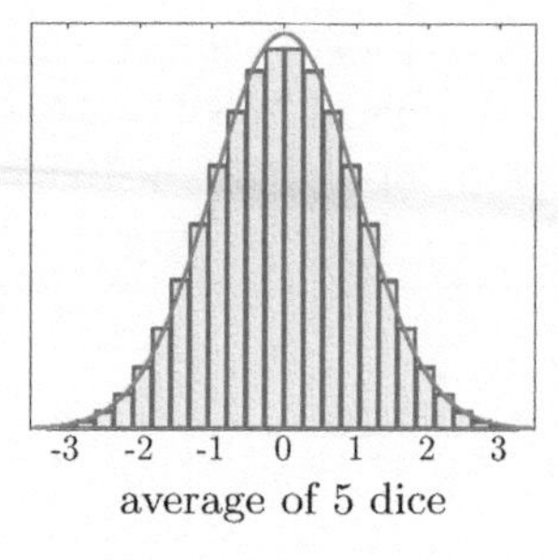

average of 5 dice

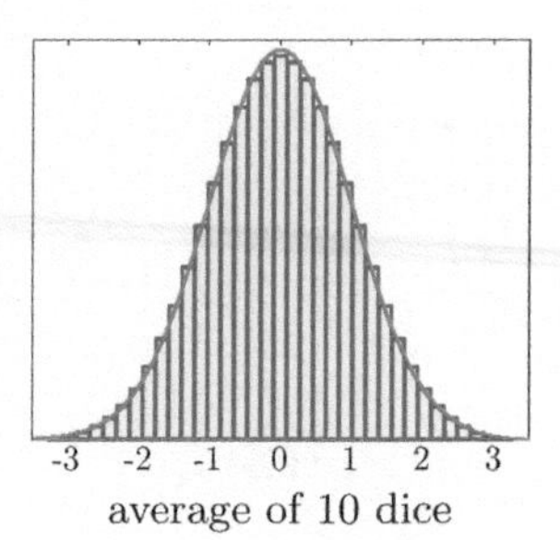

average of 10 dice

Central Limit Theorem (CLT), Laplace 1812. The emergence above of the bell-curve is perhaps the most beautiful result in probability. Simple, yet general. The PDF of the z-score for the average of n independent random variables converges to a bell-curve. It almost doesn't matter what random variables are cooked into the average. The bell-curve has a specific shape, the Gaussian or Normal distribution. Mathematically,

$$F_{\mathbf{X}}(x) \approx \phi\left(\frac{\sqrt{n}\cdot(x-\mu)}{\sigma}\right), \qquad \text{where } \phi(x) = \frac{1}{\sqrt{2\pi}}\int_{-\infty}^{x} ds\, e^{-\frac{1}{2}s^2}, \tag{21.7}$$

and $\phi(x)$ is the standard normal CDF available in most mathematics packages. The central limit theorem says that the CDF of the average of n independent random variables converges to ϕ, when $n \to \infty$. To get $F_{\mathbf{X}}(x)$, apply ϕ to the z-score of x, where $z = \sqrt{n}(x-\mu)/\sigma$. We won't prove this stunning result, but to understand it we need a closer look at ϕ.

The plot on the right shows that as $|x|$ increases, ϕ rapidly approaches 0 for $x < 0$, and ϕ rapidly approaches 1 for $x > 0$. Also, ϕ is symmetric around $\frac{1}{2}$ at $x = 0$, that is $\phi(-x) = 1 - \phi(x)$. The familiar bell curve is actually $\phi'(x) = e^{-\frac{1}{2}x^2}/\sqrt{2\pi}$, not $\phi(x)$. Asymptotically, when $x \to \infty$,

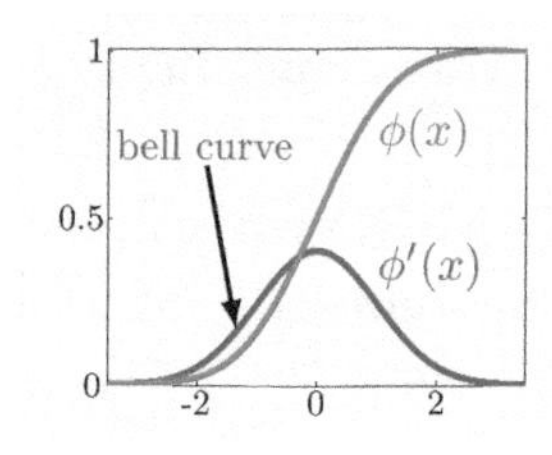

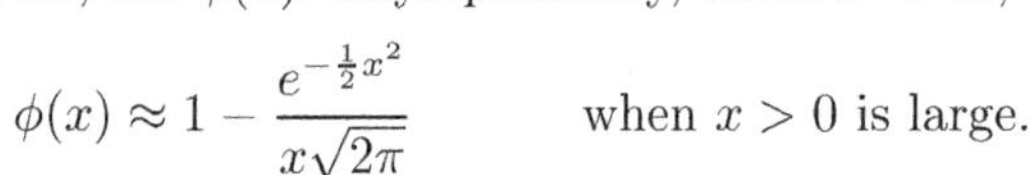

$$\phi(x) \approx 1 - \frac{e^{-\frac{1}{2}x^2}}{x\sqrt{2\pi}} \qquad \text{when } x > 0 \text{ is large.}$$

For $x = \mu + \epsilon\sigma$, the argument to ϕ in (21.7) is positive and large on account of the $\sqrt{n}$,

$$\mathbb{P}[\mathbf{X} \le \mu + \epsilon\sigma] = F_{\mathbf{X}}(\mu + \epsilon\sigma) \approx \phi(\epsilon\sqrt{n}) \to 1.$$

for $x = \mu - \epsilon$ the argument to ϕ is negative and large, and

$$\mathbb{P}[\mathbf{X} \le \mu - \epsilon\sigma] = F_{\mathbf{X}}(\mu - \epsilon\sigma) \approx \phi(-\epsilon\sqrt{n}) \to 0.$$

That is, $\mathbb{P}[\mu - \epsilon \le \mathbf{X} \le \mu + \epsilon\sigma] \approx 2\phi(\epsilon\sqrt{n}) - 1$, which approaches 1 when $n \to \infty$, for any $\epsilon > 0$. Thus, the central limit theorem implies the weak law of large numbers. Much more can be harvested from (21.7).

Exercise 21.13

(a) Assume (21.7) and show that $\mathbb{P}[|\mathbf{X} - \mu| \ge t\sigma] \approx 2(1 - \phi(t\sqrt{n}))$.

(b) Assume $t\sqrt{n}$ is large. Using the approximation for $\phi(x)$, show $\mathbb{P}[|\mathbf{X} - \mu| \ge t\sigma] \approx 2 \cdot \dfrac{e^{-\frac{1}{2}nt^2}}{\sqrt{2\pi n t^2}}$.

(Chebyshev's bound is $1/t^2$. Hoeffding (1963) proved a slightly weaker bound of $2e^{-\frac{1}{2}nt^2}$, see Problems 21.68–21.71.)

21.4 Problems

Problem 21.1. For a random variable $\mathbf{X}$, which of the following does $\sigma(\mathbf{X})$ measure?
(a) The average value of $\mathbf{X}$ you will observe if you ran the experiment many times.
(b) The average number of times you run the experiment before observing the value $\mathbb{E}[\mathbf{X}]$.
(c) The size of the deviation between the observed value of $\mathbf{X}$ and the expected value $\mathbb{E}[\mathbf{X}]$.
(d) The probability that $\mathbf{X}$ will be larger than its expected value $\mathbb{E}[\mathbf{X}]$.
(e) The number of possible values of $\mathbf{X}$.

Problem 21.2. A random variable $\mathbf{X}$ has PDF shown. Compute $\mathbb{E}[\mathbf{X}]$ and $\sigma^2(\mathbf{X})$.

x	-2	-1	0	1	2
$P_{\mathbf{X}}(x)$	$\frac{1}{10}$	$\frac{1}{10}$	$\frac{2}{10}$	$\frac{3}{10}$	$\frac{3}{10}$

Problem 21.3. We show the PDF's of two random variables $\mathbf{X}_1$ and $\mathbf{X}_2$.
(a) Guess which random variable has higher variance. Explain your guess.
(b) Compute the variances and verify your guess.

x	0	1	2	3	4
$P_{\mathbf{X}_1}(x)$	$\frac{1}{11}$	$\frac{2}{11}$	$\frac{5}{11}$	$\frac{2}{11}$	$\frac{1}{11}$
$P_{\mathbf{X}_2}(x)$	$\frac{3}{11}$	$\frac{2}{11}$	$\frac{1}{11}$	$\frac{2}{11}$	$\frac{3}{11}$

Problem 21.4. A royal family has children until they get a boy or until they have three children, whichever comes first. Let $\mathbf{B}$ be the number of princes and $\mathbf{G}$ the number of princesses. Find the mean and variance of $\mathbf{B}$ and $\mathbf{G}$.

Problem 21.5. A Poisson random variable has PDF $P(i) = e^{-\lambda}\lambda^i/i!$ for $i = 0, 1, 2, \ldots$. Show that the mean and variance are both λ. Give a plot of the PDF for $\lambda = 2$. In your plot, indicate what the mean and variance represent.

Problem 21.6. Let $\mathbf{X}$ and $\mathbf{Y}$ be the rolls of two independent fair dice and define $\mathbf{Z} = \mathbf{X} + 2\mathbf{Y}$. Compute $\sigma(\mathbf{Z})$. (The variance of a single die roll is $35/12$.)

Problem 21.7 (Ternary). Find the mean and variance of a ternary random variable which takes values in $\{-1, 0, 1\}$ with probabilities p, q, r. Specialize to the case $p = q = r = \frac{1}{3}$.

Problem 21.8. A random variable $\mathbf{X}$ has a symmetric PDF about μ, $P_{\mathbf{X}}(\mu + \Delta) = P_{\mathbf{X}}(\mu - \Delta)$. Show $\mathbb{E}[\mathbf{X}] = \mu$.

Problem 21.9. What is its PDF of a random variable $\mathbf{X}$ for which $\mathbb{E}[\mathbf{X}^2] = \mathbb{E}[\mathbf{X}]^2 = \mu^2$?

Problem 21.10. Let $\mathbf{X}$ be uniform on {-3,-2,-1,0,1,2,3}. Compute the PDF, mean and variance of $\mathbf{Y}$, where
(a) $\mathbf{Y} = \mathbf{X} + 1$. (b) $\mathbf{Y} = \mathbf{X}^2 + 1$. (c) $\mathbf{Y} = 2\mathbf{X} + 1$.

Problem 21.11. Random variables $\mathbf{X}$ and $\mathbf{Y}$ are independent with $\mathbb{E}[\mathbf{X}] = 2, \mathbb{E}[\mathbf{Y}] = 6, \sigma^2(\mathbf{X}) = 9, \sigma^2(\mathbf{Y}) = 16$.
(a) Compute $\mathbb{E}[\mathbf{X}^2 - \mathbf{Y}^2]$. (b) Compute $\sigma^2(2\mathbf{X} + 3\mathbf{Y})$.

Problem 21.12. A random variable $\mathbf{X}$ has mean 100 and variance 24. Compute:
(a) $\mathbb{E}[\mathbf{X}^2]$. (b) $\mathbb{E}[5 - 3\mathbf{X}]$. (c) $\mathbb{E}[-\mathbf{X}]$. (d) $\sigma^2(-\mathbf{X})$. (e) $\sigma^2(5 - 3\mathbf{X})$.

Problem 21.13. Prove or disprove: The variance of a sum is at most the sum of variances.

Problem 21.14. Let $\mathbf{X}$ be a random variable with mean μ and variance σ^2. Define the z-score $\mathbf{Z} = (\mathbf{X} - \mu)/\sigma$.
(a) Is the z-score $\mathbf{Z}$ a valid random variable? (b) Show that the mean of $\mathbf{Z}$ is zero and its variance is 1.

Problem 21.15. Flip a fair coin 36 times. Let $\mathbf{X}$ be the number of heads. Find the mean and variance of $\frac{1}{3}(\mathbf{X} - 5)$.

Problem 21.16. Flip a coin n times with probability p of heads. Find the mean and variance of $(\mathbf{X} - np)/\sqrt{np(1-p)}$.

Problem 21.17. You randomly pick 3 donuts from a batch of 12 in which 4 are stale. You get $\mathbf{X}$ stale donuts.
(a) Give the PDF of $\mathbf{X}$, the probability that 0,1,2,3 are stale. (b) Find the mean and variance of $\mathbf{X}$.

Problem 21.18. The temperature in a manufacturing process has a mean of 60F and a standard deviation of 5F. If instead, the temperature was reported in °C, what would the mean and variance be?

Problem 21.19. 40% of the population favors the republican candidate in an election. In a sample of 2000 voters, what is the mean and standard deviation for the number that voted republican.

Problem 21.20. Find σ^2 for the uniform distribution on $\{1, 2, 3, 4\}$. For $\{1, 2, \ldots, n\}$, show that $\sigma^2 = \frac{1}{12}(n^2 - 1)$.

Problem 21.21. Let $\mathbf{X}$ count the heads in 20 independent coin flips, with probability p of H.
(a) Give the PDF of $\mathbf{X}$, $\mathbb{P}[\mathbf{X} = k]$ (probability to get k heads) and use the PDF to find $\mathbb{E}[\mathbf{X}]$ and var$[\mathbf{X}]$.
(b) Use linearity of expectation to compute $\mathbb{E}[\mathbf{X}]$ and var$[\mathbf{X}]$.

Problem 21.22. A dealer orders a device for $100 and sells it for $200. The manufacturer repurchases unsold devices for $50. The demand for devices is a random variable $\mathbf{X}$ with a PDF $\mathbb{P}[\mathbf{X}=k]=(1-e^{-5})e^{-5k}$ for $k=0,1,\ldots$.

(a) The dealer orders n devices. Compute the mean and variance of the dealer's profit.
(b) Can you give the dealer some advice on how many devices to order (inventory management).

Problem 21.23. A couple has kids until two boys. Let $\mathbf{X}$ be the number of children the couple has.

(a) Give the PDF for $\mathbf{X}$ and use the PDF to compute the mean and variance of the waiting time.
(b) Write $\mathbf{X}$ as a sum and use that to compute the mean and variance of the waiting time.
(c) Find the the mean and variance of the waiting time if the couple were waiting for n boys.

Problem 21.24. An urn has 10 black balls. You randomly paint $\mathbf{X}$ of the balls white, where $\mathbf{X}$ is a random variable with mean $\mu=4$ and variance $\sigma^2=6$. You now randomly draw two balls with replacement.

(a) What is the probability that the first ball is white?
(b) What are the probabilities: (i) The second ball is white? (ii) The second ball is white given the first is white?
(c) What is the probability that both balls are white? When is the color of the balls independent?

Problem 21.25. The mean and variance of a sample $\{x_1,\ldots,x_n\}$, is the mean and variance of a random variable which takes those values with equal probabilities. Compute the mean and variance of these samples:

(a) {-3,-2,-1,0,1,2,3} (b) {0,1,2,3,4,5,6} (c) {0,1,2,3} (d) {1,4,7,10}

Problem 21.26. For independent dice rolls $\mathbf{X}_1$ and $\mathbf{X}_2$, find var$(\mathbf{X}_1-\mathbf{X}_2)$ without using the PDF of $\mathbf{X}_1-\mathbf{X}_2$.

Problem 21.27. For independent random variables $\mathbf{X}_1$ and $\mathbf{X}_2$, prove that $\sigma^2(\mathbf{X}_1+\mathbf{X}_2)=\sigma^2(\mathbf{X}_1-\mathbf{X}_2)$.

Problem 21.28. Prove or disprove these properties about the standard deviation.

(a) For any random variable $\mathbf{X}$: (i) $\sigma(\mathbf{X}+a)=\sigma(\mathbf{X})$. (ii) $\sigma(b\mathbf{X})=|b|\sigma(\mathbf{X})$.
(b) For independent random variables, the standard deviation of the sum is the sum of standard deviations.
(c) For independent random variables, the standard deviation of the sum is at most the sum of standard deviations.

Problem 21.29 (Spread). Let $\mathbf{X}$ be a random variable taking values $x_1,\ldots,x_n$ with probabilities $p_1,\ldots,p_n$ and having mean $\mu=\sum_{i=1}^n p_i x_i$. The spread is the expected absolute deviation as opposed to squared deviation,

$$\overline{\sigma}=\mathbb{E}[|\mathbf{\Delta}|]=\sum_{i=1}^{n} p_i|x_i-\mu|.$$

What does spread measure? Is it comparable to σ or σ^2? Prove that spread is at most the standard deviation, $\overline{\sigma}\le\sigma$.

Problem 21.30. Compute $\sigma^2(\mathbf{X})$ for $\mathbf{X}$ defined in the experiment in Problem 19.35.

Problem 21.31. Compute $\sigma^2(\mathbf{X})$ for the Martians in Problem 19.57, where $\mathbf{X}$ is the wait to 2 boys.

Problem 21.32. Let $\mathbf{X}$ be the position of a drunk on a random walk. The drunk steps right with probability p and left with probability $1-p$. Compute $\sigma^2(\mathbf{X})$, the variance of the drunk's position, after n steps.

Problem 21.33. A Bernoulli random variable $\mathbf{X}$ has $\mathbb{E}[\mathbf{X}^2]=\frac{1}{3}$.

(a) Find $\mathbb{E}[\mathbf{X}]$ and $\sigma^2(\mathbf{X})$.
(b) If $\mathbf{X}_1,\ldots,\mathbf{X}_{500}$ are independent with the same distribution as $\mathbf{X}$, compute μ and σ^2 for the average $\frac{1}{500}\sum_{i=1}^{500}\mathbf{X}_i$.

Problem 21.34. You invest $\$N$ in N independent stocks which are each worth $\$1$. Every year a stock doubles with probability $\frac{2}{3}$, or becomes worth $0 with probability $\frac{1}{3}$. Each year is independent. Consider these investing scenarios.

(i) Invest all your money into one stock.
(ii) Invest an equal share of your money in each stock.
(iii) Strategy (i) in the 1st year and strategy (ii) in the 2nd year.
(iv) Strategy (ii) in the 1st year and strategy (i) in the 2nd year.

For each strategy, compute the PDF, expectation and variance of your payoff after 1 year and after 2 years. Your grandmother is conservative. Which strategy would you recommend for her?

Problem 21.35 (Averaging). Two independent temperature measurements $\mathbf{X}_1$ and $\mathbf{X}_2$ from different thermometers on average measure the true temperature T but have variances σ_1^2 and σ_2^2. We wish to construct a better estimate of the temperature by taking an average of these measurements, $\mathbf{X}=\frac{1}{2}(\mathbf{X}_1+\mathbf{X}_2)$.

(a) Find the mean and variance of the average. Is the average a "better" estimate of the temperature?
(b) Can you do better, knowing σ_1^2 and σ_2^2? *[Hint: Consider a weighted average.]*

Problem 21.36 (Sampling Without replacement). An urn has 10 white and 20 black balls. Let $\mathbf{X}_1$ be the waiting time (number of balls sampled) until a white ball appears and $\mathbf{X}_2$ the waiting time until two white balls appear. Use indicator random variables to find the mean and variance of $\mathbf{X}_1$ and $\mathbf{X}_2$ in each setting below. (See Problem 20.37)
(a) You pick with replacement. (b) You pick without replacement. (c) Generalize to m white and n black balls.

Problem 21.37. For the waiting time to collect n out of n coupons (Example 20.6 on page 295), show

$$\sigma^2 = n^2\sum_{i=1}^{n}\frac{1}{i^2} - nH_n < n^2\sum_{i=1}^{\infty}\frac{1}{i^2} - nH_n = \frac{\pi^2 n^2}{6} - nH_n.$$

($H_n = 1 + \frac{1}{2} + \cdots + \frac{1}{n}$ is the nth Harmonic number.) Use Monte Carlo to verify the case $n = 5$.

Problem 21.38. Let the sample space be $\Omega = \mathbb{N} = \{1, 2, \ldots\}$ and define random variables $\mathbf{X}(n) = n$ and $\mathbf{Y}(n) = n^2$.
(a) Compute $\mathbb{E}[\mathbf{X}]$ and $\mathbb{E}[\mathbf{Y}]$ and var$[\mathbf{X}]$ for the probability function $P(n) = 2^{-n}$.
[Hint: $\sum_{n=1}^{\infty} na^n = a/(1-a)^2$ and $\sum_{n=1}^{\infty} n^2a^n = a(a+1)/(1-a)^3$ for $0 \le a < 1$.]
(b) How is var$[\mathbf{X}]$ related to $\mathbb{E}[\mathbf{X}]$ and $\mathbb{E}[\mathbf{Y}]$?
(c) Give upper bounds for $\mathbb{P}[\mathbf{X} \ge N]$, for $N > 1$ using the Markov and Chebyshev bounds. Now compute the exact value of $\mathbb{P}[\mathbf{X} \ge N]$ and compare your 3 answers.
(d) For the probability function $P(n) = 6/\pi^2 n^2$, compute $\mathbb{E}[\mathbf{X}]$.

Problem 21.39. 100 people toss their hats up. The hats land randomly on heads. Let the random variabls $\mathbf{X}$ be the number of people who get their hats back.
(a) Compute $\mathbb{E}[\mathbf{X}]$ and $var[\mathbf{X}]$. *[Hint: Let $\mathbf{X}_i = 1$ if person i gets their hat back and $\mathbf{X}_i = 0$ otherwise. How is $\mathbf{X}$ related to the $\mathbf{X}_i$? Are the $\mathbf{X}_i$ independent?]*
(b) Give an upper bound on the probability that more than half the people get their hats back.

Problem 21.40. Show that a random variable with mean $\mu = 1$ can have any variance.
(a) For any $M \ge 0$, construct a random variable with mean 1 and variance M. *[Hint: Two values.]*
(b) Can a positive random variable with mean 1 have any variance?

Problem 21.41. For independent $\mathbf{X}_1$ and $\mathbf{X}_2$ with the same PDF, which of these have the same variance as $\mathbf{X}_1$.
(a) $-\mathbf{X}_1$. (b) $\mathbf{X}_1 + \mathbf{X}_2$. (c) $(\mathbf{X}_1 + \mathbf{X}_2)/2$. (d) $(\mathbf{X}_1 + \mathbf{X}_2)/\sqrt{2}$.

Problem 21.42. If $\mathbf{X}_1$ and $\mathbf{X}_2$ are independent, show:
(a) $\sigma^2(\mathbf{X}_1+\mathbf{X}_2) = \sigma^2(\mathbf{X}_1-\mathbf{X}_2)$. (b) $\sigma^2(\mathbf{X}_1\mathbf{X}_2) = \sigma^2(\mathbf{X}_1)\sigma^2(\mathbf{X}_2)+\sigma^2(\mathbf{X}_1)\mathbb{E}[\mathbf{X}_2]^2+\mathbb{E}[\mathbf{X}_1]^2\sigma^2(\mathbf{X}_2)$.

Problem 21.43. For independent $\mathbf{X}_1, \ldots, \mathbf{X}_n$ with $\mathbb{E}[\mathbf{X}_i] = 0$, show that the expected sum-squared equals the sum of expected-squares: $\mathbb{E}[(\mathbf{X}_1 + \cdots + \mathbf{X}_n)^2] = \mathbb{E}[\mathbf{X}_1^2] + \cdots + \mathbb{E}[\mathbf{X}_n^2]$.

Problem 21.44. $\mathbf{X}$ and $\mathbf{Y}$ are random variables (not necessarily independent). Prove that

$$\sigma^2(\mathbf{X}+\mathbf{Y}) = \sigma^2(\mathbf{X}) + \sigma^2(\mathbf{Y}) + 2\,\mathbb{E}\,[\mathbf{X}\mathbf{Y}] - 2\,\mathbb{E}\,[\mathbf{X}]\,\mathbb{E}\,[\mathbf{Y}].$$

Problem 21.45. Let $\mathbf{X}$ and $\mathbf{Y}$ be independent and $\mathbf{Z} = \mathbf{X}\mathbf{Y}$. Prove or disprove each formula for the variance.
(a) $\sigma^2(\mathbf{Z}) = \sigma^2(\mathbf{X})\sigma^2(\mathbf{Y})$.
(b) $\sigma^2(\mathbf{Z}) = \sigma^2(\mathbf{X})\,\mathbb{E}\,[\mathbf{Y}^2] + \sigma^2(\mathbf{Y})\,\mathbb{E}\,[\mathbf{X}^2]$.
(c) $\sigma^2(\mathbf{Z}) = \sigma^2(\mathbf{X})\,\mathbb{E}\,[\mathbf{Y}]^2 + \sigma^2(\mathbf{Y})\,\mathbb{E}\,[\mathbf{X}]^2$.
(d) $\sigma^2(\mathbf{Z}) = \sigma^2(\mathbf{X})\sigma^2(\mathbf{Y}) + \sigma^2(\mathbf{X})\,\mathbb{E}\,[\mathbf{Y}]^2 + \sigma^2(\mathbf{Y})\,\mathbb{E}\,[\mathbf{X}]^2$.

Problem 21.46. For independent random variables, prove: standard deviation(sum) $\le$ sum(standard deviations).

Problem 21.47. Prove: $\sum_{i=1}^{n} x_i^2 \ge \frac{1}{n}\left(\sum_{i=1}^{n} x_i\right)^2$. *[Hint: Uniform on $x_1, \ldots, x_n$. Example 21.2.]*

Problem 21.48 (Cauchy-Schwarz, $\boldsymbol{a} \bullet \boldsymbol{b} \le \|\boldsymbol{a}\|\|\boldsymbol{b}\|$). Let $\boldsymbol{a} = [a_1, \ldots, a_n]$ and $\boldsymbol{b} = [b_1, \ldots, b_n]$, with $b_i \ne 0$. Let $\mathbf{X}$ be a random variable taking values $x_i = a_i/b_i$ with probabilities $p_i = b_i^2/\sum_{j=1}^{n} b_j^2$. Use $\mathbb{E}[\mathbf{X}^2] \ge \mathbb{E}[\mathbf{X}]^2$ to show

$$(\boldsymbol{a} \bullet \boldsymbol{b})^2 = \left(\sum_{i=1}^{n} a_i b_i\right)^2 \le \sum_{i=1}^{n} a_i^2 \sum_{j=1}^{n} b_j^2 = \|\boldsymbol{a}\|^2\|\boldsymbol{b}\|^2.$$

Problem 21.49. A graph with n nodes has degrees $d_1 \ge d_2 \ge \cdots \ge d_n$ and average degree $d = (d_1 + \cdots + d_n)/n$. Show that $\sum_{i=1}^{n} 1/(d_i + 1) \ge n/(d+1)$. *[Hint: Invent a random variable $\mathbf{X}$ and use $\mathbb{E}[\mathbf{X}^2] \ge \mathbb{E}[\mathbf{X}]^2$.]*

Problem 21.50. Let $\mathbf{X}_1, \ldots, \mathbf{X}_n$ be independent with means $\mu_1, \ldots, \mu_n$ and variances $\sigma_1^2, \ldots, \sigma_n^2$. The average is $\mathbf{X} = \frac{1}{n}(\mathbf{X}_1 + \cdots + \mathbf{X}_n)$. What are $\mu(\mathbf{X})$ and $\sigma^2(\mathbf{X})$. What would formula (21.7) on page 318 be for $\mathbf{X}$?

Problem 21.51. In Figure 21.2 on page 310 we gave the PDF for the sum of 4 and 100 dice. Use build-up method to obtain the PDF for the sum of n dice. Let $P(n, s)$ be the probability that the sum of n dice is s.

(a) What are the possible values for the sum of n dice?

(b) What are $P(1, s)$ and $P(n, n)$? For $s \geq n$, show, using total probability, that $P(n, s) = \frac{1}{6} \sum_{i=1}^{\min(6, s-n+1)} P(n-1, s-i)$.

(c) Compute $P(5, s)$ by filling the following table using (b). We filled the first two rows.

$P(n,s)$	s: 1	2	3	4	5	6	7	8	9	10	11	12	13	$\cdots$	30
n = 1	$\frac{1}{6}$	$\frac{1}{6}$	$\frac{1}{6}$	$\frac{1}{6}$	$\frac{1}{6}$	$\frac{1}{6}$	0	0	0	0	0	0	0	$\cdots$	0
				$\times 1/6$							$\times 1/6$				
2	0	$\frac{1}{36}$	$\frac{1}{18}$	$\frac{1}{12}$	$\frac{1}{9}$	$\frac{5}{36}$	$\frac{1}{6}$	$\frac{5}{36}$	$\frac{1}{9}$	$\frac{1}{12}$	$\frac{1}{18}$	$\frac{1}{36}$	0	$\cdots$	0
3	?	?	?	?	?	?	?	?	?	?	?	?	?	$\cdots$	?
4	?	?	?	?	?	?	?	?	?	?	?	?	?	$\cdots$	?
5	?	?	?	?	?	?	?	?	?	?	?	?	?	$\cdots$	?

(d) Write a program to compute the distribution $P(n, s)$ and compute the standard deviation of the average of n dice for $n = 1, \ldots, 100$. Give a plot to verify $\sigma = \sqrt{35/12n}$.

Problem 21.52. An aggressive drunk takes 10 steps $\mathbf{X}_1, \ldots, \mathbf{X}_{10}$. Each step is independent, and moves left or right with equal probability. The size of the step increases with time, $|\mathbf{X}_i| = i$.

(a) Find the PDF for the position of the drunk after the 10 steps. *[Hint: Build-up.]*

(b) Use the PDF to compute the expected value and standard deviation of the drunk's position after 10 steps.

(c) Use linearity to compute the expected value and standard deviation of the drunk's position after 10 steps.

Problem 21.53 (Maximizing Variance). A random variable $\mathbf{X}$ takes values in $[0, 1]$ and has mean μ. Prove that $\mathbb{E}[\mathbf{X}^2] \leq \mu$ and $\sigma^2(\mathbf{X}) \leq \mu(1-\mu)$. That is, the Bernoulli maximizes variance if the mean is fixed to μ.

(a) Let $\mathbf{X}$ take values $0 = x_1 < x_2 < \cdots < x_{n-1} < x_n = 1$ with probabilties $p_1, \ldots, p_n$. Suppose $p_* > 0$ for some $0 < x_* < 1$. Construct new probabilities $p'_1, \ldots, p'_n$ as follows:

$$p'_1 = p_1 + (1 - x_*)p_*; \qquad p'_* = 0; \qquad p'_n = p_n + x_* p_*.$$

(p_1, p_n increase, $p_* \to 0$; other p_j unchanged.) Show that $p'_1, \ldots, p'_n$ sum to 1 (valid PDF).

(b) Show that the random variable $\mathbf{Y}$ having PDF $p'_1, \ldots, p'_n$ has mean μ.

(c) Show that $\mathbb{E}[\mathbf{Y}^2] > \mathbb{E}[\mathbf{X}^2]$, hence $\sigma^2(\mathbf{Y}) > \sigma^2(\mathbf{X})$. Complete the proof that the Bernoulli maximizes variance.

Problem 21.54. In an exam with n questions, let p_i be the probability a student answers question i correctly.

(a) What is the condition on the p_i so that the expected grade on the exam is 80%?

(b) Show that the grade-variance is maximized when $p_i = 0.8$ (this helps to better differentiate students).

Problem 21.55. Use Chebyshev's inequality to bound the probability of 2500 ± 100 heads in 5000 fair coin flips.

Problem 21.56. You are building a circuit board and need 50 transistors. About 2% of transistors are defective. Use Chebyshev's Inequality to estimate the number of transistors you should order to ensure at least a 99% chance that you will have enough non-defective transistors. Compare with the correct number you should order.

Problem 21.57. Voltage in the US has a mean of 120V and a standard deviation of 5V. A device's operating voltage is 112-128. Use Chebyshev's inequality to bound the probability that the device will not be damaged when turned on.

Problem 21.58. In a game, you win \$1 with probability 0.4 and lose \$1 with probability 0.6. You play 100 games. Compute the probability that you will not lose money and compare with the upper bound from Chebyshev's inequality.

Problem 21.59. You send 100 bits over a wireless channel that flips bits independently with probability $\frac{1}{10}$. Compute the probability that $4 \leq$ number of errors ≤ 16. Compare with the lower bound from Chebyshev's inequality.

Problem 21.60 (Gallup poll). In a Gallup poll, we try to predict the outcome of an election by examining the votes from a sample of 1000 voters. Let p be the fraction who voted republican versus $1-p$ for democrat.

(a) Assume $p = 50\%$. Find the 3σ-range for the number in the sample who vote republican?

(b) Predict, giving reasons, who won the election when the number who voted republican is (i) 425 (ii) 480 (iii) 565.

Problem 21.61. Your commute to work is 15 min and you encounter 20 (independent) traffic lights. A traffic light causes no delay with probability $\frac{1}{4}$ and a 1 minute delay with probability $\frac{3}{4}$. Use Chebyshev to estimate your chances to get to work on time if you leave 30 min before work starts. Compare with the exact probability.

Problem 21.62. Let $\mathbf{X}$ be the waiting time with success probability p. Compute $f(n) = \mathbb{P}[\mathbf{X} \geq n]$ and $g(n)$, the Chebyshev upper bound on $\mathbb{P}[\mathbf{X} \geq n]$. Show that $f(n) \in o(g(n))$. (Chebyshev's bound can be asymptotically worse than reality.)

Problem 21.63 (Monte Carlo for Variance). Let $\mathbf{X}_1, \ldots, \mathbf{X}_n$ be independent random variables with means $\mu_1, \ldots, \mu_n$ and variances $\sigma_1^2, \ldots, \sigma_n^2$. In a Monte Carlo simulation, you use a random variable generator to generate values for $\mathbf{X}_1, \ldots, \mathbf{X}_n$. Let the values generated be $z_1, \ldots, z_n$. The average of these values is the sample mean, $\overline{z} = (z_1 + \cdots + z_n)/n$. Similarly the sample variance is the average of the squared-deviations from the sample mean,

$$s^2 = \frac{1}{n}\sum_{i=1}^{n}(z_i - \overline{z})^2.$$

(a) Show that $\mathbb{E}[\overline{z}] = (\mu_1 + \cdots + \mu_n)/n$, the average of the means.
(b) Show that $s^2 = \frac{1}{n}\sum_{i=1}^{n} z_i^2 - \overline{z}^2$ (the average of the squares minus the average squared).
(c) Show that $\mathbb{E}[s^2] = \left(\frac{n-1}{n}\right) \cdot \frac{1}{n}\sum_{i=1}^{n}\sigma_i^2 + \frac{1}{n}\sum_{i=1}^{n}\mu_i^2 - \left(\frac{1}{n}\sum_{i=1}^{n}\mu_i\right)^2$.
(A term slightly below average($\sigma_1^2, \ldots, \sigma_n^2$) plus variance($\mu_1, \ldots, \mu_n$) which measures the spread in the μ_i.)
(d) When each $\mathbf{X}_i$ has the same mean μ and variance σ^2, show that $\mathbb{E}[\overline{z}] = \mu$ and $\mathbb{E}[s^2] = \left(\frac{n-1}{n}\right)\sigma^2$.
(e) Justify the following Monte Carlo approach to estimating $\mathbb{E}[\mathbf{X}]$ and $\sigma^2(\mathbf{X})$. Generate n values for $\mathbf{X}$ having sample mean $\overline{z}$ and sample variance s^2. Estimate $\mu = \overline{z}$ and $\sigma^2 = (\frac{n}{n-1})s^2$.

Problem 21.64 (Failed Monte Carlo). Monte Carlo is a tool for estimating probabilities, and the average over repeated independent experiments is a tool for estimating expected value. The Central Limit Theorem justifies that the average will converge to the expectation. Let $\mathbf{X}$ have PDF $P_{\mathbf{X}}(k) = 1/k(k+1)$ for $k \geq 1$.
(a) Show that $P_{\mathbf{X}}$ is a valid PDF by showing it sums to 1.
(b) Run a Monte Carlo experiment to generate $\mathbf{X}$ independently and plot the average versus $\mathbf{X}$ for up to 10^6 experiments. (You must figure out how to "generate" $\mathbf{X}$.)
(c) Does the average appear to converge? Explain your observations (compute the expectation).

Problem 21.65 (Conditional variance and the Law of Total variance). The conditional variance of $\mathbf{X}$ given an event A can be defined using conditional expectations as

$$\sigma^2(\mathbf{X} \mid A) = \mathbb{E}[\mathbf{X}^2 \mid A] - \mathbb{E}[\mathbf{X} \mid A]^2.$$

Suppose there are k mutually exclusive and exhaustive cases, $C_1, C_2, \ldots, C_k$. Prove the law of total variance:

$$\sigma^2(\mathbf{X}) = \sum_{i=1}^{k}\sigma^2(\mathbf{X} \mid C_i)\,\mathbb{P}[C_i] + \sum_{i=1}^{k}\mathbb{E}[\mathbf{X} \mid C_i]^2 \cdot P[C_i] - \Big(\sum_{i=1}^{k}\mathbb{E}[\mathbf{X} \mid C_i] \cdot P[C_i]\Big)^2.$$

Total variance is the weighted sum of "within case spreads" plus "between case spread" (variance of case averages).

Problem 21.66 (Iterated Variance). Suppose $\mathbf{Y}$ depends on $\mathbf{X}$. Use Problem 21.65 to prove the law of iterated variance, $\sigma^2(\mathbf{Y}) = \mathbb{E}_{\mathbf{X}}[\sigma^2(\mathbf{Y} \mid \mathbf{X})] + \sigma^2_{\mathbf{X}}(\mathbb{E}[\mathbf{Y} \mid \mathbf{X}])$.

Problem 21.67. $\mathbf{X}_1, \ldots, \mathbf{X}_n$ are independent indicators with $p_i = \mathbb{P}[\mathbf{X}_i = 1]$ and $\mathbf{X} = \mathbf{X}_1 + \cdots + \mathbf{X}_n$. Prove:

$$\mathbb{P}[\mathbf{X} = 0] \leq e^{-\mathbb{E}[\mathbf{X}]}.$$

(a) Show that $\mathbb{P}[\mathbf{X} = 0] = \prod_{i=1}^{n}(1 - p_i) \leq \prod_{i=1}^{n} e^{-p_i}$. Hence, prove the result. *[Hint: $1 - x \leq e^{-x}$.]*
(b) 50 million people play a lottery, each independently picking a 6-digit number. To win, the number must match a randomly picked 6-digit number. Prove that the chances someone wins the lottery is at least $1 - e^{-50}$.

Problem 21.68 (Hoeffding's Lemma). Suppose $\mathbf{X}$ is a random variable taking values in $[0,1]$, with $\mathbb{E}[\mathbf{X}] = \mu$. Let λ be any positive number. Prove that:

$$\mathbb{E}[e^{\lambda(\mathbf{X}-\mu)}] \leq e^{\frac{1}{8}\lambda^2}.$$

(a) Show that e^x is convex: $e^{\alpha x + (1-\alpha)y} \leq \alpha e^x + (1-\alpha)e^y$, for $\alpha \in [0,1]$.
(b) Use the convexity of e^x to show: $e^{\lambda(\mathbf{X}-\mu)} \leq (1 - \mathbf{X})e^{-\lambda\mu} + \mathbf{X}e^{\lambda(1-\mu)}$.
(c) Show that $\mathbb{E}[e^{\lambda(\mathbf{X}-\mu)}] \leq (1-\mu)e^{-\lambda\mu} + \mu e^{\lambda(1-\mu)}$.
(d) Let $f(\lambda) = \ln\left((1-\mu)e^{-\lambda\mu} + \mu e^{\lambda(1-\mu)}\right)$. Show: $f(0) = f'(0) = 0$ and $f''(\lambda) \leq \frac{1}{4}$. *[Hint: For the last inequality, show $f''(\lambda) = xy/(x+y)^2$, where $x = (1-\mu)e^{-\lambda}$ and $y = \mu$. Now show that $xy/(x+y)^2 \leq \frac{1}{4}$ when $x + y \neq 0$.]*
(e) Use (d) and integration to show that $f(\lambda) \leq \frac{1}{8}\lambda^2$ and conclude the proof.

Problem 21.69. Suppose $\mathbf{X} \in [a, b]$, with $\mathbb{E}[\mathbf{X}] = \mu$. Let $\lambda > 0$. Use Hoeffding's Lemma from Problem 21.68 with $\mathbf{Y} = (\mathbf{X} - a)/(b - a)$ to show that: $\mathbb{E}[e^{\lambda(\mathbf{X}-\mu)}] \le e^{\frac{1}{8}\lambda^2(a-b)^2}$.

Problem 21.70 (Hoeffding's Bound). Let $\mathbf{X}_1, \ldots, \mathbf{X}_n$ be independent, taking values in $[0, 1]$ and having means $\mu_1, \ldots, \mu_n$. Let $\mathbf{X} = \frac{1}{n}(\mathbf{X}_1 + \cdots + \mathbf{X}_n)$ be the average. Prove:

$$\mathbb{P}\big[|\mathbf{X} - \mathbb{E}[\mathbf{X}]| \ge \epsilon\big] \le 2e^{-2n\epsilon^2}.$$

(a) Show that $\mathbb{P}\big[|\mathbf{X} - \mathbb{E}[\mathbf{X}]| \ge \epsilon\big] = \mathbb{P}\big[\mathbf{X} - \mathbb{E}[\mathbf{X}] \ge \epsilon\big] + \mathbb{P}\big[\mathbb{E}[\mathbf{X}] - \mathbf{X} \ge \epsilon\big]$.

(b) Explain why, for any $s > 0$, $\mathbb{P}\big[\mathbf{X} - \mathbb{E}[\mathbf{X}] \ge \epsilon\big] = \mathbb{P}\big[e^{s(\mathbf{X}-\mathbb{E}[\mathbf{X}])} \ge e^{s\epsilon}\big]$.

(c) Prove: $\mathbb{P}[\mathbf{X} - \mathbb{E}[\mathbf{X}] \ge \epsilon] \le e^{-s\epsilon} \prod_{i=1}^{n} \mathbb{E}[e^{s(\mathbf{X}_i-\mu_i)/n}]$. (Markov plus independence)

(d) Use Hoeffding's Lemma to prove that $\mathbb{P}\big[\mathbf{X} - \mathbb{E}[\mathbf{X}] \ge \epsilon\big] \le e^{-s\epsilon + s^2/8n}$ (for any $s > 0$).

(e) Set $s = 4n\epsilon$ in (d) to prove $\mathbb{P}\big[\mathbf{X} - \mathbb{E}[\mathbf{X}] \ge \epsilon\big] \le e^{-2n\epsilon^2}$.

(f) Use a similar argument for $\mathbb{P}\big[\mathbb{E}[\mathbf{X}] - \mathbf{X} \ge \epsilon\big]$ and conclude the proof using a union bound.

Problem 21.71. Let $\mathbf{X}_1, \ldots, \mathbf{X}_n$ be independent, each taking values in $[a, b]$ with mean μ and variance σ^2. Let $\mathbf{X} = \frac{1}{n}(\mathbf{X}_1 + \cdots + \mathbf{X}_n)$ be the average. Prove that

$$\mathbb{P}\big[|\mathbf{X} - \mu| \ge t\sigma\big] \le 2e^{-\frac{1}{2}nt^2}.$$

[Hint: Use Hoeffding's Inequality with $\mathbf{Y} = (\mathbf{X} - a)/(b - a)$. By Problem 21.53, $\sigma(\mathbf{Y}) \le \frac{1}{2}$.]

Problem 21.72. Use the Hoefding bound in Problem 21.71 to analyze each case by bounding a relevant probability.

(a) (A/B-testing). Assume 10% of users will click an ad when shown webpage layout A or B. Layouts A and B are shown to 1000 web-surfers. What are the chances 10 more people click the ad in layout A than B?

(b) An average student answers a question correctly 80% of the time. What are the chances a student is above average if they score 70% on a test and the test has (i) 10 questions? (ii) 50 questions? (iii) 100 questions?

(c) FOCStel claims only 1 in a thousand drives fail. You bought 100 drives and 5 failed. What are your thoughts?

Problem 21.73. For 50 independent fair coin flips, estimate $\mathbb{P}[20 \le$ number of H $\le 30]$. Compare Chebyshev's Inequality, Hoeffding's Inequality, the Central Limit Theorem and the correct value from the Binomial distribution.

Problem 21.74. A couple has kids until 5 boys. Estimate $\mathbb{P}[7 \le$ number of children $\le 13]$ using Chebyshev's inequality and compare with the true probability. Give an estimate using Hoeffding's Inequality or explain why you can't.

Problem 21.75 (Balls and Bins). Randomly throw n balls independently into n bins (each bin is equally likely).

(a) Let random variable $\mathbf{X}_i$ indicate whether bin i is nonempty, and let $\mathbf{X} = \sum_i \mathbf{X}_i$ be the number of nonempty bins. Show that, asymptotically, a constant fraction of bins are nonempty.
  (i) What is the PDF of $\mathbf{X}_1$? Are the $\mathbf{X}_i$ independent?
  (ii) Compute the mean and variance of $\mathbf{X}$. Show that $\mathbb{E}[\mathbf{X}] \to n(1 - \frac{1}{e})$ as $n \to \infty$,

(b) Let random variable $\mathbf{Y}_i$ be the number of balls which fall in bin i.
  (i) What is the PDF of $\mathbf{Y}_1$? Are the $\mathbf{Y}_i$ independent?
  (ii) Let $\mathbf{Y} = \sum_i \mathbf{Y}_i$. Compute the mean and variance of $\mathbf{Y}$.
  (iii) Give a bound on the probability that at least k balls fall in bin 1. Specifically show

$$\mathbb{P}[\mathbf{Y}_1 \ge k] \le \binom{n}{k}\left(\frac{1}{n}\right)^k \le \frac{1}{k!}.$$

[Hint: Trivial for $k < 2$. For $k \ge 2$, write $\mathbb{P}[\mathbf{Y}_1 \ge k]$ as a sum $\sum_{i=k}^{n} a_i$. Show $\frac{a_{i+1}}{a_i} \le \frac{1}{2}$ and hence $\mathbb{P}[\mathbf{Y}_1 \ge k] \le 2\binom{n}{k}(\frac{1}{n})^k$. Now show that $\frac{a_{i+1}}{a_i} \le \frac{n-k}{(k+1)(n-1)}$, hence that $\mathbb{P}[\mathbf{Y}_1 \ge k] \le \binom{n}{k}(\frac{1}{n})^k(\frac{n-1}{n})^{n-k}(1+\frac{n-k}{nk-1})$.]

(c) Let $\mathbf{Z} = \max_i \mathbf{Y}_i$ be the maximum number of balls in a bin. Prove the important result that $\mathbb{E}[\mathbf{Z}] \le c \ln n$, for some constant $c > 0$ (you expect at most $O(\ln n)$ balls in any bin).
  (i) Use a union bound and part (b) to show that $\mathbb{P}[\mathbf{Z} \ge k] \le n/k!$.
  (ii) Hence show that, for any $\alpha > 0$, $\mathbb{P}[\mathbf{Z} \ge \alpha \ln n] \to 0$ as $n \to \infty$.
  (iii) Define events $A = \{\mathbf{Y}_1 \ge \alpha \ln n\}$ and $B = \{\max(\mathbf{Y}_2, \ldots, \mathbf{Y}_n) \ge \alpha \ln n\}$. Show

$$\mathbb{E}[\mathbf{Z}] = \mathbb{E}[\mathbf{Z} \mid A]\,\mathbb{P}[A] + \mathbb{E}[\mathbf{Z} \mid \overline{A} \wedge B]\,\mathbb{P}[\overline{A} \wedge B] + \mathbb{E}[\mathbf{Z} \mid \overline{A} \wedge \overline{B}]\,\mathbb{P}[\overline{A} \wedge \overline{B}].$$

  (iv) Hence, show that $\mathbb{E}[\mathbf{Z}] \le \dfrac{n}{(\alpha \ln n)!} + \dfrac{n(n-1)}{(\alpha \ln n)!} + \alpha \ln n$.
  (v) By choosing α appropriately, prove the claim that $\mathbb{E}[\mathbf{Z}] \le c \ln n$, for some $c > 0$.

Part II

Theory of Computing

What can we compute?
What *can't* we compute?
What can we compute quickly?

Alan M. Turing (1912–1954) gave to Humanity. Among his many contributions were: a formal model of the computer; ways to crack Hitler's Enigma machine ciphers, giving Britain the upper hand over Germany in World War II; the Turing Test which measures the "intelligence" in AI. The Turing Award is the pinnacle of our sport. Win it, and you won't need this book anymore.

In return, Humanity persecuted him. In 1952, Turing reported a burglary to his home. Turing got prosecuted when the investigation revealed that Turing was gay. He was convicted of gross-indecency. Turing got to choose his punishment, prison or chemical castration, and he chose castration. Turing committed suicide by cyanide in 1954. Experiments with cyanide in his room allowed for the possibility of accidental death, an effort by Turing to alleviate his mother's misgivings about suicide. Even in death, Turing was considerate of others.

In 2009, beginning with a petition from John Graham-Cumming, Humanity began to show its conscience. On Christmas Eve 2013, under the royal prerogative of mercy, Queen Elizabeth II pardoned Turing. And what of those not as famous as Turing? Their records remain tarnished. We can avoid tragedies like Alan Turing's. It only requires a tolerance for differences in points of view and ways of life. It's worth the effort.

Sometimes it is the people no one imagines anything of who do the things that no one can imagine.

— A. M. Turing

Chapter 22

Student: "Sir, we have a list of fetishes. What's yours?"
Gödel: "Anything not on your list."

God created infinity, and man, unable to understand infinity, created finite sets. – **Gian-Carlo Rota**

An algorithm is a finite answer to infinitly many questions. – **Stephen Kleene**

No one shall expel us from the paradise that Cantor has created. – **David Hilbert**

Infinity

1: $\mathbb{N}$, $\mathbb{Z}$, $\mathbb{Q}$, Evens and Odds are all the same "size".
2: Cantor's diagonalization argument: $\mathbb{R}$ is strictly bigger than $\mathbb{N}$.

Around 1874, the genius of Georg Cantor struck down the beast Infinity. We follow in his footsteps. Why care about Infinity when any task can only involve a specific finite input? Because we may ask whether the task can be accomplished for all possible inputs. The set of all possible inputs may not be finite, and so Infinity plays a central role. The simplest property of a set is its size. For finite sets, you just count the elements. Infinite sets are a problem because we cannot count to Infinity. The solution, Cantor realized, was not to count but to compare. Though we can't count to Infinity, we can still *compare* the sizes of infinite sets.

Think back to your baby days. You couldn't count, let alone count to Infinity. You didn't know how many fingers were on each hand, but you knew it was same number on both hands by matching fingers. Similarly, we don't know how many seats are in the auditorium. But, if every student has a seat, there are as many seats as students and if students are standing, there are more students than seats. A correspondence between the elements in two sets allows us to conclude that the sets have the same size. If there is no correspondence, then one set is bigger. An injective or 1-to-1 mapping between A and B means two elements of A cannot map to the same element of B. The mapping is onto if every element of B is used. Recall these pictures:

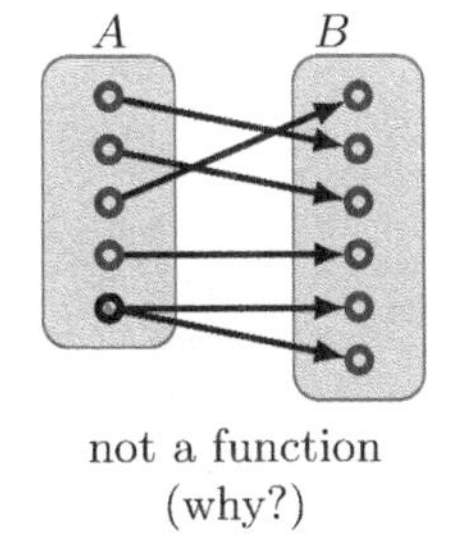

not a function
(why?)

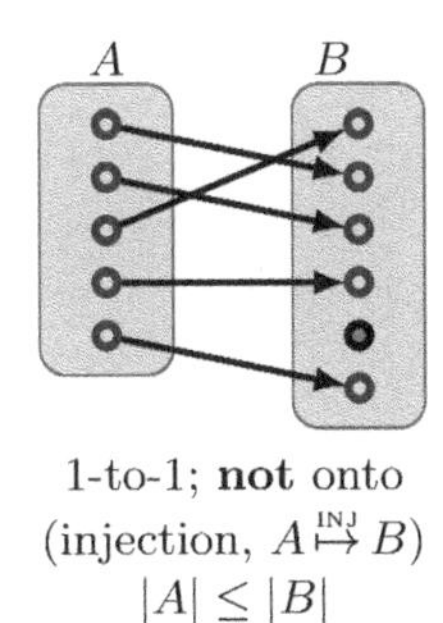

1-to-1; **not** onto
(injection, $A \overset{\text{INJ}}{\mapsto} B$)
$|A| \le |B|$

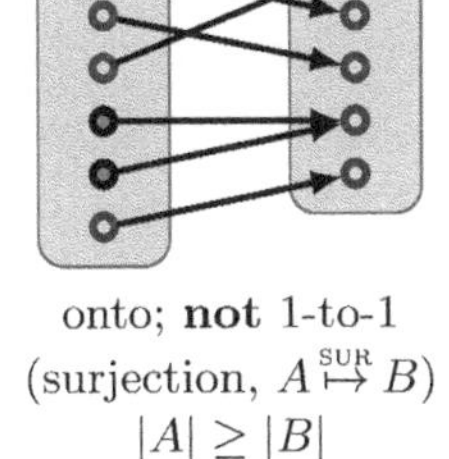

onto; **not** 1-to-1
(surjection, $A \overset{\text{SUR}}{\mapsto} B$)
$|A| \ge |B|$

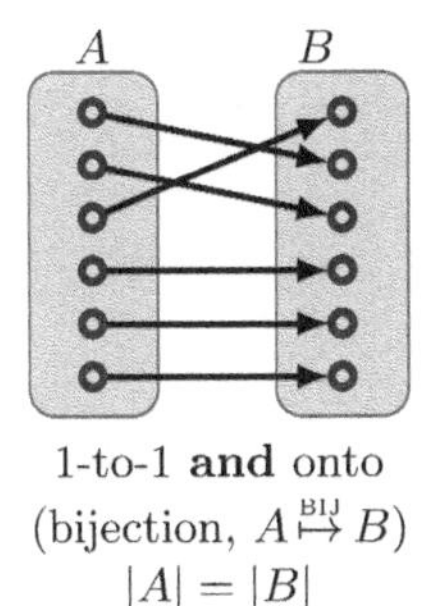

1-to-1 **and** onto
(bijection, $A \overset{\text{BIJ}}{\mapsto} B$)
$|A| = |B|$

You can conclude $|A| \le |B|$ if there is a 1-to-1 mapping from A to B and $|A| = |B|$ if there is a mapping from A to B that is both 1-to-1 and onto. A mapping that is 1-to-1 and onto is a bijection, or invertible. Cantor realized that this approach to comparing sets works not just for finite sets, but also infinite sets.

22.1 Countable

We use cardinality to describe the "size" of a set. For a set A, $|A|$ is read "cardinality of A," and equals the number of elements for finite sets. Size is ill-defined for infinite sets, but cardinality is defined and it is a useful tool for comparing infinite sets. We use mappings to compare cardinalities.

$$\begin{array}{lll} |A| \le |B| \text{ iff there is an injection } f \text{ from } A \text{ to } B,\ f : A \overset{\text{INJ}}{\mapsto} B. & (f \text{ is 1-to-1.}) \\ |A| = |B| \text{ iff there is a bijection } f \text{ from } A \text{ to } B,\ f : A \overset{\text{BIJ}}{\mapsto} B. & (f \text{ is 1-to-1 and onto.}) \end{array} \tag{22.1}$$

Cardinality gives a total order on sets. This means any two sets are comparable with respect to cardinality. Either $|A| \le |B|$ or $|B| \le |A|$, with equality when both hold,

Theorem 22.1 (Cantor-Bernstein). If $|A| \le |B|$ and $|B| \le |A|$, then |A|=|B|.

The Cantor-Bernstein Theorem is not obvious for infinite sets. To prove it, one assumes injections $f : A \overset{\text{INJ}}{\mapsto} B$ and $g : B \overset{\text{INJ}}{\mapsto} A$ are given. One must now prove existence of a bijection $h : A \overset{\text{BIJ}}{\mapsto} B$. We won't prove it here.

Exercise 22.1
(a) For $A = \{1, 2, 3\}$ and $B = \{2, 3, 4\}$, show that $|A| = |B|$.
(b) For finite $A = \{a_1, \ldots, a_n\}$ and $B = \{b_1, \ldots, b_k\}$, show: $|A| \le |B|$ if and only if $n \le k$.
(c) Prove the Cantor-Bernstein Theorem for finite sets.
(d) For arbitrary sets, show that if $A \subseteq B$, then $|A| \le |B|$.
(e) Can you always compare any two sets using the subset relation? *[Hint: Part (a).]*

For finite sets, size and cardinality are equivalent notions. Indeed the size of a set A is n if and only if there is a bijection from A to $\{1, \ldots, n\}$. For infinite sets, we have to let go all our intuitive expectations regarding size and rely purely on the strict definition of cardinality to compare sets. We need a set to compare with, and it is only natural 🙂 to use our favorite set, the natural numbers $\mathbb{N} = \{1, 2, 3, 4, 5, \ldots\}$.

Definition 22.2 (Countable). The set A is countable if $|A| \le |\mathbb{N}|$. That is, there is an injection from A to $\mathbb{N}$.

Countable means smaller than $\mathbb{N}$. To show that A is countable, find a 1-to-1 mapping from A to $\mathbb{N}$. In general, such a mapping would look something like this:

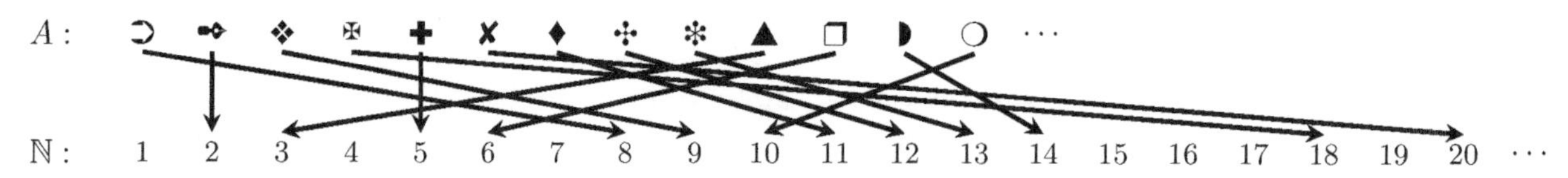

In this mapping, you cannot skip any elements of A, but you might not use every element of $\mathbb{N}$. Mathematically, you must find a function $f : A \overset{\text{INJ}}{\mapsto} \mathbb{N}$, and prove that f is an injection. This means you must prove that no two distinct elements of A map to the same element of $\mathbb{N}$. The typical way to prove an injection is by contradiction.

<u>To prove that a function $f : A \mapsto \mathbb{N}$ is an injection:</u>

1: Assume f is not an injection. This means there is a pair $x, y \in A$ for which $x \ne y$ and $f(x) = f(y)$.
2: Use $f(x) = f(y)$ to prove that $x = y$, a contradiction. Hence conclude f is an injection.

Every finite set is countable. Consider the set $A = \{3, 6, 8\}$. Here is an injection to $\mathbb{N}$,

$$3 \mapsto 1 \qquad 6 \mapsto 2 \qquad 8 \mapsto 3.$$

So, $|A| \le |\mathbb{N}|$. The injection need not use every element of $\mathbb{N}$, but you must map every element of A to distinct elements of $\mathbb{N}$. For an arbitrary finite set $A = \{a_1, a_2, \ldots, a_n\}$. Here is an injection to $\mathbb{N}$,

$$a_1 \mapsto 1 \qquad a_2 \mapsto 2 \qquad a_3 \mapsto 3 \qquad \cdots \qquad a_n \mapsto n.$$

Non-negative integers $\mathbb{N}_0 = \{0, 1, 2, \ldots\}$ are countable. How can this be? We are to show that $|\mathbb{N}_0| \le |\mathbb{N}|$, yet $\mathbb{N}_0$ contains every element in $\mathbb{N}$ plus 0. This is our first confrontation with intuition and intuition loses. Stop thinking about $|\cdot|$ as size: more is bigger. Instead, $|\cdot|$ means cardinality, and more does not necessarily mean higher cardinality. To show $|\mathbb{N}_0| \le |\mathbb{N}|$ we just need to find an injection $f : \mathbb{N}_0 \overset{\text{INJ}}{\mapsto} \mathbb{N}$. Here is one,

$$f(x) = x + 1, \qquad \text{for } x \in \mathbb{N}_0.$$

First, f is a valid function since every $x \in \mathbb{N}_0$ is mapped to a $y \in \mathbb{N}$. We show that f is an injection from $\mathbb{N}_0$ to $\mathbb{N}$. Assume f is not an injection. So, there are $x \ne y$ in $\mathbb{N}_0$ with $f(x) = f(y)$. This means

$$x + 1 = f(x) = f(y) = y + 1.$$

That is $x+1=y+1$ or $x=y$, which contradicts $x \neq y$. Therefore, f is an injection from $\mathbb{N}_0$ to $\mathbb{N}$, which proves $|\mathbb{N}_0| \leq |\mathbb{N}|$. We also have $|\mathbb{N}| \leq |\mathbb{N}_0|$ because $\mathbb{N} \subseteq \mathbb{N}_0$. Therefore, by Cantor-Bernstein $|\mathbb{N}_0| = |\mathbb{N}|$. Adding an element to $\mathbb{N}$ did not change its cardinality. We can also conclude this by noting that f is onto, so it is a bijection. The following schematic illustrates the bijection.

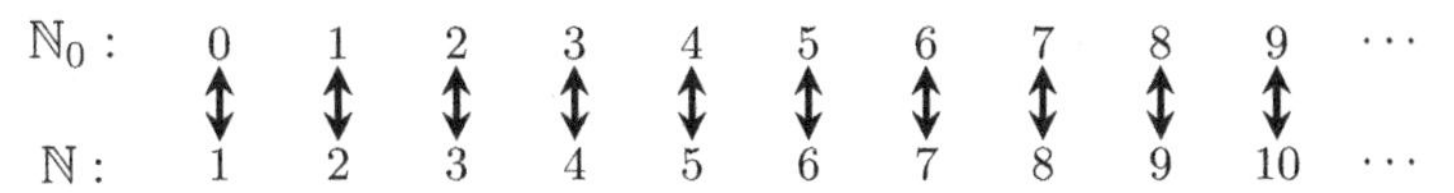

Positive even numbers $E = \{2, 4, 6, \ldots\}$ are countable. Surely, there are twice as many natural numbers? Nope. The cardinality of the two sets is the same. The bijection $f(x) = \frac{1}{2}x$ from E to $\mathbb{N}$ proves it:

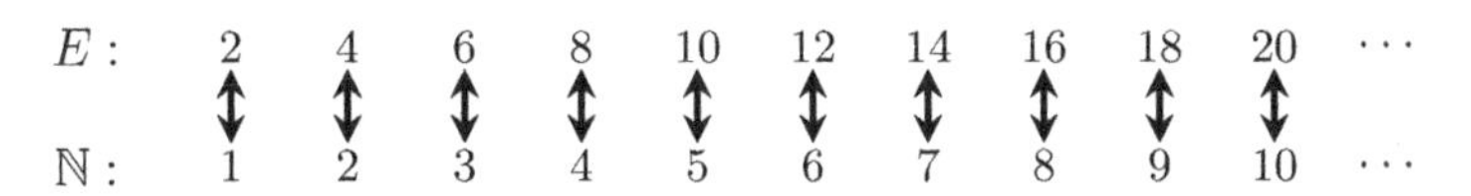

Integers $\mathbb{Z} = \{0, \pm 1, \pm 2, \ldots\}$ are countable. There appear to be twice as many integers, but, as with evens versus natural numbers, twice as many does not mean higher cardinality. Here is a bijection from $\mathbb{N}$ to $\mathbb{Z}$ which takes even natural numbers to positive integers and odd natural numbers to non-positive integers.

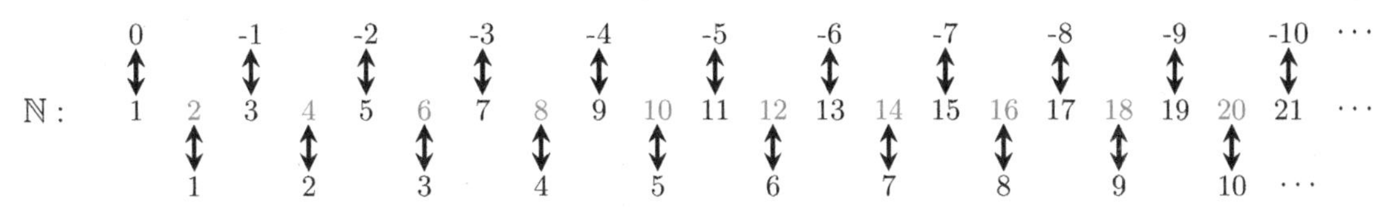

Exercise 22.2
Prove that $f(n) = \frac{1}{4}(1 + (-1)^n(2n-1))$ is a bijection from $\mathbb{N}$ to $\mathbb{Z}$.

22.1.1 Every Countable Set Can Be Listed

To formally prove that a set is countable, you must produce an injection to $\mathbb{N}$. Often, however, we are satisfied with an informal argument which lists the set. Any finite set can be shown as a list. The set $\{3, 6, 8\}$ is already a list with a first, second and third element. The same is true of an infinite countable set. The set of evens, $E = \{2, 4, 6, \ldots\}$, has a first element 2, a second element 4, and so on. There is no end to the list, but that's okay. What about the integers? Here is an attempt to list the integers.

$$\cdots, -5, -4, -3, -2, -1, 0, 1, 2, 3, 4, 5, \cdots$$

What is the first element? It's not clear. We need to be more careful about what it means to list an infinite set. Suppose, instead, we presented the integers as

$$0, \pm 1, \pm 2, \pm 3, \pm 4, \pm 5, \cdots.$$

Now, the first element is clearly 0; the second and third are ± 1; the fourth and fifth are ± 2; and so on. How we list a countable set is related to the injection that maps it to $\mathbb{N}$. Let us look again at a typical injection f from some arbitrary countable set A to $\mathbb{N}$.

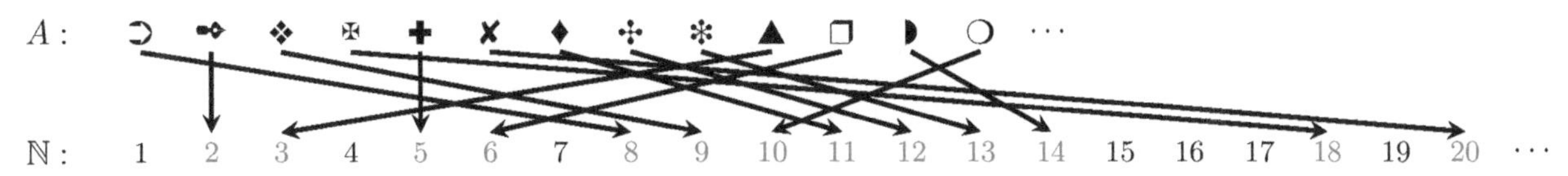

A is mapped to a subset of $\mathbb{N}$, which, by the well-ordering principle, has a minimum, in this case 2. The "first" element in A is the one which maps to this minimum, ➾ $\mapsto 2$.

Pop Quiz 22.3
Why can't there be two elements of A which map to 2 in the example above?

Excluding ➾ and 2 from A and $\mathbb{N}$ respectively, the remainder of A maps to a subset of $\mathbb{N}$ with a new minimum larger than 2. The "second" element in A is the one mapped to this new minimum. Repeating this argument, we get the "third", "fourth", etc. elements of A,

A : ➾ ▲ ✚ ❐ ➲ ❖ ❍ ◆ ✢ ❃ ◗ ✠ ✘ ⋯

$\mathbb{N}$: 1 2 3 4 5 6 7 8 9 10 11 12 13 14 15 16 17 18 19 20 ⋯

We list A using the order in which its elements are mapped by f to increasing elements of $\mathbb{N}$,

$$A = \{a_1, a_2, a_3, a_4, \ldots\}, \qquad \text{where } f(a_i) < f(a_j) \text{ for } i < j.$$

The list counts elements of A (first, second, etc.), hence A is countable. Conversely, such a list for A immediately gives an injection to $\mathbb{N}$ with $a_1 \mapsto 1$, $a_2 \mapsto 2$, etc. A set is countable if and only if you can produce a list of all its elements. It suffices to show the idea for listing the elements. Lists for $\mathbb{N}_0, E, \mathbb{Z}$ are:

$$\begin{array}{cl} \mathbb{N}_0 & \{0,1,2,3,4,5,\ldots\} \\ E & \{2,4,6,8,10,\ldots\} \\ \mathbb{Z} & \{0,+1,-1,+2,-2,+3,-3,+4,-4,\ldots\} \end{array}$$

Such informal lists of infinite countable sets usually involve "...". Recall that we urged you to avoid such ambiguous constructs. Now that we are experts, its okay to use "...", if you are careful. Your list works if:

1. Different elements of your set are assigned to different positions in the list?
2. You can determine the list-position of any element in the set, without any doubts?

Let us ask these two questions of our list for $\mathbb{Z}$. Clearly, different integers are in different list-positions. Also, we can compute the list-position of an arbitrary integer $z \in \mathbb{Z}$,

$$\text{list position of } z = f(z) = \begin{cases} 2z & z > 0; \\ 2|z| + 1 & z \leq 0; \end{cases}$$

Pop Quiz 22.4
Is $f(z)$ an injection from $\mathbb{Z}$ to $\mathbb{N}$? Using $f(z)$, compute list-positions of $z = 0, \pm 3, \pm 6$.

Theorem 22.3. The union of two countable sets is countable.

Our informal proof uses the list method. Let A and B be countable, so they can be listed:

$$A = \{a_1, a_2, a_3, a_4, a_5, \ldots\} \qquad B = \{b_1, b_2, b_3, b_4, b_5, \ldots\}.$$

To prove that $A \cup B$ is countable, we give a list for $A \cup B$ using the lists for A and B,

$$A \cup B = \{a_1, a_2, a_3, a_4, a_5, \ldots, b_1, b_2, b_3, b_4, b_5, \ldots\}.$$

So simple, but wrong! This non-list illustrates a common mistake: the use of "..." twice. To highlight the flaw, answer this question: "What is the list-position of b_1?" There is no list-position for b_1 because all the list-positions are used by the a's. Here is a valid list,

$$A \cup B = \{a_1, b_1, a_2, b_2, a_3, b_3, a_4, b_4, a_5, b_5, \ldots\}.$$

The valid list alternates between the lists for A and B. This works because we can unambiguously identify the list-position of any element in $A \cup B$,

The list-position of a_i is $2i - 1$;
The list-position of b_i is $2i$.

We have a valid list, so $A \cup B$ is countable. Since A and B were general, Theorem 22.3 is proved. The interleaving method used to list $A \cup B$ is how we listed $\mathbb{Z}$, with $A = \{0, -1, -2, -3, \ldots\}$ and $B = \{1, 2, 3, \ldots\}$.

22.1.2 Rationals are Countable

Cantor asked, "Is any set is bigger than $\mathbb{N}$?" He turned to the rational numbers. Between any two rationals is another rational. Such a property is not true of integers. Rationals should be far more numerous than integers. Cantor was quite surprised when he found the answer.

Theorem 22.4. The rationals are countable, and $|\mathbb{Q}| = |\mathbb{N}|$.

Cantor found a nice way to depict the rational numbers so he could traverse them and produce a list, proving $\mathbb{Q}$ is countable, i.e. $|\mathbb{Q}| \le |\mathbb{N}|$. Since $\mathbb{N} \subseteq \mathbb{Q}$ it follows that $|\mathbb{N}| \le |\mathbb{Q}|$ and by Cantor-Bernstein $|\mathbb{Q}| = |\mathbb{N}|$. Recall that a rational is the ratio of an integer and a natural. Here are the rationals as an $\mathbb{N} \times \mathbb{Z}$ grid,

$\mathbb{Q}$	$\mathbb{Z}$: 0	+1	−1	+2	−2	+3	−3	+4	−4	⋯
1	$\frac{0}{1}$	$\frac{+1}{1}$	$\frac{-1}{1}$	$\frac{+2}{1}$	$\frac{-2}{1}$	$\frac{+3}{1}$	$\frac{-3}{1}$	$\frac{+4}{1}$	$\frac{-4}{1}$	⋯
2	$\frac{0}{2}$	$\frac{+1}{2}$	$\frac{-1}{2}$	$\frac{+2}{2}$	$\frac{-2}{2}$	$\frac{+3}{2}$	$\frac{-3}{2}$	$\frac{+4}{2}$	$\frac{-4}{2}$	⋯
$\mathbb{N}$ 3	$\frac{0}{3}$	$\frac{+1}{3}$	$\frac{-1}{3}$	$\frac{+2}{3}$	$\frac{-2}{3}$	$\frac{+3}{3}$	$\frac{-3}{3}$	$\frac{+4}{3}$	$\frac{-4}{3}$	⋯
4	$\frac{0}{4}$	$\frac{+1}{4}$	$\frac{-1}{4}$	$\frac{+2}{4}$	$\frac{-2}{4}$	$\frac{+3}{4}$	$\frac{-3}{4}$	$\frac{+4}{4}$	$\frac{-4}{4}$	⋯
5	$\frac{0}{5}$	$\frac{+1}{5}$	$\frac{-1}{5}$	$\frac{+2}{5}$	$\frac{-2}{5}$	$\frac{+3}{5}$	$\frac{-3}{5}$	$\frac{+4}{5}$	$\frac{-4}{5}$	⋯
⋮	⋮	⋮	⋮	⋮	⋮	⋮	⋮	⋮	⋮	⋱

To produce this grid, we must list its rows and columns. We need that $\mathbb{N}$ (the rows) and $\mathbb{Z}$ (the columns) can be listed. Since $\mathbb{N}$ and $\mathbb{Z}$ are both countable, the rows and columns can be listed ☺.

Note that $+1/2$ and $+2/4$ are different rationals in our grid, though they are the same rational value. That just means $|\{\text{Rational Values}\}| \le |\mathbb{Q}|$. Start at $0/1$ and as you follow the red arrows in a snake-like manner, spit out the rationals you meet. You produce the list

$$\mathbb{Q} = \left\{\frac{0}{1}, \frac{+1}{1}, \frac{+1}{2}, \frac{0}{2}, \frac{0}{3}, \frac{+1}{3}, \frac{-1}{3}, \frac{-1}{2}, \frac{-1}{1}, \frac{+2}{1}, \frac{+2}{2}, \frac{+2}{3}, \frac{+2}{4}, \frac{-1}{4}, \frac{+1}{4}, \frac{0}{4}, \frac{0}{5}, \ldots\right\}$$

This list, which eventually hits every rational, shows that $|\{\text{Rational Values}\}| \le |\mathbb{Q}| \le |\mathbb{N}|$. Intuition suggests $|\mathbb{Q}| = |\mathbb{N}| \times |\mathbb{Z}| \gg |\mathbb{N}|$. Intuition is wrong. Intuition should be thrown out the window.

Exercise 22.5

(a) Compute the list-position of $z/n \in \mathbb{Q}$ in our list for $\mathbb{Q}$, where $z \in \mathbb{Z}$ and $n \in \mathbb{N}$.

(b) What's wrong with this list, $\mathbb{Q} = \{$rationals with denominator 1, then denominator 2,...$\}$.

(c) Prove that the union of a countable number of countable sets is countable.

(d) The "real-rationals" $\mathbb{Q}_\mathbb{R}$ are ratios of a real and a natural. Why can't the proof technique which showed $|\mathbb{Q}| = |\mathbb{N}|$ also be used to show $|\mathbb{Q}_\mathbb{R}| = |\mathbb{N}|$?

Example 22.5 (Finite Binary Strings). Computer programs are finite binary strings, hence the set $\mathcal{B}$ of all finite binary strings plays an important role in computer science.

$$\mathcal{B} = \{\varepsilon, 0, 1, 00, 01, 10, 11, 000, 001, 010, 011, 100, 101, 110, 111, 0000, \ldots\}$$

After ε, the empty string of length 0, we list strings of length 1, then length 2, and so on. Strings of a fixed length are in order of increasing value, treating the string as a binary number, e.g. 101 has value 5.

Our list shows that $\mathcal{B}$, is countable. To prove the list is valid we show how to get the (unique) list-position of any finite string $b = b_k b_{k-1} \cdots b_1 b_0$ with $k+1$ bits. The string, when seen as a binary number, has value

$$\text{value}(b) = b_0 \cdot 2^0 + b_1 \cdot 2^1 + \cdots + b_{k-1} \cdot 2^{k-1} + b_k \cdot 2^k.$$

Different strings of length $k+1$ have different values. Strings of length $k+1$ are in order of increasing value. Within strings of length $k+1$, b has position value$(b)+1$ (the $+1$ is because values start at 0 but the first position is 1). Before the strings of length $k+1$ come all strings of lengths $0, 1, \ldots, k$. There are 2^ℓ strings of length ℓ, so the number of strings which come before the first string of length $k+1$ is

$$2^0 + 2^1 + \cdots + 2^k = 2^{k+1} - 1.$$

We conclude that our string b occupies list position $2^{k+1} - 1 + \text{value}(b) + 1$, that is

$$\text{list-position of } b = 2^{\text{length}(b)} + \text{value}(b),$$

For example, 010 has length 3, value 2 and list-position $2^3 + 2 = 10$. Verify this by inspecting the list for $\mathcal{B}$ $\square$

Integers, rationals and finite binary strings are all countable. Maybe all infinite sets are countable. Cantor proved otherwise when he considered the continuum of real numbers.

22.2 Reals are Uncountable

Cantor's first proof in 1874 was very technical, using advanced tools from analysis. He revisited the result in 1891, giving an irresistible proof of supreme elegance, perhaps the most beautiful proof ever. For a prototypical uncountable set look no further than infinite binary strings. Remember, finite binary strings are countable.

Theorem 22.6. The set of all infinite binary strings is not countable.

Proof. We can't even write down a single member of this deadly set as they are all infinite, so our argument is necessarily abstract. The proof is by contradiction. Assume infinite binary strings are countable. So, there is a list all these strings, $\{b_1, b_2, b_3, \ldots\}$. Here is how such a list would look, if we could write it down.

$$\begin{array}{r|ccccccccccccccc}
b_1: & \mathbf{0} & 0 & 0 & 1 & 0 & 0 & 0 & 0 & 0 & 0 & 0 & 0 & 0 & 0 & 0\cdots \\
b_2: & 0 & \mathbf{0} & 1 & 1 & 0 & 1 & 0 & 0 & 1 & 0 & 0 & 0 & 0 & 1 & 0\cdots \\
b_3: & 1 & 1 & \mathbf{0} & 0 & 0 & 0 & 1 & 0 & 0 & 0 & 0 & 1 & 1 & 0 & 0\cdots \\
b_4: & 1 & 0 & 1 & \mathbf{0} & 0 & 1 & 0 & 0 & 0 & 0 & 1 & 0 & 0 & 0 & 0\cdots \\
b_5: & 0 & 1 & 1 & 0 & \mathbf{1} & 0 & 1 & 0 & 0 & 0 & 0 & 0 & 0 & 0 & 0\cdots \\
b_6: & 0 & 1 & 0 & 1 & 1 & \mathbf{0} & 0 & 0 & 0 & 1 & 0 & 0 & 0 & 0 & 0\cdots \\
b_7: & 0 & 0 & 1 & 0 & 0 & 1 & \mathbf{0} & 0 & 0 & 0 & 0 & 0 & 0 & 0 & 1\cdots \\
b_8: & 0 & 0 & 1 & 0 & 1 & 1 & 0 & \mathbf{1} & 0 & 0 & 0 & 0 & 1 & 0 & 0\cdots \\
b_9: & 0 & 0 & 0 & 0 & 1 & 1 & 0 & 0 & \mathbf{0} & 0 & 1 & 0 & 0 & 0 & 0\cdots \\
b_{10}: & 1 & 0 & 1 & 1 & 1 & 0 & 1 & 0 & 0 & \mathbf{1} & 1 & 0 & 0 & 0 & 0\cdots \\
\vdots & & & & & & & & & & & & & & &
\end{array}$$

Every infinite binary string is in the list. We highlight the "diagonal" entries, which continue forever. The diagonals form an infinite string $b = 0000100101\cdots$. Since the list is complete, b appears in the list. Now comes Cantor's deadly blow. Form the complementary string $\bar{b}$ by flipping the bits of b, $0 \to 1$ and $1 \to 0$):

$$\bar{b} = 1111011010\cdots$$

Just as b must appear in the list, so must $\bar{b}$. But where? Perhaps list-position 3? Let's see,

$$\begin{aligned} b_3 &= ??\mathbf{0}?????????????\cdots \\ \bar{b} &= ??\mathbf{1}?????????????\cdots \end{aligned}$$

The 3rd bit of b_3 is 0; the 3rd bit of $\bar{b}$ is 1, obtained by flipping the 3rd bit of b_3. We don't need any other bits of b_3 or $\bar{b}$ to conclude $\bar{b} \neq b_3$. This is true in general: the ith bit of $\bar{b}$ is the complement of the ith bit of b_i. So, $\bar{b} \neq b_i$ for every i and $\bar{b}$ cannot be in the list, which contradicts the list being complete. The assumption that infinite binary strings are countable is false. Infinite binary strings are uncountable. ■

The argument used in the proof of Theorem 22.6 is known as Cantor diagonalization because it uses the sequence of diagonals to construct a counter-example to the claim that a list is complete. Simple, elegant and profound. Let $\mathcal{B}_\infty$ be this set of infinite binary strings. The mapping

$$n \mapsto 00\cdots010\cdots \qquad \text{(1 in the } n\text{th position)}$$

is an injection from $\mathbb{N}$ to $\mathcal{B}_\infty$, so $|\mathbb{N}| \le |\mathcal{B}_\infty|$. By Theorem 22.6, there is no injection from $\mathcal{B}_\infty$ to $\mathbb{N}$, so $|\mathbb{N}| \ne |\mathcal{B}_\infty|$. We conclude that $|\mathcal{B}_\infty| > |\mathbb{N}|$. We have a set whose cardinality is strictly greater than $|\mathbb{N}|$.

Exercise 22.6

(a) Does Cantor's diagonalization also show that finite binary strings are uncountable?
(b) Why can't we add $\bar{b}$ into the list for $\mathcal{B}_\infty$ to counter Cantor's diagonal argument?
(c) Prove that all subsets of $\mathbb{N}$ are uncountable.
(d) Prove that the finite subsets of $\mathbb{N}$ are countable.

It is nice that we have found a set which is strictly larger than $\mathbb{N}$, but what does this have to do with the real numbers. Here is a mapping from $\mathcal{B}_\infty$ to the reals in $[0, 1]$,

$$b_1b_2b_3b_4b_5\cdots \quad \mapsto \quad 0.b_1b_2b_3b_4b_5\cdots.$$

An infinite binary string on the left is mapped to the binary expansion of a real number on the right. For example, the string $101000\cdots$ maps to $0.101000\cdots = \frac{5}{8}$. This mapping from strings to expansions is a bijection. Every string gives a different expansion and vice-versa. So, the cardinality of infinite binary strings equals the cardinality of infinite binary expansions. How do the infinite binary expansions compare with the real numbers. The binary expansion $0.b_1b_2b_3b_4b_5\cdots$ corresponds to the real number x, where

$$x = b_1 \cdot 2^{-1} + b_2 \cdot 2^{-2} + b_3 \cdot 2^{-3} + b_4 \cdot 2^{-4} + b_5 \cdot 2^{-5} + \cdots + b_k 2^{-k} + \cdots.$$

We can assign a real number in $[0, 1]$ to every infinite binary expansion. Unfortunately, this mapping is not an injection. Consider the two different binary expansions

$$0.01000000000000000\cdots$$
$$0.00111111111111111\cdots$$

We ask the reader to show that both expansions evaluate to $\frac{1}{4}$. This is not good. To show that $|\mathcal{B}_\infty| \le |[0, 1]|$, we need an injection from $\mathcal{B}_\infty$ to $[0, 1]$. Fortunately the problem is minor. Such "collisions" where two binary expansions evaluate to the same real number are rare – countable. If we remove these duplicates from $\mathcal{B}_\infty$, the remaining set, call it $\tilde{\mathcal{B}}_\infty$, is still uncountable. Indeed, if $\tilde{\mathcal{B}}_\infty$ were countable, then $\mathcal{B}_\infty$ would be the union of two countable sets, which is countable, and that isn't the case. This means $|\mathbb{N}| < |\tilde{\mathcal{B}}_\infty| \le |[0, 1]|$.

Theorem 22.7 (Reals are uncountable)**.** The continuum is strictly larger than $\mathbb{N}$, $|\mathbb{N}| < |[0, 1]|$.

We defer the details to an exercise. Cantor denoted $|\mathbb{N}|$ by $\aleph_0$ (read "aleph-naught") and $|[0, 1]|$ by $\mathfrak{c}$ (for continuum). The bijection $x \mapsto a + (b - a)x$ for $a < b$ bijectively maps $[0, 1]$ to $[a, b]$, so all intervals, large or small, have cardinality $\mathfrak{c}$. The bijection $x \mapsto \tan(x)$ maps $(-\frac{1}{2}\pi, \frac{1}{2}\pi)$ to $\mathbb{R}$, which means all intervals have the cardinality of the full continuum, and $|[a, b]| = |\mathbb{R}| = \mathfrak{c}$.

Exercise 22.7

(a) An infinite string is eventually 0 if after some point there are no 1s in the string. Show that the infinite strings which are eventually zero are countable. *[Hint: Relate eventually 0 strings to finite strings.]*
(b) Let $\mathcal{B}^0_\infty$ be the infinite strings that are eventually 0 and $\tilde{\mathcal{B}}_\infty$ the strings which are not eventually 0. Show that all infinite strings, $\mathcal{B}_\infty$, is the union $\mathcal{B}^0_\infty \cup \tilde{\mathcal{B}}_\infty$.
(c) Show that $\tilde{\mathcal{B}}_\infty$ is uncountable. *[Hint: Use contradiction.]*
(d) Prove that the mapping $b_1b_2b_3b_4b_5\cdots \mapsto 0.b_1b_2b_3b_4b_5\cdots$ is an injection from $\tilde{\mathcal{B}}_\infty$ to $[0, 1]$, and therefore that $|\tilde{\mathcal{B}}_\infty| \le |[0, 1]|$.

Is there a cardinality greater than the continuum? Cantor stunned the world by showing that there is a profusion of infinities greater than the continuum. To get there, we need to recall the power set of a set. For a set A, the power set $\mathcal{P}(A)$ is the set of all subsets of A. Cantor proved that the power set $\mathcal{P}(A)$ has larger cardinality than A, which is Cantor's Theorem, see Problem 22.38. Cantor proved:

$$\begin{array}{ccccccccccc} |\mathbb{N}| & < & |\mathcal{P}(\mathbb{N})| & < & |\mathcal{P}(\mathcal{P}(\mathbb{N}))| & < & |\mathcal{P}(\mathcal{P}(\mathcal{P}(\mathbb{N})))| & < & |\mathcal{P}(\mathcal{P}(\mathcal{P}(\mathcal{P}(\mathbb{N}))))| & < & \cdots \\ \aleph_0 & & \aleph_1 & & \aleph_2 & & \aleph_3 & & \aleph_4 & & \cdots \end{array} \tag{22.2}$$

Cantor's transfinite realm is a hierarchy of infinities, each surpassing the next – paradise. 

Continuum Hypothesis. The transfinite realm in (22.2) is quite remarkable. There is a discrete sequence of ever-increasing infinites $\aleph_0, \aleph_1, \ldots$. One can show that the cardinality of the continuum is $\aleph_1$, that is $|\mathbb{R}| = \mathfrak{c} = \aleph_1$. Cantor wondered if there can be a set whose cardinality is strictly between the naturals and the reals. Cantor believed the answer was no, and this became known as the continuum hypothesis,

$$\text{Continuum hypothesis: There is no set } \mathcal{S} \text{ with cardinality } |\mathbb{N}| < |\mathcal{S}| < |\mathbb{R}|.$$

The continuum hypothesis became the first of Hilbert's 23 problems from the 1900 International Congress of Mathematicians. Cantor tried in vain for many years to prove the continuum hypothesis. In 1940, Kurt Gödel showed that the continuum hypothesis cannot be disproved from within Zermelo-Fraenkel set theory with Choice (ZFC). In 1963, Paul Cohen showed that the continuum hypothesis also cannot be proved from within ZFC. The continuum hypothesis is independent of main stream axiomatic set theory, meaning it can be true or false without affecting set theory. Cantor opened a window to a truly uncharted realm.

22.3 Infinity and Computing

Cantor did something truly remarkable. He didn't tackle unanswered questions. He tackled unasked questions. Even the great Pythagoras, Euclid, Archimedes, Newton, Euler and Gauss all shunned away from Infinity, a dangerously beast. Cantor took Infinity head-on.[1] Fast-forward to the 20th century and Alan Turing, who faced another question, "What can we compute?" This question will occupy us for some time. But, we can hint at how Infinity will come to bear on it. Infinity shows us not only that there are things we cannot compute, but that there are many things we cannot compute.

Computer programs can be complex, like nuclear reactor simulations, or simple, like

```
int main();          //a program that does nothing
```

One thing is common. Every program is a finite string of bits. Using the ASCII code, our simple program which does nothing is the binary string

```
0110100101101110011101000010000001101101011000010110100101101110001010000010100100111011
```

Some finite strings are not valid programs, so finite strings outnumber valid programs,

$$|\{\text{valid programs}\}| \le |\{\text{finite binary strings}\}|.$$

In Example 22.5 on page 331, we saw that finite binary strings are countable. So, valid programs are countable.

Now lets talk about things we might like to compute. How about a binary function on $\mathbb{N}$? A program to compute such a function takes a natural number $n \in \mathbb{N}$ and outputs 0 or 1. We can represent a binary function by its values on all natural numbers. Each binary function f corresponds to a different infinite binary string which can be written out as

$$f(1)f(2)f(3)f(4)f(5)\cdots.$$

Wait a minute! Theorem 22.6 says infinite binary strings are uncountable. There are an uncountable number of binary functions on $\mathbb{N}$, but there are only countably many valid programs, only some of which compute binary functions. You see the dilemma. There must be some functions which we cannot compute using programs. By this argument, there are uncountably many non-computable functions. Yet, despite the abundance of non-computable functions, it is exceedingly difficult to actually catch one and put it on display for critique. Perhaps all the non-computable functions are esoteric and uninteresting. Are there useful functions that are non-computable? Stay tuned to find out.

[1] During Cantor's time, mathematics was being liberated from reality (physics) by the arrival of non-Euclidean geometries. Mathematics for mathematics-sake was coming alive and Cantor took full advantage, plunging deep into the abyss of the abstract. A similar revolution was afoot in the art-world. A canvas was no longer just a window to a visual scene frozen in time. The masters like Cézanne, Gauguin and Van Gogh brought art into an abstract realm, where paintings had lives of their own.

22.4 Problems

Problem 22.1. A barber shaves *all* people who do not shave themselves and *only* people who do not shave themselves. Who shaves the barber?

Problem 22.2. YES or NO (and explain): **"Is the answer to Problem 22.2 'NO'?"**

Problem 22.3. Explain the judge's inaction in the following anecdote.

A lawyer never won a case. Before quitting law, he declared that he would file his *last* case against his law school, sueing for a refund of his tuition.

Lawyer to Judge: They did such a bad job that I never won a case.

Judge: Hmm... reasonable. If you never win a law suit, you deserve a refund.

Nevertheless, the judge pondered forever and never made a ruling.

Problem 22.4. $A = \{a, b, c\}$; $B = \{x, y, z\}$. A function $f : A \mapsto B$ maps $a \mapsto x$; $b \mapsto x$; $c \mapsto z$. Determine which if any of the following that correctly describe f:
(a) Injection (b) Surjection (c) One-to-one (d) Bijection (e) Invertible

Problem 22.5. A function f from A to B (both finite sets) is 1-to-1 but not onto. Prove that $|A| < |B|$. Does the same hold for infinite sets A and B.

Problem 22.6. Give a definition of a surjection similar to this formal definition of an injection:

Injection: A function $f : A \mapsto B$ is an injection if $\forall a_1, a_2 \in A : f(a_1) = f(a_2) \rightarrow a_1 = a_2$.

Problem 22.7. For what values of $n \in \mathbb{Z}$ is $f(z) = z^n$ an injection from $\mathbb{Z}$ to $\mathbb{Z}$.

Problem 22.8. For each f, determine which of {injective, surjective, bijective} are true.
(a) $f : \mathbb{R} \mapsto \mathbb{R}$, where $f(x) = e^x$.
(b) $f : \mathbb{R} \mapsto \mathbb{R}_{>0}$, where $f(x) = e^x$.
(c) $f : \mathbb{R} \mapsto \mathbb{R}$, where $f(x) = x^2$.
(d) $f : \mathbb{Q} \mapsto \mathbb{R}$, where $f(x) = e^x$.
(d) $f : \mathbb{R} \mapsto \mathbb{R}_{\geq 0}$, where $f(x) = x^2$.
(e) $f : \mathbb{R} \mapsto \mathbb{R}$, where $f(x) = x(x-1)(x-2)$.
(f) $f : \mathbb{R} \mapsto \mathbb{R}_{>0}$, where $f(x) = x^2$.
(g) $f : \mathbb{N} \mapsto \mathbb{N}$, where $f(x) = \lfloor \sqrt{x} \rfloor$.

Problem 22.9. Let A be the even natural numbers and B the odd natural numbers. Let $f : A \times B \mapsto \mathbb{N}$ be defined by $f(a, b) = ab/2$. Prove or disprove: (a) f is injective. (b) f is surjective. (c) f is bijective.

Problem 22.10. A function maps $\{1, 2, 3, 4\}$ to $\{a, b, c, d, e\}$. How many such functions are
(a) Injective; (b) Surjective; (c) Bijective.

Problem 22.11. Let $f : A \mapsto B$ and $g : B \mapsto C$. The composition $g \circ f : A \mapsto C$ is given by $g \circ f(x) = g(f(x))$. Prove or disprove.
(a) f, g are bijections $\rightarrow g \circ f$ is a bijection.
(b) $g \circ f$ is a bijection $\rightarrow f, g$ are bijections.
(c) f, g are injections $\rightarrow g \circ f$ is an inijection.
(d) $g \circ f$ is an injection $\rightarrow f, g$ are injections.
(e) f, g are surjections $\rightarrow g \circ f$ is a surjection.
(f) $g \circ f$ is a surjection $\rightarrow f, g$ are surjections.

Problem 22.12. Let $f : A \mapsto B$ and $g : A \mapsto C$. The product function $f \otimes g : A \mapsto B \times C$ is given by $f \otimes g(x) = (f(x), g(x))$. Prove or disprove.
(a) IF f is an injection, THEN $f \otimes g$ is an injection.
(b) IF f and g are surjections THEN $f \otimes g$ is a surjection.
(c) IF f and g are bijections THEN $f \otimes g$ is a bijection.

Problem 22.13. Give a bijection from A to B (prove that your mapping is a bijection).
(a) $A =$ {squares of integers}; $B = \mathbb{Z}$. (b) $A =$ {positive odd numbers}; $B = \mathbb{Z}$.

Problem 22.14. Answer TRUE or FALSE.
(a) A bijection must be an injection.
(b) There is a bijection from $\mathbb{Q}$ to $\mathbb{R}$.
(c) There is a bijection from $\mathbb{Q}$ to $\mathbb{Z}$.
(d) There is an uncountable subset of $\mathbb{N} \times \mathbb{N}$.
(e) Every infinite subset of $\mathbb{R}$ is uncountable.
(f) The solutions to $x \equiv 0 \pmod 6$ are countable.

Problem 22.15. Let $\mathcal{B}$ be the finite binary strings, and $\mathcal{T}$ the finite ternary strings (strings whose characters are $0, 1$ or 2). Show that $|\mathcal{B}| = |\mathcal{T}|$. *[Hint: $0 \mapsto 00; 1 \mapsto 01; 2 \mapsto 10$.]*

Problem 22.16. Suppose $f_A : A \overset{\text{INJ}}{\mapsto} \mathbb{N}$ and $f_B : B \overset{\text{INJ}}{\mapsto} \mathbb{N}$ (A and B are countable). Use f_A and f_B to construct a function $f : A \cup B \overset{\text{INJ}}{\mapsto} \mathbb{N}$ to prove that $A \cup B$ is countable. (You must prove your f is an injection.)

Problem 22.17. Prove that IF $|A| \le |B|$ AND $|B| \le |C|$, then $|A| \le |C|$.

Problem 22.18. Determine if each method is a valid way to show that A is countable.
(a) Show an onto function from $\mathbb{N}$ to A.
(b) Show a 1-to-1 function from $\mathbb{N}$ to A.
(c) Show a bijection from $\mathbb{N}$ to A.
(d) Show an injection from $\mathbb{N}$ to A.
(e) Show there is no injection from $\mathbb{N}$ to A.
(f) Show a 1-to-1 function from A to $\mathbb{N}$.

Problem 22.19. We show a way to list integers, starting with 0. Is the method valid? If no, why? If yes, give the first 12 members of the list and the list-position of $z = 45$.

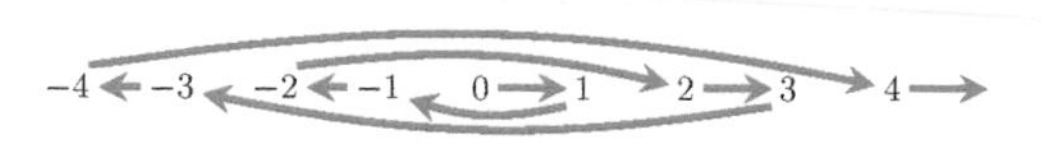

Problem 22.20. If it is possible to do so, give lists for the following sets.
(a) Positive rationals. (b) Solutions to $\sin(x) = 0$. (c) 2-tuples of integers ($\mathbb{Z} \times \mathbb{Z}$).

Problem 22.21. Prove that the unweighted finite graphs are countable. What about weighted graphs with integer weights? What if the weights are real?

Problem 22.22. True or false. Explain your answers.
(a) The positive multiples of 5 are countable.
(b) $\mathbb{Z} \cup \mathbb{Z}^2 \cup \mathbb{Z}^3$ is countable.
(c) $|\mathbb{N}| = |\{\text{square numbers}\}|$.
(d) All subsets of $\mathbb{N}$ are countable.
(e) All finite subsets of $\mathbb{N}$ are countable.
(f) All finite binary strings are countable.
(g) All infinite binary strings are countable.
(h) The angles between 0 and 2π are countable.
(i) The infinite binary strings that are eventually zero (e.g. $b_1 b_2 \cdots b_\ell 0000 \cdots$) are coutable.
(j) The functions from $\mathbb{N}$ to $\mathbb{N}$ are countable.
(k) There is a countable, infinite set for which all the subsets are countable.

Problem 22.23. Prove or disprove.
(a) The ordered pairs of integers, $\mathbb{Z}^2$, is countable, where $\mathbb{Z}^2 = \{(z_1, z_2) | z_1, z_2 \in \mathbb{Z}\}$.
(b) The ordered pairs of rationals, $\mathbb{Q}^2$, is countable, where $\mathbb{Q}^2 = \{(q_1, q_2) | q_1, q_2 \in \mathbb{Q}\}$.
(c) F is the set of all distinct functions from $\mathbb{N}$ to $\mathbb{N}$, $F = \{f | f : \mathbb{N} \mapsto \mathbb{N}\}$. F is countable.

Problem 22.24. Let A, B be countable. Prove the Cartesian product $A \times B = \{(a, b) \mid a \in A, b \in B\}$ is countable.

Problem 22.25. Determine if the cardinality of each set of functions is finite, countable or uncountable. Prove it. The functions are: (a) from $\{0\}$ to $\mathbb{N}$ (b) from $\mathbb{N}$ to $\{0\}$ (c) from $\{0,1\}$ to $\mathbb{N}$ (d) from $\mathbb{N}$ to $\{0, 1\}$.

Problem 22.26. The positive rationals are $\mathbb{Q}_+ = \{\frac{x}{y} \mid x, y \in \mathbb{N}\}$. Prove that $\mathbb{Q}_+$ is countable.
(a) Let $f(x, y) = 2^x 3^y$. Prove that f is an injection from $\mathbb{N}^2$ to $\mathbb{N}$. *[Hint: Fundamental Theorem of Arithmetic.]*
(b) Use (a) to show $|\mathbb{Q}_+| \le |\mathbb{N}|$. Show that $\mathbb{Q}_+$ being countable means $\mathbb{Q}$ must be countable.

Problem 22.27. Use ideas from Problem 22.26 to prove countable sets are closed under union and Cartesian product. Let $\{p_1, p_2, \ldots\}$ be primes. Let $\{A_1, A_2, \ldots\}$ be a countable set, where each $A_i = \{a_{i,1}, a_{i,2}, \ldots, \}$ is itself countable.
(a) For $x \in \cup_i A_i$, let A_ℓ be the first set containing x, $x \in A_\ell$ and $x \notin A_j$ for $j < \ell$. Let x be the kth element in A_ℓ. Use $f(x) = p_\ell^k$ to prove that $\cup_i A_i$ is countable. That is, the union of countably many countable sets is countable.
(b) Let $x = (x_1, x_2, \ldots, x_n)$ be an ordered n-tuple from $A_1, \ldots, A_n$, so $x \in A_1 \times A_2 \times \cdots A_n$.
  (i) Let x_i be the k_i-th element in A_i. Use $f(x_1, \ldots, x_n) = p_1^{k_1} p_2^{k_2} \cdots p_n^{k_n}$ to prove that $A_1 \times A_2 \times \cdots \times A_n$ is countable. That is, the Cartesian product of finitely many countable sets is countable.
  (ii) Why does the argument in (i) fail for an infinite Cartesian product. In fact, prove that the Cartesian product of countably many sets is uncountable, if infinitely many of the sets have size at least 2.

Problem 22.28. Prove or disprove that each intersection of the following collection of sets is countable.
(a) Countably many countable sets. (b) Uncountably many countable sets. (c) Countably many uncountable sets.

Problem 22.29. Prove that eventually constant infinite sequences on $\mathbb{N}$ are countable.

Problem 22.30. Prove that increasing sequences on $\mathbb{N}$ have the same cardinality as $\mathbb{R}$.

Problem 22.31. Let $\mathcal{X}$ be infinite, $x_0 \in \mathcal{X}$ and $\mathcal{X}_0$ the *proper* subset of $\mathcal{X}$ with all elements in $\mathcal{X}$, except x_0.

(a) Show that $|\mathcal{X}| \le |\mathcal{X}_0|$. *[Hint: Let C be any countable subset of $\mathcal{X}_0$. Construct an injection from $C \cup x_0$ to C and use this to construct an injection from $\mathcal{X}$ to $\mathcal{X}_0$.]*

(b) Prove that a set $\mathcal{X}$ is infinite if and only if there is an injection from $\mathcal{X}$ to some proper subset of $\mathcal{X}$. *[Hint: Can there be an injection from a finite set to any proper subset?]*

Problem 22.32. Prove that $f(b) = 2^{\text{length}(b)} + \text{value}(b)$ (Example 22.5 on page 331) is an injection from finite binary strings to $\mathbb{N}$. What does this imply about $|\{\text{finite binary strings}\}|$?

Problem 22.33. Prove that $[0, 1]$ has the same cardinality as the full continuum $\mathbb{R}$.

Problem 22.34 (Algebra of Infinity). Justify these "rules" for handling $\aleph_0 = |\,\mathbb{N}\,|$ (k is a constant, e.g. 2).

(a) $\aleph_0 + k = \aleph_0$. (b) $k \times \aleph_0 = \aleph_0$. (c) $\aleph_0^k = \aleph_0$. (d) $2^{\aleph_0} > \aleph_0$.

Problem 22.35. Algebraic numbers are solutions to integer-polynomial equations,

$$a_1 x^{k_1} + a_2 x^{k_2} + \cdots + a_\ell x^{k_\ell} = 0,$$

(a_i, k_i are integers and $k_1 < k_2 \cdots < k_\ell$ are positive.) A number is transcendental if it is not algebraic. Prove:

$$|\{\text{algebraic numbers}\}| = |\,\mathbb{N}\,|; \qquad |\{\text{transcendental numbers}\}| > |\,\mathbb{N}\,|.$$

(The transcendentals, e.g. π and e, far outnumber the algebraics, e.g. $2, \sqrt{2}$.)

Problem 22.36 (Irrationals have cardinality $\mathfrak{c}$). Cantor went after irrationals, a messy set for mathematicians. Prove that irrationals have the cardinality of the continuum. (There are many more irrationals than rationals.)

(a) In binary, consider the number $x = 0.1011011011011\cdots = 0.1\overline{011}$. Show that $x = \frac{5}{7}$. Argue that a rational number's binary representation either terminates or some bits eventually repeat. (You don't need a full proof.)

(b) Argue that an irrational number's binary representation is infinite and non-repeating.

(c) Let $x = 0.b_1 b_2 b_3 \cdots$ be the binary representation of a real. Let $z = 0.10b_1 110 b_2 1110 b_3 11110 b_4 \cdots$. Show that z is irrational. *[Hint: Do the digits ever repeat?]*

(d) Show that $|\,\mathbb{R}\,| \le |\{\text{irrational numbers}\}|$, and hence that $|\,\mathbb{R}\,| = |\{\text{irrational numbers}\}|$.

Problem 22.37 (Cardinality of the square, $\mathbb{R}^2$). Cantor was after a set with cardinality larger than the continuum. He was sure the square $\mathbb{R} \times \mathbb{R}$ would be it. After trying hard to show that there is no injection from $\mathbb{R} \times \mathbb{R}$ to $\mathbb{R}$, Cantor finally found one in 1877. His own words to Dedekind were "I see it but I do not believe it."

(a) Let (x, y) be reals with binary representations $x = 0.a_1 a_2 a_3 \cdots$ and $y = 0.b_1 b_2 b_3 \cdots$. Define the mapping $(x, y) \mapsto z$, where $z = 0.a_1 b_1 a_2 b_2 a_3 b_3 \cdots$. Prove that this mapping is an injection from $(0, 1) \times (0, 1)$ to $(0, 1)$.

(b) What does this tell you about $|(0, 1) \times (0, 1)|$? Prove that $|(0, 1) \times (0, 1)| = |(0, 1)|$.

Problem 22.38 (The Power Set and Cantor's Theorem). Among Cantor's many gems, this is the stunning result that bears his name. Recall that the power set of A, $\mathcal{P}(A)$, is the set of *all* subsets of A. Prove Cantor's Theorem.

Theorem 22.8 (Cantor, 1891). A set is smaller than its power-set. For any set A, $|A| < |\mathcal{P}(A)|$.

(a) Show $|A| \le |\mathcal{P}(A)|$ by giving an injection from A to $\mathcal{P}(A)$.

(b) Let $A = \{a, b, \ldots, g\}$. Here is an injection from a set $\mathcal{C}$ containing subsets of A to the elements in A.

$\mathcal{C}$ (some subsets of A):	$\{a, c, g\}$	A	$\{a, e, d\}$	$\{d\}$	$\{b, c\}$	$\{c, g\}$	
	↓	↓	↓	↓	↓	↓	
A:	a	b	c	d	e	f	g

Element a is beautiful because the set which maps to a contains a; Element c is ugly because the set which maps to c *does not contain* c. (Some elements of A may be neither beautiful nor ugly, e.g. g, because in an injection, not all elements of A need be used.) The ugly set $\mathcal{W}$ is the set of *all* ugly elements. Construct the ugly set for the injection above. Does the ugly set appear in the domain of the injection?

(c) Let f be any injection from $\mathcal{C}$ (which contains some subsets of A) to elements of A. Prove that the ugly set of f cannot be in $\mathcal{C}$ (the domain of the injection). *[Hint: Contradiction. Assume $\mathcal{W} \in \mathcal{C}$ and consider the element $x \in A$ to which $\mathcal{W}$ is mapped, $f(\mathcal{W}) = x$. Either $x \in \mathcal{W}$ or $x \notin \mathcal{W}$. Which is it?]*

(d) Set $\mathcal{C} = \mathcal{P}(A)$ and prove that, for *any* A, there is no injection from $\mathcal{P}(A)$ to A. Hence, prove Cantor's Theorem.

Problem 22.39. Prove that sets generated from recursive definitions are countable.

Problem 22.40 (Cantor Set). Construct a subset of $[0,1]$ as follows. Start with the interval $[0,1]$. At every step, remove the middle one-third of every interval in the set.

step 0 step 1 step 2 step 3

(a) At step i, show that the number of intervals is 2^i, the length of each interval is $(\frac{1}{3})^i$ and the total length of the intervals is $(\frac{2}{3})^i$. Hence, the total length of the intervals converges to 0 as $i \to \infty$. Further, the lengths of the intervals becomes 0, that is, we are left with a collection of points whose total size is zero.

(b) Let $0.t_1t_2t_3\cdots$ be the base-3 representation of a number in $[0,1]$. At step 0, all possible numbers remain. Show:
  (i) At step 1, the numbers which remain have $t_1 \in \{0,2\}$.
  (ii) At step k, the numbers which remain have $t_1,\ldots,t_k \in \{0,2\}$.
  (iii) At step i, for $i \to \infty$, all numbers with $t_1,t_2,\ldots \in \{0,2\}$ remain.

(c) Prove that the Cantor set is uncountable.

The Cantor set is uncountable, yet it has measure zero. (Measure formally quantifies "extent" for subsets of real numbers. Rationals in $[0,1]$ also have measure zero, but are countable. The irrationals in $[0,1]$ have measure 1.)

Problem 22.41 (Russell's Paradox). Let S be a collection of sets. Try to construct a set S which contains itself. Start with a singleton set $S_1 = \{\{\bullet\}\}$.

(a) Is $S_1 \in S_1$?

(b) Add S_1 into itself to create $S_2 = S_1 \cup \{S_1\}$. What is S_2. Is $S_2 \in S_2$?

(c) Keep adding the set into itself: define $S_{i+1} = S_i \cup \{S_i\}$. What is S_4?

(d) If you continued constructing the sets S_i in (c) forever, you end up with a set S_∞. Show that S_∞ is the set defined by the following recursive definition,
  (i) $\{\bullet\} \in S_\infty$. **[basis]**
  (ii) $x \in S_\infty \to x \cup \{x\} \in S_\infty$. **[constructor rule]**
  (iii) Nothing else is in S_∞. **[minimality]**

(e) Is $S_\infty \in S_\infty$?

(f) You may be wondering what you have to do to construct a set that contains itself. Consider the set $\overline{T}$ containing all things that are not turtles. Does $\overline{T}$ belong to $\overline{T}$?

(g) Suppose there are sets that contain themselves and sets that don't. Define the set W, a catalog of all the sets that *do not contain themselves*, the "well-behaved sets",

$$W = \{\text{sets } S \mid S \text{ does not contain itself}\}.$$

So, $A \in W \leftrightarrow A \notin A$. If W is well defined, either $W \in W$ or $W \notin W$. Derive a contradiction for each case. (This logically means W cannot exist and further a set cannot be *any* collection of objects. Modern set-theory is based on the Zermelo–Fraenkel (ZF) Axioms plus the Axiom of Choice (C), referred to as ZFC-set-theory.)

Problem 22.42. Here is a proof by induction of the well-ordering principle. Our claim is:

$$P(n): \text{every set } A \subset \mathbb{N} \text{ of size } n \text{ has a minimum element.}$$

We prove $P(n)\ \forall n \geq 1$ by strong induction.

[Base case] $P(1)$ is T: if $|A| = 1$, the lone element in A is the minimum element.

[Induction step] Assume $P(1),\ldots,P(n)$ and consider any set A of size $n+1$, $A = \{x_1,x_2,\ldots,x_n,x_{n+1}\}$. The set $\{x_1,x_2,\ldots,x_n\}$ has a minimum element, because $P(n)$ is T. Call this element x_*. If $x_{n+1} \leq x_*$, then x_{n+1} is a minimum element in A. Otherwise x_* is a minimum element in A. In either case, A has a minimum element. Since A was arbitrary, every set of size $n+1$ has a minimum element. Therefore, $P(n+1)$ is T, and by induction, $P(n)$ is T $\forall n \geq 1$.

This is a faulty proof of the well-ordering principle. What is wrong with it?

> Computer Science is no more about computers than astronomy is about telescopes. – **Edsger Dijkstra**
>
> What is a foreign accent? A sign of bravery. – **Amy Chua**
>
> To know but one language is to live but one life. – **Czech Proverb**
>
> Learn a language, and you'll avoid a war. – **Arab Proverb**

Chapter 23

Languages: What is Computing?

1: Describing a computing task using its language.
2: A complex computing task corresponds to a "complex" language.

We aim to capture computing as we know and love it: desktops, laptops, smartphones, smartwatches, fitness-bands, vending machines, game-consoles, GPUs, cloud, quantum, etc. What's a computer? A computer solves computing tasks. What's a computing task? Vaguely, a computing task transforms an input to an output. Let's pin it down. Here is a "simple" task, primality testing:

Decide (YES) or (NO) whether a given integer $n \in \mathbb{N}$ is prime.

For input n the output is (YES) or (NO). Here is a simple solution. List the primes in increasing order,

$$\text{primes} = \{2, 3, 5, 7, 11, 13, 17, 19, 23, 29, \ldots\}.$$

Given $n \in \mathbb{N}$, walk through this list. If you come to n say (YES). If you reach a number bigger than n, say (NO). Perhaps this is not a smart approach to primality testing, but it gets to the heart of computing, languages.

23.1 Decision Problems

We now move exclusively to the binary-(0,1)-world of computer science, with rare lapses, e.g. punctuation for easy parsing of a string as in 01#11. The primes, when written in binary, is a list of finite binary strings:

$$\mathcal{L}_{\text{prime}} = \{10, 11, 101, 111, 1011, 1101, 10001, 10011, 10111, 11101, \ldots\}.$$

Deciding whether 9 is prime is equivalent to determining if the string 1001 is in $\mathcal{L}_{\text{prime}}$.

The light on the right is off. Every push toggles between on and off. Given the number of pushes, decide whether the light is on or off. We encode the number of pushes by a binary string, e.g. 101 means 5 pushes. As with primes, we can list the binary strings for which the light is on,

$$\mathcal{L}_{\text{push}} = \{1, 01, 11, 001, 011, 101, 111, 0001, 0011, 0101, 0111, 1001, 1011, \ldots\}.$$

Note, in this case we allow strings to have leading zeros. The light is on for input w, if and only if $w \in \mathcal{L}_{\text{push}}$.

> **Pop Quiz 23.1**
> (a) Describe the numbers that are in $\mathcal{L}_{\text{push}}$. Describe the strings that are in $\mathcal{L}_{\text{push}}$.
> (b) The light starts out either on or off. Encode the initial state (on or off) and the number of pushes in a binary string and describe the strings for which the light is on. List a few of them.

An automatic door has a pressure mat that can sense someone walking on or off the mat. The door should open if a person is on the mat. We encode a person walking onto the mat with 1 and off the mat with 0. For example, the string 10110 means someone walked on, then off, then two walked on and one off. There remains 1 person on the mat, so the door should open.

Pop Quiz 23.2
Describe the inputs for which the door is open. Is the door open or closed for these inputs:
(a) 1 (b) 10 (c) 01 (d) 11 (e) 110 (f) 1100 (g) 110001

We can list the input sequences for which the door is open,

$$\mathcal{L}_{\text{door}} = \{1, 11, 101, 110, 111, 1011, 1101, 1110, 1111, \ldots\}.$$

Given an input binary string w, e.g. $w = 1011$, the door is open if and only if $w \in \mathcal{L}_{\text{door}}$.

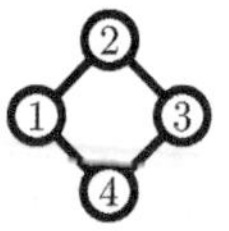

What is the distance between vertices ① and ③ in the graph on the right? The answer is 2. Let's answer an apparently simpler question. Is there a path between vertices ① and ③ of length at most 3? The answer is (YES). Why is the second question simpler? Because, the answer to the first question gives the answer to the second question instantly. If the distance is 2, there is a path of length 2, which is at most 3. Can we formulate our two graph questions as binary strings? The first question is tricky. Let us formulate the second question as a string. The string must describe the graph (vertices and edges), it must identify the vertices of interest, and lastly the target distance. Here is one way to do it.

"Is there a path of length at most 3 between vertices ① and ③ in the graph above."

becomes the string

" 1, 2, 3, 4 | (1, 2)(2, 3)(3, 4)(4, 1) | 1, 3 | 3 "

graph vertices graph edges endpoints of path target distance

Our graph problem is an ASCII string that translates, via the ASCII code, to the ungainly binary string
0011000100101100001100100010110000110011001011000011010001111100001010000011000100101100001100100010100100101000001100100010110000110011
00101001001010000011001100101100001101000010100100101000001101000010110000110001001010010111110000110001001011000011001101111100001100111.

The ASCII is easier on the eyes. The binary aspect is not crucial, the string aspect is.

Pop Quiz 23.3
Answer (YES) or (NO): " 1, 2, 3, 4, 5 | (1, 2)(2, 3)(3, 5)(3, 4) | 1, 5 | 2 "

Collect all the graph-strings for which the answer is (YES) into the set $\mathcal{L}_{\text{path}}$,

$$\mathcal{L}_{\text{path}} = \left\{ \begin{array}{l} \text{All strings of the form "vertices | edges | endpoints of path | target distance" for which} \\ \text{the distance between the endpoints in the graph is at most the target distance.} \end{array} \right\}$$

To solve an instance of the problem with a particular graph, first formulate the string w corresponding to the problem and then check whether w is in $\mathcal{L}_{\text{path}}$. Let us look more closely at our two graph problems.

1. **[Optimization, or Search]** What is distance between vertices ① and ③?
2. **[Decision]** Is there a path between vertices ① and ③ of length at most 3?

The first is an optimization problem because it asks for the path of minimum length. The second is a decision problem because the answer is a binary (YES) or (NO). The second problem is easier than the first because if you know the minimum-pathlength, it is easy to answer the decision problem. We argue that if you can solve the decision problem for a sequence of target distances, you can solve the optimization problem. Here's how:

Is there a path in the graph between vertices ⓧ and ⓨ of length at most 1? (NO)
Is there a path in the graph between vertices ⓧ and ⓨ of length at most 2? (NO)
Is there a path in the graph between vertices ⓧ and ⓨ of length at most 3? (NO)
Is there a path in the graph between vertices ⓧ and ⓨ of length at most 4? (YES)

You ask the decision question until the answer is (YES). In our example, the distance between ⓧ and ⓨ is 4. We solved the optimization problem by solving the decision problem many times. That means if you can solve either problem, you can solve the other. In that sense, the two problems are equivalent. Sometimes we care about how many decision questions you ask to solve one optimization task, but not now. We focus on what is solvable. Our discussion suggests that it suffices to understand what decision problems are solvable.

A computing problem is a decision problem.

This notion of a computing problem has withstood the test of time. Even though it looks restrictive that we are only considering (YES)/(NO) decision problems, it is not. For example, we can solve optimization problems.

Exercise 23.4
(a) How many decision problems are answered to solve the optimization problem if the distance between the two vertices is D? What do you do if there is no path between the two vertices?
(b) Can you solve the optimization problem using only $O(\log_2 D)$ decision problems?

23.2 Languages

To formulate a decision problem, state the input and the (YES) or (NO) question asked of the input. For example,

Problem: GRAPH-DISTANCE-D
Input: Finite graph G, vertices x, y and target distance D.
Question: Is there a path in G from x to y of length at most D.

All such problems can be solved in a standard way. We can always assume that the input is encoded into a finite binary string w, otherwise it is of no use to a computer. For some inputs, the answer is (YES) and for all others the answer is (NO). Collect all the inputs for which the answer is (YES) into a set, the (YES)-set.

$$\text{(YES)-set} = \{\text{input strings } w \text{ for which the answer is (YES)}\} = \{w_1, w_2, w_3, \ldots\}.$$

To solve an instance of the problem, formulate the input string w and determine if w is in the (YES)-set. If w is in the (YES)-set, the answer is (YES)and if not, the answer is (NO). This general approach worked for primality testing, the push-light, the automatic door and graph distance. It is a helpful exercise for the reader to explicitly state the input and question for the decision problems which have the (YES)-sets $\mathcal{L}_{\text{prime}}, \mathcal{L}_{\text{push}}, \mathcal{L}_{\text{door}}$.

Pop Quiz 23.5
How do we know that the (YES)-set can be listed?

Every decision problem has a (YES)-set. We may not list the (YES)-set, but it's always there. By solve the problem, we mean give a means to determine when an input string belongs to the (YES)-set. The (YES)-set represents a computing problem in a standard way, as a collection of finite binary strings. Two problems from different practical settings which have the same (YES)-set are equivalent. In fact the (YES)-set defines the computing problem. We may now make a leap and say any collection of finite binary strings is a valid (YES)-set defining a problem. The details of the decision problem no longer matter, the (YES)-set is all that matters.

A computing problem is a (YES)-set, a set of finite binary strings.

Defining a computing problem as a set of binary strings is an opportunity to divorce from practical details of a problem like GRAPH-DISTANCE-D and to focus on computing in the abstract. It is a breakthrough, because "computing problem" is vague. There is nothing vague about a set of binary strings. The (YES)-set is a language.

Definition 23.1 (Language)**.** A language $\mathcal{L}$ is a collection of finite binary strings. Any collection!

A computing problem is a language. To define a language you need an alphabet Σ, the symbols in the strings. Our alphabet is binary, $\Sigma = \{0, 1\}$. In practice we prefer ASCII, like for GRAPH-DISTANCE-D, but you can convert any string to binary so our framework is general. We list some languages using the binary alphabet. Each language is a different computing problem. We use the notation $X^{\bullet n}$ for concatenation of X with itself

n times, ε for the empty string and Σ^* for all finite binary strings (Σ^* was $\mathcal{B}$ in the previous chapter).

	$\{\varepsilon, 1, 10, 01\}$	← finite language
Σ^*	$\{\varepsilon, 0, 1, 00, 01, 10, 11, 000, 001, 010, 011, \ldots\}$	← all finite strings
$\mathcal{L}_{\text{prime}}$	$\{10, 11, 101, 111, 1011, 1101, 10001, \ldots\}$	
$\mathcal{L}_{\text{push}}$	$\{1, 01, 11, 001, 011, 101, 111, 0001, 0011, \ldots\}$	
$\mathcal{L}_{\text{door}}$	$\{1, 11, 101, 110, 111, 1011, 1101 \ldots\}$	
$\mathcal{L}_{\text{unary}}$	$\{\varepsilon, 1, 11, 111, 1111, \ldots\} = \{1^{\bullet n} \mid n \geq 0\}$	← strings of 1s
$\mathcal{L}_{(01)^n}$	$\{\varepsilon, 01, 0101, 010101, \ldots\} = \{(01)^{\bullet n} \mid n \geq 0\}$	
$\mathcal{L}_{0^n1^n}$	$\{01, 0011, 000111, \ldots\} = \{0^{\bullet n}1^{\bullet n} \mid n \geq 0\}$	
$\mathcal{L}_{\text{pal}}$	$\{\varepsilon, 0, 1, 00, 11, 000, 010, 101, 111, \ldots\}$	← palindromes
$\mathcal{L}_{\text{repeated}}$	$\{\varepsilon, 00, 11, 0000, 0101, 1010, 1111, \ldots\}$	← repeated strings

Exercise 23.6
(a) List the language $\mathcal{L}_{\text{bal}}$ of balanced strings (same number of 0s and 1s) in order of increasing length.
(b) If $\mathcal{L}_1$ and $\mathcal{L}_2$ are computing problems, are $\overline{\mathcal{L}_1}, \mathcal{L}_1 \cup \mathcal{L}_2, \mathcal{L}_1 \cap \mathcal{L}_2$ computing problems?
(c) Is the set of all possible computing problems countable or uncountable?

23.2.1 Describing a Language

A computing problem a (YES)-set. A theory of computing need not be limited to (YES)-sets from practice. Any language, treated as a (YES)-set, defines a computing problem. To describe the computing problem through its (YES)-set, we must describe the binary strings in the (YES)-set. We saw two ways to describe sets of strings: using a variable to identify a pattern the strings obey; and, using recursive definitions.

String Patterns and Variables. The strings in $\{\varepsilon, 01, 0101, 010101, \ldots\}$ have a clear pattern. We can use this pattern to define the set formally, without using "...". To do so, we use a variable w and define

$$\mathcal{L}_{(01)^n} = \{w \mid w = (01)^{\bullet n}, \text{ where } n \geq 0\}.$$

Informally, we just write $\{(01)^{\bullet n} \mid n \geq 0\}$. You can describe complex patterns using (one or more) variables. For example, the palindromes of even length are

$$\mathcal{L}_{\text{even-pal}} = \{u \bullet u^{\text{R}} \mid u \in \Sigma^*\} = \{\varepsilon, 00, 11, 0000, 0110, 1001, 1111, \ldots\}.$$

(u^{R} is the reversal of u, e.g. $1011^{\text{R}} = 1101$). Are there languages we can't describe? Yes, see Problem 23.40.

Regular Expressions are a powerful way to describe string patterns, with application to search engines, text editors, databases, etc. A command like "`ls FOCS*`" in `Unix` searches for all files which start with `FOCS`, for example `FOCS-HW1.pdf`. The `*` is called a wildcard. The notation `FOCS*` identifies strings that begin with `FOCS` concatenated with any string, the wildcard `*`. Here is a more complicated regular expression,

$$\{1, 11\} \bullet \overline{\{0, 01\}^*} \bullet (\{00\} \cup \{1\}^*). \tag{23.1}$$

After we tell you what is going on, you will have all the basics about regular expressions. The atomic units in a regular expression are finite languages. In (23.1) are the finite languages: $\{1, 11\}$, $\{0, 01\}$, $\{00\}$ and $\{1\}$. A regular expression specifies operations on these finite languages to get a new language. We are familiar with union, complement, and concatenation of strings. In a regular expression, we may concatenate languages. For example, $\mathcal{L}_1 \bullet \mathcal{L}_2 \bullet \mathcal{L}_3$ is the language formed by concatenating one string from each of $\mathcal{L}_1$, $\mathcal{L}_2$ and $\mathcal{L}_3$:

$$\mathcal{L}_1 \bullet \mathcal{L}_2 \bullet \mathcal{L}_3 = \{w_1 \bullet w_2 \bullet w_3 \mid w_1 \in \mathcal{L}_1, w_2 \in \mathcal{L}_2, w_3 \in \mathcal{L}_3\}.$$

We often write $\mathcal{L}_1\mathcal{L}_2\mathcal{L}_3$ or $w_1w_2w_3$ for concatenation. You can concatenate a language with itself,

$$\{0, 01\} \bullet \{0, 01\} = \{0, 01\}^{\bullet 2} = \{00, 001, 010, 0101\}.$$

Similarly $\{0, 01\}^{\bullet n}$ is concatenation n times. We define $\mathcal{L}^{\bullet 0} = \{\varepsilon\}$. The exotic operation in (23.1) is Kleene star, $\mathcal{L}^*$, which is all possible concatenations of a finite number of strings from $\mathcal{L}$. For example,

$$\{0,01\}^* = \{\varepsilon, 0, 01, 00, 001, 010, 0101, 000, 0010, \ldots\} = \bigcup_{n=0}^{\infty} \{0,01\}^{\bullet n};$$

$$\{1\}^* = \{\varepsilon, 1, 11, 111, 1111, 11111, \ldots\} = \bigcup_{n=0}^{\infty} \{1\}^{\bullet n}.$$

Kleene star creates infinite languages from finite ones. To satisfy the pattern in (23.1), concatenate a string in $\{1,11\}$ (e.g. 11), with a string not in $\{0,01\}^*$ (e.g. 10), with a string in $\{00\} \cup \{1\}^*$ (e.g. 00 or 111). Thus,

$$111000 \text{ and } 1110111 \text{ satisfy the regular expression } \{1,11\} \bullet \overline{\{0,01\}^*} \bullet (\{00\} \cup \{1\}^*).$$

We mention that traditional regular expressions don't use intersection and complement, for you can describe the same languages without them. We allow intersection and complement to make life easier.

Example 23.2. Here are some regular expressions and the the languages they describe. Practice.

1. $\{\varepsilon, 0\} \bullet \{\varepsilon, 1\} = \{\varepsilon, 0, 1, 01\}$
2. $\{0\}^* \bullet 1 \bullet \{0\}^* = \{\text{strings with a single } 1\}$
3. $\Sigma^* \bullet 1 \bullet \Sigma^* = \{\text{strings with one or more 1s}\}$
4. $\{0\}^* \bullet \{01\} \bullet \{1\}^* = \{\text{strings of 0s followed by 1s}\}$
5. $(\Sigma \bullet \Sigma)^* = \{\text{strings of even length}\}$
6. $(\Sigma^{\bullet 3})^* = \{\text{strings with length a multiple of 3}\}$ □

Pop Quiz 23.7

(a) For each regular expression, list all strings up to length-4.
(i) $\{0,01\} \bullet \{1,11\}$. (ii) $\{00\}^*$. (iii) $\{0,1\}^* \bullet \{00\} \bullet \{0,1\}^*$ (or, using wildcards, $*00*$).
(b) Give a regular expression for the strings in $\mathcal{L}_{\text{push}}$.
(c) What language does $\overline{*1*1*1*}$ describe? Give a regular expression that does not use complement.

Here are two interesting questions for you to ponder, but we won't answer them now. Stay tuned.

1. Is there a simple way to test if a string satisfies a regular expression. E.g. does 11110010 satisfy (23.1)?
2. Can you construct a regular expression to describe all palindromes, the strings which equal their reversal?

Recursively Defined Languages. We saw another approach to defining sets, and that is recursion. Recursion is a powerful tool for defining languages. As a review, here is a recursive definition of the palindromes.

① $\varepsilon, 0, 1 \in \mathcal{L}_{\text{pal}}$. **[basis]**

② $w \in \mathcal{L}_{\text{pal}} \to 0 \bullet w \bullet 0 \in \mathcal{L}_{\text{pal}}$ AND $1 \bullet w \bullet 1 \in \mathcal{L}_{\text{pal}}$ **[constructor rules]**

③ Nothing else is in $\mathcal{L}_{\text{pal}}$. **[minimality]**

Pop Quiz 23.8

Use the recursive definition to construct the strings of length at most 5 in $\mathcal{L}_{\text{pal}}$.

23.3 Complexity of a Computing Problem

Here are two similar looking languages: $\mathcal{L}_{0^n1^k} = \{0^{\bullet n}1^{\bullet k} \mid n, k \geq 0\}$ and $\mathcal{L}_{0^n1^n} = \{0^{\bullet n}1^{\bullet n} \mid n \geq 0\}$. Both have strings that begin with 0s and end with 1s. This superficial similarity is deceptive. These languages are very different and have very different complexities. What does complexity of a language or set of strings mean?

Exercise 23.9

Complex languages are hard to describe. Let $\mathcal{L}_{0^n1^k} = \{0^{\bullet n}1^{\bullet k} \mid n, k \geq 0\}$ and $\mathcal{L}_{0^n1^n} = \{0^{\bullet n}1^{\bullet n} \mid n \geq 0\}$.
Describe $\mathcal{L}_{0^n1^k}$ and $\mathcal{L}_{0^n1^n}$ using: (a) Regular expressions. (b) Recursive definitions.

The definition of a computing problem as a language, its (YES)-set, allows us to define the difficulty of the computing problem as the complexity of its associated (YES)-set. To solve the computing problem, we must decide if an input string is in the (YES)-set. Thus, the complexity of a (YES)-set is quantified by how hard it is to test if a string is in the (YES)-set. How does one test for membership in a language, what kinds of operations are allowed? This brings us to models of computing. Consider the computing problem $\mathcal{L}_{\text{push}}$,

$$\mathcal{L}_{\text{push}} = \{1, 01, 11, 001, 011, 101, 111, 0001, 0011, 0101, 0111, 1001, 1011, \ldots\}.$$

Only strings ending in 1 are in $\mathcal{L}_{\text{push}}$, an odd number of pushes. To test if an input string w is in $\mathcal{L}_{\text{push}}$, we must read in the string, and we do so one bit at a time from left to right. We show a read head, an input $w = 1101$ and a simple computing machine below. The read head starts left of the string, ready to process.

The interesting beast is the computing machine on the right. The machine is a directed graph with two states q_0, q_1 depicted by the two vertices in the graph. Ignore the green border around the state q_1 for now. The computing machine is a visual representation of a set of instructions for what to do every time the read head processes a bit. Each state or vertex has two arrows going out, one labeled 0 and one labeled 1. For example, the arrow from q_0 to q_1 labeled 1 stands for the instruction "If you are in state q_0 and you process a 1, transition to state q_1." Our computing machine visually encodes a set of four machine-level instructions:

1: In state q_0, when you process a 0, transition to state q_0.
2: In state q_0, when you process a 1, transition to state q_1.
3: In state q_1, when you process a 0, transition to state q_0.
4: In state q_1, when you process a 1, transition to state q_1.

A state can transition to itself. The gray arrow from nowhere to q_0 tells you the start state, in this case q_0. The machine begins in state q_0 and processes the first bit of w. If w is the empty string ε, with no bits, the machine stops in the start state and does nothing. Let's follow step-by-step as our computing machine processes $w = 1101$. We begin in state q_0. At each step, we identify the current state by shading it gray. The first bit is read in, a 1 (in red). The machine follows the red arrow labeled 1 from q_0 to q_1, instruction 2.

Now process the 2nd bit, also a 1, following the red arrow labeled 1 from q_1 to q_1, instruction 4.

The computing machine continues processing one bit at a time, transitioning from state to state.

When all bits are processed, our machine comes to rest in state q_1. The final rest state for 1101 is q_1.

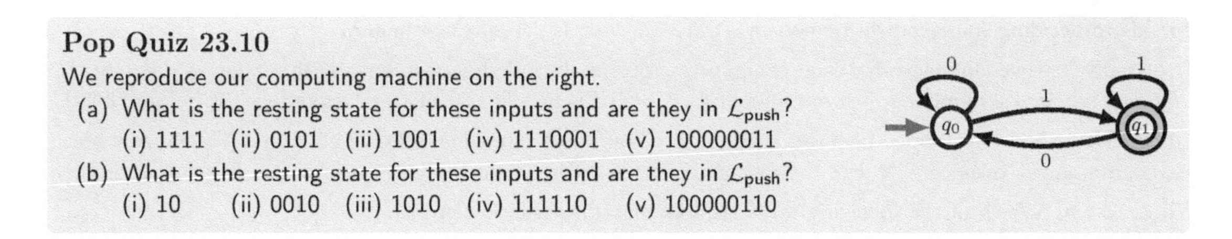

Pop Quiz 23.10

We reproduce our computing machine on the right.

(a) What is the resting state for these inputs and are they in $\mathcal{L}_{\text{push}}$?
(i) 1111 (ii) 0101 (iii) 1001 (iv) 1110001 (v) 100000011

(b) What is the resting state for these inputs and are they in $\mathcal{L}_{\text{push}}$?
(i) 10 (ii) 0010 (iii) 1010 (iv) 111110 (v) 100000110

The pop quiz should convince you that the final resting state of the machine decides membership in $\mathcal{L}_{\text{push}}$. For any input $w \in \mathcal{L}_{\text{push}}$, the machine comes to rest in the green state q_1, green for (YES). For any input $w \notin \mathcal{L}_{\text{push}}$, the machine comes to rest in q_0. To solve the computing problem $\mathcal{L}_{\text{push}}$ just pass the string through the machine and look at the final resting state to decide (YES) or (NO). The decision is (YES) if the final resting state is q_1. What are your thoughts on whether such a machine could be easily built in real life? Do you think such a machine could control a vending machine? Food for thought ....

This simple computing machine goes by many names, for example finite state machine or finite automaton. That such a simple machine can test for membership in $\mathcal{L}_{\text{push}}$ suggests that the computing problem $\mathcal{L}_{\text{push}}$ is easy. What would a harder computing problem look like? A problem can be harder in two ways.

1. The problem needs more resources. For example, the problem can be solved with a similar machine to the simple one we just discussed, except with more states.
2. The problem needs a different kind of computing machine, with superior capabilities.

The first type of harder is the focus of a follow-on algorithms course. Were you to take such a course, you would learn to efficiently solve a variety of computing problems. Efficiently means using few resources. Our focus will be on the second type of harder. Are there problems which cannot be solved by state transitioning machines like the one which solved $\mathcal{L}_{\text{push}}$, no matter how many states you give it? What kind of superior machine would solve those harder problems? We are primarily interested in what can be solved on a particular kind of machine, and what *can't be solved.* We will get there in due time. In this chapter, our focus was to formulate an abstract notion of a computing problem. A computing problem is a language. Hard problems map to complex languages. Here is a visual summary of the path we have taken.

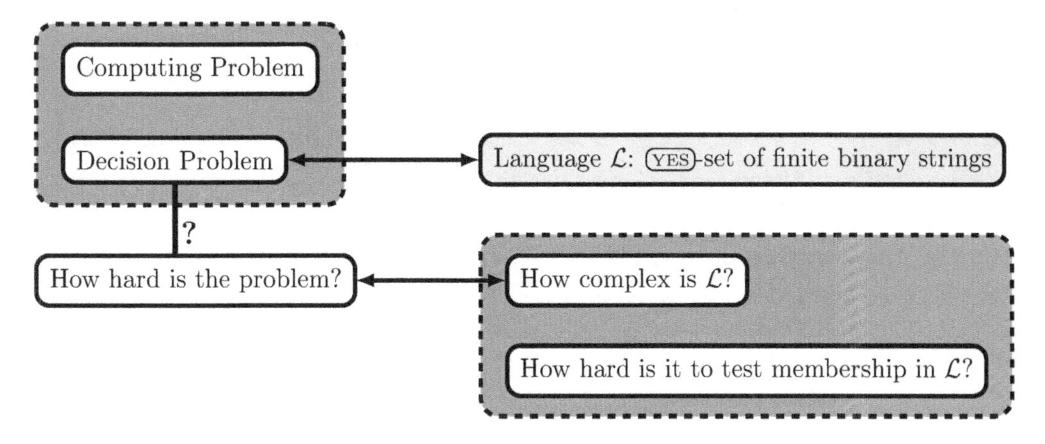

23.4 Problems

Problem 23.1. What is a computing problem, as defined in the text?
(a) Kilam says a computing problem is a subset of $\mathbb{N}$. Could Kilam be right?
(b) Ayfos says any computing problem is a function mapping $\mathbb{N}$ to $\{0, 1\}$. Could Ayfos be right?

Problem 23.2. A number $n \in \mathbb{N}$ is a younger-twin-prime if both n and $n + 2$ are prime. List a language that corresponds to deciding younger-twin-primeness. (Open problem: Is this language finite?)

Problem 23.3. Give languages for each computing problem. Include how you encode the input as a binary string.
(a) Testing whether a number n is a multiple of 4.
(b) Given a list of bits, is it sorted (all 0s before all 1s).

Problem 23.4. Starting from n counters, two players take turns removing 1,2 or 3 counters. The person who takes the last counter wins. Given $n \in \mathbb{N}$, can the first player force a win? Give the language for this computing problem.

Problem 23.5. Which of the following tasks are formulated as decision problems.
(a) An inversion in a list of distinct numbers $x_1, x_2, \ldots, x_n$ is a pair $x_i > x_j$ with $i < j$. Find the number of inversions.
(b) Given a set of line segments, determine if there is a pair of segments that intersect.
(c) Determine the maximum possible score on level 3 of Super Mario Brothers.
(d) Is there a flight itinerary from Tokyo to Roanoke with fewer than 3 stop-overs.

Problem 23.6. Reformulate each task as an appropriate decision problem, giving the input and the question. Explain how you can use the decision problem to solve the non-decision version of each problem.
(a) How many goody-bags are there with n candies of k colors?
(b) How big is a largest independent set in a graph G?
(c) How big is the largest clique in a graph G.
(d) How many colors are needed to color a graph G?
(e) What is the largest number in a list of numbers?
(f) How close are two nodes in a graph G?

Problem 23.7. True or false? Explain your answers.
(a) All languages have infinitly many strings.
(b) A language can be uncountable.
(c) A language can contain strings of infinite length.
(d) A language must contain strings of every finite length.
(e) The union of two languages is a language.
(f) The complement of any language is a language.

Problem 23.8. Is the union of *uncountably* many languages a valid language?

Problem 23.9. In Pop Quiz 23.1 you gave a language for the push-light when the start state of the light could be on or off. Construct a state transitioning computing machine to solve this computational problem (similar to the one we constructed for $\mathcal{L}_{\textsf{push}}$ in the text on page 343). When you pass an input string through your computing machine, the final resting state of the machine should tell you whether the light is on or off.

Problem 23.10. Recall concatenation: $\mathcal{L}_1 \bullet \mathcal{L}_2 = \{w_1 \bullet w_2 \mid w_1 \in \mathcal{L}_1, w_2 \in \mathcal{L}_2\}$. For $\mathcal{L}_1 = \{\varepsilon, 01\}$, $\mathcal{L}_2 = \{1, 01, 10\}$.
(a) What are $\mathcal{L}_1 \bullet \mathcal{L}_2$, $\mathcal{L}_1^{\bullet 2}$ and $\mathcal{L}_2^{\bullet 2}$
(b) Is $\mathcal{L}_1 \bullet \mathcal{L}_2 = \mathcal{L}_2 \bullet \mathcal{L}_1$?

Problem 23.11 (Kleene star). For language $\mathcal{L} = \{s_1, s_2, \ldots\}$, $\mathcal{L}^* = \{\varepsilon, s_1, s_2, s_1 \bullet s_1, s_1 \bullet s_2, \ldots\}$ is all strings obtained by concatenating zero or more strings in $\mathcal{L}$. $\Sigma^* = \{0, 1\}^*$ contains all finite binary strings.
(a) For $\mathcal{L} = \{1, 10\}$ give the strings of length at most 6 in $\mathcal{L}^*$.
(b) For $\mathcal{L}$ in (a), prove that $1110111 \in \mathcal{L}^*$ and that $11100111 \notin \mathcal{L}^*$
(c) Prove that $\mathcal{L}_1 \subseteq \mathcal{L}_2 \rightarrow \mathcal{L}_1^* \subseteq \mathcal{L}_2^*$.
(d) Prove or disprove: (i) $\mathcal{L}^*$ is a valid language for any valid language $\mathcal{L}$. (ii) $\mathcal{L}^*$ is always countable.

Problem 23.12. Let $\mathcal{L}_0 = \{0\}$ and $\mathcal{L}_1 = \{1\}$. Give English descriptions of (a) $\mathcal{L}_0^*$ (b) $\mathcal{L}_1^*$ (c) $(\mathcal{L}_0 \cup \mathcal{L}_1)^*$.

Problem 23.13. For any languages $\mathcal{L}_1$ and $\mathcal{L}_2$, prove or disprove: (a) $\mathcal{L}_1^* \cup \mathcal{L}_2^* = (\mathcal{L}_1 \cup \mathcal{L}_2)^*$ (b) $\mathcal{L}_1^* \cap \mathcal{L}_2^* = (\mathcal{L}_1 \cap \mathcal{L}_2)^*$.

Problem 23.14 (Wildcard symbol vs. Kleene star). What is the difference between $1*$ and $\{1\}^*$?

Problem 23.15. In each part, determine which strings can be generated by the corresponding regular expression.
(a) Regular expression: $\{0, 01\} \bullet \{1, 10\}$. Strings: ε; 0; 1; 00; 01; 10; 11; 0000; 0110; 1111.
(b) Regular expression: $\{1\}^* \cup \{0\}^*$. Strings: ε; 000; 11; 000111.
(c) Regular expression: $\{1\}^* \bullet \{0\}^*$. Strings: ε; 000; 11; 000111.
(d) Regular expression: $\overline{\{1\}^*} \cup \{0\}^*$. Strings: ε; 000; 11; 000111.
(e) Regular expression: $\overline{\{1\}^*} \bullet \{0\}^*$. Strings: ε; 000; 11; 000111.
(f) Regular expression: $\{0, 01\}^* \bullet \{1, 10\}^*$. Strings: 101110; 00111; 00100; 01100.
(g) Regular expression: $\{0, 01\}^* \cap \{1, 10\}^*$. Strings: 101110; 00111; 00100; 01100.
(h) Regular expression: $\overline{\{0, 01\}^*} \bullet \{1, 10\}^*$. Strings: 101110; 00111; 00100; 01100.

Problem 23.16. For each regular expression, give 3 strings in the language and 3 strings not in the language.
(a) $\{0\}^* \bullet \{1\}^*$ (b) $\{0\}^* \cup \{1\}^*$ (c) $\Sigma \bullet \{0\}^*$ (d) $\Sigma^* \bullet \{01\} \bullet \Sigma^*$ (e) $(\{0\} \bullet \{1\}^*)^*$ (f) $(\{01\} \bullet \{1\}^*)^*$.

Problem 23.17. Give a *recursive* definition of the language $L = \{001^{\bullet 2n} | n \geq 0\}$.

Problem 23.18. Give a recursive definition of $\mathcal{L}^*$ for a finite language $\mathcal{L} = \{w_1, \ldots, w_k\}$.

Problem 23.19. Prove or disporve: there is a language $\mathcal{L}$ for which $\overline{\mathcal{L}^*} = (\overline{\mathcal{L}})^*$.

Problem 23.20. Let $\mathcal{L} = \{$strings with a different number of 0s and 1s$\}$. Prove $\mathcal{L}^* = \Sigma^*$ (all finite binary strings).

Problem 23.21. For language $\mathcal{L}$, the positive concatenations $\mathcal{L}^+ = \mathcal{L}^* \cap \overline{\{\varepsilon\}} = \cup_{n=1}^{\infty} \mathcal{L}^{\bullet n}$ (nonempty strings in $\mathcal{L}^*$).
(a) Give the strings of length at most 4 in $\{0, 01\}^+$.
(b) Give a string in $\{0\} \bullet \{11\}^* \cup \{01\}^*$ which is not in $\{0\} \bullet \{11\}^+ \cup \{01\}^*$.

Problem 23.22. The set of palindromes is $\mathcal{L}_{\text{palindrome}} = \{u \mid u \in \Sigma^*, u = u^{\text{R}}\}$. Prove that

$$\mathcal{L}_{\text{palindrome}} = \{u \bullet v \bullet w \mid u \in \Sigma^*, v \in \{\varepsilon, 0, 1\}, w = u^{\text{R}}\}.$$

Problem 23.23. Recursively define $\mathcal{L}_{\text{palindrome}} = \{$strings which equal their reversal$\}$. The reversal of a length-0 or length-1 string is the string itself and $(uv)^{\text{R}} = v^{\text{R}} u^{\text{R}}$ for longer strings.

Problem 23.24 (Reversal). The reversal of $\mathcal{L}$, $\mathcal{L}^{\text{R}}$, has the reversal of all strings in $\mathcal{L}$, $\mathcal{L}^{\text{R}} = \{w^{\text{R}} \mid w \in \mathcal{L}\}$.
(a) Give regular expressions for the reversals of these languages: (i) $\{01\}^*$ (ii) $\{01\}^* \bullet \{110\}^*$ (iii) $\overline{\{01\}^*}$.
(b) For languages $\mathcal{L}_1$ and $\mathcal{L}_2$, formally define: (i) $(\mathcal{L}_1 \cup \mathcal{L}_2)^{\text{R}}$ (ii) $(\mathcal{L}_1 \cap \mathcal{L}_2)^{\text{R}}$ (iii) $(\overline{\mathcal{L}_1})^{\text{R}}$ (iv) $(\mathcal{L}_1 \bullet \mathcal{L}_2)^{\text{R}}$ (v) $(\mathcal{L}_1^*)^{\text{R}}$.
(c) Prove or disprove:
(i) $(\mathcal{L}_1 \cup \mathcal{L}_2)^{\text{R}} = \mathcal{L}_1^{\text{R}} \cup \mathcal{L}_2^{\text{R}}$ (ii) $(\mathcal{L}_1 \cap \mathcal{L}_2)^{\text{R}} = \mathcal{L}_1^{\text{R}} \cap \mathcal{L}_2^{\text{R}}$ (iii) $(\overline{\mathcal{L}_1})^{\text{R}} = \overline{\mathcal{L}_1^{\text{R}}}$ (iv) $(\mathcal{L}_1 \bullet \mathcal{L}_2)^{\text{R}} = \mathcal{L}_2^{\text{R}} \bullet \mathcal{L}_1^{\text{R}}$ (v) $(\mathcal{L}_1^*)^{\text{R}} = (\mathcal{L}_1^{\text{R}})^*$.

Problem 23.25. For a language $\mathcal{L}$, let $\mathcal{L}_{ww^{\text{R}}}$ be the palindromes formed from strings in $\mathcal{L}$, $\mathcal{L}_{ww^{\text{R}}} = \{ww^{\text{R}} \mid w \in \mathcal{L}\}$. Prove or disprove: $\mathcal{L}_{ww^{\text{R}}} = \mathcal{L} \bullet \mathcal{L}^{\text{R}}$, where $\mathcal{L}^{\text{R}}$ is the reversal of $\mathcal{L}$.

Problem 23.26. Prove or disprove: $\mathcal{L}_{\text{palindrome}}^{\bullet 2} = \mathcal{L}_{\text{palindrome}}$.

Problem 23.27. Does there exist a "nontrivial" language (not $\{\varepsilon\}$ or Σ^*) for which (a) $\mathcal{L}^{\bullet 2} = \mathcal{L}$? (b) $\mathcal{L}^* = \mathcal{L}$?

Problem 23.28. Let $\mathcal{L}_1 = 1*$ and $\mathcal{L}_2 = *110$, where the wild-card symbol $*$ can be any string in Σ^* ($1*$ is not $\{1\}^*$, the latter being Kleene-star). Informally describe each language. Explain the difference between $\mathcal{L}_1 \cap \mathcal{L}_2$ and $\mathcal{L}_1 \bullet \mathcal{L}_2$.

Problem 23.29. For each language $\mathcal{L}$, give example strings in $\mathcal{L}$ and strings not in $\mathcal{L}$.
(a) $\mathcal{L} = \{0^{\bullet n} 1^{\bullet m} \mid n \geq 0, m \geq 1\}$.
(b) $\mathcal{L} = \{w = uu^{\text{R}} \mid u \in \Sigma^*\}$.
(c) $\mathcal{L} = \{w \neq uu^{\text{R}} \mid u \in \Sigma^*\} \cap \mathcal{L}_{\text{palindrome}}$.
(d) $\mathcal{L} = \Sigma^{\bullet 3}$, where $\Sigma = \{0, 1\}$.
(e) $\mathcal{L} = \{1\}^* \bullet \{01\}^*$.
(f) $\mathcal{L} = \{1\} \bullet \{01\}^*$.

Problem 23.30. Find regular expressions for $\mathcal{L}$ and its reversal $\mathcal{L}^{\text{R}}$ (Problem 23.24), where strings of $\mathcal{L}$ satisfy:
(a) The first and last bit are the same.
(b) The number of 1s divisible by 2.
(c) Every 0 is followed by at least one 1.
(d) There is one occurrence of 111 as a substring.
(e) There is at least one occurrence of 100 as a substring.
(f) The length of the strings is a multiple of 5.

Problem 23.31. Let $\mathcal{L}_1 = \{0^{\bullet 2}\}$ and $\mathcal{L}_2 = \{0^{\bullet 3}\}$.
(a) What are $\mathcal{L}_1^*$ and $\mathcal{L}_2^*$. Give informal English descriptions.
(b) What is $(\mathcal{L}_1 \cup \mathcal{L}_2)^*$? Give an informal English description.
(c) Generalize. Let $\mathcal{L}_1 = \{0^{\bullet x}\}$ and $\mathcal{L}_2 = \{0^{\bullet y}\}$. Give an informal English description of $(\mathcal{L}_1 \cup \mathcal{L}_2)^*$. *[Hint:* $\gcd(x, y)$.*]*

Problem 23.32. True or False? (Explain your answer).
(a) $100 \in \{0\}^* \bullet \{1\}^* \bullet \{0\}^* \bullet \{1\}^*$. (b) $001 \in \{0\}^* \bullet \{1\}^* \bullet \{0\}^* \bullet \{1\}^*$.

Problem 23.33. True or False? (Explain your answer).
(a) Let $\mathcal{L}_1 = \{0\}^* \bullet \{1\}^*$ and $\mathcal{L}_2 = \{1\}^* \bullet \{0\}^*$. Then, $\mathcal{L}_1 \cap \mathcal{L}_2 = \varnothing$.
(b) Let $\mathcal{L}_1, \mathcal{L}_2, \mathcal{L}_3$ be any three languages. Then, $(\mathcal{L}_1 \bullet \mathcal{L}_2)^* \bullet \mathcal{L}_3^* = \mathcal{L}_1^* \bullet (\mathcal{L}_2 \bullet \mathcal{L}_3)^*$.
(c) Let $\mathcal{L}_1, \mathcal{L}_2$ be any two languages. Then, $\mathcal{L}_1 \bullet (\mathcal{L}_2 \bullet \mathcal{L}_1)^* = (\mathcal{L}_1 \bullet \mathcal{L}_2)^* \bullet \mathcal{L}_1$.

Problem 23.34. Give a regular expression for each language when (i) you may and (ii) you may not use complements.
(a) Strings with at most one 1 and at most one 0. (b) Strings whose number of 0s is not divisible by 4.

Problem 23.35. True or False: A regular expression without the Kleene star operation describes a finite language.

Problem 23.36 (Decision vs. calculation). Formulate a decision version of a task related to the arithmetic task of computing the product $x \times y$ of given non-negative integers x, y.

(a) How many times do you need to use the decision problem to solve the arithmetic task?
(b) What are your thoughts if x, y are positive real numbers?

Problem 23.37 (Independent set: decision vs. search). The independent set problem is to *find* an independent set of maximum size in an input graph G. This *search* version is different from the optimization version which asks only for the *size* of a maximum independent set. Here is the decision version of maximum independent set:

Problem:	INDEPENDENT-SET-K
Input:	Finite graph $G = (V, E)$ and target K.
Question:	Is there an independent set in G of size at least D.

We showed that one can use the decision problem to solve the optimization problem. Show that one can also solve the search problem. That is, one can use the decision problem to *construct* a maximum independent. For a vertex v in G, $N(v)$ are the neighbors of v. For a subset of vertices S, $G - S$ is the induced subgraph obtained by removing S.

(a) Show how to obtain $\alpha(G)$ using INDEPENDENT-SET-K.
(b) Show that if v is in an independent set of G, then $\alpha(G) = 1 + \alpha(G - \{v\} - N(v))$.
(c) Show that if v is not in any independent set of G, then $\alpha(G) = \alpha(G - \{v\})$.
(d) Show how you can construct a maximum independent set using INDEPENDENT-SET-K.
(e) What is the maximum number of calls to INDEPENDENT-SET-K that you make?

Problem 23.38 (Coloring: decision vs. search). Graph coloring has input a graph G and the task is to *construct* a valid coloring using the fewest colors. This *search* version is different from the optimization version which only asks for that *minimum number* of colors – the chromatic number $\chi(G)$. Decision version of the graph coloring:

Problem:	GRAPH-COLORING-K
Input:	Finite graph $G = (V, E)$ and target K.
Question:	Is there a valid coloring of G that uses at most K colors.

In the text, we showed that if you can solve the decision version, you can solve the optimization version. Show that you can also *construct* an optimal coloring using the decision version. Let u and v be non-adjacent vertices in G.

(a) Show how to obtain the chromatic number $\chi(G)$ using the decision version of coloring.
(b) The contraction $G^-_{u,v}$ merges u, v into one vertex w whose neighbors are all neighbors of u or v. The augmentation $G^+_{u,v}$ adds the edge (u, v). Give $G^-_{u,v}$ and $G^+_{u,v}$ for the graph shown on the right.

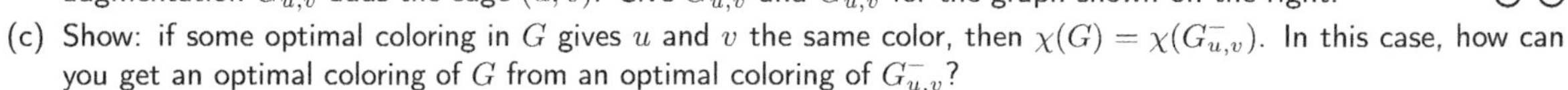

(c) Show: if some optimal coloring in G gives u and v the same color, then $\chi(G) = \chi(G^-_{u,v})$. In this case, how can you get an optimal coloring of G from an optimal coloring of $G^-_{u,v}$?
(d) Show: if every optimal coloring of G gives different colors to u, v then $\chi(G) = \chi(G^+_{u,v})$. In this case, how do you get an optimal coloring of G from an optimal coloring of $G^+_{u,v}$?
(e) Show how to get an optimal coloring of G using repeated calls to GRAPH-COLORING-K.
(f) What is the maximum number of calls to GRAPH-COLORING-K that you make?

Problem 23.39. Ayfos decides she is going to list out all the languages $\{\mathcal{L}_1, \mathcal{L}_2, \ldots\}$. Will she succeed? More specifically, will every language eventually appear on her list?

Problem 23.40 (Finite Representation of Languages). It is not satisfactory to define a language as $\{\varepsilon, 0, 11, 101, 1111, 11011, \ldots\}$, since we don't know how to continue the list. A precise definition must be finite and unambiguous. For example, $\{(01)^{\bullet n} \mid n \geq 0\}$ is a precise finite description of the language $\{\varepsilon, 01, 0101, 010101, \ldots\}$.

Assume any finite description can only use the 255 characters of the ASCII code, but it can be arbitrarily long. Prove that some languages cannot be precisely specified by a finite description. *[Hint: Use a counting argument.]*

Problem 23.41. Let $\mathcal{L}$ be an *infinite* subset of $\{0\}^*$.

(a) Prove that some such $\mathcal{L}$ cannot be described by a finite regular expression.
(b) Prove that $\mathcal{L}^*$ can always be described by a finite regular expression. *[Hint: Problem 23.31.]*

Problem 23.42. Starting on page 339 we defined languages $\mathcal{L}_{(01)^n}$, $\mathcal{L}_{0^n1^n}$, $\mathcal{L}_{\text{palindrome}}$, $\mathcal{L}_{\text{repeated}}$. Test your intuition. Place these languages in order of increasing "complexity". Explain you reasoning. (Don't cheat by reading ahead☺.)

> Cognitive revolution: (i) See. (ii) Do, then see. (iii) Imagine, do, then see.
>
> To understand a program you must become both the machine and the program.
> – **Alan Perlis**
>
> What good are computers? They only give answers. – **Pablo Picasso**
>
> Computers are stupid, but they're already in charge.

Chapter 24

Deterministic Finite Automata

1: Deterministic finite automata (DFA) model CPUs with no external memory.
2: DFA can't solve problems that require unbounded memory for scratch work.

The simplest computing machine is a deterministic finite automaton (DFA or just automaton), a central processing unit (CPU) with no scratch-paper for storing intermediate computations. We start small because it is easier to understand the theory from the ground up. And, to appreciate new capabilities it helps to know the limits of simpler models. The DFA has an elegant theory and is an important model in its own right.

A computing problem is a language of finite binary strings. To solve the problem means test if an input string is in the language. To do this, a DFA has a read-head to process input bits, one at a time. With each bit, the DFA transitions among its internal states. After processing the entire input and depending on its final resting state, the DFA either accepts by saying (YES), or rejects by saying (NO). The schematic on the right illustrates the basic model. We will add to this basic model if necessity dictates so. We need to describe the instruction set, that is how the DFA transitions among states, and how the computer makes its final (YES)/(NO) decision. DFAs have an elegant representation using a directed graph. Here is an example of a DFA.

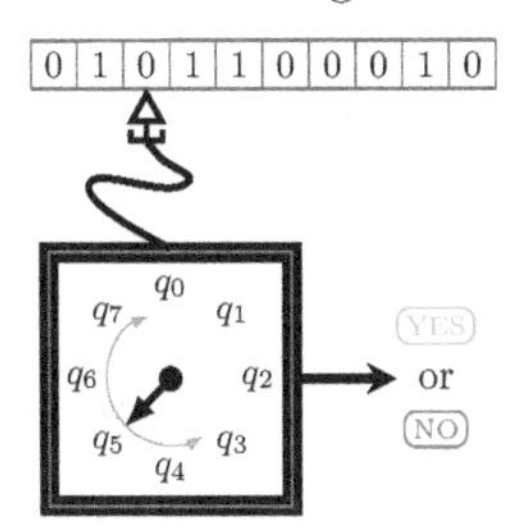

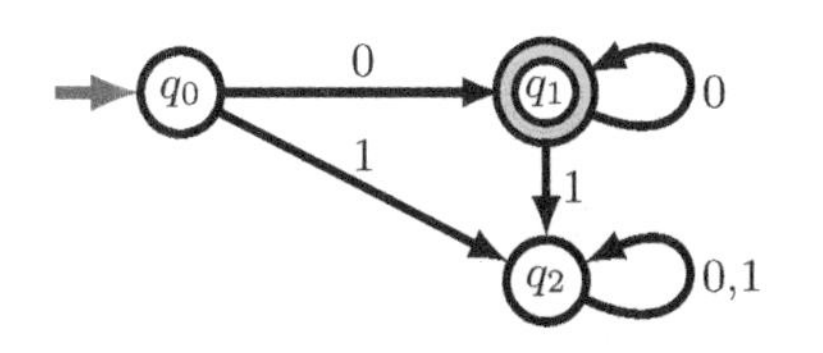

states	
$\rightarrow q_0$	(NO)
q_1	(YES)
q_2	(NO)

transitions
$1: q_0\ 0\ q_1$
$2: q_0\ 1\ q_2$
$3: q_1\ 0\ q_1$
$4: q_1\ 1\ q_2$
$5: q_2\ 0\ q_2$
$6: q_2\ 1\ q_2$

(24.1)

The states are: q_0 ((NO)-state); q_1 ((YES)-state); q_2 ((NO)-state). The start state, q_0, is shown by a gray arrow. Transition instructions are triples, `(state)-(symbol read)-(next state)`. The instruction "q_0 0 q_1" says

"`If you are in state` q_0 `and you read a 0, then transition to state` q_1."

The directed graph, called the state diagram, neatly summarizes everything. Each vertex is a state. Each vertex has two outgoing arrows labeled 0 and 1 indicating how to transition for that bit from that state. The (YES)-states are green vertices. Here are the rules for computing the output (YES) or (NO).

> 1: Start in the initial state q_0 and process the input string one bit at a time left-to-right.
> 2: For each bit, transition from the current to the next state using the transition instructions.
> 3: When there are no more bits, say (YES) if the final state is a (YES)-state, otherwise say (NO).

If the output is (YES), the DFA accepts the input; otherwise the DFA rejects. Let's walk through processing the input 010. The automaton starts in q_0, shaded gray, with the read head ready to process the first bit.

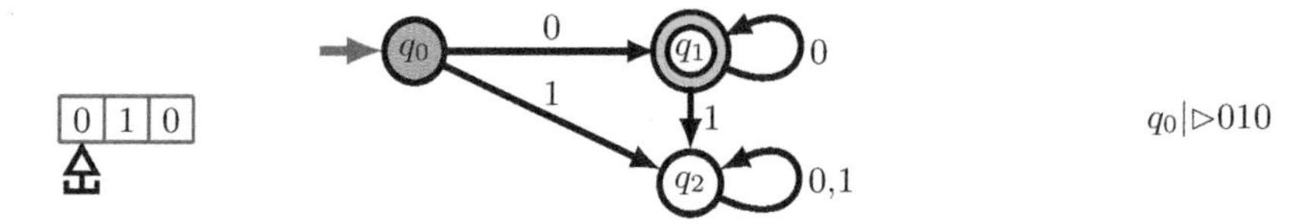

On the right is an algebraic notation $q_0|\triangleright 010$ which shows the current state q_0 with the read head $\triangleright$ pointing to the first bit. Right of $\triangleright$ is the part of the input that remains to be processed. Process the first bit 0, following the red arrow labeled 0 in the diagram, from state q_0 to q_1:

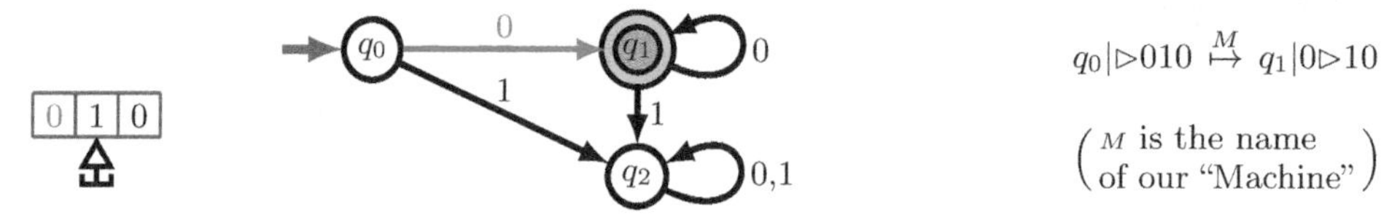

In the algebraic notation, the state changed to q_1, the substring 10 remains to be processed (right of $\triangleright$) and the substring 0 has already been processed (left of $\triangleright$). Let's process the next two bits. Follow the red arrows:

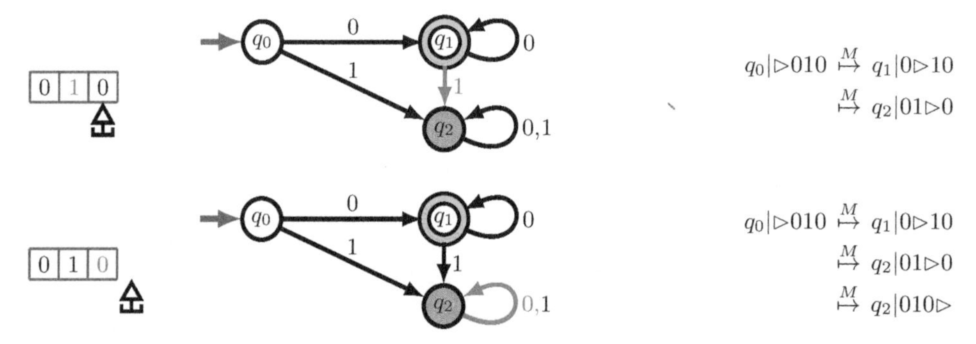

The final state is q_2, a (NO)-state. So, the automaton rejects the input. On the right, the algebraic notation gives a trace of the full computation. Part (c) in the next pop quiz illustrates that the current state and remaining bits of the input suffice to determine (YES) or (NO). This observation will be used later in the chapter.

> **Pop Quiz 24.1**
> The following questions refer to the automaton in (24.1), which we call M for machine.
> (a) Show algebraic traces for each input: (i) 0000; (ii) 1000; (iii) 0001; (iv) 0100; (v) $0^{\bullet k}1^{\bullet \ell}$?
> (b) Describe informally the set of strings that are accepted by M.
> (c) For each trace, we don't show the substring already processed. Determine (YES) or (NO). If you can't, explain why. (i) q_0 | ? $\triangleright$ 0000 (ii) q_1 | ? $\triangleright$ 0000 (iii) q_2 | ? $\triangleright$ 0000.

Recall that computing problems are languages. The computing problem solved by an automaton M is the language containing all strings which M accepts. We call this computing problem $\mathcal{L}(M)$,

> The computing problem solved by M is the language $\mathcal{L}(M) = \{w \mid M(w) = \text{(YES)}\}$.

We refer to $\mathcal{L}(M)$ as the automaton's (YES)-set. The computing problem solved by the automaton in (24.1) is easy to describe: non-empty strings containing only zeros. Let M be the automaton in (24.1). Then,

$$\mathcal{L}(M) = \{0, 00, 000, 0000, \ldots\} = \{0^{\bullet n} \mid n > 0\}.$$

There are two natural questions one might ask:

1. For an automaton M, what is the computing problem solved by M, $\mathcal{L}(M)$? What is the (YES)-set?
2. For a given computing problem $\mathcal{L}$, can one design an automaton M to solve $\mathcal{L}$?

Determining the (YES)-set of an automaton involves careful analysis, and proving it often requires some form of induction. The next exercise gives you some practice with this. The rest of the chapter deals with the second question: given $\mathcal{L}$, can one design an automaton to solve $\mathcal{L}$? Design calls for creativity.

Exercise 24.2

(a) For the automaton M in (24.1), prove that $\mathcal{L}(M) = \{0^{\bullet n} \mid n > 0\}$.

(b) Describe the strings in $\mathcal{L}(M)$ for each automaton M below.

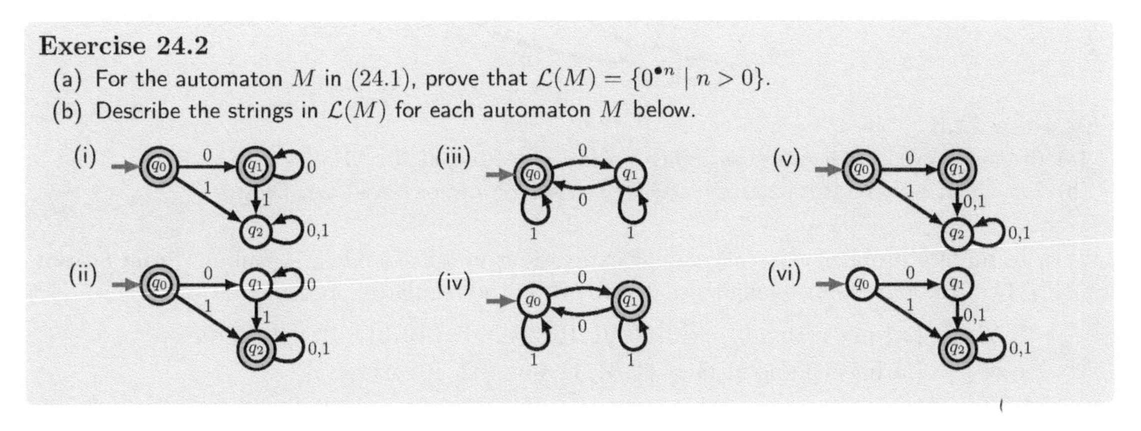

Example 24.1 (Vending Machine). We labeled the DFA-states $q_0, q_1, \ldots$, but you can use any labels you like. What matters are which states are accepting and how transitions are made from one state to another. A DFA transitions from one state to another for each input bit. One could also allow the DFA to perform other actions as it transitions. This is useful to a vending machine, which is essentially a DFA.

A vending machine accepts nickels and dimes and dispenses a soda whenever at least 25¢ has been collected. We build a vending DFA. Each state will correspond to how much money nett of sodas dispensed is in the DFA. Our DFA starts in state 0¢, →(0¢). The possible states are {0¢, 5¢, 10¢, 15¢, 20¢}. If the machine has 20¢ and receives 10¢ it must dispense a soda worth 25¢, leaving the machine with 5¢. Therefore, from the 20¢ state, receiving 10¢ causes the machine to dispense a soda and transition to the 5¢ state. We can reason similarly about all the states. The resulting DFA is shown below.

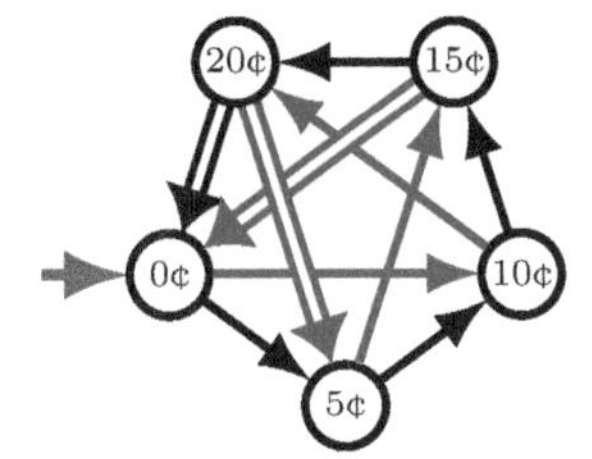

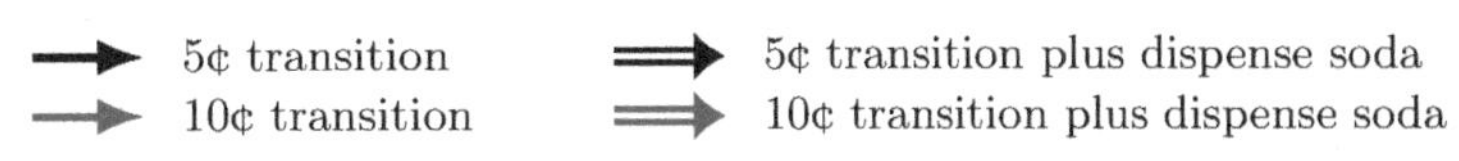

(Edges are color coded to avoid clutter. Black for 5¢ transitions and blue for 10¢ transitions. Single arrow means transition only, double arrow means transition plus dispense soda. For example, from the 15¢ state, if 10¢ is input, follow the blue (for 10¢) double arrow ⇛ to 0¢ and dispense a soda.)

If the sequence of inputs is 10¢, 10¢, 5¢, 10¢, 10¢, 10¢, then the states the DFA visits are

(0¢) → (10¢) → (20¢) ⇒ (0¢) (+ soda) → (10¢) → (20¢) ⇒ (5¢) (+ soda).

Two sodas are dispensed and 5¢ remains in the machine, which is captured by the final state. □

24.1 Regular Languages

A computing problem's (YES)-set $\mathcal{L}$ is regular if it can be solved by a DFA. This means some DFA accepts every string in $\mathcal{L}$ and no others. A finite computing problem is a finite language. Every finite language is regular. Let us walk through the logic of solving a simple finite problem with a DFA. Consider the language

$$\mathcal{L} = \{10\}.$$

Begin with the start state →(q_0), which is a (NO)-state because $\varepsilon \notin \mathcal{L}$. If the first bit is not 1, reject by transitioning to an error state E, a (NO)-state from which you can't escape. If the first bit is 1, transition to a "waiting-for-0" state q_1, to see the second bit. The beginnings of our automaton are shown on the right. From q_1 if the second bit is 1, reject into the error state; otherwise, we have our string 10, so transition to a

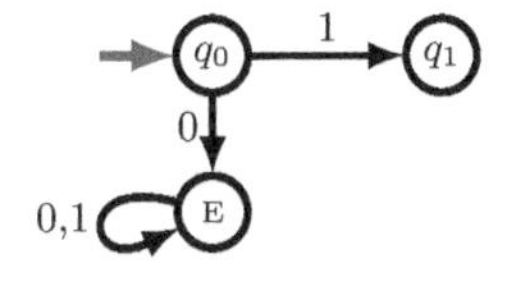

"ready-to-accept" state q_2. If no further bits arrive, accept, otherwise reject. Here is the full automaton:

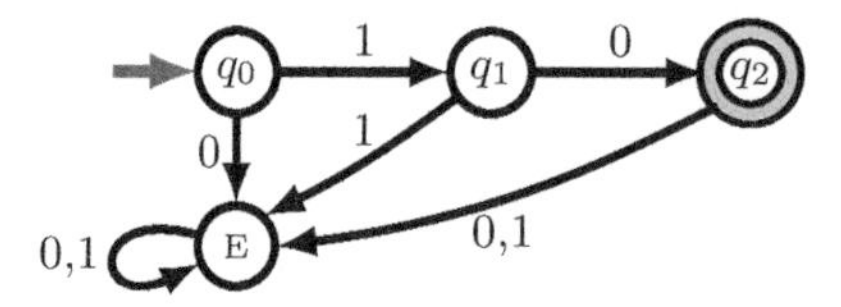

Exercise 24.3

(a) Give a DFA which solves the computing problem $\mathcal{L} = \{01, 000, 101, 111\}$.

(b) Prove that every finite language is regular by showing it can be solved by a DFA.

We now turn to infinite problems. Recall regular expressions and the wildcard symbol $*$ from Section 23.2.1 on pages 342-343. Consider the two languages described by the regular expressions $\mathcal{L}_1 = *0*$ and $\mathcal{L}_2 = *1$

$$\mathcal{L}_1 = \{\text{strings with a } 0\} = \{0, 00, 01, 10, 000, 001, 010, 011, 100, 101, 110, \ldots\}$$
$$\mathcal{L}_2 = \{\text{strings ending in } 1\} = \{1, 01, 11, 001, 011, 101, 111, \ldots\}$$

Let's build DFAs M_1 and M_2 for $\mathcal{L}_1$ and $\mathcal{L}_2$. First lets tackle $\mathcal{L}_1$. In the start state we are "waiting for 0." When we get a 0, we are ready to accept, so transition to an accept state and stay there. M_1 is

M_1 :

Now for $\mathcal{L}_2$, strings ending in 1. In the start state, we are "waiting for a 1." If we get a 1, tentatively accept, provided no 0s follow. If a 0 comes, we return to the start state to await another 1. M_2 implements this logic,

M_2 :

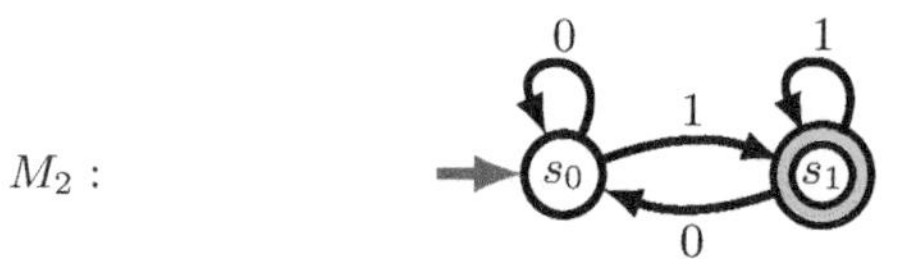

One can construct new computing problems, i.e. languages, using set-operations on $\mathcal{L}_1$ and $\mathcal{L}_2$. In such cases, can we combine M_1 and M_2 to get a DFA that solves the new problem? Here are some examples.

Complement. Consider $\overline{\mathcal{L}_1}$, the strings not in $\mathcal{L}_1$. M_1 accepts the strings in $\mathcal{L}_1$, so by reversing M_1's decision we solve $\overline{\mathcal{L}_1}$. To reverse the decision, simply make every (YES)-state a (NO)-state and *vice versa*. $\overline{M_1}$ solves $\overline{\mathcal{L}_1}$,

$\overline{M_1}$:

If there is no 0, $\overline{M_1}$ stays in q_0 and accepts. Otherwise, $\overline{M_1}$ irreversibly enters q_1 at the first 0 and rejects.

Union and Intersection. Let $\mathcal{L} = \mathcal{L}_1 \cup \mathcal{L}_2$. The DFA must accept strings in either $\mathcal{L}_1$ or $\mathcal{L}_2$. Our approach is to simulate both M_1 and M_2. Each state of M will tell us which state M_1 and M_2 are in, and M should accept if either M_1 or M_2 is in a (YES)-state. Let's begin with the start state, →(q_0s_0). Interpret this as

"M_1 is in its start state q_0 and M_2 is in its start state s_0"

If the first bit is 1, then M_1 transitions to q_0 and M_2 to s_1. So, M transitions to from q_0s_0 to q_0s_1, shown on the right. Interpret this transition instruction as

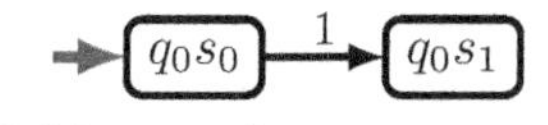

"IF M_1 is in q_0, M_2 is in s_0 and the bit is 1, THEN M_1 transitions to q_0 and M_2 to s_1."

Similarly, if the first bit is 0, M_1 transitions to q_1 and M_2 to s_0. So, M transitions to q_1s_0. Combining the transitions from the start state gives the beginings of M:

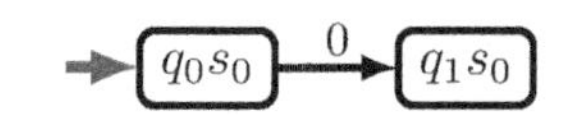

partial M :

q0s0 —1→ q0s1; q0s0 —0→ q1s0

The state-labels help to describe the logic, a useful tactic in constructing DFAs. The states q_is_j are called product states: 2-tuples of states, one from M_1 and one from M_2. To get the transitions from q_0s_1 and q_1s_0, we mimic M_1 and M_2 from their respective states. That is, q_is_j transitions to q_ks_ℓ if q_i transitions to q_k in M_1 and s_j transitions to s_ℓ in M_2. Using this rule, you should be able to produce the state transitions:

almost final M :

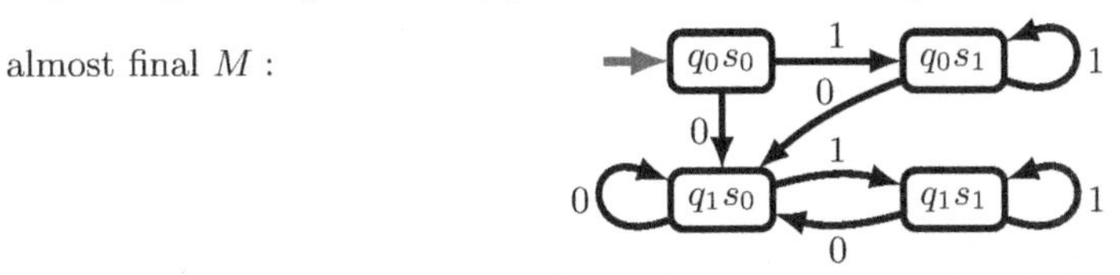

The specification of M is not complete because we still need to determine the YES-states. Our achievement is to construct a machine M which simulates the operation of both M_1 and M_2. To convince you of this, let's work through the input string 0110. Here are the algebraic traces of the computation for M_1, M_2 and M.

M_1	M_2	M
$q_0\|\triangleright 0110 \overset{M_1}{\mapsto} q_1\|0\triangleright 110$	$s_0\|\triangleright 0110 \overset{M_2}{\mapsto} s_0\|0\triangleright 110$	$q_0s_0\|\triangleright 11101 \overset{M}{\mapsto} q_1s_0\|0\triangleright 110$
$\overset{M_1}{\mapsto} q_1\|01\triangleright 10$	$\overset{M_2}{\mapsto} s_1\|01\triangleright 10$	$\overset{M}{\mapsto} q_1s_1\|01\triangleright 10$
$\overset{M_1}{\mapsto} q_1\|011\triangleright 0$	$\overset{M_2}{\mapsto} s_1\|011\triangleright 0$	$\overset{M}{\mapsto} q_1s_1\|011\triangleright 0$
$\overset{M_1}{\mapsto} q_1\|0110\triangleright$	$\overset{M_2}{\mapsto} s_0\|0110\triangleright$	$\overset{M}{\mapsto} q_1s_0\|0110\triangleright$

At every stage of the computation, M's state tells you which states M_1 and M_2 are in. That is, M effectively simulates M_1 and M_2. In this case, M_1 ends in the YES-state q_1 and M_2 ends in the NO-state s_0. Since M should accept if either M_1 or M_2 accept, q_1s_0 is a YES-state of M. The accept states of M are precisely the states q_is_j where either q_i is a YES-state of M_1 or s_j is a YES-state of M_2. Our construction of M is complete,

DFA solving $\mathcal{L}_1 \cup \mathcal{L}_2$:

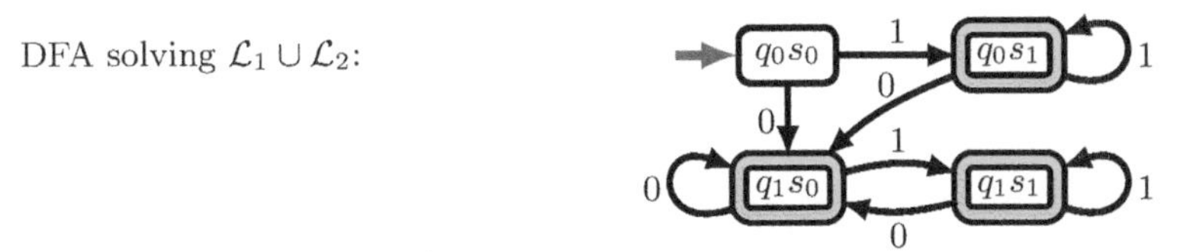

This complicated DFA solves a trivial language containing essentially all strings. The union $\mathcal{L}_1 \cup \mathcal{L}_2$ contains all strings but the empty string ε because a non-empty string either ends in 1 or contains a 0. A simpler DFA for the same problem is on the right. The method with product states is systematic but may not produce the simplest DFA.

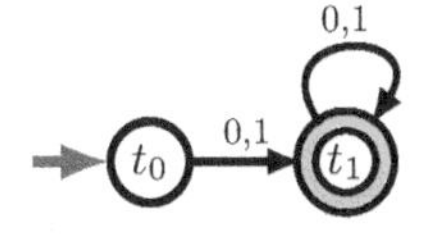

Exercise 24.4

(a) Show that strings in $\mathcal{L}_1 \cap \mathcal{L}_2$ satisfy the regular expression $*0*1$. Hence construct a DFA for $\mathcal{L}_1 \cap \mathcal{L}_2$.

(b) Use product states to construct a DFA that solves the computing problem $\mathcal{L}_1 \cap \mathcal{L}_2$.

Concatenation and Kleene Star. Let us consider the concatenation. Let $\mathcal{L} = \mathcal{L}_1 \bullet \mathcal{L}_2$. Every string in $\mathcal{L}$ is the concatenation of a string in $\mathcal{L}_1$ with a string in $\mathcal{L}_2$. Recall the definitions of $\mathcal{L}_1$ and $\mathcal{L}_2$,

$$\mathcal{L}_1 = \{\text{strings with a } 0\} = \{0, 00, 01, 10, 000, 001, 010, 011, 100, 101, 110, \ldots\}$$
$$\mathcal{L}_2 = \{\text{strings ending in } 1\} = \{1, 01, 11, 001, 011, 101, 111, \ldots\}$$

The string 10101 is in $\mathcal{L}$. To prove it, one shows $10101 = w_1 \bullet w_2$ with $w_1 \in \mathcal{L}_1$ and $w_2 \in \mathcal{L}_2$ ($10101 = 10 \bullet 101$). For a DFA to solve $\mathcal{L}_1 \bullet \mathcal{L}_2$, it must identify an appropriate $w_1 \in \mathcal{L}_1$. To do so, simply run M_1 on 10101 up to an accept state. When the trace is $10\triangleright 101$, M_1 enters its accept state q_1 as illustrated, which confirms that the prefix $w_1 = 01$ is in $\mathcal{L}_1$. We append the label s_0 to the state q_1 (of M_1) for a reason. We have found w_1 and can now test if the remainder of the string w_2 is in $\mathcal{L}_2$ by using M_2 on w_2, for which we must begin at the start state s_0 (of M_2). Hence the label q_1s_0, because from the accept state q_1 (of M_1) the machine immediately resets to the start state s_0 (of M_2) and proceeds from this hybrid state according to instructions of M_2. To accept, the DFA must end in s_1, the accept state of M_2. Combining the running of M_1 followed by M_2 is summarized in

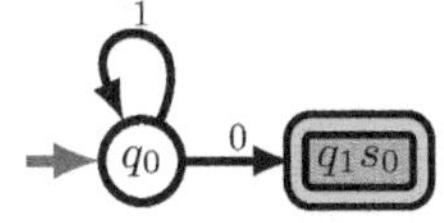

the DFA below. The left half simulates M_1 up to $q_1 s_0$, and then M_2 takes over in the right half.

DFA solving $\mathcal{L}_1 \bullet \mathcal{L}_2$:

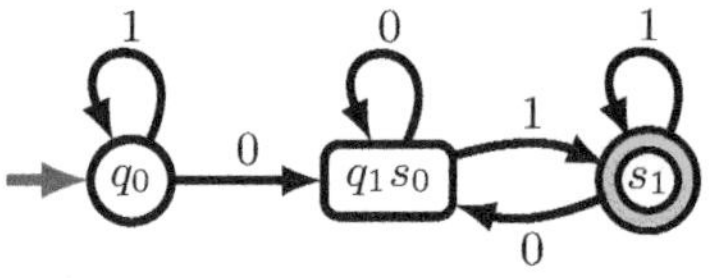

Pop Quiz 24.5

(a) Show that $\mathcal{L} = \mathcal{L}_1 \bullet \mathcal{L}_2$ from the above discussion is described by $*0*1$. Hence construct a DFA for $\mathcal{L}$.
(b) Show that $\mathcal{L} = \mathcal{L}_1 \cap \mathcal{L}_2$ and use product-states to construct a DFA to solve $\mathcal{L}$.
(c) For any two languages $\mathcal{L}_1, \mathcal{L}_2$, prove or disprove: $\mathcal{L}_1 \bullet \mathcal{L}_2 = \mathcal{L}_1 \cap \mathcal{L}_2$.

Our DFA for $\mathcal{L}_1 \bullet \mathcal{L}_2$ finds the first prefix of the input which is in $\mathcal{L}_1$ and tests if the remaining suffix is in $\mathcal{L}_2$. This works for our choices of $\mathcal{L}_1$ and $\mathcal{L}_2$, but not in general. Consider the two languages

$$\mathcal{K}_1 = \{\text{strings with an odd number of 0's}\} = \{0, 01, 10, 000, 011, 101, 110, 0001, \ldots\}$$
$$\mathcal{K}_2 = \{\text{strings with an odd number of bits}\} = \{0, 1, 000, 001, 010, 011, 100, \ldots\}$$

Pop Quiz 24.6

Find DFAs M_1' and M_2' to solve $\mathcal{K}_1$ and $\mathcal{K}_2$.

[Answer: M_1': ; M_2':]

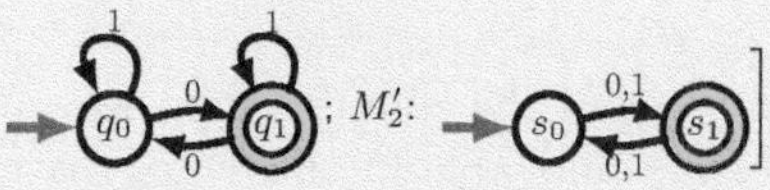

To solve $\mathcal{K}_1 \bullet \mathcal{K}_2$, first run M_1' in Pop Quiz 24.6. If it reaches its accept state q_1, jump to the start state s_0 of M_2' and follow M_2' from this dual state $q_1 s_0$. Accept if M_2' accepts, state s_1. The concatenated DFA is:

wrong DFA for $\mathcal{K}_1 \bullet \mathcal{K}_2$:

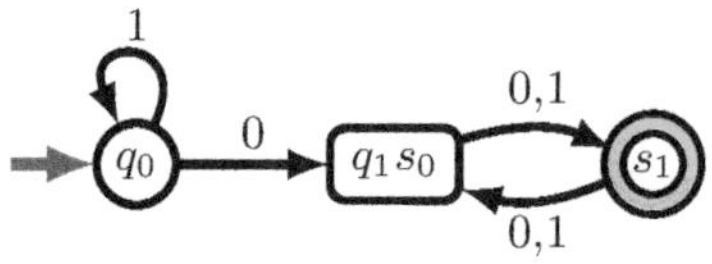

Life is good, except this DFA does not solve $\mathcal{K}_1 \bullet \mathcal{K}_2$. Consider the input $100101 = 10010 \bullet 1$, which is in $\mathcal{K}_1 \bullet \mathcal{K}_2$ because $10010 \in \mathcal{K}_1$ and $1 \in \mathcal{K}_2$. However, please verify that the DFA ends in $q_1 s_0$ and rejects. The problem arises because we commit to the first prefix that is in $\mathcal{K}_1$ and test if the remaining suffix is in $\mathcal{K}_2$. There can be multiple prefixes that are in $\mathcal{K}_1$ and only one of the corresponding suffixes need be in $\mathcal{K}_2$. The first prefix may fail but a later prefix might work. When you reach the accept state of M_1' you need to follow M_2' or continue with M_1' to test if another prefix would work. Here is an attempt at such a schizophrenic DFA.

strange DFA for $\mathcal{K}_1 \bullet \mathcal{K}_2$:

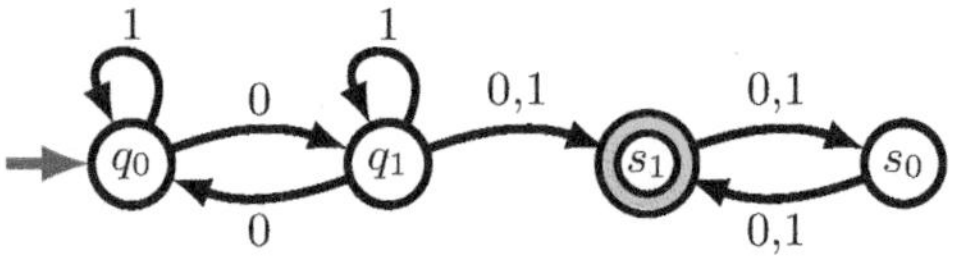

Why strange? When you run on 100101, the algebraic trace becomes $q_1|10 \triangleright 0101$. For the next bit 0, one arrow leads to q_0, continuing M_1', and another to s_1, following M_2'. Which should you follow? The action is not determined, this machine is nondeterministic. We may follow both arrows and record this in the algebraic trace as $\{q_0, s_1\}|100 \triangleright 101$. The state transitions to a set of states which captures all states the DFA can possibly be in at this stage of the computation. Think of this set of all possible states as a meta-state. Using meta-states as states in another DFA, you can remove the nondeterminacy and produce a valid DFA.

Exercise 24.7 [Subset States: Converting the Nondeterministic Automaton to a DFA]

(a) Articulate exactly what the algebraic trace $\{q_0, s_1\}|100 \triangleright 101$ means.
(b) Give the full trace for the strange DFA with input 100101. At each step track all the posisble states.
(c) How do you determine whether to accept the input from the algebraic trace?
(d) Convert the strange DFA into a valid DFA for $\mathcal{K}_1 \bullet \mathcal{K}_2$. *[Hint: DFA states are the meta-states.]*

Now consider the Kleene star, $\mathcal{L}_1^* = \mathcal{L}_1^{\bullet 0} \cup \mathcal{L}_1^{\bullet 1} \cup \mathcal{L}_1^{\bullet 2} \cup \cdots$ where $\mathcal{L}_1^{\bullet 0} = \{\varepsilon\}$. Since $\mathcal{L}_1$ contains all strings with a 0, any string in $\mathcal{L}_1^{\bullet k}$ for $k \geq 1$ must contain a 0. That means $\mathcal{L}_1^{\bullet k} \subset \mathcal{L}_1$ and therefore $\mathcal{L}_1^* = \{\varepsilon\} \cup \mathcal{L}_1$.

Exercise 24.8 [Subset States: Converting a DFA for $\mathcal{L}$ to a DFA for $\mathcal{L}^*$]

(a) Give a DFA that solves the language $\mathcal{L}_1^* = \{\varepsilon\} \cup \{\text{strings with a } 0\}$.
(b) **[Hard]** Let $\mathcal{L} = \{1, 10\}$. Construct a DFA that solves $\mathcal{L}^*$.
(c) **[Hard]** Denote the DFA on the right by M and let $\mathcal{L} = \mathcal{L}(M)$.

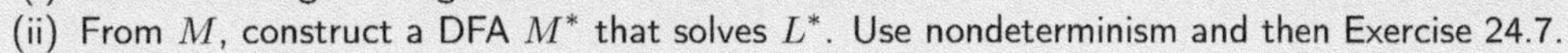

(i) Give the strings of length at most 4 which are in $\mathcal{L}$.
(ii) From M, construct a DFA M^* that solves L^*. Use nondeterminism and then Exercise 24.7.

Summary. Using DFAs for $\mathcal{L}_1$ and $\mathcal{L}_2$, we can get DFAs for $\overline{\mathcal{L}_1}$, $\mathcal{L}_1 \cup \mathcal{L}_2$, $\mathcal{L}_1 \cap \mathcal{L}_2$, $\mathcal{L}_1 \bullet \mathcal{L}_2$ and $\mathcal{L}_1^*$. Our discussion plus the exercises give you the tools to prove this is true for general $\mathcal{L}_1$ and $\mathcal{L}_2$, which proves Theorem 24.2.

Theorem 24.2 (Closure)**.** Regular languages are closed under complement, union, intersection, concatenation and Kleene star. Specifically, if $\mathcal{L}_1$ and $\mathcal{L}_2$ are regular, then, the following languages are also regular.

1. $\overline{\mathcal{L}_1}$ and $\overline{\mathcal{L}_2}$; 2. $\mathcal{L}_1 \cup \mathcal{L}_2$; 3. $\mathcal{L}_1 \cap \mathcal{L}_2$; 4. $\mathcal{L}_1 \bullet \mathcal{L}_2$ and $\mathcal{L}_2 \bullet \mathcal{L}_1$; 5. $\mathcal{L}_1^*$ and $\mathcal{L}_2^*$.

To prove Theorem 24.2, use DFAs for $\mathcal{L}_1$ and $\mathcal{L}_2$ to build a DFA for the language formed by the set operation on $\mathcal{L}_1$ and $\mathcal{L}_2$. Though we won't prove Theorem 24.2, we can appreciate its importance. It says regular languages can be combined using set operations to get more complex regular languages. The regular expressions from Section 23.2.1 describe languages built using such set operations, starting from finite languages. Finite languages are regular, so regular expressions describe regular languages. A DFA can solve any computing problem described by a regular expression. DFAs are powerful! The converse is also true. Languages solved by DFAs can be described by regular expressions. We can now answer yes to a question posed earlier,

"Can one easily determine if a given string satisfies a given regular expression?"

Why is the answer yes? Given a regular expression describing a language $\mathcal{L}$, find a DFA that solves $\mathcal{L}$ and check if the DFA accepts the string. For example, to find files of the form `FOCS*HW*.*` (e.g. `FOCS-HW-1.pdf`), find a DFA for this language, pass all filenames through the DFA, keeping only the accepted filenames.

Exercise 24.9
Show that $\mathcal{L} = \{\text{strings whose number of 1s is not divisible by 2 or 3}\}$ is regular.

24.2 Provably Non-Regular

Our computer, the DFA, solves a huge class of problems: regular expressions. It's tempting to rest on our laurels, but every rose has its thorn, and for us that thorn is the equality task. Consider the language $\mathcal{L}_{0^n1^n}$,

$$\mathcal{L}_{0^n1^n} = \{0^{\bullet n}1^{\bullet n} \mid n \geq 0\} = \{\text{strings which start with 0s followed by an equal number of 1s}\}.$$

Pop Quiz 24.10
Find a DFA to solve $\{0\}^* \bullet \{1\}^* = \{0^{\bullet n}1^{\bullet k} \mid n \geq 0, k \geq 0\} = \{\text{strings starting with 0s and ending in 1s}\}$.

The only difference between $0^{\bullet n}1^{\bullet n}$ and $0^{\bullet n}1^{\bullet k}$ is the equality constraint, but that's a biggie.

Theorem 24.3. There is no DFA that solves the computing problem $\mathcal{L}_{0^n1^n}$.

What a deep theorem! It is not about DFA-programming-skills. It is not that we aren't smart enough to solve $\mathcal{L}_{0^n1^n}$. Nobody, not even a Martian, can solve $\mathcal{L}_{0^n1^n}$ using DFAs. The intuition is in Pop Quiz 24.1(c). Suppose, after processing all the 0s, the DFA has string 11 remaining to be processed. To determine (YES) or (NO), the DFA needs to remember how many zeros (one, two, three,...) came before. For each possibility, the DFA needs to be in a different state. But, that requires a DFA with infinitely many states.

Proof. Contradiction is a good way to prove non-existence. Assume a DFA M with k states $q_0, q_1, \ldots, q_{k-1}$ solves $\mathcal{L}_{0^n1^n}$, where k is arbitrary, but finite. Let us consider M processesing a string of k zeros. M starts in state q_0 having "processed" $\varepsilon = 0^{\bullet 0}$ and transitions to a state for each additional 0,

$$q_0 = \text{state}(0^{\bullet 0}) \overset{M}{\mapsto} \text{state}(0^{\bullet 1}) \overset{M}{\mapsto} \text{state}(0^{\bullet 2}) \overset{M}{\mapsto} \cdots \overset{M}{\mapsto} \text{state}(0^{\bullet k-1}) \overset{M}{\mapsto} \text{state}(0^{\bullet k})$$

Including q_0, $k+1$ states are visited. We don't know which states are visited. But, as there are only k states, by the pigeonhole principle, two of the visited states must be the same. That is,

$$\text{state}(0^{\bullet i}) = \text{state}(0^{\bullet j}) = q \qquad \text{for some } i, j \text{ with } 0 \leq i < j \leq k$$

Consider inputs $x = 0^{\bullet i}1^{\bullet i}$ and $y = 0^{\bullet j}1^{\bullet i}$. After processing the 0s in x and y, M is in state q because $\text{state}(0^{\bullet i}) = \text{state}(0^{\bullet j}) = q$ (see figure). The computation traces are:

trace for x: $\quad q \mid 0^{\bullet i} \triangleright 1^{\bullet i}$ $\qquad\qquad$ trace for y: $\quad q \mid 0^{\bullet j} \triangleright 1^{\bullet i}$.

The same bits remain to be processed from the same state q for both x and y. Hence, M must end in the same final state q_f for both x and y. Since M solves $\mathcal{L}_{0^n1^n}$ and $x \in \mathcal{L}_{0^n1^n}$, q_f must be a (YES)-state. But $y \notin \mathcal{L}_{0^n1^n}$, so q_f must be a (NO)-state. This contradiction proves M cannot exist. ∎

What a blockbuster application of pigeonhole, to prove DFAs cannot solve so simple a problem as equality.

Pop Quiz 24.11
Prove that no DFA solves $\mathcal{L}_{\text{balanced}}$ = {strings with the same number of 0s and 1s}.

We did a full circle. We developed a model of computing, understood its capabilities – problems we can solve – and discovered some limitations – problems we cannot solve. This is an important workflow when you build models: understand the capabilities and limitations and decide if the model is both feasible and acceptable.

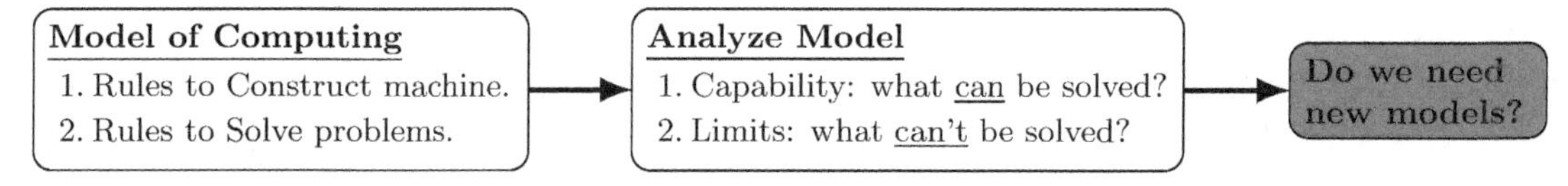

A DFA can be implemented using basic technology, so it's physically feasible. But, the DFA fails at solving so simple a problem as equality. How embarrassing! We need a new model.

24.3 Adding External Memory

What went wrong with the DFA? Why couldn't it solve equality?

"By pigeonhole, any DFA will visit some state twice and ..."

Yes, that's the proof. The intuition is scratch paper. You don't do hard math in your head. You need scratch paper to store complex calculations for later use. The DFA doesn't have scratch paper. That's the problem.

A DFA can answer the question "Was there a 1?" When a 1 arrives, the DFA transitions to a "seen-1-state" and stays there: states function as a primitive finite memory. Change the question a little, "Were there more 1s than 0s?" Now, the DFA is in trouble. The DFA needs to count 1's and 0's. For each 1, the DFA can transition "up-one-state" and for each 0 "down-one-state". But, if too many 1's arrive, you run out of states.

Stack Memory. The DFA needs external space for scratchwork. Stack memory models a file-clerk with a stack of papers. The clerk can see the top sheet, remove the top sheet by popping, or push something new onto the top of the stack. An automaton with stack memory is called a deterministic pushdown automaton or d-PDA, illustrated to the right. If you ignore the stack, it's DFA, so pushdown automata are at least as powerful as DFA. Are d-PDAs more powerful than DFAs?

Yes. With a stack, one can solve equality, $\mathcal{L}_{0^n1^n} = \{0^{\bullet n}1^{\bullet n} \mid n \geq 0\}$, which we know can't be solved by DFAs. Here is the high-level d-PDA for $\mathcal{L}_{0^n1^n}$. Push the zeros onto the stack. The stack memory is scratch paper to store the number of zeros in unary. For each 1, pop the stack, pairing 1s with 0s. If you pop an empty stack, reject as there are more 1s than 0s. When the 1s end, accept if the stack is empty as every 1 was paired. If the stack has 0s, reject, for there are more 0s than 1s. We illustrate for the input $0^{\bullet 2}1^{\bullet 2}$. The stack is left of the automaton with its top in white.

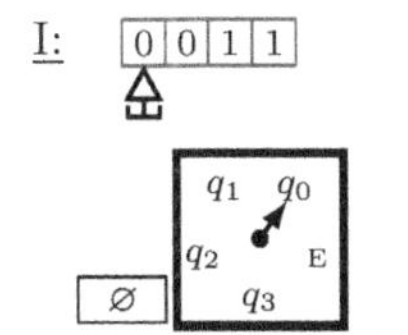

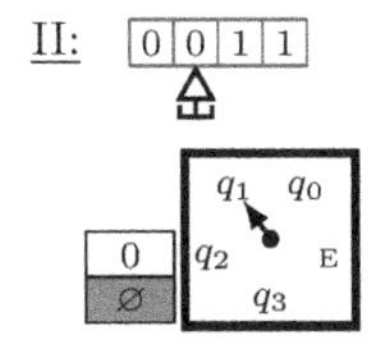

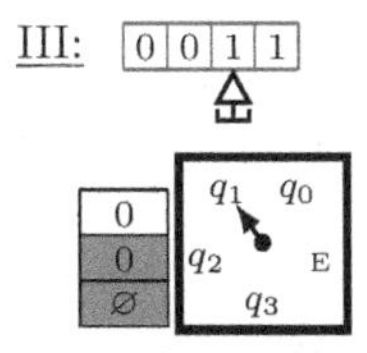

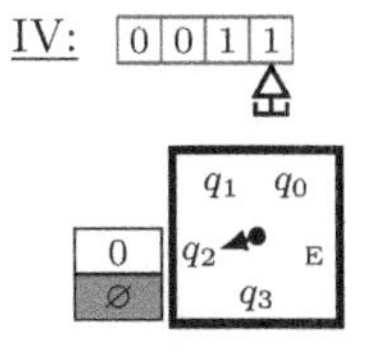

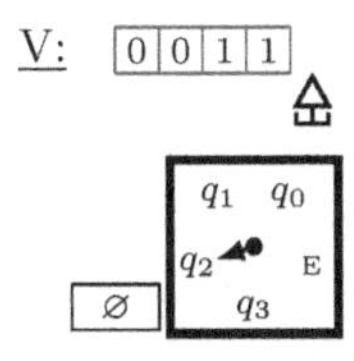

I: Start in state q_0 at the first bit with the stack empty, denoted by the empty set $\varnothing$.
II: Push the first 0 onto the stack and transition to a "reading-in-zeros" state q_1.
III: Read in all the 0's, pushing them onto the stack, while staying in state q_1.
IV: At the first 1, pop the stack and transition to a "checking-ones" state q_2. (Any 0-bit here means reject.)
V: Read in all the 1's, each time popping the stack while staying in state q_2.

At the end of the string, if the stack is empty, as in this case, transition to the accept state q_3. To convert our high-level description to a working d-PDA, we must specify low-level machine-code instructions. The input at each step can be 0,1 or EOF. We allow "reading in" ε or EOF (end of file) to explicitly identify the end of the input and make one final transition. This allows the automaton to use the stack in determining (YES) or (NO). The top of the stack can show 0 or 1, or the stack can be empty which we denote by $\varnothing$. Depending on the input and the top of the stack, the automaton transitions to a new state and manipulates the stack (does nothing; pop; push; or, change the top – pop plus push). Here is an example of a low-level instruction,

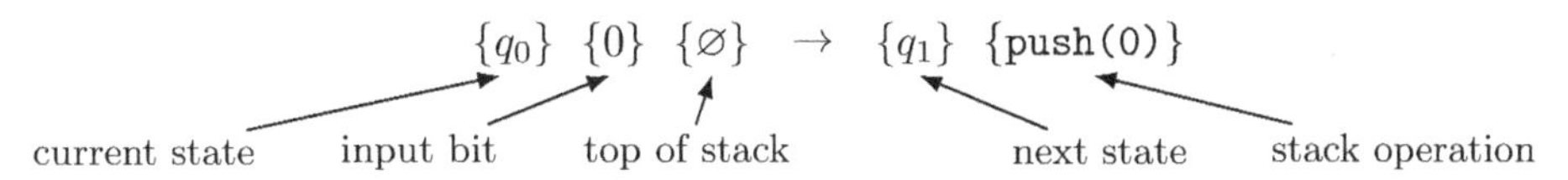

This instruction says: from state q_0, IF the input bit is 0 AND the stack is empty, THEN transition to q_1 and push 0 onto the stack. We won't delve into d-PDAs because there's a bigger fish. Also, we already achieved our modest goal, to show how a simple stack-memory gives more power, for example to solve $\mathcal{L}_{0^n1^n}$. It is now just a matter of details to convert the high-level idea into a machine-level d-PDA, which, as with the DFA, can be described by a directed graph. For the details, we invite you to the next exercise.

Exercise 24.12

We started drawing a d-PDA for $\mathcal{L}_{0^n1^n}$. Directed edges are machine-level transition instructions linking the current state to the next state of the transition. Each edge label shows the input bit and stack symbol ($\varnothing$ for empty stack) which together cause the transition. Edge labels also shows the stack operation to be performed.

$\{0,1,\varepsilon\}\{0,1,\varnothing\} \to \{\}$
$\{1\}\{\varnothing\} \to \{\}$
$\{0\}\{\varnothing\} \to \{\texttt{push(0)}\}$
$\{0\}\{0\} \to \{\texttt{push(0)}\}$

(a) Explain the high-level steps for the four instructions shown.
(b) Complete the machine-level description of the d-PDA.
(c) Show algebraic traces of your automaton for inputs 010, 00011, 0011, 00111. (At any step in the computation, the trace should show the bits processed, the bits that remain, the state and what else?)
(d) What are your thoughts on the practical feasibility of the pushdown automaton?

Epilogue. As with any form of design, designing a DFA calls for creativity. Be the automaton. Ask yourself:

"How would *I* manipulate a finite memory (the states) to decide if a string is in the language?"

If you can't do it, try proving it's impossible. If you are still stumped, don't fret. DFA-design is subtle.

Exercise 24.13

To appreciate the subtleties of designing DFAs, give a DFA for each language or prove it's impossible.
(a) $\mathcal{L}_1 = \{(01)^{\bullet n}(10)^{\bullet n} \mid n \geq 0\}$ (b) $\mathcal{L}_2 = \{$strings with the same number of 01 and 10 substrings$\}$.

24.4 Problems

Problem 24.1. You (an East-coaster) wish to tell your friend on the West-coast about your fancy new DFA.

(a) Your DFA has 5 states, $q_0, \ldots, q_4$. Identify what you must send your friend. How many bits of information is it?

(b) Our alphabet was binary, $\Sigma = \{0, 1\}$. Generalize part (a) to an alphabet $\Sigma = \{\sigma_1, \ldots, \sigma_s\}$ with s symbols, and an automaton with k states $q_0, \ldots, q_{k-1}$.

Problem 24.2. For the finite automaton on the right:

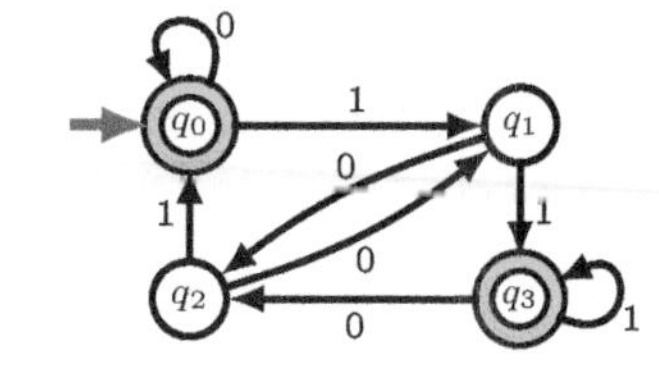

(a) What is the start state? What is the set of accept states?

(b) What sequence of states are followed for input 0011?

(c) Give all strings of length at most 6 accepted by the machine.

(d) Give the conditions on a general automaton M under which $\varepsilon \in \mathcal{L}(M)$?

Problem 24.3. Describe in words the language accepted by each automaton, and also give a regular expression.

(a) 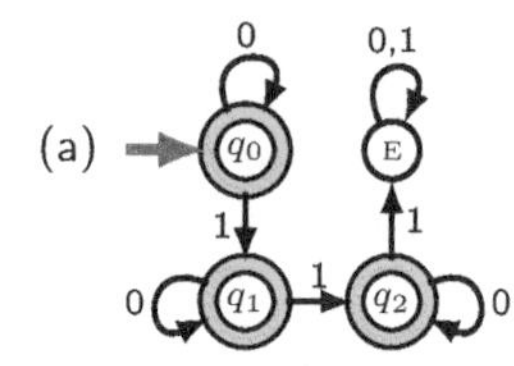

(b) 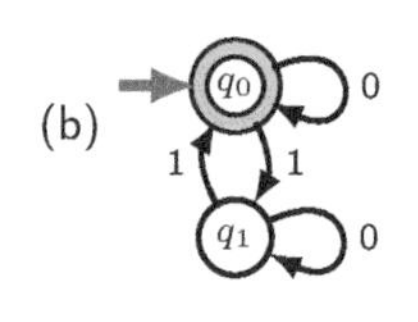

(c) 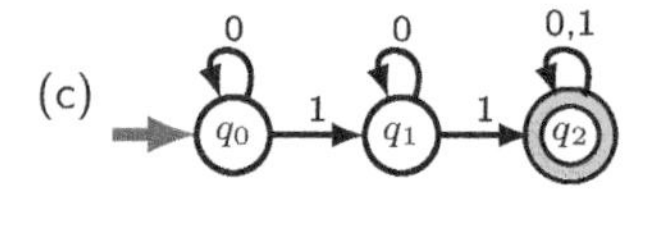

(d) 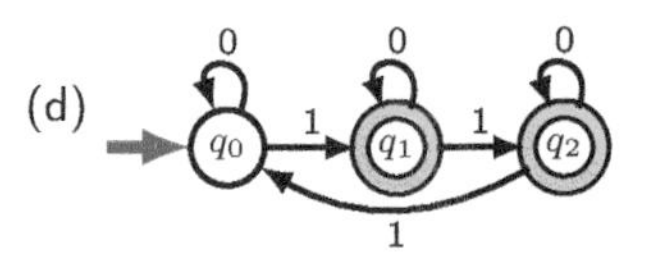

Problem 24.4. State diagrams (directed graphs) are a nice visual way to describe DFAs. One can also use a table whose rows are states. Entries in a state's row indicate where to transition for each input bit. The start state is q_0 and we use green and red for the YES and NO states. Describe in words the languages accepted by each automaton.

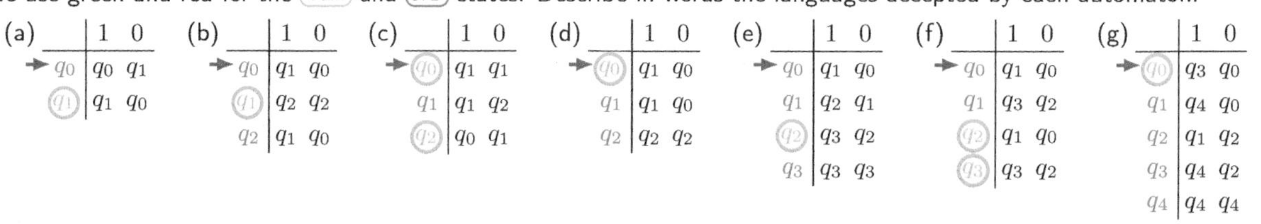

(a)

	1	0
→ q_0	q_0	q_1
(q_1)	q_1	q_0

(b)

	1	0
→ q_0	q_1	q_0
(q_1)	q_2	q_2
q_2	q_1	q_0

(c)

	1	0
→ (q_0)	q_1	q_1
q_1	q_1	q_2
(q_2)	q_0	q_1

(d)

	1	0
→ (q_0)	q_1	q_0
q_1	q_1	q_0
q_2	q_2	q_2

(e)

	1	0
→ q_0	q_1	q_0
q_1	q_2	q_1
(q_2)	q_3	q_2
q_3	q_3	q_3

(f)

	1	0
→ q_0	q_1	q_0
q_1	q_3	q_2
(q_2)	q_1	q_0
(q_3)	q_3	q_2

(g)

	1	0
→ (q_0)	q_3	q_0
q_1	q_4	q_0
q_2	q_1	q_2
q_3	q_4	q_2
q_4	q_4	q_4

Problem 24.5. Problem 24.4 shows how to describe a DFA using a table. Give the table description of the DFAs in Problem 24.3. Instead of color coding states, you may identify accept states by just circling them.

Problem 24.6. What is the probability a random 10-bit-string $b_1 b_2 \ldots b_{10}$ is accepted by each automaton?

(a) 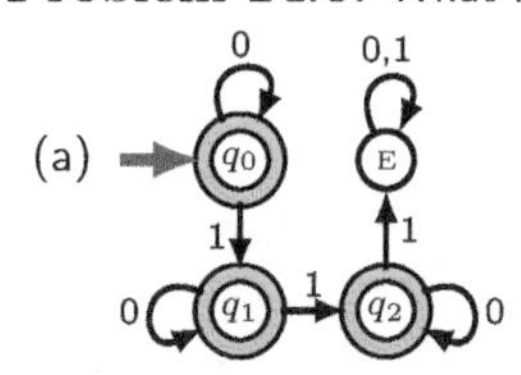

(b) 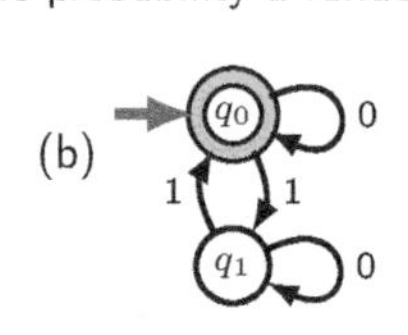

(c) 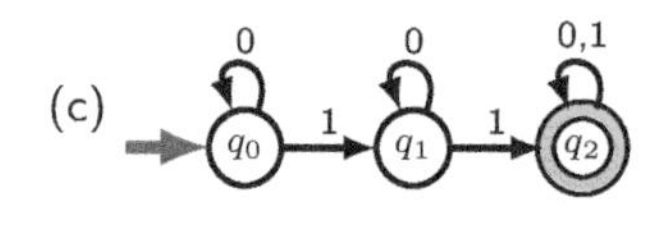

(d) 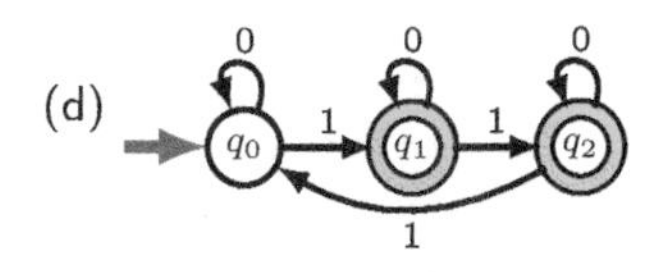

Problem 24.7. The DFA processes $b_1 \ldots b_n$, a random string of n independent bits where $b_i = 1$ with probability p. Show that $\mathbb{P}[\text{accept}] = 1 - (1-p)^n - np(1-p)^{n-1}$. *[Hint: Find a simple property of accepted strings and use the Binomial distribution.]*

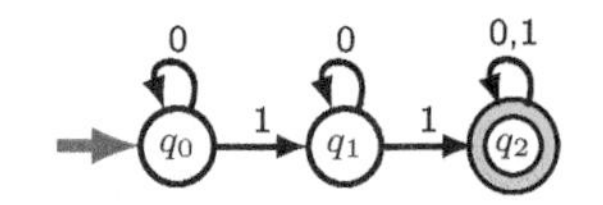

Problem 24.8. Give the simplest automaton which accepts each language.

(a) All finite strings, Σ^*. (b) No strings, $\varnothing$. (c) Just the empty string ε. (d) All strings but the empty string ε.

Problem 24.9. Give DFA's for the following computing tasks.

(a) The DFA accepts quarters and dispenses a coke each time the machine gets 3 quarters.

(b) The DFA accepts quarters and dimes and dispenses candy when the balance is at least 50¢.

(c) (i) $\mathcal{L} = \{00010, 10111\}$ (ii) $\mathcal{L} = \{\text{strings with 101 as a substring}\}$ (iii) $\mathcal{L} = \{001^{\bullet 2n} | n \geq 0\}$.

(d) Fix $d \in \mathbb{N}$. (i) $\mathcal{L} = \{1^{\bullet n} \mid n \text{ is a multiple of } d\}$ (ii) $\mathcal{L} = \{w \mid w \text{ is a binary number that is a multiple of } d\}$.

Problem 24.10. A voomba vacuum-rover ▲, when placed on one end of a dirt path, should move step by step and vacuum up all the dirt. The voomba can sense dirt in the square ahead, can rotate 90° clockwise, can move forward and transition among its internal states. Design a voomba as a DFA. In the picture, the voomba is facing north, left of the first piece of dirt.
When will your voomba succesfully vacuum all the dirt? Give an informal argument.

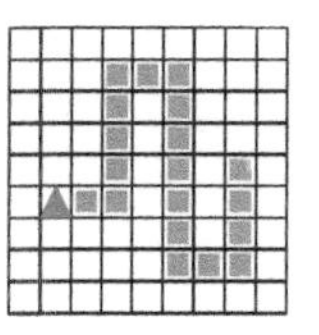

Problem 24.11. Give DFAs for the following languages, aka computing problems.

(a) Strings which end in 1.
(b) Strings which do not end in 1.
(c) Strings which begin in 1 and end in 0.
(d) Strings which do not contain any 0s.
(e) $\mathcal{L} = \{1^{\bullet 5n} \mid n \geq 0\}$.
(f) $\mathcal{L} = \{1^{\bullet 2n}01^{\bullet 2k+1} \mid n, k \geq 0\}$.
(g) Strings which begin with 10 or end with 01.
(h) Strings which begin with 10 and end with 01.
(i) Strings in which every 0 is adjacent to a 0.
(j) All strings except 10 and 100.
(k) Strings whose 3rd bit from the end is 1.
(l) Strings which begin and end in the same bit.
(m) Strings whose adjacent bits are different.
(n) *Non-empty* strings with an even number of 1s.
(o) Strings *not* of the form $0^{\bullet n}1^{\bullet k}$ for $n, k \geq 0$.
(p) Strings which contain 0101 as a substring.
(q) Strings which do not contain 001 as a substring.
(r) Strings whose even digits alternate between 0 and 1.
(s) Strings whose odd digits match the previous even digit.
(t) Strings with no 1s separated by an odd number of symbols.
(u) Strings with no 1s separated by an even number of symbols.
(v) Strings with an even number of 0s and one or two 1s.
(w) Strings whose length is divisible by 3.
(x) Strings whose length is not divisible by 2 or 3.
(y) Strings with an even number of 1s or more than two 1s.
(z) Strings with exactly two 0s and exactly two 1s.

Problem 24.12. Find a DFA for each language built from simpler languages using DFAs for the simpler languages.

(a) Strings of even length with an odd number of 0s.
(b) Strings with an odd number of 0s that end in 1.
(c) Strings with exactly two 0s and at least two 1s.
(d) Strings which do not contain exactly two 0s.
(e) Strings with exactly two 0s and exactly two 1s.
(f) Strings with matching even bits and matching odd bits.
(g) Strings whose length is not divisible by 2 or 3.
(h) Strings which do not contain the substring 01.
(i) Strings which do not contain either 01 or 10 as substrings.
(j) Strings of odd length not in $\{0\}^* \bullet \{1\}^*$.

Problem 24.13 (Transducer). A DFA-transducer resembles everyday computing. DFAs answer (YES) or (NO). Transducers also transform the input string to an output. A schematic is on the right. At each step, the DFA reads an input bit, transitions state *and* may write a string to the output. For example, consider this instruction,

It says: "If you read 1 when in state q_0, transition to q_5 and write 01."

(a) Give the output of each transducer on: (i) 00 (ii) 111 (iii) 11101 (iv) 0010101.

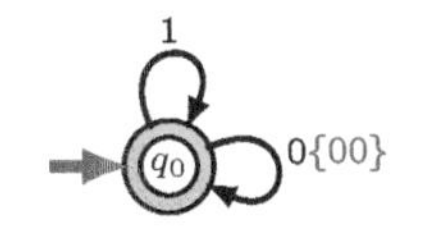

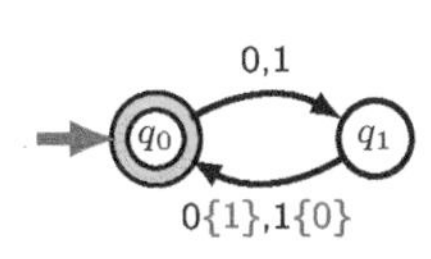

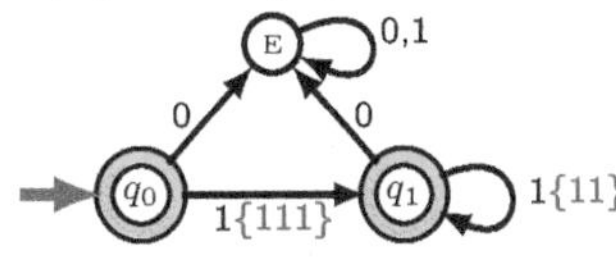

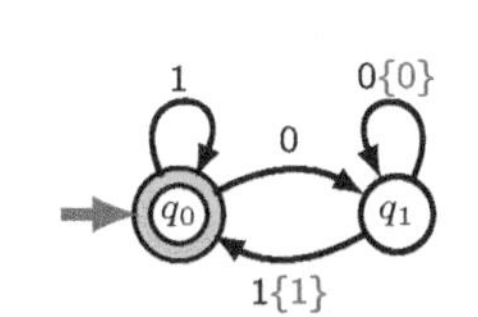

(b) Describe in words the tasks implemented by each transducer in part (a).
(c) Give a transducer whose output is every third bit of the input string flipped. For example $0011000100 \to 011$.
(d) Prove that there is no DFA-transducer that can accomplish these tasks on input w.
 (i) Write w^{R} to output. *[Hint: Consider $w = 00$ and $w = 01$.]* (ii) Write ww to output.

Problem 24.14 (Addition). These languages correspond to the arithmetic task of addition.

(a) Let $\mathcal{L} = \{w_1\#w_2\#w_3 \mid w_1 + w_2 = w_3\}$ where # is a punctuation symbol and w_1, w_2, w_3 are treated as binary numbers. For example, $101\#11\#1000 \in \mathcal{L}$ and $101\#011\#1111 \notin \mathcal{L}$. Prove that there is no DFA that solves $\mathcal{L}$.
(b) Recall that one can define languages using any alphabet Σ. Use a new alphabet Σ_3,

$$\Sigma_3 = \left\{ \left[\begin{smallmatrix}0\\0\\0\end{smallmatrix}\right], \left[\begin{smallmatrix}0\\0\\1\end{smallmatrix}\right], \left[\begin{smallmatrix}0\\1\\0\end{smallmatrix}\right], \left[\begin{smallmatrix}0\\1\\1\end{smallmatrix}\right], \left[\begin{smallmatrix}1\\0\\0\end{smallmatrix}\right], \left[\begin{smallmatrix}1\\0\\1\end{smallmatrix}\right], \left[\begin{smallmatrix}1\\1\\0\end{smallmatrix}\right], \left[\begin{smallmatrix}1\\1\\1\end{smallmatrix}\right] \right\}$$

A string in Σ_3^* can be interpreted as 3 rows of bits, each row defining a binary string. Define a language $\mathcal{L}_{\text{ADD}}$ for addition where a string is in $\mathcal{L}_{\text{ADD}}$ if the sum of the first two rows (binary numbers) equals the third. For example,

$$\left[\begin{smallmatrix}0\\0\\1\end{smallmatrix}\right]\left[\begin{smallmatrix}1\\0\\0\end{smallmatrix}\right]\left[\begin{smallmatrix}0\\1\\0\end{smallmatrix}\right]\left[\begin{smallmatrix}1\\1\\0\end{smallmatrix}\right] \in \mathcal{L}_3 \qquad \left[\begin{smallmatrix}0\\0\\1\end{smallmatrix}\right]\left[\begin{smallmatrix}1\\0\\0\end{smallmatrix}\right]\left[\begin{smallmatrix}0\\1\\1\end{smallmatrix}\right]\left[\begin{smallmatrix}1\\1\\0\end{smallmatrix}\right] \notin \mathcal{L}_3$$

Prove that $\mathcal{L}_{\text{ADD}}$ is regular. *[Hint: Build a DFA for the reversal $\mathcal{L}_{\text{ADD}}^{\text{R}}$. How does this help? See Problem 24.44.]*
(c) In the text we only used the binary alphabet $\Sigma = \{0, 1\}$. Convert $\mathcal{L}_3$ to a language $\mathcal{L}_{\text{ADD}}$ over the binary alphabet. Show that your $\mathcal{L}_{\text{ADD}}$ is regular. *[Hint: $001100010110 \in \mathcal{L}_{\text{ADD}}$ and $001100011110 \notin \mathcal{L}_{\text{ADD}}$.]*
(d) At a high level, explain the difference between $\mathcal{L}$ and $\mathcal{L}_{\text{ADD}}$, and how come $\mathcal{L}_{\text{ADD}}$ is regular but $\mathcal{L}$ is not.

(How the input is formatted for a computer (DFA) can affect whether a problem is solvable.)

Problem 24.15 (Two Input Tapes). In each setting, create a DFA to test two input strings x and y for equality.

(a) The DFA has two read-heads and x and y are on two input tapes. The DFA alternates between processing a bit from the first string and then a bit from the second string.

(b) The DFA has one input tape, and the input string is xy. *[Hint: the language* $\{ww \mid w \in \Sigma^*\}$*.]*

(c) The DFA has one input tape, and the input string has the bits of x and y interleaved, $x_1y_1x_2y_2\cdots$.

Problem 24.16 (Hidden Markov Model (HMM)). A patient can either be in a normal state, Ⓝ, or an epileptic state, Ⓔ. A patient experiences a sequence of input light stimuli. The light is off (0) or on (1). Depending on the patient's state and the stimulus, the patient transitions state and emits an output. The output is 0 for no muscle spasm or 1 for a muscle spasm. The patient is a nondeterministic automaton with transducer capabilities.

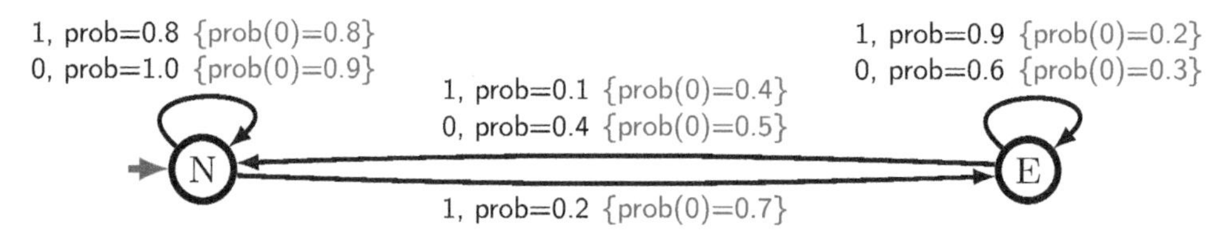

The start state is normal. The label "1, prob=0.8 {prob(0)=0.8}" on the arrow from Ⓝ to Ⓝ means: from state Ⓝ with input 1, transition to Ⓝ with probability 0.8 and output 0 with probability 0.8 or 1 with probability 0.2.

(a) Explain in words each instruction shown in the state diagram and why it intuitively make sense.

(b) Use build-up probability where needed to compute these probabilities.

(i) The input is 0111. Find the probability that the final state is epileptic. (The states are "hidden" from view.)

(ii) The input is 0111 and the output is 0110. Find the probability that the final state is epileptic.

(iii) For a random (unknown) input, the output is 0110. Find the probability that the final state is epileptic.

(Usually, the various probabilities are unknown and one tries to determine them using observed outputs. The probabilities represent the patient's "biology". More details would be covered in a course on machine learning.)

Problem 24.17. Let $\mathcal{L}$ = {strings not containing 01 as a substring, with an even number of 0s and odd number of 1s}.

(a) $\mathcal{L}$ is related to 3 simpler languages. Use DFAs for the simpler languages and product states to get a DFA for $\mathcal{L}$.

(b) Find a 5-state DFA for $\mathcal{L}$ by carefully analyzing $\mathcal{L}$ and describing it more simply.

Problem 24.18. Toss a coin and stop at the first occurrence of HH. Give a DFA that accepts $\mathcal{H}$, where the language $\mathcal{H}$ over the alphabet Σ = {H,T} contains the strings which end at their first occurrence of HH:

$$\mathcal{H} = \{w \mid w = x\text{HH}, x \text{ does not end in H or contain HH as a substring}\}.$$

Problem 24.19. Give a DFA for the language of all strings of length at most ℓ. How many states do you need? Try to minimize the number of states.

Problem 24.20. Let $\mathcal{L}_3$ = {strings whose 3rd bit from the right is 0}.

(a) Give a regular expression for $\mathcal{L}_3$.

(b) Give a DFA to solve $\mathcal{L}_3$ using at most 8 states and show that no DFA with fewer than 8 states solves $\mathcal{L}_3$.

(c) Generalize to $\mathcal{L}_k$ = {strings whose kth bit from the right is 0}. Show that 2^k states are needed.

Problem 24.21. Let $\mathcal{L}_3 = \{ww \mid w \text{ has length } 3\}$.

(a) Give a DFA to solve $\mathcal{L}_3$ using at most 8 states and show that no DFA with fewer than 8 states solves $\mathcal{L}_3$.

(b) Generalize to $\mathcal{L}_k = \{ww \mid w \text{ has length } k\}$. Show that 2^k states are needed.

Problem 24.22. Let $\mathcal{L}_1 = \{w \mid w \text{ contains } 010\}$ and $\mathcal{L}_2 = \{w \mid w \text{ begins and ends in } 1\}$. Find DFAs for:
(a) $\mathcal{L}_1$ and $\mathcal{L}_2$. (b) $\overline{\mathcal{L}_1}$ and $\overline{\mathcal{L}_2}$. (c) $\mathcal{L}_1 \cap \mathcal{L}_2$ and $\mathcal{L}_1 \cup \mathcal{L}_2$. (d) $\mathcal{L}_1 \bullet \mathcal{L}_2$ and $\mathcal{L}_2 \bullet \mathcal{L}_1$. (e) $\mathcal{L}_1^*$ and $\mathcal{L}_2^*$.

Problem 24.23. Suppose $\mathcal{L}_1$ and $\mathcal{L}_2$ are both *not* regular. Prove or disprove that these languages can't be regular:
(a) $\mathcal{L}_1 \cup \mathcal{L}_2$ (b) $\mathcal{L}_1 \cap \mathcal{L}_2$ (c) $\mathcal{L}_1 \bullet \mathcal{L}_2$ (d) $\overline{\mathcal{L}_1}$.

Problem 24.24. Two automata are the *same* if there is an isomorphism between them with (YES)-states mapping to (YES)-states and (NO)-states mapping to (NO)-states. Give two *different* automata which accept the same language.

Problem 24.25 (Counting DFAs). A DFA has *two* states a start state q_0 and another state q_1. The DFA is described by a list of its accept states and a list of its transition instructions. The order in which you list the accept states and the transition instructions does not matter. We draw a DFA as a graph with nodes q_0, q_1 and add a directed arrow for each transition instruction (the accepting states have double circles). How many different DFA's are there with two states? (*Different* DFA's *can* have the same (YES)-set)

Problem 24.26. Give regular expressions to describe each laguage in Problem 24.11.

Problem 24.27. For each language $\mathcal{L}$, give a DFA which accepts $\mathcal{L}$ and a regular expression that describes $\mathcal{L}$.

(a) Strings which contain 00 as a substring.
(b) Strings with at most two 0s.
(c) Strings with at least two 0s.
(d) Strings in which the number of 0s is even and 1s is odd.

Problem 24.28. Find DFAs for languages described by these regular expressions. (The wildcard $*$ stands for Σ^*).

(a) $(\{01\}\cup\{001\})^*$ (b) $\{0\}^*\bullet\overline{(\{10\}\cup\{11\})^*}$ (c) $\{0\}^*\cup\{1\}^*$ (d) $(\{01\}\bullet\{1\}^*)^*$ (e) $*101*1$.

Problem 24.29. Construct a regular expression for the (YES)-set of each DFA.

(a) 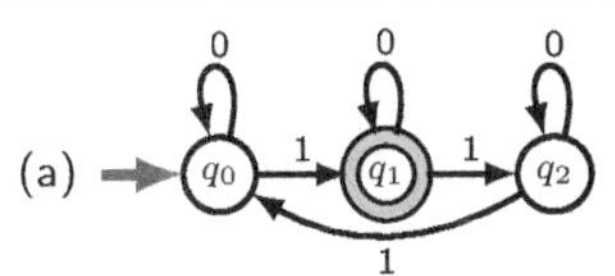

(b) 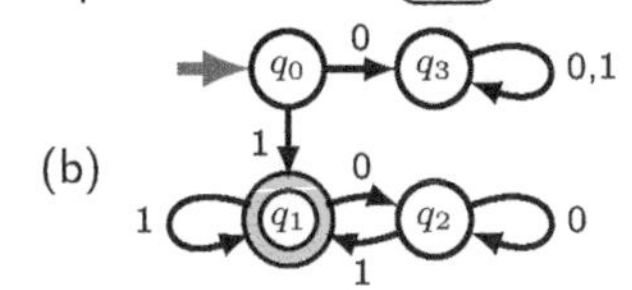

(c) 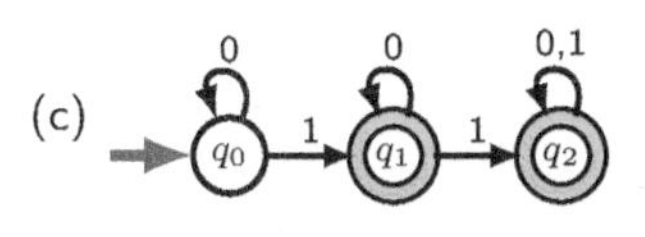

Problem 24.30 (Converting a DFA to a regular expression).

(a) M is the DFA on the right. Show that $\mathcal{L}(M)=\{0,1\}\bullet\{0\}^*\bullet(\{1\}\bullet\{0,1\}\bullet\{0\}^*)^*$.

(b) Develop a systematic way to convert a DFA to a regular expression. Number the states of the DFA $q_0,q_1,\ldots$. Let $\mathcal{L}(M)$ be the set of strings that take the automaton from its start state q_0 to any one of its (YES)-states.

Define the language (set of strings) $\mathcal{L}_k(i,j)$ to be the strings that take the automaton from state q_i to state q_j visiting *only* the states in $\{q_0,q_1,\ldots,q_{k-1}\}$ along the way. $\mathcal{L}_0(i,j)$ are the strings that take q_i directly to q_j without visiting any other state. For strings in $\mathcal{L}_1(i,j)$, the automaton is allowed to visit q_0; for strings in $\mathcal{L}_2(i,j)$, the automaton is allowed to visit states in $\{q_0,q_1\}$; and so on.

(i) What are $\mathcal{L}_0(0,0),\mathcal{L}_0(0,1),\mathcal{L}_0(1,0),\mathcal{L}_0(1,1)$?

(ii) $\mathcal{L}_1(i,j)$ are the strings that take q_i to q_j without visiting any of the states $q_1,q_2,\ldots$. So the only state visited along the way is q_0, if at all. You are certainly allowed to visit none of the other states, so $\mathcal{L}_1(i,j)$ is

$$\mathcal{L}_1(i,j)=\mathcal{L}_0(i,j)\cup\{\text{strings taking } M \text{ from } q_i \text{ to } q_j \text{ that visit } q_0 \text{ and no higher state}\}.$$

Hence, show that $\mathcal{L}_1(i,j)=\mathcal{L}_0(i,j)\cup(\mathcal{L}_0(i,0)\bullet\mathcal{L}_0(0,0)^*\bullet\mathcal{L}_0(0,j))$.

(iii) Use (ii) to obtain regular expressions for $\mathcal{L}_1(0,0),\mathcal{L}_1(0,1),\mathcal{L}_1(1,0),\mathcal{L}_1(1,1)$.

(iv) Find regular expressions for $\mathcal{L}_2(0,0),\mathcal{L}_2(0,1),\mathcal{L}_2(1,0),\mathcal{L}_2(1,1)$ by first showing that

$$L_2(i,j)=\mathcal{L}_1(i,j)\cup(\mathcal{L}_1(i,1)\bullet\mathcal{L}_1(1,1)^*\bullet\mathcal{L}_1(1,j)).$$

(v) Show that $\mathcal{L}(M)=\mathcal{L}_2(0,1)$, and hence give a regular expression for $\mathcal{L}(M)$.

(c) Does the regular expression in (b) use complement or intersection? What is the significance of your answer?

Problem 24.31. Use the method in Problem 24.30 to find regular expressions for each DFA in Problem 24.29.

Problem 24.32. Regular expressions are solved by a DFAs. Prove the converse, that computing problems solvable by DFAs can be described by regular expressions (DFAs and regular expressions are "equivalent"). Prove the theorem:

Theorem 24.4. The (YES)-set of any DFA can be described by some regular expression.

To prove it, generalize Problem 24.30 to an automaton with k states $q_0,\ldots,q_{k-1}$ whose (YES)-states are $q_\ell,\ldots,q_{k-1}$.

(a) Show that $\mathcal{L}_0(i,j)$ is a finite language, hence a regular expression.

(b) Show that for $k\geq 0$, $L_{k+1}(i,j)=\mathcal{L}_k(i,j)\cup(\mathcal{L}_k(i,k)\bullet\mathcal{L}_k(k,k)^*\bullet\mathcal{L}_k(k,j))$.

(c) Prove, by induction on n, that $L_n(i,j)$ can be described by a regular expression for all $i,j=0,1,\ldots,k-1$.

(d) Show that $\mathcal{L}(M)=\cup_{j=\ell}^{k-1}\mathcal{L}_k(0,j)$ and prove Theorem 24.4. (The union is over the (YES)-states $q_\ell,\ldots,q_{k-1}$.)

Problem 24.33. Intersection and complement, though convenient, are not needed for regular expressions. Find a regular expression that *does not* use complement to describe the language $\overline{\{0,01\}^*}$.

(a) Give a DFA for the language $\{0,01\}$.

(b) Give a nondeterministic automaton for the language $\{0,01\}^*$. *[Hint: See Exercise 24.8 on page 355.]*

(c) Use subset-states to convert your automaton in (b) into a DFA.

(d) Construct a DFA to accept the complement of the language accepted by your DFA in (c).

(e) Use the method in Problem 24.32 to find a regular expression for the DFA in (d).

Problem 24.34. Let $\mathcal{L}\subseteq\{0\}^*$ be an infinite language over a unary alphabet, and consider $\mathcal{L}^*$.

(a) Let $\mathcal{L}=\{0^{\bullet 2^n}\mid n\geq 0\}$. Do you think $\mathcal{L}$ is regular? What about $\mathcal{L}^*$?

(b) Show that $\mathcal{L}^*$ is always regular (solvable by a DFA), even if $\mathcal{L}$ is not regular. *[Hint: Problems 23.31 and 23.41.]*

(c) Prove there are *uncountably* many $\mathcal{L}\subset\{0\}^*$ which are *not* regular. *[Hint: Infinite binary strings are uncountable.]*

Problem 24.35. Give an example of two languages neither of which is regular but whose union is regular. You must prove neither language is regular and that the union is regular. Do the same for intersection. What about complement?

Problem 24.36. You have access to the state diagrams (directed graph) of DFAs M_1 and M_2.
(a) How would you determine if $\mathcal{L}(M_1)$ is empty? (b) How would you determine if $\mathcal{L}(M_1) \cap \mathcal{L}(M_2)$ is empty?

Problem 24.37. Let M be a DFA with k states whose language is $\mathcal{L}(M)$. Prove the following.
(a) $\mathcal{L}(M)$ is empty if and only if M accepts no string of length at most $k-1$. *[Hint: Suppose the shortest string M accepts has length $\ell \geq k$. Use the pigeonhole principle to show that M accepts a shorter string.]*
(b) $\mathcal{L}(M)$ is infinite if and only if M accepts some string w whose length satisfies $k \leq \text{length}(w) \leq 2k-1$.
(c) Do either of the claims in (a) or (b) depend on whether the alphabet Σ is binary?

Problem 24.38. A DFA M is provided as a black-box. You can't see any details of M except that M has at most 10 states. You can run M on any input and observe its output (YES) or (NO). Give a method to answer these questions. You may run M on inputs of your choice a finite number of times. Problem 24.37 may be useful.
(a) Is 010101 in $\mathcal{L}(M)$? (b) Is $\mathcal{L}(M)$ empty? (c) Is $\mathcal{L}(M)$ infinite? (d) Does $\mathcal{L}(M)$ contain all strings?

Problem 24.39. Two DFAs M_1 with at most k_1 states and M_2 with at most k_2 states are provided as black-boxes. You can't see any other details of M_1 or M_2. You can run the DFAs on any input and observe their outputs (YES) or (NO). Develop a method to determine whether M_1 and M_2 solve the same problem.
(a) Let $\mathcal{L}_1 = \mathcal{L}(M_1)$ and $\mathcal{L}_2 = \mathcal{L}(M_2)$. What does it mean for M_1 and M_2 to solve the same problem?
(b) The set difference $\mathcal{L}_1 \setminus \mathcal{L}_2 = \{\text{strings in } \mathcal{L}_1 \text{ that are not in } \mathcal{L}_2\}$. Is $\mathcal{L}_1 \setminus \mathcal{L}_2$ regular? *[Hint: $A \setminus B = A \cap \overline{B}$.]*
(c) Use (b) to give a method to determine if $\mathcal{L}_1 = \mathcal{L}_2$. *[Hint: Problem 24.38.]*
(d) For your solution in (c), how many times do you need to run M_1 and M_2. Does it depend on the alphabet size?

Problem 24.40 (Nondeterminism). Answer questions (i)–(iii) for each nondeterministic automaton.

(a) 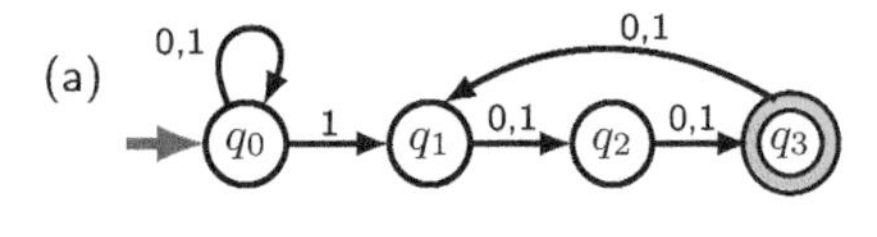

(b) 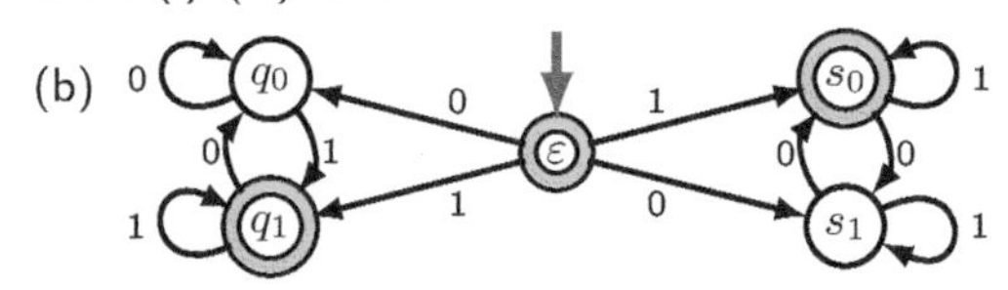

(i) One way to view the computation is that at a nondeterministic step, the automaton guesses how to proceed to the deterministic part of the computation. The automaton has the luxury to always guess correctly and accept the input if it could have been accepted. Use this view to describe in words the task solved by each automaton.
(ii) In a DFA, a computation traces a sequence of states. With nondeterminism, the path branches at every nondeterministic step, creating a tree of states rooted at the start state. Show the computation tree for input 11011.
(iii) Use subset states to convert each nondeterministic automaton to a DFA. For your DFA and the nondeterministic version, show the sequence of states for two (YES)-strings and two (NO)-strings.

Problem 24.41 (Nondeterminism and complement). For a DFA M accepting the language $\mathcal{L}(M)$, we saw that to solve the complement problem $\overline{\mathcal{L}(M)}$, you simply flip the (YES) and (NO) states in M.
(a) Give the automaton obtained by flipping the (YES) and (NO) states of the automaton in Problem 24.40(a).
(b) What is the output for the original automaton and the automaton with states flipped on the input 100?
(c) Articulate why flipping the states does not always the complement language for a nondeterministic automaton.
(d) Give a method to find the automaton for the complement language of a nondeterministic automaton?

Problem 24.42. Find DFAs for the reversal of each language, containing the reversed strings: $\mathcal{L}^{\text{R}} = \{w^{\text{R}} \mid w \in \mathcal{L}\}$.
(a) Strings which end in 1.
(b) Strings which begin in 1 or end in 0.
(c) Strings which do not contain any 0s.
(d) $\mathcal{L} = \{1^{\bullet 2n}01^{\bullet 2k+1} \mid n, k \geq 0\}$.
(e) Strings in which every 0 is adjacent to a 0.
(f) Strings whose adjacent bits are different.
(g) *Non-empty* strings with an even number of 1s.
(h) Strings *not* of the form $0^{\bullet n}1^{\bullet k}$ for $n, k \geq 0$.
(i) Strings which contain 001 as a substring.
(j) Strings which do not contain 001 as a substring.
(k) Strings whose even digits alternate between 0 and 1.
(l) Strings whose odd digits match the previous even digit.

Problem 24.43. For the DFA M, find a DFA M^{R} for the reversal of $\mathcal{L}(M)$.
(a) Follow these steps: (i) Flip the roles of two states. (ii) Change the directions of the arrows. (iii) Is the resulting automaton deterministic? What if a state has no exiting arrow for a particular input-bit? (iv) Find a DFA for $\mathcal{L}(M)^{\text{R}}$.
(b) Find a simpler DFA for $\mathcal{L}(M)^{\text{R}}$ by analyzing the language solved by M.

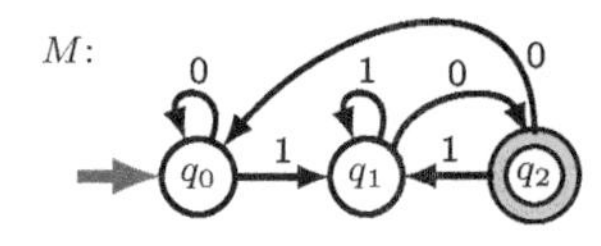

Problem 24.44. Develop a systematic way to go from a DFA for a language to a DFA for the reversal of the language.

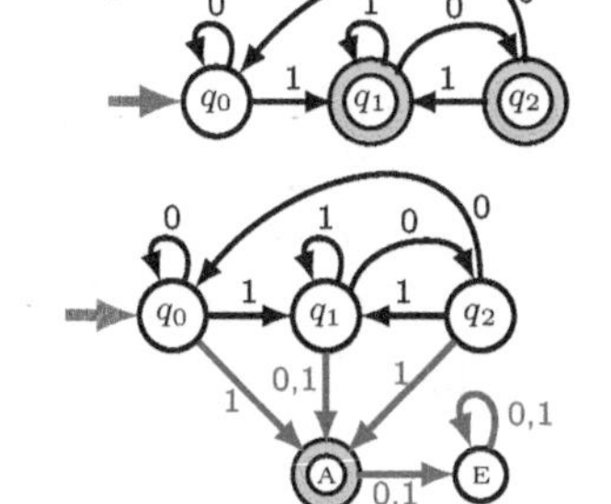

(a) We modified M from Problem 24.43 to M_1, making q_1 also a (YES)-state.
  (i) Does your procedure in part (a) work for creating M_1^{R} to slove $\mathcal{L}(M_1)^{\text{R}}$?
  (ii) Modify M_1 as follows: make q_1 and q_2 (NO)-states, and create two new states, one for accept, A, and one for error, E. Whenever M_1 would have transitioned to an accept state, we *also* allow the new DFA to transition to A. From A, if a new bit arrives, transition to E and remain there. We show the modified automaton below M_1, with newly added arrows in blue. Explain how each new arrow follows from the instructions above.
  (iii) Is the modified automaton deterministic or nondeterministic.
  (iv) Explain why the modified automaton solves the same problem as M_1.
  (v) Use the modified automaton to find a DFA M_1^{R} for $\mathcal{L}(M_1)^{\text{R}}$.

(b) Find a simpler DFA M_{1*}^{R} for $\mathcal{L}(M_1)^{\text{R}}$ by analyzing the language M_1 solves. On all strings of length 4, show the trajectory of states and final decision from M_1, the complex DFA M_1^{R} from part (b) and your simplified DFA M_{1*}^{R}.
(c) If nondeterminism is allowed, prove that an automaton with just one (YES)-state can solve any regular language.
(d) Prove that the reversal of any regular language is also regular.

Problem 24.45. Let $\mathcal{L} = \{$strings with a 1 at some multiple of 3 bits from the end$\}$.
(a) Find a DFA M^{R} for the reversal $\mathcal{L}^{\text{R}}$ and use M^{R} to get a DFA for $\mathcal{L}$ using the methods in Problem 24.44.
(b) Find a nondeterministic automaton for $\mathcal{L}$ and use subset states to convert it to a DFA. (Problem 24.40 may help.)

Problem 24.46. In each case, a language $\mathcal{L}$ is obtained from regular languages $\mathcal{L}_1, \mathcal{L}_2$. Prove that $\mathcal{L}$ is regular. Either give a regular expression for $\mathcal{L}$ or show how to get a DFA for $\mathcal{L}$ from DFAs for $\mathcal{L}_1, \mathcal{L}_2$.
(a) $\mathcal{L} = \{$strings in $\mathcal{L}_1$ which are *not* in $\mathcal{L}_2\}$. (Closure under set-difference.)
(b) $\mathcal{L} = \{$strings which are a prefix of some string in $\mathcal{L}_1\}$. (Closure under prefixing.)
(c) $\mathcal{L} = \{$strings in $\mathcal{L}_1$ which are a prefix of some string in $\mathcal{L}_2\}$. (Closure under prefixing.)
(d) $\mathcal{L} = \{$strings which are a suffix of some string in $\mathcal{L}_1\}$. *[Hint: Reversal.]* (Closure under suffixing.)
(e) $\mathcal{L} = \{$strings in $\mathcal{L}_1$ which are a suffix of some string in $\mathcal{L}_2\}$. (Closure under suffixing.)
(f) $\mathcal{L} = \{$strings whose bits are the odd bits in $\mathcal{L}_1\}$. (Closure under subsampling.)
(g) $\mathcal{L} = \{wx \mid xw \in \mathcal{L}_1\}$. (Closure under flipping.)
(h) $\mathcal{L} = \{$strings in $\mathcal{L}_1$ which do not contain any string in $\mathcal{L}_2$ as a substring$\}$. (Closure under avoidance.)
(i) $\mathcal{L} = \{w \mid w = x_1y_1x_2y_2\cdots x_ky_k$, where $x_1x_2\cdots x_k \in \mathcal{L}_1$ and $y_1y_2\cdots y_k \in \mathcal{L}_2\}$. (Closure under interleaving.)
(j) $\mathcal{L} = \{w \mid wx \in \mathcal{L}_1$ for some x with $|x| = |w|\}$. (Closure under truncation.)
(k) $\mathcal{L} = \{w \mid wx \in \mathcal{L}_1$ for some $x \in B\}$ (Closure under completion using *any* language B.)
[Hint: You can show a DFA exists without actually constructing the DFA.]

Problem 24.47. Prove these problems cannot be solved by DFAs. One method is to use the pigeonhole principle.
(a) $\mathcal{L} = \{0^{\bullet n}1^{\bullet 2^n} \mid n \geq 0\}$.
(b) $\mathcal{L}_{\text{geq}} = \{0^{\bullet n}1^{\bullet k} \mid n \geq 0, k \geq n\}$.
(c) A problem whose (YES)-set is the palindromes.
(d) $\mathcal{L} = \{ww^R|w \in \Sigma^*\}$.
(e) $\mathcal{L} = \{$strings with an equal number of 0s and 1s$\}$.
(f) $\mathcal{L} = \{0^{\bullet 2^n} \mid n \geq 0\}$.
(g) $\mathcal{L} = \{0^{\bullet n^2} \mid n \geq 0\}$.
(h) $\mathcal{L} = \{0^{\bullet n}1^{\bullet m}0^{\bullet n} \mid m, n \geq 0\}$.
(i) $\mathcal{L} = \{0^{\bullet n}1^{\bullet m} \mid m, n \geq 0, m \neq n\}$.
(j) $\mathcal{L} = \{0^{\bullet n}1^{\bullet n+5} \mid n \geq 0\}$.
(k) $\mathcal{L} = \{w \in \Sigma^*$ which are not palindromes$\}$.
(l) $\mathcal{L} = \{wxw \mid w, x \in \Sigma^*\}$.

Problem 24.48. Use closure of regular languages under set operations to prove that each language $\mathcal{L}$ is not regular.
(a) $\mathcal{L} = \{$strings with an equal number of 0s and 1s$\}$. *[Hints: Contradiction. Cosider $\mathcal{L} \cap \{0^{\bullet n}1^{\bullet k} \mid n, k \geq 0\}$.]*
(b) $\mathcal{L} = \{0^{\bullet n}1^{\bullet k} \mid k \geq n\}$. *[Hints: Contradiction. Show that $((\overline{\mathcal{L}} \cap (\{0\}^* \bullet \{1\}^*)) \bullet \{1\}) \cap \mathcal{L} = \{0^{\bullet n}1^{\bullet n} \mid n \geq 1\}$.]*

Problem 24.49. Prove each claim using closure of regular languages under set operations.
(a) If a finite set is removed from or added to a regular language, the resulting language is regular.
(b) If a finite set is removed from or added to a language that is not regular, the resulting language is not regular.

Problem 24.50. Find a DFA to solve each problem, or prove that no such DFA exists.
(a) Strings where the number of 1's is a multiple of 3.
(b) Strings with 3 times as many 0's as 1's.
(c) Strings of the form $0^{\bullet n^2}$ for $n \geq 0$.
(d) Strings of the form $0^{\bullet 2^n}$ for $n \geq 0$.
(e) $\{0^{\bullet 2^n} \mid n \geq 0\}^*$. (Kleene star)
(f) $\{0^{\bullet 2^n} \mid n \geq 1\}^*$. (Kleen star)

Problem 24.51. Appearances can deceive. In each case, find DFAs for two similar looking languages, if possible.
(a) $\mathcal{L}_1 = \{$Strings with 1 at a multiple of 3 from the front$\}$ $\mathcal{L}_2 = \{$Strings with 1 at a multiple of 3 from the end$\}$.
(b) $\mathcal{L}_1 = \{1^{\bullet n}w \mid n \geq 1, w$ has n or more 1's$\}$ $\mathcal{L}_2 = \{1^{\bullet n}w \mid n \geq 1, w$ has n or fewer 1's$\}$.
(c) $\mathcal{L}_1 = \{0^{\bullet n}w0^{\bullet n} \mid n \geq 1, w \in \Sigma^*\}$ $\mathcal{L}_2 = \{0^{\bullet n}1w0^{\bullet n} \mid n \geq 1, w \in \Sigma^*\}$.
(d) $\mathcal{L}_1 = \{0^{\bullet n}1w0^{\bullet n} \mid n \geq 1, w \in \Sigma^*\}$ $\mathcal{L}_2 = \{0^{\bullet n}1w0^{\bullet n} \mid 5 \geq n \geq 1, w \in \Sigma^*\}$.

Problem 24.52. Suppose $\mathcal{L}$ is a regular language and $\mathcal{L}^{\text{R}}$ its reversal. Prove or disprove:
(a) $\mathcal{L}\bullet\mathcal{L}^{\text{R}}$ is regular. (b) $\mathcal{L}_{ww^{\text{R}}} = \{w\bullet w^{\text{R}} \mid w \in \mathcal{L}\}$ is regular. (c) If $\mathcal{L}\bullet\mathcal{L}'$ is regular, then $\mathcal{L}'$ is regular.

Problem 24.53. The language $\mathcal{L}$ distinguishes a string x from a string y iff for some $w \in \Sigma^*$, $x\bullet w \in \mathcal{L}$ and $y\bullet w \notin \mathcal{L}$. Let $\mathcal{L}_1 = \{0^{\bullet n}1^{\bullet k} \mid n, k \geq 0\}$ and $\mathcal{L}_2 = \{0^{\bullet n}1^{\bullet n} \mid n \geq 0\}$.
(a) Find two strings x, y such that $\mathcal{L}_1$ distinguishes x from y. Do the same for $\mathcal{L}_2$.
(b) If $\mathcal{L}$ distinguishes x from y, does it mean $\mathcal{L}$ distinguishes y from x?
(c) Show: If $\mathcal{L}$ is regular and distinguishes x from y, then any DFA for $\mathcal{L}$ ends at different states on inputs x and y.
(d) $\mathcal{L}$ is a distinguisher for a set of strings S iff for every pair of distinct strings $x, y \in S$, either $\mathcal{L}$ distinguishes x from y or $\mathcal{L}$ distinguishes y from x. Find an infinite set S for which $\mathcal{L}_2$ is a distinguisher. Can you do the same for $\mathcal{L}_1$?

Problem 24.54. In each case, find an infinite set S for which the language is a distinguisher (see Problem 24.53).
(a) $\{0^{\bullet n}1^{\bullet k} \mid n \geq 0, k \geq n\}$ (b) $\{ww \mid w \in \Sigma^*\}$ (c) $\{w \mid w \in \Sigma^*, w = w^{\text{R}}\}$ (d) $\{0^{\bullet 2^n} \mid n \geq 0\}$.

Problem 24.55 (Myhill-Nerode Theorem). Suppose a language $\mathcal{L}$ is a distinguisher for a set S.
(a) Suppose $\mathcal{L}$ is regular and M is any DFA for $\mathcal{L}$. Prove that M ends in a different state for every input string in S.
(b) Prove the Myhill-Nerode Theorem: S is infinite if and only if $\mathcal{L}$ is not regular. *[Hint: Contradiction.]*
(c) Prove that the languages in Problem 24.54 are not regular.
(The Myhill-Nerode Theorem generalizes the method of proof we used in the text to show that $\{0^{\bullet n}1^{\bullet n}\}$ is not regular.)

Problem 24.56 (Pumping Lemma). Let M be a DFA with k states and let $w \in \mathcal{L}(M)$ be any string in the (YES)-set having length at least k. Prove that you can represent $w = xyz$ with $y \neq \varepsilon$ and $|xy| \leq k$ such that for all $i \geq 0$, $xy^{\bullet i}z \in \mathcal{L}(M)$ (w can be "pumped", i.e. enlarged, to $xy^{\bullet i}z = \{xz, xyz, xyyz, xyyyx, xyyyyz, \ldots\}$).
(a) Show that as M processes the first k bits of w it visits a state twice at (say) bits i and j, with $0 \leq i < j \leq k$.
(b) Show that you can choose $y = w[i+1]w[i+1]\cdots w[j]$.
(c) Construct a DFA to solve $\{0^{\bullet 2n}1^{\bullet 2m+1} \mid n, m \geq 0\}$.
  (i) How many states did you need? (ii) Give a string in the language and show how it can be pumped.
(d) Can any string in a finite language be pumped? Does this contradict the Pumping Lemma?

Problem 24.57. Use the Pumping Lemma (Problem 24.56) to prove that no DFA solves these languages.
(a) $\mathcal{L} = \{0^{\bullet n}1^{\bullet n} \mid n \geq 0\}$. (b) $\mathcal{L} = \{$balanced strings$\}$. (c) $\mathcal{L} = \{$palindromes$\}$.
[Hint: Prove a contradiction by constructing a string in $\mathcal{L}$ that cannot be pumped.]

Problem 24.58. Prove: A DFA for a *finite* language with a string of length ℓ has more than ℓ states. *[Hint: Pump.]*

Problem 24.59 (Punctuation). Let $\mathcal{L}_1\#\mathcal{L}_2 = \{w_1\#w_2 \mid w_1 \in \mathcal{L}_1, w_2 \in \mathcal{L}_2\}$ (concatenation with a punctuation symbol #). The punctuation symbol does not appear in any strings of $\mathcal{L}_1$ or $\mathcal{L}_2$. Suppose $\mathcal{L}_1$ and $\mathcal{L}_2$ are regular. Show that $\mathcal{L}_1\#\mathcal{L}_2$ is regular. Why is it easier to do concatenation with punctuation than without?

Problem 24.60. Give a high-level d-PDA for $\mathcal{L}_{\text{balanced}} = \{$strings with an equal number of 0's and 1's$\}$.

Problem 24.61. Give a high-level d-PDA for each problem. If it can't be done, give the intuition for why. # is a punctuation symbol to make some languages "easier".
(a) $\mathcal{L}_{\text{geq}} = \{0^{\bullet n}1^{\bullet k} \mid n \geq 0, k \geq n\}$.
(b) $\mathcal{L}_{\times 3} = \{0^{\bullet n}1^{\bullet 3n} \mid n \geq 0\}$.
(c) $\mathcal{L}_{+4} = \{0^{\bullet n}1^{\bullet n+4} \mid n \geq 0\}$.
(f) $\mathcal{L}_{2^n} = \{0^{\bullet 2^n} \mid n \geq 0\}$.
(g) $\mathcal{L}_{n^2} = \{0^{\bullet n^2} \mid n \geq 0\}$.
(h) $\mathcal{L}_{\text{punc-pal}} = \{w\#w^{\text{R}} | w \in \{0,1\}^*\}$.
(f) $\mathcal{L}_{\text{punc-rep}} = \{w\#w | w \in \{0,1\}^*\}$.
(g) $\mathcal{L}_{\text{even-pal}} = \{ww^{\text{R}} | w \in \{0,1\}^*\}$.
(h) $\mathcal{L}_{\text{even-rep}} = \{ww | w \in \{0,1\}^*\}$.

Problem 24.62. A nondeterministic automaton accepts if one possible final state says (YES). Strict nondeterminism requires all possible final states to say (YES). Show that strict-nondeterministic automata solve regular languages.

Problem 24.63 (Nondeterministic PDA). Nondeterminism allows an automaton to pursue multiple paths. This effectively allows the automaton to always "guess" correctly which path to follow to accept a string in the language. Nondeterministic machines can be converted to DFA by tracking the subset of possible states during the computation. What about nondeterministic PDAs? Could a nondeterministic PDA be implemented by a deterministic PDA?

> Changes and progress very rarely are gifts from above. They come out of struggles from below. – **Noam Chomsky**
>
> His sentences didn't seem to have any verbs, which was par for a politician. All nouns, no action. – **Jennifer Crusie**
>
> This is the type of arrant pedantry up with which I will not put. – **Winston Churchill**

Chapter 25

Context Free Grammars

1: Solving a computing problem by "listing out" the language.
2: Rules for Context Free Grammars, and examples.

Solving a computing problem involves recognizing valid strings. You have no problem recognizing "The cat drinks milk" as valid English, and "Dog the hill up the ran" as gibberish. In a pinch, you probably can generate a grammatically valid sentence too. The ability to generate the valid strings of a language is very useful.

Consider the abstract language $\mathcal{L}_{0^n1^n} = \{0^{\bullet n}1^{\bullet n} \mid n \geq 0\}$ and recall our discussion of recursive sets on page 91 in Chapter 7. Here is a recursive definition of $\mathcal{L}_{0^n1^n}$.

① $\varepsilon \in \mathcal{L}_{0^n1^n}$. **[basis]**
② $x \in \mathcal{L}_{0^n1^n} \to 0\bullet x\bullet 1 \in \mathcal{L}_{0^n1^n}$. **[constructor rule]**
③ Nothing else is in $\mathcal{L}_{0^n1^n}$. **[minimality]**

Start with ε and repeatedly apply the constructor rule. We get all the strings in $\mathcal{L}_{0^n1^n}$,

$$\varepsilon \to 01 \to 0011 \to 000111 \to 00001111 \to \cdots$$

Strings in $\mathcal{L}_{0^n1^n}$ are produced starting with the shortest, ε, and increasing in length by 2 bits each time. To test if 0010 is in $\mathcal{L}_{0^n1^n}$, generate the strings of $\mathcal{L}_{0^n1^n}$ in order of length and test each for a match to 0010.[1] At the 4th step, you generate 000111, which is longer than 0010. Now, you can safely output (NO) because the remaining strings in $\mathcal{L}_{0^n1^n}$ are longer than 000111 and cannot possibly match. Our method is slow. For general w, all strings up to length(w) are generated, which can be exponential for some languages. Our focus is on what can and cannot be done, not efficiency.

A context free grammar (CFG) is like a recursive definition of a set. There are rules which specify how the strings are generated. Here is the context free grammar for $\mathcal{L}_{0^n1^n}$.

1: $S \to \varepsilon$ (compare with: $\varepsilon \in \mathcal{L}_{0^n1^n}$)
2: $S \to 0S1$ (compare with: $x \in \mathcal{L}_{0^n1^n} \to 0\bullet x\bullet 1 \in \mathcal{L}_{0^n1^n}$)

The grammar consists of production rules or substitution rules. There are two rules in this case. In parentheses, we show the correspondence with the recursive definition. Each production rule has the form

`variable` $\to$ `expression`,

which means "Replace `variable` on the left with `expression` on the right," no matter where you see the variable, i.e. independent of context. Variables are typically upper case: $P, Q, R, S, T, \ldots$. Each `expression` on the right is a string of variables and terminal characters. The default terminals are $\{\varepsilon, 0, 1\}$, for binary strings. The variable on the left in the first production rule is the start variable. In this case, the start variable is S and it is also the only variable. The process for generating a string is summarized next.

---

[1] We assume there is a machine that can determine whether two strings match, see Problem 24.15.

1: Write down the start variable form the first production rule, typically S.
2: Replace one variable (say) X in the current string with the RHS from a production rule that starts with X. The production rule looks like $X \to$ RHS.
3: Repeat step 2 until no variables remain in the string.

For our CFG, we start with S. Rule 1 gives $S \Rightarrow \varepsilon$ and rule 2 gives $S \Rightarrow 0S1$. The hybrid string $0S1$ contains a variable and terminals. Continuing from $0S1$ gives the strings of $\mathcal{L}_{0^n1^n}$ in order of increasing length:

$$\begin{array}{ccccccccccc} S & \stackrel{2:}{\Longrightarrow} & 0S1 & \stackrel{2:}{\Longrightarrow} & 00S11 & \stackrel{2:}{\Longrightarrow} & 000S111 & \stackrel{2:}{\Longrightarrow} & 0000S1111 & \stackrel{2:}{\Longrightarrow} & \cdots \\ \Downarrow 1: & & \Downarrow 1: & & \Downarrow 1: & & \Downarrow 1: & & \Downarrow 1: & & \\ \varepsilon & & 01 & & 0011 & & 000111 & & 00001111 & & \end{array}$$

The strings generated by a CFG, its language, form a context free language (CFL). For brevity, we collect all production rules for a single variable into one mega-rule which is just a shorthand for the original rules,

$$1{:}\ S \to \varepsilon \mid 0S1$$

The vertical | stands for OR, so S can be replaced by ε OR $0S1$. Let us denote our grammar for $\{0^{\bullet n}1^{\bullet n}\}$ by $\text{CFG}_{0^n1^n}$. Now consider the similar looking grammar, which we denote CFG_{bal},

$$\text{CFG}_{\text{bal}} \qquad 1{:}\ S \to \varepsilon \mid 0S1S \mid 1S0S \tag{25.1}$$

Here is a derivation of the string 0110 in CFG_{bal}. Each step in the derivation is called an inference.

$$\boldsymbol{S} \stackrel{1:}{\Rightarrow} 0S1S \stackrel{1:}{\Rightarrow} 0\boldsymbol{S}11S0S \stackrel{1:}{\Rightarrow} 0\varepsilon 11S0\boldsymbol{S} \stackrel{1:}{\Rightarrow} 0\varepsilon 11\boldsymbol{S}0\varepsilon \stackrel{1:}{\Rightarrow} 0\varepsilon 11\varepsilon 0\varepsilon = 0110$$

We use $S \stackrel{*}{\Rightarrow} 0110$ to mean some derivation starting from S yields 0110. Our derivation has length 5, the number of production rules invoked. In each step the bold variable on the left is replaced by the red string on the right. The rule being used is above the arrow (there is just one production rule). Be aware that the CFG-variable S is not a mathematical-variable. The two occurrences of S in the hybrid string $0S1S$ are replaced independently. The first S becomes ε and the second becomes 10. In contrast, the mathematical-variable x in $0x1x$ is just an unknown string (e.g. $x = 11$ gives **011111**). Think of a CFG-variable as representing a type of string, i.e. a language. Each occurrence of the CFG-variable is replaced by a string of that type.

Pop Quiz 25.1
Can each string be generated by the CFG on the right. If yes, give a derivation.
(a) 0011 (b) 0110 (c) 00011 (d) 010101
Informally describe the context free language generated by the grammar.

$$\begin{aligned} 1{:}\ S &\to \varepsilon \mid T_0T_1 \mid T_0A \\ 2{:}\ X &\to T_0T_1 \mid T_0A \\ 3{:}\ A &\to XT_1 \\ 4{:}\ T_0 &\to 0 \\ 5{:}\ T_1 &\to 1 \end{aligned}$$

Example 25.1 (CFGs for English and programming). Here is a very simplified CFG for English.

1: S → <phrase><verb>
2: <phrase> → <article><noun>
3: <article> → A␣ | The␣
4: <noun> → cat␣ | dog␣
5: <verb> → walks. | runs. | walks.␣S | runs.␣S

The CFG-variables are S, the start variable, and <phrase>,<verb>,<article>,<noun> (we used variable names from English grammar). The terminals are letters, period"." and space "␣" (punctuation). The start variable S represents the language of well formed English sentences. Here is a derivation.

S ⇒(1:) <phrase><verb> ⇒(5:) <phrase>walks. ⇒(2:) <article><noun>walks. ⇒(3:) A␣<noun>walks. ⇒(4:) A␣cat␣walks.

Pop Quiz 25.2
Give a derivation for the string: A␣cat␣runs.␣The␣dog␣walks.

Here is an extremely simplified CFG for declaring and assigning variables in programs.

```
1:          S → <stmt>;S | <stmt>;
2:     <stmt> → <assign> | <declare>
3:  <declare> → int␣<variable>
4:   <assign> → <variable>=<integer>
5:  <integer> → <integer><digit> | <digit>
6:    <digit> → 0 | 1 | 2 | 3 | 4 | 5 | 6 | 7 | 8 | 9
7: <variable> → x | x<variable>
```

The variables are S, <stmt>,<declare>,<assign>,<integer>,<digit>,<variable> and the terminals are digits and some symbols for declaring statements, {;, ␣, x, =, int, 0, 1, 2, 3, 4, 5, 6, 7, 8, 9}.

Exercise 25.3

(a) Give derivations for these snippets of code using the programming grammar:
(i) `int␣x;int␣xx;x=22;xx=8;` (ii) `x=8;int␣x;` (iii) `int␣x;xx=8;`

(b) Which snippets in (a) are correct "programs"? (All three are syntactically valid and derivable within the grammar. Only one is semantically correct.)

(c) White space W is any string of spaces, "␣", or new-lines, "\n". Update the program-CFG to allow white space between statements. (Most programming languages allow white space almost anywhere.)

A programming language like C^{++} has a much more complex grammar than ours, but the basic structure is similar. A valid C^{++} program must follow all rules of C^{++} syntax. That means the program, treated as a gigantic string, must be derivable within the grammar. A compiler determines program validity.[2] □

Let's walk through building a CFG. Creativity is often required, and experience with recursion helps. Consider

$$\mathcal{L}_{\text{bal}} = \{\text{strings with an equal number of 1's and 0's}\}.$$

The start variable S represents a string from $\mathcal{L}_{\text{bal}}$. As with recursive definitions, let's relate the string S to smaller strings. In our case, if S is not ε, then it starts with 0 or 1. Now for the crucial observation. Consider a valid string which starts with 0, for example 001011010110. We can decompose the string as

$$001011010110 = 0\bullet\mathbf{0101}\bullet 1\bullet\mathbf{010110} = 0w_1 1w_2, \qquad \text{where } w_1, w_2 \in \mathcal{L}_{\text{bal}}.$$

We could write $0w_1 1w_2$ as $0S1S$ since each S independently stands for any string in $\mathcal{L}_{\text{bal}}$.

Pop Quiz 25.4

Prove that every non-empty string in $\mathcal{L}_{\text{bal}}$ is $0w_1 1w_2$ or $1w_1 0w_2$ for some $w_1, w_2 \in \mathcal{L}_{\text{bal}}$.

Every large string in $\mathcal{L}_{\text{bal}}$ is formed recursively from smaller ones. The production rules $S \to 0S1S$ and $S \to 1S0S$ capture this recursion. The colors emphasize that all the S's can be different. The red S stands for the big string in $\mathcal{L}_{\text{bal}}$. The blue and green S's stand for independent smaller strings in $\mathcal{L}_{\text{bal}}$. There is no other way to get a string in $\mathcal{L}_{\text{bal}}$, and so we arrive at the production rules for CFG$_{\text{bal}}$ in (25.1),

$$\text{CFG}_{\text{bal}} \qquad\qquad S \to \varepsilon \mid 0S1S \mid 1S0S.$$

Does the grammar work? Does CFG$_{\text{bal}}$ generate all strings in $\mathcal{L}_{\text{bal}}$ and only those strings? Can we prove:

(i) Every string generated by CFG$_{\text{bal}}$ is in $\mathcal{L}_{\text{bal}}$?
(ii) Every string in $\mathcal{L}_{\text{bal}}$ can be derived by CFG$_{\text{bal}}$?

The intuition for (i) is that every production rule adds the same number of 0's and 1's, maintaining balance. To prove (ii), we use the fact that any balanced string can be built from smaller balanced strings. So, if the smaller balanced strings can be derived, then so can the large one. Here is the formal proof that CFG$_{\text{bal}}$ works.

[2] Compilers also ensure semantic correctness. The phrases "A cat barks." and "A dog barks." are both syntactically correct English, but only the latter is semantically correct (meaningful). Semantic correctness is context sensitive, not context free: "bark" is allowed in the context of "dog", not "cat". We won't discuss context sensitive grammars.

(i) If $S \overset{*}{\Rightarrow} w$, then $w \in \mathcal{L}_{bal}$. We use strong induction on the length of the derivation, that is the number of production rules invoked. The base case is 1 step, producing ε. For the induction step, let $\ell > 0$ and assume every derivation of length less than ℓ yields a string in $\mathcal{L}_{\text{bal}}$. Consider any derivation of length ℓ yielding string w. We must show that $w \in \mathcal{L}_{\text{bal}}$. The derivation must start

$$S \to 0S1S \to \cdots \qquad \text{or} \qquad S \to 1S0S \to \cdots$$

Both cases are similar so we just analyze the first. Each instance of S will follow a shorter derivation to yield two (independent) strings. That is, $w = 0x1y$ with $S \overset{*}{\Rightarrow} x$, $S \overset{*}{\Rightarrow} y$ and the derivations of x and y are shorter than ℓ. By the induction hypothesis, $x, y \in \mathcal{L}_{\text{bal}}$ and so have an equal number of 0's and 1's. Since w adds a 1 and a 0 to x and y, w has the same number of 0's and 1's and is in $\mathcal{L}_{\text{bal}}$, concluding the induction.

(ii) If $w \in \mathcal{L}_{bal}$, then $S \overset{*}{\Rightarrow} w$. We use strong induction on the length of the string. Base case is ε and clearly $S \overset{*}{\Rightarrow} \varepsilon$. For the induction step, assume every string of length less than ℓ can be derived and consider any string w in $\mathcal{L}_{\text{bal}}$ of length ℓ. By Pop Quiz 25.4, either $w = 0w_1 1w_2$ or $w = 1w_1 0w_2$, where w_1, and w_2 are in $\mathcal{L}_{\text{bal}}$ and have length less than ℓ. By the induction hypothesis, $S \overset{*}{\Rightarrow} w_1$ and $S \overset{*}{\Rightarrow} w_2$. We get w using:

$$S \Rightarrow 0S1S \overset{*}{\Rightarrow} 0w_1 1S \overset{*}{\Rightarrow} 0w_1 1w_2 \qquad \text{or} \qquad S \Rightarrow 1S0S \overset{*}{\Rightarrow} 1w_1 0S \overset{*}{\Rightarrow} 1w_1 0w_2.$$

We used the steps in $S \overset{*}{\Rightarrow} w_1$ on the red S and the steps in $S \overset{*}{\Rightarrow} w_2$ on the blue S.

Exercise 25.5

(i) Give CFGs for each language $\mathcal{L}$. Prove you can derive (ii) only strings in $\mathcal{L}$, and (iii) every string in $\mathcal{L}$.

(a) $\mathcal{L} = \{1^{\bullet k} \mid k \geq 0\}$.
(b) $\mathcal{L} = \{\text{strings ending in } 1\}$.
(c) $\mathcal{L} = \{\text{strings containing } 00\}$.
(d) $\mathcal{L} = \{1^{\bullet n}0^{\bullet n} \mid n \geq 0\}$.
(e) $\mathcal{L} = \{1^{\bullet k}0^{\bullet k}1^{\bullet \ell} \mid k, \ell \geq 0\}$.
(f) $\mathcal{L} = \{\text{palindromes}\}$.

Union, Concatenation and Kleene star. It is surprisingly easy to combine CGFs to get the union or concatenation of context free languages. Here is an example. Let

$$\mathcal{L}_1 = \{0^{\bullet n}1^{\bullet n} \mid n \geq 0\} \qquad \text{and} \qquad \mathcal{L}_2 = \{1^{\bullet n}0^{\bullet n} \mid n \geq 0\}.$$

These two are context free languages, respectively generated by the two grammars

$$A \to \varepsilon \mid 0A1 \qquad \text{and} \qquad B \to \varepsilon \mid 1B0.$$

For union, we use the trick $S \to A \mid B$. CFG-variables represent strings of a particular type, so, S becomes a string of type A or B. For concatenation, instead of $S \to A \mid B$, we use the trick $S \to AB$, so S becomes a string from A followed by a string from B. The grammars for A and B must not use any of the same variables.

$\mathcal{L}_1 \cup \mathcal{L}_2$:
1: $S \to A \mid B$
2: $A \to \varepsilon \mid 0A1$
3: $B \to \varepsilon \mid 1B0$

$\mathcal{L}_1 \bullet \mathcal{L}_2$:
1: $S \to AB$
2: $A \to \varepsilon \mid 0A1$
3: $B \to \varepsilon \mid 1B0$

In addition to union and concatenation, context free languages are also closed under Kleene star (next exercise). Unfortunately they are not closed under intersection or complement.

Exercise 25.6 [Union, Concatenation and Kleene star]

Give CFGs for the following languages.

(a) $\mathcal{L} = \{\text{strings containing 0 or } 1\}$.
(b) $\mathcal{L} = \{0^{\bullet k}1^{\bullet k+\ell}0^{\bullet \ell} \mid k, \ell \geq 0\}$.
(c) $\mathcal{L}^*$ where $\mathcal{L} = \{0^{\bullet n}1^{\bullet n} \mid n \geq 0\}$.
(d) $\mathcal{L} = \{\text{strings not containing } 00\}$.

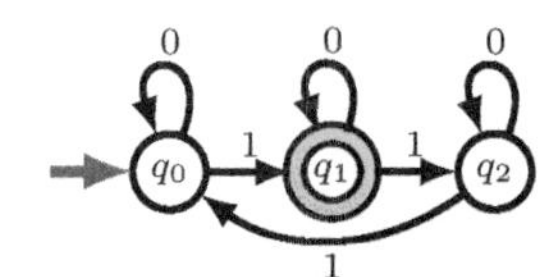

Example 25.2 (CFGs can implement DFAs). CFGs are more powerful than DFAs. The DFA on the right accepts strings whose number of 1s is $3k+1$ for $k = 0, 1, 2, \ldots$. We can build a CFG from the DFA. Define three types of strings, Q_0, Q_1 and Q_2 which are the strings accepted by the DFA starting from states q_0, q_1 and q_2 respectively.

The language of the automaton is Q_0 because the automaton starts in state q_0. Let's build a string in Q_0. Such a string is accepted from state q_0. If the first bit is 0, the automaton remains in q_0 hence the string must be of the form $0Q_0$. If the first bit is 1, the automaton moves to q_1 hence the string must be of the form $1Q_1$. That is, Q_0 has the form $0Q_0$ or $1Q_1$. Here is the beginning of our CFG,

$$Q_0 \rightarrow 0Q_0 \mid 1Q_1.$$

Now, lets build a string in Q_1. If it starts with 0, the string is of the form $0Q_1$; if it starts with 1, it is of the form $1Q_2$. Lastly, since Q_1 is a (YES)-state, $\varepsilon \in Q_1$. Summarizing,

$$Q_1 \rightarrow \varepsilon \mid 0Q_1 \mid 1Q_2.$$

Using a similar reasoning for Q_2 gives the rule $Q_2 \rightarrow 0Q_2 \mid 1Q_0$. Combining the rules gives the full grammar,

$$\begin{aligned} &1: Q_0 \rightarrow 0Q_0 \mid 1Q_1 \\ &2: Q_1 \rightarrow \varepsilon \mid 0Q_1 \mid 1Q_2 \\ &3: Q_2 \rightarrow 0Q_2 \mid 1Q_0 \end{aligned} \tag{25.2}$$

The start variable is Q_0. For illustration, we derive 0110011 using our grammar,

$$Q_0 \Rightarrow 0Q_0 \Rightarrow 01Q_1 \Rightarrow 011Q_2 \Rightarrow 0110Q_2 \Rightarrow 01100Q_2 \Rightarrow 011001Q_0 \Rightarrow 0110011Q_1 \Rightarrow 0110011$$

The CFG in (25.2) is quite special. All production rules replace a variable with a string containing at most one other variable at the rightmost end. Such grammars are called right-linear. □

Exercise 25.7 [Chomsky Normal Form]

Different CFGs can generate the same CFL. Chomsky Normal Form is useful because all derivations only involve primitive steps. For an example, see Pop Quiz 25.1. A grammar is in Chomsky Normal Form if:

- The start variable does not appear on the RHS of any rule.
- Only the start variable may be replaced by ε.
- Every rule has the form $A \rightarrow BC$ or $A \rightarrow t$, where B, C are variables and t is a terminal.

(a) Give an equivalent grammar in Chomsky Normal Form for the CFG $S \rightarrow \varepsilon \mid 0S1S \mid 1S0S$.
(b) For the Chomsky Normal Form, show that deriving a string of length $\ell > 0$ takes $2\ell - 1$ steps.
(c) How does (b) help with recognizing if an input belongs to a context free language.

25.1 Parse Trees

Consider the language $\mathcal{L}_{0^n\#1^n} = \{0^{\bullet n}\#1^{\bullet n} \mid n \geq 0\}$, which is basically $\mathcal{L}_{0^n1^n}$ with punctuation separating 0s from 1s, which doesn't materially change the computing problem. Here is a CFG for $\mathcal{L}_{0^n\#1^n}$,

$$S \rightarrow \# \mid 0S1,$$

with terminals $\{0, 1, \#\}$. Here is a derivation of 000#111,

$$S \Rightarrow 0S1 \Rightarrow 00S11 \Rightarrow 000S111 \Rightarrow 000\#111$$

We build the parse tree as follows. The start variable is the root of the parse tree. Each step in the derivation creates a new branch from the variable being replaced to children, one child for each token on the RHS of the production rule. The left-to-right order of the children matches the order in the production rule. Here is the parse tree, built up step by step for the derivation above. We show the full parse tree in a box on the right.

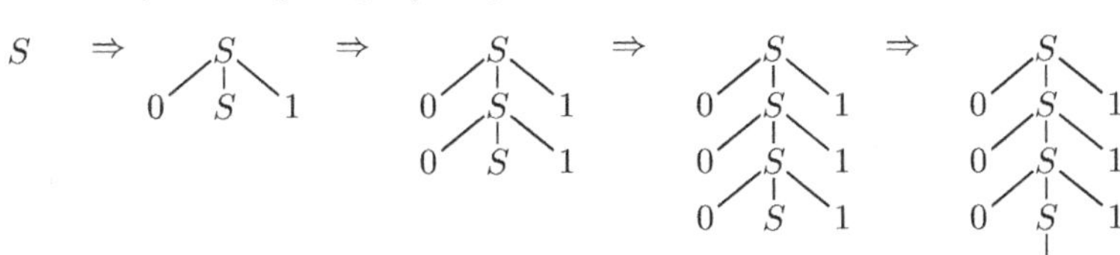

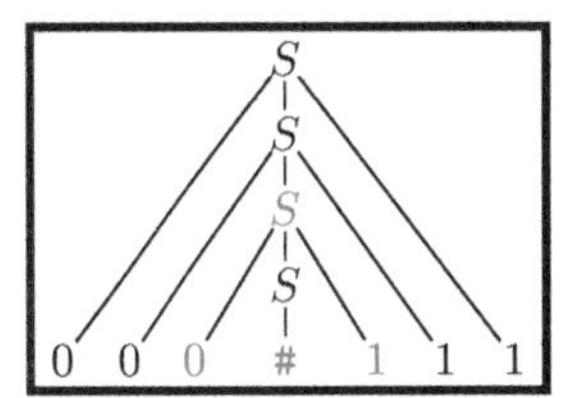

The leaves of the full tree in left-to-right order form the final string. The parse tree is more informative than a derivation because it shows how a substrings results from its parent variable. For example, the red substring is formed from the leaves of the child-subtree produced by the red parent variable.

A string can have multiple derivations each with their own parse tree. These parse trees may or may not be different. Consider this grammar for a language of arithmetic expressions involving 2,

$$S \to S+S \mid S\times S \mid (S) \mid 2 \tag{25.3}$$

with terminals $\{+, \times, (,), 2\}$. Some strings derivable in this grammar are $2+2$, $2+2\times 2$ and $(2+2)\times(2+2+2)$. In the next quiz, you'll show that these two different derivations of $2+2$ have the same parse tree,

$$\begin{aligned} S &\Rightarrow S+S \Rightarrow 2+S \Rightarrow 2+2 \\ S &\Rightarrow S+S \Rightarrow S+2 \Rightarrow 2+2 \end{aligned} \tag{25.4}$$

Pop Quiz 25.8
Give the two parse trees for the different derivations of $2+2$ above. You should get the same parse tree.

The parse tree gives a useful interpretation of a string's structure within the context of the grammar. Consider $2+2\times 2$. Here are two derivations along with parse trees,

$$S \Rightarrow S+S \Rightarrow S+S\times S \overset{*}{\Rightarrow} 2+2\times 2 \qquad\qquad S \Rightarrow S\times S \Rightarrow S+S\times S \overset{*}{\Rightarrow} 2+2\times 2$$

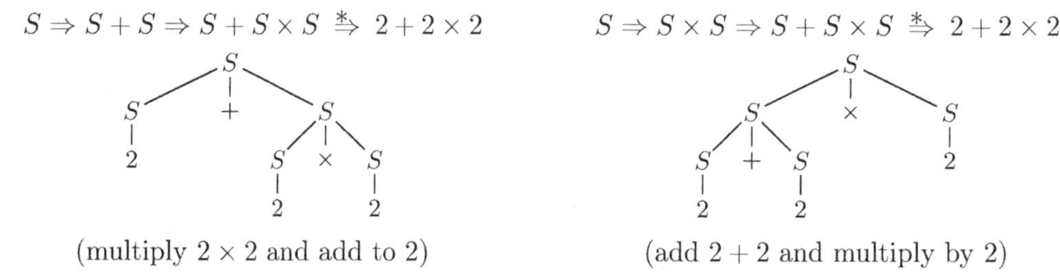

(multiply 2×2 and add to 2) (add $2+2$ and multiply by 2)

The parse trees are different, reflecting different arithmetic interpretations of $2+2\times 2$ as either $2+(2\times 2)=6$ or $(2+2)\times 2=8$. Is the answer 6 or 8? The standard rules of precedence say 6, matching the left parse tree. It is unsettling when $2+2\times 2$ has different parse trees, which leads to ambiguity in interpreting the string.

Parse trees should be unique for strings to have precise meaning. Here is another grammar for arithmetic.

$$\begin{aligned} &1{:}\ S \to P \mid S+P \\ &2{:}\ P \to T \mid P\times T \\ &3{:}\ T \to 2 \mid (S) \end{aligned} \tag{25.5}$$

The language of this grammar is the same as the language of the original grammar in (25.3). That the grammars in (25.5) and (25.3) generate the same strings is not a given and has to be proved (see Problem 25.15). The advantage of the new grammar in (25.5) is that the precedence rules of arithmetic are embedded within. For example, there is only one parse tree for $2+2\times 2$. Here is a derivation, and *the* parse tree

$$\begin{aligned} S &\Rightarrow S+P \\ &\Rightarrow S+P\times T \\ &\Rightarrow P+P\times T \\ &\Rightarrow P+T\times T \\ &\Rightarrow T+T\times T \\ &\overset{*}{\Rightarrow} 2+2\times 2 \end{aligned}$$

How does the grammar in (25.5) embed the precedence rules of arithmetic? The first rule, $S \to P \mid S+P$, is crucial. This rule produces an expression as a sum of "products" of type P,

$$S \Rightarrow S+P \Rightarrow S+P+P \Rightarrow \cdots \Rightarrow S+P+P+\cdots+P \Rightarrow P+P+P+\cdots+P.$$

The product sub-expressions are derived and then added.[3] A product sub-expression is a product of terms of type T generated by the rule $P \to T \mid P\times T$, where a term is either "2" or another expression S in parentheses.

Example 25.3 (Programming and Markup Languages)**.** CFGs were invented by Noam Chomsky to formalize linguistic structure. Today, CFG's and parse trees have become indispensable to computer science. Whenever data must be structured so that it can be interpreted and processed later, CFGs play a central role in defining the structure, and the parse tree is instrumental for interpreting a string to get its meaning.

[3]Expression parse trees are evaluated using post-order traversal: deeper operations are evaluated first.

We gave a baby programming grammar in Example 25.1. Naturally, a full grammar would be very complex. Such formal grammars are essential for defining a programming language's syntax. In compilers, parse trees are the data structure of choice for analyzing a program (huge string). Parse trees facilitate the translation of the program into machine-level code, which tells the CPU how to interpret and execute the program as instructions – the program's meaning. Markup languages, like `HTML` and `XML`, have a document-type-definition (DTD) which is essentially a CFG that produces structured strings like:

```
<p>I <em>hate</em>:<ul><li>spinach</li><li>cats</li></ul></p>
```

A browser will then interpret i.e. parse this `HTML` code and render it as a webpage similar to:

I hate:
- spinach
- cats

Program strings should have unique parse trees so that programs are unambiguously interpreted into to a sequence of instructions. Similarly, `HTML` code should render unambiguously as a webpage. If a grammar is carefully engineered, then it is often possible to ensure that strings have unique parse trees. □

Exercise 25.9
(a) Give another derivation of $2 + 2 \times 2$ using the CFG in (25.5), and its parse tree.
(b) Give derivations of $(2 + 2) \times (2 + 2 \times 2)$ using the CFGs in (25.5) and (25.3).
(c) Consider the CFG $S \to \varepsilon \mid 1 \mid SS$.
  (i) Give two different derivations of 111 with different parse trees.
  (ii) For the same language, construct a grammar that has unique parse trees.

25.2 Pushdown Automata (PDA)

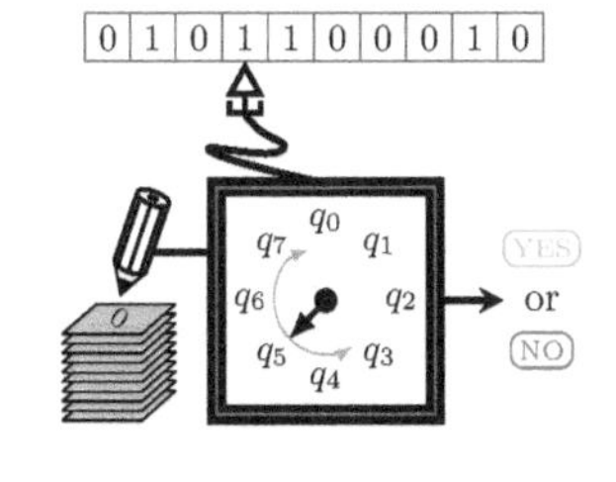

In Section 24.3 we introduced the d-PDA, a DFA with stack memory, to solve equality, an impossible task without a stack. When there is a stack, the DFA transitions state and/or performs an operation to the top of the stack (pop, push or replace), depending on its current state, the input and the top of the stack. To save energy for Turing Machines, we won't delve deep into d-PDA, but let's explore some of their capabilities and the relationship to context free languages. The stack enables a DFA to solve $\mathcal{L}_{0^n1^n} = \{0^{\bullet n}1^{\bullet n}\}$. A CFG can generate $\mathcal{L}_{0^n1^n}$ too, $S \to \varepsilon \mid 0S1$.

Consider the palindromes with a punctuation symbol # to separate w from its reversal w^{R},

$$\mathcal{L}_{\text{punc-pal}} = \{w\#w^{\mathrm{R}} \mid w \in \{0,1\}^*\}.$$

Recall that w^{R} is the reverse of w, so $01001^{\mathrm{R}} = 10010$. A non-empty string w either starts with a 0 or a 1, so we can write $w = 0x$ or $w = 1x$ for some $x \in \Sigma^*$. We then have

$$w\#w^{\mathrm{R}} = 0x\#x^{\mathrm{R}}0 \qquad \text{or} \qquad w\#w^{\mathrm{R}} = 1x\#x^{\mathrm{R}}1.$$

Since $x\#x^{\mathrm{R}} \in \mathcal{L}_{\text{punc-pal}}$, a large string in $\mathcal{L}_{\text{punc-pal}}$ can be built from smaller strings in $\mathcal{L}_{\text{punc-pal}}$ by either adding a 0 at both ends or a 1 at both ends. This suggests that a CFG for $\mathcal{L}_{\text{punc-pal}}$ would be

$$S \to \# \mid 0S0 \mid 1S1. \tag{25.6}$$

We encourage you to prove that this CFG does generate all and only the strings in $\mathcal{L}_{\text{punc-pal}}$.

Pop Quiz 25.10
Give a derivation and parse tree for 011#110 using the grammar in (25.6).

To solve $\mathcal{L}_{\text{punc-pal}}$, a d-PDA would use the stack to store w. Then, after reading in #, it matches the forthcoming bits of w^{R} with the bits on the stack, as it pops the stack. Here is an illustration with $w = 01\#10$.

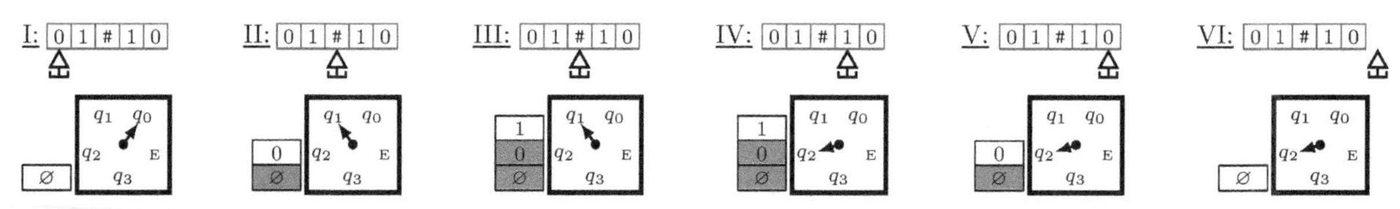

I: Start in state q_0 at the first input bit with the stack empty, denoted by $\varnothing$.
II: Push the first bit onto the stack and transition to a "reading-in-w" state q_1.
III: Push all bits of w onto the stack while staying in state q_1.
IV: On reading in # transition to a "checking-w^{R} state q_2
V: Pop the stack as long as the input matches the top of the stack, and stay in state q_2.
VI: At the end (input is EOF), accept if the stack is empty (as is the case here).

We omitted several details such as what to do if there is no # or multiple #'s in the input, etc. You may fill in these details by converting our high-level description to low level machine-code for the full d-PDA.

Exercise 25.11

Review Section 24.3 and Exercise 24.12 on page 357. We started to draw a d-PDA for $w\#w^{\text{R}}$. Directed edges link the current state to the next state of a transition. Edge labels show the input bit and stack symbol ($\varnothing$ for empty stack) which cause the transition, and the stack operation to be performed.

(a) Complete the machine-level description of the d-PDA.

(b) Show algebraic traces for inputs $0110, 01\#01, 01\#10$. (At each step, the trace should show the status of the automaton, the bits processed and the bits that remain. What else should the status of the automaton capture?)

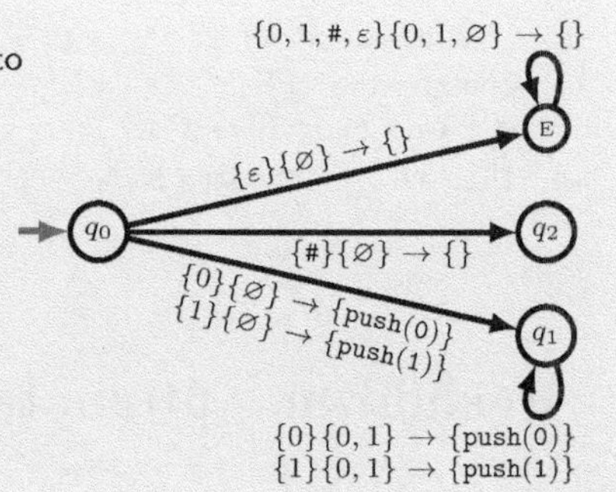

Now for a twist. Remove the punctuation and solve ww^{R}. Modify the grammar in (25.6) to $S \to \varepsilon \mid 0S0 \mid 1S1$ and you generate all strings of the form ww^{R}. That was painless. Can a DFA with stack memory solve this problem? No! The punctuation tells the automaton when to stop pushing bits onto the stack and start popping to check the reversal. Our deterministic automaton with a stack has run up against a wall.

Nondeterminism to the rescue. We mentioned nondeterminism in Section 24.1 when discussing how to solve the concatenation of two regular languages given by DFAs M_1 and M_2. We used M_1 to recognize a prefix in $\mathcal{L}(M_1)$ and then M_2 to test if the remaining suffix was in $\mathcal{L}(M_2)$. The challenge was to figure out when the correct suffix begins, i.e., when to stop using M_1 and switch over to M_2. The solution was nondeterminism, which allows the automaton to try both actions. We have a similar issue here. The automaton does not know when w^{R} begins i.e., when to stop pushing and start popping. The solution is similar. Allow the automaton at every step to follow two paths: push, in case w is continuing; or, pop, in case w^{R} is starting. Such a PDA is nondeterministic. We won't get into the details, but a nondeterministic PDA can solve ww^{R}.

Determinism is not essential for automata because one can use subset states to convert a nondeterministic automaton to a DFA, see Exercise 24.7. This not true for nondeterministic PDA: ww^{R} can only be solved by a nondeterministic PDA, not a deterministic PDA. Every CFL can be solved by a nondeterministic PDA and every nondeterministic PDA solves a CFL, so nondeterministic PDAs and CFLs are equivalent. The proof of this claim is beyond our scope. Let us instead ask whether CFLs are the end of our journey.

25.3 Provably Not Context Free

We are now at the cross-roads where we ask if there are important problems that CFGs cannot solve. CFGs are very powerful and important in computer science. For example, they are the basis for compilers, `HTML`, etc.

Unfortunately, there are also some simple important problems which CFGs cannot solve.

repetition	multiple-equality	squaring	exponentiation
$\{w\#w\}$	$\{0^{\bullet n}1^{\bullet n}0^{\bullet n}\}$	$\{0^{\bullet n^2}\}, \{0^{\bullet n}1^{\bullet n^2}\}$	$\{0^{\bullet 2^n}\}, \{0^{\bullet n}1^{\bullet 2^n}\}$

Are we certain no CFG solves any of the above problems? Just as we used the pigeonhole principle to show that there is no DFA that solves $0^{\bullet n}1^{\bullet n}$, one can use pigeonhole to show that the above languages are not solvable by CFGs (see the Pumping Lemma in Problem 25.29). Without giving technical details, let's see the intuition by asking how a PDA could solve $w\#w^{\text{R}}$, $w\#w$ and $0^{\bullet n}1^{\bullet n}0^{\bullet n}$. The punctuation is added so that we do not have to deal with nondeterminism.

$w\#w^{\text{R}}$

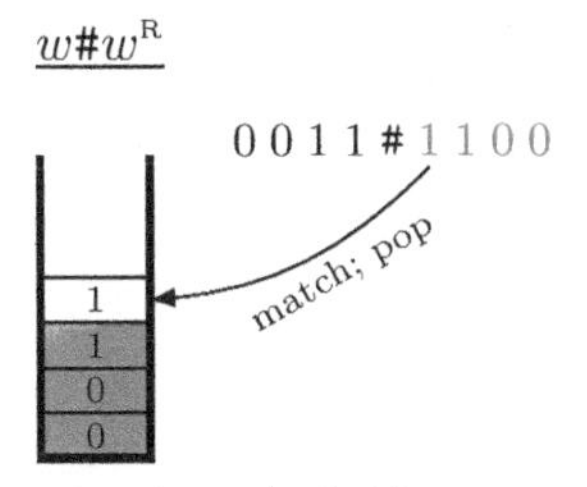

0011 is pushed. To process 1100, pop and match the bits at the top of the stack. No problem here.

$w\#w$

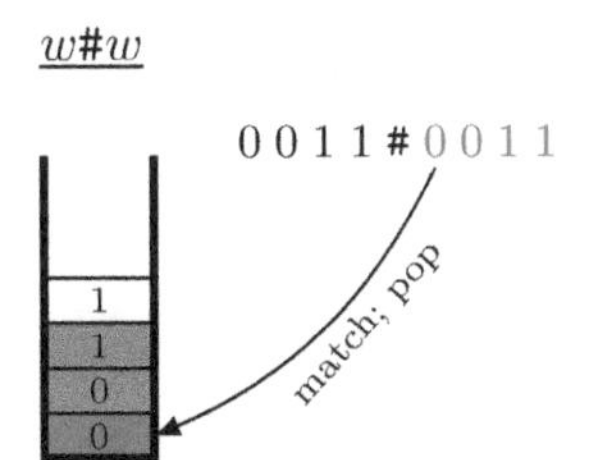

0011 is pushed. To process 0011, we need access to bits at the bottom of the stack (not possible).

$0^{\bullet n}1^{\bullet n}0^{\bullet n}$

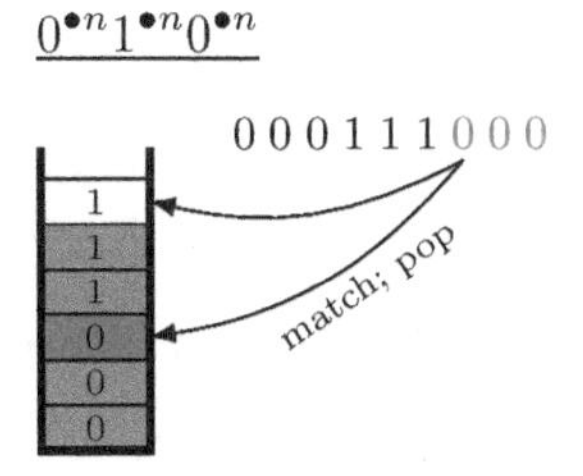

000111 is pushed. To process 000, match each 0 to a 1 (on top) and a 0 in the middle (not possible).

The PDA can't solve $w\#w$ and $0^{\bullet n}1^{\bullet n}0^{\bullet n}$ because it only has access to the top of the stack, but needs to check bits at other positions. An external memory or scratch-pad with top-only access is not enough. We need a form of random access memory, a storage which the automaton can browse to find what it needs.

> The file clerk who only has access to the top of a stack of papers has fundamentally less power than the file clerk who has a filing cabinet with access to all the papers.

Exercise 25.12 [CFLs are not closed under intersection]

CFLs are closed under union, concatenation and Kleene star. You can now prove that CFLs are not closed under intersection and complement. You may assume that $\mathcal{L} = \{0^{\bullet n}1^{\bullet n}0^{\bullet n} \mid n \geq 0\}$ is not context free.

(a) Prove that $\mathcal{L}_1 = \{0^{\bullet n}1^{\bullet n}0^{\bullet m} \mid m, n \geq 0\}$ and $\mathcal{L}_2 = \{0^{\bullet m}1^{\bullet n}0^{\bullet n} \mid m, n \geq 0\}$ are both context free.

(b) What is the intersection, $\mathcal{L}_1 \cap \mathcal{L}_2$? Hence, prove that CFLs are not closed under intersection.

(c) Use part (c) and closure under union to prove that CFLs are not closed under complement.

To solve $w\#w$, $0^{\bullet n}1^{\bullet n}0^{\bullet n}$, and many other problems, we need a new computing model. We need a DFA with a random access memory (`RAM`). We summarize our current state of affairs in a picture, a zoo of acronyms.

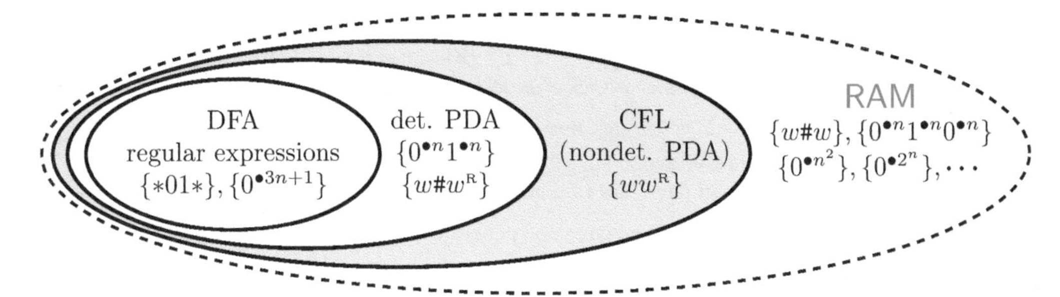

This new model of computing that we seek, a DFA with RAM, is called a Turing Machine.

25.4 Problems

Problem 25.1. Consider the ambiguous sentence "I love to cook my family and my dog."
(a) Use knowledge of English and parse trees to show two possible meanings of the sentence, one of them quite eerie.
(b) In English grammer, we use punctuation to distinguish between these parse trees, and hence convey the correct meaning. Give the punctuated sentences for each possible interpretation.

Problem 25.2. Give English descriptions for the languages generated by each CFGs:
(a) $S \to S$ (b) $S \to 0S \mid 1S1S \mid \epsilon$ (c) $S \to \varepsilon \mid 0 \mid 1 \mid SS$ (d) $S \to A00A$, $A \to \varepsilon \mid 0 \mid 1 \mid AA$ (e) $S \to 0S1 \mid 1A \mid A0$, $A \to \varepsilon \mid 0A \mid 1A$

Problem 25.3. Use the descriptions of each language in Problem 25.2 to give a CFG for the complement language.

Problem 25.4. Rewrite the CFG on the right with all production rules for a variable on one line.
(a) Give a string in this CFL with length longer than 5 and give a string *not* in this CFL.
(b) Describe the language in words.
(c) Give a Chomsky Normal Form for the grammar (see also Exercise 25.7).

$S \to 00S1$
$T \to 0S1$
$S \to 0T$
$S \to 01 \mid \epsilon$

Problem 25.5. Give a Chomsky Normal Form for each grammar in Problem 25.2 (see also Exercise 25.7).

Problem 25.6. Give a parse tree and derivation of 001011001 for CFG $S \to 0S \mid 1S1S \mid \epsilon$. What is the language?

Problem 25.7. Give a DFA and a CFG for each problem.
(a) $\mathcal{L} = \{01^{\bullet n} | n \geq 0\}$ (b) $\mathcal{L} = \{0^{\bullet n}1^{\bullet n} | 0 \leq n \leq 5\}$ (c) $\mathcal{L} =$ {strings which end in a 1}.

Problem 25.8. Find CFGs for these languages.
(a) $\{0^{\bullet n}1^{\bullet n+k} \mid n, k \geq 0\}$.
(b) Strings of the form $0^{\bullet 3n}$ for $n \geq 0$.
(c) Strings of the form $0^{\bullet n}1^{\bullet 3n+1}$ for $n \geq 0$.
(d) Strings with an even number of 1's.
(e) Strings with at least three 1s.
(f) Strings with more 0s than 1s.
(g) Strings *not* of the form $0^{\bullet n}1^{\bullet n}$.
(h) Strings with twice as many 0s as 1s.
(i) $\{0^{\bullet m}1^{\bullet n} \mid m \neq n\}$.
(j) $\{0^{\bullet n} \mid n$ is *not* a multiple of 3$\}$.
(k) $\{0^{\bullet m}1^{\bullet n} \mid n \neq m$ and $n \neq 3m\}$.
(l) Strings with a 1 before a 0, that is $*1*0*$.
(m) Strings with an odd number of bits and middle bit 0.
(n) Strings whose first and last bit are the same.
(o) $\{0^{\bullet n}1^{\bullet m} \mid 0 \leq n \leq m \leq 2n\}$.
(p) $\{0^{\bullet n}1^{\bullet m}0^{\bullet m}1^{\bullet n} \mid n, m \geq 0\} \cup \{0^{\bullet n}1^{\bullet m}0^{\bullet n+m} \mid n, m \geq 0\}$.
(q) $\{0^{\bullet m}1^{\bullet n}0^{\bullet \ell} \mid m, n, \ell \geq 0$ and $(n \neq m$ OR $n \neq \ell)\}$.
(r) Strings $w\#v$ where w^{R} is a substring of v.
(s) All palindromes w where $w = w^{\text{R}}$ (not only of the form ww^{R}).
(t) Strings which are not palindromes.
(u) Strings not of the form ww (non-equality).
(v) Strings in which every prefix has at least as many 0s as 1s.

Problem 25.9. Construct CFGs for these languages using union and/or concatenation.
(a) $\{0^{\bullet n}1^{\bullet k}0^{\bullet m} \mid n, m \geq 0$ and $k > n + m\}$.
(b) $\{0^{\bullet n}1^{\bullet n}0^{\bullet n} \mid n \geq 0\}$.
(c) $\{0^{\bullet n}1^{\bullet k}0^{\bullet m} \mid n, m \geq 0$ and $k > n + 1\}$.
(d) Strings with an unequal number of 0s and 1s.

Problem 25.10. Give a CFG to generate reversal of strings in the CFG: $S \to 00S1 \mid 1S0 \mid \epsilon$.

Problem 25.11. Suppose $\mathcal{L}_1$ and $\mathcal{L}_2$ are context free. Show that these languages are context free.
(a) $\mathcal{L}_1 \cup \mathcal{L}_2$ (union) (b) $L_1 \bullet \mathcal{L}_2$ (concatenation) (c) $\mathcal{L}_1^*$ (Kleene star) (d) $\mathcal{L}^{\text{R}} = \{w^{\text{R}} \mid w \in \mathcal{L}\}$ (reversal).
[Hint: For reversal, reverse the hybrid string on the RHS of production rules and use induction.]

Problem 25.12. Construct a CFG for $\mathcal{L} =$ {strings *not* containing 00} as follows.
(a) Construct a DFA for $\overline{\mathcal{L}} =$ {strings containing 00}, and use that to find a DFA for $\mathcal{L}$.
(b) Use the technique in Example 25.2 on page 368 to construct a CFG for $\mathcal{L}$.

Problem 25.13. Prove that the CFG in (25.2) on page 369 generates all strings whose number of ones $\equiv 1 \pmod 3$.

Problem 25.14. Prove that the CFG $S \to \# \mid 0S0 \mid 1S1$ generates all strings of the form $w\#w^{\text{R}}$.

Problem 25.15. Prove by induction on string length that the CFG's in (25.3) and (25.5) generate the same strings.

Problem 25.16. For each language $\mathcal{L}$, (i) Give a CFG that generates the strings in $\mathcal{L}$. (ii) Prove by induction that your CFG generates only strings in $\mathcal{L}$. (iii) Prove by induction that every string in $\mathcal{L}$ can be generated by your CFG.
(a) $\mathcal{L} =$ {strings with an odd number of 1s}
(b) $\mathcal{L} =$ {strings with equal number of 0s and 1s}.
(c) $\mathcal{L} =$ {strings with *more* 1s than 0s}
(d) $\mathcal{L} =$ {strings with *more* 1s than 0s in every prefix}

Problem 25.17. Consider the language $\mathcal{L} = \{\epsilon, 1, 11, 111, \ldots\} = \{1\}^*$.

(a) Show that the CFG $S \to \varepsilon \mid 1 \mid 1S$ generates $\mathcal{L}$. Give a derivation of 111.

(b) Show that the CFG $S \to \varepsilon \mid 1 \mid SS$ generates $\mathcal{L}$. Give two *different* derivations of 111.

(c) A *leftmost* (*rightmost*) derivation replaces the leftmost (rightmost) variable at every step. For the grammar in part (b), give leftmost and rightmost derivations of 111.

Problem 25.18. For the CFG on the right, give parse trees for leftmost and rightmost derivations of: (a) 00101 (b) 1001 (c) 00011. (See Problem 25.17(c) for the definition of leftmost and right derivations.)

1: $S \to A1B$
2: $A \to \varepsilon \mid 0A$
3: $B \to \varepsilon \mid 0B \mid 1B$

Problem 25.19. Give CFGs for these languages:
(a) $\mathcal{L}_1 = \{0^{\bullet n}1^{\bullet n}0^{\bullet m}1^{\bullet m} \mid n, m \geq 1\}$. (b) $\mathcal{L}_2 = \{0^{\bullet n}1^{\bullet m}0^{\bullet m}1^{\bullet n} \mid n, m \geq 1\}$. (c) $\mathcal{L}_1 \cup \mathcal{L}_2$ and $\mathcal{L}_1 \bullet \mathcal{L}_2$.

Problem 25.20. For your CFG which generates $\mathcal{L}_1 \cup \mathcal{L}_2$ in Problem 25.19(c), give two different leftmost derivations of 00110011 and the (different) parse trees for those derivations. (Your grammar is ambiguous because there are two different parse trees for the same string. In fact, every grammar that generates this language is ambiguous.)

Problem 25.21. For CFG $S \to 0S \mid S1 \mid 0 \mid 1$, prove no string has 10 as a substring. *[Hint: Induction on length.]*

Problem 25.22. What is wrong with this proof that $0^{\bullet n}1^{\bullet 2n}0^{\bullet n}$ is a CFL. Let $\mathcal{L}_1 = 0^{\bullet n}1^{\bullet n}$ and $\mathcal{L}_2 = 1^{\bullet n}0^{\bullet n}$, both of which are CFL's. Since CFLs are closed under concatenation, $\mathcal{L}_1 \bullet \mathcal{L}_2 = 0^{\bullet n}1^{\bullet n}1^{\bullet n}0^{\bullet n} = 0^{\bullet n}1^{\bullet 2n}0^{\bullet n}$ is a CFL.

Problem 25.23. Consider the problem $\mathcal{L} = \{0^{\bullet n}1^{\bullet n+m}0^{\bullet m} \mid n, m \geq 0\}$.
(a) Show how a deterministic pushdown automaton (stack memory) can solve $\mathcal{L}$. (b) Find a CFG for $\mathcal{L}$.

Problem 25.24. In each case explain intuitively why a d-PDA cannot solve $\mathcal{L}$ and find a CFG for $\mathcal{L}$.
(a) $\mathcal{L} = \{0^{\bullet m}1^{\bullet n}0^{\bullet k} \mid n = m \text{ or } n = k\}$. (b) $\mathcal{L} = \{w \mid w\text{'s second half has a } 1\} = \{xy \mid |x| \geq |y|,\ y \text{ has a } 1\}$.

Problem 25.25. A CFG is *right-linear* if every production rule replaces a variable with a string that has at most one variable, and this variable is at the rightmost end of the replacing string: all production rules are of the form

$$A \to x \quad \text{or} \quad A \to xB \qquad (x \text{ is a string of terminals}).$$

Show that every regular language has a right-linear grammar. (It turns out that the converse is also true, that every right linear grammar generates a regular language.) *[Hint: Let the variables be states of the DFA.]*

Problem 25.26. Suppose a language $\mathcal{L}_1$ is solved by a d-PDA and $\mathcal{L}_2$ is solved by a DFA. Use product states to prove that $\mathcal{L}_1 \cap \mathcal{L}_2$ is a CFL. (More generally, a CFL intersected with a regular language is a CFL.)

Problem 25.27. Answer these questions about the language $\mathcal{L}$ of the CFG on the right.

1: $S \to 0 \mid 0A$
2: $A \to 0S$

(a) Prove that all strings in $\mathcal{L}$ have an odd number of 0's.

(b) Prove $\mathcal{L}$ is regular. (Ginsburg-Rice, 1962: CFLs on unary alphabets are regular.)

Problem 25.28 (Pumping). We restate the CFG from Pop Quiz 25.1 on the right. We emphasize some important facts (see also Exercise 25.7). There are 4 variables, in addition to the start variable. The start variable S is not on the RHS of any rule. All rules are of the form either $A \to BC$ or $A \to t$, where A, B, C are variables and t a terminal. All derivations of a non-empty string of length ℓ have $2\ell - 1$ steps.

1: $S \to \varepsilon \mid T_0T_1 \mid T_0A$
2: $X \to T_0T_1 \mid T_0A$
3: $A \to XT_1$
4: $T_0 \to 0$
5: $T_1 \to 1$

(a) Give the parse tree for $w = 000111$. Remove all the leaves (terminals), what remains is a binary tree whose root is Ⓢ and all other vertices are variables. Explain why this binary tree is full (vertices have either 2 or no children).

(b) There is a path in the parse tree from Ⓢ to a terminal-leaf in which the variable A appears twice. How many variables are in this path other than Ⓢ? We illustrate the situation on the right. Since $S \overset{*}{\Rightarrow} w$, the leaves of the tree rooted at S form w. We decomposed w as $w = axbyc$, where (first)$A \overset{*}{\Rightarrow} xby$ and (second)$A \overset{*}{\Rightarrow} b$. That is, the leaves of the subtree rooted at the first A form xby and the leaves of the subtree rooted at the second A form b. Determine a, x, b, y, c (one or more can be ε).

(c) The reoccurence of a variable in the path from S to a terminal leaf is similar to the situation in a DFA when the DFA "loops" back to the same state when processing a string. Explain why we can replace the subtree rooted at the second A by the entire subtree rooted at the first A and get a valid parse tree/derivation (see right).

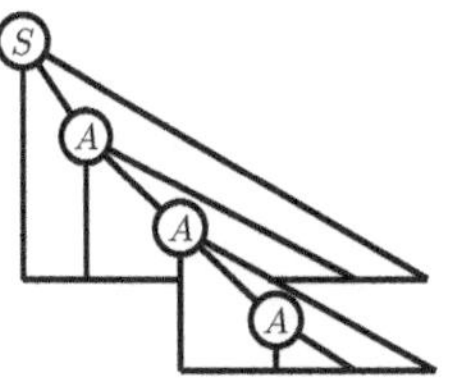

(i) What is the string whose parse tree is on the right (in terms of a, x, b, y, c).

(ii) In (b), can you replace the subtree rooted at the first A with the subtree rooted at the second A? What string is derived? Why can't both x and y be empty?

(iii) Prove that $ax^{\bullet i}by^{\bullet i}c$ can be generated for $i \geq 0$. (w can be *pumped*.)

Problem 25.29 (Pumping Lemma). Prove the pumping lemma for a CFG in Chomsky Normal Form.

> **Pumping Lemma.** For any CFL, there is a parameter p, the pumping length, such that if w is in the language and has length $\ell \geq p$, then w can be decomposed into $w = axbyc$ such that
> (i) length$(xby) < p$; (ii) Both x, y are not ε; (iii) $ax^{\bullet i}by^{\bullet i}c$ is in the language for $i \geq 0$.

Generalize Problem 25.28 to an arbitrary CFG in Chomsky Normal Form with a start variable S and k additional variables. Recall, from Exercise 25.7: Only the start variable S can transition to ε, and S is not on the RHS of any rule. Other than (possibly) $S \to \varepsilon$, all other rules are of the form either $A \to BC$ or $A \to t$, where A, B, C are variables and t a terminal. All derivations of a non-empty string of length ℓ have $2\ell - 1$ steps.

(a) Let w be a string of length ℓ. The leaves in the parse tree are terminals each produced by a transition of a variable directly to a terminal. Remove these terminal-leaves. What remains is a binary tree of variables. Suppose $\ell > 2^k$.
  (i) Show that some path p from the root Ⓢ to a leaf x in the remaining tree has length at least $k+1$
  (ii) Start at x and move up toward S until a variable (say) A is repeated. Show that at most k steps are made.
  (iii) Show that the substring in w derived from the (repeated) variable from (ii) has length at most 2^k.
  (iv) Prove that w can be decomposed as $w = axbyc$ with length$(xby) \leq 2^k$ and not both x, y being ε such that $ax^{\bullet i}by^{\bullet i}c$ can be generated by the CFG for $i \geq 0$. Hence, prove the pumping lemma.

(b) Use the pumping lemma to prove that $\mathcal{L} = \{0^{\bullet n}1^{\bullet n}0^{\bullet n} \mid n \geq 0\}$ is not context free. Use these steps as a guide.
  (i) Let p be the pumping length and $w = 0^{\bullet p+1}1^{\bullet p+1}0^{\bullet p+1}$. Why are the only possibilities for xby: entirely in the left 0s; overlapping left 0s and 1s; entirely in the 1s; overlapping 1s and right 0s; entirely in the right 0s.
  (ii) Consider each case in (i) and show that w cannot be pumped, contradicting the pumping lemma.

Problem 25.30. Using the pumping lemma, show that these languages are not CFL's.

(a) $0^{\bullet n^2}$ for $n \geq 0$.
(b) $0^{\bullet n}1^{\bullet n^2}$, where $n \geq 0$.
(c) $0^{\bullet n}1^{\bullet m}0^{\bullet k}$ where $0 \leq n \leq m \leq k$.
(d) $\{0^{\bullet m}1^{\bullet n} \mid m$ is not divisible by $n\}$.
(e) Palindromes with an equal number of 0s and 1s.
(f) Strings of the form ww where $w \in \{0,1\}^*$.
(g) Strings of the form $w\#w$ where $w \in \{0,1\}^*$.
(h) $0^{\bullet n}1^{\bullet 2^n}$, where $n \geq 0$.
(i) $0^{\bullet 2^n}$, where $n \geq 0$.
(j) $0^{\bullet m}1^{\bullet n}$, where m is divisible by n.

Problem 25.31. Prove that a CFG generates an infinite language if and only if it generates some string whose length satisfies $p \leq$ length$(w) \leq 2p$, where p is the pumping length from Problem 25.29.

Problem 25.32. Suppose a CFG generates a unary language $\mathcal{L}$, $\mathcal{L} \subseteq \{1\}^*$. Let p be the pumping length from Problem 25.29. Prove that if $1^{\bullet 0}, 1^{\bullet 1}, \ldots, 1^{\bullet p+p!}$ are all in $\mathcal{L}$, then $\mathcal{L} = \{1\}^*$. Follow these steps.

(a) For $p \leq k$, if $1^{\bullet k} \in \mathcal{L}$, use the pumping lemma to show that $1^{\bullet k+n\alpha} \in \mathcal{L}$ for some $1 \leq \alpha < p$ and $n \geq 0$.
(b) Using $\{np! \mid n \geq 0\} \subset \{n\alpha \mid n \geq 0\}$, show that $1^{\bullet k+np!} \in \mathcal{L}$ for $p \leq k \leq p!$ and $n \geq 0$. Hence, prove the claim.

Problem 25.33. In each case $\mathcal{L}_1$ and $\mathcal{L}_2$ look similar. Give a CFG for $\mathcal{L}_1$ and prove that $\mathcal{L}_2$ is not a CFL.

(a) $\mathcal{L}_1 = \{(01)^{\bullet n}(01)^{\bullet n} \mid n \geq 0\}$, $\mathcal{L}_2 = \{0^{\bullet n}1^{\bullet n}0^{\bullet n}1^{\bullet n} \mid n \geq 0\}$.
(b) $\mathcal{L}_1 = \{0^{\bullet n}0^{\bullet 2n}0^{\bullet 3n} \mid n \geq 0\}$, $\mathcal{L}_2 = \{0^{\bullet n}\#0^{\bullet 2n}\#0^{\bullet 3n} \mid n \geq 0\}$.
(c) $\mathcal{L}_1 = \{ww^{\text{R}}\}$, $\mathcal{L}_2 = \{wxw^{\text{R}} \mid$ length$(w) =$ length$(x)\}$.
(d) $\mathcal{L}_1 = \{$strings $w\#v$ where w^{R} is a substring of $v\}$, $\mathcal{L}_2 = \{$strings $w\#v$ where w is a substring of $v\}$.
(e) $\mathcal{L}_1 = \{w \mid w$'s mid-third has a 1$\} = \{xyz \mid |x| = |z| \geq |y|, y$ has a 1$\}$, $\mathcal{L}_2 = \{w \mid w$'s mid-third has two 1s$\}$.

Problem 25.34 (Context sensitive grammar). In each production rule of grammars I and II below, an instance of the string on the LHS can be replaced by the string on the RHS. For each grammar:

(a) Give derivations of three different strings.
(b) Guess the problem solved by the grammar.
(c) Informally justify your guess (no need of proof).
(d) Is there a contradiction with any claims in Section 25.3 on page 372?

Grammar I

1:	$S \to \varepsilon \mid 0SBC$
2:	$CB \to BC$
3:	$0B \to 0X$
4:	$XB \to XX$
5:	$XC \to XY$
6:	$YC \to YY$
7:	$X \to 1$
8:	$Y \to 0$

Variables: S, B, C, X, Y.

Grammar II

1:	$S \to A0B$
2:	$A \to \varepsilon \mid AD$
3:	$D0 \to 00D$
4:	$DB \to B$
5:	$B \to \varepsilon$

Variables: S, A, B, D.

> It is possible to invent a single machine which can be used to compute any computable sequence. – **Alan Turing**
>
> Where a calculator like the ENIAC today is equipped with 18,000 vacuum tubes and weighs 30 tons, computers in the future may have only 1,000 vacuum tubes and perhaps weigh only $1\frac{1}{2}$ tons. – **Popular Mechanics, March 1949**

Chapter 26

Turing Machines

1: Tape memory (RAM) and the read-write-move head.
2: High-level descriptions of Turing Machines: pseudocode.
3: Low-level descriptions of Turing Machines: machine-code.

Starting as early as Chapter 1, we heftily hyped up the Turing Machine, TM for short.

> ...a grand model, a model of the digital computer – a model of computing. We want a realistic model that captures your desktop as well as smartphone. But, it should be simple enough to analyze, because we have deep questions to ask.
> 1. What can we compute?
> 2. What *can't* we compute?
> 3. Are there things we can compute in principle, but it takes too long?

Turing Machines are more powerful than computers, but nevertheless are the accepted model, having stood the test of time. There are many equivalent variants, which gives us the flexibility to pick a convenient form. Let us illustrate the general setup for the non-context free language $\{w\#w\}$, specifically using input 001#001.

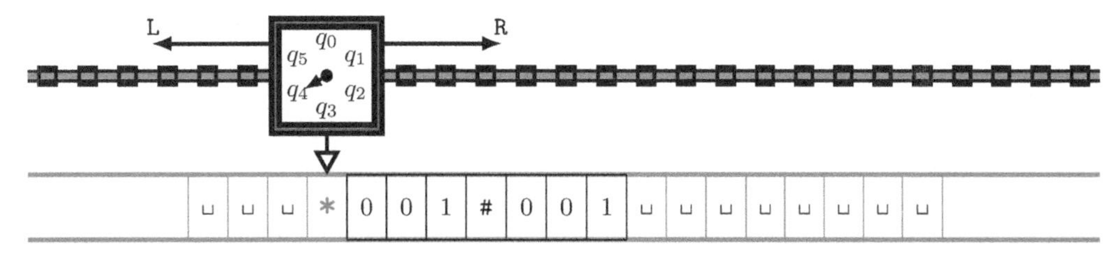

The Turing Machine, like the d-PDA, is a finite automaton (think "CPU") with access to an external memory. Unlike the d-PDA, the memory is not a stack but a tape that extends indefinitely on both sides.[1] As illustrated, the automaton can move left and right to access different parts of the tape, a type of random access memory.

The tape is segmented into memory slots with default blank symbols "␣" and a beacon-symbol "$*$" to which the automaton can always return. The input is loaded onto the tape as shown, right of "$*$". The machine processes the input by moving left and right to accesses different parts of the tape. It may transition between internal states and write to the tape. Ultimately, the machine accepts the input by transitioning to a (YES)-state (A) and halting, or rejects by transitioning to a (NO)-state (E) and halting. Halting is a crucial new twist. Unlike a DFA, the input is not fed in one-bit at a time, hence there is no well defined end to a computation. Instead, the Turing Machine moves around, accessing the tape until it decides the verdict and halts.

Let us see the birds eye view of how a machine endowed with tape memory and mobility can solve $\{w\#w\}$. The idea is to use mobility to check that the first bit of the first string matches the first bit of the second string. Then check the second bit, and so on. We break the computation into several smaller tasks.

[1] Unlimited memory is not practical. In this sense, the TM is more powerful than a computer. The model is too grand ☺.

1: Check for one "#", otherwise REJECT. A DFA can do this.

2: Return to "$*$".

3: Move right to first non-marked bit before "#".
If you reach "#" before any non-marked bit, GOTO step 5.
Otherwise, mark the location and "remember" the bit.

4: Move right to first non-marked bit after "#".
If you reach "␣" before any non-marked bit, REJECT.
If the bit does not match the bit from step 3, REJECT.
Otherwise (bit matches), mark the location. GOTO step 2.

5: Move right to first non-marked bit after "#".
If you reach "␣" before any non-marked bit, ACCEPT.
If you find a bit, the string on the right is too long, REJECT.

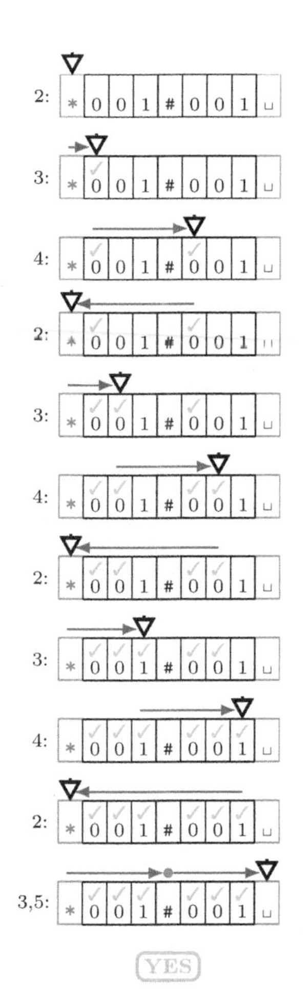

Follow the TM as it works on the right. We show the computation after step 1. The loop between steps 2–4 repeatedly checks each bit of the first string for a match with the corresponding bit in the second string. The automaton REJECTS if there is no corresponding bit because the first string is longer, or if there is a mismatch. If every bit successfully matches and you hit "#" in step 3, the automaton goes to step 5 and looks for additional bits in the second string. If there are no additional bits in the second string, the automaton ACCEPTS. Follow these steps on the tape as shown on the right. The zig-zagging behavior is typical.

The Turing Machine can mark the tape, a feature we use liberally and often. Strictly speaking, Turing Machines can only read or write alphabet symbols. To mark the tape, a purist would introduce new symbols into the alphabet such as a marked-1, "✓1". Replacing 1 with ✓1 effectively marks the 1 on the tape. To avoid alphabet-bloat, we simply say mark the 1.

Pop Quiz 26.1
Show the TM's behavior with inputs: (a) 0110; (b) 01#10; (c) 101#10; (d) 10#101.

Turing Machines are much more powerful than CFGs. We already came up with a relatively simple TM that solves $\{w\#w\}$ for which there is no CFG. Our high-level description is like pseudocode. We can also produce more formal machine-code. A Turing Machine begins with its read-write head at $*$ in its start state q_0. At every step in its computation, the machine reads the tape at its current location and performs these actions:

1. Change what is written on the tape, possibly leaving it unchanged;
2. Transition to a new state, possibly staying in the same state;
3. Move the read-write head left (L), right (R) or not at all, i.e. stay put (S).

A machine-level instruction is shown below, together with its graphical counterpart,

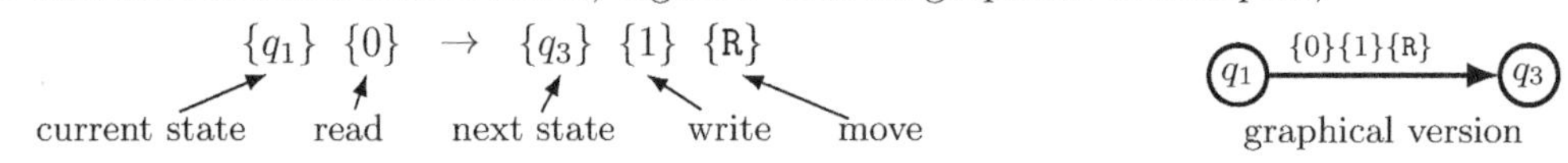

This instruction says: IF in state q_1 and the tape reads 0, THEN transition to q_3, write 1 to the tape and move right one step. Here is what the execution of this instruction would look like on a Turing Machine,

Notice that the 0 in the shaded spot changed to 1. Let us agree that, by default, the only symbols on the tape are $*$, 0, 1, # and ␣. To mark tape locations, we will use symbols like ✓, ✗ written above normal symbols.

Pop Quiz 26.2

Practice with the notation. Translate each instruction into words and give the graphical version. {} means do nothing for that part of the instruction. When there is only a mark, mark the symbol on the tape that way; otherwise, replace whatever is on the tape with the symbol being written.

(a) {q}{0}→{r}{0}{R}	(e) {q}{0}→{r}{✓}{R}	(i) {q}{✓}→{r}{}{L}
(b) {q}{0}→{r}{}{R}	(f) {q}{0,1}→{r}{✓1}{L}	(j) {q}{0}→{r}{␣}{L}
(c) {q}{✓0}→{r}{}{}	(g) {q}{✓0,✓1}→{r}{0,1}{L}	(k) {q}{␣}→{r}{#}{L}
(d) {q}{0}→{r}{✓}{}	(h) {q}{✓}→{r}{0}{L}	(l) {q}{✓}→{r}{✓0}{}

We now give the machine-code for our Turing Machine, one piece at a time for each step in the pseudocode.

Step 1: Check for one #. The finite automaton on the right solves this problem without writing to the tape. It starts in state (step 1), looking for "#" and moving right each step. If there is no "#", a "␣" will arrive when the input ends and the automaton transitions to the halting red error state E, and rejects. On the other hand, if a "#" arrives, the automaton transitions to q_1 to ensure there is only one "#". If another '#" arrives, halt and reject. Otherwise, if "␣" arrives, transition to (step 2). The state (step 2) marks the success of step 1.

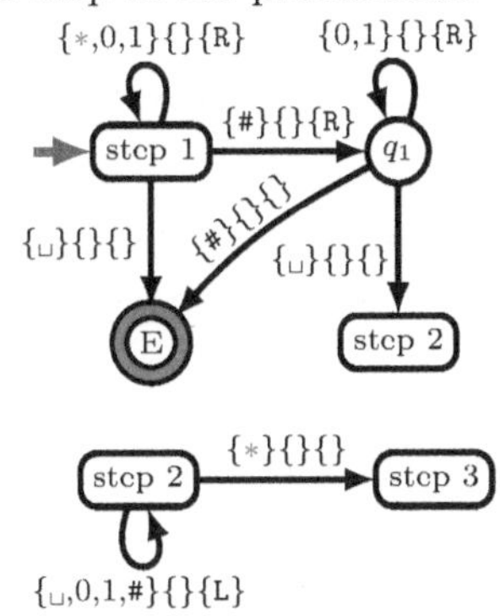

Step 2: Return to ∗. A finite automaton also solves this problem. After step 1 succeeds, the automaton is in state (step 2). A second automaton takes over, moving to the left until ∗ at which it stops and transitions to this step's success state (step 3). The meat of the algorithm, steps 3&4, take over from here.

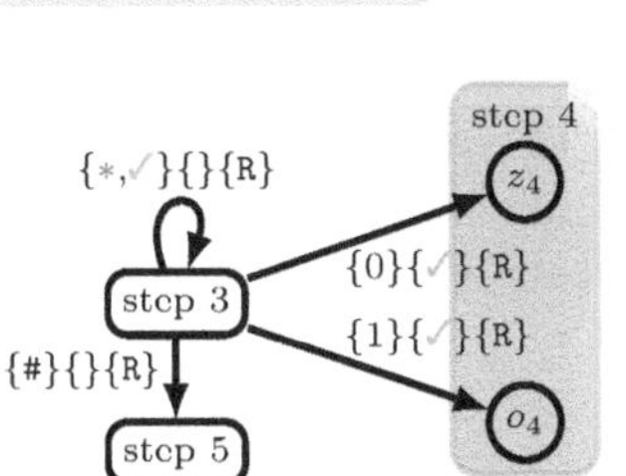

Pop Quiz 26.3

Why does the error state (E) not have any outgoing arrows?

Show how to combine the two automata above to get an automaton that solves steps 1&2.

Step 3: Find first unmarked bit before #. After steps 1&2 succeed, the automaton is in state (step 3) at ∗. The input bits are to the right of ∗. The symbols as one moves right fall into one of four categories.

1. The symbol is marked: move right and remain in (step 3).
2. The symbol is unmarked 1: mark it and remember the bit.
3. The symbol is unmarked 0: mark it and remember the bit.
4. Symbol is #: GOTO (step 5).

To remember the bit marked, the automaton transitions to z_4 for 0 (z for zero) and o_4 for 1 (o for one). The states z_4 and o_4 are an internal memory. Arriving at z_4 or o_4 means step 3 succeeded and step 4 can begin.

Step 4: Match to first unmarked bit after # and return to ∗. The automaton is in state z_4 trying to match a 0 or state o_4 trying to match a 1. Both cases is similar. Move right, ignoring unmarked bits. When # is reached, transition to z_5 (resp. o_5) and find the first unmarked symbol, which means:

1. Ignore marked symbols and move right.
2. If the first unmarked symbol matches (0 for z_5 or 1 for o_5), mark it and return to ∗. Return to ∗ is implemented by transitioning to (step 2)
3. If the first unmarked symbol is a mismatch, halt and reject. Or, if the automaton reaches ␣, halt and reject as the string right of # is too short.

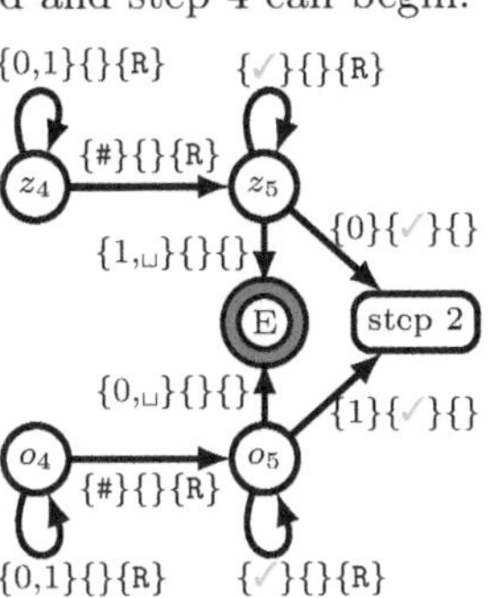

The success of step 4 is marked by transitioning to (step 2) and the loop continues.

Step 5: No additional bits in right string. The automaton comes here from step 3, if there are no more left-bits to match. All that remains is to check that all right-bits are marked. So move right, to the first non-marked symbol. If you come to "␣" first, halt and ACCEPT (green state). Otherwise halt and REJECT.

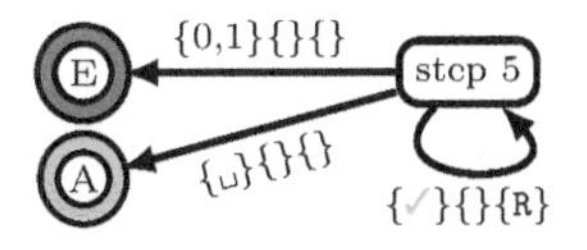

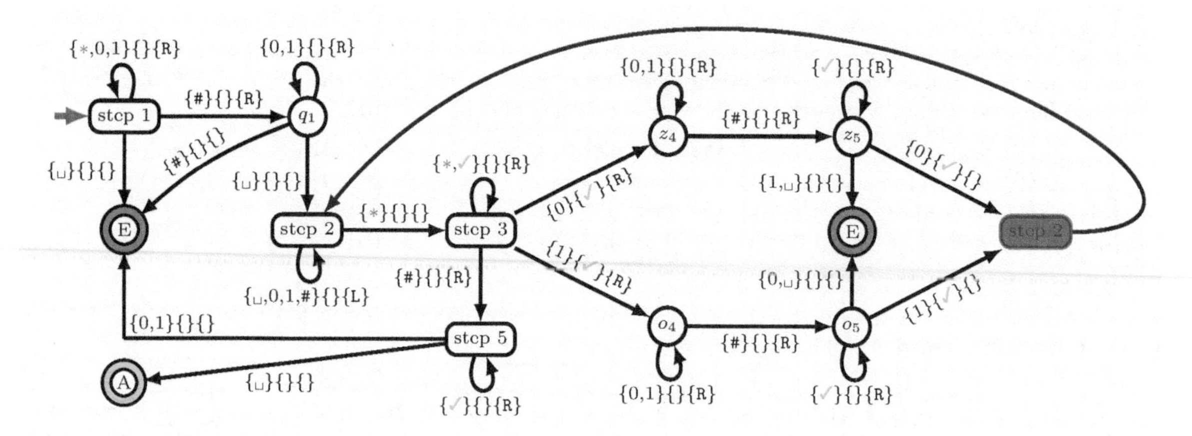

Figure 26.1: Turing machine to solve $\{w\#w\}$, based on the pseudocode on page 378.

We snap together the modules of each step at their common states to get the Turing Machine in Figure 26.1. Note the Turing Machine's priviledged halting states Ⓔ and Ⓐ, which a DFA doesn't have. The computation must reach a halting state to end. It is entertaining to see a low-level Turing Machine in action.

Pop Quiz 26.4
Show how the five modules "snap" together to give the Turing machine in Figure 26.1. For each input, give the sequence of states followed by the Turing machine. (a) 01#01 (b) 01#10 (c) 0#01 (d) 01#0

Example 26.1. Here is a language that corresponds to multiplication,

$$\mathcal{L}_{\text{mult}} = \{0^{\bullet i}\#1^{\bullet j}\#0^{\bullet k} \mid i, j > 0 \text{ and } k = i \times j\}$$

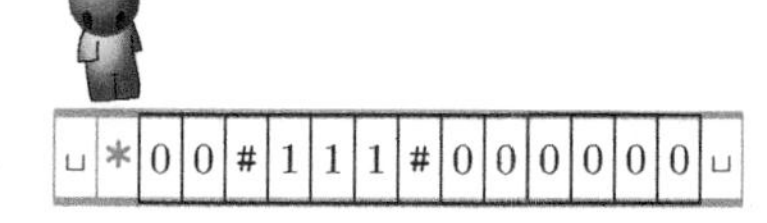

Consider input $0^{\bullet 2}\#1^{\bullet 3}\#0^{\bullet 6}$. Imagine you are on the tape and can only look down. You can't see the bits to the left or right. You can read, write, move about, and remember only finitely many things. How would you verify that the number of right-0's equals the number of left-0's times the number of 1's? First you should check that the input format is correct.

1: Verify the input format is $0^{\bullet i}\#1^{\bullet j}\#0^{\bullet k}$. A DFA can solve this.
2: Return to ∗.

From grade-school, we know that multiplication is repeated addition, $2 \times 3 = 3 + 3$ (two blocks of 3). More generally, in $0^{\bullet i}\#1^{\bullet j}\#0^{\bullet k}$, we just need to to check that k can be broken into i blocks of size j. To check this, for each left-0, mark j right-zeros. At the end, if there are no unmarked right-0s remaining, halt and accept.

3: Move right and mark the first unmarked left-0. Then, move right to "#".
   If there are no unmarked left-0's (you reach "#"), GOTO step 6.
4: Move right and mark the first unmarked 1.
   If all 1's are marked (you reach "#") move left, unmarking all 1's, and GOTO step 2.
5: Move right to find an unmarked right-0.
   If there are no unmarked right-0's (you come to "␣"), REJECT
   Otherwise, mark the 0, move left to the first marked 1 and GOTO step 4.
6: Move right to verify there are no unmarked right-zeros.
   If you come to an unmarked right-zero, REJECT; if you come to "␣" ACCEPT.

For each left-0, the Turing machine zig-zags between the 1's and right-0's, marking a right-0 for each 1. After steps 3,4 and 5 have been executed once, the status of the tape is

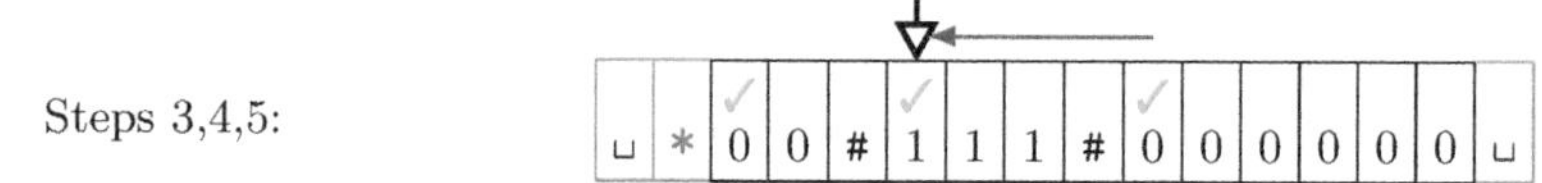

From here, the loop in steps 4,5 will mark each 1 and a corresponding 0.

Steps 4,5 (loop):

⊔	*	0	0	#	1	1	1	#	0	0	0	0	0	0	⊔

⊔	*	0	0	#	1	1	1	#	0	0	0	0	0	0	⊔

⊔	*	0	0	#	1	1	1	#	0	0	0	0	0	0	⊔

⊔	*	0	0	#	1	1	1	#	0	0	0	0	0	0	⊔

The Turing Machine now finds out that all 1's are marked when it moves right to "#", at which point it moves left, unmarking the 1's and goes to step 2 where it returns to $*$:

Steps 4,2:

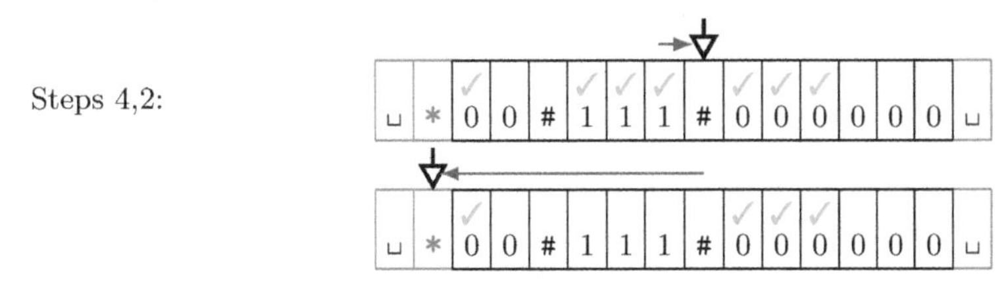

The Turing Machine has now processed the first left-0 and it continues to process each left-0 in this way.

Exercise 26.5
Give machine-code for steps 1–6 and snap all these modules together to give a low-level description of a Turing Machine to solve the multiplication problem $\mathcal{L}_{\text{mult}}$.

□

Our Turing Machine is more like a calculator that solves a specific task than a computer which solves general problems. Also, it looks nothing like a program. So much for our model of computing. In old times, when I walked uphill to and from school 🙂, people did program in machine-code. Now, we are pampered with high-level programming languages like C^{++}. Good programmers go to an even higher level and write pseudocode for a problem before manually translating the pseudocode to a structured C^{++} program.[2] A compiler automatically translates the program into machine-instructions, so we never see the machine-level instructions that are the basis of Turing Machines. We do have a computer. We just don't see it yet.

Exercise 26.6
In each case: (i) Give pseudocode of a Turing Machine for the problem. (ii) Give a machine-level description of each module in your pseudocode. (iii) Combine modules to get your Turing Machine for the problem.
(a) $\mathcal{L} = *01* = \{\text{strings containing } 01\}$ (regular). (b) $\mathcal{L} = \{ww \mid w \in \{0,1\}^*\}$ (repetition).

26.1 Transducer Turing Machines

In a DFA or d-PDA, the input is read from left to right and the computation ends with a (YES) or (NO). A Turing Machine can change the tape, leaving the tape in an altered state when it halts and delivers its (YES) or (NO) verdict. We can treat the altered tape as the output. Such a Turing Machine is a transducer (a device that transforms a signal). Let us use the multiplication example. The tape starts with $0^{\bullet i}\#1^{\bullet j}$. The machine moves around reading and writing and eventually halts, having performed the multiplication $i \times j$. When the machine halts, we don't care about the (YES) or (NO) decision. We only care about the altered tape, and we

[2]Pseudocode outlines high-level tasks. It's hard to define, but "You know it when you see it." – Justice Potter Stewart.

want the tape to read $0^{\bullet i}\#1^{\bullet j}\#0^{\bullet i\times j}$. For $i = 2, j = 3$, here is the tape at the start of the computation.

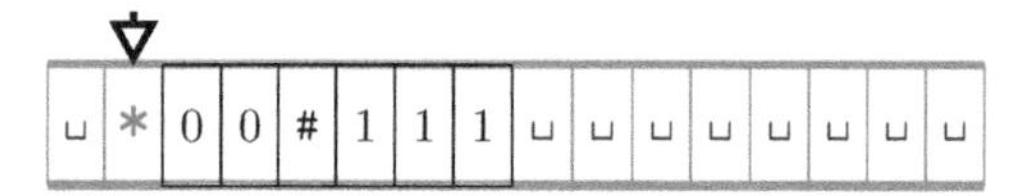

At the end, after returning the read-write head back to $*$ and halting, the tape should be $0^{\bullet 2}\#1^{\bullet 3}\#0^{\bullet 6}$,

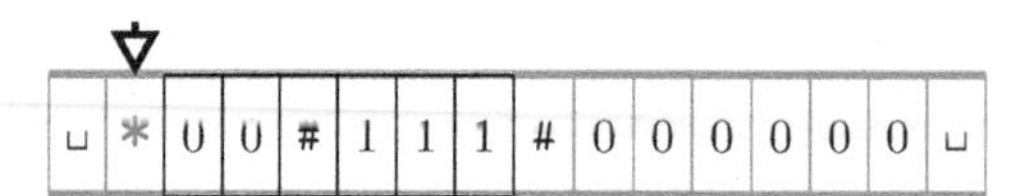

A transducer produces an output, whereas a decider just spits out (YES) or (NO). If we feed in 00#111 via (say) stdin, our calculator spits out 000000 via (say) stdout. Transducers better resemble everyday computers. Turing Machines are just as good transducers as they are deciders. We can turn our Turing Machine that decided $0^{\bullet i}\#1^{\bullet j}\#0^{\bullet i\times j}$ into a transducer which multiplies. Instead of marking the right-0's, we write 0's.

1: Verify the input format is $0^{\bullet i}\#1^{\bullet j}$ and write a # at the first ␣.
2: Return to $*$.
3: Move right and mark the first unmarked left-0. Then, move right to "#".
    If there are no unmarked left-0's (you reach "#"), return to $*$ and halt.
4: Move right and mark the first unmarked 1.
    If all 1's are marked (you reach "#"), move left, unmarking all 1's, and GOTO step 2.
5: Move right to "␣" and write a 0 there.
6: Move left to the first marked 1 and GOTO step 4.

Pop Quiz 26.7
For input 00#111, show the result after each of the steps 1-6 in the "algorithm" above.

In Pop Quiz 26.7, you trace steps 1–6 for our multiplication example. The tape configuration should now be:

Steps 1–6:

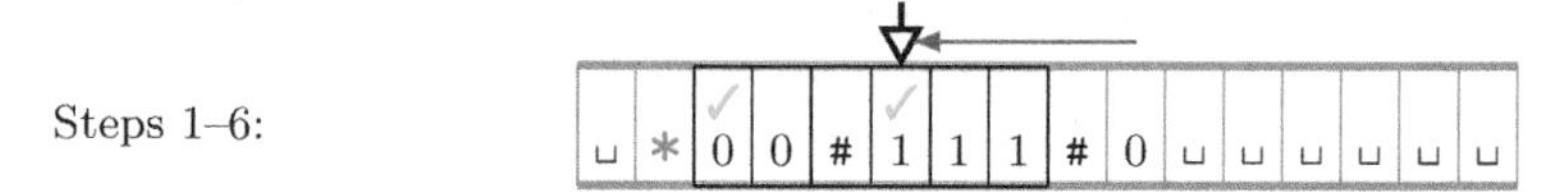

From here, the transducer repeats steps 4,5,6 until there are no more unmarked 1's:

Steps 4,5,6 (loop):

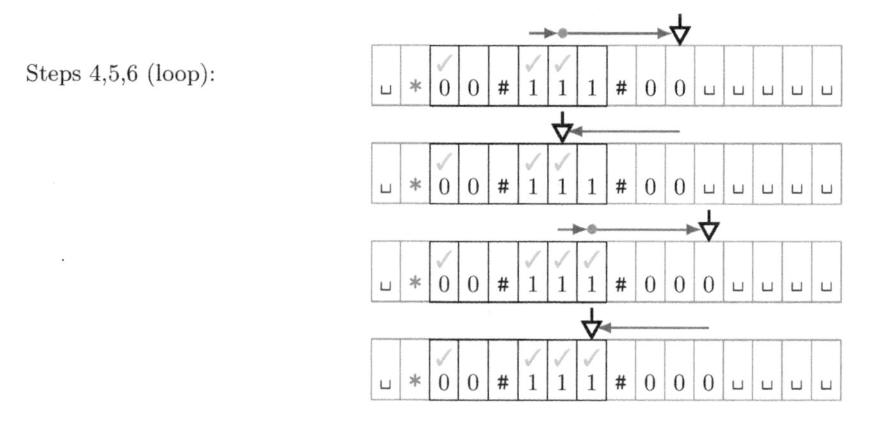

Now, the transducer moves right to "#", finding no more unmarked 1's. Hence, it exits the loop at step 4, unmarking the 1's, and returns to $*$ where it is ready to process the next left-0:

Steps 4,2:

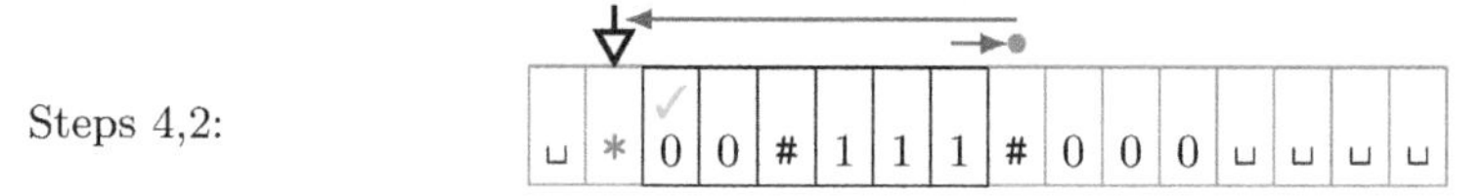

The transducer zig-zags as does the decider. Transducers are not more powerful than deciders. They are just more reminiscent of what modern computers do.[3] For example, we can multiply by running the decider on $0^{\bullet i}\#1^{\bullet j}\#0^{\bullet k}$ for $k = 1, 2, 3, \ldots$. The value of k when we hear (YES) is the product we seek. It's inefficient, but it does the job. Our foray into the theory of computing – what is computable – will continue to use decision problems or languages to model computing tasks, even though transducers are more useful in practice.

Exercise 26.8

For each problem (i) Give pseudocode for a transducer that solves the problem. (ii) Give a decision version of the problem formulated as a language.

(a) (Copying) The input is a string w and the final state of the tape is $w\#w$.

(b) (Copying, without punctuation) The input is w and the final state of the tape is ww.

(c) (Squaring) The input is $0^{\bullet n}$ and the final state of the tape is $0^{\bullet n}\#1^{\bullet n^2}$.

(d) (Reversal) The input is w and the final state of the tape is w^{R}.

26.2 Infinite Loops

Our small examples should convince you that Turing Machines perform complex tasks just like computers. Turing Machines also suffer the same pitfalls as computers. Remember your nightmares as a young programmer debugging non-terminating programs that had fallen into infinite loops. A Turing Machine can also enter an infinite loop. Study the Turing Machine shown (it's not too complex) and do the Pop Quiz.

Pop Quiz 26.9

What states are visited by the Turing Machine on the right for inputs:

(a) #. (b) 0#. (c) 101.

What is the simplest Turing Machine that can infinitely loop?

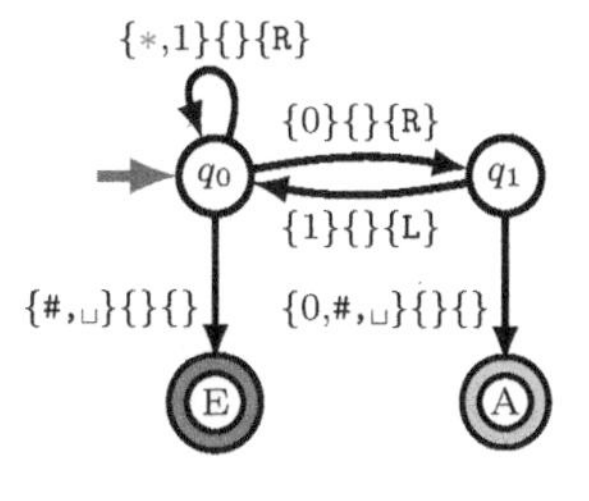

The Turing Machine on the right can infinitely loop because it may move right and then left, allowing it to jiggle forever on some inputs. In contrast, DFAs only "move" right to process input bits, and the computation ends when the input ends.

A Turing Machine has halting states to announce the end of a computation. Unfortunately, every computation may not reach a halting state. A Turing Machine's ability to move around is essential for solving complex problems. But, that mobility is what produces infinite loops. So, infinite loops are a necessary evil. One of three things can happen when you run a Turing Machine M on an input w:

$$M(w) = \begin{cases} \text{Halts in an accept state} & \to \text{ACCEPT} \\ \text{Halts in a reject state} & \to \text{REJECT} \\ \text{Does not halt} & \to ? \end{cases}$$

$M(w)$ loosely refers to what happens when M runs on w. A Turing Machine that does not halt is unacceptable. A computer that could loop forever is not a solution to any problem. If infinite loops are even just a remote possibility, a definite (YES) or (NO) could be 1 minute away or not coming at all, and you won't know which. To discuss these issues in a principled way, we need to get more formal.

The language $\mathcal{L}(M)$ of Turing Machine M is the set of inputs on which M halts and accepts, its (YES)-set:

$$\begin{aligned} w \in \mathcal{L}(M) &\leftrightarrow M(w) = \text{halt and (YES)}; \\ w \notin \mathcal{L}(M) &\leftrightarrow M(w) = \text{halt and (NO) or loop forever.} \end{aligned}$$

The Turing Machine M recognizes the language $\mathcal{L}(M)$, which means that M will halt and say (YES) for any string $w \in \mathcal{L}(M)$. The language $\mathcal{L}$ is recognizable if there is some Turing Machine M for which $\mathcal{L}(M) = \mathcal{L}$, i.e. M recognizes $\mathcal{L}$. If $w \notin \mathcal{L}(M)$, we don't know what will happen. Either M halts and says (NO) or M loops forever, not giving any answer. Even for $w \in \mathcal{L}(M)$, you will be in an unsavory limbo because you do not know when the answer will come. A Turing Machine that can loop forever is called a recognizer.

[3]Remember that deciders can also solve all kinds of problems, e.g. optimization, see Chapter 23, page 341.

A recognizer is a useful theoretical concept that is of limited use in practice, because any practical computation must always stop. We care about Turing Machines that always halt, returning (YES) or (NO). A Turing Machine that always halts is called a decider. For a decider,

$$w \in \mathcal{L}(M) \leftrightarrow M(w) = \text{halt and (YES)};$$
$$w \notin \mathcal{L}(M) \leftrightarrow M(w) = \text{halt and (NO)}.$$

A Turing Machine M that always halts decides the language $\mathcal{L}(M)$. When $w \notin \mathcal{L}(M)$, a recognizer may loop forever but a decider may not. A Turing Machine that always halts, a decider, is the mathematical formulation of what we intuitively call an algorithm, a procedure that always produces an answer in finite time.

Church-Turing Thesis. A computing problem $\mathcal{L}$ (a language) that is solvable by an algorithm' is one that can be solved by a Turing Machine that is a decider, an automaton with a random-access read-write memory that always halts and delivers a (YES)/(NO) answer.

The Church-Turing Thesis is not a theorem. It is an empirically valid belief that Turing Machines solve all problems humans can solve. This belief is plausible because the human brain is a finite controller which computes with the aid of external scratch-paper. A computing problem $\mathcal{L}$ is Turing-decidable (or just decidable) if some Turing Machine decides $\mathcal{L}$. Similarly, $\mathcal{L}$ is Turing-recognizable if some Turing Machine recognizes $\mathcal{L}$.

Pop Quiz 26.10
Is the set of decidable languages contained in the set of recognizable languages?

The Turing Machine is our final mathematical model of a computer, more specifically an algorithm. Solvable problems are those that can be decided by a Turing Machine. All the problems in this chapter are decidable.

Are there undecidable problems, problems that cannot be solved by a computer? Alan Turing and Alonzo Church independently answered this question while addressing Hilbert's 1928 *Entscheidungsproblem*: "Is there a decision process to determine if a logical proposition can be derived from a set of axioms?" First, one has to precisely define "decision process". For Turing, that was the Turing Machine. For Church, it was the λ-calculus. Both formalizations of a decision process are equivalent. To understand Turing's undecidable problem, we need one more concept, that of Turing Machine encodings.

26.3 Encodings of Turing Machines

You just created a beautiful Turing Machine M and wish to communicate it to a friend who is half way across the world. Your friend needs a mathematical description of M, with the following details.

Mathematical Description of a Turing Machine

1. **States Q.** The first state is the start state, the halting states are (E) and (A).
2. **Symbols Σ.** By default these are $\{*, 0, 1, \sqcup, \#\}$.
3. **Machine-level transition instructions.** Each instruction has the form

{state}{read-symbol}{next-state}{written-symbol}{move}

The instructions map each (state, symbol) pair to a (state, symbol, move) triple and thus form a transition function $\delta : Q \times \Sigma \mapsto Q \times \Sigma \times \{\texttt{L},\texttt{R},\texttt{S}\}$.

To mark the tape, one adds marked versions of the symbols into the alphabet, like $\not{0}$. Note that the transition function is only a partial function since it does not need to map halting states to actions. Let us convert the graphical description of the infinitely looping Turing Machine on page 383 into a mathematical description.

1. **States.** $\{q_0, q_1, \text{A}, \text{E}\}$
2. **Symbols.** $\{*$, 0, 1, ␣, #$\}$
3. **Machine-level transition instructions.**

```
{q0}{*}{q0}{*}{R}
{q0}{1}{q0}{1}{R}
{q0}{0}{q1}{0}{R}
{q0}{#}{E} {#}{S}
{q0}{␣}{E} {␣}{S}
{q1}{1}{q0}{1}{L}
{q1}{0}{A} {0}{S}
{q1}{#}{A} {#}{S}
{q1}{␣}{A} {␣}{S}
```

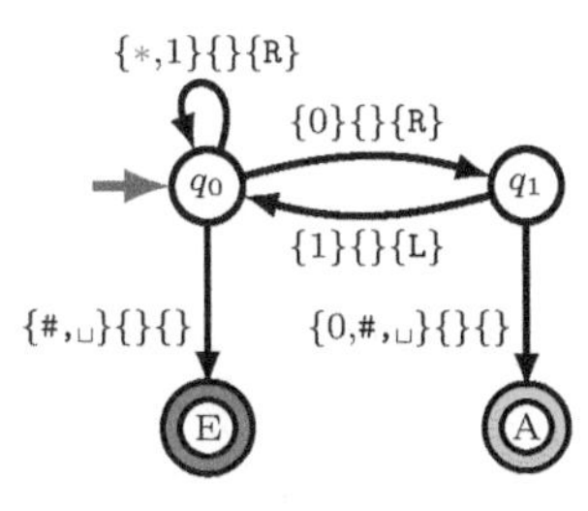

Of course, we much prefer the look of the graphical description on the right, but the mathematical description on the left is what you would send via email to your friend. Now for the key observation. The mathematical description on the left is written using ASCII, and it can be converted to a binary string using the ASCII code (ignoring subscripts). For example "{"→ 01111011 and "q0"→ 0111000100110000. We can perform this conversion to binary for the description of any Turing Machine. The conclusion is quite profound.

The description of a Turing Machine is a finite binary string.

Not all binary strings are Turing Machines, but any Turing Machine has a unique binary description. If you change the order of the instructions, functionally you have the same Turing Machine, but mathematically we treat it as a different Turing Machine with a different binary description. The unique binary description of Turing Machine M is the encoding of M into binary, which we denote $\langle M\rangle$. You can construct binary encodings for pretty much any object. Our focus here is binary encodings of Turing Machines. Since every Turing Machine maps to a unique finite binary string, and finite binary strings are countable, the Turing Machines are countable and can be listed: $\{M_1, M_2, \ldots\}$. The corresponding languages $\{\mathcal{L}(M_1), \mathcal{L}(M_2), \ldots\}$ also form a countable set. That is, the problems solvable by Turing Machines are countable.

Now consider all computing problems, i.e. languages. We can describe a language using its membership sequence with respect to the list of binary strings, illustrated below.

binary strings	ε	0	1	00	01	10	11	000	001	010	011	100	101	110	111	$\cdots$
language $\mathcal{L}$	0	1	1	1	1	0	1	0	0	0	1	0	0	1	0	$\cdots$

The membership sequence for this language $\mathcal{L}$ is the infinite binary string $011110100010010\cdots$. The ones in the membership sequence identify the strings in $\mathcal{L}$. If the ith bit is 1, then $\mathcal{L}$ contains the ith binary string,

$$\mathcal{L} = \{0, 1, 00, 01, 11, 011, 110, \ldots\}.$$

Every infinite binary string gives a different language. Since infinite binary strings are uncountable,

There are uncountably many computing problems (languages).

Computing problems are uncountable, but solvable problems are countable. Hmm ....

There are computing problems that cannot be solved by Turing Machines.

Stay tuned. We're going to catch one of these unsolvable problems and put it on display. It's an important problem, and no matter how smart you are, you won't be able to solve it on a computer.

Exercise 26.11

Let $\mathcal{L} = \{\langle M_1\rangle, \langle M_2\rangle, \ldots\}$ be the binary encodings of all valid Turing Machines. Give a high-level description of a Turing Machine decider for $\mathcal{L}$. Describe in words the problem your Turing Machine solves.

26.4 Problems

Problem 26.1. Order these sets of languages using the subset relation:

DFA-solvable: The set of languages that can be solved by Deterministic Finite Automata.
CFG-solvable: The set of languages that can be solved by Context Free Grammars.
TM-solvable: The set of languages that can be solved by Turing Machines.

Problem 26.2. What is the difference between a recognizer and a decider? Which is an algorithm? Why?

Problem 26.3. Give machine-code of a Turing Machine for the language $*01$. Zig-zagging over the tape is common behavior for a Turing Machine. How many times does your machine need to scan over the tape. Informally explain why.

Problem 26.4. Find the (YES)-sets of Turing Machines M_1 and M_2. Which Turing Machine do you prefer and why?

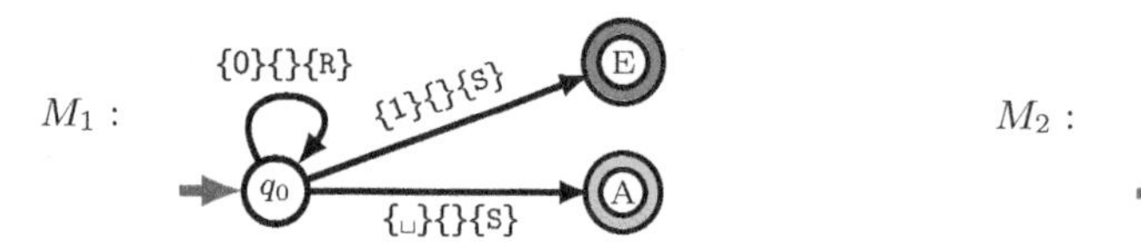

Problem 26.5. In each case: (i) Give pseudocode of a Turing Machine for the problem. (ii) Give machine-code for each module in your pseudocode. (iii) Combine your modules to get machine-code of a Turing Machine for the problem.

(a) $\mathcal{L} = \{0^{\bullet n} | n \geq 0\}$ (only zeros).
(b) $\mathcal{L} = \{0^{\bullet n}1^{\bullet n} | n \geq 0\}$ (testing equality).
(c) $\mathcal{L} = \{0^{\bullet 2n} | n \geq 0\}$ (parity-check).
(d) $\mathcal{L} = \{0^{\bullet 2^n} \mid n \geq 0\}$ (exponentials).
(e) $\mathcal{L} = \{$palindromes $w = w^{\mathrm{R}}\}$
(f) $\mathcal{L} = \{$strings with as many 0's as 1's$\}$.
(g) $\mathcal{L} = \{$strings with twice as many 0's as 1's$\}$.
(h) $\mathcal{L} = \{$strings *not* containing twice as many 0's as 1's$\}$.
(i) $\mathcal{L} = \{0^{\bullet i}\#1^{\bullet j}\#0^{\bullet k} \mid i, j > 0$ and $k = i + j\}$ (addition).
(j) $\mathcal{L} = \{w_1\#w_2\#\cdots\#w_\ell \mid w_i \neq w_j$ for $i \neq j\}$ (distinct elements).

Problem 26.6. In each case, give high level pseudocode for a Turing Machine M for the problem.

(a) Regular languages: (i) $\mathcal{L}_1 = \{*01*\}$ (ii) $\mathcal{L}_2 = \{*01\}$.
(b) Not CFL: $\mathcal{L} = \{0^{\bullet n}\#1^{\bullet n}\#0^{\bullet n}\}$ (# is punctuation).
(c) Squaring: $\mathcal{L} = \{0^{\bullet n}\#1^{\bullet n^2}, n \geq 0\}$ (# is punctuation).
(d) Exponential: $\mathcal{L} = \{0^{\bullet n}\#1^{\bullet 2^n}, n \geq 0\}$ (# is punctuation).
(e) Repetition: $\mathcal{L} = \{ww | w \in \{0,1\}^*\}$.
(f) Palindromes: $\mathcal{L} = \{w | w \in \{0,1\}^*, w = w^{\mathrm{R}}\}$.
(g) Add Two: $\mathcal{L} = \{0^{\bullet n}1^{\bullet n+2}\}$.
(h) Inequality: $\mathcal{L} = \{0^{\bullet m}1^{\bullet n} \mid n \geq m^2\}$.

Problem 26.7. Can both of the problems $\mathcal{L}_1 = \{0^{\bullet n}\#0^{\bullet n^2} \mid n \geq 0\}$ and $\mathcal{L}_2 = \{0^{\bullet n^2} \mid n \geq 0\}$ be solved on a Turing Machine? Which problem do you think is trickier (give the intuition for why)?

Problem 26.8. In each case, give high level pseudocode for a transducer Turing Machine M for the problem.

(a) Add Two: The input is $0^{\bullet n}$ and M halts with $0^{\bullet n+2}$ on the tape.
(b) Multiplication by 2: The input is $0^{\bullet n}$ and M halts with $0^{\bullet 2n}$ on the tape.
(c) Squaring: The input is $0^{\bullet n}$ and M halts with $0^{\bullet n^2}$ on the tape.
(d) Exponentiate: The input is $0^{\bullet n}$ and M halts with $0^{\bullet 2^n}$ on the tape.
(e) Copying: The input is w and M halts with ww on the tape.
(f) Reversal: The input is w and M halts with w^{R} on the tape.
(g) Switching: The input is $w\#v$ and M halts with $v\#w$ on the tape.
(h) Delete first: The input is xw where $x \in \Sigma$ and $w \in \Sigma^*$, and M halts with w on the tape.
(i) Prefixing: The input is $w \in \Sigma^*$ and M halts with $0w$ on the tape.
(j) Binary to unary: The input w is the binary representation of n and M halts with $0^{\bullet n}$ on the tape.
(k) Unary to binary: The input is $0^{\bullet n}$ and M halts with binary representation of n on the tape. .
(l) Binary addition: The input is $w_1\#w_2$, two binary strings and M halts with $w_1 + w_2$ (binary addition) on the tape.
(m) Division: The input is $0^{\bullet n}$. M rejects if n is odd. If n is even, M accepts with $0^{\bullet n/2}$ on the tape.

Problem 26.9. An LR-Turing Machine must move left or right at every step. An LRS-Turing Machine can move left, right or stay put at every step. Prove that the LRS-TM model is *not* more powerful than the LR-TM model. That is, any language that can be decided by an LRS-TM can also be decided by an LR-TM. *[Hint: "stay" = LR.]*

Problem 26.10. If $\mathcal{L}$ is decidable, show that $\overline{\mathcal{L}}$ is decidable. How do you get a decider for $\overline{\mathcal{L}}$ from one for $\mathcal{L}$?

Problem 26.11. If a Turing Machine can't write on slots containing the input, prove that it can't decide $\{0^{\bullet n}1^{\bullet n}\}$. (More generally, the language of such a TM must be regular.)

> A pessimist sees the difficulty in every opportunity; an optimist sees the opportunity in every difficulty. – **Winston Churchill**
>
> The best way out is always through. – **Robert Frost**
>
> Good things are fragile, for there are many ways to fail.
> – **Anna Karenina principle (paraphrased)**

Chapter 27

Unsolvable Problems

1: Programmable Turing Machines: the universal Turing Machine.
2: The Halting Problem is unsolvable.

Turing Machines that always halt are our model of computing, a precise definition of algorithm.

Intuitive notion of algorithm	$\equiv$	Turing Machine
Solvable problem	$\equiv$	Turing-decidable language

A programmer would love an all powerful ultimate-debugger-tool that tells whether a program halts or loops forever. The ultimate-debugger solves the HALTING PROBLEM. Can we build an ultimate-debugger?

Pop Quiz 27.1 [The Teaching-Assistant-Tormentor]

An Intro-To-CS assignment asks for a program to print "Hello World!" to a file and exit. The TA created AUTO-GRADE to grade the submissions. A diabolical student handed in this program, shown in pseudocode:

```
// Dear TA: If you correctly grade my program you will be famous☺.
for(n = 4,6,8...)
   if(n is not a sum of two primes) print("Hello World!") and exit;
```

(a) Explain the student's cryptic comment about the TA becoming famous.
(b) Show how to use an ultimate-debugger to resolve Goldbach's conjecture.
(c) A program CONFUSED runs AUTO-GRADE on CONFUSED, i.e. itself. If AUTO-GRADE says (NO), CONFUSED prints "Hello World!" and halts; if AUTO-GRADE says (YES), CONFUSED halts with no output. When you run CONFUSED, does it print "Hello World" or not? Is your head spinning yet?

27.1 Sketching Turing Machines

Like any algorithm, Turing Machines can be described at different depths, the deepest being the full description with all machine-level instructions. The high-level description summarizes the steps, showing how the read-write head is controlled, without full machine-level instructions (e.g. the high-level Turing Machine for $w\#w$ on page 387). The shallowest description is a sketch that ignores all implementation details such as how the read-write head moves. Let us illustrate sketches on the graph-connectivity problem,

$$\mathcal{L} = \{\langle G\rangle \mid G \text{ is a connected graph, having a path between every pair of vertices}\}.$$

Recall that $\langle G\rangle$ is the encoding of graph G as a string. One way to encode G is to list nodes, then undirected edges. An encoding for the graph on the right with semi-colons separating list-entries is

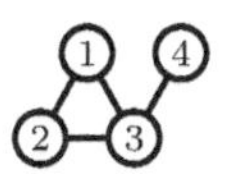

$$\langle G\rangle = \texttt{1;2;3;4\#1,2;2,3;1,3;3,4}.$$

For visual clarity, we kept the encoding in ASCII, but it can be converted to binary using the ASCII code. Here is a sketch of a Turing Machine that takes $\langle G\rangle$ as input and solves the graph connectivity problem.

M = Turing Machine for graph connectivity
INPUT: $\langle G\rangle$, the encoding of a graph G.
1: Check that $\langle G\rangle$ is a valid encoding of a graph and mark the first node in G.
2: REPEAT: Find an edge in G between a marked and an unmarked node.
Mark the unmarked node or GOTO step 3 if there is no such edge.
3: REJECT if there is an unmarked node remaining in G; otherwise ACCEPT.

Behold! Turing Machine sketches look very much like pseudocode.

Exercise 27.2
Show how the algorithm works on the example graph above. Convert the sketch to a high-level description, explaining how the read-write head moves over $\langle G\rangle$ at each step.

Example 27.1 (Decidable languages are closed under union). If $\mathcal{L}_1$ and $\mathcal{L}_2$ are decidable, then so is $\mathcal{L}_1 \cup \mathcal{L}_2$. Let M_1 and M_2 be deciders for $\mathcal{L}_1$ and $\mathcal{L}_2$. Here is a sketch of a Turing Machine M that decides $\mathcal{L}_1 \cup \mathcal{L}_2$.

M = Turing Machine that decides $\mathcal{L}_1 \cup \mathcal{L}_2$ given deciders M_1 and M_2 for $\mathcal{L}_1$ and $\mathcal{L}_2$.
INPUT: w
1: Run M_1 on w. If M_1 accepts, then ACCEPT. If M_1 rejects, perform step 2.
2: Run M_2 on w. If M_2 accepts, then ACCEPT. If M_2 rejects, then REJECT.

Since M_1 and M_2 always halt, M always halts. If $w \in \mathcal{L}_1$, M accepts in step 1. If $w \notin \mathcal{L}_1$, but $w \in \mathcal{L}_2$, then M accepts in step 2. How does M first run M_1 and then M_2 (as "subroutines")? The challenge is that M_1 may alter the input and M cannot "Run M_2 on w," since there is no w anymore. A solution is to copy w onto a second tape. Now run M_1 on the first tape (with w), and then M_2 on the second tape (with w). But, a Turing Machine has only one tape. A trick to simulate two tapes using a single tape is to merge the two tapes onto one tape, using the even slots for the first tape and the odd slots for the second tape.

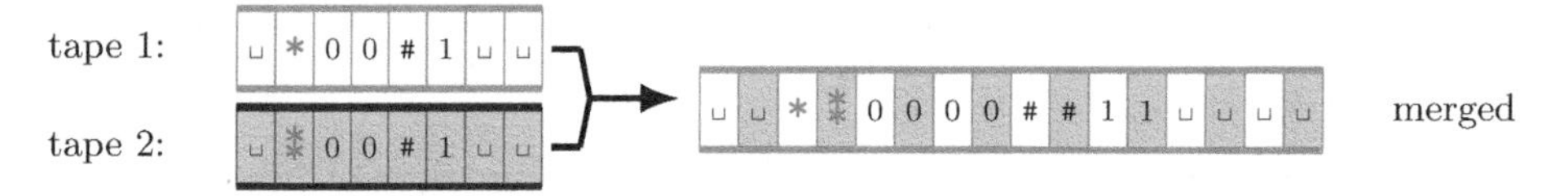

First M replicates w and interleaves the two copies of w. Then, starting at $*$, M runs M_1 on w except that whenever M_1 moves right or left, M moves 2 steps right or left to stay on the "correct tape". If M_1 accepts, M accepts. If M_1 rejects, M moves to ⁑ and simulates M_2, again moving 2 steps for every move M_2 makes. By the way, you see that two tapes are not more powerful than one when it comes to what one can solve, because one tape can simulate two tapes. Parallelism can't change what you can and cannot solve.

Exercise 27.3
Does our construction of M work for showing that recognizable languages are closed under union? Explain.

□

27.2 Programmable Turing Machines

Computers solve different problems by executing different programs. The deficiency of a Turing Machine is that it solves one task. Our Turing Machines for $w\#w$ and graph connectivity are different machines. We can't build a new machine for every problem. We need a programmable Turing Machine which takes as input the encoding of another Turing Machine M (the "program") and a string w. The programmable Turing Machine should run M on w. Rather than build M, we feed its encoding $\langle M\rangle$ into the programmable Turing Machine. Such a universal Turing Machine that can simulate any Turing Machine exists. We call it a computer.

We name our universal Turing Machine U_{TM} and stress that U_{TM} is a Turing Machine. The novelty in U_{TM} is that its input string has the special format $\langle M\rangle\#w$ where $\langle M\rangle$ is the binary encoding of some Turing Machine M and w is a binary string which is the input of M. The encoding of M and its input w are separated by some punctuation character # which does not appear anywhere else. Note, the input to U_{TM} is $\langle M\rangle\#w$ and the input to M is w. U_{TM} works by processing $\langle M\rangle\#w$ and then outputting whatever M outputs on w:

$$U_{\text{TM}}(\langle M\rangle\#w) = \begin{cases} \text{halt with ACCEPT} & \text{if } M(w) = \text{halt with ACCEPT;} \\ \text{halt with REJECT} & \text{if } M(w) = \text{halt with REJECT;} \\ \text{loop forever} & \text{if } M(w) = \text{loop forever;} \end{cases}$$

> U_{TM} outputs on $\langle M\rangle\#w$ whatever M outputs on w

U_{TM} is our programmable Turing Machine, $\langle M\rangle$ is its program and w the input to the program. U_{TM} executes or simulates M on w. The first universal Turing Machine was proposed by Alan Turing in his seminal 1936 paper, and it played an important role in the history of stored-program computers. We won't exhibit a full implementation of a universal Turing Machine. We just say one or two things about what is involved.

The challenge is that U_{TM} is fixed, with a fixed number of states and fixed instructions. Yet, U_{TM} must simulate any Turing Machine, even one with a billion states. The key is to simulate M on the tape. The encoding of M must list the states and transition instructions of M. By marking the tape, U_{TM} keeps track of M's state (●) and the position of M's read-write head (▽). In the illustration below, the gray region stores the program $\langle M\rangle$. U_{TM} moves around examining M to find out what to do on w (stored next to $\langle M\rangle$).

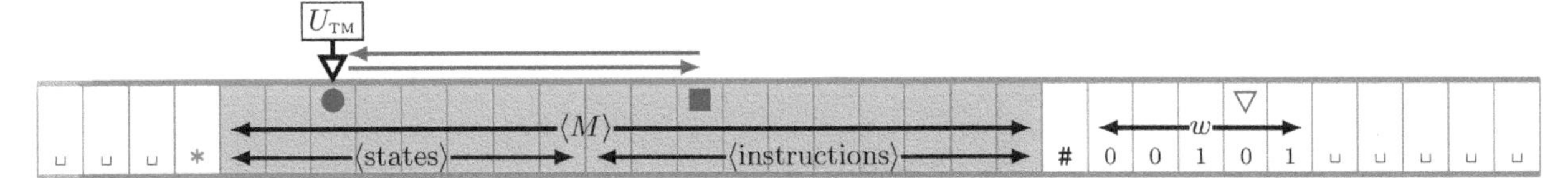

- U_{TM} zig-zags between the states and instructions in $\langle M\rangle$ to find the instruction that matches the current state at ● and the current bit at ▽. The appropriate instruction is temporarily marked ■.
- The instruction at ■ tells U_{TM} the next state for M. The previous state is unmarked and more zig-zaging is used to locate and mark the next state. The transition-instruction also indicates any change to the bit at ▽ and how M's read-write head ▽ should be moved (L, R, S).
- The simulation of one step is complete with ● and ▽ repositioned. U_{TM} is ready for M's next step.

Pop Quiz 27.4
Why does U_{TM} have to zig-zag to find the right transition instruction? That is, why can't U_{TM} remember the current state and find the correct transition with a single scan?

If our sketch doesn't convince you that U_{TM} is well defined, go ahead and build it (fewer than 20 states suffice). Of more interest to us is the language recognized by any universal Turing Machine. Define the strings accepted by U_{TM} as $\mathcal{L}_{\text{TM}}$, strings of the form $\langle M\rangle\#w$ where M is a Turing Machine and M accepts w, i.e. $w \in \mathcal{L}(M)$,

$$\mathcal{L}_{\text{TM}} = \{\langle M\rangle\#w \mid M \text{ is a Turing Machine and } M \text{ accepts } w, \text{ so } U_{\text{TM}} \text{ outputs (YES) on } \langle M\rangle\#w\}. \tag{27.1}$$

$\mathcal{L}_{\text{TM}}$ is the language of successful Turing Machines. By construction, $\mathcal{L}_{\text{TM}}$ is recognizable, and U_{TM} recognizes $\mathcal{L}_{\text{TM}}$. U_{TM} is only a recognizer because it loops forever when M loops forever on w. What a thrill it would be to have a decider for $\mathcal{L}_{\text{TM}}$. A decider for $\mathcal{L}_{\text{TM}}$ would be like an oracle. If M accepts w, the decider accepts $\langle M\rangle\#w$, just like U_{TM}. If M does not accept w, the decider must halt and reject $\langle M\rangle\#w$. In contrast, U_{TM} runs into a problem if M loops forever on w because U_{TM} simulates M. Somehow our decider has to detect that M will loop forever and reject, i.e. our decider implicitly solves the HALTING PROBLEM. From a programmer's perspective, $\mathcal{L}_{\text{TM}}$ contains programs which terminate successfully. A decider for $\mathcal{L}_{\text{TM}}$ is a program that looks at another program and determines ahead of time whether it terminates successfully.

The idea of a program taking another program as input is not absurd. A compiler does exactly that. A compiler, among other tasks, determines if the input program is syntactically valid. Perhaps we can go a step further and make a mega-compiler that determines not only if the program is valid, but also if it will terminate successfully. Don't hold your breath. We will prove that such a mega-compiler is impossible.

27.3 $\mathcal{L}_{\text{TM}}$ is Undecidable: There's No Mega-Compiler

In 1931, Kurt Gödel caused tremors in mathematics. He showed that axiomatic systems powerful enough to contain arithmetic are either inconsistent or incomplete. Gödel gave a precise construction of the claim

"This proposition cannot be proved."

Is the claim F, i.e. provable? If so, a falsity is provable and mathematics is inconsistent. In a consistent mathematics only truths are provable and the claim must be T, i.e. unprovable. A true claim is unprovable and mathematics is incomplete. Mathematics must be consistent, hence it is incomplete. Hilbert's dream of an axiomatic system in which all true statements are provable is a fantasy.

Alan Turing, in 1936, did a similar thing to computing. First, he invents a model of computing, the Turing Machine. Then, he unveils important problems that simply cannot be computed. If the smartest alien species in the universe threatened us with extinction, we could save ourselves by asking them to create a program that would determine if the software running their ship was infinite-loop-free. Turing's proof is actually not too hard, but it is an abstract proof by contradiction, similar to Gödel's proof of incompleteness.

Let us assume $\mathcal{L}_{\text{TM}}$ is decidable and A_{TM} is a decider for $\mathcal{L}_{\text{TM}}$, which by assumption exists. Construct the following diabolical "Diagonal" Turing Machine D, a decider that uses A_{TM} as a subroutine.

D = "Diagonal" Turing Machine derived from A_{TM} (the decider for $\mathcal{L}_{\text{TM}}$)
INPUT: $\langle M\rangle$ where M is a Turing Machine.
1: Run A_{TM} with input $\langle M\rangle\#\langle M\rangle$.
2: If A_{TM} accepts then REJECT. If (A_{TM} rejects then ACCEPT.

The input $\langle M\rangle\#\langle M\rangle$ to A_{TM} is curious, hence the term "Diagonal" for D. We are used to A_{TM}'s input being $\langle M\rangle\#w$. But, w can be any binary string, in particular the encoding of M itself. In Step 1, running A_{TM} on $\langle M\rangle\#\langle M\rangle$ outputs what M says when run on itself. Step 1 always halts because A_{TM} is a decider. Therefore, D always halts and is a decider. This diabolical Diagonal Turing Machine D will be the undoing of A_{TM}.

Finite binary strings are countable, see Example 22.5 on page 331. Turing Machines map uniquely (injectively) to finite binary strings, so Turing Machines are countable and can be listed. Here is such a list,

List of Turing Machines: $\langle M_1\rangle, \langle M_2\rangle, \langle M_3\rangle, \langle M_4\rangle, \ldots, \langle D\rangle, \ldots$

Our diabolical machine D must be on this list. Here is a table of the result when A_{TM} runs on $\langle M_i\rangle\#\langle M_j\rangle$.

$A_{\text{TM}}(\langle M_i\rangle\#\langle M_j\rangle)$	$\langle M_1\rangle$	$\langle M_2\rangle$	$\langle M_3\rangle$	$\langle M_4\rangle$	$\cdots$	$\langle D\rangle$	$\cdots$
$\langle M_1\rangle$	ACCEPT	ACCEPT	REJECT	ACCEPT	$\cdots$	ACCEPT	$\cdots$
$\langle M_2\rangle$	REJECT	REJECT	REJECT	ACCEPT	$\cdots$	ACCEPT	$\cdots$
$\langle M_3\rangle$	ACCEPT	ACCEPT	REJECT	REJECT	$\cdots$	ACCEPT	$\cdots$
$\langle M_4\rangle$	ACCEPT	REJECT	REJECT	REJECT	$\cdots$	ACCEPT	$\cdots$
$\vdots$			$\vdots$		$\cdots$	$\vdots$	$\cdots$
$\langle D\rangle$	REJECT	ACCEPT	ACCEPT	ACCEPT	$\cdots$	ACCEPT / REJECT ?	$\cdots$
$\vdots$			$\vdots$		$\cdots$	$\vdots$	$\ddots$

For example, A_{TM} rejects $\langle M_2\rangle\#\langle M_3\rangle$. This means M_2 either rejects or loops forever on the input $\langle M_3\rangle$. The diagonal entries are what happens when M_i runs on its own description $\langle M_i\rangle$. By construction, D rejects $\langle M_i\rangle$ if and only if M_i accepts $\langle M_i\rangle$. That is, the row for $\langle D\rangle$ is the opposite of the underlined diagonal entries in the table. This is reminiscent of Cantor diagonalization to show reals can't be listed. We use diagonalization to show that D can't exist. The problem is the diagonal entry in the row for $\langle D\rangle$. This entry is the opposite of itself! That's a contradiction. Let us work through the contradiction for both cases.

(i) $A_{TM}(\langle D\rangle\#\langle D\rangle)$ = YES —D outputs opposite of A_{TM}→ $D(\langle D\rangle)$ = NO
A_{TM} says what D does → $D(\langle D\rangle)$ = YES

(ii) $A_{TM}(\langle D\rangle\#\langle D\rangle)$ = NO —D outputs opposite of A_{TM}→ $D(\langle D\rangle)$ = YES
A_{TM} says what D does on $\langle D\rangle$ → $D(\langle D\rangle)$ = NO

Both cases give a contradiction, so D cannot exist. But, to have D, all we need is A_{TM}. Hence, A_{TM} cannot exist. If A_{TM} cannot exist, then $\mathcal{L}_{TM}$ must be undecidable.

Theorem 27.2. $\mathcal{L}_{TM}$ is undecidable. No mega-compiler exists.

Analyzing a program to say if it terminates successfully on an input is not solvable by an algorithm on any computing platform. ☹

Automated program analysis of a general program on a general input is not possible. For particular cases, it may be possible to analyze the program and determine the outcome, but this analysis cannot be made into a general algorithm. It turns out that there is also a demonic fixed program, i.e., Turing Machine, whose behavior on a general input is undecidable. Automated analysis of this single program is not possible.

Exercise 27.5
Show that some demonic fixed Turing Machine U has an undecidable language $\mathcal{L}(U)$. Recall that $\mathcal{L}(U)$ contains the strings on which U halts and accepts. U may infinitely loop on NO-strings. *[Hint: Why U?]*

Our model of computing, the Turing Machine, is powerful enough to solve every problem solvable on a modern computer. We even have the programmable Turing Machine U_{TM}, so you only need to build one machine (hardware) that can simulate any other machine M from its description $\langle M\rangle$ (software). The precise format for encoding Turing Machines into strings is a programming language. We are at our usual crossroads, confronted by a quite natural problem that is unsolvable. No Turing Machine can determines whether a given program will terminate successfully on its input. Do we need a better model of computing?

Unfortunately, the situation is similar to Gödel's incompleteness of mathematics. Any consistent mathematical system complex enough to include arithmetic must contain statements that are true but cannot be proven. Similarly with computing. Once you have a model of computing that is powerful enough to construct a powerful universal machine U_{TM} that simulates any other machine from a description, you open the door to "incompleteness". An unsolvable problem like $\mathcal{L}_{TM}$ becomes inevitable. Just as in mathematics, there are truths that cannot be proved, in computing there are problems that cannot be solved. Unsolvable problems are a fact of life. To survive, we must know what is unsolvable, so we can focus efforts elsewhere.

Exercise 27.6
Assume $\mathcal{L}_{TM}$ is solvable and A_{TM} decides $\mathcal{L}_{TM}$. Sketch a Turing Machine that determines if Goldbach's Conjecture is true. Does this mean Goldbach's Conjecture is unprovable?

27.4 Other Unsolvable Problems: Reduction

Once Turing proved that $\mathcal{L}_{TM}$ is undecidable, it opened the flood gates. Any problem harder than $\mathcal{L}_{TM}$ must also be unsolvable. How can one show that a problem is harder than $\mathcal{L}_{TM}$? The technique is reduction.

Reducing one problem to another is a powerful. Later, in an algorithms course, you will learn classic algorithms like sorting, linear programming, max-flow, shortest paths, etc. These algorithms not only solve important problems, but also form the basis for solving other problems using reduction. Suppose you want to find the minimum of a list, but only know how to sort using a black-box sorter. Can you find the minimum? Yes. Use the black-box sorter and take the first element in the sorted list.

IF you can sort, THEN you can find the minimum.

Our argument shows that finding the minimum is easier than sorting, which prompts the notation

$$\text{finding the minimum} \le_{\text{R}} \text{sorting}.$$

On a hardness-scale, finding the minimum is less than equal to sorting. The subscript-R is for reduction. We say that finding the minimum is reducible to sorting. Here is an algebraic example. Addition, subtraction and division by 2 (shift) are basic operations in binary. Suppose you can square a number using only basic operations. Can you multiply two arbitrary numbers? Yes, and here is why:

$$xy = \left(\tfrac{1}{2}(x+y)\right)^2 - \left(\tfrac{1}{2}(x-y)\right)^2.$$

The formula shows that multiplication is not harder than squaring. Multiplication reduces to squaring,

IF you can square, THEN you can multiply;
multiplication $\le_{\text{R}}$ squaring.

This is counter intuitive because multiplying arbitrary numbers seems more general than squaring (multiplying a number with itself), yet it is true. We now use a reduction to show that the ultimate-debugger, which tells you whether a program will halt or loop, does not exist. That is, the HALTING PROBLEM is unsolvable by an algorithm. Define the language $\mathcal{L}_{\text{HALT}}$ which corresponds to the HALTING PROBLEM,

$$\mathcal{L}_{\text{HALT}} = \{\langle M\rangle\#w \mid M \text{ halts when run on } w\}.$$

A decider for $\mathcal{L}_{\text{HALT}}$ is the ultimate-debugger that decides whether Turing Machine M halts on w. A decider for $\mathcal{L}_{\text{TM}}$ is similar, deciding whether M accepts w. We show that if you can solve $\mathcal{L}_{\text{HALT}}$, you can solve $\mathcal{L}_{\text{TM}}$.

Theorem 27.3. IF $\mathcal{L}_{\text{HALT}}$ is decidable, THEN $\mathcal{L}_{\text{TM}}$ is decidable. That is, $\mathcal{L}_{\text{TM}} \le_{\text{R}} \mathcal{L}_{\text{HALT}}$.

Theorem 27.3 says $\mathcal{L}_{\text{TM}}$ is reducible to $\mathcal{L}_{\text{HALT}}$, that is $\mathcal{L}_{\text{TM}}$ is easier than $\mathcal{L}_{\text{HALT}}$. Theorem 27.3 asserts an implication, which doesn't prove anything useful until we add more information (recall our discussion of logical implication in Chapter 4 on page 41). The additional known information is that $\mathcal{L}_{\text{TM}}$ is undecidable.

Theorem 27.4. $\mathcal{L}_{\text{HALT}}$ is undecidable. The HALTING PROBLEM is unsolvable and there is no ultimate-debugger.

Proof. (Contradiction) Assume $\mathcal{L}_{\text{HALT}}$ is decidable. By Theorem 27.3, $\mathcal{L}_{\text{TM}}$ is decidable, a contradiction. ■

Let's now prove Theorem 27.3 which establishes that $\mathcal{L}_{\text{HALT}}$ is harder than $\mathcal{L}_{\text{TM}}$.

Proof. (of Theorem 27.3) We use a direct proof of the implication. Assume that $\mathcal{L}_{\text{HALT}}$ is decidable, and let H_{TM} be a decider for $\mathcal{L}_{\text{HALT}}$. We use H_{TM} to construct A_{TM}, a decider for $\mathcal{L}_{\text{TM}}$. Here is the idea. Run H_{TM} to determine if M halts. If M does not halt, reject. If M does halt, then simulate M on w by running a universal Turing Machine U_{TM} on $\langle M\rangle\#w$ to determine accept or reject. Here is the sketch of A_{TM}.

A_{TM} = Turing Machine derived from H_{TM} (the decider for $\mathcal{L}_{\text{HALT}}$)
INPUT: $\langle M\rangle\#w$ where M is a Turing Machine and w an input to M.
1: Run H_{TM} on input $\langle M\rangle\#w$. If H_{TM} rejects, then REJECT and halt.
2: Run U_{TM} on input $\langle M\rangle\#w$ and output the decision U_{TM} gives.

In step 1, the decider H_{TM} must halt. Step 2 only runs if H_{TM} accepts $\langle M\rangle\#w$, which means M halts on w, so U_{TM}, when it simulates M on w, must halt. Thus, A_{TM} always halts. Further, A_{TM} accepts $\langle M\rangle\#w$ if and only if U_{TM} accepts $\langle M\rangle\#w$ in step 2, which happens if and only if M accepts w. Therefore, A_{TM} decides $\mathcal{L}_{\text{TM}}$. ■

We summarize the steps in our proof that $\mathcal{L}_{\text{HALT}}$ is unsolvable into a general method for proving undecidability.

To prove that a problem $\mathcal{L}$ is undecidable:

1: Find an undecidable problem $\mathcal{L}_*$ which you believe is easier than $\mathcal{L}$. Usually $\mathcal{L}_* = \mathcal{L}_{\text{TM}}$ or $\mathcal{L}_{\text{HALT}}$.
2: Show that $\mathcal{L}_* \le_{\text{R}} \mathcal{L}$, that is, $\mathcal{L}$ is indeed harder than an undecidable problem. You must show:

IF there is a decider M for $\mathcal{L}$, THEN there is a decider M_* for $\mathcal{L}_*$.

To show this, you must explicitly sketch a decider M_* for $\mathcal{L}_*$, which uses M as a subroutine.

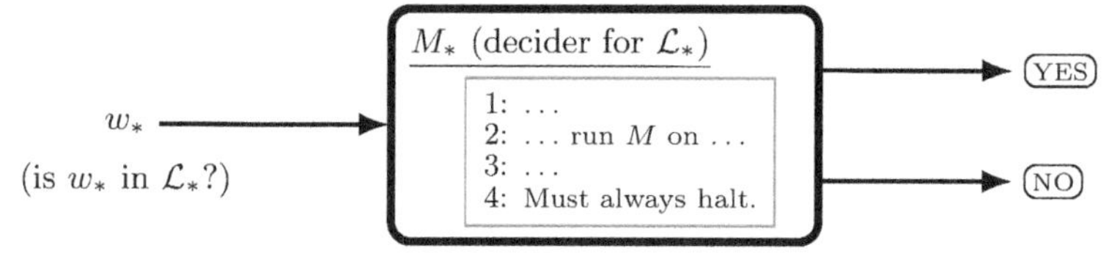

A common confusion in such undecidability proofs arises because:

- You are trying to prove that $\mathcal{L}$ is undecidable.
- Yet, you actually prove that $\mathcal{L}_*$ is decidable, to get a contradiction.

Overcome this confusion by understanding why you do it this way. Don't memorize. Be careful in such proofs, because the direction of the reduction is very important. You must show that your problem is harder than a known undecidable problem (often $\mathcal{L}_{\text{TM}}$ or $\mathcal{L}_{\text{HALT}}$). The proof takes getting used to, but know this fact:

There is no ultimate-debugger to tell if a program halts or loops forever. ☹

Exercise 27.7
In each case, formulate a language and show that the problem is unsolvable.
(a) Determining whether a Turing Machine M accepts any strings.
(b) Determining if two Turing Machines are equivalent and accept the same strings.

27.4.1 Post's Correspondence Problem (PCP)

The HALTING PROBLEM and $\mathcal{L}_{\text{TM}}$ look esoteric and abstract, dealing with intricacies of Turing Machines. Recall the domino problem from Section 1.4, which is easy to grasp as a visual puzzle. You have an unlimited supply of three dominoes d_1, d_2, d_3, where the top and bottom entry of each domino is a binary string:

$$\begin{array}{ccc} d_1 & d_2 & d_3 \\ \begin{bmatrix} 0 \\ 100 \end{bmatrix} & \begin{bmatrix} 01 \\ 00 \end{bmatrix} & \begin{bmatrix} 110 \\ 11 \end{bmatrix} \end{array} \tag{27.2}$$

Dominoes can be lined up in any order, with repetition, to produce a combined domino in which the top string is the concatenation of all the top strings in order, and similarly for the bottom string. For example,

$$d_3d_2d_3d_1 = \begin{bmatrix} 110 \\ 11 \end{bmatrix}\begin{bmatrix} 01 \\ 00 \end{bmatrix}\begin{bmatrix} 110 \\ 11 \end{bmatrix}\begin{bmatrix} 0 \\ 100 \end{bmatrix} = \begin{bmatrix} 110011100 \\ 110011100 \end{bmatrix}$$

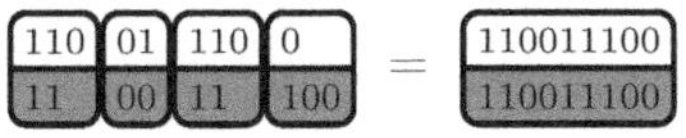

In this example, the combined top and bottom strings are equal. That is the goal, and $d_3d_2d_3d_1$ is a solution. This domino problem is called Post's Correspondence Problem, PCP. Here is another instance of PCP,

$$\begin{array}{ccc} d_1 & d_2 & d_3 \\ \begin{bmatrix} 10 \\ 101 \end{bmatrix} & \begin{bmatrix} 011 \\ 11 \end{bmatrix} & \begin{bmatrix} 101 \\ 011 \end{bmatrix} \end{array} \tag{27.3}$$

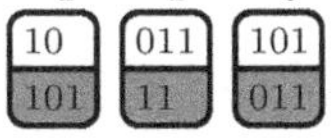

Here is an attempt to match the top and bottom string in the combined domino,

$$d_1d_3d_3 = \begin{bmatrix} 10 \\ 101 \end{bmatrix}\begin{bmatrix} 101 \\ 011 \end{bmatrix}\begin{bmatrix} 101 \\ 011 \end{bmatrix} = \begin{bmatrix} 10101101 \\ 101011011 \end{bmatrix}$$

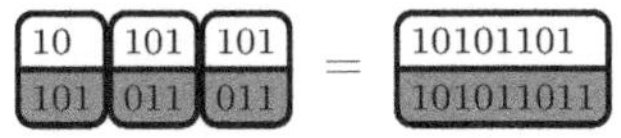

As you can see, the top and bottom strings do not match, for the top string is one bit shorter.

Exercise 27.8
Prove that no finite sequence of dominos has equal top and bottom strings for the instance of PCP in (27.3).

We can encode a general instance of PCP with n dominoes into a string as follows,

$$\alpha_1\#\alpha_2\#\cdots\#\alpha_n\#\#\beta_1\#\beta_2\#\cdots\#\beta_n$$

where α_i and β_i are the top and bottom string in domino d_i. The task is to determine if some finite sequence of dominoes has equal top and bottom string. We can formulate a language $\mathcal{L}_{\text{PCP}}$ corresponding to PCP,

$$\mathcal{L}_{\text{PCP}} = \left\{ \alpha_1\#\cdots\#\alpha_n\#\#\beta_1\#\cdots\#\beta_n \;\middle|\; \begin{array}{c} \text{for some } \ell > 0 \text{ and } 1 \le i_1, \ldots, i_\ell \le n, \\ \alpha_{i_1}\alpha_{i_2}\cdots\alpha_{i_\ell} = \beta_{i_1}\beta_{i_2}\cdots\beta_{i_\ell} \end{array} \right\}.$$

One can reduce $\mathcal{L}_{\text{TM}}$ to $\mathcal{L}_{\text{PCP}}$, showing PCP is harder than $\mathcal{L}_{\text{TM}}$ and hence undecidable. A computing problem that a 3-year-old could grasp is not solvable by an algorithm. You can't win the $1,000 on offer in Section 1.4.

Theorem 27.5. PCP is undecidable. There is no algorithm to solve a general instance of the domino puzzle.

The proof takes an input $\langle M\rangle\#w$ and constructs an instance of PCP that has a solution if and only if M accepts w. So, if you have a decider for $\mathcal{L}_{\text{PCP}}$, you get a decider for $\mathcal{L}_{\text{TM}}$ by using the PCP-decider on the instance of PCP constructed from $\langle M\rangle\#w$. You may refer to more advanced texts on the theory of computing for the details. We just wanted to show you that "real" problems can be undecidable. Another example is Hilbert's 10th problem which asks for an algorithm to decide whether an integer polynomial equation has integer solutions. In 1970, Yuri Matiyasevich, building on prior work, proved that this problem is undecidable.

Exercise 27.9
Prove that if the strings in the dominos are unary (consisting of only 1's), then PCP is decidable. Sketch a Turing Machine that decides unary-PCP.

27.4.2 Program Verification: "Hello World!"

Recall the industrious TA who created AUTO-GRADE in Pop Quiz 27.1. "Hello World!" could be any string, so let's simplify and use "0". AUTO-GRADE verifies that a program prints only the string "0" to the file and exits. We can formulate a language $\mathcal{L}_{\text{HW}}$ (for Hello World) which AUTO-GRADE decides:

$$\mathcal{L}_{\text{HW}} = \left\{ \langle M\rangle\#w \;\middle|\; \begin{array}{l} M \text{ is a Turing Machine that halts on } w, \\ \text{leaving only the output 0 on the tape.} \end{array} \right\}.$$

```
>Hello World!
>▯
```

Pop Quiz 27.1 shows $\mathcal{L}_{\text{HW}}$ is unsolvable by using CONFUSE to get a self-referential paradox, just like the diagonal argument proving $\mathcal{L}_{\text{TM}}$ is undecidable.

Here is a proof by reduction from the HALTING PROBLEM. Suppose HW_{TM} decides $\mathcal{L}_{\text{HW}}$. We sketch a decider H_{TM} for $\mathcal{L}_{\text{HALT}}$. The decider HW_{TM} solves the HALTING PROBLEM with the additional test that 0 is left on the tape. We just run HW_{TM} and skip testing the tape for 0. The problem is, we do not know how HW_{TM} works. Instead of skipping HW_{TM}'s test for 0, we can ensure that M, after it halts, writes 0 to the tape. Now, HW_{TM} will accept M whenever it halts. Here is a sketch of H_{TM}, built from HW_{TM} using this idea.

H_{TM} = Decider for $\mathcal{L}_{\text{HALT}}$ derived from HW_{TM} (the decider for $\mathcal{L}_{\text{HW}}$)
INPUT: $\langle M\rangle\#w$ where M is a Turing Machine and w an input to M.
1: Modify M to M' as follows:

> M' = Modified version of M
> Run M on its input w.
> Erase the tape, write 0 to the tape's first spot and halt.

2: Obtain $\langle M'\rangle$, the encoding of M'. The encoding of M' depends on $\langle M\rangle$.
3: Run HW_{TM} on $\langle M'\rangle\#w$ and output the decision of HW_{TM}.

Step 2 uses an algorithm to encode Turing Machines to strings. The sketch has some interesting points:

- One can take a Turing Machine $\langle M\rangle$ as input and modify it to $\langle M'\rangle$.
- M or M' are never actually run in H_{TM}. Only their encodings are used, in particular as input to HW_{TM}, which *is* run. Steps 1 and 2 are finite. Since HW_{TM} is a decider, step 3 must halt, so H_{TM} is a decider.
- If M does not halt on w, then M' does not halt and HW_{TM} rejects in step 3. If M halts on w, M' erases the tape, writes 0 and halts. Isn't the tape infinite? Can M' ever finish its task and halt? The insight is that M' only has to erase that part of the tape M ever touched. Since M halted, it only touched a finite part of the tape. So M' halts with 0 on the tape and and HW_{TM} accepts in step 3. Thus H_{TM} is a decider that accepts if and only if M halts on w. That is H_{TM} decides $\mathcal{L}_{\text{HALT}}$, and so HW_{TM} cannot exist.

Exercise 27.10
(a) Sketch a COUNTER that counts the number of steps a Turing Machine executes. *[Hint: Use a second tape and the trick in Example 27.1 on page 388 to merge tapes.]*
(b) A Turing Machine runs for n steps. How many tape-slots can be touched?
(c) Sketch how to implement "Erase the tape," which is used in the sketch of H_{TM}.

You didn't hear this from us. In a programming course, the TAs use an elaborate AUTO-GRADER to grade the many homework submissions. We proved no AUTO-GRADER can exist, so you may have grounds to dispute any grades assigned by such a system.

Exercise 27.11
How should a homework be worded so that an auto-grader can assign valid grades?

27.4.3 Non-Recognizable Languages

Just as a decidable language has a Turing Machine-decider, a recognizable language has a Turing Machine-recognizer. Turing Machines are encoded as finite binary strings which are countable. There are only countably many Turing Machines, hence there can be only countably many recognizable languages. A general language, however, corresponds to an infinite binary string. Recall the argument: let $\{b_1, b_2, \ldots\}$ be a list of all finite strings. A language $\mathcal{L}$ is a subset of these strings which can be identified by the 1's in the infinite string.

infinite binary string →	1	0	1	1	0	0	0	0	1	0	⋯
subset of the finite strings →	b_1	b_2	b_3	b_4	b_5	b_6	b_7	b_8	b_9	b_{10}	⋯

A 1 at position i means $b_i \in \mathcal{L}$. Infinite binary strings are uncountable by Theorem 22.6 on page 332. Hence, the languages are uncountable and so the unrecognizable languages must be uncountable.

Every decidable language is recognizable. So being unrecognizable is worse than being undecidable. Can we exhibit a concrete language that is unrecognizable, given that there are uncountably many of them. Yes. Every undecidable problem implicitly defines at least one unrecognizable problem. We know $\mathcal{L}_{\text{TM}}$ is recognizable and U_{TM} is a recognizer for $\mathcal{L}_{\text{TM}}$. Consider the complement of $\mathcal{L}_{\text{TM}}$,

$$\overline{\mathcal{L}_{\text{TM}}} = \{\langle M \rangle\#w \mid \text{It is not the case that } M \text{ is a Turing Machine that accepts } w\}.$$

You won't be able to come up with a recognizer for $\overline{\mathcal{L}_{\text{TM}}}$. The next exercise proves why.

Exercise 27.12
(a) Prove that $\mathcal{L}$ is decidable if and only if both $\mathcal{L}$ and $\overline{\mathcal{L}}$ are recognizable.
(b) Prove that if $\mathcal{L}$ is undecidable then one or both of $\mathcal{L}$ and $\overline{\mathcal{L}}$ are non-recognizable.
(c) Prove that $\overline{\mathcal{L}_{\text{TM}}}$ and $\overline{\mathcal{L}_{\text{HALT}}}$ are non-recognizable.

We are at the end of our journey on computability, the study of what algorithms can and cannot do. The shaded region below sums up what we can compute (some set inclusions are proved in the problems).

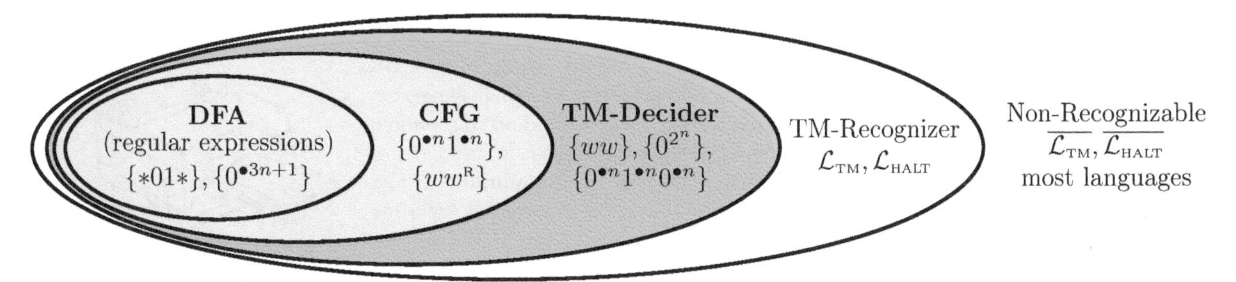

Our answer to the question "What can we compute?" revealed a surprising conclusion. Most problems are not solvable, not even recognizable. Don't fret. Many real world problems are solvable and for these, a good computer scientist must create efficient solutions. We now ask

"What can we compute efficiently?"

Just like the divide between solvable and unsolvable, there is a divide between efficient and inefficient.

27.5 Problems

Problem 27.1. Answer YES or NO and explain your reasoning. "Is the correct answer to Problem 27.1 'NO'?"

Problem 27.2. A collection of sets $\mathcal{C}$ is closed under union and complement. Prove that $\mathcal{C}$ is closed under intersection. If $\mathcal{C}$ were closed under union and intersection, is it necessarily closed under complement?

Problem 27.3. Given an ultimate-debugger which takes $\langle M\rangle\#w$ and decides if TM M halts on input w, show that every recognizer of a language $\mathcal{L}$ can be converted into a decider for the language.

Problem 27.4. Given an untimate-debugger that determines if a program halts, show how to resolve each conjecture.
(a) Goldbach's conjecture that every even number greater than 2 is a sum of two primes.
(b) The twin primes conjecture that n and $n+2$ are prime for infinitely many n.
(c) The Collatz $(3n+1)$ conjecture in Problem 1.43 on page 14.
[Hint: If necessary, you can use the ultimate-debugger on a program which itself uses the ultimate-debugger.]

Problem 27.5. Identify which of DFA, CFG or Turing Machine can solve each problem.
(a) $\mathcal{L} = \{$programs that HALT$\}$ (b) $\mathcal{L} = \{$strings with an even number of 1s$\}$ (c) $\mathcal{L} = \{0^{\bullet n}\#0^{\bullet n^2}, n \geq 0\}$.

Problem 27.6. For $p \geq 0$, define the language $\mathcal{L}_p = \{w \mid \text{length}(w) < p\}$. For what p is $\mathcal{L}_p$ decidable?

Problem 27.7. Define a strange language, $\mathcal{L} = \{w \mid \text{length}(w) < \text{weight of God in lbs}\}$. Is $\mathcal{L}$ decidable?

Problem 27.8 (Hilbert's 10th Problem). A polynomial $p(x;\mathbf{a}) = x^n + a_1x^{n-1} + a_2x^{n-2} + \cdots + a_n$, where $a_i \in \mathbb{Q}$. One must decide if $p(x;\mathbf{a})$ has an integral root, that is $p(x_*;\mathbf{a}) = 0$ for an integer $x_* \in \mathbb{Z}$. Define the language

$$\mathcal{L}_{\text{root}} = \{\langle\mathbf{a}\rangle \mid n \geq 1,\ p(x;\mathbf{a}) \text{ has an integral root}\}.$$

Prove that $\mathcal{L}_{\text{root}}$ is decidable. *[Hint: Show that any root satisfies $|x_*| < (n+1)\max_i |a_i|$. Matiyasevich's Theorem implies no such bound is possible for the multivariate version of Hilbert's 10th problem, which is only recognizable.]*

Problem 27.9. Prove that any regular language is TM-decidable. *[Hint: Encode a DFA in a sketch of a TM.]*

Problem 27.10. Prove that any CFL is TM-decidable. *[Hint: Encode a CFG in a sketch of a TM and use Exercise 25.7]* (Problems 27.9 and 27.10 prove the set inclusions on page 395 that DFA $\subset$ CFG $\subset$ TM.)

Problem 27.11. Show that one can encode a TM in unary, using only 0's. Specifically, sketch a TM that takes a "regular" encoding of a TM as in Section 26.3 and produces the unary encoding. *[Hint: TMs are countable.]*

Problem 27.12. Sketch a universal TM to simulate a TM M on input w from a unary encoding of M (Problem 27.11).

Problem 27.13 (Program Translation). Given a TM M in some encoding $\langle M\rangle_1$, the task is to "translate" it into another encoding $\langle M\rangle_2$. Do you think this problem is solvable by an algorithm?

Problem 27.14 (Enumerators). The ability to generate the strings of a language is useful. A language $\mathcal{L}$ is *enumerable* if some Turing Machine M_{E} sequetially generates all the strings of $\mathcal{L}$, with possible repetition. Envision M_{E} being hooked up to a printer (a second tape). Every now and again, M_{E} prints out a string. Every printed string must be in $\mathcal{L}$ and eventually, every string in L must be printed. So, M_{E} outputs strings $s_1, s_2, \ldots$ where $s_i \in \mathcal{L}$ and if $w \in \mathcal{L}$, then for some i, $s_i = w$. You can stop M_{E} after it has printed i strings and perform operations on the strings $s_1, \ldots, s_i$.
(a) Sketch a recognizer M_{R} for $\mathcal{L}$ given an enumerator M_{E}.
(b) Sketch an enumerator M_{E} for $\mathcal{L}$ given a recognizer M_{R}. Be careful. *[Hint: Let $\Sigma^* = \{w_1, w_2, \ldots\}$. Simulate M_{R} on each of $w_1, \ldots, w_i$ for i steps.]*
(c) Prove that a language is enumerable if and only if it is recognizable.

Problem 27.15. The binary strings in lexicographic order are $\Sigma^* = \{\varepsilon, 0, 1, 00, 01, 10, 11, 000, \ldots\}$. Shorter strings appear first and strings of the same length appear in order of increasing value. Prove that a language $\mathcal{L}$ is decidable if and only if there is an enumerator for $\mathcal{L}$ which prints the strings in lexicographic order.

Problem 27.16. Prove that any recognizable language that is infinite has a decidable subset that is infinite. *[Hint: Problems 27.14 and 27.15.]*

Problem 27.17. You learned that $\mathcal{L}_{\text{TM}}$ is undecidable. You are interested in a problem $\mathcal{L}$ and you suspect that it is unsolvable by an algorithm. Explain how to show that $\mathcal{L}$ is unsolvable.

Problem 27.18. Do you think $\mathcal{L}_{\text{HALT}} \leq_{\text{R}} \mathcal{L}_{\text{TM}}$? Explain your intuition and then give a proof.

Problem 27.19. Intuitively explain the difficulty in constructing a recognizer for the language $\mathcal{L}_{\text{TM-reject}}$, where

$$\mathcal{L}_{\text{TM-reject}} = \{\langle M\rangle\#w \mid M \text{ is a Turing Machine that does not accept } w\}.$$

Prove that $\mathcal{L}_{\text{TM-reject}}$ is non-recognizable. *[Hint: How is $\mathcal{L}_{\text{TM-reject}}$ related to $\overline{\mathcal{L}_{\text{TM}}}$.]*

Problem 27.20. In each case you are given some information and asked to answer a question.
(a) A is reducible to B and A is undecidable. What can you say about B?
(b) A is reducible to B and A is decidable. What can you say about B?
(c) A is reducible to B and B is undecidable. What can you say about A?
(d) A is reducible to B and B is decidable. What can you say about A?

Problem 27.21. Which of the following do you think is decidable? Give your intuition.
(a) Input: $\langle M\rangle$. Does Turing Machine M accept at least one string?
(b) Input: $\langle M\rangle$. Does Turing Machine M accept all strings?
(c) Input: $\langle M\rangle$. Does Turing Machine M accept 011?
(d) Input: $\langle M_1\rangle\#\langle M_2\rangle$. Does Turing Machine M_1 accept more strings than Turing Machine M_2?
(e) Input: $\langle M\rangle\#w$. Does Turing Machine M run for more than 10^6 steps on input w

Definition 27.6. As with $\mathcal{L}_{\text{TM}}$, one can define several interesting problems based on properties of languages and computing machines. We will refer to the list below in later problems.
(a) $\mathcal{L}_{\text{DFA}} = \{\langle M\rangle\#w \mid M \text{ is a DFA and } M \text{ accepts } w.\}$
(b) $\mathcal{L}_{\text{CFG}} = \{\langle C\rangle\#w \mid C \text{ is a CFG and } C \text{ generates } w.\}$
(c) $\mathcal{L}_{\text{TM}} = \{\langle M\rangle\#w \mid M \text{ is a TM and } M \text{ accepts } w.\}$
(d) $\mathcal{L}_{\text{DFA-00}} = \{\langle M\rangle \mid M \text{ is a DFA and } M \text{ accepts the string } 00.\}$
(e) $\mathcal{L}_{\text{CFG-00}} = \{\langle C\rangle \mid C \text{ is a CFG and } C \text{ generates the string } 00.\}$
(f) $\mathcal{L}_{\text{TM-00}} = \{\langle M\rangle \mid M \text{ is a TM and } M \text{ accepts the string } 00.\}$
(g) $\mathcal{L}_{\text{EMPTY-DFA}} = \{\langle M\rangle \mid M \text{ is a DFA and } M \text{ accepts no strings, } \mathcal{L}(M) = \varnothing.\}$
(h) $\mathcal{L}_{\text{EMPTY-CFG}} = \{\langle C\rangle \mid C \text{ is a CFG and } C \text{ generates no strings, } \mathcal{L}(C) = \varnothing.\}$
(i) $\mathcal{L}_{\text{EMPTY-TM}} = \{\langle M\rangle \mid M \text{ is a TM and } M \text{ accepts no strings, } \mathcal{L}(M) = \varnothing.\}$
(j) $\mathcal{L}_{\text{EQ-DFA}} = \{\langle M_1\rangle\#\langle M_1\rangle \mid M_1, M_2 \text{ are DFAs that accept the same strings, } \mathcal{L}(M_1) = \mathcal{L}(M_2).\}$
(k) $\mathcal{L}_{\text{EQ-CFG}} = \{\langle C_1\rangle\#\langle C_2\rangle \mid C_1, C_2 \text{ are CFGs that generate the same strings, } \mathcal{L}(C_1) = \mathcal{L}(C_2).\}$
(l) $\mathcal{L}_{\text{EQ-TM}} = \{\langle M_1\rangle\#\langle M_2\rangle \mid M_1, M_2 \text{ are TMs that accept the same strings, } \mathcal{L}(M_1) = \mathcal{L}(M_2).\}$
(m) $\mathcal{L}_{\text{ALL-DFA}} = \{\langle M\rangle \mid M \text{ is a DFA that accepts all strings, } \mathcal{L}(M) = \Sigma^*.\}$
(n) $\mathcal{L}_{\text{ALL-CFG}} = \{\langle C\rangle \mid C \text{ is a CFG that generates all strings, } \mathcal{L}(C) = \Sigma^*.\}$
(o) $\mathcal{L}_{\text{ALL-TM}} = \{\langle M\rangle \mid M \text{ is a TM that accepts all strings, } \mathcal{L}(M) = \Sigma^*.\}$
(p) $\mathcal{L}_{\text{FINITE-DFA}} = \{\langle M\rangle \mid M \text{ is a DFA that accepts a finite language, } \mathcal{L}(M) \text{ is finite.}\}$
(q) $\mathcal{L}_{\text{FINITE-CFG}} = \{\langle C\rangle \mid C \text{ is a CFG that generates a finite language, } \mathcal{L}(C) \text{ is finite.}\}$
(r) $\mathcal{L}_{\text{FINITE-TM}} = \{\langle M\rangle \mid M \text{ is a TM that accepts a finite language, } \mathcal{L}(M) \text{ is finite.}\}$

Problem 27.22. Answer these questions for the DFA M on the right.
(a) Explain how to get an encoding for the DFA, $\langle M\rangle$.
(b) Is $\langle M\rangle\#011 \in \mathcal{L}_{\text{DFA}}$? Does it depend on your encoding $\langle M\rangle$?
(c) Are $\langle M\rangle$ and/or $\langle M\rangle\#\langle M\rangle$ in these languages? Does it depend on your encoding $\langle M\rangle$?
(i) $\mathcal{L}_{\text{DFA}}$ (ii) $\mathcal{L}_{\text{DFA-00}}$ (iii) $\mathcal{L}_{\text{EMPTY-DFA}}$ (iv) $\mathcal{L}_{\text{EQ-DFA}}$ (v) $\mathcal{L}_{\text{ALL-DFA}}$ (vi) $\mathcal{L}_{\text{FINITE-DFA}}$ (vii) $\mathcal{L}_{\text{TM-00}}$

Problem 27.23. Guess if each problem in Definition 27.6 is decidable, recognizable or neither. Give your intuition.

Problem 27.24. Prove that $\mathcal{L}_{\text{DFA}}$ is decidable (give a sketch of a TM-decider). Is $\mathcal{L}_{\text{DFA-00}}$ decidable?

Problem 27.25. Sketch a TM which can decide if a (YES) state is reachable from the start state of a DFA. Hence, prove that $\mathcal{L}_{\text{EMPTY-DFA}}$ is decidable? *[Hint: Traverse the state diagram of a DFA, which is a directed multigraph.]*

Problem 27.26. Use a decider for $\mathcal{L}_{\text{EMPTY-DFA}}$ to sketch a TM that decides if the language of one DFA is a subset of the language of another DFA. *[Hints: $\mathcal{L}_1 \subseteq \mathcal{L}_2$ iff $\overline{\mathcal{L}_1} \cap L_2 = \varnothing$. Regular languages are closed under set operations.]*

Problem 27.27. Use Problems 27.25 and 27.26 to prove that $\mathcal{L}_{\text{EQ-DFA}}$ is decidable by sketching a TM for $\mathcal{L}_{\text{EQ-DFA}}$.

Problem 27.28. Use Problem 27.25 to prove that $\mathcal{L}_{\text{ALL-DFA}}$ is decidable by sketching a TM for $\mathcal{L}_{\text{ALL-DFA}}$.

Problem 27.29. Prove that $\mathcal{L}_{\text{FINITE-DFA}}$ is decidable by sketching a TM for $\mathcal{L}_{\text{FINITE-DFA}}$. *[Hint: Problem 24.37.]*

Problem 27.30. Prove that $\mathcal{L}_{\text{CFG}}$ is decidable. Is $\mathcal{L}_{\text{CFG-00}}$ decidable? *[Hint: Chomsky Normal Form, Exercise 25.7.]*

Problem 27.31. Prove that $\mathcal{L}_{\text{EMPTY-CFG}}$ is decidable. *[Hint: Work "backwards". Mark all terminals. Repeat: Mark a variable on the left of a production rule if the string produced on the right of the rule has only marked variables.]*

Problem 27.32. By Problem 27.31, one can decide if a CFG generates no strings. Build a decider for $\mathcal{L}_{\text{ALL-CFG}}$ as follows. Given a CFG C for $\mathcal{L}$, construct a CFG $\overline{C}$ for $\overline{L}$ and decide if $\overline{C}$ generates no strings using Problem 27.31. What is wrong with this proof that $\mathcal{L}_{\text{ALL-CFG}}$ is decidable? (Unlike $\mathcal{L}_{\text{ALL-DFA}}$ & $\mathcal{L}_{\text{EQ-DFA}}$, $\mathcal{L}_{\text{ALL-CFG}}$ & $\mathcal{L}_{\text{EQ-CFG}}$ are undecidable.)

Problem 27.33. Sketch a recognizer for $\overline{\mathcal{L}_{\text{EQ-CFG}}}$. What is the difficulty with recognizing $\mathcal{L}_{\text{EQ-CFG}}$?

Problem 27.34. Prove that $\mathcal{L}_{\text{FINITE-CFG}}$ is decidable. *[Hint: Problems 25.29 and 27.30.]*

Problem 27.35. Show that each problem is solvable. You may find it useful to review the closure properties of regular languages and Problems 27.25-27.31.

(a) Determine if a DFA accepts no string with an odd number of 1's.
(b) Determine if a DFA accepts all strings with an odd number of 1's.
(c) Determine if a DFA accepts w^{R}, the reversal of w, whenever it accepts w.
(d) Determine if a DFA, for some string w, accepts both w as well as the reversal w^{R}.

Problem 27.36. Show that each problem is solvable. You may find Problem 25.26 useful.

(a) Determine if a DFA accepts some string of the form $0^{\bullet n}1^{\bullet n}$.
(b) Determine if a DFA accepts some balanced string with an equal number of 1's and 0's.
(c) Determine if a DFA accepts some string with more 1's than 0's.

Problem 27.37. Show that each problem is solvable. You may assume a generalization of Problem 25.26, that the intersection of a CFL with a regular language is context free. Problem 27.31 may be useful.

(a) Determine if a DFA accepts some string which is a palindrome.
(b) Determine if a CFG generates some string whose length is not a multiple of 3.
(c) Determine if a CFG generates some string in $\{1\}^*$.
(d) Determine if a CFG generates all strings in $\{1\}^*$. *[Hint: Problem 25.32.]*

Problem 27.38. Suppose that $A_{\text{TM-00}}$ is a decider for $\mathcal{L}_{\text{TM-00}}$. On the right, we sketch another TM which uses $A_{\text{TM-00}}$.

(a) Does A ever run M on w?
(b) Prove that A is a decider.
(c) Prove that A accepts $\langle M\rangle\#w$ if and only if M accepts w.
(d) What language from Definition 27.6 does A decide?
(e) Prove that $\mathcal{L}_{\text{TM-00}}$ is undecidable.

Make sure you appreciate the difference between running M' on some input versus creating $\langle M'\rangle$ and running $A_{\text{TM-00}}$ on it.

A = TM that uses $A_{\text{TM-00}}$.
INPUT: $\langle M\rangle\#w$
1: Create a new TM M' with encoding $\langle M'\rangle$.
  M' = New TM taking INPUT x
  1: If $x = 00$, run M on w.
     Accept if M accepts.
  2: Otherwise, reject.
2: Output the decision of $A_{\text{TM-00}}$ on $\langle M'\rangle$.

Problem 27.39. Suppose that E is a decider for $\mathcal{L}_{\text{EMPTY-TM}}$. On the right, we sketch another TM which uses E.

(a) Does A ever run M on w?
(b) Prove that A is a decider.
(c) Prove that A accepts $\langle M\rangle\#w$ if and only if M accepts w.
(d) What language from Definition 27.6 does A decide?
(e) Prove that $\mathcal{L}_{\text{EMPTY-TM}}$ is undecidable.

Make sure you appreciate the difference between running M' on some input versus creating $\langle M'\rangle$ and running E on it.

A = TM that uses E.
INPUT: $\langle M\rangle\#w$
1: Create a new TM M' with encoding $\langle M'\rangle$.
  M' = New TM taking INPUT x
  1: If $x = w$, run M on w.
     Accept if M accepts.
  2: Otherwise, reject.
2: Output the opposite decision of E on $\langle M'\rangle$.

Problem 27.40. Problem 27.39 proved that $\mathcal{L}_{\text{EMPTY-TM}}$ is undecidable. Sketch a decider for $\mathcal{L}_{\text{EMPTY-TM}}$ given a decider for $\mathcal{L}_{\text{EQ-TM}}$, and hence prove that $\mathcal{L}_{\text{EQ-TM}}$ is undecidable. *[Hint: Use a vacuous TM whose language is empty.]*

Problem 27.41. Given a TM $\langle M\rangle$, the task is to determine if its language is regular and could be decided by a DFA.

(a) Formulate a language which corresponds to the task. Call this language $\mathcal{L}_{\text{REG-TM}}$.

(b) Let R be a decider for $\mathcal{L}_{\text{REG-TM}}$. On the right, we sketch another TM which uses R.
 (i) Does A ever run M on w?
 (ii) What language does M' accept if M accepts w?
 (iii) What language does M' accept if M does not accept w?
 (iv) Prove that A is a decider which accepts $\langle M\rangle\#w$ if and only if M accepts w.
 (v) Prove that $\mathcal{L}_{\text{REG-TM}}$ is undecidable.

(c) Use the same technique as in (b) to show that no algorithm can decide if a TM accepts a language which is a CFL.

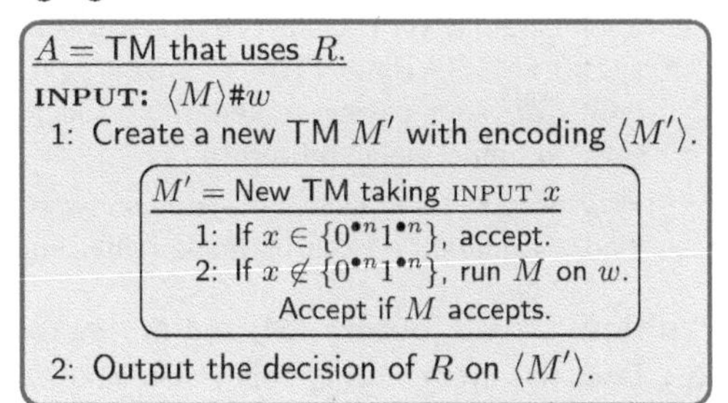

Problem 27.42. Use methods similar to Problems 27.38-27.41 to show that $\mathcal{L}_{\text{ALL-TM}}$ and $\mathcal{L}_{\text{FINITE-TM}}$ are undecidable.

Problem 27.43 (Rice's Theorem). Problems 27.38-27.42 show that testing a TM for a property is undecidable. Indeed this is true for any non-trivial property. Let $\mathcal{L}_{\text{P-TM}}$ be the language of all TMs with property P,

$$\mathcal{L}_{\text{P-TM}} = \{\langle M\rangle \mid M \text{ is a TM that has property } P\}.$$

Property P depends only on the language of the TM, so if $\mathcal{L}(M_1) = \mathcal{L}(M_2)$, then $\langle M_1\rangle \in \mathcal{L}_{\text{P-TM}}$ iff $\langle M_2\rangle \in \mathcal{L}_{\text{P-TM}}$. Property P is non-trivial, which means both $\mathcal{L}_{\text{P-TM}}$ and $\overline{\mathcal{L}_{\text{P-TM}}}$ are nonempty (some TM has property P and some TM does not). Let T_P be a TM with property P, so $\langle T_p\rangle \in \mathcal{L}_{\text{P-TM}}$. Let $T_\varnothing$ be the trivial TM that rejects all strings, so $\mathcal{L}(T_\varnothing) = \varnothing$. Without loss of generality, you may assume that $\langle T_\varnothing\rangle \notin \mathcal{L}_{\text{P-TM}}$. Suppose that $A_{\text{P-TM}}$ decides $\mathcal{L}_{\text{P-TM}}$.

(a) Explain why it is without loss of generality that we may assume $\langle T_\varnothing\rangle \in \mathcal{L}_{\text{P-TM}}$.

(b) On the right, we sketch a TM which uses $\mathcal{L}_{\text{P-TM}}$, T_P and $T_\varnothing$.
 (i) Does A ever run M on w?
 (ii) What language does M' accept if M accepts w?
 (iii) What language does M' accept if M does not accept w?
 (iv) Prove that A is a decider which accepts $\langle M\rangle\#w$ if and only if M accepts w. (Intuitively, A uses $\mathcal{L}_{\text{P-TM}}$'s ability to distinguish between $\langle T_\varnothing\rangle$ and $\langle T_P\rangle$ to decide $\mathcal{L}_{\text{TM}}$.)

(c) Prove Rice's Theorem: $\mathcal{L}_{\text{P-TM}}$ is undecidable for non-trivial P.

(d) Use (c) to prove undecidability of these languages.
 (i) $\mathcal{L}_{\text{TM-00}}$. (ii) $\mathcal{L}_{\text{EMPTY-TM}}$. (iii) $\mathcal{L}_{\text{ALL-TM}}$. (iv) $\mathcal{L}_{\text{FINITE-TM}}$.

(e) Does Rice's Theorem imply that $\mathcal{L}_{\text{EQ-TM}}$ is undecidable?

A = TM that uses $\mathcal{L}_{\text{P-TM}}$, T_P and $T_\varnothing$.
INPUT: $\langle M\rangle\#w$
1: Create a new TM M' with encoding $\langle M'\rangle$.
 M' = New TM taking INPUT x
 1: Run M on w.
 2: If M accepts w, run T_P on x. Accept if T_P accepts.
 3: If M rejects w, reject.
2: Output the decision of $A_{\text{P-TM}}$ on $\langle M'\rangle$.

Problem 27.44. Show that determining if a TM accepts w^{R} (reversal) whenever it accepts w is undecidable.

Problem 27.45. Find a solution to these instances of PCP: (a)

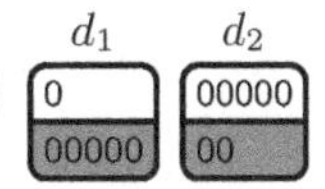

(b)

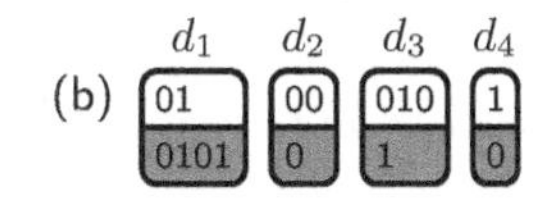

Problem 27.46. Consider a variant of PCP with the restriction that the top and bottom string in every domino must be the same length. Prove that this variant of PCP is decidable by sketching a Turing Machine that solves it.

Problem 27.47. We showed that PCP is undecidable. Is PCP recognizable?

Problem 27.48. Prove that there exists an undecidable language which is a subset of $\{1\}^*$.

Problem 27.49. In your favorite language (e.g. python), write a program that prints an exact copy of itself to a file or stdout. Such a program is called a self-replicating program or *quine*. If you don't think it is possible, explain why.

Problem 27.50. Prove directly by contradiction, not using a reduction from the undecidable problems in this Chapter, that "Hello-World" is undecidable. Obtain a paradox as in Pop Quiz 27.1.

Problem 27.51. Prove the undecidability of an *easier* version of the "Hello-World" autograding task, to determine if a Turing Machine halts with the first bit after the $*$ being 0. (The rest of the tape need not be empty.)

$$\mathcal{L} = \{\langle M\rangle\#w \mid M \text{ is a TM that halts on } w \text{ with 0 as the first bit on the tape after } *\}.$$

Problem 27.52 (Viruses). Define a virus as a program that writes an exact copy of itself to a file and exits.

(a) Prove that virus detection is an undecidable problem.

(b) For a more general type of virus, is virus detection easier or harder?

(c) Look carefully on the antivirus package on the top right. Do you see a 100% GUARANTEE*? Ofcourse, there is an asterisk to fine print. ☹ Fancy paying around fifty bucks for a program that claims to solve an undecidable problem.

How do you think such anti-virus software actually works, and what kinds of guarantees can be made (what kind of fine print is needed)?

Problem 27.53. Suppose M_1 and M_2 are recognizers for $\mathcal{L}_1$ and $\mathcal{L}_2$. Sketch a recognizer M for $\mathcal{L}_1 \cup \mathcal{L}_2$.

(a) Does this attempt at M work? On input w, run $M_1(w)$ and then $M_2(w)$. If M_1 or M_2 accept, M says (YES).

(b) For Turing Machines M_1 and M_2 and input w, give a high-level Turing Machine M which computes $M_1(w)$ and $M_2(w)$ *in parallel*: M should implement a step of M_1's computation, then a step of M_2's computation, then M_1's and so on. That is, M interleaves the computations of $M_1(w)$ with those of $M_2(w)$.

(c) Use (b) to sketch M and show it recognizes $\mathcal{L}_1 \cup \mathcal{L}_2$. Thus, *recognizable* languages are closed under union.

(Alert readers may see a resemblence to proof that countable languages are closed under union in Theorem 22.3.)

Problem 27.54. If $\mathcal{L}$ and $\overline{\mathcal{L}}$ are recognizable, show that $\mathcal{L}$ is decidable by sketching a decider for $\mathcal{L}$. Be careful. You must show how to construct a *decider* for $\mathcal{L}$ given *recognizers* for $\mathcal{L}$ and $\overline{\mathcal{L}}$.

Problem 27.55. Prove that the decidable languages are closed under:
(a) Union. (b) Intersection. (c) Complement. (d) Concatenation. (e) Kleene star. (f) Reversal

Problem 27.56. Prove that the recognizable languages are closed under:
(a) Union. (b) Intersection. (c) Concatenation. (d) Kleene star. (e) Reversal

Problem 27.57. Explain why recognizable languages are not closed under complement.

Problem 27.58. Recall the task to test if two TMs are equivalent, $\mathcal{L}_{\text{EQ-TM}}$ from Definition 27.6.

(a) Show that $\mathcal{L}_{\text{EQ-TM}}$ is non-recognizable. To do this, show that you can use a recognizer for $\mathcal{L}_{\text{EQ-TM}}$ to sketch a recognizer for $\overline{\mathcal{L}_{\text{HALT}}}$ and derive a contradiction from there.

(b) Show that $\overline{\mathcal{L}_{\text{EQ}}}$ is non-recognizable. (A language and its complement can both be non-recognizable.)

Problem 27.59. Recall the task to test if a TM accepts no strings (not even ε), $\mathcal{L}_{\text{EMPTY-TM}}$ from Definition 27.6.

(a) Show that $\overline{\mathcal{L}_{\text{EMPTY-TM}}}$ (the complement of $\mathcal{L}_{\text{EMPTY-TM}}$) is recognizable. Be careful.

(b) What difficulty do you face in trying to construct a recognizer for $\mathcal{L}_{\text{EMPTY-TM}}$? Prove $\mathcal{L}_{\text{EMPTY-TM}}$ is non-recognizable.

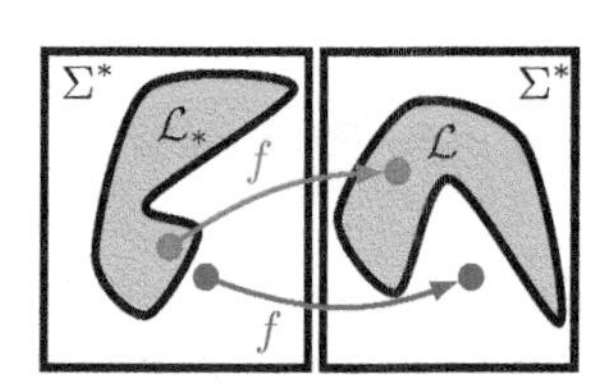

Problem 27.60 (Mapping Reduction). Problem $\mathcal{L}$ is undecidable if a TM M for $\mathcal{L}$ can be used to solve a known undecidable problem $\mathcal{L}_*$. The formal framework is mapping reduction. A computable function f is a transducer-TM that halts on any input w, leaving $f(w)$ on the tape, $f : \Sigma^* \mapsto \Sigma^*$. f *reduces* $\mathcal{L}_*$ to $\mathcal{L}$ if for every w,

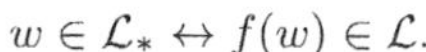

$$w \in \mathcal{L}_* \leftrightarrow f(w) \in \mathcal{L}.$$

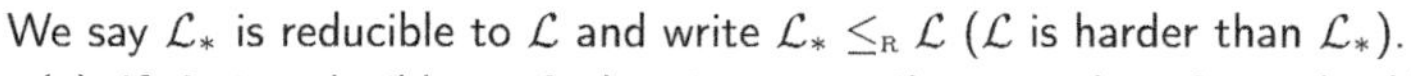

We say $\mathcal{L}_*$ is reducible to $\mathcal{L}$ and write $\mathcal{L}_* \leq_{\text{R}} \mathcal{L}$ ($\mathcal{L}$ is harder than $\mathcal{L}_*$).

(a) If $\mathcal{L}_*$ is reducible to $\mathcal{L}$, does it necessarily mean that $\mathcal{L}$ is reducible to $\mathcal{L}_*$?

(b) If $\mathcal{L}_*$ is reducible to $\mathcal{L}$, does it necessarily mean that $\mathcal{L}$ is reducible to $\overline{\mathcal{L}_*}$?

(c) If $\mathcal{L}_*$ is reducible to $\mathcal{L}$, does it necessarily mean that $\overline{\mathcal{L}}$ is reducible to $\overline{\mathcal{L}_*}$?

(d) If $\mathcal{L}$ is decidable and $\mathcal{L}_*$ is reducible to $\mathcal{L}$, then prove that $\mathcal{L}_*$ is decidable.

(e) If $\mathcal{L}$ is decidable and $\mathcal{L}_*$ is reducible to $\overline{\mathcal{L}}$, then prove that $\mathcal{L}_*$ is decidable.

(f) If $\mathcal{L}$ is recognizable and $\mathcal{L}_*$ is reducible to $\mathcal{L}$, then prove that $\mathcal{L}_*$ is recognizable.

(g) If $\mathcal{L}$ is regular and $\mathcal{L}_*$ is reducible to $\mathcal{L}$, does that mean $\mathcal{L}_*$ is regular. Why or why not?

(h) If $\mathcal{L}_*$ is undecidable and $\mathcal{L}_*$ is reducible to $\mathcal{L}$, then prove that $\mathcal{L}$ is undecidable.

(i) If $\mathcal{L}_*$ is undecidable and $\mathcal{L}_*$ is reducible to $\overline{\mathcal{L}}$, then prove that $\mathcal{L}$ is undecidable.

(j) If $\mathcal{L}_*$ is non-recognizable and $\mathcal{L}_*$ is reducible to $\mathcal{L}$, then prove that $\mathcal{L}$ is non-recognizable.

(k) If $\mathcal{L}$ is recognizable and $\mathcal{L} \leq_{\text{R}} \overline{\mathcal{L}}$, then prove that $\mathcal{L}$ is decidable.

Problem 27.61. Show that any recognizable language is reducible to $\mathcal{L}_{\text{TM}}$. *[Hint: Use a recognizer for the language.]*

Problem 27.62. Recall that $\mathcal{L}_{\text{TM}}$ is recognizable, but not decidable.

(a) Suppose $\mathcal{L}_{\text{TM}}$ is reducible to $\mathcal{L}$, so $\mathcal{L}_{\text{TM}} \le_{\text{R}} \mathcal{L}$. Prove that $\mathcal{L}$ is undecidable.
(b) Suppose $\overline{\mathcal{L}_{\text{TM}}}$ is reducible to $\mathcal{L}$, so $\overline{\mathcal{L}_{\text{TM}}} \le_{\text{R}} \mathcal{L}$. Prove that $\mathcal{L}$ is non-recognizable.
(c) Suppose $\mathcal{L}_{\text{TM}}$ is reducible to $\overline{\mathcal{L}}$, so $\mathcal{L}_{\text{TM}} \le_{\text{R}} \overline{\mathcal{L}}$. Prove that $\mathcal{L}$ is non-recognizable.

Problem 27.63. Problem 27.62 will be useful to answer these questions.

(a) Give a mapping reduction from $\mathcal{L}_{\text{TM}}$ to $\overline{\mathcal{L}_{\text{EMPTY-TM}}}$. What does it prove? *[Hint: Problem 27.39.]*
(b) Sketch a recognizer for $\overline{\mathcal{L}_{\text{EMPTY-TM}}}$.
(c) Prove there is no mapping reduction from $\mathcal{L}_{\text{TM}}$ to $\mathcal{L}_{\text{EMPTY-TM}}$. *[Hint: $\mathcal{L}_{\text{TM}} \le_{\text{R}} \mathcal{L}_{\text{EMPTY-TM}}$ implies $\overline{\mathcal{L}_{\text{TM}}} \le_{\text{R}} \overline{\mathcal{L}_{\text{EMPTY-TM}}}$.]*

Problem 27.64. Use mapping reduction to prove that both $\mathcal{L}_{\text{EQ-TM}}$ and $\overline{\mathcal{L}_{\text{EQ-TM}}}$ are non-recognizable.

(a) Give a mapping reduction from $\mathcal{L}_{\text{TM}}$ to $\overline{\mathcal{L}_{\text{EQ-TM}}}$. What does it prove? *[Hint: Sketch a transducer-TM which takes input $\langle M\rangle$#w and produces $\langle M_1\rangle$#$\langle M_1\rangle$ where M_1 is a TM which rejects every string and M_2 is a TM which accepts every string if M accepts w.]*
(b) Give a mapping reduction from $\mathcal{L}_{\text{TM}}$ to $\mathcal{L}_{\text{EQ-TM}}$. What does it prove? *[Hint: Sketch a transducer-TM which takes input $\langle M\rangle$#w and produces $\langle M_1\rangle$#$\langle M_1\rangle$ where M_1 is a TM which accepts every string and M_2 is a TM which accepts every string if M accepts w.]*

Problem 27.65. A linearly bounded Turing Machine is a machine with restricted memory. It cannot move off the slots occupied by the input. You can imagine a second beacon symbol ⁑ placed on the right of the input beyond which the machine cannot move. The TM can mark the tape in different ways, so the symbols that can appear on the tape are ␣, $0, 1, \check{0}, \check{1}$, etc. Let g be the number of symbols that can appear on the tape. Suppose the input w has length n.

(a) Show that the number of possible strings that can be on the part of the tape occupied by the input is g^n. (The amount of tape memory available for the machine is $n \log_2 g$ bits, linear in the input size.)
(b) As a computation proceeds, we can describe the configuration of the system (TM and tape) by the position of the TM head, the state of the TM and the string on the available n slots of tape. Show that the number of possible system-configurations for a TM with q states is qng^n.
(c) If the computation takes more than qng^n steps, prove that the TM loops for ever on input w.
(d) Sketch a decider H_{LB} that decides if a linearly bounded TM M halts or loops forever on input w. Note, the input to H_{LB} is $\langle M\rangle$#w where M is linearly bounded, but H_{LB} can be a regular TM not necessarily linearly bounded.
(e) Sketch a decider A_{LB} for the language $\mathcal{L}_{\text{TM-LB}} = \{\langle M\rangle\#w \mid M \text{ is a linearly bounded TM which accepts } w\}$.

Problem 27.66. Let $\mathcal{L}_{\text{TM-DECIDER}} = \{\langle M\rangle \mid M \text{ is a decider}\}$ be the language containing descriptions of all TMs that are deciders. Prove that $\mathcal{L}_{\text{TM-DECIDER}}$ is not decidable. That is, no algorithm can tell if some other program halts on all inputs. This should not surprise you because it looks very similar to the halting problem.

Use a proof by contradiction. Assume $A_{\text{TM-DECIDER}}$ is a decider for $\mathcal{L}_{\text{TM-DECIDER}}$. We sketched another TM on the right that uses $A_{\text{TM-DECIDER}}$. Is this TM a decider? What language does it decide?

A = TM that uses $A_{\text{TM-DECIDER}}$.
INPUT: $\langle M\rangle$#w
1: Create TM M' with encoding $\langle M'\rangle$.
  M' = New TM taking INPUT x
  1: Ignore x and run M on w.
  2: Accept.
2: Output the decision of $A_{\text{TM-DECIDER}}$ on $\langle M'\rangle$.

Problem 27.67. Prove that the language of all deciders $\mathcal{L}_{\text{TM-DECIDER}}$ from Problem 27.66 is not recognizible. Use a proof by contradiction. Assume $\mathcal{L}_{\text{TM-DECIDER}}$ is recognizable. Sketch a Turing Machine E which prints the TMs in $\mathcal{L}_{\text{TM-DECIDER}}$ in some order, $M_1, M_2, \ldots$ (see Problem 27.14). Similarly, sketch a Turing Machine S which prints the strings of Σ^* in some order $s_1, s_2, \ldots$ (for example lexicographic order). Consider the decisions Turing Machine M_i makes on strings s_j. We show what these decisions might look like in the table, in which we highlighted the diagonal.

	s_1	s_2	s_3	s_4	$\cdots$
$\langle M_1\rangle$	YES	YES	NO	YES	$\cdots$
$\langle M_2\rangle$	NO	NO	NO	YES	$\cdots$
$\langle M_3\rangle$	YES	YES	NO	NO	$\cdots$
$\langle M_4\rangle$	YES	NO	NO	NO	$\cdots$
$\vdots$			$\vdots$		$\ddots$

(a) Use the diagonal to construct a language $\mathcal{L}$ which is not decided by any of the M_i.
(b) Sketch a decider for $\mathcal{L}$ from part (a). (Prove that you have a decider.) *[Hint: On input w, first run S until it prints w. Suppose $s_i = w$. Now run M_i on s_i. How will you get M_i? Must M_i halt? What is the final output?]*
(c) Prove that $\mathcal{L}_{\text{TM-DECIDER}}$ is not recognizable.

You have proved that any recognizable language containing only encodings of deciders can't be complete.

Problem 27.68. A real number in binary is $x = 0.b_1 b_2 \cdots = \sum_i b_i 2^{-i}$. The number x is computable if there is a TM M which, for any input $i \in \mathbb{N}$, halts and accepts if b_i=1 or halts and rejects if $b_i = 0$.

(a) Show that each of these numbers is computable (also give the first 10 binary digits): (i) $1/3$ (ii) $1/\sqrt{2}$ (iii) $1/\pi$.

(b) Prove there are uncountably many non-computable numbers.

(c) Prove that each of the numbers defined below is not computable. Let $\{M_1, M_2, \ldots\}$ be a list of all TMs.
 (i) The ith digit b_i is 1 if and only if M_i accepts 00.
 (ii) The ith digit b_i is 1 if and only if M_i accepts $\langle M_i \rangle$.

Problem 27.69 (Busy Beaver). In 1962, Tibor Radó described a non-computable function $B : \mathbb{N} \mapsto \mathbb{N}$. Given n, consider all possible n-state TMs which halt on the empty input ε. The busy beaver function $B(n)$ is the largest number of steps made by any of these halting n-state TMs. Busy beaver captures the maximum activity you can get from a fixed complexity machine, where complexity is measured by number of states.

(a) Prove that $B(n)$ is a non-computable function. To do so, assume that some transducer-TM M_{BB} always halts on input n with $B(n)$ remaining on the tape. Sketch a TM which decides $\mathcal{L}_{\text{TM}}$. *[Hint: Embed $\langle M \rangle$#w into a TM which runs M on w and use M_{BB} to determine how long to run to decide if M halts on w.]*

(b) Let $f(n)$ be any computable function. Prove that $B(n) > f(n)$ for infinitely many n. That is, in a sense, $B(n)$ is larger than *any* computable function. *[Hint: Modify the proof in (a) to use $f(n)$ instead of $B(n)$.]*

Problem 27.70 (Kolmogorov Complexity, Information and Randomness). For a string x, $\langle M \rangle$#w is a *description* of x if TM M when run with input w halts with x left on the tape. The Kolmogorov complexity $\mathcal{K}(x)$ is the length of the shortest description of x (also called the descriptive complexity),

$$\mathcal{K}(x) = \min_{\langle M \rangle \#w \text{ is a description of } x} |\langle M \rangle \#w|.$$

(a) Which of these two strings do you think is more "complex" or "contains" more information? Give your intuition.

$$x_1 = 00110011001100110011001100110011001100110011001100110011001100110011$$
$$x_2 = 10001101000101101110101110000000010010101110101011110100010101111101$$

(b) Show that there is a universal constant c for which $\mathcal{K}(x) \le |x| + c$ for all x. (Descriptive complexity can't be much worse than using the string itself, but it can be much smaller.) *[Hint: Use a trivial TM in the description.]*

(c) A string is compressible if $\mathcal{K}(x) < x$. Prove that for every $n \in \mathbb{N}$, there is at least one incompressible string of length n. *[Hint: Use a counting argument.]*

(Incompressible strings have many properties of a "typical" random string, e.g. about the same number of 0s and 1s.)

Problem 27.71. The Kolmogorov complexity $\mathcal{K}(x)$ in Problem 27.70 is a function from Σ^* to $\mathbb{N}$. Prove that $\mathcal{K}(x)$ is a non-computable function by following these steps. Assume a TM Q on any input x halts with $\mathcal{K}(x)$ on the tape.

(a) Let $\{s_1, s_2, \ldots\}$ be a lexicographic ordering of strings in Σ^*. We use Q to sketch another TM A on the right. Prove that A halts on any input n and outputs x_n.
One may use A to produce a sequence of strings $x_1, x_2, \ldots$, where x_n is produced by running A on n. By construction of A, what is a lower bound for $\mathcal{K}(x_n)$, for $n = 1, 2, \ldots$?

> A = TM that uses Q.
> **INPUT:** $n \in \mathbb{N}$.
> 1: **for** $x = s_1, s_2, \ldots$ **do**
> 2: Run Q on x to get $\mathcal{K}(x)$.
> 3: If $\mathcal{K}(x) \ge n$, print x and HALT.

(b) Prove that $|\langle A \rangle|$ is some universal constant c. The main complication is the statement "for $x = s_1, s_2, \ldots$". You may wish to give a more detailed sketch of A.

(c) Show that $\langle A \rangle$#$\langle n \rangle$ is the description of x_n. Use $|\langle A \rangle$#$\langle n \rangle|$ to get an upper bound $\mathcal{K}(x_n)$ which is in $O(\log_2(n))$.

(d) Use your upper bound from (c) and lower bound from (a) to get a contradiction, and hence prove Q doesn't exist.

Trial and error. ~~$E = ma^2$.~~
~~$E = mb^2$.~~
$E = \ldots$

We haven't money, so we have to think. – **Ernst Rutherford**

We are to do battle against an old foe, counting.

Chapter 28

Efficiency: The Class P

1: Computability versus efficiency: time complexity.
2: P, the polynomialy solvable problems.

The Church-Turing Thesis has withstood the test of time. Turing Machines are the gold standard for "solvable". However, a problem may be solvable in principle, but infeasible in practice if it requires too many resources.

We show a road network between towns A,B,C,D, with distances in miles. A traveling salesperson (TSP) at A visits each town once and returns to A. What is the shortest path for this tour? If you check all 6 possible paths, the shortest is 17 miles, A → B → C → D → A. That was easy. What if there are 50 cities? You have to check $49 \times 48 \times \cdots \times 1 = 49!$ paths which on a 10GHz computer would take more than 10^{50} years. The universe is no more than 10^{12} years old, so good luck. This problem is solvable in principle. Is it solvable in practice?

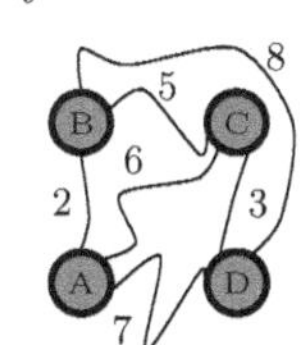

Efficiently solving a problem, quickly and using little memory, is as important as solving it. We need a framework for analyzing efficiency, especially runtime. Let's start by sketching a Turing Machine for $\{0^{\bullet n}\#1^{\bullet n}\}$.

> M = Turing Machine that solves $\{0^{\bullet n}\#1^{\bullet n}\}$
> **INPUT:** Binary string w.
> 1: Check that the input has the correct format and return to $*$.
> 2: Match each 0 left of # to a 1 right of #.
> 3: If a match fails or there are more 1's, REJECT. Otherwise ACCEPT.

Such a high-level sketch is not of much use in determining how long this Turing Machine takes on an input. We need to look deeper. In particular, we need to give some of the details on how step 2 is accomplished. The machine needs to zig-zag, going back and forth between 0's and 1's, each time marking a 0 and a 1,

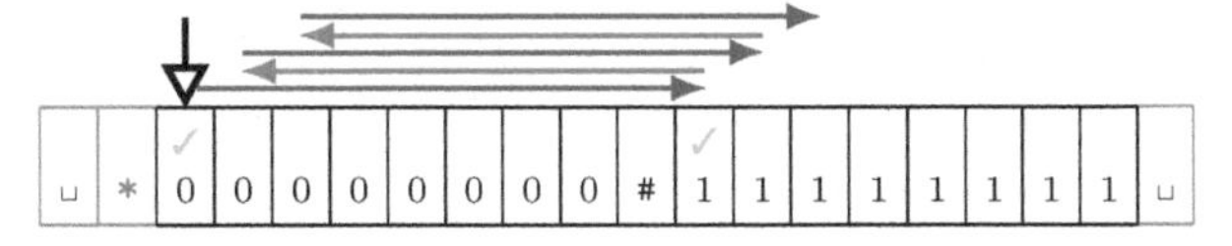

Implementing this idea, we can flesh out step 2 in our Turing Machine sketch to obtain:

> M = Turing Machine that solves $\{0^{\bullet n}\#1^{\bullet n}\}$ with step 2 expanded
> **INPUT:** Binary string w.
> 1: Check that the input has the correct format and return to $*$.
> 2: Match each 0 (left of #) to a 1 (right of #):
> → Move right and mark the first unmarked 0 (if none, GOTO step 3).
> Move right and mark the first unmarked 1 (if none, REJECT).
> Move left to the first marked 0.
> 3: If there are any unmarked 1's, REJECT. Otherwise ACCEPT.

28.1 Time Complexity

We now analyze the runtime of M, the decider for $\{0^{\bullet n}\#1^{\bullet n}\}$ on the previous page. What does analyze runtime mean? The runtime of M will be different, depending on the input w. There are two sides to this.

- Tasks generally take longer for bigger inputs. For example, to determine if the input format is correct you have to examine all of w and that takes longer when w is bigger.
- Runtimes can vary even for inputs of the same size. For example if the input starts with a 1, you can reject immediately. Otherwise you check the next bit.

Worst case analysis. Since the input is unknown, the safest approach is to consider the worst input of a given size. Worst case analysis is by far the norm, and algorithms with small worst case runtime generally perform well in practice, in part because the worst case runtime is a performance guarantee. How do you know which input has the worst runtime? Part of the analysis involves identifying that worst input. There are three basic steps when analyzing worst case runtime of an algorithm or Turing Machine M:

1. Identify a parameter to quantify the size or complexity of the input.
2. Fix the size of the input to n and identify the worst input w_* of size n.
3. Determine the runtime of M for the input w_*.

The result is a worst case runtime that depends on n. As we embark on a runtime analysis, Chapter 9 on comparing runtimes using big-Theta and big-Oh notation will be helpful. We repeat two important points:

- We are interested in runtimes for the asymptotic regime of very large inputs ($n \to \infty$).
- We disregard additive and multiplicative constants and focus on the growth rate of the runtime as a function of n, as captured by $\Theta(\cdot)$ and $O(\cdot)$ notation.

The freedom to ignore lower order terms and constants makes runtime analysis easier. For example, we don't care if the Turing Machine uses 4 or 12 instructions in a step, because any constant number of instructiions per step will not factor in the growth rate. Only the number of steps matters as long as each step is at most a constant number of instructions. Let's use these considerations to analyze M.

Worst case runtime analysis of M. Let n be the size of the input (number of bits). Step 1 uses two scans of the input and Step 3 uses 1 scan for a total of at most $3n$ steps. The bulk of the work is in step 2 which only runs for valid inputs. So, the worst case runtime is when the input is valid, when the machine moves back and forth at most $n/2$ times using at most $2n$ steps each time, for a total of $n/2 \times 2n = n^2$ steps. The grand total about $3n + n^2$ steps, which is in $\Theta(n^2)$. We say that

$$M \text{ is a } \Theta(n^2)\text{-time Turing Machine.}$$

Rough calculations are justified for getting growth rates. Embrace the idea and you will avoid migraines.

Our Turing Machine is inefficient because it marks only one 0 and one 1 in a scan. There is a faster Turing Machine. You can mark half the unmarked 0's and half the unmarked 1's in each scan. To mark half the unmarked 0's in one scan, simply mark every other unmarked 0. Here is an example showing two scans.

		✓	✗	✓		✓	✗	✓			✓	✗	✓		✓	✗	✓		
␣	*	0	0	0	0	0	0	0	0	#	1	1	1	1	1	1	1	1	␣

For clarity, we used ✓ for the first scan and ✗ for the second scan. After two more scans, all 0's are marked and all 1's are marked, and you can accept. If all the 0's are marked and some 1's remain or *vice versa*, you can reject. This idea almost works. Unfortunately, there is a small hiccup illustrated by the next example.

		✓		✓		✓			✓		✓		✓		✓				
␣	*	0	0	0	0	0	0	#	1	1	1	1	1	1	1	␣	␣	␣	␣

After one scan, the are as many unmarked 0's as 1's, so the algorithm ultimately accepts, which is wrong. We can diagnose a problem at the beginning because the total number of bits is odd, which cannot possibly lead to a match. Here is another example which should be rejected, even though the total number of bits is even.

		✓		✓		✓			✓		✓		✓		✓				
␣	*	0	0	0	0	0	0	#	1	1	1	1	1	1	1	1	␣	␣	␣

This time, the problem is diagnosed after the first scan when the number of unmarked bits becomes odd. Our new idea seems to work. First check that the number of unmarked bits is even. If so, mark every other unmarked 0 and every other unmarked 1, starting with the first of each. Now repeat.

Exercise 28.1

(a) Show that if the number of 0's and 1's are equal then all 0's and 1's get marked.

(b) Show that if the number of 0's and 1's are not equal, then at some point the number of unmarked bits will be odd. *[Hint: Induction.]*

(c) Give a Turing Machine to solve $\{0^{\bullet n}\#1^{\bullet n}\}$ with worst case runtime in $\Theta(n \log n)$. Prove it.

By halving the unmarked bits in each scan, we only need $\Theta(\log n)$ scans, for a runtime in $\Theta(n \log n)$. Can we do better? Yes, but only with more resources. A Turing Machine with two tapes and independently controlled read-write heads can copy the 0's from tape 1 to tape 2 in one scan. After copying, continue scanning right on tape 1 and retrace left on tape 2, matching each 1 with a 0, shown on the right below.

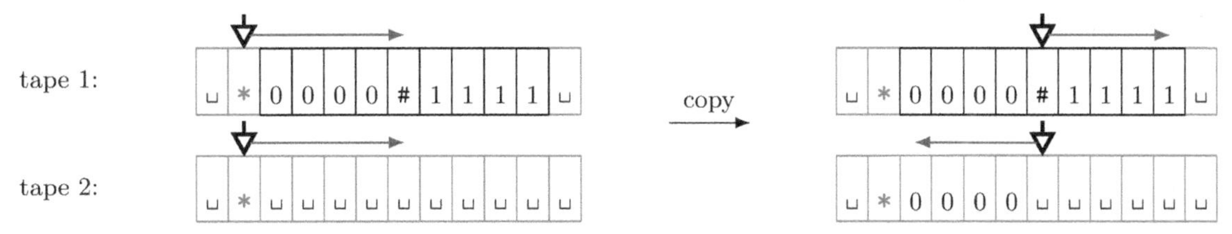

In all there are about $2n$ steps, so this is a two-tape Turing Machine with runtime in $\Theta(n)$. In summary

Solutions for $\{0^{\bullet n}\#1^{\bullet n}\}$	Runtime
Simple brute-force algorithm	$\Theta(n^2)$
Smarter halving algorithm	$\Theta(n \log n)$
Better two-tape architecture	$\Theta(n)$

There are two ways to improve the runtime. (i) Move to a better architecture that is more suited to your problem. This is not common in practice because your computer, a universal Turing Machine, is bought and paid for. You can't buy a new type of computer for every different problem. (ii) Use a smarter algorithm, i.e., write a more efficient program. This is where most of a computer scientist's efforts are spent.

28.2 Efficiently Solvable Problems: The Class P

When it comes to computability, we ask if a problem is solvable. We don't care about how efficiently it can be solved. The HALTING PROBLEM is unsolvable on any variant of the Turing Machine, even one with a zillion tapes, because a zillion tapes can be simulated by one tape and the problem is unsolvable with one tape.

When it comes to efficiency, the specific architecture of the machine can affect the runtime, as we saw in the previous section. So, what would it mean to say that there is no way to efficiently solve a problem. Is n^2 efficient? Is e^n efficient? Can a problem be efficiently solvable on one architecture but not another? We need a theoretical notion of efficient that is architecture independent. In practice, a machine's architecture matters, and we do care that a two-tape machine can solve a problem more quickly than a one-tape machine. However, to build a general theory, we need to step back and view efficiency from a broader perspective. In doing so, we will define the class of polynomialy solvable problems, P. Here is what we will gain:

- A robust definition of a tractable problem, independent of machine architecture.
- A clear divide between the tractable and the intractable. Polynomial solvability equates to efficiently solvable, just as decidable equates to solvable.
- Relevance to practice. Polynomial solvability generally translates to tractable in practice. If a problem is not polynomialy solvable, its time to move on to other problems.

We approach polynomial solvability through the notion of a fast algorithm. Let the worst case runtime of a Turing Machine be upper bounded by the increasing function $f(n)$, where n is the size of the input.

A Turing Machine is fast if the worst case runtime is bounded by a function $f(n)$ which increases by at most a constant factor λ when you double the size of the input from n to $2n$.

$$\text{worst case runtime} \leq f(n) \qquad \text{and} \qquad f(2n) \leq \lambda f(n).$$

We hope you agree that this is a reasonable and intuitive definition of a fast algorithm, one whose scaling behavior as you double the input-size is bounded by some constant λ.

Pop Quiz 28.2

Which of these Turing Machine worst case runtimes are fast?

$\log n \qquad \sqrt{n} \qquad n \qquad n^2 \log_2 n \qquad (\log_2 n)^{\log_2 n} \qquad n^{\log_2 n} \qquad 2^{\sqrt{n}} \qquad 2^n$

Theorem 28.1 (Fast means polynomial). A Turing Machine M is fast if and only if its worst-case runtime on an input of size n is in $O(n^k)$, for a constant k. Fast algorithms run in polynomial time.

Proof. (Not essential to moving on.) There are two directions to an if and only if claim.
(i) Suppose M is fast. So, runtime$(M) \leq f(n)$ and $f(2n) \leq \lambda f(n)$. We show $f(n) \leq Cn^k$, for constants C, k, which proves the worst case runtime is in (n^k). By a straightforward induction, $f(2^\ell) \leq \lambda^\ell f(1)$. Let $n = 2^\ell + r$, where $\ell = \lfloor \log_2 n \rfloor$ and $r < 2^\ell$. Since f is increasing,

$$f(n) = f(2^\ell + r) \leq f(2^{\ell+1}) \leq \lambda^{\ell+1} f(1) = \lambda f(1) 2^{\ell \log_2 \lambda} = \lambda f(1)(2^\ell)^{\log_2 \lambda}.$$

Since $2^\ell = n - r$, by choosing $C = \lambda f(1)$ and $k = \log_2 \lambda$, we have proved that

$$f(n) \leq \lambda f(1)(n-r)^{\log_2 \lambda} \leq \lambda f(1) n^{\log_2 \lambda} = Cn^k.$$

(ii) Suppose runtime is in $O(n^k)$, i.e., runtime is upper bounded by Cn^k. Then, we can set $f(n) = Cn^k$ and $f(2n) = C(2n)^k = 2^k f(n)$, which means M is fast with $\lambda = 2^k$. ∎

We could have simply defined fast as polynomial runtime. That would seem arbitrary so we thought it better to start from an intuitive notion of fast and show that it is equivalent to polynomial. The main complaint about our definition of fast is that we do not require any bound on the doubling constant λ, which translates logarithmically to the growth rate of the polynomial. So $\lambda = 2$ (linear runtime) and $\lambda = 2^{10}$ (n^{10} runtime) are both "fast." In practice we would never dream of running a $\Theta(n^{10})$-algorithm as it wouldn't finish for an input of size 1,000. In theory we call n^{10} fast because we are envisioning another kind of runtime which blows away n^{10} or any polynomial. Consider $f(n) = 2^n$, then $f(2n) = 2^{2n} = 2^n \cdot 2^n = 2^n f(n)$ and $\lambda = 2^n$. You can see how $\lambda = 10$ pales in comparison to $\lambda = 2^n$. If $f(n) = 2^n$, the runtime exponential.

Exercise 28.3

Let $\lambda = n$ and $f(2n) = nf(n)$. Show that $f(n) = f(1)\sqrt{n^{\log_2 n+1}}$ for n a power of 2.

We will see that our notion of fast creates a clean theoretical divide between the tractable and intractable. This motivates the definition of the class of polynomialy solvable problems.

Definition 28.2 (P, polynomialy solvable). A problem $\mathcal{L}$ is in P if there exists a fast, polynomial runtime, Turing Machine that decides $\mathcal{L}$. The class P is a set of problems (languages).

You may object that we speak of polynomial solvability as a property of a problem, yet the definition invokes a Turing Machine. We saw that runtime can depend on the type of Turing Machine and algorithm (brute force or smart). For example, are we allowed to use two-tape Turing Machines? We must reconcile this definition of P with the considerable flexibility that is available in designing Turing Machines.

Let's start with the type of algorithm, e.g. brute force versus smart. You always choose the Turing Machine with the fastest runtime. If that's polynomial, the problem is in P. Just because you or I can't find a Turing Machine with polynomial runtime, doesn't mean there isn't one. To prove a problem is not in P, one must show that no decider can be fast. That is usually hard to do. We will see an example later.

What about different architectures? Here, we reap the benefits from our definition of fast. On two-tapes, we got a runtime $\Theta(n)$. The best with one tape was $\Theta(n \log n)$. It doesn't matter. Both runtimes are bounded by polynomials, hence fast. That's interesting. Is it true in general? Yes, but we are not going to make it precise nor prove it. You can take the next assertion as a definition of reasonable Turing Machine architecture.

Extended Church-Turing Thesis. Any efficiently solvable problem can be decided by a fast Turing Machine. Or, fast on any "reasonable" Turing Machine architecture, means fast on our one-tape Turing Machine. The class P is independent of Turing Machine architecture.

Example 28.3 (Simulating a Two-Tape Turing Machine with One Tape)**.** Let's build a two-tape Turing Machine to decide $w\#w$. The idea is similar to our solution for $0^{\bullet n}\#1^{\bullet n}$. First copy w to the second tape; then use a scan to match the second string to the first. We illustrate the algorithm for the input 011#011:

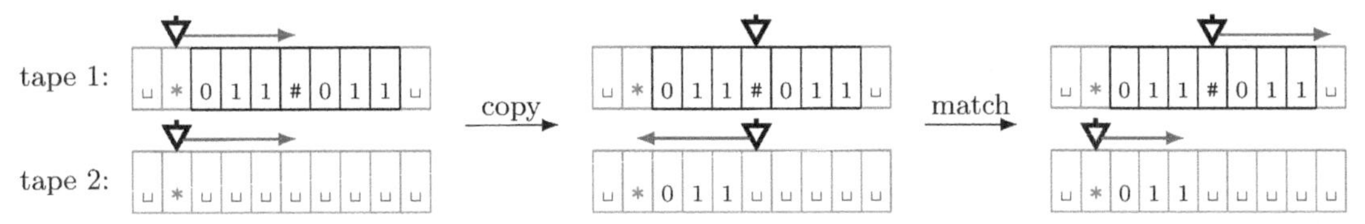

That was easy. Here is a sketch of a two-tape Turing Machine M_{two} corresponding to our algorithm.

M_{two} = Two-tape Turing Machine that solves $\{w\#w\}$
INPUT: Binary string w.
1: Check the input format and return to $*$. (2 scans)
2: Copy the string to the left of # onto tape 2 and return head-2 to $*$. ($1\frac{1}{2}$ scans)
3: Move both heads right and match the bits one by one. (1 scan)
4: ACCEPT if both heads come to ␣ or REJECT if there is ever a mismatch.

A scan traverses the input once making $\Theta(n)$ transitions. About $4\frac{1}{2}$ scans are used to complete steps 1–3, hence this is a two-tape Turing Machine that decides $w\#w$ with worst case runtime in $\Theta(n)$.

A one-tape Turing Machine can solve $w\#w$ (the first Turing Machine in Chapter 26). Here, we use a different approach to build a one-tape machine M_{one} for $w\#w$, by simulating M_{two}. The two main ideas are:

- Interleave two tapes into one. Even slots are tape-1 and odd slots are tape-2 (Example 27.1 on page 388).
- Remember the positions of the read heads in M_{two} by marking their positions on the single tape of M_{one}.

M_{one} = One-tape Turing Machine that solves $\{w\#w\}$ by simulating M_{two}
INPUT: Binary string w.
1: Reconfigure the tape to odd-even format, with the input in the even (tape 1) slots.
2: Mark the positions of head-1 and head-2.
3: ...

The situation after reconfiguring the tape is shown below, with even slots (tape-1) having the input bits.

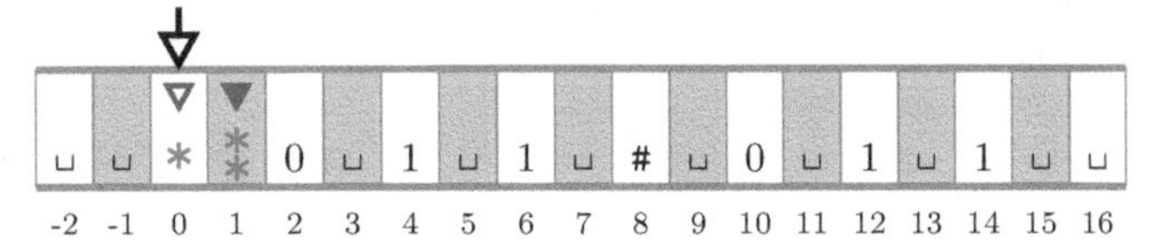

The tape slots are numbered for ease of reference. The unshaded even slots are "tape-1" and the shaded odd slots are "tape-2;" ▽ marks the position of head-1 on its tape and ▼ the position of head-2 on its tape.

Pop Quiz 28.4
Give the details of step 1 in M_{one} and show that it can be done in $\Theta(n^2)$ steps.

In each step, M_{two} performs an action with one of the heads. For each such step, M_{one} does the following:

- For the current step, find the marker of the appropriate head (▽ or ▼).
- Erase the marker and perform the appropriate actions for the current head. If the head of M_{two} moves, then M_{one} moves its actual head two steps to stay on the appropriate tape.
- SWITCH: mark the current spot with the marker for the current head and possibly switch heads.

Let's take a closer look at copying a bit (part of step 2 in M_{two}) and see how M_{one} simulates the copy.

$\underline{M_{\text{two}}}$ (copy)

1: Move head-1 R.
2: Read and remember bit on tape-1.
3: Move head-2 R. Write bit to tape-2.

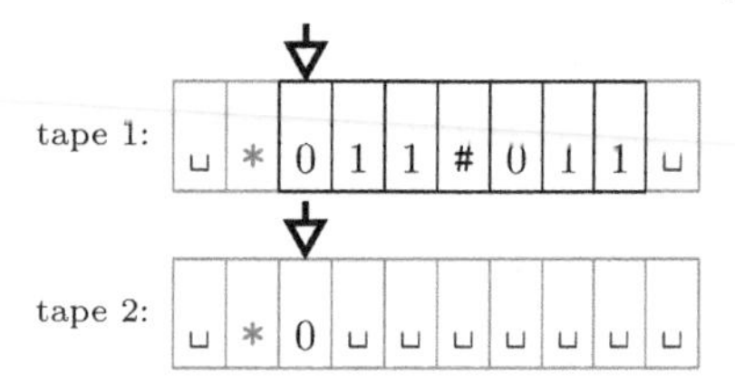

$\underline{M_{\text{one}}}$ (simulate copy)

1: SWITCH (to head-1). Move two steps R.
2: SWITCH (to head-1). Read and remember bit.
3: SWITCH (to head-2). Move two steps R.
4: SWITCH (to head-2). Write bit.

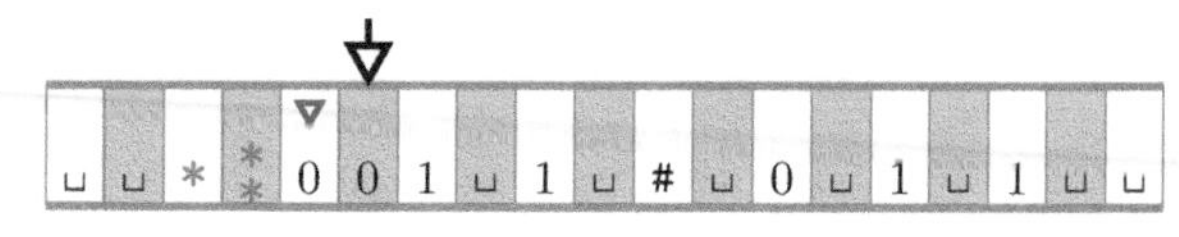

The new SWITCH operation in M_{one} is straightforward in principle, but can take many steps to implement because you don't know where the mark of the other tape head might be. If the SWITCH is to the same tape-head, there is nothing to do. If the SWITCH is to another tape-head, there are 3 steps:

(i) remember the position of the current tape-head (by marking it);
(ii) move to the position of the next tape-head by finding the appropriate mark;
(iii) unmark the slot (M_{one}'s head is now positioned and ready to perform actions on the next tape).

Pop Quiz 28.5
If M_{two} has implemented t steps, show that SWITCH can be implemented in $O(t)$ steps.

Fleshing out the four steps in M_{two} which switches between head-1 and head-2, we obtain our simulator M_{one}.

$\underline{M_{\text{one}} = \text{One-tape Turing Machine that simulates } M_{\text{two}} \text{ which solves } \{w\#w\}}$
INPUT: Binary string w.
1: Reconfigure the tape to odd-even format, with the input in the even (tape 1) slots.
2: Mark the positions of head-1 and head-2.
3: SWITCH (to head-1); check the input format; return to $*$.
4: Copy the first string onto tape 2 and return head-2 to ⁑.
- SWITCH (to head-1); move two R; read bit.
- SWITCH (to head-2).
- If bit $\neq$ #, move two R, write bit and continue with step 4.
  If bit = # move L to ⁑ and exit step 4.

5: Move the heads right and match the bits one by one.
- SWITCH (to head-1); move two R; read bit1.
- SWITCH (to head-2); move two R; read bit2.
- If bit1 $\neq$ bit2: halt and REJECT. If bit1 = bit2 = ␣: halt and ACCEPT.
  If bit1 = bit2 $\neq$ ␣: continue step 5.

Exercise 28.6
(a) Prove that M_{one} is fast, in particular its runtime is in $\Theta(n^2)$.
(b) Prove the following simulation theorem, that one tape can simulate two tapes in polynomial time.
Theorem 28.4 (Polynomial simulation). A two-tape Turing Machine M_{two} with runtime in $O(t(n))$ can be implemented by a one-tape Turing Machine M_{one} with runtime in $O(t(n)^2)$.
(The theorem shows that if M_{two} is fast, then M_{one} is fast, with at most quadratic slowdown. You can use the same technique to go from k tapes to one tape with at most a quadratic slowdown.)

Let's pause to digest the practical implications of the simulation theorem in Exercise 28.6. Even if you didn't do the exercise, you can still appreciate the message. A multi-tape Turing Machine is like a parallel computer. A single-tape Turing Machine is like a single-CPU sequential computer. The simulation theorem says that you can get no more than a polynomial speedup in going from a sequential to a parallel architecture. This says a lot for the class P. If a problem is in P for one architecture, it is in P for all architectures. That does not mean there is no use for parallelism. In practice, we do care very much about polynomial speedups. □

Here is a tiny sample of the problems in P. We know how to solve them efficiently. In an algorithms course you study fast algorithms for such classic problems. You may challenge yourself by: (a) Formulating an appropriate language for the problem; (b) Finding a polynomial-runtime Turing Machine to solve the problem.

- PATH: Given a graph and two nodes, is there are path connecting the two nodes?
- SHORTEST-PATH: Given a graph and two nodes, what is the distance between the two nodes?
- MAKE-CHANGE: Make change for n using the fewest coins in a given coin-system (e.g. 1¢, 3¢, 6¢, 10¢).
- FIND-MINIMUM: What is the minimum in a list of numbers?
- MATCH: Given a group of students with preferences (who they like and dislike), can one match the students into pairs so that every student likes their partner?
- EULER-PATH: Given a road network between points of interest, can one clean the snow off the roads, with the snowplow driving down every road exactly once?
- MAX-FLOW: Given a network (e.g. the internet) with bandwidth constraints along each edge, determine the maximum transmission rate of packets from a source node to a destination node.

Many interesting problems are in P. Are there problems not in P. Certainly. We know there are undecidable problems like $\mathcal{L}_{\text{TM}}$. If a problem cannot be decided, it certainly cannot be decided in polynomial time, so any undecidable problem is not in P. A more interesting question is whether some decidable problem is not in P.

Exercise 28.7
Prove that these problems are decidable by sketching Turing Machines for them. Do your Turing Machines have polynomial runtime?
(a) HAM-PATH: Is there a cycle that uses every node in a graph once?
(b) CLIQUE: Given a graph with n nodes, is there a clique of size at least $n/2$

If you could not construct polynomial time Turing Machines in Exercise 28.7, you are in good company. Many smart people have tried and so far all have failed. Though we can't find a polynomial algorithm, we also can't prove there isn't one. We seek a decidable problem which is provably not in P.

28.3 A Decidable Non-Polynomial Problem

There is no decider to tell whether a program will terminate successfully because $\mathcal{L}_{\text{TM}}$ is undecidable. Is there an algorithm to decide if a program will quickly terminate successfully. More formally, decide whether a given Turing Machine on input w halts within $2^{|w|}$ steps and says (YES). Define the problem $\mathcal{L}_{\text{EXP}}$,

$$\mathcal{L}_{\text{EXP}} = \{\langle M\rangle\#w \mid M \text{ accepts } w \text{ within at most } 2^{|w|} \text{ steps}\}.$$

For $\langle M\rangle\#w$ to be in $\mathcal{L}_{\text{EXP}}$, M must accept w "quickly", within exponential time. This quickness requirement makes $\mathcal{L}_{\text{EXP}}$ decidable even though $\mathcal{L}_{\text{TM}}$ is undecidable. To decide $\mathcal{L}_{\text{EXP}}$, simply run M on input w for $2^{|w|}$ steps. If during that time M accepts, say (YES). Otherwise say (NO). This idea can be implemented by modifying a universal Turing Machine U_{TM} that would normaly just simulate M on w. The modification is to add a step counter to U_{TM} so that it will count the number of steps of M that have been simulated. If M halts before the counter reaches $2^{|w|}+1$, U_{TM} reports whatever decision M returns. Otherwise, if the counter reaches $2^{|w|}+1$, U_{TM} rejects. The modified U_{TM} always halts, and hence is a decider for $\mathcal{L}_{\text{EXP}}$.

To show $\mathcal{L}_{\text{EXP}}$ is not in P, we must show that any decider for $\mathcal{L}_{\text{EXP}}$ cannot be polynomial. It seems obvious. What else can you do but run M on w for $2^{|w|}$ steps? To find a needle in a haystack, what else could you do but search the whole haystack? Well, you can bring a powerful magnet near the haystack and pull the needle out, which is quicker than searching. What else can you do reasoning won't hold up in court.

To prove $\mathcal{L}_{\text{EXP}}$ is not in P, we use contradiction and diagonalization, just as for proving $\mathcal{L}_{\text{TM}}$ is undecidble. Assume that E_{TM} is a decider for $\mathcal{L}_{\text{EXP}}$ with polynomial worst case runtime,

$$E_{\text{TM}}(\langle M\rangle\#w) = \begin{cases} \text{ACCEPT} & \text{if } M \text{ accepts } w \text{ within at most } 2^{|w|} \text{ steps;} \\ \text{REJECT} & \text{otherwise.} \end{cases}$$

Polynomial runtime means runtime $\le Cn^k$, where $n = |\langle M\rangle\#w|$ is the length of the input to E_{TM}. We use E_{TM} to build a diabolical diagonal Turing Machine D whose input can be any Turing Machine $\langle M\rangle$.

> D = "Diagonal" Turing Machine derived from E_{TM} (the decider for $\mathcal{L}_{\text{EXP}}$)
> **INPUT:** $\langle M\rangle$ where M is a Turing Machine.
> 1: Run E_{TM} with input $\langle M\rangle\#\langle M\rangle$.
> 2: If E_{TM} accepts then REJECT; otherwise (E_{TM} rejects) ACCEPT

The output of D is the opposite of $E_{\text{TM}}(\langle M\rangle\#\langle M\rangle)$. Let us list the Turing Machines (D appears on this list) and consider the behavior of E_{TM} on the pairs $\langle M_i\rangle\#\langle M_j\rangle$. Here is what E_{TM}'s decisions might look like.

$E_{\text{TM}}(\langle M_i\rangle\#\langle M_j\rangle)$	$\langle M_1\rangle$	$\langle M_2\rangle$	$\langle M_3\rangle$	$\langle M_4\rangle$	$\cdots$	$\langle D\rangle$	$\cdots$
$\langle M_1\rangle$	ACCEPT	ACCEPT	REJECT	ACCEPT	$\cdots$	ACCEPT	$\cdots$
$\langle M_2\rangle$	REJECT	REJECT	REJECT	ACCEPT	$\cdots$	ACCEPT	$\cdots$
$\langle M_3\rangle$	ACCEPT	ACCEPT	REJECT	REJECT	$\cdots$	ACCEPT	$\cdots$
$\langle M_4\rangle$	ACCEPT	REJECT	REJECT	REJECT	$\cdots$	ACCEPT	$\cdots$
$\vdots$			$\vdots$		$\cdots$	$\vdots$	$\cdots$
$\langle D\rangle$	REJECT	ACCEPT	ACCEPT	ACCEPT	$\cdots$	ACCEPT / REJECT ?	$\cdots$
$\vdots$			$\vdots$		$\cdots$	$\vdots$	$\ddots$

For example, E_{TM} rejects $\langle M_2\rangle\#\langle M_1\rangle$: either M_2 rejects $\langle M_1\rangle$ within $2^{|\langle M_1\rangle|}$ steps or runs for more than $2^{|\langle M_1\rangle|}$ steps. The row for D is the opposite of the diagonal entries. The problem is at $E_{\text{TM}}(\langle D\rangle\#\langle D\rangle)$, and since E_{TM} is a fast decider, it must output something here. Let us consider all possibilities.

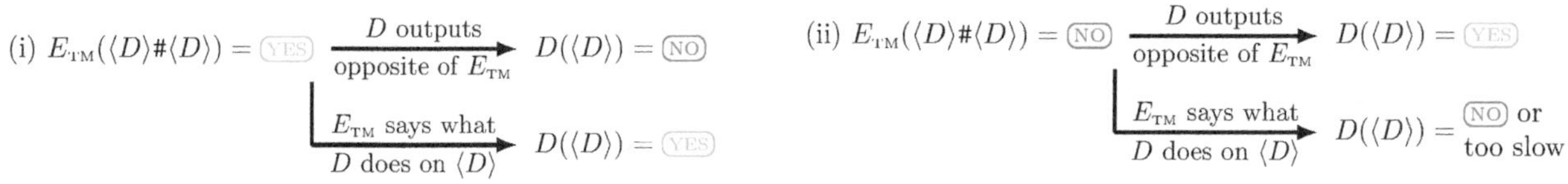

(i) $E_{\text{TM}}(\langle D\rangle\#\langle D\rangle) =$ YES —(D outputs opposite of E_{TM})→ $D(\langle D\rangle) =$ NO
 —(E_{TM} says what D does on $\langle D\rangle$)→ $D(\langle D\rangle) =$ YES

(ii) $E_{\text{TM}}(\langle D\rangle\#\langle D\rangle) =$ NO —(D outputs opposite of E_{TM})→ $D(\langle D\rangle) =$ YES
 —(E_{TM} says what D does on $\langle D\rangle$)→ $D(\langle D\rangle) =$ NO or too slow

Case (i) is clearly a contradiction. Case (ii) is interesting. It is possible that $D(\langle D\rangle)$ is YES, but it takes a long time to compute, in which case E_{TM} says NO. Therefore, case (ii) is not immediately a contradiction. To get a contradiction in case (ii), we must be sure that D runs quickly on $\langle D\rangle$. If we prove that the runtime of $D(\langle D\rangle)$ is at most $2^{|\langle D\rangle|}$, the too slow option is ruled out and we have our contradiction because E_{TM} says $D(\langle D\rangle) =$ NO. The contradiction proves D cannot exist and hence E_{TM} cannot exist.

So far, we didn't use the runtime of E_{TM}. We need it now. The runtime of D on $\langle D\rangle$ is essentially the runtime of E_{TM} on $\langle D\rangle\#\langle D\rangle$. Since E_{TM} is polynomial, D can't take too long. That is the essence of the argument to get the contradiction. Here are the technical details. Using the runtime bound of E_{TM},

$$\text{runtime of } E_{\text{TM}} \text{ on } \langle D\rangle\#\langle D\rangle \le C(2|\langle D\rangle|+1)^k \;\rightarrow\; \text{runtime of } D \text{ on } \langle D\rangle \le C(2|\langle D\rangle|+1)^k + \text{const}\cdot|\langle D\rangle|^2$$

The additional runtime for D comes from needing to copy $\langle D\rangle$ to prepare the input for E_{TM} and any few additional steps. Now we remind you of an undesirable phenomenon called program bloat, i.e. making a program longer without changing its functionality. Similarly, we can bloat a Turing Machine by adding useless states that are never visited. We can bloat $|\langle D\rangle|$ indefinitely without altering its functionality. The runtime of D is growing polynomialy as it bloats, and so eventually the runtime of D on $\langle D\rangle \le 2^{|\langle D\rangle|}$. We're done.

Theorem 28.5. $\mathcal{L}_{\text{EXP}} \notin$ P, which means there is no decider for $\mathcal{L}_{\text{EXP}}$ with polynomial worst case runtime.

> There is no algorithm to tell if a program will terminate successfully.
> There is no efficient algorithm to tell if a program will quickly terminate successfully.

28.4 Boundary Between Efficient and Inefficient

Turing Machines are the gold standard for defining solvable as well as efficiently solvable. Let's recap.

- We defined a robust, architecture independent notion of an efficiently solvable problem, the class P. The class P contains problems for which there is a polynomial decider, having polynomial worst case runtime.
- There are many interesting problems which are polynomialy solvable.
- There are problems that cannot be solved in polynomial time. $\mathcal{L}_{\text{EXP}}$ is one, but it's not likely to occur in practice. Some games like generalized go and chess are also provably exponential, but again not typical use cases in practice. Are there problems from common practice that are non-polynomial?

What about problems like the traveling salesperson, which started this chapter, and CLIQUE? We can certainly solve these problems, but all known solutions are inefficient (non-polynomial). Yet, we cannot prove that a polynomial solution is impossible. These problems are on the efficient-inefficient boundary. A beautiful theory, called NP-completeness connects all these problems, and we will catch a glimpse of this theory in the next chapter. Nevertheless, computer-science moves on, almost independently of which side of the boundary these problems sit. If these problems can't be solved in polynomial time, well, we need to confront them anyway, because they are important problems in practice. Approximations are called for. On the flip side, if they can be solved in polynomial time, for example using a $\Theta(n^{18})$ Turing Machine, well who cares. Such a polynomial algorithm wouldn't finish on an input of size $n = 100$. Approximations are called for.

In practice, we behave as we should. We're practical. The theory says polynomial is polynomial is polynomial, and if a polynomial solution is possible on one architecture, then it's possible on all architectures. Nevertheless, a plethora of different computing platforms have evolved to trade off different aspects of efficiency, for example runtime for memory, trading off one polynomial for another. For example:

- Supercomputer, cluster, cloud and multicore architectures reduce runtime using parallelism: more tapes with independent heads and coordination among the different heads. We saw examples in this chapter.
- Mobile platforms optimize for power and memory, often at the expense of increased runtimes.
- Distributed platforms spread the data among multiple CPUs and must solve the problem with limited inter-CPU communication.
- Streaming platforms have limited memory with which to process a continuously arriving data-"stream".
- Randomized algorithms tolerate a small chance of failure.
- Quantum computing uses quantum mechanical properties to speed up computation, etc.

Our discussion has focused on runtime, which is by far the most important aspect of efficiency, but memory is also a big concern in computing. What can be computed using only a polynomialy sized tape? Many programs will sacrifice speed in order to use less memory, since memory is a hard physical limitation whereas runtime, as long as we are willing to wait, is unbounded. We didn't have space 🙂 to discuss these issues.

Exercise 28.8 [Factoring]

Give sketches for transducer Turing Machines to solve the following problems.

(a) The input is $n \in \mathbb{N}$ represented in unary by $1^{\bullet n}$ on the tape. M_{unary} should REJECT if n is prime. If n is composite, M_{unary} should ACCEPT with $1^{\bullet n}\#0^{\bullet p}$ left on the tape, where p is any prime factor of n. Give the worst-case runtime of your Turing Machine M_{unary}; it should be polynomial in n.

(b) Same as (a), but now the input n is represented in binary on the tape. If your machine M_{binary} ACCEPTS, then $w_n\#w_p$ should be left on the tape where w_p is any prime factor p in binary. What is the worst-case runtime of your Turing Machine M_{binary}? Is it polynomial in $|w_n|$?

The input format is part of the problem specification. A problem can be in P for one input format, but not another. The norm is that numbers should be in binary, or any other radix system with base at least 2.

28.5 Problems

Problem 28.1. Which worst-case runtimes are fast and which are slow. Justify your answers mathematically. Plot all the functions versus n on a log-log plot. Explain why your plot visually justifies the separation between fast and slow.

$\sqrt{n}$ $\quad n \log\log n$ $\quad 2^{\log n}$ $\quad 2^{\log^2 n}$ $\quad 2^{\sqrt{n}}$ $\quad 2^n$ $\quad n^3$ $\quad n^{100}$

Problem 28.2. Show that each problem is in P (Sketch a Turing Machine and analyze the worst-case runtime). A transducer is polynomial if its worst-case runtime is polynomial in the sum of the input and output sizes.

(a) Regular language: $\mathcal{L}_1 = \{*01*\}$ and $\mathcal{L}_2 = \{*01\}$.
(b) Not CFL: $\mathcal{L} = \{0^{\bullet n}\#1^{\bullet n}\#0^{\bullet n}\}$ (# is a 'punctuation' symbol).
(c) Squaring: $\mathcal{L} = \{0^{\bullet n}\#1^{\bullet n^2}, n \geq 0\}$ (# is a 'punctuation' symbol).
(d) Exponentiating: $\mathcal{L} = \{0^{\bullet n}\#1^{\bullet 2^n}, n \geq 0\}$ (# is a 'punctuation' symbol).
(e) Repetition: $\mathcal{L} = \{ww | w \in \{0,1\}^*\}$.
(f) Palindromes: $\mathcal{L} = \{w | w \in \{0,1\}^*, w = w^{\mathrm{R}}\}$.
(g) Addition of 2: $\mathcal{L} = \{0^{\bullet n}1^{\bullet n+2}\}$.
(h) Addition of 2: The input is $0^{\bullet n}$. Halt with $0^{\bullet n+2}$ on the tape.
(i) Multiplication by 2: The input is $0^{\bullet n}$. Halt with $0^{\bullet 2n}$ on the tape.
(j) Squaring: The input is $0^{\bullet n}$. Halt with $0^{\bullet n^2}$ on the tape.
(k) Exponentiate: The input is $0^{\bullet n}$. Halt with $0^{\bullet 2^n}$ on the tape.
(l) Exponentiate: The input w is the binary representation of n. Halt with 2^n in binary on the tape.
(m) Copying: The input is a string w. Halt with ww on the tape.
(n) Reversal: The input is w. Halt with w^{R} on the tape.
(o) Switching: The input is $w\#v$. Halt with $v\#w$ on the tape.
(p) Deleting first: The input is $xw \in \Sigma^*$. Halt with w on the tape.
(q) Prefixing: The input is $w \in \Sigma^*$. Halt with $0w$ on the tape.
(r) Binary to unary: The input w is the binary representation of n. Halt with $0^{\bullet n}$.
(s) Unary to binary: The input is $0^{\bullet n}$. Halt with the binary representation of n on the tape.
(t) Binary addition: The input is two binary strings $w_1\#w_2$. Halt with $w_1 + w_2$ (binary addition) on the tape.
(u) Division: For input $0^{\bullet n}$, rejects if n is odd. If n is even, accept with $0^{\bullet n/2}$ on the tape.
(v) Division: The input w binary for n. Reject if n is odd. If n is even, accept with $n/2$ in binary on the tape.

Problem 28.3. Prove that P is closed under union, intersection, concatenation, and complement.

Problem 28.4. Formulate each task as a language and show that it is in P. If appropriate, use a transducer-TM.

(a) MAKE-CHANGE: Make change for n using the fewest coins in a given coin-system (e.g. 1¢, 3¢, 6¢, 10¢).
(b) NUM-CHANGE: Find the number of ways to make change for n in a given coin-system (e.g. 1¢, 3¢, 6¢, 10¢).
(c) RELPRIME: Given two integers x, y in binary, determine if they are relatively prime.
(d) PATH: Given a graph and two nodes, determine if there are path connecting the two nodes.
(e) COMPOSITE-VERIFY: Given n and a factor $1 < p < n$, verify that p divides n.
(f) COLOR-VERIFY: Given a graph and a coloring of the vertices, verify that the coloring is valid.
(g) HAMILTONIAN-VERIFY: Given a graph and a Hamiltonian path, verify that the path is Hamiltonian.
(h) CLIQUE-VERIFY: Given a graph and a K-clique, verify that it is a K-clique.

Problem 28.5. Prove that every regular language is in P.

Problem 28.6. The decider for a CFL in Problem 27.10 uses the Chomsky Normal Form. Given input w of length n, the TM checks every derivation of length $2n - 1$. Is this TM polynomial? Does this mean CFL's are not in P?

Problem 28.7. Prove that every context free language is in P. Use a build-up method. Let the CFG be in Chomsky Normal Form and consider input string w. Let $w_{i,j}$ be the substring of w from position i to j, where $i \leq j$.

(a) Let $S_{i,j}$ be the subset of variables that can generate $w_{i,j}$. How do you determine $S_{i,i}$?
(b) Given $S_{i,j}$ for all $w_{i,j}$ up to length k (strong induction), show how to determine $S_{i,j}$ for $w_{i,j}$ of length $k + 1$.
(c) Suppose you have computed $S_{1,n}$. How do you determine if the CFG can generate w.
(d) Sketch a TM for the CFL and prove that it's polynomial. *[Hint: How many choices are there for $w_{i,j}$?]*

Problem 28.8. Prove that there is no decider for $\mathcal{L}_{\text{EXP}}$ with worst case runtime in $o(2^n)$, where $n = |\langle M\rangle\#w|$. The argument follows the same general line we used to prove there is no polynomial decider for $\mathcal{L}_{\text{EXP}}$.

Chapter 29

Hard Problems: NP

1: Verifiable versus solvable.
2: NP-completeness.

You are head of IT at a chain-supermarket. Marketing neads to identify products which are bought together, sometimes called a frequent basket or just frequent items. Items purchased simultaneously by many people are related, and should be displayed near each other to increase sales. Here is a sample of customer-data.

		beer	chips	milk	diapers	cheese
Alice	(A)	1	1	0	1	0
Bob	(B)	1	1	0	1	1
Charles	(C)	0	0	1	1	0
David	(D)	1	1	1	1	1

The items {beer, chips, diapers} are a basket of size 3. Three people (A, B and D) purchased this basket – people drink beer, eat chips and watch TV while babysitting. Your boss asks for a basket with 10 or more items purchased by at least 5,000 customers. The full data has 10^6 customers $\times$ 10^4 items. You couldn't find a fast solution, so you might soon be back in the CS-job market. Given the predicament, any sane person would take counter measures and read Chapter 29 to brush up on CS-theory. You learned something that saved your job. This "simple" supermarket problem is at the heart of the burning open question in computer science. To start the discussion, let us categorize computing problems into three broad classes:

- **Unsolvable.** Problems we can't solve, for example program verification ($\mathcal{L}_{\text{TM}}$) and the ultimate-debugger ($\mathcal{L}_{\text{HALT}}$). Too bad.
- **Slow.** Problems we can solve, but not efficiently (e.g. $\mathcal{L}_{\text{EXP}}$). Problems with provably exponential runtime are rare in practice.
- **Fast.** Problems we can solve efficiently, the problems that are in P, for which we get polynomial runtimes. There are many of these.

UNSOLVABLE
SLOW
NP
P
FAST

We should be able classify every problem into unsolvable, slow or fast. We can't. There's a gray-zone between fast and slow that is filled with important problems, such as: scheduling; assigning radio frequencies; finding cliques in social networks; picking small teams to solve tasks; and, our supermarket problem. We don't know whether these gray-zone problems can be solved quickly.[1]

29.1 Verifiable versus Solvable

The gray zone is NP. The name stands for nondeterministic polynomial-time which is the type of Turing Machine that efficiently solves these problems. Wait! Didn't we say polynomial on one architecture means polynomial on all architectures. It's time to confess. The word is still out for nondeterministic Turing Machines. Does polynomial on the (theoretical) nondeterministic Turing Machine mean polynomial on our good old fashoined single tape deterministic Turing Machine? That is literally the million dollar question.

[1]The popular expert-opinion is that we can't solve any of these gray-zone problems with a fast algorithm.

We will see nondeterminism later. For now, let's develop a more earthy characterization of NP. Define two simple problems for a multi-set $S = \{s_1, \ldots, s_n\}$ of n positive numbers with repetition allowed, for example

$$S = \{3, 5, 3, 11, 6, 2\}.$$

LARGE-SUM: Given S and k, is there a subset $A \subseteq S$ with $|A| \le k$ and $\text{sum}(A) \ge \frac{1}{2}\text{sum}(S)$?

PARTITION: Given S, is there a subset $A \subseteq S$ with $\text{sum}(A) = \frac{1}{2}\text{sum}(S)$?

LARGE-SUM asks for a small subset with a large sum. PARTITION doesn't care about subset-size and simply asks if any subset has a sum exactly half the total sum. The problems look similar, but they are very different.

Pop Quiz 29.1

(a) For $S = \{3, 5, 3, 11, 6, 2\}$ and $k = 2$ is the answer to LARGE-SUM (YES) or (NO).

(b) Is the answer to PARTITION (YES) or (NO) for (i) $S = \{3, 5, 3, 11, 6, 2\}$ (ii) $S = \{3, 6, 2, 11, 6, 2\}$.

Both LARGE-SUM and PARTITION are solvable. Here are the algorithms:

LARGE-SUM: Sum the k largest elements and ACCEPT if this sum is at least $\frac{1}{2}\text{sum}(S)$.

PARTITION: Compute all subset-sums and ACCEPT if any one equals $\frac{1}{2}\text{sum}(S)$.

By now, you agree that any procedure or "algorithm" to solve a problem can be turned into a Turing Machine for the problem. Our algorithm for LARGE-SUM is fast (polynomial, see Problem 29.14). Our algorithm for PARTITION is slow (exponential), since it may compute the subset-sum of all 2^n possible subsets. There is nothing new here. We already knew that some Turing Machines have polynomial runtime and some do not. The question is whether a smarter algorithm for PARTITION could be polynomial? We don't know.

PARTITION is an example of an NP-complete problem. Our goal is to explain exactly what that means.

29.1.1 NP: Polynomialy Verifiable

You are now the head of research at a startup, faced with two instances of PARTITION:

$$S_1 = \{3, 5, 3, 11, 6, 2\}; \qquad \text{and} \qquad S_2 = \{3, 6, 2, 11, 6, 2\}.$$

You can't solve these problems, but Ayfos, a newly minted PhD from a school in Troy NY, tells you the answers: (NO) for S_1 and (YES) for S_2. Being skeptical, you want proofs. To prove the (NO)-answer for S_1, Ayfos can list out all the subsets of S_1 and verify that none sum to 15. That's long and tedious. How about proving the (YES)-answer for S_2? That's easy. The string 110010 is the "proof": the 1's at positions 1,2 and 5 identify elements $\{3, 6, 6\}$ at those positions in S_2. Simple addition confirms the sum. In the diagram, you, the manager, are the certifier. You have the input S_2. Ayfos provides evidence for the (YES)-answer. This evidence is called a witness or certificate. In our case, the evidence is a solution to the problem, a string that encodes a subset with the correct sum. Given the input and evidence, the certifier can quickly verify the solution. Verification must be quick (polynomial), which means the evidence can't be too large when compared to the input $|\langle S_2 \rangle|$. This means two things:

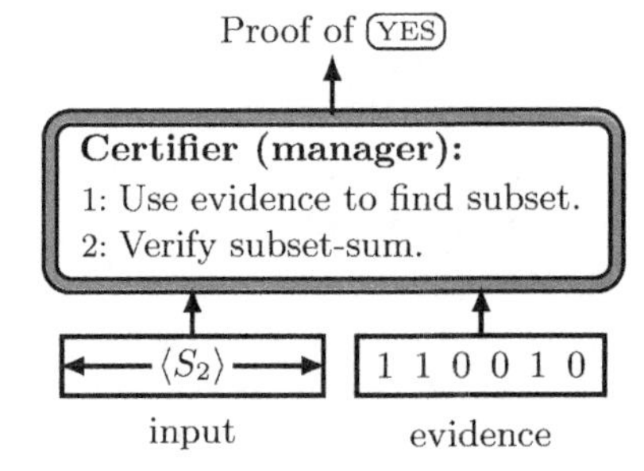

1. The certifier (a Turing Machine) must have polynomial worst-case runtime.
2. The evidence must have polynomial size in the length of the input.

The second requirement follows from the first because a polynomial certifier cannot possibly examine a non-polynomial amount of evidence. There is an asymmetry when it comes to proof. It appears as hard to prove a (NO)-answer as it is to solve PARTITION. Proving (YES) is almost trivial given the right evidence.

Exercise 29.2

(a) Give another evidence that proves S_2 is a (YES)-instance of PARTITION.

(b) Give a certifier to prove a (NO)-answer of PARTITION. Is it polynomial?

(c) Show how to use a (YES)-certifier to solve PARTITION. Is your decider polynomial?

Exercise 29.3
For each problem, which is easier to prove, the (YES)-answer or (NO)-answer?
(a) SUBSET-SUM: Given a set S and k, is there a subset with subset-sum equal to k?
(b) CLIQUE: Given a graph G and $k > 1$, is there a clique of size at least k?
(c) COLORING: Given a graph G and $k > 1$, is there a valid k-coloring of G?
(d) IS-PRIME: Given $n > 1$, is n prime?
(e) ISOMORPHIC: Given graphs G_1 and G_2, are they the same graph, i.e. isomorphic?

We are now ready to define NP. NP, like P, is a set of problems. Recall that P contains all problems which can be solved quickly. NP contains all problems whose yes-answer can be verified quickly.

A problem is in NP if a (YES)-answer can be quickly verified from a little evidence.

Note the asymmetry. We care about verifying (YES)-answers, not (NO)-answers. We also don't care about where the evidence came from. But, given the evidence, however obtained, one can quickly verify the (YES)-answer.

Definition 29.1 (NP). A problem $\mathcal{L}$ is in NP if there is a polynomial Turing Machine C, the certifier, which takes as input $w\#\text{E}$, an input w and evidence E, and uses the evidence E to verify whether $w \in \mathcal{L}$. This means:

1. If $w \notin \mathcal{L}$, $C(w\#\text{E}) =$ (NO), no matter what evidence E is provided.
2. If $w \in \mathcal{L}$, there exists an evidence E with $|\text{E}| \le p(|w|)$ for which $C(w\#\langle\text{E}\rangle) =$ (YES).

In Definition 29.1, $p(x)$ is a fixed polynomial. The formal definition matches our informal discussion. There's asymmetry between (YES) and (NO). The evidence, often the object we seek, is succint. Verifying (YES) is quick.

Example 29.2 (CLIQUE is in NP). This is not earth-shattering news because pretty much any problem in practice is in NP, and proving so is usually routine. To show that a problem is in NP, construct a certifier and show that it has polynomial worst-case runtime for the appropriate evidence. The evidence must be succinct but you need not worry about how hard it is to produce the evidence. Consider the CLIQUE problem,

CLIQUE: Given a graph G and $k > 1$, is there a clique of size at least k?

To encode the graph G, number the vertices $1, 2, \ldots, n$ and specify its $\frac{1}{2}n(n-1)$ edges as follows,

$$\langle G\rangle = e_{1,2}\ e_{1,3}\ \cdots e_{1,n}\ e_{2,3}\ e_{2,4}\ \cdots\ e_{2,n}\ e_{3,4}\ e_{3,5}\ \cdots\ e_{3,n}\ \cdots\ e_{(n-1),n}$$

where $e_{i,j} = 1$ if edge (i, j) is in G. The graph on the right encodes to the input string

$$\langle G\rangle = e_{1,2}\ e_{1,3}\ e_{1,4}\ e_{1,5}\ e_{2,3}\ e_{2,4}\ e_{2,5}\ e_{3,4}\ e_{3,5}\ e_{4,5} = 1010110101.$$

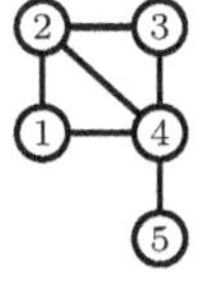

The input $\langle G\rangle$ is a binary string of length $\frac{1}{2}n(n-1)$. To recover the graph from the input, first obtain n from the length of $\langle G\rangle$, and then read off the edges one-by-one from the bits of the input.

Pop Quiz 29.4
Draw the graphs for inputs: (a) 111001100011 (b) 100110011010100100110

For our graph with $k = 3$, the answer to CLIQUE is (YES). What evidence could prove this? Almost always, the evidence is the actual object we seek, in this case a 3-clique. Identify the vertices in the clique using a binary string, for example 11010. The positions of the 1's identify the clique as vertices $\{1, 2, 4\}$. We now construct the certifier C. The input to C is the graph G together with the clique size k plus a k-clique as evidence:

$$\text{input to } C = \langle G\rangle\,\#\,\langle k\rangle\,\#\,\text{E} = 1010110101\,\#\,11\,\#\,11010.$$

(k is in binary, so $11 = 3$). Technically, we should write $\langle\text{E}\rangle$ for an encoding of the evidence, but the evidence is already a binary string, so we just use E. First, the certifier checks that there are at least k 1's in the evidence E, to confirm that the alleged clique has size at least k. Then, for each pair of 1's in the evidence E, verify that the corresponding edge is present in $\langle G\rangle$. If everything works out, then C has verified the (YES)-answer.

Our certifier C works for a general (YES)-instance of k-clique. We described C at a high level. You should be getting comfortable with such descriptions. To conclude that CLIQUE $\in$ NP, we must show that C has polynomial runtime. The input to C has length $|\langle G\rangle|+|\langle k\rangle|+|\mathrm{E}| \leq n^2$. Hence, we must show that runtime(C) is at most some polynomial in n. A rough analysis will do because we don't distinguish between runtimes n^{1000} and n^2 (both are "fast"). Here are two useful rules for quickly analyzing high-level algorithms.

- A sum or product of polynomialy many polynomials is a polynomial.
- A polynomial evaluated with a polynomial as input is a polynomial.

For example, if $f(n) = n^2 + n$ and $g(n) = n^3$, then

$$f(n)g(n) = n^5 + n^4 \quad \text{and} \quad f(g(n)) = g(n)^2 + g(n) = n^6 + n^3.$$

We need to check $O(n^2)$ pairs of vertices. If each check takes polynomial time, the total runtime is bounded by the product of two polynomials, which is polynomial.

Pop Quiz 29.5
Give a more detailed sketch of the certifier for CLIQUE. Analyze the worst-case runtime and show that it is at most a polynomial in n. What is the order of your polynomial?

Exercise 29.6
(a) Show that COLORING (see Exercise 29.3) is in NP.
(b) Show that every problem in P is in NP, that is P $\subseteq$ NP.

□

The relationship between P and NP has plagued theoretical computer science for many decades.

Does P equal NP?
That is, are polynomialy verifiable problems also polynomialy solvable?
Or, if a (YES)-answer can be verified quickly, can the answer itself be found quickly?

Can we solve PARTITION, CLIQUE & COLORING in polynomial time? We don't have much hard evidence either way. The inclinations are that P $\neq$ NP. Why? Intuitively, verifying an answer should be easier than finding the answer. Many great people have tried in vain to find polynomial algorithms for the harder problems in NP. A simple explanation for the failures is that those problems can't be solved in polynomial time.

Another nagging question: "Why the asymmetry between (YES) and (NO)?" If (YES) is polynomialy verifiable, shouldn't (NO) also be polynomialy verifiable? We don't know!

29.1.2 NP and Nondeterminism

Nondeterminism allows a machine to simultaneously try different things before making a decision. As such, it cannot really be implemented in practice, but it is a beautiful theoretical concept. We used nondeterminism to show that the concatenation of regular languages is regular (Section 24.1 on page 354). To refresh your memory, here is the nondeterministic finite automaton from that discussion.

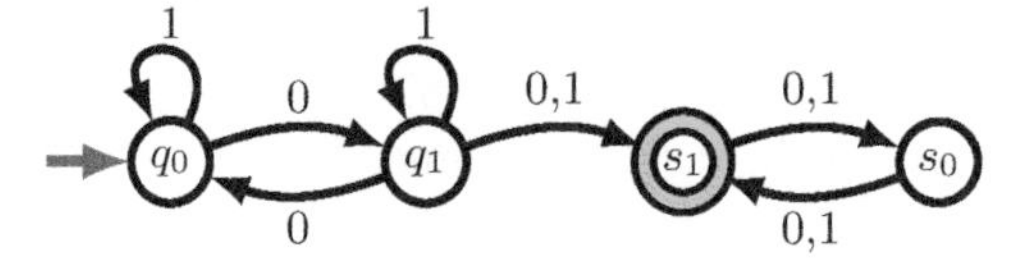

The interesting state is q_1, where the instructions are ambiguous. If the bit is 0, does the automaton transition to q_0 or s_1? The action is not determined, hence the name nondeterministic automaton. We allow the automaton to try both actions. Let us illustrate with the computation-tree for input 100101.

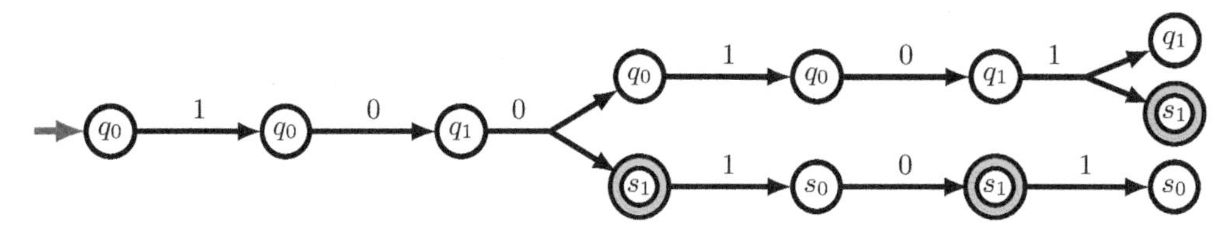

The automaton starts in state q_0 and transitions $q_0 \to q_0 \to q_1$. The computation branches in state q_1 because there are two possible actions. Each time the automaton is in state q_1 the computation branches. At the end, there are three possible computation paths. The automaton accepts if any of these computation paths accept, as is the case here. To implement such a nondeterministic machine, one must keep track of all the possible computation paths, more specifically all possible final states. A DFA can do so, see Exercise 24.7.

> Nondeterminism is a theoretical tool that allows an automaton to try multiple computation-paths with the flexibility to ACCEPT if any path accepts. A Nondeterministic automaton has an equivalent DFA.

Pop Quiz 29.7

Are these automata nondeterministic? For each, which of $\varepsilon, 0, 1, 00, 01, 10, 11$ are accepted. If you switch (YES) and (NO) states in a DFA, you get a DFA that solves the complement of the original problem. Is the same true for a nondeterministic automaton? Explain why or why not.

Nondeterminism extends to Turing Machines. A Turing Machine writes to tape, transitions states and moves. In a nondeterministic Turing Machine, each of these actions can have multiple options. The Turing Machine can write one of a subset of the symbols, transition to one of a subset of the states and move L/R or stay. A Turing Machine instruction is shown on the left. A similar nondeterministic instruction is shown on the right.

Pop Quiz 29.8

Explain exactly what each instruction above tells the Turing Machine to do.

Nondeterministic Turing Machines branch, just like nondeterministic automata. We must keep track of all the branches, and accept if any computation path accepts. A nondeterministic Turing Machine is polynomial if the longest computation path is polynomial in the length of the input. The punchline is that if a problem is polynomialy-verifiable, it is polynomialy-solvable by a nondeterministic Turing Machine. Here is how.

Suppose the problem $\mathcal{L} \in$ NP. There is a deterministic polynomial certifier C such that for any $w \in \mathcal{L}$, there is evidence E with $|\text{E}| \leq p(|w|)$ for which $C(w\#\text{E}) =$ (YES). The nondeterministic Turing Machine has the ability to try different things and accept if any one of them works. This is a very powerful capability. We can use nondeterminism to try every possible piece of evidence and if one works, ACCEPT. If none works, REJECT.

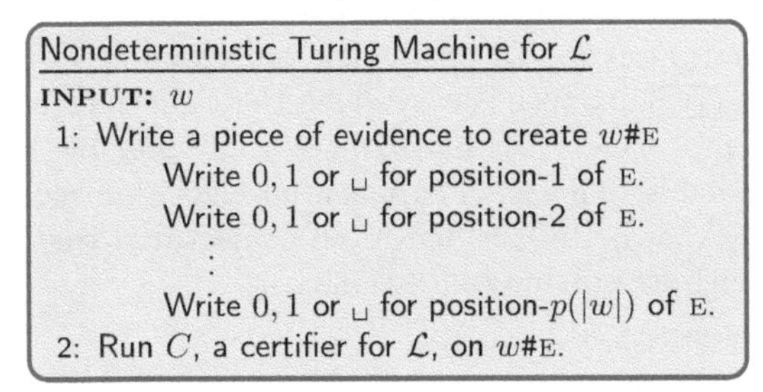

Nondeterministic Turing Machine for $\mathcal{L}$

INPUT: w

1: Write a piece of evidence to create w#E
   Write $0, 1$ or ␣ for position-1 of E.
   Write $0, 1$ or ␣ for position-2 of E.
   ⋮
   Write $0, 1$ or ␣ for position-$p(|w|)$ of E.
2: Run C, a certifier for $\mathcal{L}$, on w#E.

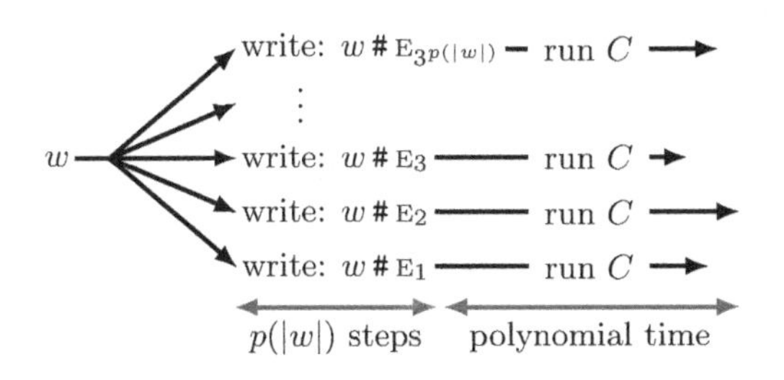

Step 1 has $p(|w|)$ nondeterministic actions, writing 0, 1 or ␣ for each symbol in E. The computation branches into $3^{p(|w|)}$ possibile paths. Each branch is polynomial, taking $p(|w|)$ steps to write E plus polynomial time to run the certifier C. The nondeterministic Turing Machine benefits from an unbounded parallelism, testing every possible evidence simultaneously. To simulate this process on a deterministic Turing Machine, write and test each piece of evidence in turn, which takes $\Omega(3^{p(|w|)})$ time in the worst case, not polynomial. The P equals NP question asks if this awesome parallelism wielded by the nondeterministic Turing Machine can be simulated by a polynomial deterministic Turing Machine. It seems unlikely, but we don't know.

29.2 A Hardest Problem in NP

Polynomial time is the the gold standard, the bar for a task to be tractable. NP has easy problems, e.g. every problem in P, and hard problems for which we don't yet have polynomial algorithms. These hard problems, called NP-complete problems, are harder than any other problem in NP. Glory to thee who solves one.

NP-complete problems are the hardest in NP. A polynomial solver for any single NP-complete problem provides a polynomial solver for every problem in NP.

29.2.1 Circuits and Satisfiability

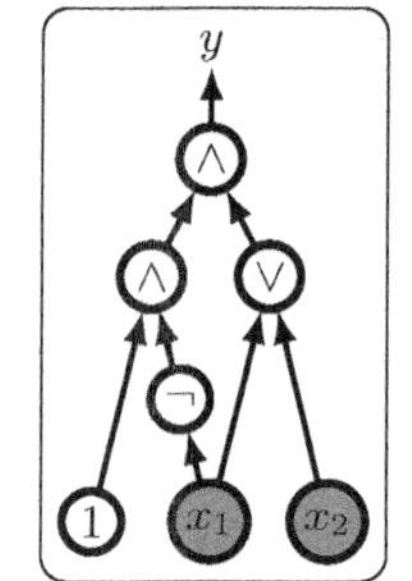

To unravel the cryptic statement above, we start at the begining, with Boolean circuits. A circuit is a directed acyclic graph with AND ($\wedge$), OR ($\vee$) and NOT ($\neg$) gates, for example the circuit on the right). Vertices output a Boolean value, 0 for F and 1 for T. Directed edges feed the output of a node into the input of another node. For example, ① feeds into Ⓐ; x_1 feeds into ⊖ which then outputs the negation $\overline{x_1}$ into Ⓐ. So, the inputs to the first Ⓐ are 1 and $\overline{x_1}$, and the output is $1 \wedge \overline{x_1}$. There are three types of vertices:

- vertices with a hard-coded constant output, e.g. ①;
- input vertices, whose value is set by the user, e.g. (x_1) and (x_2);
- Boolean logic gates Ⓐ, Ⓥ and ⊖, which output a Boolean operator of its inputs.

A Boolean gate must always have the right number of inputs for its Boolean operator. The output of a vertex can be the input for multiple vertices, as with x_1. The inputs to the Ⓥ are x_1 and x_2, and the output is $x_1 \vee x_2$. Lastly, the inputs to the second Ⓐ are $1 \wedge \overline{x_1}$ and $x_1 \vee x_2$, and the final output is

$$y = (1 \wedge \overline{x_1}) \wedge (x_1 \vee x_2).$$

The output y is the Boolean function computed by the circuit, which is a combination of Boolean operations on the inputs x_1, x_2. The circuit is satisfied when the output $y = 1$.

Pop Quiz 29.9
(a) What is the output y for inputs $x_1 = x_2 = 1$. (b) Find values for x_1, x_2 that satisfy the circuit.

We are now ready to define a decision problem for circuits called satisfiability.

CIRCUIT-SAT: Given a circuit built from Ⓐ, Ⓥ, ⊖, and having inputs $x_1, \ldots, x_n$, is there a Boolean assignment to $x_1, \ldots, x_n$ for which the circuit is satisfied?

CIRCUIT-SAT is in NP. The evidence for a (YES)-instance is the string of binary assignments to $x_1, \ldots, x_n$. The certifier checks by plugging into the circuit whether the output is 1. To prove that our example circuit is satisfiable, set $x_1x_2 = 01$ and verify that $y = 1$. Verifying a (YES)-instance is easy given the right evidence.

Can we solve CIRCUIT-SAT? For the general case of n inputs $x_1, \ldots, x_n$, one can try all 2^n possible binary assignments for the inputs. If one works, the circuit is satisfiable. This is an exponential algorithm requiring at least 2^n steps. Is there a polynomial algorithm? None is known. In fact, it is even conjectured that there is no algorithm which is substantially faster than 2^n. So much for solving CIRCUIT-SAT. ☹

29.2.2 CIRCUIT-SAT is Harder than Every Problem in NP

Turing Award winner Steve Cook in 1971 proved a gargantuan result, the Cook-Levin Theorem. (Leonid Levin independently proved the same result in 1973.)

Theorem 29.3 (CIRCUIT-SAT is NP-complete)**.** Suppose CIRCUIT-SAT can be solved in polynomial time. Then every problem in NP can be solved in polynomial time using a polynomial solver for CIRCUIT-SAT.

Theorem 29.3 can be taken literally. An alien gives you a black-box which tells whether a circuit is satisfiable in polynomial time. You can't see how the black-box works, but you can use it any number of times. Theorem 29.3

says that this black-box is powerful enough to solve any NP-problem in polynomial time. To show you why this is so, we will need a link between fast Turing Machines and small circuits.

Circuits and Turing Machines. Circuits, like Turing Machines, are computing devices. Unlike Turing Machines which process inputs of any length, a circuit has a fixed, harded-coded number of inputs. Fix the input-length to n bits. Each Turing Machine step executes an instruction such as

"if in state q with the head at slot i reading '0': write '1'; move L; transition to s."

Such instructions can be implemented by small circuits, and by combining the circuits for all the steps, it is plausible that we can simulate the entire computation of the Turing Machine in a circuit.

Theorem 29.4. Suppose a Turing Machine with worst-case runtime $t(n)$ computes a Boolean decision function $f_n(w)$ on inputs w of size n. In poly($t(n)$)-time, one can compute a circuit with poly($t(n)$) gates that computes the same function $f_n(w)$.

poly($t(n)$) is short for polynomial in $t(n)$. We omit the proof of Theorem 29.4 (see Problems 29.25 and 29.26). The bottom line is that small circuits can implement efficient Turing Machines.

To prove Theorem 29.3, let $\mathcal{L}$ be any NP-problem and C a polynomial certifier for $\mathcal{L}$. Let w be a YES-string of length n. There is an evidence E of length $p(n)$ for which $C(w\#\text{E}) =$ YES, where $p(\cdot)$ is a polynomial. More generally, for fixed w, C computes a Boolean function of the evidence E, an unknown variable of length $p(n)$. By Theorem 29.4, since C runs in polynomial time, we can quickly construct a small circuit that computes the same function C computes on E. The situation is illustrated below.

The certifier C on the left is a Turing Machine with input $w\#\text{E}$ and output 1 if the evidence E implies w is in $\mathcal{L}$. On the right is a small circuit that computes the same function of E. This circuit depends on C, the input w which is hard-coded and how the evidence E is used. The bits of E are input vertices in the circuit and the number of inputs is $|\text{E}| = p(n)$). The input w is in $\mathcal{L}$ if and only if the small circuit on the right is satisfiable. The alien's black-box can tell if this circuit is satisfiable, which allows us to decide if w is in $\mathcal{L}$.

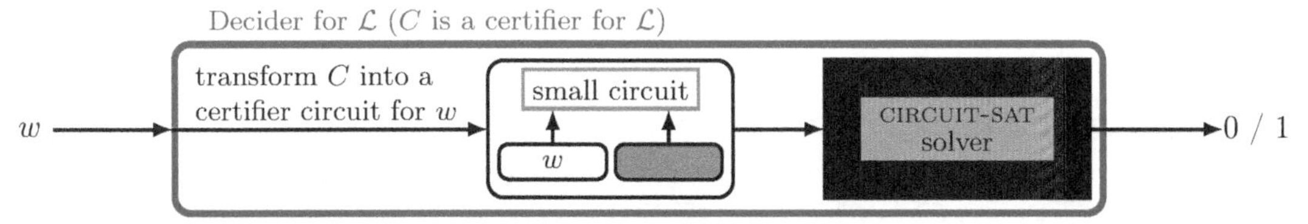

The input to our decider is w. The input to the alien black-box is the circuit that verifies whether there is some piece of evidence that corroborates w's membership in $\mathcal{L}$. The evidence remains unknown. The black-box decides whether some evidence will work. If so, $w \in \mathcal{L}$; if not, $w \notin \mathcal{L}$.

Exercise 29.10

(a) Show that the runtime of our decider for $\mathcal{L}$ is polynomial. You may assume Theorem 29.4.
(b) In general, the evidence has size at most $p(n)$, not exactly $p(n)$. How do you accomodate this?

Example 29.5 (Reducing CLIQUE to CIRCUIT-SAT). Let's use the alien black-box to solve CLIQUE, a concrete problem. Does the graph on the right from Example 29.2 have a clique of size at least 3? Our approach is to convert the problem to a circuit on which to use the alien black-box. We develop an algorithm to convert CLIQUE problems into CIRCUIT-SAT problems. The graph's edge-list is

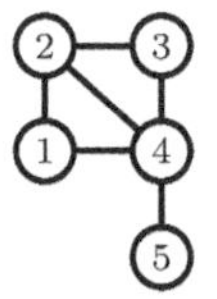

$$\langle\text{graph}\rangle = e_{1,2}\, e_{1,3}\, e_{1,4}\, e_{1,5}\, e_{2,3}\, e_{2,4}\, e_{2,5}\, e_{3,4}\, e_{3,5}\, e_{4,5} = 1010110101.$$

An alleged clique, e.g. vertices $\{2,3,4\}$, is encoded by the sequence $x_1x_2x_3x_4x_5 = 01110$, where the 1's identify the clique-vertices. Let's build a circuit to verify that 01110 is a valid solution satisfying the two conditions: the clique-size is at least 3; and, there is an edge between every pair of clique-vertices. We use seperate circuits to check each condition. To ensure both conditions hold, we will take the AND of the outputs from each circuit.

First, we design the circuit to verify the size of the clique, i.e. if a string has 3 or more ones (more generally k or more ones). This is not as trivial as it sounds. The naive approach uses too many gates (Problem 29.21). For the black-box CIRCUIT-SAT-solver to be efficient, its input must be small – a polynomial in the graph's size. Then, the runtime will be polynomial in this polynomial-sized input which is a polynomial. We count the number of 1's using an indirect approach by first sorting the string, illustrated on the right. Now, the AND of the leftmost k bits verifies if there are k or more 1's (in our case $k = 3$). To complete the size-verifier, we ask you to provide circuits for sorting and computing a many-input AND in the next exercise.

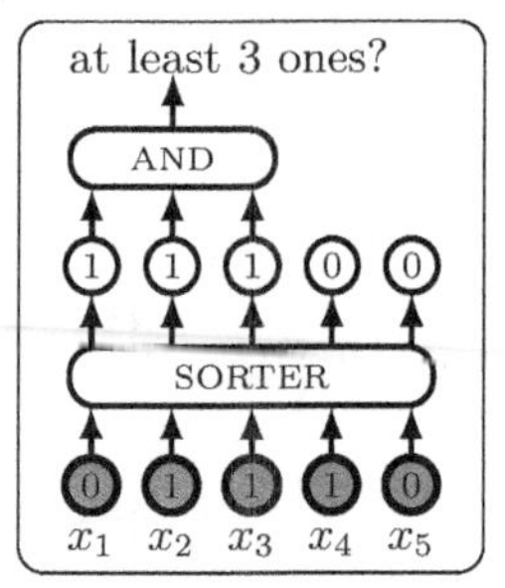

Exercise 29.11

(a) AND$(x_1, \ldots, x_\ell)$ evaluates to one if $x_i = 1$ (all the bits are 1) and zero otherwise. Give a circuit to compute AND of ℓ Boolean inputs. How many gates are needed?

(b) Give a circuit that sorts n input bits by moving all 1's to the left using a polynomial-in-n number of gates. We suggest shooting for $\Theta(n^2)$ gates, though one can do better. Prove your circuit works.

(Efficient hardware requires compact circuits for AND, OR, ADDERS, MULTIPLIERS, SORTERS, etc. This beautiful realm of circuit complexity theory is of extreme importance to chip design.)

Now we build a circuit to verify the clique. The basic constraint is that if vertices i and j are in the alleged clique, then edge (i,j) is in the graph and $e_{i,j} = 1$. That is $e_{i,j} \vee \overline{x_i} \vee \overline{x_j}$ must be T. A circuit $C_{i,j}$ which computes

$$e_{i,j} \vee \overline{x_i} \vee \overline{x_j}$$

is shown on the right. To verify this basic constraint for every pair of vertices, we construct separate circuits for the 10 possibile tuples of $(e_{i,j}, x_i, x_j)$. The vertices form a clique if and only if every $C_{i,j}$ outputs 1, which we ensure by taking the AND of the outputs from all the $C_{i,j}$ circuits. The AND of the clique-verifier and the size-verifier gives the full verifier circuit:

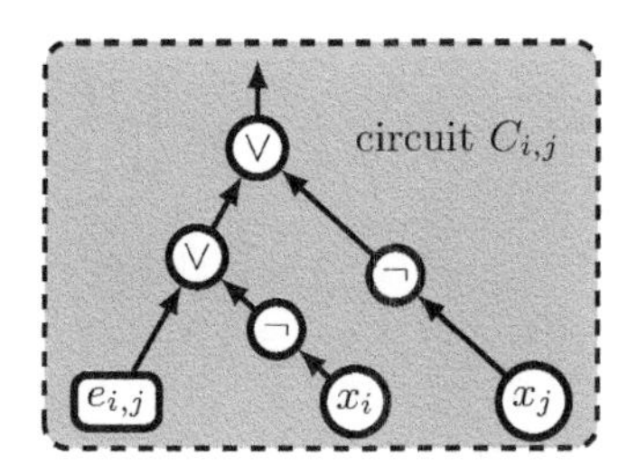

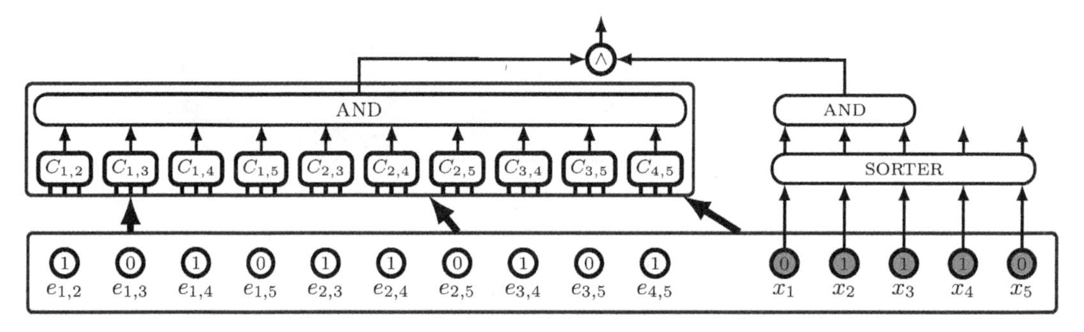

The size-verifier on the right uses only the clique-string. The clique-verifier on the left uses both the clique-string and edge list. The three inputs of each $C_{i,j}$ circuit connect to $e_{i,j}$, x_i and x_j, e.g. $C_{1,2}$ to $e_{1,2}, x_1, x_2$.

Pop Quiz 29.12

(a) Show that the output of our verifier-circuit above is 1. What does this mean?

(b) How many gates are in the verifier-circuit for our 5-vertex graph with $k = 3$?

We are ready to use the black-box CIRCUIT-SAT-solver. Instead of using 01110 for the clique, we treat it as an unknown input $x_1x_2x_3x_4x_5$. We want to know if some assignment to $x_1x_2x_3x_4x_5$ satisfies the circuit. If yes, then there is a clique of size at least 3. To find out, feed the circuit into the black-box CIRCUIT-SAT-solver:

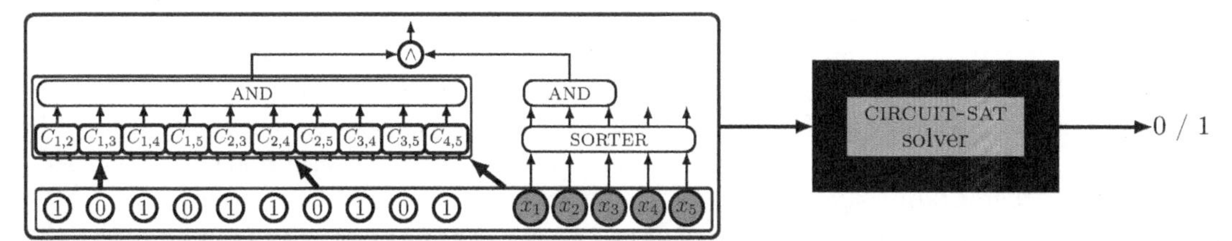

If the output is 1, there is a 3-clique. If not, there is no 3-clique. Though we only considered the specific graph 1010110101 and $k = 3$, our construction is systematic and general. Given the encoding of a graph on n vertices and $k > 1$, construct the corresponding circuit and plug it into the black-box. Two things are crucial:

1. The circuit must be small, polynomial in the size of the original input $\langle G \rangle$, to ensure that the black-box has polynomial runtime in $|\langle G \rangle|$. Our circuit-size is linear in $|\langle G \rangle|$, so we are good.
2. The circuit must be constructed quickly, in polynomial time. True in this case.

We can solve CLIQUE problems by reducing them to CIRCUIT-SAT problems. We say CLIQUE is polynomialy reducible to CIRCUIT-SAT, written CLIQUE $\leq_P$ CIRCUIT-SAT for "CLIQUE is easier than CIRCUIT-SAT". Beware. We can't polynomialy solve CIRCUIT-SAT – we do not have the black-box. We only have a relationship between CIRCUIT-SAT and CLIQUE which says CLIQUE is easier than CIRCUIT-SAT.

Exercise 29.13
An independent set in a graph contains vertices which are pairwise non-adjacent.

IND-SET: Given a graph G and $k > 1$ is there an independent set of size at least k?

Show how to use the CIRCUIT-SAT-solver to solve IND-SET for our graph and $k = 3$.

□

CIRCUIT-SAT is harder than every NP-problem. Every NP-problem is polynomialy reducible to CIRCUIT-SAT. The chaotic gray area between fast and slow – NP – has gained some order, in which CIRCUIT-SAT is a star that is a beacon to all of NP. If we can find a fast solution for this single problem, we would have fast solutions for every problem in NP. The status of the entire NP revolves around the status of just one problem in NP! There turn out to be other "hardest" problems in NP which, like CIRCUIT-SAT, hold the fate of NP in their hand. In the rest of the chapter we will see some of these other hardest problems.

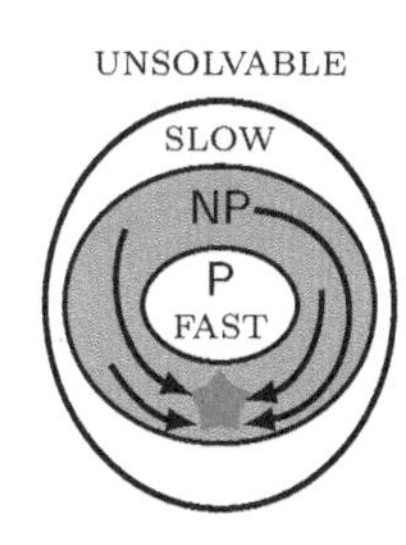

29.3 Other Hardest Problems: NP-completness

CIRCUIT-SAT is NP-complete. This means, CIRCUIT-SAT is harder than every NP-problem, or, more technically, that every NP-problem $\mathcal{L}$ is polynomialy reducible to CIRCUIT-SAT:

$$\text{IF CIRCUIT-SAT is polynomialy solvable, THEN } \mathcal{L} \text{ is polynomialy solvable.} \tag{29.1}$$

The proof was deep, because it had to work for every $\mathcal{L} \in$ NP, i.e. any problem with an efficient certifier. But now the floodgate is open. If we can show the converse for some problem $\mathcal{L}_* \in$ NP, namely that

$$\text{IF } \mathcal{L}_* \text{ is polynomialy solvable, THEN CIRCUIT-SAT is polynomialy solvable,} \tag{29.2}$$

it means $\mathcal{L}_*$ is harder than CIRCUIT-SAT which is harder than every NP-problem. It follows that $\mathcal{L}_*$ is harder than every NP-problem. Showing this converse for $\mathcal{L}_*$ shouldn't be that hard because it is for a specific $\mathcal{L}_*$.

Pop Quiz 29.14
Suppose that (29.2) is true. Prove that $\mathcal{L}_*$ is NP-complete.

Is there any problem $\mathcal{L}_*$ which is harder than CIRCUIT-SAT? Such a problem, if efficiently solved, would give an efficient algorithm for CIRCUIT-SAT which, in turn, gives efficient solutions to every NP-problem.

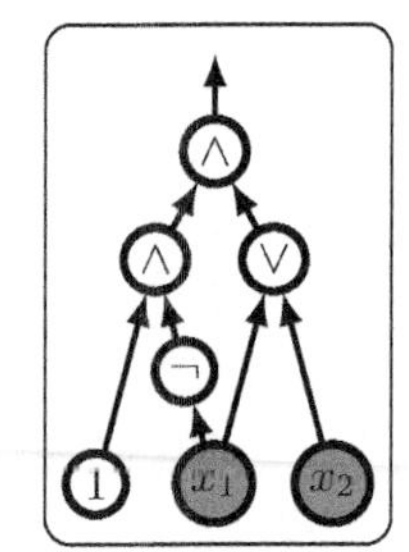

Our instance of CIRCUIT-SAT, reproduced on the right, computes $(1 \wedge \overline{x_1}) \wedge (x_1 \vee x_2)$. Deciding whether the circuit is satisfiable amounts to deciding if this Boolean expression is satisfiable. If you can polynomialy decide satisfiability of general Boolean expressions, you can polynomialy solve CIRCUIT-SAT. We conclude that satisfiability of general Boolean expressions is harder than CIRCUIT-SAT. This is no surprise because general Boolean expressions contain CIRCUIT-SAT expressions as special cases. We now show that determining satisfiability of a special kind of Boolean expression is harder than CIRCUIT-SAT.

We also show the same circuit with non-input vertices replaced by variables $v_1, \ldots, v_5$. The variables represent a node's output. To reproduce the original circuit, we should set

$$v_1 = 1 \qquad v_2 = \overline{x_1} \qquad v_3 = v_1 \wedge v_2 \qquad v_4 = x_1 \vee x_2 \qquad v_5 = v_3 \wedge v_4.$$

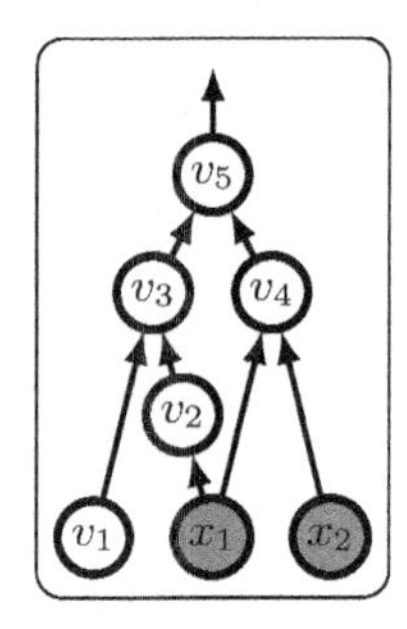

These constraints are propagation rules for the circuit, telling us how to compute the output v_5. For example, if $x_1 = 1$ and $x_2 = 1$, then

$$v_1 = 1 \quad v_2 = \overline{1} = 0 \quad v_3 = 1 \wedge 0 = 0 \quad v_4 = 1 \vee 1 = 1 \quad v_5 = 0 \wedge 1 = 0,$$

and the output is 0. The circuit is satisfied if the output is 1, which means every propagation constraint is satisfied AND $v_5 = 1$. The circuit is satisfied if and only if

$$(v_1 = 1) \wedge (v_2 = \overline{x_1}) \wedge (v_3 = v_1 \wedge v_2) \wedge (v_4 = x_1 \vee x_2) \wedge (v_5 = v_3 \wedge v_4) \wedge (v_5 = 1).$$

is a true expression, that is every clause is true.

> **Pop Quiz 29.15**
> Convert each constraint above into logical expressions by first showing:
> (a) $u = 1 \leftrightarrow u$ is true and $u = 0 \leftrightarrow \overline{u}$ is true
> (b) $u = v \leftrightarrow (u \vee \overline{v}) \wedge (\overline{u} \vee v)$ is true
> (c) $u = v \vee w \leftrightarrow (u \vee \overline{v}) \wedge (u \vee \overline{w}) \wedge (\overline{u} \vee v \vee w)$ is true
> (d) $u = v \wedge w \leftrightarrow (\overline{u} \vee v) \wedge (\overline{u} \vee w) \wedge (u \vee \overline{v} \vee \overline{w})$ is true
> Each constraint should become an AND of ORS.

By Pop Quiz 29.15 each constraint transforms into a logical formula which must be T.

$$\begin{aligned}
(v_1 = 1) &\leftrightarrow (v_1) \text{ is true;}\\
(v_2 = \overline{x_1}) &\leftrightarrow (v_2 \vee x_1) \wedge (\overline{v_2} \vee \overline{x_1}) \text{ is true;}\\
(v_3 = v_1 \wedge v_2) &\leftrightarrow (\overline{v_3} \vee v_1) \wedge (\overline{v_3} \vee v_2) \wedge (v_3 \vee \overline{v_1} \vee \overline{v_2}) \text{ is true;}\\
(v_4 = x_1 \vee x_2) &\leftrightarrow (v_4 \vee \overline{x_1}) \wedge (v_4 \vee \overline{x_2}) \wedge (\overline{v_4} \vee x_1 \vee x_2) \text{ is true;}\\
(v_5 = v_3 \wedge v_4) &\leftrightarrow (\overline{v_5} \vee v_3) \wedge (\overline{v_5} \vee v_4) \wedge (v_5 \vee \overline{v_3} \vee \overline{v_4}) \text{ is true;}\\
(v_5 = 1) &\leftrightarrow (v_5) \text{ is true.}
\end{aligned}$$

Each propagation constraint becomes an AND of a bunch of clauses, where a clause is the OR of a bunch of variables or their negations. The circuit is satisfied if and only if every constraint is satisfied, which means every clause above must be true. Here are all the clauses.

$$(v_1)(v_2 \vee x_1)(\overline{v_2} \vee \overline{x_1})(\overline{v_3} \vee v_1)(\overline{v_3} \vee v_2)(v_4 \vee \overline{x_1})(v_4 \vee \overline{x_2})(\overline{v_4} \vee x_1 \vee x_2)(\overline{v_5} \vee v_3)(\overline{v_5} \vee v_4)(v_5 \vee \overline{v_3} \vee \overline{v_4})(v_5)$$

This is a special Boolean expression, an AND of a bunch of clauses. Each clause is the OR of at most 3 terms, where a term is a variable or negation of a variable. The circuit is satisfiable if and only if every clause above can be simultaneously satisfied. We thus define the problem 3-SAT,

3-SAT: Given n clauses $C_1, \ldots, C_n$, where each clause is an OR of at most 3 terms, does some assignment of truth values to the variables make every clause true?

We can polynomialy solve CIRCUIT-SAT using a polynomial solver for 3-SAT on the clauses of the circuit.

Theorem 29.6 (3-SAT is NP-complete). IF 3-SAT $\in$ P, THEN CIRCUIT-SAT $\in$ P. Further, a polynomial solver for 3-SAT can be transformed into a polynomial solver for any problem in NP.

We have a second NP-complete problem. We won't formally prove Theorem 29.6, though all the ingredients of the proof are embedded in our discussion. The only part missing is to show that the number of clauses created is polynomial in the size of the CIRCUIT-SAT instance. This follows because each vertex in the circuit gives one constraint which gives at most 3 clauses, hence the number of clauses is linear in the size of the circuit.

Let's push on. Are there other NP-complete problems? Here is an instance of 3-SAT,

$$(y \vee x \vee z)(\overline{x} \vee z)(\overline{x} \vee \overline{z})(x \vee \overline{y} \vee \overline{z})$$

The clauses are satisfiable if and only if one term from each clause can be made true without conflicts. If x is true from the first clause, then $\overline{x}$ can't be true from the second clause as that conflicts with x. Here is a visual. Let each clause be a group of vertices. Each vertex is labeled by its clause and term it represents in the clause. Now add edges between vertices to indicate that those two terms cannot both be picked. So all vertices in a clause are linked, since you pick one term from a clause. Conflicting terms in different clauses are also linked, e.g. x in clause 1 gets an edge to the $\overline{x}$ in clause 2. Here is the full picture.

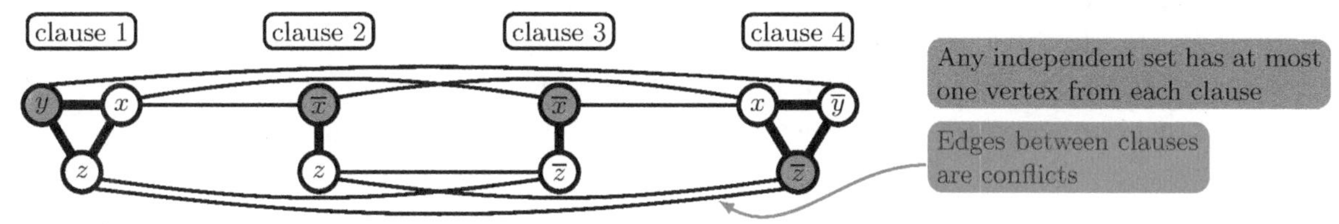

The graph above is a conflict-graph. No two of the shaded vertices (one in each clause) are adjacent, hence they are an independent set. This means the shaded terms do not conflict and can each be set to true. Setting $y = \text{T}$, $\overline{x} = \text{T}$, $\overline{z} = \text{T}$, we have the truth assignment $(x, y, z) = (\text{F}, \text{T}, \text{F})$. It is not hard to verify that these truth values satisfy every clause. Any independent set of size 4 would work.

Pop Quiz 29.16
Give all size-4 independent sets and the corresponding truth-assignments to (x, y, z).

We showed that an independent set of size 4 in the conflict graph of the clauses gives a satisfying truth assignment to the variables. Conversely, a satisfying truth assignment gives an independent set of size 4, by taking one satisfied term from each clause. The 3-SAT instance is satisfiable if and only if there is an independent set of size 4 in the conflict-graph. Let us define the general independent set problem,.

IND-SET: Given a graph G and $k > 1$ is there an independent set of size at least k?

Our argument generalizes. Given a black-box that solves IND-SET, we can solve a k-clause instance of 3-SAT by using the black-box on the conflict-graph of the 3-SAT problem. The conflict graph has at most $3k$ vertices and we seek an independent set of size k. Since the IND-SET-solver is polynomial, the runtime will be polynomial in k, and so we have a polynomial solver for 3-SAT..

Theorem 29.7 (IND-SET is NP-complete). IF IND-SET $\in$ P, THEN 3-SAT $\in$ P. Further, a polynomial solver for IND-SET can be transformed into a polynomial solver for any problem in NP.

The theme is that any NP-complete problem can be used to show that a harder problem is NP-complete. We now have three NP-complete problems: CIRCUIT-SAT, 3-SAT and IND-SET.

Showing another NP-problem $\mathcal{L}$ is NP-complete
1. Choose some NP-complete problem $\mathcal{L}_*$.
2. Show: IF $\mathcal{L}$ is polynomialy solvable, THEN $\mathcal{L}_*$ is polynomialy solvable.

Exercise 29.17
(a) Use IND-SET to show that CLIQUE is NP-complete.
(b) Use IND-SET to show that VERTEX-COVER is NP-complete. A set of vertices are a vertex cover if every edge has at least one of its end-points in the vertex cover. The problem VERTEX-COVER is:

VERTEX-COVER: Given a graph G, is there a vertex cover of size at most k?

The path we took is shown on the right. An arrow from one problem to another indicates that if the first is polynomialy solvable, then so is the second. Since CIRCUIT-SAT points to all of NP, all the named problems are equally hard. If any one is polynomialy solvable, then so is all of NP. If any one is not polynomialy solvable, then none are. The problems on the right are just the tip of the iceberg. Karp's seminal 1972 paper gave 21 NP-complete problems of different flavors. The list has since exploded to hundreds of problems in various areas (graphs, network design, sets and partitions, scheduling, distributed computing, optimization, algebra, number theory, games/puzzles, etc., see the classic *Computers and Intractability* by Carey & Johnson). NP-completeness is the beautiful theory connecting all the hardest problems in NP. Solve one, solve them all!

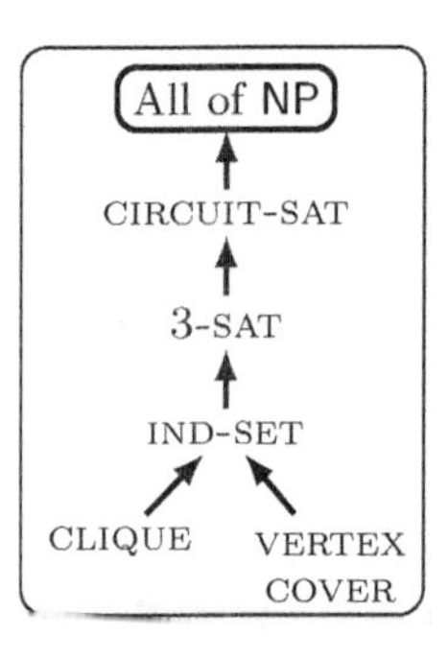

Example 29.8 (Data mining frequent baskets). The customer data in the supermarket problem which started this chapter is a binary matrix A, where the (i, j)-entry $A_{i,j}$ is 1 if customer i bought item j. Given a size k and popularity n, is there a k-item-basket $B = \{j_1, \ldots, j_k\}$ which is bought by n customers $C = \{i_1, \ldots, i_n\}$, which means $A_{i,j} = 1$ for $i \in C$ and $j \in B$. Such a basket, represented by k columns of A, is n-frequent.

FREQ-ITEMS: Given A, n and k, are there k columns which are n-frequent?

For the sample data on page 413, we can identify A and a basket which is 3-frequent:

$$A = \begin{pmatrix} 1 & 1 & 0 & 1 & 0 \\ 1 & 1 & 0 & 1 & 1 \\ 0 & 0 & 1 & 1 & 0 \\ 1 & 1 & 1 & 1 & 1 \end{pmatrix} \quad \text{and} \quad \begin{array}{l} B = \{1, 2, 4\}; \\ C = \{1, 2, 4\}. \end{array} \quad (B \text{ is 3-frequent})$$

FREQ-ITEMS is in NP. To prove a (YES)-instance, use, as evidence, the columns B and corresponding rows C. The verifier checks that $A_{i,j} = 1$ for those row-column pairs.

Theorem 29.9 (FREQ-ITEMS is NP-complete). IF FREQ-ITEMS $\in$ P, THEN CLIQUE $\in$ P. Further, a polynomial solver for FREQ-ITEMS can be transformed into a polynomial solver for any problem in NP. □

Exercise 29.18

(a) Prove that BIG-CLIQUE is NP-complete by reduction from CLIQUE

BIG-CLIQUE: Given $G = (V, E)$ and $k > |V|/2$, is there a k-clique in G?

(b) **[Hard]** Prove that FREQ-ITEMS is NP-complete by reduction from CLIQUE.

Example 29.8 reflects an unfortunate reality. Many problems in practice are NP-complete. ☹ How did this save your job? You didn't tell your boss you can't solve the problem. You reported that Turing himself can't solve the problem efficiently. Now your boss is impressed since you appear to be on the same plane as a legend.

The supermarket still needs those 10 items that are bought by at least 5,000 customers. It is widely accepted that P $\neq$ NP, so we may never have a polynomial solution. How do we cope? An exponential algorithm may have reasonable runtime on the specific instance you encounter in practice. If not, there is some recourse:

SURVIVOR'S HANDBOOK

HOW TO BEAT:
Quicksand
Crocodiles
NP-completeness

1. Modify the task. For the supermarket, there's a tradeoff betweem basket-size k and basket-popularity n. We want a basket with large k and large n. If you just need large $k + n$, that's polynomialy solvable. If you need large $k \times n$, that's NP-complete. Subtle changes can drastically affect a problem's solvability.

2. Narrow the task. The general problem may be hard, but if your instance has some special structure, then it could be much easier to solve efficiently.

3. Use partial or approximate solutions. Optimal is not practical. Unfortunately, we need another book to cover approximations. This book has run out of steam.

The Case for P = NP. By far, the prevailing bias is that P $\neq$ NP. Why is it not a slam dunk that searching for a solution has to be harder than verifying a solution? Here is an analogy. It is simple enough to verify if a piece of straw is a steel needle. What about searching for that needle in a haystack? One laborious way is to test if each straw is the needle. A smarter and very efficient alternative is to just bring a magnet to the haystack and tease the needle out. There could be an efficient "magnet" for 3-SAT. We just don't know it.

29.4 Problems

Problem 29.1. The average earth-to-moon distance is 238,855 miles. Express this distance using Roman numerals. How is your answer relevant to the way we define if a problem is hard? *[Hint: Unary vs. radix in a base larger than 1.]*

Definition 29.10. Here is a small list useful problems, some of which we proved are NP-complete.
(a) PATH-DIR(G, s, t): Is there a path from vertices s to t in the directed graph G?
(b) k-SAT$(C_1, \ldots, C_m)$: Each clause C_i is an OR of at most k terms. Is there a truth assignment to the variables satisfying every clause?
(c) IND-SET(G, k): Is there an independent set with k or more vertices in the undirected graph G?
(d) CLIQUE(G, k): Is there an clique with k or more vertices in the undirected graph G?
(e) k-COLORING(G): Is there a valid coloring of undirected graph G using at most k colors?
(f) VERTEX-COVER(G, k): Is there a vertex cover with k or fewer vertices in the undirected graph G?
(g) DOM-SET(G, k): Is there a dominating set with k or fewer vertices in the undirected graph G?
(h) SUBSET-SUM(S, t): Is there a subset of the multiset S whose elements sum to the target t?
(i) FACTOR(n, k): Is the kth bit of the smallest prime divisor of n a 1?

Problem 29.2. For each problem in Definition 29.10, is it easier to give evidence for a (YES) or (NO) answer?

Problem 29.3. Prove each problem in Definition 29.10 is in NP by giving the evidence E and a polynomial certifier C. (For part (i), you may assume that testing primality is in P.)

Problem 29.4. Why is every problem in P also in NP? What is the evidence E and polynomial certifier C?

Problem 29.5. Prove that PATH-DIR is in P.

Problem 29.6. If PATH-DIR is NP-complete, prove that P = NP. Do you think PATH-DIR is NP-complete?

Problem 29.7. Prove that for any fixed k, e.g. $k = 10$, determining if a graph G has a clique of size k is in P. Why then do we say that CLIQUE is NP-completeand that we do not know of a polynomial algorithm for CLIQUE.

Problem 29.8. A problem's (YES)-answer is polynomialy verifiable. Does it mean its (NO)-answer is also polynomialy verifiable? Show that the answer is affirmative for all problems in P.

Problem 29.9. A sorter outputs all the bits in the n-bit input, but with all the 1's on the left. For the problem IS-SORTER defined below, which is easier to verify given the right evidence: (YES) or (NO)?

IS-SORTER: Given a circuit that takes n inputs, determine if the circuit is a valid sorter.

Problem 29.10 (coNP). The set coNP contains all problems whose (NO)-answer can be verified in polynomial time. Prove that FACTOR $\in$ NP $\cap$ coNP. (**Burning question:** Is NP = coNP?)

Problem 29.11. We introduced two notions for comparing problems $\mathcal{L}_1$ and $\mathcal{L}_2$: $\mathcal{L}_1 \le_{\text{R}} \mathcal{L}_2$ in Chapter 27 and $\mathcal{L}_1 \le_{\text{P}} \mathcal{L}_2$ in this chapter. Carefully explain both notions and the difference between them.

Problem 29.12. The problem $\mathcal{L}_*$ is in NP-complete. What can you conclude about the problem $\mathcal{L}$?
(a) An instance w of $\mathcal{L}$ can be converted to an instance w_* of $\mathcal{L}_*$ and $w \in \mathcal{L} \leftrightarrow w_* \in \mathcal{L}_*$.
(b) An instance w of $\mathcal{L}$ can be quickly converted, in polynomial time, to an instance w_* of $\mathcal{L}_*$ and $w \in \mathcal{L} \leftrightarrow w_* \in \mathcal{L}_*$.
(c) An instance w_* of $\mathcal{L}_*$ can be converted to an instance w of $\mathcal{L}$ and $w \in \mathcal{L} \leftrightarrow w_* \in \mathcal{L}_*$.
(d) An instance w_* of $\mathcal{L}_*$ can be quickly converted, in polynomial time, to an instance of w $\mathcal{L}$ and $w \in \mathcal{L} \leftrightarrow w_* \in \mathcal{L}_*$.

Problem 29.13. PATH is the same problem as PATH-DIR, but for undirected graphs. Prove that PATH $\le_{\text{P}}$ PATH-DIR.

Problem 29.14. Sketch a fast Turing Machine that implements the solution of LARGE-SUM in Section 29.1 on page 414 and argue that the runtime of your Turing Machine is polynomial.

Problem 29.15. The certifier for a problem in NP takes the input w, a certificate c with $|c| \le p(|w|)$ and has worst-case runtime $q(|w| + |c|)$, where $p(\cdot)$ and $q(\cdot)$ are polynomials.
How do you *solve* the problem using the certifier? Is your worst-case runtime polynomial?

Problem 29.16. DIRECTED-HAM-PATH is the task of determining if a directed graph G, has a Hamiltonian path.
(a) Similar to Example 29.2, what would be a simplified encoding for a directed graph G?
(b) Show that DIRECTED-HAM-PATH $\in$ NP.

Problem 29.17. Prove that NP is closed under the Kleene star operation. That is, if $\mathcal{L} \in$ NP then $\mathcal{L}^* \in$ NP.

Problem 29.18. Prove that P is closed under the Kleene star operation. That is, if $\mathcal{L} \in$ P then $\mathcal{L}^* \in$ P. *[Hint: Use a build-up method (dynamic programming). For string $w = b_1 b_2 \cdots b_n$, define $Q(i) = 1$ if $b_1 \cdots b_i \in \mathcal{L}^*$ for $i = 1, \ldots, n$.]*

Problem 29.19. A circuit is a directed *acyclic* graph of gates. We show a cyclic circuit on the right. What is the output y? Explain your reasoning.

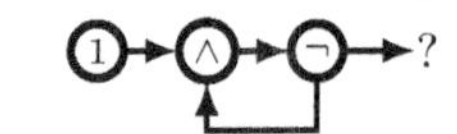

Problem 29.20. In each case, is the instance of 3-SAT satisfiable? Give a proof of your answer.

(a) $(x \vee y \vee z)(x \vee \overline{y} \vee z)(x \vee \overline{y} \vee \overline{z})(\overline{x} \vee y \vee z)(\overline{x} \vee y \vee \overline{z})(\overline{x} \vee \overline{y} \vee \overline{z})$.

(b) $(x \vee y \vee z)(x \vee y \vee \overline{z})(x \vee \overline{y} \vee z)(x \vee \overline{y} \vee \overline{z})(\overline{x} \vee y \vee z)(\overline{x} \vee y \vee \overline{z})(\overline{x} \vee \overline{y} \vee z)(\overline{x} \vee \overline{y} \vee \overline{z})$.

Problem 29.21. Build a 'naive" circuit to determine if the input-string $x_1 \cdots x_n$ has at least k 1's.

(a) Let $S_{i_1,i_2,\ldots,i_k}$ be a circuit that takes the AND of bits $x_{i_1}, \ldots, x_{i_k}$. How many different circuits $S_{i_1,i_2,\ldots,i_k}$ are there, and how many gates are in each of them?

(b) Show that the OR of the outputs of all the $S_{i_1,i_2,\ldots,i_k}$ is 1 if and only if the input-string has at least k ones.

(c) How many gates do you need to implement the gigantic OR?

(d) How many gates does the entire circuit need? For $k = n/2$, show that the number of gates is exponential in n.

Problem 29.22. Is $\mathcal{L} = \{0^{\bullet n} 1^{\bullet n} \mid n \geq 1\}$ in NP?

(a) Give a Boolean circuit which takes four inputs $x_1 x_2 x_3 x_4$ with output 1 if and only if $x_1 x_2 x_3 x_4 \in \mathcal{L}$.

(b) Transform the Boolean circuit to an instance of 3-SAT such that the Boolean circuit is satisfied if and only if the instance of 3-SAT is satisfied. How many variables and clauses do you need?

(c) Transform the instance of 3-SAT to an instance of IND-SET. Find an independent set of the appropriate size and use that to find a satisfying assignment to the variables for the instance of 3-SAT.

Problem 29.23. A problem is in the set EXP if it can be solved by a Turing Machine M with at most exponential runtime, which means for a polynomial $p(\cdot)$, the worst-case runtime of M on input w is at most $p(2^{|w|})$. Show:

(a) P $\subseteq$ NP $\subseteq$ EXP (b) P $\subset$ EXP (c) Either P $\subset$ NP or NP $\subset$ EXP

Problem 29.24. Show that if a problem is solved by a non-deterministic Turing Machine in polynomial time, the problem has a deterministic polynomial-time certifier. *[Hint: If the answer is* (YES)*, some branch in the non-deterministic computation accepts. The choices made along that computation-path are the evidence. To prove* (YES)*, you can run the non-deterministic Turing Machine, while making the choices dictated by the evidence.]*

Problem 29.25. A Turing machine has 2 states q_0, q_1, and takes at most 3 steps on an input of size 2. Let bits $s_0 s_1$ represent the state; so 10 is state q_0 and 01 is state q_1. Let $w_0 w_1 w_2 w_3$ be the bits at tape-slots 0,1,2,3 ($*$ is at slot 0) – the Turing Machine will not read or write to other slots. Let $p_0 p_1 p_2 p_3$ be the head's position, so 0100 means the head is at tape-slot 1. The *configuration* of the Turing Machine is represented by $s_0 s_1 \# w_0 w_1 w_2 w_3 \# p_0 p_1 p_2 p_3$.

(a) What is the configuration at the begining for input $w = 01$.

(b) The configuration is $01\#{*}11{\sqcup}\#0100$. What does this mean? Build a circuit to implement the instruction:

"In state q_1 with the head at slot 1 reading '1': write '0'; move L; transition to q_0."

(The circuit takes an input configuration and outputs the next configuration.) Apply your circuit to $01\#{*}11{\sqcup}\#0100$.

Problem 29.26 (Turing Machines and Circuits). A Turing Machine M has worst-case runtime $t(|w|)$ on input w. Show that the function computed by M on inputs of size n can be computed by a circuit with $O(t(n)^2)$ gates.

Problem 29.27. Prove that HAM-CYCLE $\leq_{\text{P}}$ HAM-PATH, where

HAM-CYCLE: Given a graph G, is there a Hamiltonian cycle using every vertex once?

HAM-PATH: Given a graph G, is there a Hamiltonian path using every vertex once?

(a) Consider any edge $e = (u, v)$ in G. Construct G' from G by adding vertices u', v' and edges (u', u) and (v', v). Show that there is a Hamiltonian cycle in G if and only if there is a Hamiltonian path in G'.

(b) Show that IF HAM-PATH $\in$ P THEN HAM-CYCLE $\in$ P.

(c) How many times does your solver for HAM-CYCLE use the blackbox-solver for HAM-PATH?

(d) Can you find a reduction which uses the blackbox-solver for HAM-PATH just once?

Problem 29.28. Show that the problem BOUNDED-k defined below is NP-complete by reducing every problem in NP to BOUNDED-k, just as we reduced every problem in NP to CIRCUIT-SAT.

BOUNDED-k: Given a Turing Machine M and k, is there some input w for which M halts after at most k steps?

Problem 29.29. The problem BIPARTITE is to determine if an input graph is bipartite. Show that BIPARTITE $\in$ NP. Show also that BIPARTITE is polynomialy solvable and hence that 2-COLORING is in P. Does this mean P = NP?

Problem 29.30 (BALANCED-BIPARTITE-CLIQUE). Show that FREQITEMS remains NP-complete even when the popularity and basket sizes are equal. *[Hint: Exercise 29.18(b); add spurious customers who buy every item.]* (A problem can be easier when restricted (not the case here). With this restriction, FREQITEMS is equivalent to BALANCED-BIPARTITE-CLIQUE, NP-complete problem GT24 in *Computers and Intractability* by Garey & Johnson.)

Problem 29.31. Why is PARTITION a special case of SUBSET-SUM? Nevertheless, prove that PARTITION is not easier than SUBSET-SUM, that is SUBSET-SUM $\le_{\text{P}}$ PARTITION. *[Hint: To solve* SUBSET-SUM(S,t) *add* $\sum_{x_i\in S} x_i - 2t$ *to* S.*]*

Problem 29.32. Consider the instance of 3-SAT: $\varphi = (x_1 \vee x_2 \vee x_3)(\overline{x_1} \vee x_3)(\overline{x_1} \vee \overline{x_3})(x_1 \vee \overline{x_2} \vee \overline{x_3})$.

(a) Is φ satisfiable? Let ℓ be the number of variables, and k the number of clauses in φ. What are ℓ and k?

(b) Corresponding to φ, construct $2(\ell+k)$ numbers, each with $\ell+k$ digits. Corresponding to each variable x_i for $i = 1,\ldots,\ell$ are two numbers $a_i, \overline{a_i}$ (2ℓ numbers), and corresponding to each clause C_j for $j = 1,\ldots,k$ are two buffer numbers $b_j, \overline{b_j}$. The least significant k digits correspond to clauses and the most significant ℓ digits correspond to the variables. The digits of a_i indicate the variable and the clauses containing that variable. The digits of $\overline{a_i}$ indicate the variable and the clauses containing the negation of that variable. The digits of b_i and $\overline{b_i}$ simply indicate the clause. For φ, we partially filled a table with one row for each number.

	variables			clauses			
	x_1	x_2	x_3	c_1	c_2	c_3	c_4
a_1	1	0	0	1	0	0	1
$\overline{a_1}$	1	0	0	0	1	1	0
a_2	0	1	0	1	0	0	0
$\overline{a_2}$							
a_3							
$\overline{a_3}$							
b_1	0	0	0	1	0	0	0
$\overline{b_1}$	0	0	0	1	0	0	0
b_2	0	0	0	0	1	0	0
$\overline{b_2}$							
b_3							
$\overline{b_3}$							
b_4							
$\overline{b_4}$							
t	1	1	1	3	3	3	3

(i) Complete the table by filling in the digits for all the numbers.
(ii) At the bottom of the table is a target number t whose digits are ℓ 1's followed by k 3's. Find a subset of the numbers which sums to t.
(iii) In your subset of numbers, explain why exactly one of a_i or $\overline{a_i}$ must be picked.
(iv) Use your subset to assign $x_i = \text{T}$ if and only if a_i is in the subset.
(v) What is the truth value of φ for the assignment you obtained.
(vi) Prove the φ is satisfiable if and only if some subset-sum equals t.
(vii) Generalize the construction to an arbitrary instance of 3-SAT with ℓ variables and k clauses. Hence, prove that SUBSET-SUM is NP-complete.

(c) Prove that PARTITION is NP-complete.

Problem 29.33. Consider SUBSET-SUM with set $S = \{3,5,3,11,6,2\}$ and target $t = 9$. Build a table in which the columns are labeled by the possible subset-sums up to t, $0,1,\ldots,t$ and the rows are labeled by the possible prefixes of S, that is $S_0 = \varnothing, S_1 = \{3\}, S_2 = \{3,5\},\ldots$. The entry in cell (S_i, j) is 1 if the prefix-subset S_i has a subset with sum j and 0 otherwise. We filled the first 3 rows.

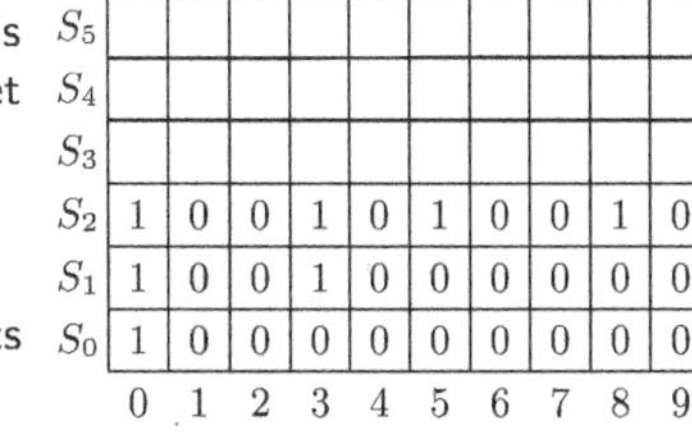

S_6										
S_5										
S_4										
S_3										
S_2	1	0	0	1	0	1	0	0	1	0
S_1	1	0	0	1	0	0	0	0	0	0
S_0	1	0	0	0	0	0	0	0	0	0
	0	1	2	3	4	5	6	7	8	9

(a) Explain row S_0, and how to get row S_1 from S_0 and row S_2 from row S_1.
(b) Complete the table. How do tell if the answer is (YES) from the filled table?
(c) Sketch an algorithm to solve SUBSET-SUM for a general set with n elements and target t. Show that your algorithm's runtime is polynomial in n and t.
(d) Since SUBSET-SUM is NP-complete, have you proved that P = NP?

Problem 29.34. Determine whether these two instances of 2-SAT are satisfiable,

$$\varphi_1 = (x_1 \vee x_2)(x_1 \vee \overline{x_2})(\overline{x_1} \vee x_3)(\overline{x_1} \vee \overline{x_3}) \qquad \text{and} \qquad \varphi_2 = (x_1 \vee x_2)(x_1 \vee \overline{x_2})(\overline{x_1} \vee x_3).$$

Construct a graph for an expression as follows. For l each variables x_i, add two vertices x_i and $\overline{x_i}$. To satisfy a clause $(a \vee b)$, if $a = \text{F}$ the $b = \text{T}$ and if $b = \text{F}$ then $a = \text{T}$, hence add two directed edges $\overline{a} \to b$ and $\overline{b} \to a$.

(a) Construct the graphs G_1, G_2 for φ_1, φ_2.
(b) If there is a directed path from a vertex a to a vertex b and $a = \text{T}$, what can you conclude about b? Explain.
(c) In G_1, find a pair of vertices $x_i, \overline{x_i}$ that are on the same directed cycle. Hence prove that ϕ_1 is unsatisfiable.
(d) In G_2, is there a pair of vertices $x_i, \overline{x_i}$ that are on the same directed cycle?

Use G_2 to assign truth values to the variables in φ_2 as follows. For any unassigned variable x_i, either there is no path from x_i to $\overline{x_i}$, in which case let $x_i = \text{T}$ or there is no path from $\overline{x_i}$ to x_i, in which case let $\overline{x_i} = \text{T}$. Now give T to all vertices reachable from that assigned vertex and F to their negations. Continue until all variables have been assigned. What is the assignment you get? Show that for your assignment, φ_2 is satisfied. *[Hint: To prove correctness, observe that if there is a path from a to b then there is also a path from $\overline{b}$ to $\overline{a}$.]*

(e) Prove that 2-SAT is in P. (You may assume PATH-DIR is in P.)

Problem 29.35 (Interval Graphs). Give efficient (linear time) algorithms for solving these NP-complete problems when restricted to an interval graph. Assume that the graph is specified by a set of intervals.
(a) IND-SET. (b) CLIQUE. (c) COLORING.

Problem 29.36. Give a polynomial algorithm for 2-COLORING. That is, show that 2-COLORING is in P.

Problem 29.37. Reduce this instance of 3-SAT, $\varphi = (x_1 \vee x_2 \vee x_3)(\overline{x_1} \vee x_3)$ to 3-COLORING.

(a) Start with a triangle with vertices corresponding to T, F and base B colored green, red and blue. For each variable x_i, add vertices x_i and $\overline{x_i}$ and form a triangle with B. We illustrate with x_1. Give the graph after adding all variable vertices. Prove that in any valid 3-coloring of the graph, one of a variable's vertices will be green and one red.

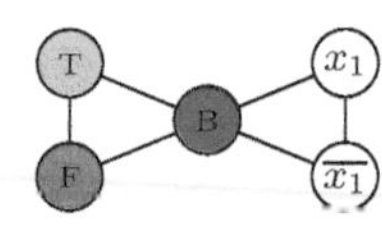

(b) We show an OR-gadget which corresponds to the clause $(a \vee b)$. Prove that in any valid 3-coloring of this OR-gadget, at least one of a or b must be colored green which corresponds to T and hence implies that the clause $(a \vee b)$ is T. Construct a similar OR-gadget for $(a \vee b \vee c)$ and prove it. *[Hint: $(a \vee b \vee c) = (a \vee (b \vee c))$.]*

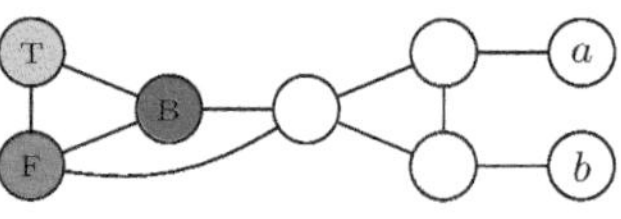

(c) Combine the gadgets in (a) and (b) to get a graph which is 3-colorable if and only if φ is satisfiable. Prove it.

(d) Generalize the argument to arbitrary instances of 3-SAT and prove that 3-COLORING is NP-complete.

Problem 29.38. For $k > 3$, prove k-COLORING is NP-complete. *[Hint: To solve 3-COLORING add $k - 3$ vertices.]*

Problem 29.39. Use a reduction from VERTEX-COVER to show that DOM-SET is NP-complete. *[Hints: Why can you remove isolated vertices? For each edge $e = (v_i, v_j)$ add a new vertex v_{ij} and edges $(v_i, v_{ij}), (v_j, v_{ij})$.]*

Problem 29.40 (Bin Packing). Disks have capacity M and you have n files of (positive) sizes $S = \{x_1, \ldots, x_n\}$. The task is to determine if k disks will suffice to hold all the files (a file cannot be split between disks).

BIN-PACKING(S, M, k): Can the values in S be partitioned into k bins with the sum of values in each bin at most M.

(a) Determine if the values in each instance of partition can be packed into two bins of capacity 15:
(i) $S = \{3, 5, 3, 11, 6, 2\}$ (ii) $S = \{3, 6, 2, 11, 6, 2\}$.

(b) Prove that a set can be partitioned into two equal sets if and only if the values can be placed into two bins of an appropriate capacity (what is that capacity). Hence, prove that BIN-PACKING is NP-complete (even fixing $k = 2$).

Problem 29.41. Here is a greedy algorithm, first fit, to pack the values $x_1, \ldots, x_n$ into as few bins of capacity M as possible (see Problem 29.40). Label the bins $B_1, B_2, \ldots$. Process the values one by one, placing each value into the first available bin with enough space. Let k be the number of bins used and k_* the minimum number of bins needed.

(a) Prove that at least $k - 1$ bins are more than half full. Hence, prove that $\sum_i x_i > \frac{1}{2}M(k - 1)$.

(b) Prove that first fit uses at most twice the optimal number of bins, $k \leq 2k_*$.

(c) Prove that if P $\neq$ NP, no polynomial algorithm guarantees $k < \frac{3}{2}k_*$. *[Hint: Use the algorithm to solve PARTITION.]*

(d) First fit decreasing processes the values in decreasing order $x_1 \geq x_2 \cdots \geq x_n$. Prove that first fit decreasing uses at most $\frac{3}{2}k_*$ bins. *[Hint: Suppose ℓ of the x_i are larger than $\frac{1}{2}M$. Consider the two cases $\ell \geq \frac{2}{3}k$ and $\ell < \frac{2}{3}k$.]*

Problem 29.42 (Knapsack). A truck has capacity c, and n packages of sizes $S = \{s_1, \ldots, s_n\}$ have corresponding values $V = \{v_1, \ldots, v_n\}$. The task is fill the truck with as much value as possible without exceeding it's capacity. As a decision problem, is there a subset packages having total size at most c with total value at least v?

KNAPSACK(S, V, c, v): Is there a subset $I \subseteq [n]$ for which $\sum_{i \in I} s_i \leq c$ and $\sum_{i \in I} v_i \geq v$?

(a) Let S be an instance of PARTITION with total sum M. Construct an instance of KNAPSACK with sizes S and values S with capacity $c = \frac{1}{2}M$ and target value $v = \frac{1}{2}M$. Prove that the answer to PARTITION(S) is (YES) if and only if the answer to KNAPSACK$(S, S, \frac{1}{2}M, \frac{1}{2}M)$ is (YES). Hence, prove that KNAPSACK is NP-complete.

(b) Use build up (dynamic programming) to sketch an algorithm for KNAPSACK with worst-case runtime poly(n, s, v).

Problem 29.43. The maximization version of KNAPSACK (Problem 29.42) asks for the maximum value of items given the capacity c. An item's efficiency is $e_i = v_i/s_i$. Order items by decreasing efficiency, $e_1 \geq e_2 \geq \cdots \geq e_n$.

(a) In the fractional version of KNAPSACK (see Problem 29.42), one can place a fractional part of an item in the truck. Greedy picks items in order of decreasing efficiency, and the last item picked may be fractional. Prove that Greedy is polynomial and maximizes the value that can be fit into capacity c. Let the values of items picked by Greedy be $v_1, \ldots, v_k$. Prove that for non-fractional KNAPSACK, Greedy would pick $v_1, \ldots, v_{k-1}$ and possibly v_k.

(b) Let v_* be the optimal value that can be packed into capacity c and v the value packed by Greedy. Give an example to show that v_*/v can be arbitrarily large.

(c) Prove that $v_* \leq v_1 + v_2 + \cdots + v_k$. Hence, modify Greedy to obtain a value at least half of optimal.

Problem 29.44 (Scheduling). Each student in $S = \{s_1, \ldots, s_n\}$ is taking a subset of courses in $C = \{c_1, \ldots, c_m\}$. Each course must be assigned to one of k final exam slots such that two courses in the same final exam slot cannot have a student in common. Formulate this problem as a language and show that it is NP-complete. *[Hint: Reduce from* COLORING. *Let each edge in the input graph to* COLORING *be a student and each vertex a course.]*

Problem 29.45 (Integer Programming is NP-complete). An instance of 3-SAT has variables $x_1, \ldots, x_\ell$. For each x_i, define a $z_i \in \{0, 1\}$. For each clause form an inequality constraint. For example $(\overline{x_1} \vee x_3)$ becomes $(1 - z_1) + z_3 \geq 0$, where if x_i is in the clause, z_i is in the constraint and if $\overline{x_i}$ is in the clause, $(1 - z_i)$ is in the constraint.

(a) Give all the constraints for $\varphi = (x_1 \vee x_2 \vee x_3)(\overline{x_1} \vee x_3)(\overline{x_1} \vee \overline{x_3})(x_1 \vee \overline{x_2} \vee \overline{x_3})$.
(b) Find $z_i \in \{0, 1\}$ so that all constraints are obeyed. Use the values for z_i to get a satisfying assignment for φ.
(c) Prove that φ is satisfiable if and only if every constraint in (a) is satisfied for some $z_i \in \{0, 1\}$.
(d) Generalize to an arbitrary instance of 3-SAT and prove that determining if a set of linear inequality constraints over Boolean variables can all be simultaneously satisfied is NP-complete. (Formally define a problem INT-PROGRAM.)

Problem 29.46 (Solitaire). Many versions of solitaire are NP-complete. Here is a simple version. Each square on an $n \times n$ board has either a red or blue stone, or no stone. The player removes stones one-by-one, but must keep at least one stone in each row. The goal is to make each column monochromatic, having stones of only one color. The task is to determine if the game is winnable. Prove that this version of solitaire is NP-complete. *[Hint: Reduce from* 3-SAT. *For an instance of* 3-SAT *with variables* $x_1, \ldots, x_n$ *and clauses* $c_1, \ldots, c_m$, *if* $x_i \in c_j$ *place a blue stone in square* (c_j, x_i), *and if* $\overline{x_i} \in c_j$ *place a red stone in square* (c_j, x_i). *What do you do if* $m \neq n$?*]*

(Most non-trivial 2-player games (e.g. checkers/draughts, chess, go) are much harder, *requiring* exponential time to solve.)

Problem 29.47. Assume 3-SAT is in P. This just means that you can quickly determine if an instance of 3-SAT is satisfiable. The task now is to find a satisfying assignment for the variables. Sketch a polynomial algorithm to find a satisfying assignment for the variables. *[Hint: Set* $x_1 = \text{T}$ *and obtain a new instance of* 3-SAT. *If this new instance is satisfiable, then you can set* $x_1 = \text{T}$. *Continue with* x_2 *and so on. Is the algorithm polynomial?]*

Problem 29.48. Assume FACTOR is in P. Sketch a polynomial algorithm to factor an integer into its prime divisors.

Problem 29.49. Assume SUBSET-SUM is in P. Sketch a polynomial algorithm to *find* a subset with sum t.

Problem 29.50. Assume IND-SET is in P. Sketch a polynomial algorithm to find a *maximum* independent set. *[Hints: First find the size of the maximum independent set; Problem 23.37.]*

Problem 29.51. Assume CLIQUE is in P. Sketch a polynomial algorithm to find a *maximum* clique.

Problem 29.52. Exact-3-SAT or X3-SAT is the special case of 3-SAT where all clauses have exactly 3 variables.

(a) Show that for $(\overline{z_1} \vee z_2 \vee z_3)(\overline{z_1} \vee \overline{z_2} \vee z_3)(\overline{z_1} \vee z_2 \vee \overline{z_3})(\overline{z_1} \vee \overline{z_2} \vee \overline{z_3})$ to be satisfied, z_1 must be F.
(b) Show, by a reduction from 3-SAT that X3-SAT is NP-complete.

Problem 29.53. Prove that any instance of X3-SAT (see Problem 29.52) with fewer than 8 clauses is satisfiable.

Problem 29.54. Consider an instance φ of 3-SAT with n variables $x_1, \ldots, x_n$ and m clauses.

(a) Sketch a deterministic brute force algorithm with $O(m2^n)$ steps by trying all possible assignments to the variables.
(b) Suppose that φ is satisfiable and let $\boldsymbol{\alpha} = \alpha_1\alpha_2 \cdots \alpha_n$ be a satisfying assignment. Pick a random assignment $\mathbf{x}$
  (i) Let A_k be the event that $\mathbf{x}$ has k disagreements with $\boldsymbol{\alpha}$. Show that $\mathbb{P}[A_k] = \binom{n}{k}2^{-n}$.
  (ii) Repeat up to n times if the current assignment does not satisfy φ: pick any unsatisfied clause and flip the bit of a random variable in the clause. Show that with probability at least $\frac{1}{3}$, the number of disagreements between $\boldsymbol{\alpha}$ and $\mathbf{x}$ decreases by 1.
  (iii) Show that if the first k flips in (ii) are successful, increasing the agreement with $\boldsymbol{\alpha}$ by 1 each time, then you succesfully find a satisfying assignment. Hence, prove that

$$\mathbb{P}[\text{success}] \geq 2^{-n} \sum_{k=0}^{n} \binom{n}{k} 3^{-k}.$$

  Evaluate the sum on the right to show that $\mathbb{P}[\text{success}] \geq (\frac{2}{3})^n$.
  (iv) Repeat in t independent trials, succeeding if any trial succeeds. Give a t so that $\mathbb{P}[\text{success}] \geq 1 - 1/n^{100}$.
(c) Give a randomized decider M for 3-SAT with the following properties on an instance φ.
  (i) If φ is unsatisfiable, M says (NO). If φ is satisfiable, M says (YES) with probability at least $1 - 1/n^{100}$.
  (ii) The worst-case runtime of M is poly$(n) \times (\frac{3}{2})^n$. What is your poly$(n)$?

(By modifying (b)(ii) to repeat up to $3n$ times and anaysing the probability that in the first $3k$ flips at most k fail to improve the agreement with $\boldsymbol{\alpha}$, one gets a poly$(n) \times (\frac{4}{3})^n$ runtime. The best known is poly$(n) \times 1.31^n$ runtime.)

Problem 29.55. Let φ be an instance of 3-SAT with n variables $x_1, \ldots, x_n$ and m clauses. Even if φ is unsatisfiable, one often wants to assign the variables to maximize the number of clauses that are satisfied (e.g. to maximize the number of constraints that can be satisfied).

(a) Show that one of the assignments all $x_i = \text{T}$ or all $x_i = \text{F}$ satisfies at least half the clauses. *[Hint: Pigeonhole.]*

(b) One can do better. For simplicity, let φ be an instance of X3-SAT (every clause has 3 variables). Assign each variable randomly to T or F. Compute the expected number of satisfied clauses and hence show that there is always an assignment which satisfies at least $(\frac{7}{8})$-th of the clauses.

(c) Sketch an algorithm to satisfy at least $(\frac{7}{8})$-th of the clauses in any instance of X3-SAT. *[See also Problem 20.62.]*

Problem 29.56 (Boolean Games). A Boolean game is based on a Boolean formula $Q(x_1, x_2, \ldots, x_n)$ with n variables $x_1, x_2, \ldots, x_n$. Alice sets T/F for x_1, then Bob sets T/F for x_2, then Alice sets T/F for x_3, and so the game continues until all variables are set. Alice wins if at the end the Boolean formula is T. Assume players are optimal.

(a) Show that Alice wins for $Q(x_1, x_2, x_3) = (x_1 \vee x_2) \wedge (x_2 \vee x_3) \wedge (\overline{x_2} \vee \overline{x_3})$. True or false: $\exists x_1 \forall x_2 \exists x_3 : Q(x_1, x_2, x_3)$.

(b) Show that Bob wins for $Q(x_1, x_2, x_3) = (x_1 \vee x_2) \wedge (x_2 \vee x_3) \wedge (x_2 \vee \overline{x_3})$. True or false: $\exists x_1 \forall x_2 \exists x_3 : Q(x_1, x_2, x_3)$.

(c) For a general Q, show that Alice wins if and only if $\exists x_1 \forall x_2 \exists x_3 \forall x_4 \cdots : Q(x_1, x_2, \ldots, x_n)$ is true.

(More generally a quantified Boolean formula (QBF) is in prenex normal form if all quantifiers are listed first. Alice sets existentially quantified variables and Bob sets universaly quantified variables. The order of play is the order in which the variables appear. Determining if Alice wins amounts to determining if the QBF is true, known as the TQBF problem. It is not known whether TQBF is in NP.)

Problem 29.57 (Zero Knowledge Proof (ZKP)). The ATM-setting in Problem 17.39 requires a test which you can pass with the password but which you pass or fail randomly without the password. The important requirement is that when you pass the test with the password, you should give the ATM no knowledge about your password. That is the hard part. Analyze the following approach to such a test that uses an NP-hard problem (we choose CLIQUE).

Your "account number" is a large graph $G = (V, E)$ with n vertices, e.g. $n = 1000$ in which there is a clique C of size $n/2$. Your password is the clique C. Both you and the ATM know the graph G. Only you know the password C. When you arrive at the ATM, here is the test you will face.

1: You construct a random isomorphism which randomly permutes the vertices and correspondingly relabels the edges of G. The isomorphism is a function $f : V \mapsto V$.
2: You apply f to G, constructing the adjacency matrix of the transformed graph. You *commit* to this adjacency matrix, i.e. it cannot be changed. The clique in the transformed graph is $f(C)$.
3: The ATM randomly tests you by asking you to do one of two things:
   (i) Reveal all entries of the transformed adjacency matrix and the isomorphism f. The ATM has the original graph G, and so can verify if f is an isomorphism, in which case you pass the test.
   (ii) Reveal the edges in the transformed adjacency matrix involving all vertices in the clique $f(C)$. The user *does not* reveal f. If all revealed edges are 1, you pass the test.

(a) Even though the ATM knows the graph G, explain why your passward is "safe".

(b) Why don't you reveal any information about the password, when you answer either of the two tests correctly?

(c) One way for an imposter with your ATM-card (i.e. the graph G) to try to get access to your money is to commit to the adjacency matrix which is all 1. What is the probability the imposter wins?

(d) Alternatively, the imposter commits to a random isomorphism, and if asked to reveal the clique, he randomly picks vertices. Which test might the imposter fail. Give an upper bound on the probability the imposter wins.

(Some critical issues with regard to implementing the scheme above are: (i) How does the user generate their account graph G with an embedded clique C of size $n/2$ which they know through the process of generating the G, but which is hard to find given only the graph G. (ii) In the test the user must *commit* to the transformed adjacency matrix. A separate cryptographic protocol exists to ensure that the user cannot change the edges after commitment (otherwise an imposter can easily pass the test). (iii) One must also ensure that after the user reveals clique edges, the ATM cannot access anything that the user did not reveal (the isomorphism or unrevealed edges in the transformed adjacency matrix), otherwise information about the password gets leaked. Again, standard cryptographic protocols can be used here.)

A large part of mathematics which becomes useful developed with absolutely no desire to be useful, and in a situation where nobody could possibly know in what area it would become useful; and there were no general indications that it ever would be so.
– **John von Neumann**

Epilogue

We covered a basic foundation in discrete mathematics and probability. We then applied that foundation to develop a theory of the digital computer which is perhaps the defining technology of the 21st century. No one doubts the digital computer's impact to society, but few appreciate that this high technology is essentially mathematical. A millenium from now, the face of computing may look different. Perhaps we'll be wearing computers in our brains. Humanity's trajectory is hard to predict. New technologies rise. Some stay and others become fads. It's not that way with mathematics. What is true in this book today will be true a millenium from now. Don't hold your breadth for quantum-supercomputers to save us from the halting problem. Don't waste your time looking for a friendship network with 11 people, all of who have 5 friends.

Where to go from here? The most profitable next step is a course in algorithms at the level of Dasgupta et al. [2006], Levitin [2011] or Skiena [2013]. From there, paths may diverge. Here are some popular directions.

- *Software and Programming Languages.* Perhaps this is the traditional route with lots of scope for theory and application, see, for example, Pierce [2002], Aho et al. [2007].
- *Theory and algorithms.* Standard texts to get you started on this path are Kleinberg and Tardos [2005], Cormen et al. [2009].
- *AI, machine learning and data science.* Russell and Norvig [2002] is a comprehensive introduction to AI and Abu-Mostafa et al. [2012] gives a foundational introduction to learning from data. Blum et al. [2020] discusses the foundations of data science focusing more on the algorithmic side.
- *Parallel and distributed paradigms.* Such paradigms have many applications including cloud computing, edge computing, fog computing, distributed ledgers and blockchain/bitcoin, etc. See, for example, Leighton [1992], Lynch [2009], Wattenhofer [2019].
- *Robotics and autonomous systems.* A discipline which combines algorithms, probability and AI. Starter texts in this area are Thrun et al. [2005], Siegwart et al. [2011], Corke [2017].
- *Networks.* An area in which graphs and probability play a big role, see, for example, Barabasi [2002], Easley and Kleinberg [2010], Newman [2018].

Ultimately, a more theoretical reader may get involved in newer areas like quantum computing (e.g. Mermin [2007], Nielsen and Chuang [2011], Lipton and Regan [2014]) or a more applied reader may combine with another discipline such as biology (e.g. Gusfield [1997]).

Our list of possible trajectories is neither complete nor static. It is hard to predict the path a reader will take and perhaps harder to predict what paths will be available given how rapidly the field evolves.

It would appear that we have reached the limits of what it is possible to achieve with computer technology, although one should be careful with such statements, as they tend to sound pretty silly in 5 years.
– John von Neumann, 1948

I think there is a world market for maybe five computers. – Thomas J. Watson, IBM, 1943

We're headed for a world where you're either going to be able to write algorithms and speak that language or be replaced by algorithms. – Ray Dalio, 2018

What we can say is that if you build a solid theoretical foundation, you will be poised to take any path.

Digging Deeper. This book only set the stage for a deeper exploration into Discrete Mathematics and Computing. If you did all the problems, you are already quite far into that exploration. Use it as a springboard into broader and deeper waters, for there remains a huge breadth of tools in discrete mathematics that are worth mastering. For example, we hardly covered generating functions and other transforms, which find applications in recursion, counting, probability, etc. Indeed, topics to which we devoted just a single chapter have entire volumes of advanced material. Here is some brief guidance along those lines.

A technically more challenging coverage of general discrete mathematics is *Concrete Mathematics* by Graham, Knuth and Patashnik. Many of these topics are also addressed in depth from the algorithmic perspective in the sequence of books *The Art of Computer Programming* by Knuth. We suggest the following resources as starting points for specific discrete mathematics and theory of computing topics. We hope the reader will take up the challenge of working through some of these books.

- *Logic and proof.* For a gentler introduction to proofs, we recommend Hammack [2018]. Readers interested in the abstract foundations of mathematics and logic should look to formal treatments of logic and set theory, for example Johnstone [1987], Ebbinghaus et al. [1996], Enderton [2001].
- *Number theory and cryptography.* A computer scientist consumes number theory usually in the context of cryptography. Good introductory texts are Paar [2010], Katz and Lindell [2014]. A slightly more advanced treatment is Koblitz [1994].
- *Graphs.* Graphs are an essential discrete object in computer science and effort spent mastering graphs and graph algorithms is effort well spent. West [1996] and Bollobás [2001] are good places to start. More advanced treatments are in Berge [1983] and Diestel [2000]. The notion of a random graph has become a popular model for real networks. To learn about random graphs try Erdős and Rényi [1959], Albert and Barabási [2002], and for advanced material see Bollobás [2002].
- *Counting.* Combinatorics is a topic which is intertwined with counting, graphs and probability. Accessible texts are van Lint and Wilson [1993], Grimaldi [2003] and Brualdi [2009]. For a deep and extensive treatement of counting, see Stanley [2011].
- *Probability.* Today's computer scientist needs probability. For data scientists, it is indisputable. But, probability is now also woven into the fabric of algorithm design. The introductory text DeGroot and Schervish and more advanced texts Feller [1968] and Grimmett and Strizaker [2001] give good coverage. Use of probability in algorithm design is possible due to tail inequalities like Chernoff [1952] and Hoeffding [1963]. The practical impact is that a randomized algorithm can work an overwhelming majority of the time. This has led to an explosion in randomized algorithms with texts like Motwani and Raghavan [1995], Alon and Spencer [2000] and Mitzenmacher and Upfal [2005] making the field accessible.
- *Theory of Computing.* A standard resource is Sipser [2012], but many others exist, for example Hopcroft et al. [2006], Lewis and Papadimitriou [2007], Papadimitriou [1995]. On the more advanced side is Arora and Barak [2009]. When it comes to decidability, not much more can be done. On the other hand, the study of hard NP-complete problems is vibrant. A good resource on NP-completeness is Garey and Johnson [1979]. When it comes to hard problems, the predominant direction is to develop efficient approximation algorithms, see for example Hochbaum [1996] and Vazirani [2001].

THE END

Further Reading

Y. Abu-Mostafa, M. Magdon-Ismail, and H.-T. Lin. *Learning From Data: A Short Course.* amlbook.com, 2012.

M. Agrawal, N. Kayal, and N. Saxena. PRIMES is in P. *Annals of Mathematics*, 160(2):781–793, 2002.

A. Aho, M. Lam, R. Sethi, and J. Ullman. *Compilers: Principles, Techniques and Tools.* Addison-Wesley, 2007.

M. Aigner, G. Ziegler, and K. Hofmann. *Proofs from THE BOOK.* Springer, 6th edition, 2018.

R. Albert and A.-L. Barabási. Statistical mechanics of complex networks. *Rev. Mod. Phys.*, 74:47–97, 2002.

N. Alon and J. Spencer. *The Probabilistic Method.* Wiley, 2nd edition, 2000.

S. Arora and B. Barak. *Computational Complexity: A Modern Approach.* Cambridge University Press, 2009.

A.-L. Barabasi. *Linked: The New Science of Networks.* Perseus, 2002.

R. E. Bellman. *Dynamic Programming.* Princeton University Press, 1957.

R. E. Bellman. On a routing problem. *Quarterly of Applied Mathematics*, 16:87–90, 1958.

C. Berge. *Graphs.* North-Holland, 1983.

E. R. Berlekamp, J. H. Conway, and R. K. Guy. *Winning Ways for Your Mathematical Plays.* Academic Press, 1982.

N. L. Biggs. *Discrete Mathematics.* Oxford University Press, 2nd edition, 2013.

N. L. Biggs, E. K. Lloyd, and R. J. Wilson. *Graph theory 1736-1936.* Clarendon Press, 1999.

A. Blum, J. Hopcroft, and R. Kannan. *Foundations of Data Science.* Cambridge University Press, 2020.

B. Bollobás. *Random Graphs.* Cambridge University Press, 2nd edition, 2001.

B. Bollobás. *Modern Graph Theory.* Springer, 2002.

R. A. Brualdi. *Introductory Combinatorics.* Prentice-Hall, 2009.

L. Carroll. *Symbolic Logic.* Crown, 1977.

L. Carter and M. Wegman. Universal classes of hash funtions. *J. Computer and System Sciences*, 18(2):143–154, 1979.

G. Chartrand and P. Zhang. *Introduction to Graph Theory.* McGraw-Hill, 2004.

H. Chernoff. A measure of asymptotic efficiency for tests of a hypothesis based on the sum of observations. *Annals of Mathematical Statistics*, 23:493–509, 1952.

S. Cook. The complexity of theorem proving procedures. In *Proc. Symp. Th. of Comp., STOC*, pages 151–158, 1971.

P. Corke. *Robotics, Vision and Control: Fundamental Algorithms In MATLAB.* Springer, 2nd edition, 2017.

T. Cormen, C. Leiserson, R. Rivest, and C. Stein. *Introduction to Algorithms.* MIT Press, 3rd edition, 2009.

S. Dasgupta, C. Papadimitriou, and U. Vazirani. *Algorithms.* McGraw-Hill, 2006.

M. H. DeGroot and M. J. Schervish. *Probability and Statistics.* Addison–Wesley,ISBN: 0201524880, 3rd edition.

R. Diestel. *Graph Theory.* Springer, 2000.

E. W. Dijkstra. A note on two problems in connection with graphs. *Numerische Matematik*, 1:269–271, 1959.

D. Easley and J. Kleinberg. *Networks, Crowds, and Markets: Reasoning about a Highly Connected World.* Cambridge University Press, 2010.

H.-D. Ebbinghaus, J. Flum, and W. Thomas. *Mathematical Logic.* Springer, 2nd edition, 1996.

H. Enderton. *A Mathematical Introduction to Logic.* Academic Press, 2nd edition, 2001.

S. Epp. *Discrete Mathematics with Applications.* Cengage Learning, 5th edition, 2019.

P. Erdős and A. Rényi. On random graphs. *Publicationes Mathematicae*, 6:290âĂŞ297, 1959.

P. Erdős. Beweis eines satzes von tschebyshef (proof of a theorem of Tschebyshef). *Acta Sci. Math*, 5:194–198, 1930-1932.

L. Euler. Solutio problematis ad geometriam situs pertinentis. *Commentarii academiae scientiarum Petropolitanae*, pages 128–140, 1741.

W. Feller. *An Introduction to Probability Theory and its Applications*, volume 1–2. Wiley, 3rd edition, 1968.

R. W. Floyd. Algorithm 245 (treesort). *Communications of the ACM*, 7:701, 1964.

L. R. J. Ford and D. R. Fulkerson. *Flows in Networks.* Prentice-Hall, 1962.

D. Gale and L. Shapley. College addmissions and the stability of marriage. *Am. Math. Monthly*, 69:9–15, 1962.

M. Garey and D. Johnson. *Computers and Intractability: A Guide to the Theory of NP-Completeness.* Freeman, 1979.

K. Gödel. Über formal unentscheidbare sätze der principia mathematica und verwandter systeme, I. *Monatshefte für Mathematik und Physik*, 38(1):173–198, 1931.

R. L. Graham, D. E. Knuth, and O. Patashnik. *Concrete Mathematics.* Addison-Wesley, 1994.

R. P. Grimaldi. *Discrete and Combinatorial Mathematics.* Addison-Wesley, 5th edition, 2003.

G. Grimmett and D. Strizaker. *Probability and Random Processes.* Oxford University Press, 3rd edition, 2001.

D. Gusfield. *Algorithms on Strings, Trees, and Sequences: Computer Science and Computational Biology.* Cambridge University Press, 1997.

D. R. Gusfield and R. W. Irving. *The Stable Marriage Problem: Structure and Algorithms.* MIT Press, 1989.

P. Hall. On representation of subsets. *J. London Mathematical Society*, 10:26–30, 1935.

R. Hammack. *Book of Proof.* Richard Hammack, 3rd edition, 2018.

D. Hochbaum, editor. *Approximation Algorithms for NP-Hard Problems.* PWS Publishing, 1996.

W. Hoeffding. Probability inequalities for sums of bounded random variables. 58(301):13–30, 1963.

J. Hopcroft, R. Motwani, and J. Ullman. *Introduction to Automata Theory, Languages, and Computation.* Pearson, 3rd edition, 2006.

T. R. Jensen and B. Toft. *Graph Coloring Problems.* Wiley Interscience, 1995.

P. Johnstone. *Notes on Logic and Set Theory.* Cambridge University Press, 1987.

D. Karger and C. Stein. A new approach to the minimum cut problem. *J. of the ACM*, 43(4):601–640, 1996.

R. M. Karp. Reducibility among combinatorial problems. In R. Miller and J. Thatcher, editors, *Complexity of Computer Computations*, pages 85–103. Plenum Press.

J. Katz and Y. Lindell. *Introduction to Modern Cryptography.* Chapman & Hall, 2nd edition, 2014.

B. Kernighan and S. Lin. An efficient heuristic procedure for partitioning graphs. *The Bell System Technical Journal*, 49(2):291–307, 1970.

J. Kleinberg and E. Tardos. *Algorithm Design.* Pearson, 2005.

D. Knuth. *The Art of Computer Programming*, volume 1–4. Addison-Wesley, 2011.

D. E. Knuth. Algorithms. *Scietific American*, 236(4):63–80, 1977.

N. Koblitz. *A Course in Number Theory and Cryptography.* Springer, 2nd edition, 1994.

E. Lehmann, F. T. Leighton, and A. R. Meyer. Mathematics for computer science. 12th Media Services, 2017. Also available as MIT open source notes.

F. T. Leighton. *Introduction to Parallel Algorithms and Architectures.* Morgan Kaufmann, 1992.

L. Levin. Universal search problems (in russian). *Problemy Peredachi Informatsii*, 9(3):265–266, 1973.

A. Levitin. *Introduction to the Design and Analysis of Algorithms.* Pearson, 3rd edition, 2011.

H. R. Lewis and C. H. Papadimitriou. *Elements of the Theory of Computation.* Prentice Hall, 4th edition, 2007.

R. Lipton and K. Regan. *Quantum Algorithms via Linear Algebra: A Primer.* MIT Press, 2014.

L. Lovász, J. Pelikán, and K. Vesztergombi. *Discrete Mathematics: Elementary and Beyond.* Springer, 2003.

N. A. Lynch. *Distributed Algorithms.* Elsevier, 2009.

D. Mermin. *Quantum Computer Science: An Introduction.* Cambridge University Press, 2007.

S. Milgram. The small world problem. *Psychology Today*, 1967.

M. Mitzenmacher and E. Upfal. *Probability and Computing: Randomized Algorithms and Probabilistic Analysis.* Cambridge University Press, 2005.

R. Motwani and P. Raghavan. *Randomized Algorithms.* Cambridge University Press, 1995.

G. L. Nemhauser and L. A. Wolsey. *Ubteger and Combinatorial Optimization.* Wiley, 1988.

M. Newman. *Networks.* Oxford University Press, 2nd edition, 2018.

M. Nielsen and I. Chuang. *Quantum Computation and Quantum Information.* Cambridge University Press, 10th anniversary edition, 2011.

C. Paar. *Understanding Cryptography: A Textbook for Students and Practitioners.* Springer, 2010.

C. H. Papadimitriou. *Computational Complexity.* Addison-Wesley, 1995.

B. C. Pierce. *Types and Programming Languages.* MIT Press, 2002.

G. Polya. *How to Solve It: A New Aspect of Mathematical Method.* Princeton University Press, 2014.

K. H. Rosen. *Discrete Mathematics and Its Applications.* McGraw-Hill, 7th edition, 2011.

S. Russell and P. Norvig. *Artificial Intelligence: A Modern Approach.* Prentice-Hall, 2nd edition, 2002.

E. A. Scheinerman. *Mathematics: A Discrete Introduction.* Brooks Cole, 3rd edition, 2012.

R. Sedgewick and K. Wayne. *Algorithms.* Addison-Wesley, 4th edition, 2011.

C. E. Shannon and W. Weaver. *The Mathematical Theory of Communication.* University of Illinois Press, 1949.

R. Siegwart, I. R. Nourbakhsh, and D. Scaramuzza. *Introduction to Autonomous Mobile Robots.* MIT Press, 2nd edition, 2011.

M. Sipser. *Introduction to the Theory of Computation.* Cengage Learning, 3rd edition, 2012.

S. Skiena. *The Algorithm Design Manual.* Springer, 2nd edition, 2013.

R. Smullyan. *What is the Name of this Book?: The Riddle of Dracula and Other Logical Puzzles.* Prentice-Hall, 1978.

R. P. Stanley. *Enumerative Combinatorics*, volume 1-2. Cambridge University Press, 2nd edition, 2011.

S. Thrun, W. Burgard, and D. Fox. *Probabilistic Robotics.* MIT Press, 2005.

A. M. Turing. On computable numbers, with an application to the entscheidungsproblem. *Proceedings of the London Mathematical Society*, 2(42):230–265, 1936.

J. H. van Lint and R. M. Wilson. *A Course in Combinatorics.* Cambridge University Press, 1993.

V. Vazirani. *Approximation Algorithms.* Springer, 2001.

R. Wattenhofer. *Blockchain Science: Distributed Ledger Technology.* Independently published, 2019.

D. Watts. *Six Degrees: The Science of a Connected Age.* Norton, 2002.

D. B. West. *Introduction to Graph Theory.* Prentice Hall, 2nd edition, 1996.

P. Zeitz. *Art Craft Problem Solving.* Wiley, 2016.

Glossary of Notation

$\lvert\cdot\rvert$	absolute value, or cardinality (of a set), or determinant (of a matrix)
$\aleph_0, \aleph_1, \ldots$	different cardinalities of infinity, $\aleph_0 = \lvert\mathbb{N}\rvert$, $\aleph_1 = \lvert\mathcal{P}(\mathbb{N})\rvert = \lvert\mathbb{R}\rvert = \mathfrak{c}$
$\alpha(G)$	independence number of graph G, the size of a maximum independent set
$O(\cdot)$	big-oh, asymptotically smaller than a constant multiple of argument
$\Omega(\cdot)$	big-omega, asymptotically larger than a constant multiple of argument
$\Theta(\cdot)$	big-theta, asymptotically comparable to a constant multiple of argument
$o(\cdot)$	little-oh, asymptotically negligible compared to argument
$\omega(\cdot)$	little-omega, asymptotically infinitely larger than argument
	beacon symbol on a TM's tape
Bernoulli(p)	Bernoulli distribution, 1 with probability p and 0 with probability $1-p$
$\mathcal{B}$	all finite binary strings, including the empty string ε, $\mathcal{B} = \{\varepsilon, 0, 1, 00, 01, 10, 11, 000, 001, \ldots\}$
$\mathcal{B}_\infty^0$	all infinite binary strings that are eventually 0 (after some point all bits are 0), e.g. $010000\cdots$
$\mathcal{B}_\infty$	all infinite binary strings
$\tilde{\mathcal{B}}_\infty$	all infinite binary strings that are not eventually 0, there is no point after which all bits are 0
$B(k; n, p)$	Binomial probability of k heads in n coin flips with $\mathbb{P}[\mathrm{H}] = p$, $B(k; n, p) = \binom{n}{k} p^k (1-p)^k$
$B(n, p)$	binomial distribution with n flips and success probability p, $\mathbb{P}[\mathbf{X} = k] = \binom{n}{k} p^k (1-p)^{n-k}$
$\binom{r}{k}$	generalized Binomial coefficient for arbitrary r, $\binom{r}{k} = r^{\underline{k}}/k! = r(r-1)(r-2)\cdots(r-k+1)/k!$
$[\![\cdot]\!]$	Boolean indicator function equal to 1 if the argument is true, and 0 if false
$A \times B$	cartesian product, 2-tuples (a, b) where $a \in A$ and $b \in B$(e.g. $\mathbb{N} \times \mathbb{Z}$)
X^d	d-tuples $(x_1, \ldots, x_d)$ where $x_i \in X$, e.g. $\mathbb{R}^d$
C_n	nth Catalan number, $C_n = \frac{1}{n+1}\binom{2n}{n}$
CDF	cumulative distribution function, probability to be at most a specific value
CFG	context free grammar
CFL	context free language, a language generated by a CFG
$\chi, \chi(G)$	chromatic number of graph G, the minimum number of colors that produce a valid coloring
$\binom{n}{k}$	Binomial coefficient n-choose-k (number of k-combinations from n items), $\binom{n}{k} = n!/k!(n-k)!$
$\binom{n}{k_1, \ldots, k_r}$	multinomial coefficient, $\binom{n}{k_1, \ldots, k_r} = n!/k_1! k_2! \cdots k_r!$
CLT	Central Limit Theorem
$w_1 \bullet w_2$	concatenation, e.g. $01 \bullet 10 = 0110$
$w^{\bullet k}$	concatenated power, e.g. $(01)^{\bullet 2} = 0101$
coNP	problems whose (NO)-answer is polynomialy verifiable
$\mathfrak{c}$	cardinality of the continuum, $\mathfrak{c} = \lvert\mathbb{R}\rvert$
C_n	cycle graph on n vertices
d-PDA	deterministic pushdown automaton, a DFA with stack memory
δ_i	degree of vertex v_i in a graph with vertices $\{v_1, \ldots, v_n\}$
$\Delta, \Delta(G)$	maximum degree in a graph G, $\Delta = \max_i \delta_i$
$\boldsymbol{\delta}$	degree sequence $\boldsymbol{\delta} = [\delta_1, \ldots, \delta_n]$, the degrees of all the vertices $\{v_1, \ldots, v_n\}$
D_n	number of derangements of n items, $D_n = n! \sum_{k=0}^{n} (-1)^k/k!$
$D_{n,k}$	number of partial derangements of n items, with k staying in place
$\frac{d(\cdot)}{dx}$	derivative with respect to x

DFA	deterministic finite automaton
$d(\cdot,\cdot)$	distance between two objects, e.g. $d(v_1, v_2)$ is the distance between two vertices in a graph
$d\|n$	d divides n, which means $n = kd$ for $k \in \mathbb{Z}$
e	universal constant, Euler's number (base of natural logarithms), $e = 2.718281828\cdots$
$\varnothing, \{\}$	empty set, containing no elements
E	edge set of graph, for example $E = \{(v_1, v_2), (v_3, v_6)\}$
ε	empty string, containing non symbols, similar to the empty set $\varnothing$
$\langle\cdot\rangle$	encoding of some object, usually into binary, e.g. $\langle M\rangle$ encodes the TM M to a binary string
E	evidence used by a certifier for an NP-prooblem
$\exists$	existential quantifier THERE EXISTS, e.g. $\exists x : 3x > x^2$
e^x	exponent of x in the base $e = 2.71828\cdots$
$\mathbb{E}[\mathbf{X}\|A]$	conditional expectation of $\mathbf{X}$ given event A
$\mathbb{E}[\mathbf{Y}\|\mathbf{X}]$	conditional expectation of $\mathbf{Y}$ given $\mathbf{X}$
$\mathbb{E}[\cdot]$	expected value of argument
$\mathbb{E}_{\mathbf{X}}[\cdot]$	expected value with respect to the random variable $\mathbf{X}$
$F_{\mathbf{X}}(x)$	cumulative probability distribution of $\mathbf{X}$, $F_{\mathbf{X}}(x) = \mathbb{P}[\mathbf{X} \le x]$
$k!$	factorial, $k! = k(k-1)(k-2)\cdots 3 \times 2 \times 1$
$x^{\underline{k}}$	factorial or falling power, $x^{\underline{k}} = x(x-1)(x-2)\cdots(x-k+1)$, e.g. $6^{\underline{2}} = 30$
F_n	nth Fibonacci number, $F_1 = F_2 = 1$, and $F_n = F_{n-1} + F_{n-2}$ for $n > 2$
$\forall$	universal quantifier FOR ALL, e.g. $\forall x : x^2 > 0$
$g \circ f(x)$	composition of g with f, $g \circ f(x) = g(f(x))$
$f \otimes g(x)$	cartesian product function, $f \otimes g(x) = (f(x), g(x))$
γ	universal Euler-Macheroni constant, the $\gamma = \lim_{n\to\infty} H_n - \ln n = 0.577215664\cdots$
$\gcd(m,n)$	greatest common divisor of m and n, e.g. $\gcd(27, 12) = 3$
$G(s)$	generating function for sequence $A_0, A_1, A_2, A_3, \ldots$, $G(s) = A_0 + A_1 s^1 + A_2 s^2 + A_3 s^3 + \cdots$
$G = (V, E)$	graph G with vertices V and edges E; usually $n = \|V\|$ and $m = \|E\|$
$\overline{G}$	complement graph, where the edge set of $\overline{G}$ is the complement of the edge set E of G
H_k	Hadamard matrix, a $2^k \times 2^k$ orthogonal matrix whose entries are all $\pm 2^{-k/2}$
H_n	nth harmonic number, $H_n = 1 + \frac{1}{2} + \frac{1}{3} + \frac{1}{4} + \cdots + \frac{1}{n}$
$\mathrm{H}(w)$	hash function, $\mathrm{H}(w)$ maps w uniformly to a rndom number in a range $[0, L]$
$\mathrm{height}(T)$	height of rooted tree T, length of the longest path from the root to a leaf
$\text{in-deg}(v_i)$	in-degree of vertex v_i in a directed graph
$\int$	integral
$[a, b]$	interval of real numbers from a to b, where the context indicates $a \le b$ are real
$[i, j]$	interval of integers when $i \le j$ are integers, e.g. $[4, 7] = \{4, 5, 6, 7\}$
K_n	clique or complete graph on n vertices
$K_{n,m}$	complete bipartite graph on a bipartite graph with partitions of sizes n and m
$\mathcal{K}(x)$	Kolmogorov complexity, shortest description of string x
$\mathcal{L}$	language, set of finite strings over an alphabet Σ
$\mathcal{L}_1 \bullet \mathcal{L}_2$	concatenation of languages, strings formed by appending a string in $\mathcal{L}_2$ to a string in $\mathcal{L}_1$
$\mathcal{L}^{\bullet k}$	strings formed by concatenating k strings from $\mathcal{L}$
$\mathcal{L}^*$	Kleene-star, all possible concatenations of strings from $\mathcal{L}$, including the empty string ε
$\mathcal{L}^+$	all positive or non-empty concatenations of strings from $\mathcal{L}$ (excludes the empty string ε)
$\mathcal{L}_{\text{HALT}}$	language of halting TMs $\{\langle M\rangle\#w\}$, where M is a TM that halts on w
$\mathcal{L}_{\text{TM}}$	language of successful TMs $\{\langle M\rangle\#w\}$, where M is a TM that accepts w
$\mathcal{L}^{\text{R}}$	language reversal, reversal of the strings in $\mathcal{L}$
$\mathrm{lcm}(m,n)$	least common multiple of m and n, e.g. $\gcd(2, 3) = 6$
LHS	left hand side, for example in an equation, inequality or implication
$\mathrm{length}(w)$	length of the string w (number of symbols), e.g. $\mathrm{length}(1101) = 4$
$L(G)$	line graph of G (edges become vertices, and edges incident with the same vertex are linked)
ln	logarithm in base $e = 2.71828\cdots$
L_n	path or line on n vertices

$\log_{10}$	logarithm in base 10
$\log_2$	logarithm in base 2
$\wedge$	logical AND, e.g. $p \wedge q \wedge r$
$\overset{\text{eqv}}{\equiv}$	logical equivalence, e.g. $p \overset{\text{eqv}}{\equiv} q$ means p is equivalent to q
$\leftrightarrow$	logical if and only if (equivalence), e.g. $p \leftrightarrow q$ means p IF AND ONLY IF q
$\rightarrow$	logical implication, e.g. $p \rightarrow q$ means p IMPLIES q, or IF p, THEN q
$\vee$	logical OR, e.g. $p \vee q \vee r$
$a \oplus b$	bitwise OR, e.g. $0001110010 \oplus 1000111000 = 1001111010$
μ	mean (expected value) of a random variable
$A \overset{\text{BIJ}}{\mapsto} B$	mapping A bijectively to B, i.e. 1-to-1 and onto, so $\lvert A\rvert = \lvert B\rvert$
$A \overset{\text{INJ}}{\mapsto} B$	mapping A injectively to B, i.e. 1-to-1, so $\lvert A\rvert \leq \lvert B\rvert$
1-to-1	mapping that distinct inputs to distinct outputs, an injection
onto	mapping that uses all possible outputs (every output is mapped to by some input), a surjection
$A \overset{\text{SUR}}{\mapsto} B$	mapping A surjectively to B, i.e. onto, so $\lvert A\rvert \geq \lvert B\rvert$
$\max(\cdot,\cdot)$	maximum of the two arguments, e.g. $\max(1,2) = 2$
$\min(\cdot,\cdot)$	minimum of the two arguments, e.g. $\min(1,2) = 1$
$a \equiv b \pmod d$	a is congruent to b modulo d, or $d \mid (a-b)$, e.g. $2 \equiv 12 \pmod 5$
$[n]$	in the context of counting, the set $\{1, 2, \ldots, n\}$, e.g. $[4] = \{1, 2, 3, 4\}$.
$\neg(\cdot)$	negation, for example $\neg p$ means NOT(p)
$N(v)$	neighborhood of vertex v, the vertices to which v has an edge
(NO)	rejecting output of a decider when testing a string for membership in a language
$\lVert\cdot\rVert$	Euclidean norm, $\lVert\mathbf{x}\rVert = (x_1^2 + \cdots + x_d^2)^{1/2}$
NP	nondeterministic polynomial, problems whose (YES)-answer is polynomialy verifiable on a TM
$\nu_p(x)$	largest power of prime p that divides x, $x = \prod_{\text{primes } p} p^{\nu_p(x)}$, e.g. $\nu_3(18) = 2$
$\mathbb{N}$	natural numbers, $1, 2, 3, \ldots$
$\mathbb{Q}$	rationals, ratio of an integer over a natural number
$\mathbb{R}$	real numbers
$\mathbb{Z}$	integers, $0, \pm1, \pm2, \pm3, \ldots$
ω	outcome of a random experiment
Ω	sample space (possible outcomes)
$<, \leq, >, \geq$	binary ordering relations
out-deg(v_i)	out-degree of vertex v_i in a directed graph
P	polynomialy solvable problems on a TM
PDF	probability distribution function, probability to be a specific value
φ	golden ratio, $\varphi = \frac{1}{2}(1 + \sqrt{5}) = 1.618\cdots$
$\phi(x)$	normal CDF, $\phi(x) = \frac{1}{\sqrt{2\pi}} \int_{-\infty}^{x} ds\; e^{-\frac{1}{2}s^2}$
$\phi(n)$	Euler's totient function, the number of co-prime positive divisors of n, e.g. $\phi(9) = 6$
π	universal constant ratio of circumference to diameter, $\pi = 3.141592654\cdots$
$\mathcal{P}(A)$	power set of A containing all subsets of A including the empty set $\varnothing$
$P(n)$	predicate stating a claim depending on n, often used to define an induction claim
$\mathbb{P}[A]$	probability of event A
$P(\omega)$	probability function defined for outcomes in the outcome space, $\omega \in \Omega$
$\mathbb{P}[A \cap B]$	probability of event A and event B occuring
$\mathbb{P}[A \mid B]$	probability of event A conditioned on event B occuring, $\mathbb{P}[A \mid B] = \mathbb{P}[A \cap B] / \mathbb{P}[B]$
$P_{\mathbf{X}}(x)$	probability distribution of $\mathbf{X}$, $P_{\mathbf{X}}(x) = \mathbb{P}[\mathbf{X} = x]$
$P_{\mathbf{XY}}(x,y)$	joint probability distribution of $\mathbf{X}$ and $\mathbf{Y}$
$\prod$	product, e.g. $\prod_{i=1}^{10} i^2 = 1 \times 4 \times 9 \times \cdots \times 100$
q_i	state in a DFA or a TM
$R(k,s)$	Ramsey number, the minimum number of vertices to guarantee a k-clique or an s-war
$\mathcal{L}_1 \leq_{\text{P}} \mathcal{L}_2$	$\mathcal{L}_1$ is polynomialy-reducible to $\mathcal{L}_2$, that is $\mathcal{L}_1$ is polynomialy solvable if $\mathcal{L}_2$ is
$\mathcal{L}_1 \leq_{\text{R}} \mathcal{L}_2$	$\mathcal{L}_1$ is TM-reducible to $\mathcal{L}_2$, that is $\mathcal{L}_1$ is solvable if $\mathcal{L}_2$ is

rem(n,d)	remainder when n is divided by d where $0 \leq \text{rem}(n,d) < d$, e.g. rem$(22,6) = 4$
w^{R}	reversal of string w, e.g. $001^{\text{R}} = 100$
RHS	right hand side, for example in an equation, inequality or implication
RBT	rooted binary tree, each vertex has at most two children
RFBT	rooted full binary tree, each vertex is a leaf or has two children
RFTT	rooted full ternary tree
RST	rooted short tree
RT	rooted tree
RTT	rooted ternary tree, each vertex has at most three children
$\{x\}$	round to nearest integer ($\frac{1}{2}$ is rounded up), e.g. $\{1.6\} = 2$, $\{1.1\} = 1$ and $\{-1.1\} = -1$
$\lceil x \rceil$	round up, i.e. ceiling, e.g. $\lceil 1.1 \rceil = 2$ and $\lceil -1.1 \rceil = -1$
$\lfloor x \rfloor$	round down, i.e. floor, e.g. $\lfloor 1.1 \rfloor = 1$ and $\lfloor -1.1 \rfloor = -2$
$\{\cdots\}$	set of elements enclosed within curly parentheses, e.g. $\{1,2,3\}$
$\overline{(\cdot)}$	complement of a set, e.g. $\overline{A} = \{\text{items not in } A\}$, or negation of a variable, e.g. $\overline{x} = \text{NOT}(x)$
$\overline{b}$	flipped binary variable b, with 1's replaced by 0's and *vice versa*, e.g. $\overline{0100} = 1011$
$A \cap B$	A intersected with B, the elements in both A and B, e.g. $\{1,2\} \cup \{2,3\} = \{2\}$
$A \setminus B$	A with the elements of B removed, e.g. $\{1,2\} \setminus \{2,3\} = \{1\}$
$A \cup B$	A union B, the elements of A and B combined, e.g. $\{1,2\} \cup \{2,3\} = \{1,2,3\}$
$\sigma^2, \sigma^2(\mathbf{X})$	variance of a random variable $\mathbf{X}$
Σ	alphabet (also used for summation), e.g. $\Sigma = \{0,1\}$ is the binary alphabet
Σ^+	all nonempty strings that can be formed using an alphabet Σ
Σ^*	all strings that can be formed using an alphabet Σ, e.g. for $\Sigma = \{0,1\}$, Σ^* is all binary strings
size(T)	size of rooted tree T, equal to the number of vertices
S_n	star graph on n vertices; also used for the sum up of a series up to n terms
Ⓐ, Ⓔ	halting state of a TM for accept and reject (error)
→○	start state in a DFA or TM
◎	yes-state in a DFA, states without the green border are no-states
$\left[n \atop k \right]$	Stirling number of the first kind, partitions of n items into k non-empty labeled sets
$\left\{ n \atop k \right\}$	Stirling number of the second kind, partitions of n items into k non-empty unlabeled sets
$\sum_i^j$	summation, e.g. $\sum_{i=1}^{10} i^2 = 1 + 4 + 9 + \cdots + 10^2$
$\sigma(n)$	sum of the divisors of n, including n, e.g. $\sigma(6) = 12, \sigma(12) = 28$
✓0, ✓1	marked symbols on a TM's tape
#	punctuation symbol used to separate different parts of strings
␣	blank symbol, one of the default symbols on a TM's tape
$T(n)$	runtime of an algorithm or Turing Machine on an input of size n
TM	Turing machine
U_{TM}	universal TM
$U[n]$	uniform distribution on $1, \ldots, n$, $\mathbb{P}[\mathbf{X} = k] = 1/n$ for $k = 1, \ldots, n$
value(b)	integer value of binary string $b = b_k b_{k-1} \cdots b_1 b_0$, e.g. value$(101) = 5$
var$(\mathbf{X})$	variance of a random variable $\mathbf{X}$
V	vertex set of graph
$W(k,\ell)$	Expected wait to k successes and ℓ failures in n independent trials with success probability p
W_n	wheel graph on n vertices
$w*$	wildcard symbol, e.g. $1* = 1 \bullet \Sigma^*$ is the set of all strings starting with 1
$\mathbf{X}$	random variable, a measurement in an experiment, mathematically a function $\mathbf{X} : \Omega \mapsto \mathbb{R}$
$\mathbf{Y}$	random variable, a measurement in an experiment, mathematically a function $\mathbf{Y} : \Omega \mapsto \mathbb{R}$
(YES)	accepting output of a decider when testing a string for membership in a language
(YES)-set	set of strings for which the answer to a problem is yes, i.e. the strings in the language
$\mathbf{Z}$	random variable, a measurement in an experiment, mathematically a function $\mathbf{Z} : \Omega \mapsto \mathbb{R}$
z-score	z-score is a random variable $\mathbf{Z}$ derived from $\mathbf{X}$, $\mathbf{Z} = (\mathbf{X} - \mu(\mathbf{X}))/\sigma(\mathbf{X})$
ZFC	Zermelo-Fraenkel set theory with the axiom of choice

Index